Spin Glass Theory and Far Beyond

Replica Symmetry Breaking After 40 Years

Editors

Patrick Charbonneau
Duke University, USA

Enzo Marinari
Sapienza University of Rome, Italy

Marc Mézard
Bocconi University, Italy

Giorgio Parisi
Sapienza University of Rome, Italy

Federico Ricci-Tersenghi
Sapienza University of Rome, Italy

Gabriele Sicuro
King's College London, UK

Francesco Zamponi
École Normale Supérieure, France

World Scientific

NEW JERSEY · LONDON · SINGAPORE · BEIJING · SHANGHAI · HONG KONG · TAIPEI · CHENNAI · TOKYO

Published by

World Scientific Publishing Co. Pte. Ltd.

5 Toh Tuck Link, Singapore 596224

USA office: 27 Warren Street, Suite 401-402, Hackensack, NJ 07601

UK office: 57 Shelton Street, Covent Garden, London WC2H 9HE

Library of Congress Control Number: 2023939014

British Library Cataloguing-in-Publication Data
A catalogue record for this book is available from the British Library.

First published 2023 (hardcover)
Reprinted 2024 (in paperback edition)
ISBN 978-981-12-9687-1 (pbk)

SPIN GLASS THEORY AND FAR BEYOND
Replica Symmetry Breaking After 40 Years

ISBN 978-981-127-391-9 (hardcover)
ISBN 978-981-127-392-6 (ebook for institutions)
ISBN 978-981-127-393-3 (ebook for individuals)

For any available supplementary material, please visit
https://www.worldscientific.com/worldscibooks/10.1142/13341#t=suppl

Desk Editor: Joseph Ang

Typeset by Stallion Press
Email: enquiries@stallionpress.com

Preface

Patrick Charbonneau[*], Enzo Marinari[†], Marc Mézard[‡],
Federico Ricci-Tersenghi[†], Gabriele Sicuro[§] and Francesco Zamponi[¶]

[*]*Department of Chemistry and Department of Physics, Duke University, Durham,
North Carolina, USA*
[†]*Department of Physics, Sapienza Università di Roma, and Nanotec-CNR and Infn
Sezione di Roma, Rome, Italy*
[‡]*Department of Computing Sciences, Bocconi University, Milan, Italy*
[§]*Department of Mathematics, King's College London, London, United Kingdom*
[¶]*Laboratoire de Physique, École normale supérieure, Paris, France*

About sixty years ago, the anomalous magnetic response of some magnetic alloys drew the attention of theoretical physicists. It soon became clear that their understanding would require to develop a new branch of statistical physics for disordered and strongly interacting systems. As physical materials, spin glasses were found to be as useless as they were exotic. They were nevertheless recognized as paradigmatic examples of *complex* systems.

Theoretical efforts to describe spin glasses took speed with the complete formulation of *replica symmetry breaking* by Giorgio Parisi in 1979 [1, 2] and the discovery of its physical content in the following years. The book *Spin glass theory and beyond* [3] (familiarly known as the *Beyond*), published in 1987, presented the concepts and consequences of replica symmetry breaking, as well as a first look at some applications that one could foresee at that time. Indeed, in the introduction to that book, the authors wrote "We are firmly convinced that the techniques developed for spin glasses: the replica theory, the TAP approach and the cavity method can be applied to a myriad of other problems that otherwise are difficult to handle". It turns out that the set of ideas and techniques that originated from spin glasses have since given rise to an intellectual *cornucopia* [4]; it has led to a huge number of applications to problems as diverse as neural networks, amorphous solids, biological molecules, social and economic interactions, information theory and constraint satisfaction problems.

In 2019, some of us co-organized a conference to celebrate the 40th anniversary of the complete formulation of replica symmetry breaking theory. Within this context, the idea emerged of inviting colleagues to participate in a collective effort at writing a new book, the *Far Beyond* that would give an idea of the development of the field after the release of the *Beyond*. Of course, the recognition of the importance of these ideas by the Nobel committee in 2021 gave further momentum to the project, and eventually led to its completion.

This book aims at presenting an overview of the broad scope of applications of spin glass theory. We tried to invite as many as possible of the researchers that have contributed to these applications over the last decades, and we asked them to present the connection between spin glasses and their own research field in a pedagogical way, having in mind a reader with a good scientific background (not necessarily in physics), but generally unfamiliar with the specific field. We have striven for an encyclopedic work, in which a reader can find a general description of the ideas, together with a set of references to a more technical and complete discussion. The reader who wants to follow the technical developments, or get deeper into one of the presented subjects, is invited to study first some of the available textbooks, e.g. [3, 5–8].

The book is organized into thematic chapters. Some chapters contain a single contribution, coauthored by a small set of colleagues. Other chapters contain several distinct (but related) contributions, each written by one or a few authors. In the latter case, we added a short introductory paragraph to describe the contributions and their articulation. In the spirit of an encyclopedia, each chapter can be read independently of the others, so the reader can pick those chapters that are closer to their interests.

A final chapter, written by Giorgio Parisi, describes his own perspective on the state and direction of the field.

We are grateful to all the hundred and one authors who accepted to embark on this challenging endeavor with us.

References

[1] G. Parisi, *J. Phys. A.* **13**, 1101, (1980).
[2] P. Charbonneau, *IAMP News Bulletin.* **2022**(October), 5–25, (2022).
[3] M. Mézard, G. Parisi, and M. A. Virasoro, *Spin glass theory and beyond: An Introduction to the Replica Method and Its Applications.* vol. 9, (World Scientific Publishing Company, 1987).
[4] P. W. Anderson, *Physics Today.* **42**(9), 9, (1989).
[5] K. Fischer and J. Hertz, *Spin glasses.* (Cambridge University Press, 1991).
[6] H. Nishimori, *Statistical physics of spin glasses and information processing: an introduction.* Number 111, (Clarendon Press, 2001).
[7] M. Mézard and A. Montanari, *Information, physics, and computation.* (Oxford University Press, 2009).
[8] G. Parisi, P. Urbani, and F. Zamponi, *Theory of simple glasses: exact solutions in infinite dimensions.* (Cambridge University Press, 2020).

Contents

Chapter 1

Simulated Annealing, Optimization, Searching for Ground States

Sergio Caracciolo*, Alexander Hartmann[†], Scott Kirkpatrick[‡] and Martin Weigel[§]

Department of Physics, University of Milan and INFN Milan Section, Milan, Italy
sergio.caracciolo@mi.infn.it
[†]*Institut für Physik, Universität Oldenburg, Oldenburg, Germany*
a.hartmann@uni-oldenburg.de
[‡]*School of Engineering and Computer Science, Hebrew University, Jerusalem, Israel*
kirk@cs.huji.ac.il
[§]*Institut für Physik, Technische Universität Chemnitz, Chemnitz, Germany*
martin.weigel@physik.tu-chemnitz.de

The chapter starts with a historical summary of first attempts to optimize the spin glass Hamiltonian, comparing it to recent results on searching largest cliques in random graphs. Exact algorithms to find ground states in generic spin glass models are then explored in Sec. 1.2, while Sec. 1.3 is dedicated to the bidimensional case where polynomial algorithms exist and allow for the study of much larger systems. Finally Sec. 1.4 presents a summary of results for the assignment problem where the finite-size corrections for the ground state can be studied in great detail.

1.1. Introduction

A theme which unites this chapter is the study by simulation of finite random systems in order to test the predictions and insights that arose as new kinds of order were defined and realized in spin glasses. The tools of this chapter have found use in many applied contexts. In physics, phase spaces of physical systems have typically been considered. In applied mathematics, problems, either idealized or based on real-world data, are solved to optimize target functions or to satisfy constraints. Over the years, it has been gradually accepted in the mathematics and physics communities that these two realms are very similar to each other.

Replicas, when introduced by Brout [1], were large patches of a perfectly ordered lattice. Edwards and Anderson (EA) [2] looked for order in the similarity of behavior across multiple identical copies of random spins and their interactions. In the Brout and EA work, the free energy was extracted as the linear term in an expansion of the partition function in powers of n, the number of replicas. EA defined order as a self-correlation of spin orientation in different replicas, since this could represent correlation over long times. Sherrington and Kirkpatrick (SK) [3], after simplifying the problem to an infinite ranged Ising system with i.i.d. random Gaussian interactions of strength

1

$1/\sqrt{N}$ in hopes of making it *soluble*, explicitly used the identity,

$$\ln Z = \lim_{n \to 0} \frac{Z^n - 1}{n},\tag{1.1}$$

despite the obvious fact that the meaning of Z^n anywhere except at integer values of n was unclear. A careful treatment of the extrapolation of the resulting equations for the free energy, F, showed an entropy at zero temperature which was negative, an impossibility in a discrete model, while other features such as a susceptibility cusp seemed plausible. The predicted ground state energy, $E_0 = (2/\pi)^{1/2} = -0.798...$, could be tested in simulation.

Fortunately, computers in 1975 had almost reached the point where they might be able to address questions about asymptotic values of quantities such as E_0. Powerful generally available computers such as IBM's 370-168 and later 3033 could hold as much as 10 MB of data in random access memory, and process instructions at a few MIPS. (The first supercomputer, the Cray-1, in 1975 also had no more than about 10 MB of RAM, but ran its instructions 4–6 times faster.) This amount of RAM permitted simulating a small number of samples with 500–1000 spins, so with a floating point coprocessor attached to their IBM mainframe to provide more Cray-like processing speeds, Kirkpatrick and Sherrington (KS) [4] in 1978 could report that E_0 was in fact between -0.75 and -0.77, excluding the replica symmetric result. Improvements on that estimate have continued for the next 30+ years. The most recent estimate of the asymptotic result, using Parisi's full RSB formulas and Padé approximants to extrapolate both upper and lower bounds to E_0, yields the currently accepted value of $-0.76321...$ [5]. The improvements in theory that have made this the accepted result required several decades, and are discussed elsewhere. Improving the experiments to test it also required some years for computing speeds to increase so that better statistics could emerge from simulations. Graphs with N up to 2000 sites have been studied [6], but understanding the size dependence of E_0 remains a subject of research. Simulations agree with theory, and have grown more accurate as the bounds on the theoretical result have also grown tighter. New methods of finding the ground state energies in the simulated model were required, intially and as the models got larger and the accuracy required grew narrower. These methods, such as simulated annealing, have taken on a life of their own, with many applications in complex systems outside of the simple models of statistical mechanics.

Simulated annealing [7] is an obvious idea if you are statistical physicists, like KS when first studying their spin glass model, and also V. Černý [8] and K. Wilson [9]. Kirkpatrick and Černý studied the Travelling Salesman as an easily described example. Wilson used annealing to optimize packing of parallel processor code generated in a compiler he wrote for his quantum chromodynamics simulations. All of these authors realized that allowing a Markov chain of states to evolve at a series of decreasing finite temperatures (*annealing*) would tend to reach larger and deeper minima than simple gradient descent for a complex function space with many local minima.

At the time the preferred methods used gradient descent with many random restarts and tricks to jump to new starting points, applied only when a search gets stuck. The large number of possible local minima, mostly at higher energies, makes this ineffective.

In addition, study of properties such as susceptibilities and specific heat (obtained from the fluctuations of a Boltzmann system) could guide the development of effective annealing schedules. Ranges of temperature at which large fluctuations were seen, possibly signalling a phase boundary, give a signal to slow the annealing process to allow large changes to occur.

Kirkpatrick and IBM colleagues [7] were also at the time studying the problems presented by design automation tools used to place and route transistors and small VLSI circuits in IBM's next-generation computers, and included simplified examples of both practical problems in their paper. These tools were successfully used and incorporated into IBM's internal product development tool sets, and adopted in other industries.

The IBM group learned important lessons from exposure to the engineering environment. First, expressing complex constraints as energetic costs in a Hamiltonian framework provided valuable flexibility, and the annealing framework met the constraints simultaneously or in order of importance rather than one at a time. Second, they soon realized that finding the exact optimum in a problem like circuit design was not really the objective of an engineering team, who simply needed to find solutions that were good enough, soon enough, to ship as products. For that sort of objective, robustness of a methodology and the ability to incorporate many esoteric constraints was at least as important as its efficiency. Optimality of the solution obtained, if possible, was a bonus, but not the only objective.

Simulated annealing has been accepted as another tool for at least approximately solving messy but useful and important problems. Probably its greater impact has been to stimulate the incorporation of statistical physics frameworks as an active part of applied mathematics. One recent review by a respected practitioner of constraint satisfaction [10] considers the 1990s to be the era of phase transitions, with the 2000s introducing more refined techniques such as survey propagation [11] and cavity constructions [12]. Phase diagrams with pictures of changes in the shapes of possible sets of solutions and different degrees of ergodicity in the phase space of a problem's solutions [13, 14] now shape the discussions of the fundamental differences between different complexity classes of combinatorial and computational problems [15].

The simplest problems in combinatorial optimization are proving explicitly some property of a random graph, or proving that the property does not hold in that graph. An example would be testing if a clique, or completely connected cluster of sites, of size K exists in an Erdős–Rényi graph $G(N, p = 0.5)$ of size N, with half of the bonds selected at random, the rest absent. This is a stylization of a common question data scientists might ask of the social networks tracking interaction on today's internet, where such graphs may describe populations of billions, and the bonds might be demonstrated common interests or communication. We know what is possible by just calculating expectations. The largest cliques, of size $K_{\max}$, that form naturally in this model will not exceed $2 \log_2 N$ in size, with finite-size corrections making the actual limiting size of such a *MaxClique* much less. Simple linear algorithms, with costs proportional to the number of bonds, thus N^2, fail to find solutions with clique size K more than a few sites bigger than $\log_2 N$. A staircase of steps at which increasingly larger maximum cliques are found thus bounds a *hard* phase in which large numbers of cliques with sizes greater

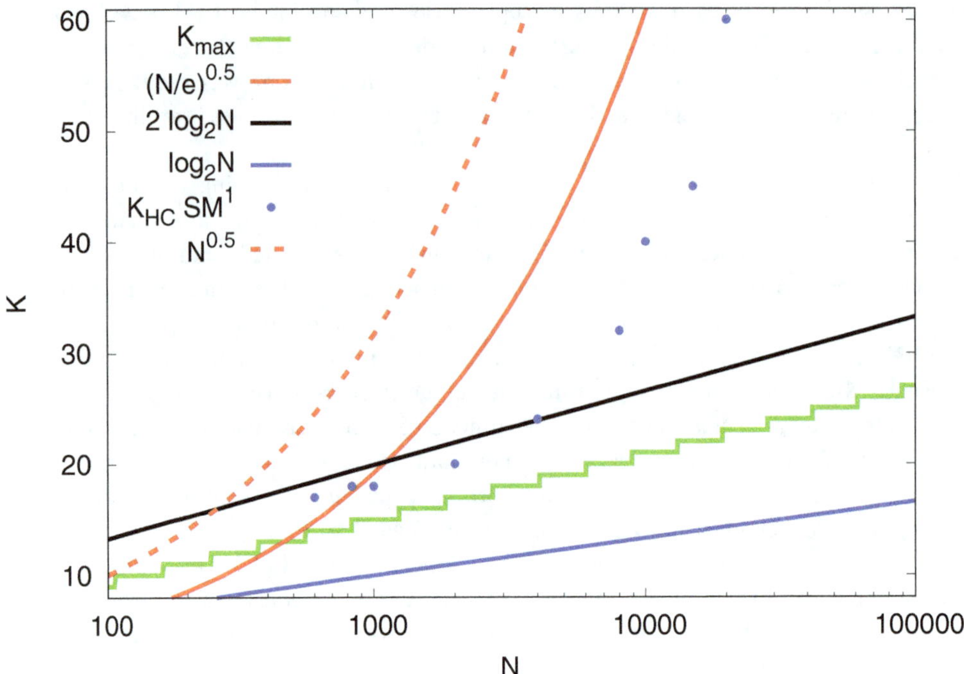

Fig. 1.1.　Hidden clique sizes K_{HC} of interest in $G(N, p = 0.5)$ lie between the $K_{\max}$ staircase and the proven or experimentally observed lower limits that can be found with spectral methods (dashed red line) or message-passing techniques (solid red line). Sizes of the smallest hidden cliques identified by a simple greedy search from all initial sites, stopping as soon as evidence for the hidden clique is found, are shown with blue dots and lie well below both limits.

than $\log_2 N$ must exist, but cannot be found without introducing some more expensive nonlinear search, such as backtracking.

A popular extension of this problem is to add a *hidden clique* to the random graph which is larger than those which occur at random. Since this clique is unique, it should be easier to find, but the best methods proven to work with quasi-linear cost (but large prefactors) can only find hidden cliques of size greater than $\sqrt{N/e}$. So an easy region for this related problem exists when the hidden clique is bigger than this line. The resulting phase diagram is shown in Fig. 1.1 [16].

Some recent work has returned to the original intuition of EA that correlations of activity between identical replicas of random, symmetry-less systems were an indication of ordering that might serve in place of a traditional order parameter. Consider simulating the evolution of multiple copies of a random system at steadily lowered temperatures, or at a number of different temperatures, and passing information about improved solutions between the different replicas, a methodology called *parallel tempering* in physics [17]. This has proved capable of finding hidden cliques in very large graphs when the hidden clique barely exceeds the size of naturally occurring cliques [18], as well as to find maximum independent sets very efficiently [19]. Annealing multiple replicas in this way has the disadvantage that it cannot be proven to have only polynomial cost (in the size of the problem) asymptotically, although experience and empirical knowledge of the problem may allow tuning the method for affordable costs on large practical problems. It may also provide a path to overcoming the confusion that impedes the search for optimal configurations in combinatorial problems where many suboptimal configurations overlap and confuse any local search, such as coloring or maximum clique [16].

The extra search power that parallel tempering seems to provide suggests that there may be other ways to exploit the original insight of Edwards and Anderson, that ordering in random systems might show up as a correlation between behavior observed in multiple copies or regions of a complex system. Replica symmetry breaking implies ordering which may take on a range of values, and study of the correlations seen in multiple replicas at low temperatures may add physical insight into such ordering. A further step could be to model systems which are basically similar but subject to weak local environmental corrections with a set of replicas, each slightly different. The objective would be to identify from the differences between solutions in each replica a functional variation of the response of ordering to the different local influences. Such local variations are typical of much of the vast amounts of social data available for study in today's highly instrumented world. This is just one more possible, but as yet unrealized, impact of spin glasses on applied mathematics and statistics.

The original SK Ising model with Gaussian-distributed interactions is only one of the situations which has stimulated further exploration to tease out the lowest energy ground states. Different ways of combining different tools of optimization have proved valuable in this and different lessons emerge, as covered in the further sections of this chapter.

1.2. Focusing on Ground States

Consider the spin-glass (SG) model in zero field with Hamiltonian [2]

$$\mathcal{H} = -\sum_{\langle i,j \rangle} J_{ij} s_i s_j. \tag{1.2}$$

We focus on Ising spins $s_i = \pm 1$ placed on the vertices of a graph, but other symmetries of the order parameter have been considered. The Ising symmetry has the advantage that the related statistical physics problems are combinatorial. The sum $\langle i, j \rangle$ runs over all edges of the graph. For the Edwards–Anderson (EA) model the graph is a hypercubic lattice in d dimensions, but also other graph structures like the fully connected Sherrington–Kirkpatrick model corresponding to the $d \to \infty$ limit of (1.2) have been studied. As discussed in section 1.1, the physics of this mean-field problem is well understood, in many aspects since the 1980s. The situation in low dimensions is less clear and so much of the work in recent decades has focused on studying the problem in 2, 3 and 4 dimensions with numerical methods.

Next to Monte Carlo simulations used to study the vicinity of the spin-glass transition and the behavior in the ordered phase (see Chapter 5), much work has been invested in studying ground states and low-lying excitations above them in order to gauge the low-temperature behavior. Alternative theories for the nature of the spin-glass phase make contrasting predictions about the energetic and geometric properties of such excitations. Based on generalizations of Peierls' argument for the stability of the ferromagnetic phase, researchers have argued that excitations with energies diverging with length will lead to spin-glass phases that are stable against thermal fluctuations, such that one of the prime goals of studying ground states for spin-glass systems is to understand the nature of the prevalent low-energy excitations and how their sizes and energies are related.

The search for ground states for spin glasses with discrete symmetry amounts to a combinatorial optimization problem as there is a countable number of candidate solutions [20]. Such problems can hence be solved by a brute-force enumeration of all configurations, with an effort that grows exponentially with the number of spins. As discussed in Sec. 1.3, a clever organization of this enumeration can lead to massive gains in efficiency of this process, but will not alter the overall exponential scaling of the algorithm. This corresponds to the fact that the problem in $d \geq 3$ is known to be *NP* hard [21]. In some special cases, however, the ground-state problem can be mapped onto auxiliary optimization problems that permit solutions in *polynomial* time. This will be explained in Sec. 1.4. Beyond the ground states of spin glasses, many optimization problems have caught the attention of physicists [22, 23]. An example for a recently studied model is the assignment problem, which is discussed in Sec. 1.5.

1.3. Exact Algorithms for Hard Problems

Here, exact and general algorithms for finding ground states (GSs) for Ising SGs are considered, although the presented methods are very general. As an extension of Eq. (1.2), here also an interaction with local fields h_i is included. For most studied systems no local field is present, but for some of the algorithms presented below, such a term might arise for sub-problems to be solved. In this case, the energy of a SG is given by the Hamiltonian

$$\mathcal{H}(s) = -\sum_{i<j} J_{ij} s_i s_j - \sum_i h_i s_i \,, \tag{1.3}$$

where $s = (s_1, \ldots, s_N)$ is a configuration and the bonds J_{ij}, corresponding to the edges of the graph, are quenched random variables. The sum runs here, in the most general case, over all pairs of spins. Thus, if all bonds are nonzero, the system is of mean-field type. For finite-dimensional lattices, most bonds are zero, suitably selected. The nonzero bonds are typically drawn from a Gaussian or a bimodal $J_{ij} = \pm 1$ distribution.

Here, three types of algorithms are presented, which have frequently been used to calculate exact GSs for three-dimensional SGs. First, the *branch-and-bound* method is explained, which is based on enumerating many states in a sophisticated way. Next, the *linear programming* approach is outlined, which is based on rewriting the Hamiltonian as a linear function, relaxing the condition $s_i = \pm 1$, plus adding additional constraints, called *cutting planes* or *cuts*. Finally, the combination of both approaches, the *branch-and-cut* algorithm is presented, which yields the currently fastest exact method to obtain spin-glass ground states.

1.3.1. *Branch-and-bound*

The basic idea of the branch-and-bound approach [24] to find the minima of Eq. (1.3) is to represent all spin configurations as a binary tree, where at each node the configuration space is, for a node-dependent selected spin i_0, subdivided into the configurations with $s_{i_0} = +1$ and those with $s_{i_0} = -1$, respectively. The spin configurations are given by the 2^N leafs of this tree. The simplest approach to the GS problem would be to obtain all configurations by enumeration, and simply pick those with the minimum energy, yielding an $O(2^N)$ running time.

This running time can be improved, although still being exponential in the worst case, by omitting parts of this tree via considering *bounds* on the achievable energies in sub-trees [25]. Here we present the refined algorithm described in Ref. [26]. The branching is performed always on the last spin of the sub-problem, i.e., it starts with spin N. The energies for the sub problems with $s_N = +1$ and $s_N = -1$ can be written using Eq. (1.3) for $\bar{s} = (s_1, \ldots, s_{N-1})$ as follows:

$$\mathcal{H}^+(\bar{s}) = -\sum_{i<j}' J_{ij} s_i s_j - \sum_i' h_i s_i - \sum_i' J_{iN} s_i - h_N, \tag{1.4}$$

$$\mathcal{H}^-(\bar{s}) = -\sum_{i<j}' J_{ij} s_i s_j - \sum_i' h_i s_i + \sum_i' J_{iN} s_i + h_N, \tag{1.5}$$

where the sums $\sum'$ run from 1 to $N-1$. If one defines

$$\mathcal{H}^*_{N-1} = \min_{s_1,\ldots,s_{N-1}} -\sum_{i<j}' J_{ij} s_i s_j, \tag{1.6}$$

one obtains, using the relation $\min_s(f_1(s)+f_2(s)) \geq \min_s f_1(s) + \min_s f_2(s)$, the bounds

$$\mathcal{H}^+(\bar{s}) \geq \mathcal{H}^*_{N-1} + \min_{s_1,\ldots,s_{N-1}} \sum_i' (-h_i - J_{iN})s_i - h_N, \tag{1.7}$$

$$\mathcal{H}^-(\bar{s}) \geq \mathcal{H}^*_{N-1} + \min_{s_1,\ldots,s_{N-1}} -\sum_i' (-h_i + J_{iN})s_i + h_N. \tag{1.8}$$

These bounds are available because the minima $\mathcal{H}^*_{N-1}, \mathcal{H}^*_{N-2}, \ldots$ can be obtained recursively while the branching tree is built. Furthermore, the minimum of a linear function $\sum_s \sum_i a_i s_i$, here $a_i = -h_i - J_{iN}$ or $a_i = -h_i + J_{iN}$, respectively, is simply given by $-\sum_i |a_i|$. Thus, as a first way to restrict the size of the branching tree, if one or two of the branches exhibit bounds above a known threshold, the corresponding branches can be omitted. Such thresholds may come from low lying configurations found already in other branches or by heuristic algorithms, or simply given as part of the problem in case an enumeration of a specified range of low-lying configurations is sought.

A second type of bound [26] works as follows. Using $d(\bar{s}) = -2\sum_i' J_{iN} s_i - 2h_N$ one can rewrite Eqs. (1.4) and (1.5) as $\mathcal{H}^+(\bar{s}) = \mathcal{H}^-(\bar{s}) + 2d(\bar{s})$. Therefore, we obtain the implications

$$\max_{s_1,\ldots,s_{N-1}} d(\bar{s}) = 2\sum_i |J_{iN}| - 2h_N \leq 0 \implies \mathcal{H}^+(\bar{s}) \geq \mathcal{H}^-(\bar{s}),$$

$$\min_{s_1,\ldots,s_{N-1}} d(\bar{s}) = -2\sum_i |J_{iN}| - 2h_N \geq 0 \implies \mathcal{H}^+(\bar{s}) \leq \mathcal{H}^-(\bar{s}).$$

These bounds are easy to calculate and allow sometimes for omitting one of the two branches, before any branch has to be evaluated.

Such branch-and-bound algorithms have been used, e.g., to analyze the low-temperature landscape [27–30] of SGs. More broadly, in the field of statistical mechanics of optimization problems [22, 23], the branch-and-bound approach has been applied to other problems like the satisfiability problem [31] or the vertex-cover problem [32]. For the latter, a branch-and-bound approach was used, where the variable to branch on was not selected in a given order but determined by a local heuristic for further reduction of the branching tree. For simple variants of these algorithms, it has also been possible to calculate analytically the typical running time for ensembles of random problems, which exhibit transitions between typically polynomial and typically exponential behavior [33, 34].

1.3.2. *Linear programming and cutting planes*

A different approach works by translating the quadratic Hamiltonian into a linear problem. For convenience, here we consider the form of Eq. (1.2). Note that the field term present in Eq. (1.3) can be written as a quadratic term by introducing a "ghost spin" $s_0 = 1$ matching the given equation.

We describe the system by a graph $G = (V, E)$ where V denotes the set of sites where the spins are located and E the set of edges $\{i, j\}$ between the interacting sites. For any set $V' \subset V$ in G the *cut* $\delta(V') \subset E$ denotes the set of edges where one endpoint is in V' and the other is not, i.e., those connecting the two sets V' and $V \setminus V'$. For each configuration, the spins can be partitioned into two sets $V^+ = \{i | s_i = +1\}$ of "up" spins and $V^+ = \{i | s_i = -1\} = V \setminus V^+$ of "down" spins. If two spins s_i and s_j are oriented identically, they contribute the energy $-J_{ij} = +0 - J_{ij}$, while they contribute the energy $J_{ij} = 2J_{ij} - J_{ij}$ if they are oriented differently. Thus, using the cut, we can write

$$\mathcal{H}(s) = 2 \sum_{\{i,j\} \in \delta(V^+)} J_{ij} - \sum_{ij} J_{ij}. \tag{1.9}$$

By introducing $c_{ij} = -J_{ij}$, $S = \sum_{ij} J_{ij}$ and variables $x_{ij} = 1$ if $\{i, j\} \in \delta(V^+)$ and $x_{ij} = 0$ else, this reads

$$\mathcal{H}(x) = -2 \sum_{i,j} c_{ij} x_{ij} - S, \tag{1.10}$$

where $\sum_{i,j} c_{ij} x_{ij}$ is called the *weight* of the cut represented by x. Therefore, since S is only a constant, finding the *minimum energy* of Eq. (1.2) corresponds to finding the maximum cut in a graph with edge weights c_{ij}. Note that Eq. (1.10) is a *linear function* with integer variables, which means we have transformed the quadratic optimization problem into a linear one, but with additional constraints since x must describe a cut. This problem is called *integer linear program*.

To include the constraints describing the cut, we note that for any cycle in the graph G the cut must be crossed an even number of times. This can be conveniently described by linear inequalities [35] for the variables x as follows: For any cycle $C \subset E$, i.e., a path that (?) starts and ends at the same vertex, and any odd cardinality subset $Q \subset C$,

$$\sum_{\{i,j\}\in Q} x_{ij} - \sum_{\{i,j\}\in C\setminus Q} x_{ij} \leq |Q| - 1 \tag{1.11}$$

must hold, which defines a cut comprehensively.

The basic idea of the *cutting-plane* approach is now to *relax* the variables $x_{ij} = 0, 1$ to $0 \leq x_{ij} \leq 1$ and look for a maximum of Eq. (1.10) given the linear inequalities Eq. (1.11). The name cutting plane comes from the fact that all inequalities describe hyper-planes which cut off one part from the space of possible solutions. The resulting problem is called a *linear program* (LP). The good news is that LPs, i.e., with the relaxed variables, can be solved [36] in worst-case polynomial time in the problem size using the *ellipsoid method*. Still, in a practical context methods like the *simplex approach* [37] or the *dual simplex approach*, which exhibit no polynomial bound, perform much faster. Still, the bad news is that the number of inequalities is in principle exponentially large, which would yield an exponential running time right-on. Therefore, instead of adding all constraints immediately to the LP, one starts with no or few constraints and calculates a first solution. Since fewer constraints than necessary are contained in the relaxed problem, typically the obtained cut weight will be higher, i.e., an upper bound of the true maximum cut for the integer LP. Hence, the solution obtained will typically not correspond to a cut and not be pure integer-valued. Thus, there may be some of the exponentially many inequalities which are violated. The second basic idea of the cutting plane approach is to look specifically for violated inequalities, without searching all possible ones, and add the violated ones to a growing set of inequalities included in the LP. An exact polynomial algorithm to find violated inequalities is based on solving a series of shortest-path problems [35], which can be done in $O(N^3)$. This is polynomial but rather slow. Fortunately, there exist, in particular for physical lattice structures, several heuristics which run in linear $O(N)$ time [38] and are most of the time sufficient to generate additional inequalities for violated conditions. If at some point no further violated inequalities are found and the solution is fully integer-valued, a true optimum has been found, and the algorithm stops. But if on the contrary some variables are still non-integer, one can resort to branching as explained in the next subsection.

Nevertheless, for some combinatorial problems it has been observed that a cutting plane approach alone may lead to a valid optimum solution of the integer problem. For example for vertex-cover problems on Erdős–Rényi random graphs a different kind of cycle inequalities has been considered [39]. When varying the average number c of neighbor nodes in the graphs, a phase transition has been observed. In the thermodynamic limit $N \to \infty$, for small values $c < c^* = e \approx 2.71$, typically all instances can be solved completely in a polynomial running time, while for larger values of c this is not possible. Interestingly, this *easy-hard transition* coincides with the critical connectivity where replica-symmetry breaking of the vertex-cover problem occurs [32]. At this point a complex structure of the solution space has been observed [40], where the so-called *leaf-removal core* [41] starts to percolate.

Finally, note that there is a set of cutting planes, so-called *Gomory cuts* [42], which can be constructed generally for all relaxed linear problems. They are based on iden-tifying violated inequalities directly from a given non-integer solution, actually in the so-called *tableau* [36] used by the simplex algorithm to solve the LP. It is proven that this, possibly exponentially large, set of inequalities is complete, i.e., *any* integer programming problem can be solved in principle by generating *just* these cutting planes. Still, in practice, any finite numerical accuracy leads to convergence problems, such that this and many other cutting-plane approaches turned out to be actually efficient in combination with branching, as explained next.

1.3.3. *Branch-and-cut*

If for a relaxed linear system describing maximum cuts the solution is still non-integer, one considers for some variable $x_{ij} \neq 0, 1$ both possibilities $x_{ij} = 0$ and $x_{ij} = 1$ and solves the corresponding sub-problems recursively. This means one branches. The combination of these approaches is therefore called *branch-and-cut* [38, 43]. Note that here several other bounds, in addition to those mentioned above, can be used. This can be lower bounds obtained from the cut weight of any valid cut x^* or upper bounds obtained from suitable relaxations like the LP.

Currently, the branch-and-cut approach can be considered as the most powerful exact algorithm to obtain GSs for hard SG instances. A publicly accessible implementation of a branch-and-cut algorithm is the *spin-glass server* [44] hosted by the University of Bonn. The server was originally implemented at the University of Cologne by several members and collaborators of the research groups of F. Liers and M. Jünger. At the server, you can submit SG instances as a file and, if the system is not too large, a corresponding GS will be returned.

Branch-and-cut approaches have been applied to finite-dimensional SGs in several occasions. To our knowledge the largest three-dimensional instances were $N = 12^3$ as considered in a study of low-lying excitations [45].

The approach has also been applied for a mean-field random-bond Ising model, which is a generalization of the standard SG with a variable fraction of negative bond as controlled by a non-zero mean of the bond values. Here, a phase transition of the typical branch-and-cut running time, as measured by the number of LPs solved, between an easy and a hard phase has been observed near the transition between ferromagnetic and SG behavior [46].

1.4. Ground States in Two Dimensions

We now turn to the case of ground-state problems permitting a polynomial-time solution. For the EA model of Eq. (1.2) this is the case in dimensions $d < 3$. Since the 1d problem is rather trivial, the much more interesting case of this type is the EA model in two dimensions.

A relevant mapping of the EA ground state to a minimum-weight perfect matching (MWPM) problem on an auxiliary graph was first proposed in Ref. [47]. It is based on the observation that frustrated plaquettes [48], i.e., elementary lattice faces including an odd number of antiferromagntic couplings, must have an odd number of broken bonds with $J_{ij}s_is_j < 0$, while non-frustrated plaquettes have an even number of broken bonds. Hence a spin configuration can be depicted as a configuration of defect lines of broken bonds that start and end at frustrated plaquettes. A ground state configuration is then a perfect pairing (matching) of frustrated plaquettes through defect lines of minimum total weight. MWPM can be solved in polynomial time based on the blossom algorithm [49] and its variants [50]. However, this approach is still not ideal as it operates on the complete graph of the F frustrated plaquettes with $F(F-1)$ edges, and the edge weights need to be computed in a preparatory step using a suitable approach such as Dijkstra's algorithm [51] before attacking the matching problem. This approach allows one to study systems of a typical maximum linear size of $L \approx 500$ [52].

As was shown more recently [53, 54], an alternative mapping is significantly more efficient as it operates on a sparse graph with similar connectivity as the original lattice. It relies on an auxiliary graph that replaces each vertex of the dual lattice by a complete graph K_4 of four nodes, also known as Kasteleyn city. Edge weights are set to J_{ij} for the original edges and to zero for the internal K_4 bonds. The solution of a matching problem on this graph then corresponds to a set of closed loops on the original lattice, separating domains of opposite spin orientations, cf. the illustration in Fig. 1.2. The configuration of minimum weight corresponds to a ground state of the spin-glass sample. Due to the sparsity of the auxiliary graph, significantly larger systems can be studied with this method as compared to the one proposed in [47], and calculations for square lattices up to $L = 10,000$ have been reported in Ref. [55].

A widely applied method for studying the excitations out of the ground states that take a central role in the theory of the spin-glass phase, consists of systematic modifications of boundary conditions (BCs). It is argued that the defect energy connected to a change from periodic to antiperiodic BCs in one direction,

$$E_{\mathrm{def}} = |E_{\mathrm{P}} - E_{\mathrm{AP}}|, \tag{1.12}$$

can act as a proxy for a typical low-energy excitation of the system [56]. Here, E_{P} and E_{AP} refers to the ground-state energy for periodic and antiperiodic BCs, respectively.

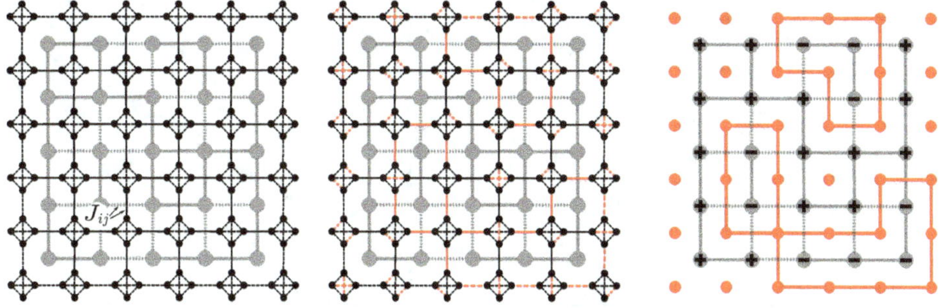

Fig. 1.2.   Mapping of the Ising ground-state problem to a matching problem on an auxiliary graph with Kasteleyn cities. Left: expansion of the Ising lattice, replacing each vertex by a complete graph K_4. Edge weights in the K_4 subgraphs are set to 0, the remaining weights are J_{ij}. Middle: A minimum-weight perfect matching on the auxiliary graph. Right: Back-transformation from the decorated graph to the original lattice. The matching then results in a set of closed loops separating up from down spins.

One expects that E_{def} scales as [57, 58],

$$E_{\mathrm{def}} \sim L^{\theta} \tag{1.13}$$

with the *spin-stiffness exponent* θ, where $\theta > 0$ should indicate the stability of the spin-glass phase at non-zero temperatures, while for $\theta < 0$ the transition temperature $T_{\mathrm{SG}} = 0$ and $\theta = -1/\nu$ governs the divergence of the spin-glass correlation length as $T \to T_{\mathrm{SG}}$ [59]. For Gaussian exchange couplings J_{ij} one finds a stiffness exponent $\theta \approx -0.3$ [52], with the most accurate estimate being [55],

$$\theta = -0.2793(3). \tag{1.14}$$

This is illustrated in Fig. 1.3(a) showing the scaling of defect energies over a wide range of system sizes. The change of boundary conditions induces a domain-wall defect that spans the system; a typical configuration of the overlap between the ground states for periodic and antiperiodic BCs is shown in the left panel of Fig. 1.4. The boundary of the flipped domain is a fractal curve, and the domain-wall length is hence expected to show fractal scaling of the form

$$\langle \ell \rangle_J = A_\ell L^{d_{\mathrm{f}}}. \tag{1.15}$$

As is illustrated in Fig. 1.3(b), this is indeed borne out in the data to high accuracy, and the fractal dimension is estimated as $d_{\mathrm{f}} = 1.27319(9)$.

For technical reasons the matching approach can only handle samples on planar graphs, i.e., lattices with periodic boundary conditions in at most one direction [47]. More precisely, runs for systems with fully periodic boundaries yield the same result for periodic and for antiperiodic BCs in each of the two directions, such that the configuration returned is a ground state for one out of four possible BCs. As pointed out in Ref. [53], the approach hence effectively optimizes over BCs as well as spin variables. To circumvent this problem and allow treatment of systems with fully periodic BCs with the resulting smaller scaling corrections, one may use a windowing technique as

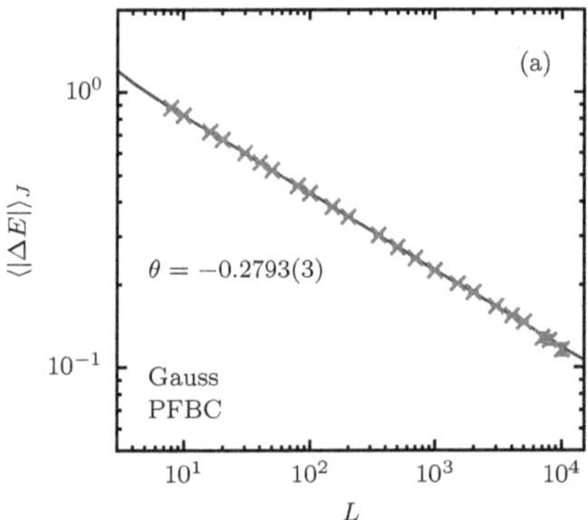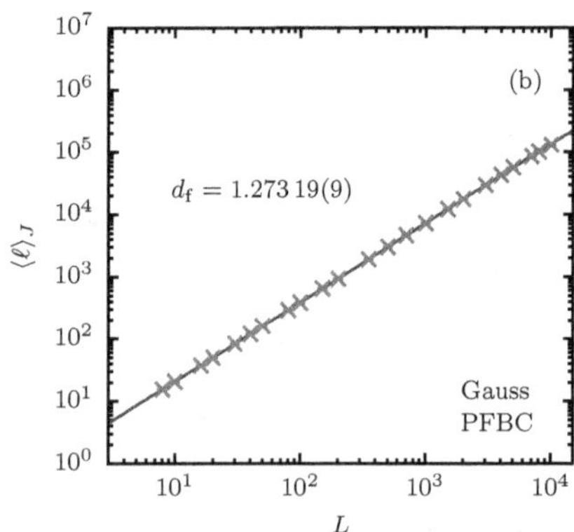

Fig. 1.3.   (a) Scaling of defect energies E_{def} for the Gaussian EA model on the square lattice with periodic boundaries in x direction and free boundaries in y direction. The line shows a fit of the data to the functional form $E_{\mathrm{def}} = A_\theta L^\theta + C_\theta / L^2$ [55]. (b) Scaling of the domain-wall length between periodic and antiperiodic BCs. The line corresponds to a fit of the functional form (1.15) to the data.

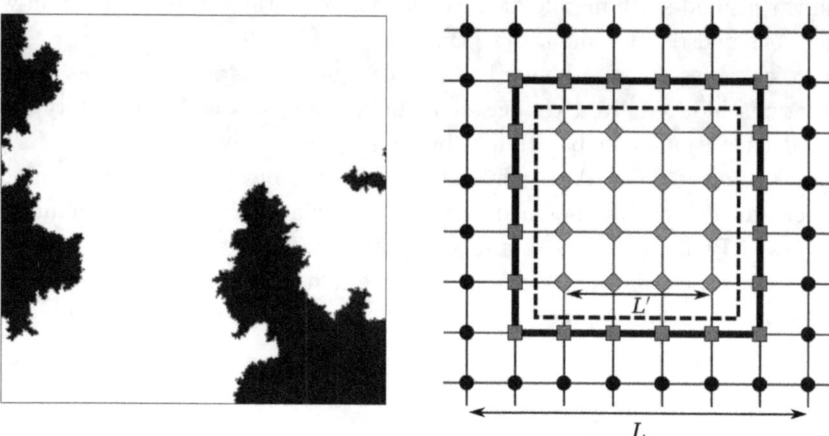

Fig. 1.4. Left: The domain wall separating regions of equal and opposite ground-state configurations for a specific disorder sample considered with periodic and with antiperiodic boundaries. Right: Setup used for the windowing technique to compute ground states for samples with fully periodic boundary conditions.

illustrated in the right panel of Fig. 1.4: since MWPM can be used to find exact ground states for planar graphs, in order to treat a periodic $L \times L$ system one applies it to a square subset of edge length $L - 2$ ("window") while keeping the relative orientation of the outside spins fixed. Randomly displacing the window location over the (periodic) lattice, repeated applications of the window optimizations lead to a quick convergence of the result. This prescription results in a stochastic algorithm, whose success probability can be arbitrarily improved by using m independent runs,

$$P_s(\{J_{ij}\}) = 1 - [1 - P_n(\{J_{ij}\})]^m. \tag{1.16}$$

Numerically, one finds that the number of required repetitions for a given success probability is independent of system size, such that the computational complexity of the algorithm remains the same as that of the MWPM approach for planar graphs, which scales as L^κ with $\kappa \approx 2.2$ [55] for the Blossom V algorithm [50].

The system with bimodal couplings can also be studied with matching techniques. Here, one finds no asymptotic decay of E_{def}, but a convergence to a positive limiting value as $L \to \infty$ [52]. While this was initially taken as evidence for a lower-critical dimension $d_l = 2$, it was later on realized that it is rather a signature of an additional zero-temperature renormalization-group fixed point that is not relevant for the physics at non-zero temperatures [60] and, instead, there is evidence for $d_l = 2.5$ [61, 62]. A signature of this system is the extensive degeneracy of the ground state, leading to a finite ground-state entropy. This creates a difficulty for the matching approach as it does not pick the individual ground states with equal probabilities. In its simplest form, it is deterministic and will hence always return the same ground state. Some simple randomizations through changing the order of considering bonds or adding some noise onto the couplings improve on this, but still lead to biased sampling methods [55]. Unbiased sampling can be achieved via a suitably constructed Monte Carlo sampling technique in the ground-state manifold, thus allowing for estimates of the domain-wall fractal dimensions and related quantities [55].

Matching techniques can also be used to sample other excitations than the domain-wall perturbations induced by a change of boundary conditions. Different types of droplet-shaped excitations can be studied by fixing the relative orientation of spins through "hard" bonds [63, 64]. Also, while matching is the most widely used technique for this problem, an alternative approach based on a calculation of the partition function through the use of Pfaffians allows to also study finite-temperature properties exactly and in polynomial time [65–67]. Recently, such methods have been extended to also enable the study of correlation functions and further related properties [68–70].

1.5. The Assignment Problem

In this section we will discuss some new results for the *assignment problem*. In order to define the question in its simplest version we have to consider a square matrix of size n, $W := \{w_{ij}\}_{i,j=1}^n$, with real entries. For each permutation π in the symmetric group $\mathcal{S}_n$ consider the matrix $\Pi := \{\pi_{ij}\}_{i,j=1}^n$ with entries zero or one, such that

$$\pi_{ij} = \delta_{j,\pi(i)} = \begin{cases} 1 & \text{if } \pi(i) = j \\ 0 & \text{elsewhere} \end{cases} \tag{1.17}$$

and ask for a permutation of the columns of W in order to get a minimum of the trace, that is of the Hamiltonian

$$\mathcal{H}(\Pi, W) := \operatorname{tr}\left(W^T \cdot \Pi\right) = \sum_{i,j=1}^n w_{ij}\pi_{ij} = \sum_{i,j=1}^n w_{ij}\delta_{j,\pi(i)} = \sum_{i=1}^n w_{i,\pi(i)}. \tag{1.18}$$

Without loss of generality we can take the entries of W to be nonnegative: $w_{ij} \geq 0$. Indeed, in *combinatorial optimization* they are usually referred to as *costs*. In different words, this is the classical *matching problem* on the *bipartite complete graph* $\mathcal{K}_{n,n}$. The solution of the problem is a permutation π^*, with corresponding matrix $\Pi^*(W)$, that realizes the minimum cost and brings to the determination of

$$\mathcal{H}^*(W) := \min_{\pi \in \mathcal{S}_n} \mathcal{H}(\Pi, W) = \mathcal{H}\left(\Pi^*(W), W\right) \tag{1.19}$$

the optimal value of the total cost. The optimal solution can be seen as the ground state of the Hamiltonian of a *disordered* system defined by the cost-matrix W, an analogy which can be made useful, for example, by *simulated annealing* [7].

The introduction of a probability on the space of the possible costs allows the investigation of the properties of the *typical* solutions and the artillery from statistical physics shows its whole power [22, 23, 71]. In their seminal works Mézard and Parisi [72–74] (but see also [75]) could solve, by using the replica trick, the matching, the assignment and the Travelling Salesman Problem in the case in which the entries w_{ij}

are independent random variables, equally distributed, with a probability distribution density of the form

$$\rho(w) = w^r \sum_{k=0}^{\infty} \eta_k w^k \qquad (1.20)$$

with $\eta_0 \neq 0$. More precisely, in the asymptotic limit of an infinitely large size n, replica symmetry is not broken, and the optimal solution is determined by the application of the saddle-point method as the solution of an integral equation in which only the parameter r enters. In particular

$$E_n := \mathbb{E}\left[\mathcal{H}^*(W)\right] \sim n^{1-\frac{1}{r+1}}, \qquad (1.21)$$

where the expectation value is taken on the possible weights and with $\sim$ we indicate that both sides of the relation scale with large n in the same way so that their ratio converges in the limit of an infinite number of points. For a recent work in which the first finite-size corrections are reconsidered after Refs. [76, 77] and the extension to non-integer value of the parameter r see Ref. [78].

A new class of problems arises when the vertices of the graph $\mathcal{K}_{n,n}$ are identified with points in $\Omega \subset \mathbb{R}^d$ seen as a subset of a Euclidean space. We thus have two sets of points of cardinality n: we denote them as the red points $\mathcal{R}$, respectively blue points $\mathcal{B}$, with positions $x_i \in \mathbb{R}^d$, respectively $y_i \in \mathbb{R}^d$, with $i \in \{1,\dots,n\} = [n]$. Then the cost of the assignment of the i-th red point with the j-th blue point is assumed to be a function of the Euclidean distance between the two points $|x_i - y_j|$. We shall restrict to the cases

$$w_{ij} = f(|x_i - y_j|) = |x_i - y_j|^p \qquad (1.22)$$

parametrized by the real number $p \in \mathcal{R}$. Let us introduce the *empirical* probability measures associated to the two sets of points

$$\rho_{\mathcal{R}}(x) = \frac{1}{n}\sum_{i=1}^{n}\delta(x-x_i); \qquad \rho_{\mathcal{B}}(y) = \frac{1}{n}\sum_{i=1}^{n}\delta(y-y_j) \qquad (1.23)$$

and look, for $p \geq 1$, at the p-th Wasserstein (elsewhere associated to the names of Kantorovich and Rubinstein) distance of two probability measures, that is at the variational problem

$$W_p(\rho_1,\rho_2) := \left(\inf_{\gamma \in \Gamma(\rho_1,\rho_2)} \int dx\,dy\,\gamma(x,y)\,|x-y|^p\right)^{\frac{1}{p}}, \qquad (1.24)$$

where $\Gamma(\rho_1,\rho_2)$ is the set of measures on $\Omega \times \Omega$ with marginals ρ_1 and ρ_2. This is nothing but the *optimal transport* (or Monge–Kantorovich) problem of a unit mass distributed according to ρ_1 to a distribution ρ_2 [79, 80]. A function $\gamma(x,y)$ defines a *transportation plan*, indeed, the marginality conditions

$$\int dx\,\gamma(x,y) = \rho_2(y); \qquad \int dy\,\gamma(x,y) = \rho_1(x) \qquad (1.25)$$

constraining the mass moved into the point y and from the point x are what is required. In the case of the two empirical probability measures the possible transportation plans reduce to the set of permutations and therefore their Wasserstein distance is simply related to the optimal cost [81]

$$\mathcal{H}^*(W) = n\, W_p^p(\rho_\mathcal{R}, \rho_\mathcal{B}). \tag{1.26}$$

A random matrix, whose elements depend on the Euclidean distance between points randomly distributed in space is called *Euclidean*. The spectra of Euclidean random matrices have been studied in [82].

In order to fix the ideas, let us consider the case in which $\Omega = [0,1]^d$, periodic boundary conditions are chosen, so that we are really on a torus of unit volume and the positions of red and blue points are taken at random with flat probability. A natural length scale is therefore $n^{-\frac{1}{d}}$ and one can simply assume that for each red point there is at least a blue point to match in a ball of radius of order $n^{-\frac{1}{d}}$, so that we can guess that

$$E_n \sim n^{1-\frac{p}{d}}. \tag{1.27}$$

But it is well known [83] that this can be true only in $d \geq 2$. It was proven that in $d = 2$

$$E_n \sim n\left(\frac{\log n}{n}\right)^{\frac{p}{2}}, \tag{1.28}$$

i.e., a logarithmic violation appears. A much more detailed analysis is possible in $d = 1$ [84] where an intriguing relation with Brownian processes is explored [85]. It is shown that, for a generic distribution probability ρ with cumulative Φ, the average total cost is

$$E_n = n^{1-\frac{p}{2}}\frac{2^p}{\sqrt{\pi}}\Gamma\left(\frac{p+1}{2}\right)\int_0^1 dx\,\frac{[\Phi(x)(1-\Phi(x))]^{\frac{p}{2}}}{\rho^{p-1}(x)} + o(n^{-\frac{p}{2}}) \tag{1.29}$$

at least when the integral is convergent. Otherwise an anomalous scaling emerges [86]. In the case of open boundary conditions, with flat distribution, the average cost can be evaluated even for finite size by means of Selberg integrals [87]

$$E_n = n\,\frac{\Gamma\left(1+\frac{p}{2}\right)}{p+1}\frac{\Gamma(n+1)}{\Gamma\left(n+1+\frac{p}{2}\right)}. \tag{1.30}$$

Also the case $p \leqslant 0$ has been studied [88], where, instead, for flat distribution

$$\lim_{n\to\infty}\frac{E_n}{n} = \frac{1}{2^p}. \tag{1.31}$$

When $0 < p < 1$ the cost function becomes concave. In [89] it is argued that

$$E_n \sim \begin{cases} n^{1-p} & \text{for } 0 < p < \frac{1}{2}, \\ \sqrt{n}\log n & \text{for } p = \frac{1}{2}, \\ \sqrt{n} & \text{for } \frac{1}{2} < p < 1, \end{cases} \tag{1.32}$$

so that a change in the phase diagram occurs at $p = \frac{1}{2}$.

An amusing exact result has been obtained for the flat distribution in $d = 2$ for the particular value $p = 2$, in [90, 91], that is

$$\lim_{n\to\infty}\frac{E_n}{\log n} = \frac{1}{2\pi}. \tag{1.33}$$

This has been rigorously proven in Ref. [92] (see also Ref. [93] for improvements). Let us follow the field theoretic approach introduced in Ref. [94] and let us introduce the vector *transport field* $\mu(x)$ which joins the red point in x to the blue point in $y = x + \mu(x)$ and consider the Lagrangian

$$\mathcal{L}[\mu, \phi] := \frac{1}{2} \int \mu^2(x)\rho_\mathcal{R}(dx) + \int [\phi(x + \mu(x))\rho_\mathcal{R}(dx) - \phi(x)\rho_\mathcal{B}(dx)] \tag{1.34}$$

to be minimized, where the scalar field $\phi(x)$ is a Lagrangian multiplier which implements a matching between blue and red points. In the limit of a large number of points n, when the red and blue points are extracted with the same distribution ρ so that $\delta\rho := \rho_\mathcal{R} - \rho_\mathcal{B}$ and the optimal μ goes to zero and we expect a good approximation by using the only the quadratic terms in the Lagrangian, that is

$$\mathcal{L}[\mu, \phi] := \int \left[\frac{1}{2}\mu^2(x) + \mu(x) \cdot \nabla\phi(x)\rho(dx) \right] + \int \phi(x)\delta\rho(dx), \tag{1.35}$$

which has Euler–Lagrangian equations

$$\mu = -\nabla\phi, \qquad \nabla \cdot [\rho\,\mu] = \delta\rho, \tag{1.36}$$

revealing a strict analogy with an electrostatic problem where μ plays the role of the electric field, ϕ is the scalar potential and indeed is the Lagrangian multiplier which implements the Gauss law, red and blue points have opposite unit charge, being null the total charge, while ρ is the dielectric function of a linear dielectric medium. As a consequence

$$-\nabla \cdot [\rho\,\nabla\phi] = \rho \tag{1.37}$$

is solved by means of the classical Green's function $G_\rho(x, y)$ of the operator $-\nabla \cdot [\rho\,\nabla\bullet]$, so that an explicit approximate solution at fixed disorder is given by

$$\mu(x) = \int \nabla_x G_\rho(x, y)\,\delta\rho(dy). \tag{1.38}$$

After averaging over disorder, in the simple case of a flat measure (see Ref. [95] for the non-constant case) we get

$$\lim_{n \to \infty} E_n(\Omega) = -2\,\mathrm{tr}\,\Delta_\Omega^{-1}, \tag{1.39}$$

where the Laplacian Δ_Ω is defined on the domain Ω. This formula is correct in $d = 1$ but it simply provides a divergence on both sides for $d > 1$. It is an ultraviolet divergence which has been introduced by the linearization in the infinite number of modes, but the approximation cannot be true at very short distances. In the exact non-linear theory higher modes are cut off and we expect that

$$E_n(\Omega) = 2 \int_{0+}^{\infty} \frac{F\left(\frac{\lambda}{n}\right)}{\lambda}\,d\mathcal{N}_\Omega(\lambda), \tag{1.40}$$

where $\mathcal{N}_\Omega(\lambda)$ is number of the eigenvalue less than λ for the Laplace operator and the unknown function F interpolates between 1 for $\lambda \lesssim n$ and 0 for $\lambda \gtrsim n$.

By the Weyl law [96] on the asymptotics of the eigenvalue counting function for the Laplace–Beltrami operator we know that, for a $2d$ manifold with unit volume (under Neumann boundary conditions which are appropriate for our problem)

$$\mathcal{N}_\Omega(\lambda) = \frac{1}{4\pi}\left(\lambda + \sqrt{\lambda}\,|\partial\Omega|\right) + o\left(\sqrt{\lambda}\right).\tag{1.41}$$

In $d = 2$ it is easy now to evaluate the leading logarithmic singularity in the number of points and in agreement with Ref. [97] we expect that

$$E_n(\Omega) = \frac{1}{2\pi}\log n + 2c_*(n) + 2c_\Omega + o(1),\tag{1.42}$$

where $c_*(n) = O(\log n)$ is a universal function not depending on Ω. As a further consequence,

$$\lim_{n\to\infty}\left[E_n(\Omega) - E_n(\Omega')\right] = 2\lim_{n\to\infty}\int_{0+}^\infty \frac{F\left(\frac{\lambda}{n}\right)}{\lambda}\left[d\mathcal{N}_\Omega(\lambda) - d\mathcal{N}_{\Omega'}(\lambda)\right],\tag{1.43}$$

but the r.h.s. is convergent even in the absence of regularization thus

$$\lim_{n\to\infty}\left[E_n(\Omega) - E_n(\Omega')\right] = 2\int_{0+}^\infty \frac{d\mathcal{N}_\Omega(\lambda) - d\mathcal{N}_{\Omega'}(\lambda)}{\lambda},\tag{1.44}$$

an expression that has been tested in Ref. [98] on various $2d$ manifolds, by using both the Green's function method as other classical tools as the Dedekind's limit formulas, thus confirming the predictions of the field theoretic approach.

For a similar method applied to a more general context see Refs. [99–101].

Once more this relatively simple combinatorial optimization problem is revealing intriguing and fruitful connections with so many different research fields.

References

[1]   R. Brout, *Phys. Rev.* **115**(4), 824, (1959).
[2]   S. F. Edwards and P. W. Anderson, *J. Phys. F.* **5**, 965, (1975).
[3]   D. Sherrington and S. Kirkpatrick, *Phys. Rev. Lett.* **35**(26), 1792, (1975).
[4]   S. Kirkpatrick and D. Sherrington, *Phys. Rev. B.* **17**(11), 4384, (1978).
[5]   A. Crisanti and T. Rizzo, *Phys. Rev. E.* **65**(4), 046137, (2002).
[6]   S.-Y. Kim, S. J. Lee, and J. Lee, *Phys. Rev. B.* **76**(18), 184412, (2007).
[7]   S. Kirkpatrick, C. D. Gelatt, and M. P. Vecchi, *Science.* **220**(4598), 671–680, (1983).
[8]   V. Černỳ, *Journal of optimization theory and applications.* **45**(1), 41–51, (1985).
[9]   K. G. Wilson. Personal communication to Scott Kirkpatrick, (1990).
[10] B. Selman. The next generation of automated reasoning methods, (2021). Slides of lecture CS6700 at Cornell University.
[11] M. Mézard, G. Parisi, and R. Zecchina, *Science.* **297**(5582), 812–815, (2002).
[12] M. Mézard and G. Parisi, *J. Stat. Phys.* **111**(1), 1–34, (2003).
[13] F. Krzakała, A. Montanari, F. Ricci-Tersenghi, G. Semerjian, and L. Zdeborová, *Proc. Natl. Acad. Sci. U.S.A.* **104**(25), 10318–10323, (2007).
[14] L. Zdeborova, *Acta Physica Slovaca.* **59**, (2009).
[15] D. Gamarnik, *Proc. Natl. Acad. Sci. U.S.A.* **118**(41), e2108492118, (2021).
[16] R. Marino and S. Kirkpatrick, *Sci. Rep.,* **13**(1), 3671 (2023).
[17] K. Hukushima and K. Nemoto, *J. Phys. Soc. Jpn.* **65**(6), 1604–1608, (1996).
[18] M. C. Angelini, *J. Stat. Mech.: Theory Exp.* **2018**(7), 073404, (2018).

[19] M. C. Angelini and F. Ricci-Tersenghi, *Phys. Rev. E.* **100**(1), 013302, (2019).

[20] A. K. Hartmann and H. Rieger, *Optimization Algorithms in Physics.* (Wiley, 2002).

[21] F. Barahona, *J. Phys. A.* **15**, 3241, (1982).

[22] A. K. Hartmann and M. Weigt, *Phase Transitions in Combinatorial Optimization Problems: Basics, Algorithms and Statistical Mechanics.* (Wiley, 2006).

[23] M. Mézard and A. Montanari, *Information, physics, and computation.* (Oxford University Press, 2009).

[24] A. H. Land and A. G. Doig, *Exonometrica.* **28**, 497, (1960).

[25] S. Kobe and A. Hartwig, *Comp. Phys. Commun.* **16**(1), 1–4, (1978).

[26] A. Hartwig, F. Daske, and S. Kobe, *Comp. Phys. Commun.* **32**(2), 133–138, (1984).

[27] T. Klotz and S. Kobe, *J. Magn. Magn. Mat.* **177-181**, 1359–1360, (1998).

[28] T. Klotz, S. Schubert, and K. H. Hoffmann, *Europ. Phys. J. B.* **2**(3), 313–317 (1998).

[29] J. Krawczyk and S. Kobe, *Physica A.* **315**(1), 302–307, (2002).

[30] S. Schubert and K. H. Hoffmann, *Comp. Phys. Commun.* **174**(3), 191–197, (2006).

[31] R. Monasson, R. Zecchina, S. Kirkpatrick, B. Selman, and L. Troyansky, *Nature.* **400**, 133, (1999).

[32] M. Weigt and A. K. Hartmann, *Phys. Rev. Lett.* **84**, 6118, (2000).

[33] S. Cocco and R. Monasson, *Phys. Rev. Lett.* **86**, 1654, (2001).

[34] M. Weigt and A. K. Hartmann, *Phys. Rev. Lett.* **86**, 1658, (2001).

[35] F. Barahona and A. R. Mahjoub, *Math. Program.* **36**(2), 157–173 (1986).

[36] M. Padberg, *Linear Programming and extensions.* (Springer, 1995).

[37] G. B. Dantzig, *Bull. Amer. Math. Soc.* **54**, 1074–1074, (1948).

[38] F. Liers, M. Jünger, G. Reinelt, and G. Rinaldi. In eds. A. K. Hartmann and H. Rieger, *New Optimization Algorithms in Physics*, p. 47. Wiley-VCH, (2004).

[39] T. Dewenter and A. K. Hartmann, *Phys. Rev. E.* **86**, 041128, (2012).

[40] W. Barthel and A. K. Hartmann, *Phys. Rev. E.* **70**, 066120, (2004).

[41] M. Bauer and O. Golinelli, *Eur. Phys. J. B.* **24**, 339, (2001).

[42] R. E. Gomory, *Bull. Am. Math. Soc.* **64**(5), 275–278, (1958).

[43] F. Barahona, M. Grötschel, M. Jünger, and G. Reinelt, *Operations Research.* **36**(3), 493, (1988).

[44] S. Mallach. Spin-glass Server. `http://spinglass.uni-bonn.de/`, (2022). Accessed: 2022-05-04.

[45] M. Palassini, F. Liers, M. Juenger, and A. P. Young, *Phys. Rev. B.* **68**, 064413 (2003).

[46] F. Liers, M. Palassini, A. K. Hartmann, and M. Jünger, *Phys. Rev. B.* **68**, 094406 (2003).

[47] I. Bieche, R. Maynard, R. Rammal, and J. P. Uhry, *J. Phys. A.* **13**, 2553, (1980).

[48] G. Toulouse, *Commun. Phys.* **2**, 115, (1977).

[49] J. Edmonds, *J. Res. Natl. Bur. Stand. B.* **69**, 125, (1965).

[50] V. Kolmogorov, *Math. Prof. Comp.* **1**, 43, (2009).

[51] A. Gibbons, *Algorithmic Graph Theory.* (Cambridge University Press, 1985).

[52] A. K. Hartmann and A. P. Young, *Phys. Rev. B.* **64**(18), 180404, (2001).

[53] C. K. Thomas and A. A. Middleton, *Phys. Rev. B.* **76**, 220406, (2007).

[54] G. Pardella and F. Liers, *Phys. Rev. E.* **78**, 056705, (2008).

[55] H. Khoshbakht and M. Weigel, *Phys. Rev. B.* **97**, 064410, (2018).

[56] J. R. Banavar and M. Cieplak, *Phys. Rev. Lett.* **48**, 832, (1982).

[57] A. J. Bray and M. A. Moore, *J. Phys. C.* **17**, (1984).

[58] W. L. McMillan, *J. Phys. C.* **17**, 3179, (1984).

[59] A. J. Bray and M. A. Moore. In eds. J. L. van Hemmen and I. Morgenstern, *Heidelberg Colloquium on Glassy Dynamics*, p. 121, (1987). Springer.

[60] T. Jörg and F. Krzakala, *J. Stat. Mech.: Theory Exp.* **2012**(01), L01001, (2012).

[61] S. Boettcher, *Phys. Rev. Lett.* **95**, 197205, (2006).

[62] A. Maiorano and G. Parisi, *Proc. Natl. Acad. Sci. U.S.A.* **115**(20), 5129–5134, (2018).

[63] A. K. Hartmann and M. A. Moore, *Phys. Rev. Lett.* **90**, 127201, (2003).

[64] A. K. Hartmann, *Phys. Rev. B.* **77**, 144418, (2008).

[65] J. A. Blackman and J. Poulter, *Phys. Rev. B.* **44**, 4374–4386, (1991).

[66] L. Saul and M. Kardar, *Phys. Rev. E.* **48**(5), R3221, (1993).

[67] A. Galluccio, M. Loebl, and J. Vondrák, *Phys. Rev. Lett.* **84**(26), 5924, (2000).

[68] C. K. Thomas and A. A. Middleton, *Phys. Rev. E.* **80**, 046708, (2009).

[69] C. K. Thomas, D. A. Huse, and A. A. Middleton, *Phys. Rev. Lett.* **107**, 047203, (2011).

[70] C. K. Thomas and A. A. Middleton, *Phys. Rev. E.* **87**, 043303 (2013).

[71] M. Mézard, G. Parisi, and M. Virasoro, *Spin glass theory and beyond: An Introduction to the Replica Method and Its Applications.* vol. 9, (World Scientific Publishing Company, 1987).

[72] M. Mézard and G. Parisi, *J. Phys. Lett. (France).* **46**(17), 771–778, (1985).

[73] M. Mézard and G. Parisi, *J. Phys. (France).* **47**(1986), 1285–1296, (1986).

[74] M. Mézard and G. Parisi, *Europhys. Lett.* **2**(12), 913–918, (1986).

[75] H. Orland, *J. Phys. (France) - Lettres.* **46**(17), 773–770, (1985).

[76] M. Mézard and G. Parisi, *J. Phys. (France).* **48**(9), 1451–1459, (1987).

[77] G. Parisi and M. Ratiéville, *Eur. Phys. J. B.* **29**(3), 457–468 (2002).

[78] S. Caracciolo, M. P. D'Achille, E. M. Malatesta, and G. Sicuro, *Phys. Rev. E.* **95**, 052129, (2017).

[79] C. Villani, *Optimal transport: old and new.* vol. 338, (Springer Science & Business Media, 2008).

[80] L. Ambrosio, *Mathematical Aspects of Evolving Interfaces*, vol. 1812, *Lecture Notes in Mathematics (Fondazione C.I.M.E., Firenze)*, chapter Lecture notes on optimal transport problems, pp. 1–52. Springer, (2003).

[81] H. Brezis, *Comptes Rendus Mathematique.* **356**(2), 207–213, (2018).

[82] M. Mézard, G. Parisi, and A. Zee, *Nuclear Physics B.* **559**(3), 689–701, (1999).

[83] M. Ajtai, J. Komlós, and G. Tusnády, *Combinatorica.* **4**(4), 259–264, (1984).

[84] E. Boniolo, S. Caracciolo, and A. Sportiello, *J. Stat. Mech.* **11**, P11023, (2014).

[85] S. Caracciolo and G. Sicuro, *Phys. Rev. E.* **90**, 042112, (2014).

[86] S. Caracciolo, M. P. D'Achille, and G. Sicuro, *J. Stat. Phys.* **174**(4), 846–864, (2019).

[87] S. Caracciolo, A. Di Gioacchino, E. M. Malatesta, and L. G. Molinari, *J. Stat. Mech.* p. 063401, (2019).

[88] S. Caracciolo, M. P. D'Achille, and G. Sicuro, *Phys. Rev. E.* **96**, 042102, (2017).

[89] S. Caracciolo, M. P. D'Achille, V. Erba, and A. Sportiello, *J. Phys. A.* **53**(6), 064001 (25pp), (2020).

[90] S. Caracciolo, C. Lucibello, G. Parisi, and G. Sicuro, *Phys. Rev. E.* **90**, 012118, (2014).

[91] S. Caracciolo and G. Sicuro, *Phys. Rev. E.* **91**, 062125, (2015).

[92] L. Ambrosio, F. Stra, and D. Trevisan, *Probab. Theory Relat. Fields.* **173**, 433–477, (2019).

[93] L. Ambrosio, F. Glaudo, and D. Trevisan, *Discrete Cont. Dyn. A.* **39**, 1078–0947, (2019).

[94] S. Caracciolo and G. Sicuro, *Phys. Rev. Lett.* **115**(23), 230601, (2015).

[95] D. Benedetto and E. Caglioti, *J. Stat. Phys.* **181**, 854–869, (2020).

[96] V. Ivrii, *Bull. Math. Sci.* **6**(3), 379–452, (2016).

[97] L. Ambrosio and F. Glaudo, *J. Éc. Polytech. Math.* **6**, 737–765, (2019).

[98] D. Benedetto, E. Caglioti, S. Caracciolo, M. P. D'Achille, G. Sicuro, and A. Sportiello, *J. Stat. Phys.* **183**, 34, (2021).

[99] P. Koehl, M. Delarue, and H. Orland, *Phys. Rev. Lett.* **123**, 040603, (2019).

[100] P. Koehl and H. Orland, *Phys. Rev. E.* **103**, 042101, (2021).

[101] P. Koehl, M. Delarue, and H. Orland, *Phys. Rev. E.* **103**, 012113, (2021).

Chapter 2

Beyond the Ising Spin Glass I
m-Vector, Potts, p-Spin, Spherical, Induced Moment, Random Graphs

David Sherrington[*] and Jairo R. L. de Almeida[†]

[*]*Rudolf Peierls Centre for Theoretical Physics, Oxford OX1 3PU, UK*
david.sherrington@physics.ox.ac.uk
[†]*Departamento de Física, Universidade Federal de Pernambuco, Recife, Brazil*
jairorolimalmeida19@gmail.com

This chapter presents extensions of Ising spin glass models to different kinds of variables (spins/pseudo-spins) and types of interactions which have led to new concepts and enriched the physical understanding of these systems.

2.1. Introduction

When one of us introduced the SK model [1] in 1975, following the very innovative paper of Edwards and Anderson (EA) [2] earlier that same year, he made two choices that have proven to be influential: (i) an infinite-range intensive exchange distribution, and (ii) Ising spins. The first was made in the hope of enabling an exact solution by analogy with and extension of previously known work on pure magnets and to provide the correct mean-field solution; the second to simplify some of the technicalities. In the event, the correct mean-field solution turned out to be much more subtle and interesting than was anticipated, thus revealing that mean-field theory need not be trivial — a common perspective at the time. The use of discrete Ising spins was serendipitous in highlighting a problem with a 'natural' (replica-symmetric) ansatz, recognized through an unphysical negative entropy feature already in SK. (The problem would not have been obvious for continuous classical spins where such a feature is a known pathology.)[a] The probable origin of the unphysical entropy was later shown by the demonstration of an instability in an excitation mode in replica-space by the other of us and Thouless (AT) [3], eventually leading Parisi, between 1979 [4] and 1983 [5], to identify the correct and highly impactful (full) replica symmetry breaking (RSB) resolution.

In this chapter we introduce systems with spins and interactions of different symmetries and indicate some of the qualitatively new consequences that arise. Mainly, we concentrate on systems with quenched infinite-range interactions, drawn randomly and independently from identical distributions, in conceptual analogy with SK, in the expectation of mean-field solvability in the thermodynamic limit $N \to \infty$ and the definition of

---

[a]EA considered Heisenberg $m = 3$ spins, presumably because the stimulating experiments at the time involved Heisenberg spins.

the appropriate associated mean-field theories. We concentrate on equilibrium/Gibbsian statistical mechanics (statics), leaving dynamics to later chapters.

Note that we pre-assume a qualitative understanding of what constitutes a spin glass, the replica method for studying averaged physical observables, the Ising infinite-ranged Sherrington-Kirkpatrick model, the replica-symmetric approximation to the SK model, the Almeida-Thouless replicon instability and its implications for the need to break replica-symmetry, Parisi's mathematical ansatz for SK and its physical meaning. For readers without this prior knowledge, it is recommended to first read the introductory chapters of the earlier book "Spin Glass Theory and Beyond" (see Chapter 0).

2.2. Binary Interaction Models

In this section we consider models that retain a pairwise interaction structure.

2.2.1. *Local moment spins of $O(m)$ symmetry*

We first consider systems with classical m-vector spins $\mathbf{S}_i$ (m integral) beyond Ising ($m = 1$) and with SK-like scalar-product interactions.

In the absence of anisotropy these models have the Hamiltonian

$$H = -\sum_{(ij)} J_{ij}\mathbf{S}_i \cdot \mathbf{S}_j, \tag{2.1}$$

with J_{ij} drawn independently randomly and symmetrically ($J_{ij} = J_{ji}$) à la SK, from a Gaussian distribution of mean[b] J_0/N and variance J^2/N. The subsequent behaviour is essentially as for the $m = 1$ case. (For RS analysis, see Refs. [7, 8]). In particular, if the spin length normalisation is chosen as $|\mathbf{S}| = \sqrt{m}$ the spin glass transition temperature (in units with Boltzmann's constant set to unity $k_B = 1$) is $T = J$.

Something different arises when anisotropic terms are included.

First, consider the application of a uniform uni-directional magnetic field, in a direction denoted below by 1,

$$H = -\sum_{(ij)} J_{ij}\mathbf{S}_i \cdot \mathbf{S}_j - \sum_i hS_i^1. \tag{2.2}$$

In 1981, Gabay and Toulouse [9] pointed out that this system would then have a new transition to a spin glass phase transverse to the field direction (i.e. symmetric in the $m \neq 1$ hyper-plane) beneath a characteristic GT line in (h, T), starting from $T = 1$ for $h = 0$ and with h_{GT} going asymptotically to ∞ as $T \to 0$. Replica symmetry breaks beneath this line, gradually and strongly in the transverse direction (as for an $(m - 1)$-dimensional spin glass), but also weakly in the 1-direction, until a cross-over to stronger RSB around an AT-like (h, T) line [10–13]; see Figs. 2.1 and 2.2. However, for a $J_0 = 0$ $m > 2$-vector system with external fields randomly and independently distributed over the full m-hypersphere there is no GT analogue, only AT lines which are m-dependent [14]; see Fig. 2.3.

---

[b]The inclusion of a finite positive mean, originally by Sherrington and Southern [6], aims to emulate the concentration-dependence of experimental spin glass systems. However, most other theoretical authors have concentrated on the zero-mean case ($J_0 = 0$) to emphasise the spin glass features.

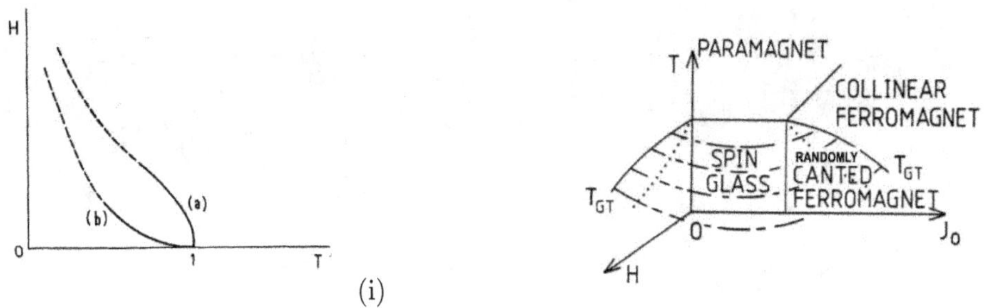

Fig. 2.1. m-vector phase diagrams: (i) $J_0 = 0$ in an applied field H: (a) GT transverse spin-glass onset line, (b) AT crossover; (ii) including a positive exchange distribution mean J_0. Solid lines denote phase transitions, dashed lines denote quasi-AT crossovers. Reprinted with permission from (i) M. Gabay and G. Toulouse, Phys. Rev. Lett. **47**, 201 (1981) [9]. ©(1981) American Physical Society; (ii) D. Sherrington, Springer Lecture Notes in Physics **192**, 125 (1983) [13]. ©(1983) Springer-Verlag [13].

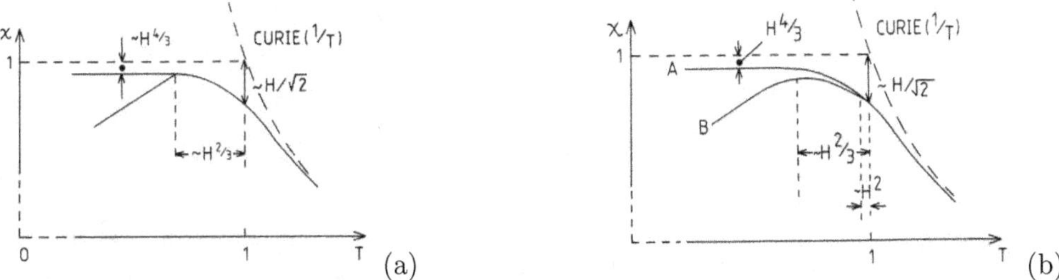

Fig. 2.2. Schematic longitudinal spin glass susceptibilities in field H for (a) Ising, and (b) m-vector spins. The upper curves are field-cooled, the lower ones are zero-field-cooled, reflecting the difference between $[1 - \int dx q_{||}(x)]/T$ and $[1 - q_{||\max}]/T$. Reprinted with permission from D. Sherrington, Springer Lecture Notes in Physics **192**, 125 (1983) [13]. ©(1983) Springer-Verlag.

Second, consider the case with quadratic single-site anisotropy

$$H = -\sum_{(ij)} J_{ij}\mathbf{S}_i \cdot \mathbf{S}_j - \sum_i h S_i^1 - \sum_i D(S_i^1)^2. \tag{2.3}$$

It exhibits three different spin glass phases already for $J_0 = 0, h = 0$, as shown in Fig. 2.4. RSB is fully obtained in all three phases. For a more general situation, including $J_0 \neq 0, h \neq 0$, RSB and Parisi solutions, see [15].

2.2.2. *Potts spins*

All m-vector spins, including Ising ($m = 1$) spins, have definiteness symmetry with pairwise interactions, J_{ij} and $-J_{ij}$ each leading to a unique relative ordering of the pair of spins i and j to minimize their energy. This is not the case for p-state Potts spins [17] with $p > 2$, where a ferromagnetic J prefers identical Potts states on i and j, whereas an antiferromagnetic J leads to $(p - 1)$ degenerate optima. To investigate possible consequences of the lack of this symmetry, Elderfield and Sherrington (1983) [18]

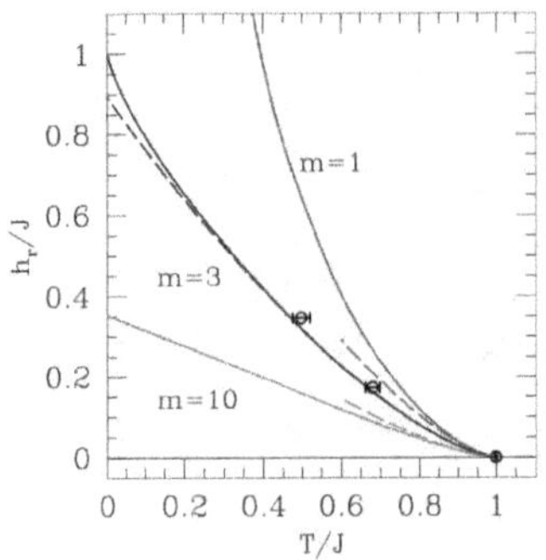
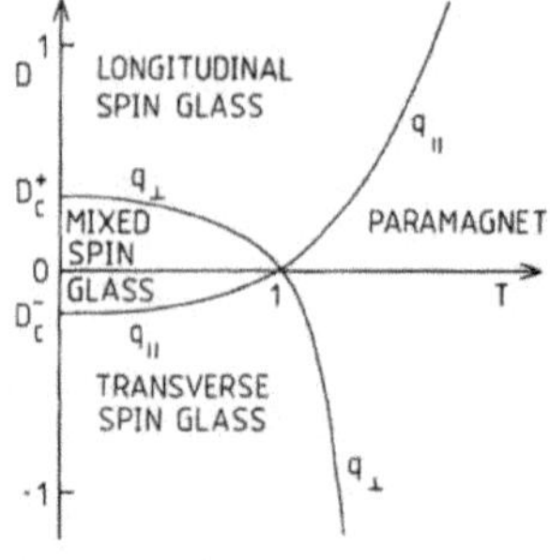

Fig. 2.3.   AT line for m-vector spin glasses in quenched m-vector local random fields. Reprinted with permission from A. Sharma and A. P. Young, Phys. Rev. E **81**, 061115 (2010) [14]. ©(2010) American Physical Society.

Fig. 2.4.   Phase diagram of anisotropic spin glass [16]. Reprinted with permission from D. M. Cragg and D. Sherrington, Phys. Rev. Lett. **49**, 1190 (1982) [10]. ©(1982) American Physical Society.

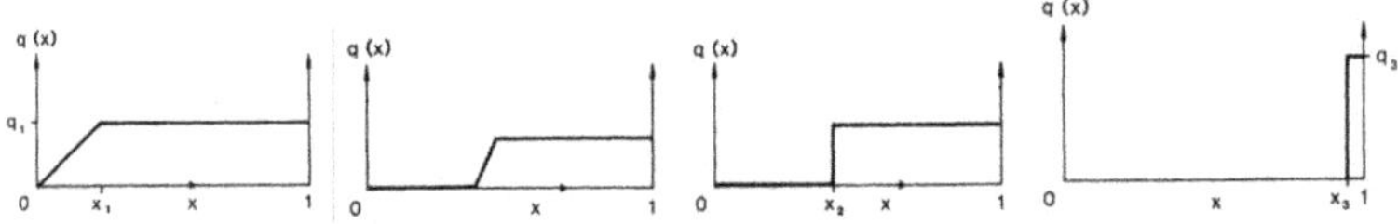

Fig. 2.5.   Parisi order functions of Potts Glasses for small $\tau = (T_c - T)/T_c$; (i) $p = 2 \equiv$ Ising (FRSB), (ii) $p_{c1} > p > 2$, (iii) $p_{c2} > p > p_{c1}$ (C1RSB), (iv) $p > p_{c2}$ (D1RSB). Reprinted with permission from D. Sherrington, Prog. Theor. Phys. Supp. **87**, 180 (1986) [21]. ©(1986) Phys. Soc. Japan.

considered the p-state Potts extension of SK[c]

$$H = \sum_{(ij)} J_{ij}(p\delta_{\pi(i)\pi(j)} - 1); \pi = 1, \ldots, p \tag{2.4}$$

where the J_{ij} are distributed as in Eq. (2.1).

This system turns out to have unusual RSB behaviour compared with m-vector systems [18, 20, 21], as illustrated in Fig. 2.5 for the Parisi order function $q(x); x \in (0,1)$ for increasing p, based on formulae interpolated to real p.

There are two critical Potts dimensions characterising significant changes in the overlap distribution. First, $p_{c1} = 2.82$ separates a range of overlaps continuous between peaks at $q = 0$ and a finite q_{EA}, i.e. full RSB, and another with 1RSB, itself split into two parts, the first onsetting continuously up to the second critical value $p_{c2} = 4$, the second for $p > p_{c2}$, for which the 1RSB onset is discontinuous one-step [20] but without latent heat, now known as a random first order transition (RFOT) [22] in recognition of the discontinuity in state-overlap as opposed to normal Ehrenfest first order; see Fig. 2.5. Corresponding overlap distributions, $\overline{P(q)}$, are illustrated in Fig. 2.6. Qualitatively similar behaviour is found in other systems lacking symmetry of definiteness (see e.g. [23]).

---

[c]Erzan and Lage [19] also introduced and studied the model, contemporaneously but independently.

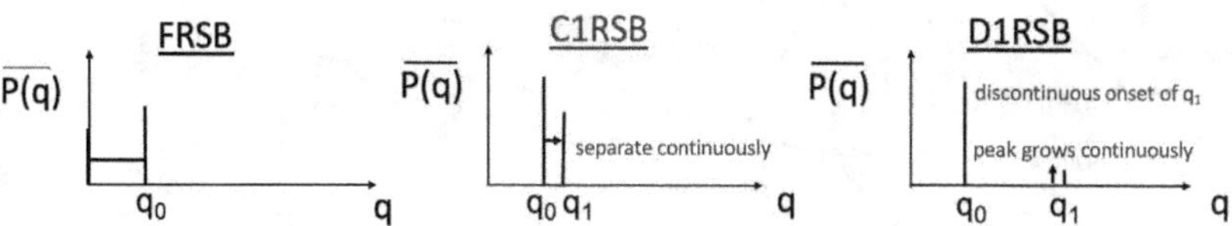

Fig. 2.6. Types of RSB $\overline{P(q)}$: (i) FRB ($p_{c1} > p > 2$); (ii) C1RSB (continuous onset) ($p_{c2} > p > p_{c2}$) (iii) D1RSB (discontinuous onset) ($p > p_{c2}$).

2.3. p-Spin Interactions

Another interesting and influential extension of the original binary-interaction SK model was introduced by Derrida in 1980 with the binary interaction term in the SK Hamiltonian replaced by one involving p interacting spins [24, 25].

2.3.1. *Ising spins*

Derrida considered p interacting Ising spins,

$$H_p = - \sum_{(i_1 i_2 \ldots i_p)} J_{i_1 \ldots i_p} \sigma_{i_1} \sigma_{i_2} \ldots \sigma_{i_p}; \quad \sigma = \pm 1 \tag{2.5}$$

with the $J_{i_1 \ldots i_p}$ randomly chosen from a Gaussian probability distribution of variance $J^2/N^{(p-1)}$. For $p \to \infty$ Derrida showed that the problem simplifies into a random energy model (REM), which he solved exactly, demonstrating freezing into the lowest energy state below a critical temperature, corresponding to 1RSB but without the need for a replica formulation. In 1984, Gross and Mézard subsequently discussed this model using several of the methods used for the SK model—including the replica method — to explicitly identify the low-temperature phase as 1RSB with a discontinuous transition [26].

In further important study in 1985 [27], Gardner demonstrated for p-spin Ising systems that (i) for all $p > 2$ the spin glass transition from paramagnet to spin glass is 1RSB (whereas for $p=2$ (SK) the transition is FRSB), and (ii) that for $2 < p < \infty$ there is also a lower temperature (Gardner) transition to full RSB. Both observations have had further important ramifications subsequently, to be discussed in Chap. 12.

2.3.2. *Spherical models*

A solvable extension of the normal ferromagnetic Ising model, known as the spherical model, was introduced by [28], replacing the Ising variables $\sigma = \pm 1$ on each site $i = 1 \ldots N$ by a single (hyperspherical) condition $\sum_{i=1}^{N} \sigma_i^2 = N$, with the individual σ otherwise able to take any real value. A corresponding spherical extension of the (infinite-range $p = 2$) SK Ising spin glass model was introduced and solved by Kosterlitz *et al.* [29], using several different procedures—including without resorting to replicas — and shown to exhibit a spin glass phase without replica symmetry breaking.

In a later study of the equilibrium statistical mechanics (statics) for the case of a spherical extension of the general-p-spin infinite-range (SK-extended) model, Crisanti

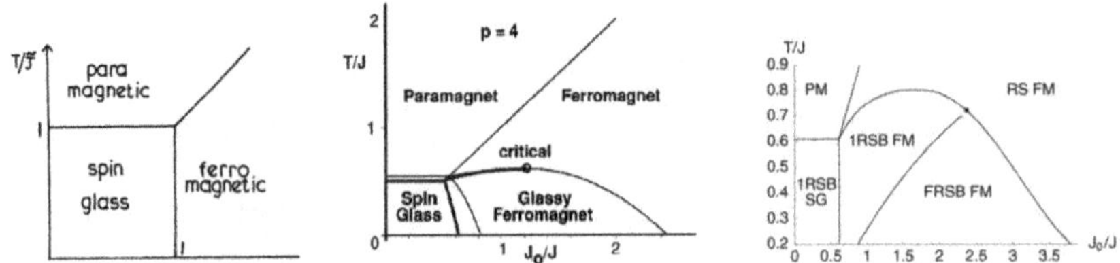

Fig. 2.7. Spin glass phase diagrams: (i) spherical spins $p = 2$, statics, no RSB; (ii) spherical spins $p = 4$, statics (solid lines), dynamics (fine lines), dot (critical point, discontinuous 1RSB to left, continuous 1RSB to right); (iii) Ising $p = 5$ statics, showing also 1RSB to FRSB transition. Reprinted with permission from (i) J. M. Kosterlitz, D. J. Thouless and R.C. Jones, Phys. Rev. Lett. **36**, 1217 (1976) [29]. ©(1976) American Physical Society; (ii) J. A. Hertz, D. Sherrington and Th. M. Nieuwenhuizen, Phys. Rev. E **60**, R2460 (1999) [34]. ©(1999) American Physical Society; (iii) P. Gillin, D. Sherrington and H. Nishimori, J. Phys. A **34**, 2949 (2001) [35]. ©(2001) IOPP.

and Sommers (1992) showed that for $p > 2$ the spin glass state is 1RSB, with onset discontinuous below a critical magnetic field, continuous above it [30]. In a further (1993) paper on the relaxational dynamics with Horner [31], they demonstrated several further intriguing features, including that the onset temperatures for 1RSB is higher for dynamics than that given by equilibrium statics. Later work recognised that the dynamical 1RSB onset corresponds to marginal stability of the statics.

Also in 1993, Cugliandolo and Kurchan [32] made a different study of the dynamics of the p-spin spherical model at long but finite times, demonstrating many unexpected but important new features, including 'weak' ergodicity breaking and aging effects, leading to much activity and results Chapter 9.

Even though the $p = 2$ spherical model does not exhibit RSB, it was shown also to have non-trivial dynamics [33].

Figure 2.7 shows examples of several models with various p-spin random zero-mean SK-extended interactions together with 2-spin ferromagnetic interactions, demonstrating several phases, including glassy ferromagnetism, and transitions.

There has also been significant interest in mixed-p spin glasses with infinite-ranged extended-SK interactions, particularly spherical models because of their solvability advantages along with realisation that they (mixed-p systems) can have FRSB as well as 1RSB, as well as more complicated issues, both static and dynamic, of potential relevance to the understanding of other glasses; see e.g. [36–38].

2.4. Finite-Connectivity Graph Models

Although the infinite-ranged SK model was introduced for its putative solvability rather than to mimic specific experimental systems, subsequent interest (and extension of the model) turned to many problems where spatial separation is irrelevant, e.g., communication through the world wide web and random satisfiability in computer science. Several such problems are discussed in later chapters, but we here (briefly) discuss one, which appeared early on in the field.

In 1985, Viana and Bray introduced a dimension-free but (on-average) finite-connectivity alternative to the SK spin glass model [39], in which active spins are effectively located on an Erdös-Renyi graph of average connectivity c with interactions on linked sites quench-randomly chosen from a distribution $P_c(J)$:

$$H = -\sum_{(ij)} J_{(ij)}\sigma_i\sigma_j; \quad P(J_{ij}) = (c/N)P_c(J_{ij}) + (1 - c/N)\delta(J_{ij}). \tag{2.6}$$

As for the EA and SK models, a spin glass phase results from sufficient frustration in $P_c(J)$, in purest form with $P_c(J) = P_c(-J)$, but without need for N-scaling of the variance for c finite.

In 1986, Fu and Anderson showed the relationship of this model with graph bi-partitioning,[d] including a demonstration of mapping the extensively connected graph problem to the SK model [40].

The Erdös–Renyi graph above has variable connectivity (with average c) on different sites, but there is also some interest—particularly in computer science — in random *regular* graphs, for which all vertices have the same connectivity c, but are still quench-disordered. This problem, with finite c, independent of the total number of vertices N, was considered numerically by Banavar *et al.* [41] in connection with optimal graph bi-partitioning, finding evidence for several of the novel features of the Parisi SK solution. The full analytical solution has proven harder than for SK, but RSB was found [42–44]. Further finite-connectivity random graph optimization studies, and extensions to classic computer science such as random satisfiability, have led to many new concepts.

2.5. Induced Moment Spin Glasses

Models considered thus far have non-zero spins (moments) even in the absence of interactions. For some systems, however, interactions are required to bootstrap-induce moments and exhibit cooperative (including spin glass) magnetism. Ferromagnetic examples have been known for centuries and recognised for many decades, but here we make the case for spin glasses.

2.5.1. *Discrete spins*

Stimulated by the consideration of local crystal field splitting favouring a singlet ground state, a discrete/'hard'-spin example of an induced-moment spin glass was introduced in 1977 by Ghatak and Sherrington (GS) [45], with Hamiltonian

$$H = -D\sum_i S_i^2 - \sum_{ij} J_{ij}S_iS_j; \ S = 0, \pm 1, \tag{2.7}$$

with the J_{ij} Gaussian-distributed around zero mean. In the absence of the interaction term, for $D > 0$ the local term alone favours $S = \pm 1$, but for $D < 0$ it favours all $S = 0$, i.e., no moments. Consequently, for $D > 0$ the full system (including the interaction term) behaves qualitatively analogously to the SK model, while for $D < 0$ there is a critical maximum $|D|$ to permit bootstrap-induced cooperative order. At the RS level of

---

[d]In optimal graph bipartioning one seeks a separation of vertices into two groups of equal size with the minimal number of graph edges between them. This problem is equivalent to that of finding the ground state of a system of Ising spins on the vertices of the graph interacting ferromagnetically along the edges but with a frustrating constraint of zero overall magnetization.

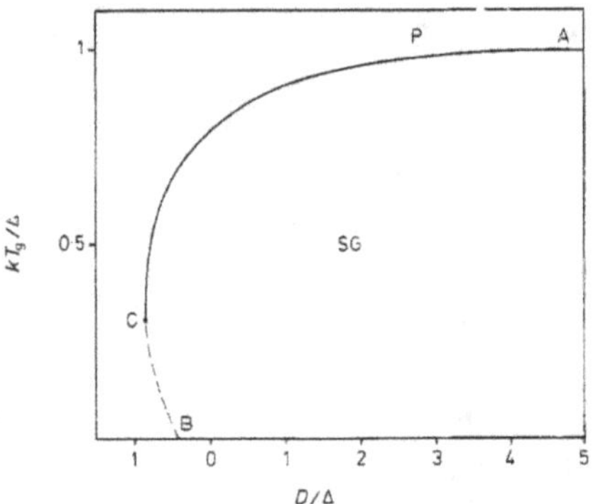

Fig. 2.8. Phase diagram of the GS model. The solid curve indicates a continuous transition between paramagnet and spin glass, the dashed curve a thermodynamic first-order transition. The spin glass phase is full RSB. Reprinted with permission from S. K. Ghatak and D. Sherrington, J. Phys. C. **10**, 3149–3156, (1977) [45]. ©(1977) IOPP.

description, the phase diagram is as shown in Fig. 2.8 and demonstrates both continuous and (Ehrenfest) first-order phase transitions from paramagnet to spin glass, along with re-entrance/inverse-freezing from spin glass to paramagnet. Including RSB modifies the details of the first-order transition line but retains its qualitative character [46].

2.5.2. *Itinerant spin glasses*

A simple soft-spin model was initially proposed in 1973 by Sherrington and Mihill (SM) [47, 48], to try to explain the magnetic behaviour of the transition metal spin glass alloy RhCo; see Fig. 2.9 [49].[e] Starting from a disordered Hubbard model alloy of ions with different Coulomb U, transforming to auxiliary local magnetization fields and with some simplification, including static approximation, leads to an effective Hamiltonian

$$H = \sum_i \{\kappa_i |\mathbf{m}_i|^2 + \lambda_i |\mathbf{m}_i|^4\} - \sum_{(ij); i \neq j} J(\mathbf{R}_{ij}) \mathbf{m}_i . \mathbf{m}_j, \qquad (2.8)$$

where the i, j label sites, the $\mathbf{m}_i$ are unconstrained local magnetization variables, the local coefficients κ_i and λ_i depend on the type of atom at site i, and the $J(\mathbf{R}_{ij})$ are inter-site interaction energies.[f]

$\kappa < 0$ would favour local moments [50] (ground state with $m \neq 0$ in the absence of interaction), the analogue of $D > 0$ in the GS model. But for both Rh and Co the κ are positive, so that the local harmonic terms alone favour no moment, $|\mathbf{m}| = 0$. Inclusion of the interaction term, however, offers the potential for bootstrapped collective order if the resultant binding energy can overcome the local cost. For pure Co this results in ferromagnetism, but the same is not true of Rh,[g] which consequently is not magnetic. Hence, without need for computation, in analogies with local moment spin glasses (such as Au Fe) and itinerant ferromagnets (such as Ni), one can immediately anticipate a phase diagram with three low-temperature phases as a function of increasing Co

---

[e]Pure bulk Rh is non-magnetic, pure bulk Co is an itinerant ferromagnet, but isolated Co ions in Rh do not carry a long-lived moment and at very low concentrations RhCo is Pauli paramagnetic. However, at intermediate concentrations of Co a spin glass was observed, along with magnetic clustering features.

[f]In terms of the Hubbard model parameters, $\kappa_i = (1 - U_i \chi_{ii})$ and $J(\mathbf{R}_{ij}) = (\sqrt{U_i U_j} \chi_{ij})$, where the U are the appropriate (site-occupation dependent) Hubbard potentials and χ_{ij} is the two-site conduction-band susceptibility.

[g]$(1 - U_{\mathrm{Co}} \sum_j \chi_{ij}) < 0$, $(1 - U_{\mathrm{Rh}} \sum_j \chi_{ij}) > 0$.

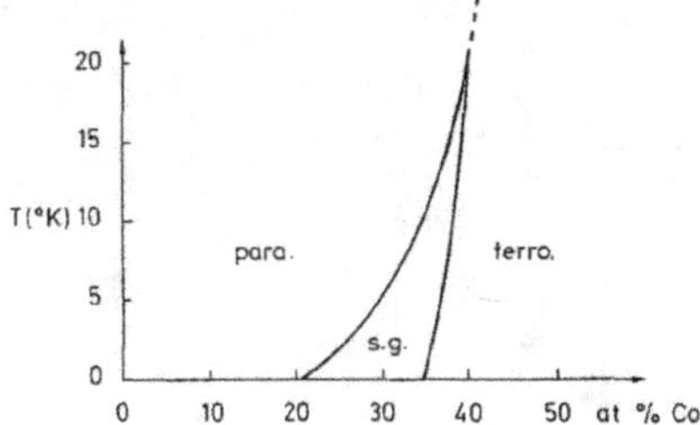

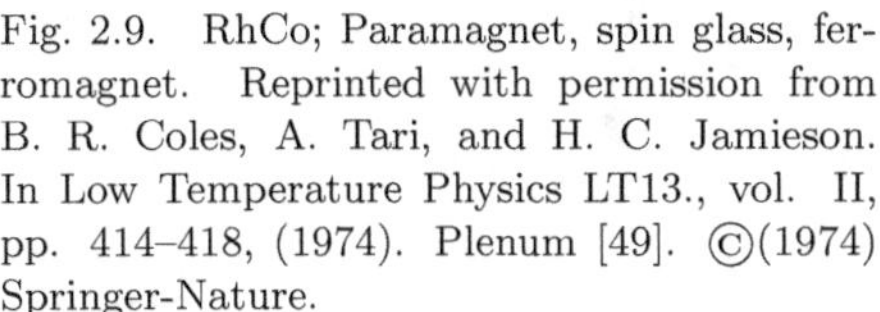

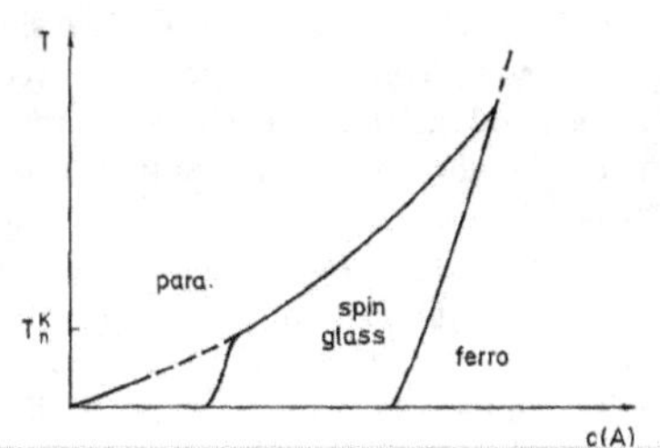

Fig. 2.9. RhCo; Paramagnet, spin glass, ferromagnet. Reprinted with permission from B. R. Coles, A. Tari, and H. C. Jamieson. In Low Temperature Physics LT13., vol. II, pp. 414–418, (1974). Plenum [49]. ©(1974) Springer-Nature.

Fig. 2.10. Schematic prediction for RhCo-type alloy. Reprinted with permission from D. Sherrington and K. Mihill, J. de Physique **5**, C4, 199 (1974) [47]. ©(1974) EPS.

concentration of Pauli paramagnet, itinerant spin glass, and itinerant ferromagnet; see Fig. 2.10.[h]

2.5.3. *Relaxor ferroelectrics as 'soft' pseudo-spin glasses*

A similar reasoning provides a likely explanation for a long-standing puzzle in some displacive ferroelectric alloys and also opens up a potentially interesting new direction for random-field magnets.

Examples of pure displacive ferroelectrics are found in ionic crystalline compounds based on the generic formula ABO_3 with charges A^{2+}, B^{4+}, and O^{2-} and at high temperature have cubic perovskite structure; see Fig. 2.11. Inter-ionic interactions can lead to spontaneous structural distortions to lower symmetry at lower temperature if the consequential interaction energy lowering is great enough to overcome local displacement costs. With several ionic types within the unit cell with different harmonic displacement coefficients, the displacements of the different ion types relative to their locations in the higher-temperature phase are themselves different, leading to spontaneous intra-cell electric dipole moments and hence ferroelectricity.[i] $BaTiO_3$ (BT) and $PbTiO_3$ (PT) are two classic examples and have been studied theoretically quantitatively using non-disordered and three-dimensional analogues of Eq. (2.8), with the local magnetizations replaced by displacements; *e.g* by [53, 54];[j] see again Fig. 2.11.[k]

The present interest, however, concerns substitutional alloys. Already in the 1950s, experimental behaviour retrospectively reminiscent of corresponding behaviour later

---

[h]Pre-EA, SM [47, 48] were motivated by a desire to include statistically occurring local moment-like clustering. Post-EA, Hertz [51] examined a similar starting model, concentrating on prediction of an extended itinerant spin glass phase. He proposed to name it *Stoner glass* in recognition of the pioneering work of Stoner [52] on itinerant (conduction electron) magnetism.

[i]Displacive ferroelectricity is thus an analogue of itinerant ferromagnetism.

[j]First-principles quantum-mechanical calculations are used to determine the parameters in effective classical Hamiltonians whose subsequent thermodynamic consequences are then explored through computer simulations.

[k]BT and PT transform from cubic to tetragonal as the temperatures are reduced, with also different ionic intracell relative displacements.

Fig. 2.11. ABO_3 perovskite. Circles show high T cubic cell: A (open), B (central black dot), O (dark shaded circles). Unit cell distorts to tetragonal ($c > a = b$) beneath T_c. Arrows show ionic displacements in the ferroelectric phase relative to the tetragonal cell. $PbTiO_3$. Reprinted with permission from A. Garcia and D. Vanderbilt, Phys. Rev. B **54**, 3817-3824 (1996) [54]. ©(1996) American Physical Society.

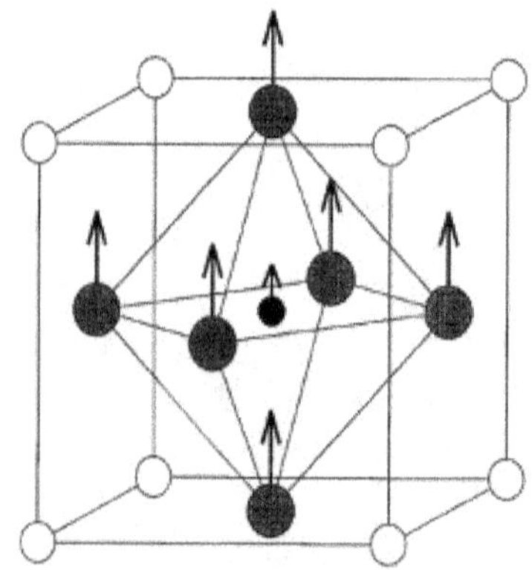

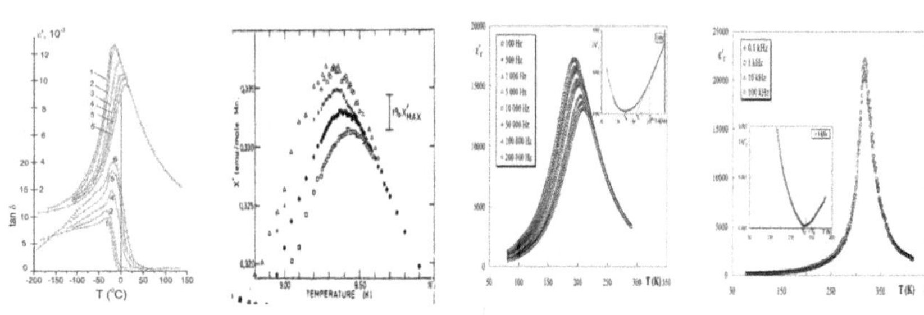

Fig. 2.12.   AC susceptibilities: (i) heterovalent relaxor $PbMg_{1/3}Nb_{2/3}O_3$ (PMN) [57] (1960); (ii) spin glass **CuMn**; (iii) homovalent relaxor $BaZr_{0.35}Ti_{0.65}O_3$ (BZT); (iv) ferroelectric $BaZr_{0.20}Ti_{0.80}O_3$. Reprinted with permission from (i) G. Smolenskii, J. Phys. Soc. Japan Suppl. **28**, 26 (1970) [63]. ©(1970) Phys. Soc. Japan; (ii) C. Mulder, A. van Duyneveldt and J. Mydosh, Phys. Rev. B **23**, (1981) [56]. ©(1981) American Physical Society; (iii)-(iv) A. Simon, J. Ravez and M. Maglione, J. Phys.: Condens. Matter **16**, 963–970 (2004) [64]. ©(2004) IOPP.

seen in experimental spin glasses [55, 56] was observed in the alloy $PbMg_{1/3}Nb_{2/3}O_3$ (PMN) [57, 58]; high, sharpish, strongly frequency-dependent peaks in AC susceptibility, see Figs. 2.12(i) and (ii), but with no change in overall lattice structure and no ferroelectricity, again reminiscent of early spin glass experimentation that demonstrated spin freezing without periodicity. Other characteristic spin glass features, such as differences between FC and ZFC static susceptibilities beneath the static/low frequency susceptibility peak temperature, were observed later; see *e.g.* Fig. 2.13. Initially referred to simply as a *ferroelectric with diffusive phase transition*, later the name *relaxor* was attributed to the new phase. Given their experimental similarity, theoretical comparison with spin glasses, with induced electric dipoles the analogues of local magnetizations, seems natural [59–62].

PMN is a substitutional $A(B/B')O_3$ perovskite alloy in which the Ti^{4+} B-ions in $PbTiO_3$ (PT) are replaced randomly and heterovalently by Mg^{2+} and Nb^{4+} in the charge-conserving ratio 1:2. However, it is instructive to consider first the more recently discovered alloy $BaZr_xTi_{1-x}O_3$ (BZT) [64], in which the Ti and Zr B-ions are homovalent (both 4+) and so without the extra, potentially complicating, charge — and hence effective field — disorder of PMN. The AC susceptibility for BZT with $x = 0.35$ is shown in Fig. 2.12(iii). It looks very similar to those shown for PMN and CuMn, suggesting similar physics. (Again, the average crystal structure remains cubic perovskite,

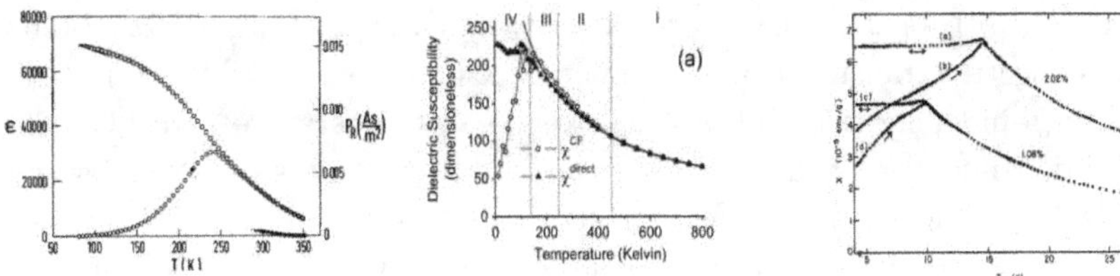

Fig. 2.13. Field cooled (FC) vs. zero-field cooled (ZFC) static susceptibilities; (i) PMN; (ii)BZT$_{50/50}$ simulation; (iii) CuMn spin glass. Reprinted with permission from (i) A. Levstik, Z. Kutnjak, C. Filipič and R. Pirc, Phys. Rev. B **57**, 11204–11211 (1998) [65]. ©(1998) American Physical Society; (ii) R. Akbarzadeh, S. Prosandeev, E. J. Walter, A. Al-Barakaty and L. Bellaiche, Phys. Rev. Lett. **108**, 257601 (2012) [61]. ©(2012) American Physical Society; (iii) S. Nagata, P. H. Keesom and H. R. Harrison, Phys. Rev. B **19**, 1633–1638 (1979) [66] ©(1979) American Physical Society.

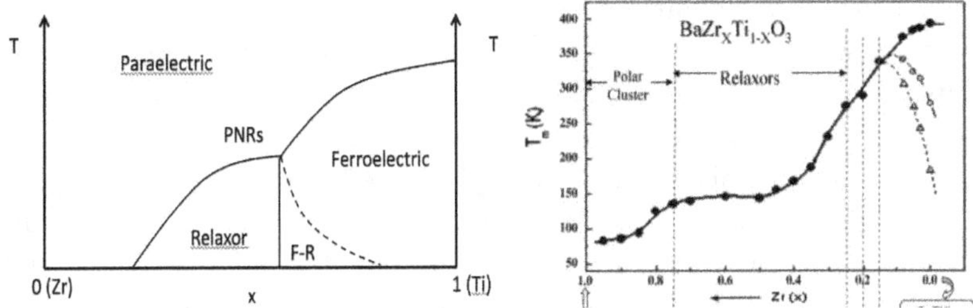

Fig. 2.14. Left: Heuristic phase diagram for BZT, by analogy with spin glass. Polar nano-regions (PNRs) refer to locally correlated statistical clusters above the extended cooperative transition [62]; F-R refers to a possible mixed ferroelectric-relaxor. Right: Experimental phase diagram for BZT. Reprinted with permission from T. Maiti, R. Guo and A. S. Bhalla, J. Am. Ceram. Soc. **91**, 1769–1780 (2008) [68]. ©(2008) Am. Ceram. Soc.

without global electric order.) The preparation-dependence of static susceptibilities also look similar, with a separation between field cooled and zero field cooled susceptibilities onsetting at the transition and growing as temperature is reduced; see Fig. 2.13.

Noting that pure BaZrO$_3$ is experimentally found not to exhibit ferroelectricity, in contrast to BaTiO$_3$, one can already deduce that the local harmonic displacement coefficient of Zr must be significantly greater than that of Ti, too large for the interaction terms to overcome it.[1]

The relaxor phase of BZT, as discussed above, is straightforwardly explainable by analogy with the induced-moment discussion above for a spin glass phase in RhCo, with Zr the analogue of Rh, Ti of Co, and the relaxor the analogue of a spin glass, with in-cell ionic displacements analogues of local magnetizations; see Fig. 2.14. Simulations of BZT$_{50/50}$ using a model as discussed above have been performed by [61] (FC/ZFC, Fig. 2.13 (ii)) and [67] (AC susceptibility), in good accord with experiments.

It is also interesting to compare the frequency-dependence of the location of the peaks in experimental AC susceptibility curves of BaZr$_x$Ti$_{1-x}$O$_3$ for concentrations of the Zr ions above and below the critical concentration separating ferroelectric and

---

[1]Because Zr^{4+} and Ti^{4+} are isovalent, the strengths of the ionic Coulombic interactions in BT and BZ are essentially the same. The local displacement coefficients can be calculated from numerical first-principles quantum mechanics. Another crude indicator comes from comparing ionic radii.

relaxor; see Fig. 2.12(iv) for $x = 0.20$, ferroelectric, and Fig. 2.12(iii) for $x = 0.035$, relaxor. The ferroelectric transition peak temperature of AC susceptibility of BZT is essentially frequency-independent while the relaxor peak temperature in BZT35:65 is highly frequency-dependent, as indeed are the peaks for spin-glass onset in low concentration CuMn (Fig. 2.12(ii)) and heterovalent relaxor PMN (Fig. 2.12(i)). It seems likely that the greater dispersion of the relaxors and spin glass, compared with their ferro counterparts, are consequences of the rugged and chaotically-evolving *free energy landscape* that underlies RSB.

Let us now return to the original, canonical and much studied relaxor PMN. It differs from BZT in that its site-occupation disorder is heterovalent, with the two types of B ions carrying different charges, Mg being 2+ and Nb 5+, rather than the 4+ of the normal pure (ABO_3) template. Being also randomly distributed, they lead to extra quenched random fields in an extension of Eq. (2.8), in three dimensions.

Noting that Mg^{2+} has a similar ionic radius to Zr^{4+} and Nb^{5+} a similar ionic radius to Ti^{4+}, one can expect some B-ordering tendencies in PMN similar to those in BZT [69]. However, since $PbZr_xTi_{1-x}O_3$ (PZT) has not been observed to exhibit relaxor behaviour, the random fields appear to be also necessary for the favouring of spin glass behaviour in PMN.[m] This further raises the issue of possible (quasi-)spin-glass behaviour in even-simpler systems with a combination of frustrated but non-random interactions and quenched local disorder only through random fields. Given that truly three-dimensionally random local magnetic fields are impossible to produce experimentally, heterovalent relaxor alloys may provide fruitful alternative *experimental laboratories* for the study of their consequences.

A third feature observed experimentally in relaxors, and considered as one of their key characteristics, is of clusters of locally ordered regions above the (susceptibility-peak) transition temperature, generally referred to as Polar Nano-regions (PNRs). Within the picture outlined above they are simply explainable for homovalent systems (such as BZT) as quench-statistically-occurring localized states in an analogue of Anderson localization [70] in which a *'mobility' edge* determines the separation of cooperative extended order and insufficiently correlated PNRs, while a density-of-states *band edge* emulates the limit of PNR observability [62, 71].

A minimal SK-analogue induced-moment model is [72]

$$H = \sum_i (rm_i^2 + um_i^4) - \sum_{(ij)} J_{ij} m_i m_j, \tag{2.9}$$

with the $\{J_{ij}\}$ drawn independently randomly from the infinite-ranged SK distribution, offering the possibility of exact solution.[n] However, because all the eigenstates of the SK-distribution for $\{J_{(ij)}\}$ are extended, no PNRs should result.

---

[m] Note that Pb^{2+} is significantly more easily displaceable than Ba^{2+}; in ferroelectric BT the relative displacements of Ba:Ti is 1:4 while in PT the relative displacements of Pb:Ti is 7:3, so that the undiluted A-site (Pb) ions play the dominant role in PMN, in contrast to the diluted B-site Ti-ions in BZT. This is in accord with the smaller ionic radius of Pb^{2+} compared with Ba^{2+}.

[n] It has also recently been proposed and studied in connection with low temperature vibrational excitations of structural glasses [73].

In summary, in this sub-section we have drawn attention to displacive relaxor ferroelectrics that display features that are reminiscent of spin glasses.[o] Although these features were observed already six decades ago and have led to considerable practical applications, their understanding nevertheless remains controversial. We have argued for an explanation as induced pseudo-spin glass. Furthermore, by comparison of two different relaxor examples, homovalent and heterovalent, we speculate on an important role for quenched random fields in systems with spatially frustrated interactions, and on heterovalent relaxors as potentially valuable experimental 'laboratories' for the study of three-dimensionally random local field systems, which are not easily available for magnetic systems.

2.6. Short-Range and Lattice Models

While the discussions above have been principally in terms of range-free systems, real experimental systems are normally lattice-based in physical dimensions, normally $d = 3$, sometimes with relatively short-ranged but still frustrated interactions (*e.g.* $Eu_xSr_{1-x}S$), sometimes long-ranged but decaying with separation (e.g., AuFe, CuMn). There has been much theoretical investigation concerning whether such systems can have RSB, whether there is a lower critical dimension d_l for an AT transition in a field and, if so, what. These issues will not however be further discussed here.

2.7. Conclusion

We have introduced several extensions of the Ising SK spin glass model to different kinds of variables/spins/pseudo-spins and several types of interactions, mostly still randomly drawn from range-free intensive distributions, indicating several of the new features that have been exposed by theorists' *blue sky* curiosity, mainly from the first few decades of spin glass research. We have also noted two examples of conceptual and technical transfers, to graph partitioning and relaxor ferroelectrics.

Later chapters will extend these developments, expose much further theoretical enlightenment and its application, and fruitful conceptual and practical progress in application to problems far beyond understanding the metallic alloys that stimulated the theory of spin glasses half a century ago.

References

[1]　D. Sherrington and S. Kirkpatrick, *Phys. Rev. Lett.* **35**, 1792–1796, (1975).
[2]　S. F. Edwards and P. W. Anderson, *J. Phys. F.* **5**, 965–974, (1975).
[3]　J. R. L. de Almeida and D. J. Thouless, *J. Phys. A.* **11**, 983–990, (1978).
[4]　G. Parisi, *Phys. Rev. Lett.* **43**, 1754–1756, (1979).
[5]　G. Parisi, *Phys. Rev. Lett.* **50**, 1946–1948, (1983).
[6]　D. Sherrington and B. Southern, *J. Phys. F.* **5**, L49–L53, (1975).
[7]　S. Kirkpatrick and D. Sherrington, *Phys. Rev. B.* **17**, 4384–4403, (1978).

---

[o]For a discussion of spin glass-like behaviour in other material systems with pre-formed moments, see [74].

[8] J. R. L. de Almeida, R. C. Jones, J. M. Kosterlitz, and D. J. Thouless, *J. Phys. C.* **11**, L871–L875, (1978).

[9] M. Gabay and G. Toulouse, *Phys. Rev. Lett.* **47**, 201–203, (1981).

[10] D. M. Cragg, D. Sherrington, and M. Gabay, *Phys. Rev. Lett.* **49**, 158–161, (1982).

[11] D. Elderfield and D. Sherrington, *J. Phys. A.* **15**, L199–L203, (1982).

[12] G. Toulouse, M. Gabay, T. C. Lubensky, and J. Vannimenus, *J. Physique Lett.* **43**, 109–113, (1982).

[13] D. Sherrington. In *Heidelberg Colloquium on Spin Glasses.*, vol. 192, *Lecture Notes in Physics*, pp. 125–136. Springer-Verlag, (1983).

[14] A. Sharma and A. P. Young, *Phys. Rev. E.* **81**(061115), (2010).

[15] D. Elderfield and D. Sherrington, *J. Phys. C.* **16**, 4865–4888, (1983).

[16] S. A. Roberts and A. Bray, *J. Phys. C.* **15**, L527–L531, (1982).

[17] F. Y. Wu, *Rev. Mod. Phys.* **54**, 235–268, (1982).

[18] D. Elderfield and D. Sherrington, *J. Phys. C.* **16**, L497–L503, (1983).

[19] A. Erzan and E. J. S. Lage, *J. Phys. C.* **16**, L555–L560, (1983).

[20] D. J. Gross, I. Kanter, and H. Sompolinsky, *Phys. Rev. Lett.* **47**, 304–307, (1985).

[21] D. Sherrington, *Prog. Theor. Phys. Supp.* **87**, 180–190, (1986).

[22] T. R. Kirkpatrick, D. Thirumalai, and P. Wolynes, *Phys. Rev. A.* **40**, 1045–1054, (1989).

[23] P. M. Goldbart and D. Sherrington, *J. Phys. C.* **18**, 1923–1940, (1985).

[24] B. Derrida, *Phys. Rev. Lett.* **45**, 79–82, (1980).

[25] B. Derrida, *Phys. Rev. B.* **24**, 2613–2626, (1981).

[26] D. J. Gross and M. Mézard, *Nucl. Phys.* **B240**, 431–452, (1984).

[27] E. Gardner, *Nuc. Phys.* **B257**, 747–765, (1985).

[28] T. H. Berlin and H. Kac, *Phys. Rev.* **86**, 821–835, (1952).

[29] J. M. Kosterlitz, D. J. Thouless, and R. C. Jones, *Phys. Rev. Lett.* **36**, 1217–1220, (1976).

[30] A. Crisanti and H.-J. Sommers, *Z. Phys. B.* **87**, 341–354, (1992).

[31] A. Crisanti, H. Horner, and H.-J. Sommers, *Z. Phys. B.* **92**, 257–271, (1993).

[32] L. Cugliandolo and J. Kurchan, *Phys. Rev. Lett.* **71**, 173–176, (1993).

[33] L. Cugliandolo and D. Dean, *J. Phys. A.* **28**, 4213–4234, (1995).

[34] J. A. Hertz, D. Sherrington, and T. M. Nieuwenhuizen, *Phys. Rev. E.* **60**, R2460–R2463, (1999).

[35] P. Gillin, D. Sherrington, and H. Nishimori, *J. Phys. A.* **34**, 2949–2964, (2001).

[36] A. Crisanti and L. Leuzzi, *Phys. Rev. Lett.* **93**(217203), (2004).

[37] A. Crisanti and L. Leuzzi, *Phys. Rev. B.* **76**(184417), (2007).

[38] G. Folena, S. Franz, and F. Ricci-Tersenghi, *Phys. Rev. X.* **10**(031045), (2020).

[39] L. Viana and A. J. Bray, *J. Phys. C.* **18**, 3037–3051, (1985).

[40] Y. Fu and P. W. Anderson, *J. Phys. A.* **19**, 1605–1620, (1986).

[41] J. R. Banavar, D. Sherrrington, and N. Sourlas, *J. Phys. A.* **20**, L1–L8, (1987).

[42] K. Y. M. Wong and D. Sherrington, *J. Phys. A.* **21**, L459–L466, (1988).

[43] S. Franz, M. Leone, F. Ricci-Tersenghi, and R. Zecchina, *Phys. Rev. Lett.* **87**(127209), (2001).

[44] M. Mézard and G. Parisi, *Eur. Phys. J. B.* **20**, 217–233, (2003).

[45] S. K. Ghatak and D. Sherrington, *J. Phys. C.* **10**, 3149–3156, (1977).

[46] A. Crisanti and L. Leuzzi, *Phys. Rev. B.* **70**(014409), (2004).

[47] D. Sherrington and K. Mihill, *J. Physique Supp.* **5 C4**, 199–201, (1974).

[48] D. Sherrington and K. Mihill. In *Proc. Int. Conf. Mag. (Moscow 1973)*, vol. 1 (1), pp. 238–287, Moscow, (1974). Nauka.

[49] B. R. Coles, A. Tari, and H. C. Jamieson. In *Low Temperature Physics LT13*, vol. II, pp. 414–418, Plenum, (1974).

[50] P. W. Anderson, *Phys. Rev.* **124**, 41–53, (1961).

[51] J. A. Hertz, *Phys. Rev. B.* **19**, 4796–4804, (1979).

[52] E. C. Stoner, *Proc. Roy. Soc. A.* **165**, 372– 414, (1938).

[53] W. Zhong, D. Vanderbilt, and K. M. Rabe, *Phys. Rev. B.* **52**, 6301–6312, (1995).

[54] A. Garcia and D. Vanderbilt, *Phys. Rev. B.* **54**, 3817–3824, (1996).

[55] V. Cannella and J. A. Mydosh, *Phys. Rev. B.* **6**, 4220–4237, (1972).

[56] C. Mulder, A. van Duyneveldt, and J. Mydosh, *Phys. Rev. B.* **23**, 1384–1396, (1981).

[57] G. A. Smolenskii, V. A. Isupov, A. I. Agranovskaya, and S. N. Popov, *Fiz. Tverd. Tela.* **2**(11), 2906–2918, (1960).

[58] G. A. Smolenskii, V. A. Isupov, A. I. Agranovskaya, and S. N. Popov, *Sov. Phys. Solid State.* **2**(11), 2584–2594, (1961).

[59] D. Viehland, M. Wuttig, and L. E. Cross, *Ferroelectrics.* **120**, 71–77, (1991).

[60] R. Pirc and R. Blinc, *Phys. Rev. B.* **60**, 13470–13478, (1994).

[61] A. R. Akbarzadeh, S. Prosandeev, E. J. Walter, A. Al-Barakaty, and L. Bellaiche, *Phys. Rev. Lett.* **108**(257601), (2012).

[62] D. Sherrington, *Phys. Rev. Lett.* **111**(227601), (2014).

[63] G. A. Smolenskii, *J. Phys. Soc. Jpn. Supp.* **26**, 26–37, (1970).

[64] A. Simon, J. Ravez, and M. Maglione, *J. Phys.: Condens. Matter.* **16**, 963–970, (2004).

[65] A. Levstik, Z. Kutnjak, C. Filipič, and R. Pirc, *Phys. Rev. B.* **57**, 11204–11211, (1998).

[66] S. Nagata, P. H. Keesom, and H. R. Harrison, *Phys. Rev. B.* **19**, 1633–1638, (1979).

[67] D. Wang, A. A. Bokov, Z.-G. Ye, J. Hlinka, and L. Bellaiche, *Nature Comm.* **7**(11014), (2016).

[68] T. Maiti, R. Guo, and A. S. Bhalla, *J. Am. Ceram. Soc.* **91**, 1769–1780, (2008).

[69] D. Sherrington, *Phys. Rev. B.* **89**(064105), (2014).

[70] P. W. Anderson, *Phys. Rev.* **109**, 1492–1505, (1958).

[71] D. Sherrington. In *Frustrated Materials and Ferroic Glasses*, vol. 275, *Springer Materials Science*, pp. 1–29. Springer, (2018).

[72] D. Sherrington, *Phase Transitions.* **88**, 202–221, (2015).

[73] E. Bouchbinder, E. Lerner, C. Rainone, P. Urbani, and F. Zamponi, *Phys. Rev. B.* **103**, 174202, (2021).

[74] K. Binder and J. Reger, *Adv. Phys.* **41**(6), 547–627, (1992).

Chapter 3

Beyond the Ising Spin Glass II
Spin glass without replicas

J. Michael Kosterlitz

Department of Physics, Brown University, Providence, Rhode Island, USA
J_Kosterlitz@brown.edu

This chapter considers a couple of spin glass models that do not (always) exhibit RSB.

3.1. Spherical Spin Glass

Shortly after the EA and SK models were formulated Kosterlitz, Thouless and Jones [1] considered the Ising spin glass in the spherical limit. The problem is then readily soluble, at least for uniform interactions in any spatial dimensions [2]. Although this model is physically unrealistic, its thermal averaging is straightforward. It is then possible to concentrate on the more controversial disorder averaging in a way which does not need the replica method. For N spins in the spherical limit [1], the N constraints $S_i^2 = 1$ are replaced by the single global constraint $\sum_i S_i^2 = N$ with Hamiltonian

$$H = -\sum_{(i,j)=1}^{N} J_{ij} S_i S_j - h \sum_i S_i \tag{3.1}$$

where the interaction J_{ij} is infinitely long ranged with probability density

$$P(J_{ij}) = (2\pi\sigma^2)^{-1/2} \exp\left[-(J_{ij} - J_0)^2/2\sigma^2\right], \tag{3.2}$$

where the standard deviation $\sigma = \tilde{J} N^{-1/2}$ and the mean $J_0 = \tilde{J}_0 N^{-1}$. We use the intensive variables $\tilde{J}$ and $\tilde{J}_0$ to obtain a sensible thermodynamic limit and firstly consider the case when the mean $\tilde{J}_0 = 0$.

The symmetric random matrix J_{ij} is diagonalized by an orthogonal transformation so that

$$S_i = \sum_\lambda \langle i|\lambda\rangle S_\lambda \tag{3.3}$$

where $\langle i|\lambda\rangle$ is the orthonormal eigenvector of J_{ij} belonging to the eigenvalue J_λ. Since the density of eigenvalues obeys the semicircular law [3]

$$\rho(J_\lambda) = (4\tilde{J}^2 - J_\lambda)^2)^{1/2}/2\pi\tilde{J}^2 \tag{3.4}$$

for $J_0 = 0$ in the $N \to \infty$ limit, we can perform the standard spherical model manipulations with the constraint $\sum_i S_i^2 = N$. The partition function becomes

$$Z = \frac{1}{2\pi i} \int_{c-i\infty}^{c+i\infty} dz \exp \left\{ N[z - (2N)^{-1} \sum_\lambda \ln(z - J_\lambda/2T)] \right\} \tag{3.5}$$

where the integration contour lies to the right of the largest eigenvalue $2\tilde{J}$ and we have omitted the trivial normalization factor. Note that we interchanged the orders of integration over z and S_λ before taking the thermodynamic limit $N \to \infty$. This is justified because, when N is sufficiently large, the probability of finding an eigenvalue $J_\lambda > 2\tilde{J}$ is so small that the error is negligible [4].

The integral in the exponent of Eq. (3.5) is dominated by the saddle point value of z so that, using $1/N \sum_\lambda \to \int dJ\rho(J)$, we find

$$z - (z^2 - \tilde{J}^2/T^2)^{1/2} = \tilde{J}^2/T^2. \tag{3.6}$$

Equation (3.6) has the solution $z = \frac{1}{2}(1 + \tilde{J}^2/T^2)$ for $T > \tilde{J} = T_c$ and the saddle solution sticks at $z = \tilde{J}/T$. The disorder averaged free energy per site is

$$\langle f(T) \rangle = \begin{cases} -\tilde{J}^2/4T - \frac{1}{2}T(1 + \ln 2), & T > T_c, \\ \frac{1}{2}T\ln(T/2\tilde{J}) - \tilde{J} + \frac{1}{4}T, & T < T_c \end{cases} \tag{3.7}$$

which implies a specific heat per site of $\tilde{J}^2/2T^2$ when $T > T_c$ and $1/2$ when $T < T_c$. Note that this model has an unphysical negative low temperature entropy which diverges logarithmically as $T \to 0$. This pathology is also present in the short ranged uniform spherical model.

When a uniform magnetic field h is applied, the saddle point equation becomes

$$1 = \int dJ\rho(J) \left[\frac{1}{2(z - J/2T)} + \frac{h^2(J)}{4T^2(z - J/2T)^2} \right], \tag{3.8}$$

where $h(J_\lambda) = h \sum_i \langle i|\lambda \rangle$. On average, $h^2(J) \to h^2$ when it is obvious that Eq. (3.8) has the solution $z > \tilde{J}/T$ so that there is no transition in the presence of a uniform magnetic field. This is because a uniform field has a component $h_{2\tilde{j}}$ corresponding to the largest eigenvalue which plays the role of an ordering field.

A few years later, Crisanti and Sommers introduced a soluble spherical model with p-spin interactions [5] which has a RSB phase in contrast to the original spherical spin glass of Kosterlitz *et al.* [1].

3.2. *XY* Spin Glass

A natural way to investigate order in any system is to compute the domain wall or droplet energy [6] where one *assumes* a picture of a spin glass which has a finite set of ground states (GS) connected by some symmetry operation. In such a situation, one can create a defect or domain wall *relative to the GS* by changing the boundary conditions in say the x direction so that the spins want to be reversed relative to their ground state configuration. For our random system it is certainly not obvious how this can be achieved but it is simple for a ferromagnet with nearest neighbor interactions.

We start with a ferromagnetic system of linear size L with periodic boundary conditions (BC) in all directions so that all spins are parallel in the GS. To induce a domain wall normal to x we change the BC along x so that the new GS is such that $S(x+L,y,z) = -S(x,y,z)$, which is accomplished by introducing a strip of interactions of reversed signs perpendicular to $\hat{\mathbf{x}}$. Averaging over disorder is done in the most naive way possible by repeating the measurement for N samples or realizations of disorder and then averaging the measured quantities O_i by $\langle O \rangle = N^{-1} \sum_1^N O_i$ again avoiding the replica method. We note that Bray and Moore argue that there is no replica symmetry breaking in less than six spatial dimensions d so that this naive disorder averaging will be valid [7]. Also, the absence of a de Almeida–Thouless (AT) line in $d = 3$ spin glasses [8] shows that replica symmetry is not broken. These arguments imply that, for a $d = 3$ vector spin glass, replica symmetry is not broken and the most naive averaging over disorder is valid.

The general idea behind a domain wall renormalization group (DWRG) is to compute, either analytically or numerically, the energy $\Delta E(L)$ of a domain wall in a system of linear size L for a particular realization of disorder and fit the average over disorder to a finite size scaling form

$$\langle \Delta E(L) \rangle \sim L^\theta, \tag{3.9}$$

where θ is the stiffness exponent, whose sign is of fundamental importance. If $\theta < 0$, $\langle \Delta E(L) \rangle$ vanishes in the thermodynamic limit $L \to \infty$ which implies that, when $T > 0$, the probability of the defect $P(L) \sim e^{-\Delta E(L)/k_B T} \to 1$ as $L \to \infty$. In turn, this implies that the density of such defects is finite when $T > 0$ and the system will have no long-range order or stiffness, just like the vanishing of the shear modulus in a liquid. By contrast, if $\theta > 0$, such defects will have zero probability when $L \to \infty$ and the system has finite stiffness at sufficiently small $T > 0$.

One would like to use this strategy as suggested by Anderson for *random* systems like a spin glass [9, 10]. However, it is unclear how to proceed because, for a particular realization of disorder, neither the GS spin configuration nor the compatible BC are known so computing the defect energy $\Delta E(L)$ is problematical. However, assuming $\Delta E(L)$ can be found, the stiffness exponent is defined by Eq. (3.9). To the best of our knowledge, it is not known how to calculate analytically either the GS energy nor the energy $E_D(L)$ of the same system with an induced domain wall defect relative to this unknown GS. We must therefore proceed with the appropriate numerical method. However, several conceptual and technical difficulties are immediately apparent. The first, and most important, is the technical problem of computing the energy difference $\Delta E(L)$ between the lowest energies of the same system subject to two different BC. Because we are limited to rather small system size L, it is vital to choose the boundary conditions very carefully to avoid inducing spurious irrelevant excitations which will cause large corrections to the assumed scaling form of Eq. (??). For a uniform ferromagnet, the obvious choice is periodic BC for the ground state and anti-periodic BC in one direction with periodic BC in the others to induce a single domain wall relative to the ground state. This choice yields excellent scaling even for very small system sizes, $\Delta E(L) = E_{\mathrm{ap}}(L) - E_{\mathrm{p}}(L) \sim L^{d-n}$ where $n = 1$ for discrete spins and $n = 2$ for XY or

Heisenberg spins. If one imposes some arbitrary choice of BC which does not respect the ground state configuration to define E_{GS} and reverse the BC in the chosen direction to obtain E_D, the energy difference $\Delta E(L)$ does not obey the required form. The lesson from this simple example is that it is key to pick the BC very carefully so that the resulting $\Delta E(L)$ actually is the energy of a single domain wall relative to the true ground state. Otherwise, $\Delta E(L)$ is just the energy difference between two unknown excitations and there is no reason to expect this to scale as L^θ.

It is very CPU intensive to compute the $\Delta E(L)$ for random systems because it is necessary to obtain $E_D(L)$ and $E_{\mathrm{GS}}(L)$ essentially exactly, so the error in the difference $\Delta E(L)$ is small enough that fitting $\langle \Delta E(L) \rangle$ to the assumed scaling form L^θ is meaningful. The phase space explored therefore ought to be as small as possible. We can accomplish this by converting the original phase to a Coulomb gas representation which is already a local energy minimum. Any deviation of the phases from this corresponds to an increase of energy so that the problem is reduced to exploring these local minima. The price of this is the introduction of long-range Coulomb interactions between integer valued charges. However, the boundary conditions consistent with the unknown lowest energy ground state can be also determined during the numerical minimization in the charge representation.

This section discusses the existence of a spin glass phase in d spatial dimensions for two-component systems ($m = 2$) with random $\pm J$ interactions using the Coulomb gas representation. We do not use the replica method to perform the averaging over interaction strengths but return to the original idea where the average of the expectation value of some operator $O[S_i, J_{ij}]$ is

$$\langle O \rangle = \int DJ P[J] O[J] \tag{3.10}$$

where $P[J]$ is the probability distribution of the coupling constants J_{ij}. This requires the evaluation of $\langle O[S_i, J_{ij}] \rangle_T$ for several realizations of the random couplings J_{ij} followed by an averaging over the probability distribution $P[J_{ij}]$. Clearly, this is a very tedious and time consuming procedure and using the replica method would make life easier. However, that method still has not been fully accepted.

In view of this, we decided to look at the spin glass version of the XY ($m = 2$) magnet which is described by a Hamiltonian

$$H = -J \sum_{\langle ij \rangle} V(\theta_i - \theta_j - A_{ij}) \tag{3.11}$$

where $V(\phi + 2\pi) = V(\phi)$ is 2π periodic and $A_{ij} = 0, \pi$ with probability $1/2$. Thus, this Hamiltonian describes an XY spin glass with nearest neighbor coupling constants $J_{ij} = \pm J$ on a $2D$ square or a $3D$ simple cubic lattice. The partition function for a gauge glass model is

$$Z = \int_{-\pi}^{+\pi} \prod_i d\theta_i \sum_{\{n_{ij}\}} \exp\left(-\beta J \sum_{\langle ij \rangle} (\theta_{ij} - A_{ij})^2 \right) \tag{3.12}$$

where $\theta_{ij} = \theta_i - \theta_j - 2\pi n_{ij}$ with $n_{ij} = -n_{ji}$ an integer on the bond $\langle ij \rangle$. After some simple but very tedious algebra, the partition function can be written in Coulomb gas language as [11, 12]

$$Z = Z_0 \sum_{\{\mathbf{q_r}\}} \sum_{q_\mu} \exp\left[-\beta H(\mathbf{q_r}, \mathbf{f_r}, q_{\mu 1}, f_{\mu 1})\right],$$

$$H = (2\pi)^2 J \sum_{\mathbf{r},\mathbf{r'}} (\mathbf{q_r} - \mathbf{f_r}) \cdot (\mathbf{q_{r'}} - \mathbf{f_{r'}}) G(\mathbf{r} - \mathbf{r'})$$

$$+ \tfrac{J}{2L}\left(\tfrac{\pi}{L}\sum_{\mathbf{r}}(zp_{\mathbf{r}}^y - yp_{\mathbf{r}}^z) + Q_x\right)^2 + \tfrac{J}{2L}\left(\tfrac{\pi}{L}\sum_{\mathbf{r}}(xp_{\mathbf{r}}^z - zp_{\mathbf{r}}^x) + Q_y\right)^2$$

$$+ \tfrac{J}{2L}\left(\tfrac{\pi}{L}\sum_{\mathbf{r}}(yp_{\mathbf{r}}^x - xp_{\mathbf{r}}^y) + Q_z\right)^2, \tag{3.13}$$

where $\mathbf{p_r} = \mathbf{q_r} - \mathbf{f_r}$ and $G(\mathbf{r}) = L^{-3} \sum_{\mathbf{k}\neq 0}[\exp(i\mathbf{k}\cdot\mathbf{r}) - 1]/(6 - 2\cos k_x - 2\cos k_y - 2\cos k_z)$ is the Green's function on a simple cubic lattice in $3D$ with periodic boundary conditions. The quantities Q_μ are

$$Q_x = \pi \sum_{\mathbf{r}} (zp_{\mathbf{r}}^y \delta_{y,1} - yp_{\mathbf{r}}^z \delta_{z,1}) + 2\pi L(q_{x1} - f_{x1}), \tag{3.14}$$

with Q_y and Q_z obtained from Q_x by cyclic permutations of xyz. f_{x1} is the circulation of A_{ij} along the selected loop in the x direction around the hypertorus,

$$2\pi f_{x1} = \sum_{x=1}^{L} A^x_{\mathbf{r}=(x,1,1)} \tag{3.15}$$

and similarly for f_{y1} and f_{z1}. The *integers* $q_{\mu 1}$ are the circulations of the phase round the three independent global loops encircling the hypertorus.

Equations (3.13) and (3.14) give the energy of the system of size L with boundary conditions which are determined by choosing values for the $f_{\mu 1}$ of Eq. (3.15). To obtain the lowest or GS energy $E^0(L)$, we adjust the integer valued variables $\mathbf{q}_i$ and also the global frustrations $q_{\mu 1} - f_{\mu 1}$. A domain wall normal to the x direction relative to this GS is induced by $f_{x1} \to f_{x1} + 1/2$ which is equivalent to imposing a twist of π in the phase of the spins round a loop round the hypertorus in the x direction. The minimum energy $E_D(L)$ of the system containing an extra domain wall is found by minimizing the energy with respect to the integer valued $\mathbf{q}_i$. The actual domain wall energy $\Delta E^{\mathrm{BT}}(L)$ in a system of size L is the difference $\Delta E^{\mathrm{BT}}(L) = E^D(L) - E^0(L)$ which we fit to the postulated finite size scaling form

$$\Delta E^{\mathrm{BT}}(L) = E^D(L) - E^0(L) \sim L^{\theta_{\mathrm{BT}}}. \tag{3.16}$$

Here the superscript BT means that we have adjusted the boundary conditions to get the true lowest energies of the size L system and then inducing a domain wall relative to this particular GS by imposing a phase twist of π in the chosen direction [12].

This calculation must be done numerically using finite size L^d systems. Attempts have been made by defining the defect energy $\Delta E(L)$ as the energy difference of the L^d system with periodic and antiperiodic boundary conditions in the chosen direction. For a random system, periodic or antiperiodic BC are just arbitrary choices of BC and there is no reason to expect that one of $E_p(L)$ or $E_{ap}(L)$ is larger than the other. The obvious comparison is for a ferromagnet for which periodic BC are compatible with the GS configuration while antiperiodic BC induce a domain wall when the system will obviously have a higher energy, $E_{ap}(L) > E_p(L)$. This inequality is not necessarily obeyed in a spin glass. This is an important observation because, for a random system, finding the lowest energy is very difficult and very CPU intensive and it is vital to apply appropriate BC on the rather small systems accessible. This is extremely important

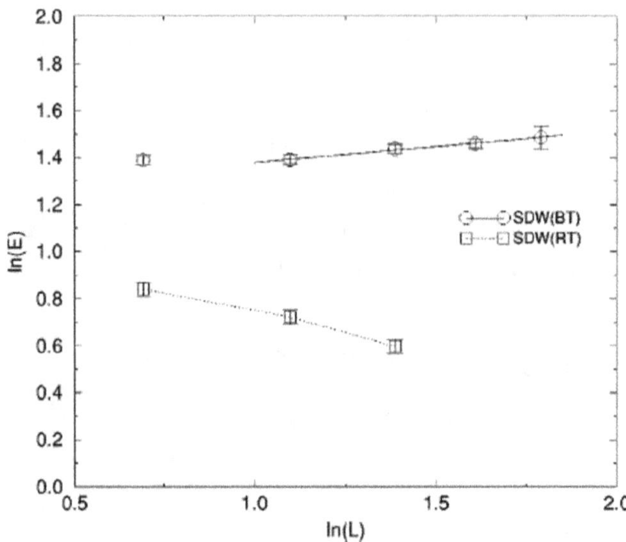

Fig. 3.1. L-dependence of the spin domain wall energies $\Delta E_S^{\mathrm{BT}}(L)$ and $\Delta E_s^{\mathrm{RT}}(L)$ in $d = 3$. The error in the $L = 6$ point is because of averaging over rather few samples. The solid line is a power law fit and the dotted line is a guide for the eye. Note the discrepancy between the best and random twist measurements. Reprinted figure with permission from [N. Akino and J. M. Kosterlitz, Phys. Rev. B 66, 054536 (2002)] Copyright (2002) by the American Physical Society [12].

when fitting the data to the scaling ansatz $\Delta E(L) \sim L^\theta$. The system sizes L are restricted to $L \leq 7$ in $d = 3$ and $L \leq 14$ in $d = 2$ because of limited computer power. To fit the very limited number of data points to verify the postulated FSS scaling form and to extract the exponent requires that the data is extremely accurate and that the errors are just the standard statistical errors $O(N^{-1/2})$ where N is the number of samples.

Akino and Kosterlitz [12] realized that it was possible to study the XY gauge glass and spin glass (a special case of the gauge glass) by rewriting the problem in terms of the Coulomb gas representation whose Hamiltonian is shown above and finding the defect energy sufficiently accurately by performing the minimization with the correct BC. This was not an easy problem and our method is still being questioned by those who have not understood the problem in sufficient depth. The reason that our system sizes are so small is that our CPU resources were limited and I think that even if we had access to the biggest and fastest machines available today, we still could not do much larger sizes. There are some more recent studies of the stiffness exponent in $3D$ but using different boundary conditions which obtain very different values for θ_s and θ_c [13]. An important constraint on the simulations is the only exact analytic result known to this author is the equality of the spin and chiral stiffness exponents in $\theta_s = \theta_c < 0$ in $d = 2$ [14]. This equality is not satisfied in many simulations but it is in [11, 12, 14] which gives some support for the validity of these simulations. Although not rigorous, the conjecture of [14] is the only analytic result known to this author for the XY spin glass and it is reasonable to use this as a check on the validity of the simulation method used. It is of interest to note that almost all simulations fail this test which, in the author's very biased opinion, makes the conclusions from these very suspect, as discussed in Ref. [11]. In Fig. 3.1, the lower curve is our random twist RT measurement of the spin stiffness exponent from the domain wall energy $\Delta E^{\mathrm{RT}}(L) \sim L^{\theta_{\mathrm{RT}}}$, which is obtained from comparing measurements with conventional periodic and antiperiodic BC. This label recalls that the true lowest energy GS is obtained by applying the best twist BT boundary conditions. Periodic and antiperiodic BC are just two arbitrary choices of BC relative to the best twist BC of the true GS energy minimum and there is no reason to expect that $E_{ap} > E_p$.

Our results for the stiffness exponent θ suggest that there is no low-temperature $d = 2$ spin glass phase, $\theta_{2D} = -0.37 \pm 0.010$, but there is in $d = 3$ with $\theta_{3D}^{XY} = +0.10 \pm 0.03$ [12, 14]. This is to be compared with the stiffness exponent $\theta_S^I = 0.24 \pm .02$ for the $d = 3$ Ising spin glass [15, 16]. It is to be expected that $\theta_S^I > \theta_S^{XY}$ which implies that the Ising spin glass is more stable than the XY spin glass. At the time the lowest critical dimension for a Heisenberg SG was $d_l = 4$.

In summary, our investigation of the XY spin glass with short-range interactions by converting the problem into an equivalent Coulomb gas problem reduces the volume of phase space to a size which can be explored numerically. This allows us to demonstrate that an XY spin glass phase does exist in $d \geq 3$, which is consistent with the estimate of the spin glass lower critical dimension $d_l = 2.5$ [15, 17, 18]. It does not, however, say anything about the transition to a spin glass phase at finite T.

References

[1] J. M. Kosterlitz, D. J. Thouless, and R. C. Jones, *Phys. Rev. Lett.* **36**, 1217–1220, (1976).

[2] T. H. Berlin and M. Kac, *Phys. Rev.* **86**, 821–835, (1952).

[3] M. L. Mehta, *Random Matrices and the Statistical Theory of Energy Levels.* (Academic Press, 1967). p. 240.

[4] B. V. Bronk, *J. Math. Phys.* **5**(12), 1661–1663, (1964).

[5] A. Crisanti and H.-J. Sommers, *Z. Phys. B.* **87**(3), 341–354, (1992).

[6] D. S. Fisher and D. A. Huse, *Phys. Rev. Lett.* **56**, 1601–1604, (1986).

[7] M. A. Moore and A. J. Bray, *Phys. Rev. B.* **83**, 224408, (2011).

[8] A. P. Young and H. G. Katzgraber, *Phys. Rev. Lett.* **93**, 207203, (2004).

[9] P. W. Anderson, *J. Less-common Met.* **62**, 291–294, (1978).

[10] P. W. Anderson and C. M. Pond, *Phys. Rev. Lett.* **40**, 903–906, (1978).

[11] J. M. Kosterlitz and N. Akino, *Phys. Rev. Lett.* **82**, 4094–4097, (1999).

[12] N. Akino and J. M. Kosterlitz, *Phys. Rev. B.* **66**, 054536, (2002).

[13] M. Weigel and M. J. P. Gingras, *Phys. Rev. Lett.* **96**, 097206, (2006).

[14] M. Ney-Nifle and H. J. Hilhorst, *Phys. Rev. B.* **51**, 8357–8369, (1995).

[15] S. Boettcher, *Phys. Rev. Lett.* **95**(19), 197205, (2005).

[16] A. K. Hartmann, *Phys. Rev. E.* **59**(1), 84, (1999).

[17] S. Franz, *Europhys. Lett.* **73**(4), 492, (2006).

[18] A. Maiorano and G. Parisi, *Proc. Nat. Acad. Sci. U.S.A.* **115**(20), 5129–5134, (2018).

Chapter 4

Renormalization Group in Spin Glasses

The renormalization group treatment of spin glasses has been a theoretical challenge since shortly after the formulation of the Sherrington–Kirkpatrick model. This chapter brings three perspectives on this topic. Section 4.1, by **T. Lubensky**, reviews the early replica symmetric description of the problem, which predate and in some ways anticipate the discovery of the instability of that treatment by de Almeida and Thouless. The perturbative renormalization group approach to the ensuing transition is presented in Sec. 4.2, contributed jointly by **T. Temesvari** and **I. Kondor**. The findings of this approach motivate the consideration of non-perturbative renormalization group schemes, which are discussed in Sec. 4.3 written by **M. C. Angelini**.

4.1. Mean-Field and ϵ-Expansion for Spin Glasses

Tom Lubensky

Department of Physics and Astronomy, University of Pennsylvania,
Philadelphia PA, USA
tom@sas.upenn.edu

This section reviews my first article with Brooks Harris [1] presenting a Landau–Wilson (LW) free energy [2–6] and our follow-up work [7] about a model exhibiting transitions from the paramagnetic (P) to the ferromagnetic state (M) and from M to a spin glass (SG) in addition to a P to SG transition. This last transition was found to have an upper critical dimension, $d_u = 6$, rather than the $d_u = 4$ of familiar thermodynamic transitions. Critical exponents to first order in $\epsilon = d - d_u$ could then be obtained. The usual ϵ-expansion protocol that had been applied with great success to thermodynamic [4, 8, 9] and quantum [10, 11] phase transitions, dilute and semi-dilute polymeric solutions [12], percolation [13, 14] and branched polymers [15, 16], however, appeared not to work for SG, at least not without further tweaks. One might say that this breakdown was the *canary in a mine shaft* that provided early warning that SG models were going to require new ideas. They soon arrived in the form of replica-symmetry breaking [17] after the de Almeida and Thouless demonstration that the Sherrington–Kirkpatrick (SK) SG state is unstable [18, 19].

4.1.1. *Constructing a Landau–Wilson free energy*

Consider first the MF phases and phase transitions associated with the model Landau–Wilson free-energy density $\mathcal{F}$ describing a random microscopic O_m model with quenched random exchange interactions with average value, $[J]_{\mathrm{av}}$, and second cumulant

45

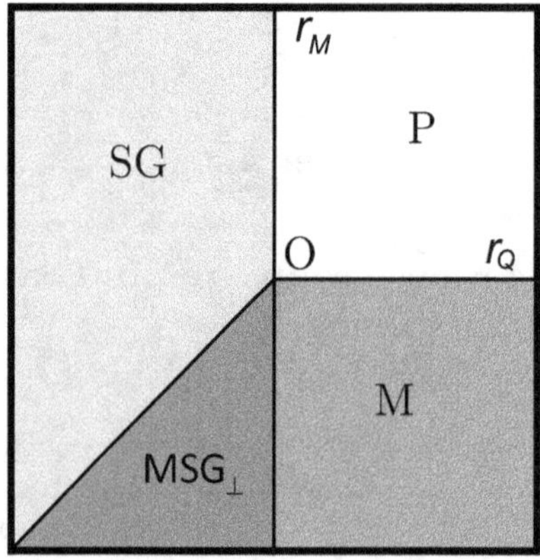

Fig. 4.1. MF phase diagram showing the P, SG, M, and MSG$_\perp$ phases and the multicritical point C. The vertical axis is r_M and the horizontal axis is r_Q. The two axes intercept at the origin $O = (r_Q, r_M)$. For $m = 1$, no distinct MSG$_\perp$ phase exist; it becomes part of M.

$([J^2]_{\mathrm{av}} - [J]_{\mathrm{av}}^2)$. $\mathcal{F}$ is a functional of the replicated [20] local magnetization $\vec{M}$ with components M_i^α and the Edwards–Anderson (EA) [20, 21] spin-glass (SG) order parameter $\overleftrightarrow{Q}$ with components $Q_{ij}^{\alpha\beta}$ with replica indices α and β running from 1 to n and O_m indices i and j running from 1 to m. The $n = 0$ procedure [22, 23] is used to produce a homogeneous energy for the random system. As usual, the diagonal elements with respect to $\alpha\beta$ of $Q_{ij}^{\alpha\beta}$ are zero, and the trace with respect to the ij indices of the off-diagonal α–β parts are equal to $[\langle \vec{S}(\mathbf{x})\rangle \cdot \langle \vec{S}(\mathbf{x})\rangle]_{\mathrm{av}}$ and are thus greater than or equal to zero. The SK model [24, 25] is a long-range version of this *local* model, which has been used, for example, in Refs. [26–28].

$\mathcal{F}$ naturally decomposes into three parts:

$$\mathcal{F} = \mathcal{F}_M + \mathcal{F}_Q + \mathcal{F}_{MQ}, \tag{4.1}$$

where [29]

$$\mathcal{F}_Q = \left[\frac{1}{4} r_Q \mathrm{Tr}\, \overleftrightarrow{Q}^2 + \frac{1}{4}\mathrm{Tr}(\nabla \overleftrightarrow{Q})^2 - w_Q \mathrm{Tr}\, \overleftrightarrow{Q}^3 + u_Q \mathrm{Tr}\, \overleftrightarrow{Q}^4 - v_Q (\mathrm{Tr}\, \overleftrightarrow{Q}^2)^2 \right] \tag{4.2}$$

$$\mathcal{F}_M = \left[\frac{1}{2} r_M \vec{M} \cdot \vec{M} + \frac{1}{2}\nabla_j \vec{M} \cdot \nabla_j \vec{M} + u_M \sum_\alpha M_i^\alpha M_i^\alpha M_j^\alpha M_j^\alpha - v_M (\vec{M} \cdot \vec{M})^2 \right]$$

$$\mathcal{F}_{MQ} = -w_{MQ} Q_{ij}^{\alpha\beta} M_i^\alpha M_j^\beta$$

and where $r_Q = a_Q(T - T_Q)$ with $T_Q \sim [J^2]_{\mathrm{av}} - [J]_{\mathrm{av}}^2$ and $r_M = a_M(T - T_M)$ with $T_M \sim [J]_{\mathrm{av}}$. (The Einstein summation convention is here used.) All of the energy coefficients $w_Q, w_M, u_Q, \cdots$ except for r_Q and r_M are taken to be positive.

4.1.2. *Mean-field theory*

The MF analysis of this Landau–Wilson description captures qualitative SG features of the Edwards–Anderson (EA) [20, 21] and SK [24, 25] models. It produces, in particular, an essentially identical phase diagram to that of the latter.

Under the assumption that replica symmetry is not broken, both M_i^α and $Q_{ij}^{\alpha\beta}$ are independent of the indices. O_m rotational symmetry can, however, be broken leading to $\vec{M} = M\mathbf{e}$, where $\mathbf{e}$ is the m-component unit vector parallel to $\vec{M}$. The breaking of rotational symmetry by $\vec{M}$ requires the isotropy of the Edwards–Anderson SG order parameter $Q_{ij}^{\alpha\beta}$ to be broken with a component, $Q_{||}$, parallel to $\vec{M}$ and a component, $Q_\perp$, perpendicular to $\vec{M}$:

$$Q_{ij}^{\alpha\beta} = [Q_{||}e_i e_j + Q_\perp(\delta_{ij} - e_i e_j)](1 - \delta^{\alpha\beta}). \tag{4.3}$$

The $(1 - \delta^{\alpha\beta})$ factor forces all diagonal α–β components in $Q_{ij}^{\alpha\beta}$ to be zero. When M is zero, $Q_{||} = Q_\perp$ and $Q_{ij} = Q\delta_{ij}(1 - \delta^{\alpha\beta})$. The MF components of $\mathcal{F}$ are [29]

$$\mathcal{F}_M = n\left(\frac{1}{2}r_M M^2 + u_M M^4\right), \tag{4.4a}$$

$$\mathcal{F}_Q = n(n-1)\left\{\frac{1}{4}r_Q[(m-1)Q_\perp^2 + Q_{||}^2] - w_Q(n-2)[(m-1)Q_\perp^3 + Q_{||}^3]\right.$$

$$\left. + \tilde{u}_Q[(m-1)Q_\perp^4 + Q_{||}^4]\right\}, \tag{4.4b}$$

$$\mathcal{F}_{MQ} = -n(n-1)w_{MQ}M^2 Q_{||}, \tag{4.4c}$$

where $\tilde{u}_Q = (n^2 - 3n + 3)u_Q$ approaches $3u_Q$ as $n \to 0$. Note that the v_M and v_Q terms have been omitted because, being proportional to n^2, their contribution to $\mathcal{F}/n$ vanishes in the $n \to 0$ limit. The equations of state for M, $Q_{||}$, and $Q_\perp$ are

$$\frac{\partial\mathcal{F}}{n\partial M} = (r_M + 4u_M M^2 - 2(n-1)w_{MQ}Q_{||})M = 0, \tag{4.5a}$$

$$\frac{\partial\mathcal{F}}{n\partial Q_{||}} = (n-1)\left(\frac{1}{2}r_Q - 3(n-2)w_Q Q_{||} + 4\tilde{u}_Q Q_{||}^2\right)Q_{||} \tag{4.5b}$$

$$-(n-1)w_{MQ}M^2 = 0, \tag{4.5c}$$

$$\frac{\partial\mathcal{F}}{n\partial Q_\perp} = (n-1)(m-1)\left(\frac{1}{2}r_Q Q_\perp - 3(n-2)w_Q Q_\perp^2\right)Q_\perp = 0. \tag{4.5d}$$

Their solution determines the thermodynamic properties of M, $Q_{||}$, and $Q_\perp$ and the full phase diagram. Note that the solution to Eq. (4.5d) for $Q_\perp$ does not depend on M. An important feature of these equations is that they permit solutions with M and Q equal to zero, with $M = 0$ and $Q_{||} > 0$, and with $Q_{||}$ and M^2 greater than zero, but there is no phase with $Q_{||} = 0$ and $M \neq 0$. We will begin with a study of the SG phase in some detail and then discuss the full phase diagram.

4.1.3. *The spin-glass sector*

In the SG phase, $M = 0$, $Q_{||} = Q_\perp = Q$, and

$$Q_{ij}^{\alpha\beta} = Q\delta_{ij}(1 - \delta^{\alpha\beta}). \tag{4.6}$$

The δ_{ij} factor here implies that the pure SG state is isotropic. The LW energy for this SG state is then

$$\frac{\mathcal{F}}{mn(n-1)} = \frac{1}{4}r_Q Q^2 - w_Q(n-2)Q^3 + 4\tilde{u}_Q\,Q^4. \tag{4.7}$$

Several properties of this expression require further comment:

(1) Note the $mn(n-1)$ factor in the denominator of the right-hand side. We are interested in the limit $n \to 0$, and the normal procedure is to put the factor $(n-1)$, which is then negative, on the right side of the equation. The resulting change in the effective free-energy *equilibrium* extremum from a minimum to a maximum is unsettling. Taken at face value, the factor $n(n-1)$ is the number of degrees of freedom in the replica portion of the $\overleftrightarrow{Q}$ matrix so long as $n > 1$. An interpretation [22, 28] that avoids the extremum dilemma is to view this factor as the number of degrees of freedom even in the analytic continuation $n \to 0$. In this interpretation, the right-hand side can be viewed as a free-energy density per degree of freedom, which has the usual property of being zero when the order parameter Q is zero and negative when r_Q becomes negative and a phase transition occurs. Unfortunately, as we shall see, the *number-of-degrees-of-freedom* interpretation presents problems when ferromagnetic as well as SG order is considered.

(2) As emphasized after Eq. (4.1), Q is constrained to be positive. The free energy in the negative half plane can therefore be ignored.

(3) There is a third-order term in Q. Normally this implies a MF first-order transition [9], in which the sign of Q in the ordered phase is opposite to that of the coefficient of Q^3 in the free-energy function. When $n > 2$, the coefficient is negative implying a first-order transition to a state of positive Q. When $n < 2$, the coefficient is positive implying a first-order transition to negative Q, which is not permitted. Rather, there is a second-order transition at $r_Q = 0$ to a state with the required positive Q. An identical behavior is noted in the treatment of percolation using the $s \to 1$ limit of the s-state Potts model [13, 14]. There, the order parameter is the (necessarily positive) probability that the diluted lattice has a connected cluster that traverses the sample in all directions. The third-order term in the Potts energy changes sign at $s = 2$, and at $s = 1$ the percolation transition is second-order with an upper critical dimension of $d_u = 6$.

Minimization of Eq. (4.7) leads to the equation of state for Q in the SG state as $r_Q \to 0$:

$$\left(\frac{1}{2} r_Q - 3(n-2)w_Q Q + 4\tilde{u}_Q Q^2 \right) Q = 0, \tag{4.8}$$

with solution

$$Q = \frac{1}{8\tilde{v}} \left[3(2-n)w_Q - \sqrt{[3(2-n)w_Q]^2 - 8r_Q\tilde{u}_Q} \right]$$

$$\approx \frac{r_Q}{6(2-n)w_Q} \xrightarrow{n \to 0} -\frac{r_Q}{12 w_Q}. \tag{4.9}$$

As in the SG state (Eqs. (4.8) and (4.9)), the $\tilde{u}_Q$ terms are neglected in Eqs. (4.5a) and (4.5b). The contribution of the fourth-order $\tilde{u}_Q$ term to Q vanishes as $r_Q \to 0$, regardless of its sign, and near the phase transition, $Q \sim (-r_Q)^\beta$, where $\beta = 1$ rather than the usual $\beta = 1/2$. The alternative solution for Q with a $+$ sign before the radical corresponds to the negative value of Q (when $n = 0$) and can be ignored. Note that the positive solution for Q emerges when $r_Q < 0$ only because the $n - 2$ term is negative when $n = 0$. If it remained positive, a first-order rather than a second-order transition would be predicted.

4.1.4. *The full phase diagram*

The solutions to Eq. (4.5) produce the phase diagram with the P, M, SG and MSG$_\perp$ phases (Fig. 4.1). The point C $= (r_Q = 0, r_M = 0)$ is tricritical for $m = 1$ and tetracritical for $m > 1$. All of the other phase transitions are second order, so the phase boundaries are set by the vanishing of order parameters or inverse susceptibilities. The phases and their boundaries (all with $n = 0$) are then as follows.

- The paramagnetic (P) phase has the trivial solutions $M = 0$ and $Q_{||} = Q_\perp = 0$. The inverse M and SG susceptibilities are

$$\chi_M^{-1} = r_M; \qquad \chi_Q^{-1} = \chi_{Q_{||}}^{-1} = \chi_{Q_\perp}^{-1} = r_Q. \tag{4.10}$$

  Their zeros determine the limits of stability of the P phase and thus the PM and P-SG phases boundaries limiting P to $r_Q > 0$ and $r_M > 0$.

- The spin glass (SG) phase has $M = 0$, $r_Q < 0$, and

$$Q = Q_{||} = Q_\perp = -r_Q/12w_Q \tag{4.11}$$

  with susceptibilities

$$\chi_Q^{-1} = \chi_{Q_{||}}^{-1} = \chi_{Q_\perp}^{-1} = -\frac{1}{2}r_Q, \tag{4.12a}$$

$$\chi_M^{-1} = r_M - (w_{MQ}/6w_Q)r_Q. \tag{4.12b}$$

  These equations define the boundaries, as shown in Fig. 4.1, of the SG phase to be the P-SG boundary on the line $r_Q < 0$ for $r_M > 0$ and the M-SG boundary on the line $r_M = (w_{MQ}/6w_Q)r_Q$ for $r_M < 0$ beyond which M grows from zero. Our model does not have any $Q_\perp$-M^2 coupling, and $Q_\perp$ follows Eq. (4.11) throughout the entire region $r_Q < 0$ and is insensitive to the MSG boundary. However, there is a $Q_{||}$-M^2 coupling, and $Q_{||}$ follows Eq. (4.12a) until the M-SG boundary whereupon it changes behavior.

- The magnetic (M and MQ$_\perp$) phases both exhibit both M and $Q_{||}$ order. The MQ$_\perp$ phase additionally has $Q_\perp$. For $m = 1$, however, there is no $Q_\perp$. The M phase is then determined by the two separate equations showing interactions between M and $Q_{||}$:

$$M^2 = (1/w_{MQ})\left(\frac{1}{2}r_Q Q_{||} + 6w_Q Q_{||}^2\right) \tag{4.13a}$$

$$Q_{||} = (w_{MQ}/24u_M w_Q)\left\{-A + [A^2 - (24u_M w_Q/w_{MQ})r_M]^{1/2}\right\}, \tag{4.13b}$$

where $A = w_Q + (v/w_{MQ})r_Q$. Clearly, $Q_{||}$ and thus M vanish when $r_M = 0$. The P-M boundary is therefore along $r_M = 0$. When $r_M = (w_{MQ}/6w_Q)r_Q$, $\frac{1}{2}r_Q + 6w_Q Q_{||} = 0$, thus verifying that $M = 0$ on the M-SG line. Both $Q_{||}$ and M^2 must be positive in the

M and $MQ_\perp$ phases. It is straightforward to see that M is nonzero for $r_M < 0$ near the P-M phase boundary, and zero for $r_M > 0$. It is also true, albeit more complicated to show, that M^2 grows continuously from zero for displacements with positive changes, Δr_Q, to r_Q perpendicular to the M-SG boundary defined by $r_M = w_{MQ}/(6w_Q)$. For $m > 1$, $Q_\perp$ is nonzero throughout the $r_Q < 0$ subspace because there is no coupling between it and either M or $Q_\parallel$.

The M and $MQ_\perp$ phases, which exhibit both $\overleftrightarrow{Q}$ and $\vec{M}$ order, present greater difficulties in interpreting the $n(n-1)$ factor that, as discussed in Sec. 4.1.3, either represents the number of degrees of freedom in $\overleftrightarrow{Q}$ or signals an energy that is maximized rather than minimized in the SG phase. In the M-SG case, the $\vec{M}$ component does not have the $n-1$ problem but the $\overleftrightarrow{Q}$ part does, making it difficult to interpret $n(n-1)$ as the number of degrees of freedom. This problem can be discerned in the expressions for fluctuation corrections to the MF response function arising from the $\mathcal{F}_{MQ}$. $\mathcal{F}_M$ contains a term $\frac{1}{2}r_M\vec{M}\cdot\vec{M}$. To one-loop order in perturbation theory, r_M experiences a correction proportional to $-(n-1)w_{MQ}^2$ at point C arising from a one-loop diagram.

4.1.5. *Critical exponents and the ϵ-expansion*

The MF order-parameter exponent β and correlation-length exponent ν determine the upper critical dimension $d = d_u$, via the relation $\beta = (1/2)(d_u - 2)\nu$. In MF, Eq. (4.9) sets $\beta = 1$, and Eq. (4.2) implies $\nu = 1/2$ so that $d_u = 6$. The third-order term in $\mathcal{F}$ then becomes relevant in the ϵ-expansion renormalization scheme (see Table 1).

The momentum-shell renormalization-group-recursion relations for an ϵ-expansion about $d = 6$ are [29]

$$\frac{dr_M}{dl} = (2 - \eta_M)r_M - 4m(n-1)\frac{\tilde{w}_{MQ}^2}{(1+r_M)(1+r_Q)}, \tag{4.14a}$$

$$\frac{dr_Q}{dl} = (2 - \eta_Q)r_Q - 36m(n-2)\frac{\tilde{w}_Q^2}{(1+r_Q)^2} - \frac{4\tilde{w}_{MQ}^2}{(1+r_M)^2} \tag{4.14b}$$

$$\frac{d\tilde{w}_Q}{dl} = \frac{1}{2}(\epsilon - 3\eta_Q)\tilde{w}_Q + 36[(n-3)m+1]\tilde{w}_Q^3 + (4/3)\tilde{w}_{MQ}^3, \tag{4.14c}$$

$$\frac{d\tilde{w}_{MQ}}{dl} = \frac{1}{2}(\epsilon - \eta_Q - 2\eta_M)\tilde{w}_{MQ} + 4\tilde{w}_{MQ}^3 + 12m(n-2)\tilde{w}_Q\tilde{w}_{MQ}^2, \tag{4.14d}$$

where $\tilde{w}_S = \sqrt{K_6}w_S$ for $S = Q, M, MQ$ ($K_d = \Omega_d/(2\pi)^d$ with Ω_d the solid angle subtended by a sphere in d dimensions), and

$$\eta_Q = [12(n-2)m\tilde{w}_Q^2 + (4/3)\tilde{w}_{MQ}^2], \qquad \eta_M = (4/3)(n-1)m\tilde{w}_{MQ}^2. \tag{4.15}$$

Table 1. Exponents for the SG fixed point.

Exponent	$\lambda_Q - 2$	$\nu_Q - (1/2)$	$\lambda_M - 2$	$\phi_M - 1$	η_Q	η_M	ψ_Q	ψ_M
Value	$-\dfrac{5m\epsilon}{3(2m-1)}$	$\dfrac{5\epsilon}{12(2m-1)}$	$-\dfrac{m\epsilon}{3(2m-1)}$	$\dfrac{5m\epsilon}{6(2m-1)}$	$-\dfrac{m\epsilon}{(2m-1)}$	0	$-\epsilon$	$\dfrac{7m-3}{12m-6}\epsilon$

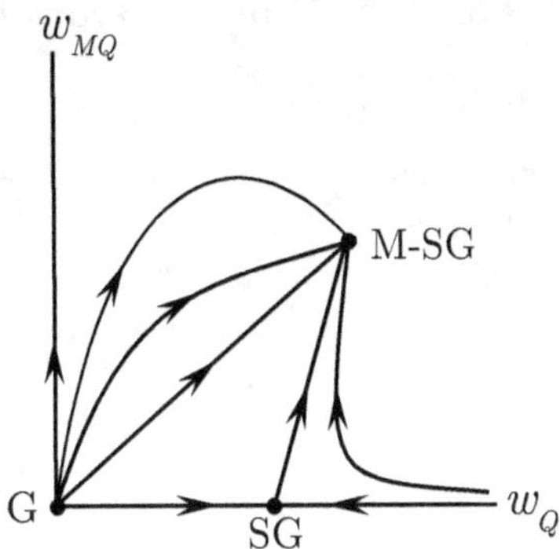

Fig. 4.2.   Schematic RG flow for Eqs. (4.14) and (4.15) showing the G, SG and M-SG FP. Note that the SG FP is unstable to flow toward the M-SG one.

Table 2.   Exponents for the multicritical point C.

Exponent	$\lambda_+ - 2$	$\lambda_- - 2$	η_Q	η_M	ψ_Q	ψ_M
$m = 1$	$-8\epsilon/3$	$-5\epsilon/3$	$-\epsilon/3$	$-\epsilon/3$	$-\epsilon$	$-5\epsilon/3$
$m = 2$	$(-1.150 + 0.3247i)\epsilon$	$(-1.150 - 0.3247i)\epsilon$	-0.2149ϵ	-0.2451ϵ	$-\epsilon$	-1.079ϵ
$m = 3$	$-(0.9407 + 0.2539i)\epsilon$	$-(0.9407 - 0.2539i)\epsilon$	0.1960ϵ	-0.2253ϵ	$-\epsilon$	-0.8686

The outputs of Eqs. (4.14) and (4.15) are their fixed points and the standard zoo of critical exponents. A first observation is that there are three fixed points, depicted in Fig. 4.2, in the space of $w_Q > 0$ and $w_{MQ} > 0$: the Gaussian (G) fixed point at $w_Q = w_{MQ} = 0$, the SG fixed point at $w_Q = w_Q^* > 0$, $w_{MQ} = 0$, and the M-SG-fixed point at $w_Q = w_Q^{**} > 0$, $w_{QM}^{**} > 0$. The exponents $\lambda_Q = \nu_Q^{-1}$ and $\phi_M = \phi_M \lambda_Q$, where ν_Q is the correlation length exponent for Q and ϕ_M, the crossover exponent for M, are those that govern the growth of r_Q and r_M near the P-SG transition. η_Q and η_M control the behavior of correlations of Q and M, respectively, on the P-SG transition line. Finally, ψ_Q and ψ_M are the *stability* exponents that control the behavior of w_Q and w_{MQ} near their fixed point.

Tables 1 and 2 summarize the exponents for the SG transition and the M-SG multicritical point. At the G fixed point, both $\psi_Q = \psi_M = \epsilon/2$, and $\lambda_Q = \lambda_M = 2$. The SG fixed point has $\psi_Q < 0$, and is stable with respect to changes in w_Q, indicating that it describes the transition to the SG phase as long as $\vec{M}$ or w_{MQ} is zero. Because both λ_M and ψ_M are positive, both r_M and w_{QM} are relevant variables that *run away* from any initial values other than zero (see Ref. [28]). The M-SG-fixed point is the most stable one with both ψ_Q and ψ_M negative. The equations for r_Q and r_M are coupled, and, as a result, their exponents λ_+ and λ_- are associated with linear combinations of them. Curiously, λ_+ and λ_- are complex conjugates of each other. There are other peculiarities to the RG flows even for the Ising ($m = 1$) SG case, which unlike for $m > 1$ does not have complex exponents at the M-SG fixed point.

It is therefore clear that the early and naive treatment presented in this section raises more questions than it answers. The rest of this chapter reviews the significant progress on these matters made since the 1970s.

4.2. Field Theory for the de Almeida–Thouless Transition

Tamás Temesvári*, Imre Kondor[†]

*Theoretical Physics Department, Institute of Physics, Eötvös Loránd University,
Budapest, Hungary*
temtam@helios.elte.hu
[†]*Complexity Science Hub, Vienna, Austria, and London Mathematical Laboratory,
London, UK*
kondor.imre@gmail.com

MF theory is exact for the Ising spin glass on the fully connected lattice, i.e. the SK model, and its simplest solution has a transition from the paramagnet to the replica symmetric (RS) SG state in zero external field [30]. This RS phase, however, was soon proven to be unstable for zero as well as for any nonzero magnetic field whenever the temperature is low enough [18]. This instability is now understood to indicate the onset of replica symmetry breaking (RSB) in both cases. Yet the nature of the instability differs in one from the other:

- $H = 0$: The high-temperature paramagnetic phase has a unique degenerate mass m [with multiplicity $n(n-1)/2$ in the replicated theory, with n being the replica number]. The MF transition at the SG critical point T_c^{mf} has the character of a paramagnet to RSB SG transition, instability of the paramagnet is signaled by $m \to 0$.
- $H > 0$: The high-T phase has three different masses: replicon m_R, anomalous m_A, and longitudinal m_L. (For $n = 0$, the latter two are degenerate.) Upon lowering T, m_R vanishes at the de Almeida–Thouless (AT) instability, whereas the other two modes remain noncritical. This kind of transition is now considered to be the *true* SG transition, physically resulting in the SG susceptibility to diverge, whereas the zero-field case is multicritical.

An AT transition can take place even when $H = 0$, but only for $n \gtrsim 0$ [31]. By extending the finite n calculation to $H > 0$, one can contrast the phase diagram with that for $n = 0$ (Fig. 4.3). We note the following:

(i) The finite n phase boundary has a maximum, and hence the RS phase reenters at low T.

(ii) The high-T endpoint of the finite n AT line is separated from T_c^{mf} by a *stable* RS SG phase.

(iii) The $T \to 0$ and $n \to 0$ limit is strongly singular: the H axis for $n = 0$ is simultaneously the innermost part of the RSB phase, and the $n \to 0$ limit of the low-T wing of the AT line.

4.2.1. *RS field theory for the AT transition*

Going beyond MF theory in d dimensions is commonly done by building an effective field theory which is suited to the calculation of perturbative corrections, and may be considered as an initial condition for iterating the renormalization group flows. For this

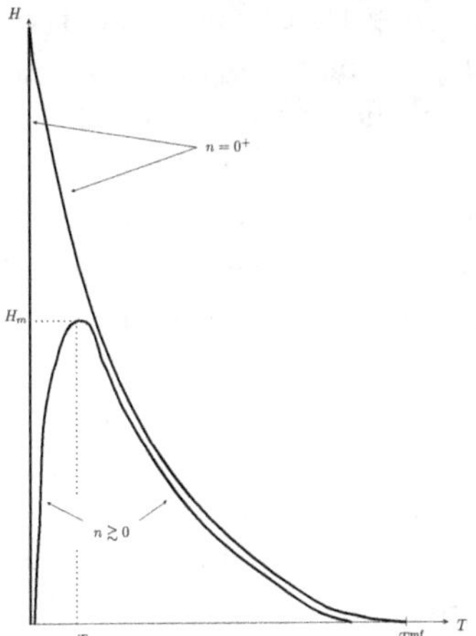

Fig. 4.3.   MF phase diagram of the Ising spin glass for $n = 0^+$ and $n \gtrsim 0$. The maximum asymptotically scales as $T_m \sim n \left[\ln(n^{-2})\right]^{1/2}$ and $H_m \sim \left[\ln(n^{-2})\right]^{1/2}$. The low-$T$ AT line terminates at $T_{\min} \sim n \left[\ln(n^{-2})\right]^{-1/2}$ (not marked in the figure) for $H = 0$, signalling the RS reentrance.

purpose, it is usual to apply the Gaussian integral representation of the replicated and averaged partition function [5, 32, 33]:

$$\overline{Z^n} \sim \int [d\phi]\, e^{-\mathcal{L}(\phi)}, \qquad \mathcal{L}(\phi) = \mathcal{L}^{(G)}(\phi) + \mathcal{L}^{(I)}(\phi)$$

with

$$\mathcal{L}^{(G)} = \frac{1}{2} \sum_{\mathbf{p}} \left[\left(\frac{1}{2}(pa\rho)^2 + m_1 \right) \sum_{\alpha\beta} \phi_{\mathbf{p}}^{\alpha\beta} \phi_{-\mathbf{p}}^{\alpha\beta} + m_2 \sum_{\alpha\beta\gamma} \phi_{\mathbf{p}}^{\alpha\gamma} \phi_{-\mathbf{p}}^{\beta\gamma} + m_3 \sum_{\alpha\beta\gamma\delta} \phi_{\mathbf{p}}^{\alpha\beta} \phi_{-\mathbf{p}}^{\gamma\delta} \right], \tag{4.16}$$

and

$$\mathcal{L}^{(I)} = -\frac{1}{3!\,\sqrt{N}} \sideset{}{'}\sum_{\mathbf{p_1 p_2 p_3}} \sum_{i=1}^{8} w_i\, I_i^{(3)}(\phi) - \frac{1}{4!\,N} \sideset{}{'}\sum_{\mathbf{p_1 p_2 p_3 p_4}} \sum_{i=1}^{23} u_i\, I_i^{(4)}(\phi) - \ldots \tag{4.17}$$

where the fluctuating fields obey $\phi_{\mathbf{p}}^{\alpha\beta} = \phi_{\mathbf{p}}^{\beta\alpha}$ with $\phi_{\mathbf{p}}^{\alpha\alpha} = 0$, the number of the lattice sites $N \to \infty$ in the thermodynamic limit, while ρa is the interaction range. One can define the effective coordination number as $z \equiv \rho^d$. (Momentum conservation is understood in the primed sums.) The cubic and quartic RS invariants[a] in the interaction Lagrangian $\mathcal{L}^{(I)}$ have been exhibited in Refs. [33, 34], some examples are displayed below:

$$I_1^{(3)}(\phi) = \sum_{\alpha\beta\gamma} \phi_{\mathbf{p_1}}^{\alpha\beta} \phi_{\mathbf{p_2}}^{\beta\gamma} \phi_{\mathbf{p_3}}^{\gamma\alpha}, \quad I_2^{(3)}(\phi) = \sum_{\alpha\beta} \phi_{\mathbf{p_1}}^{\alpha\beta} \phi_{\mathbf{p_2}}^{\alpha\beta} \phi_{\mathbf{p_3}}^{\alpha\beta}, \quad I_3^{(3)}(\phi) = \sum_{\alpha\beta\gamma} \phi_{\mathbf{p_1}}^{\alpha\beta} \phi_{\mathbf{p_2}}^{\alpha\beta} \phi_{\mathbf{p_3}}^{\alpha\gamma},$$

and

$$I_1^{(4)} = \sum_{\alpha\beta\gamma\delta} \phi_{\mathbf{p_1}}^{\alpha\beta} \phi_{\mathbf{p_2}}^{\beta\gamma} \phi_{\mathbf{p_3}}^{\gamma\delta} \phi_{\mathbf{p_4}}^{\delta\alpha}, \quad I_2^{(4)} = \sum_{\alpha\beta} \phi_{\mathbf{p_1}}^{\alpha\beta} \phi_{\mathbf{p_2}}^{\alpha\beta} \phi_{\mathbf{p_3}}^{\alpha\beta} \phi_{\mathbf{p_4}}^{\alpha\beta}, \quad I_5^{(4)} = \sum_{\alpha\beta\gamma} \phi_{\mathbf{p_1}}^{\alpha\beta} \phi_{\mathbf{p_2}}^{\alpha\beta} \phi_{\mathbf{p_3}}^{\alpha\gamma} \phi_{\mathbf{p_4}}^{\beta\gamma}.$$

---

[a] $I_j^{(k)}$ are deemed RS invariant because they are unaffected by the global transformation $\phi_{\mathbf{p}}^{\prime\,\alpha\beta} = \phi_{\mathbf{p}}^{P_\alpha P_\beta}$, where P is any permutation of the n replicas.

The stationary condition, which requires the linear term in the interaction part to vanish, gives that masses and couplings depend on temperature T, magnetic field H and replica number n, thus providing an effective field theory beyond the close vicinity of the zero-field multicritical point. One can therefore also study the $T \to 0$ regime. Exact relations further relate some couplings, the most important being $w_3 = -3w_2 = -2w_5$.

A hierarchy of the masses and couplings emerges close to T_c^{mf}. For the paramagnet, m_1, w_1, u_1, u_2, and u_3 are the only nonzero bare parameters (up to quartic order). In the crossover region, the Lagrangian can be written as $\mathcal{L} = \mathcal{L}_{\mathrm{para}} + \delta\mathcal{L}$ with $\delta\mathcal{L}$ having additionally the parameters m_2, w_2, w_3, w_5, u_5 etc., all of which are proportional to the reduced temperature $\tau = (T_c^{\mathrm{mf}} - T)/T_c^{\mathrm{mf}}$. It is clear that the above representation of the system by the RS invariants with unrestricted replica summations and couplings belonging to them is well suited to the system close to the zero-field multicritical point where the paramagnet becomes unstable.

Close to $T = 0$, however, a new system of couplings must be chosen. We then decompose the fluctuating field as

$$\phi_{\mathbf{p}}^{\alpha\beta} = (\phi_{\mathbf{p}}^{R})^{\alpha\beta} + (\phi_{\mathbf{p}}^{A})^{\alpha\beta} + (\phi_{\mathbf{p}}^{L})^{\alpha\beta}$$

where

- the replicon (R) field has the property $\sum_{\beta}(\phi_{\mathbf{p}}^{R})^{\alpha\beta} = 0$ for any α, so the number of independent components is $n(n-3)/2$;
- the anomalous (A) field can be built up from $n-1$ one-replica fields $(\phi_{\mathbf{p}}^{A})^{\alpha}$ with the property $\sum_{\alpha}(\phi_{\mathbf{p}}^{A})^{\alpha} = 0$ as $(\phi_{\mathbf{p}}^{A})^{\alpha\beta} = \frac{1}{2}\left[(\phi_{\mathbf{p}}^{A})^{\alpha} + (\phi_{\mathbf{p}}^{A})^{\beta}\right]$, $\alpha \neq \beta$;
- the single component longitudinal (L) field is constant: $(\phi_{\mathbf{p}}^{L})^{\alpha\beta} = (\phi_{\mathbf{p}}^{L})$, $\alpha \neq \beta$.

$\mathcal{L}^{(G)}$ is diagonal in this new representation, whereas the cubic part of $\mathcal{L}^{(I)}$ takes the form

$$
-\frac{1}{3!\sqrt{N}} \sideset{}{'}\sum_{\mathbf{p_1 p_2 p_3}} \Bigg\{ g_1 \cdot \sum_{\alpha\beta\gamma}(\phi_{\mathbf{p_1}}^{R})^{\alpha\beta}(\phi_{\mathbf{p_2}}^{R})^{\beta\gamma}(\phi_{\mathbf{p_3}}^{R})^{\gamma\alpha} + \frac{1}{2}g_2 \cdot \sum_{\alpha\beta}(\phi_{\mathbf{p_1}}^{R})^{\alpha\beta}(\phi_{\mathbf{p_2}}^{R})^{\alpha\beta}(\phi_{\mathbf{p_3}}^{R})^{\alpha\beta}
$$

$$
+ 3g_3 \cdot \sum_{\alpha\beta}(\phi_{\mathbf{p_1}}^{R})^{\alpha\beta}(\phi_{\mathbf{p_2}}^{R})^{\alpha\beta}(\phi_{\mathbf{p_3}}^{A})^{\alpha} + 3g_4 \cdot \sum_{\alpha\beta}(\phi_{\mathbf{p_1}}^{R})^{\alpha\beta}(\phi_{\mathbf{p_2}}^{R})^{\alpha\beta}(\phi_{\mathbf{p_3}}^{L})
$$

$$
+ 3g_5 \cdot \sum_{\alpha\beta}(\phi_{\mathbf{p_1}}^{R})^{\alpha\beta}(\phi_{\mathbf{p_2}}^{A})^{\alpha}(\phi_{\mathbf{p_3}}^{A})^{\beta} + g_6 \cdot \sum_{\alpha}(\phi_{\mathbf{p_1}}^{A})^{\alpha}(\phi_{\mathbf{p_2}}^{A})^{\alpha}(\phi_{\mathbf{p_3}}^{A})^{\alpha}
$$

$$
+ 3g_7 \cdot \sum_{\alpha}(\phi_{\mathbf{p_1}}^{A})^{\alpha}(\phi_{\mathbf{p_2}}^{A})^{\alpha}(\phi_{\mathbf{p_3}}^{L}) + g_8 \cdot (\phi_{\mathbf{p_1}}^{L})(\phi_{\mathbf{p_2}}^{L})(\phi_{\mathbf{p_3}}^{L}) \Bigg\}. \tag{4.18}
$$

See [33] for the relation between the two sets of couplings, the g_i's and the w_i's.

To calculate corrections to MF theory near $T = 0$, we must know how the bare parameters behave in its vicinity along the MF (or tree-approximation) AT line. It is then convenient to study the $n = 0$ and $n \gtrsim 0$ cases separately (see Fig. 4.3).

- $n = 0$: The two fully-replicon cubic vertices (i.e. with all the three legs being R) diverge as

$$
g_1 = g_2 \sim T^{-1}, \tag{4.19}
$$

whereas the others vanish like $\sim T \ln T$. Surprisingly, the longitudinal mass $m_L = m_A$ does *not* become infinitely large in this limit, instead $\lim_{T \to 0} m_L = O(1)$. Interestingly, it is not monotonic along the AT line, but has a maximum at some intermediate temperature.

- $n \gtrsim 0$: In the low temperature regime, where the $n \gtrsim 0$ line deviates from the $n = 0$ one, the two replicon vertices behave again as in Eq. (4.19). The other six vertices behave at most as $g_i \sim T^{-1} \cdot n^2$. The AT line, however, reaches the temperature axis ($H = 0$) at $T_{\min} \sim n \left[\ln(n^{-2}) \right]^{-1/2}$, and the $n \to 0$ limit finally makes these vertices vanish.

4.2.2. *Perturbative correction to the mean field AT line*

Because perturbative considerations are somewhat modified at $d = 6$, our study in this subsection is restricted to $d > 6$.

(i) **The high-temperature endpoint of the AT line for $H = 0$:**

When both the replica number n and the magnetic field H are zero, the replicon mass is negative, $m_R = -\frac{4}{3}\tau^2$, thus yielding an ill-defined replicon propagator. We must therefore resort to regularization by n or H:

- $n \gtrsim 0$ and $H = 0$. The RS phase is stable between τ_c and τ_{AT}, and it can also be proved that τ_c is at the same time the temperature (at one-loop level) where the paramagnet becomes unstable and the RS order parameter changes sign from negative to positive value.

  As for τ_{AT}, applying *conventional* perturbative method with $1/z \ll n \ll 0$ at one-loop order and contemplating the higher order corrections suggests the form

$$\tau_{AT} = n \cdot f_1(1/nz) + n^2 \cdot f_2(1/nz) + \dots ,$$

and by fixing z while $n \to 0$, the high-argument limit of the f functions will yield the $1/z$ expansion of $\tau_{AT}(H = 0)$.

- $n = 0$ and $H^2/(kT_c^{\mathrm{mf}})^2 \gtrsim 0$. In this case, one can compute the AT temperature for a given, small magnetic field perturbatively:

$$\tau_{AT} = \tau_0 + O(1/z) , \qquad \text{with} \qquad \tau_0 \equiv \left[\frac{3}{4} \frac{H^2}{(kT_c^{\mathrm{mf}})^2} \right]^{1/3} .$$

The loop expansion is generated for a given, albeit small, magnetic field with $1/z \ll \tau_0 \ll 1$. One can expect that a resummation of the whole series provides

$$\tau_{AT} = \tau_0 \cdot \bar{f}(1/\tau_0 z) + \text{correction terms},$$

and a nontrivial zero-field limit follows if $\lim_{u \to \infty} \bar{f}(u) \sim u$, resulting in

$$\tau_{AT}(H = 0) \sim \frac{1}{z},$$

in agreement with the previous regularization scheme.

(ii) **The zero-temperature limit of the AT line for $n = 0$:**

Close to $T = 0$ the loop-expansion is valid for $1/z \ll (T/T_c^{\mathrm{mf}})^2 \ll 1$, providing the result

$$\frac{H_{\mathrm{AT}}^2}{(kT_c^{\mathrm{mf}})^2} = \ln z + \ln\left(\frac{8}{9\pi} u\right) + O(u) \equiv \ln z + g(u) \qquad \text{with} \qquad u = \frac{1}{z}\left(\frac{T_c^{\mathrm{mf}}}{T}\right)^2.$$

The $T = 0$ critical field is expected to be finite for a system with finite connectivity z, in contrast to the SK model. This means that $\lim_{u \to \infty} g(u)$ must be finite, providing

$$H_{\mathrm{AT}}^2(T = 0) = (kT_c^{\mathrm{mf}})^2 \cdot [\ln z + g(\infty)].$$

4.2.3. *Perturbative RG for the cubic field theory*

MF theory and its perturbative corrections provide insight into the transition to the RSB phase. The renormalization group (RG) can also usually provide the correct phase diagrams and universal critical parameters for finite d, short-range systems (z finite). As discussed in Sec. 4.1, the $H = 0$ case was initially studied by Wilson's RG, which identified a stable fixed point in the first order of the ϵ-expansion, $\epsilon = 6 - d$ [1, 7]. Later works extended the calculation of the critical exponents η and ν up to third order [35]. An attempt of the RG study for the RS spin glass phase (again for $H = 0$), with the result of finding its instability, was also done in [36]. Except in this last work, a single mass m_1 and cubic coupling w_1 were considered (see Eqs. (4.16) and (4.17)), and it is the replicated paramagnet which becomes unstable on the critical surface belonging to this stable fixed point. This single critical mass is actually a direct consequence of the extra symmetry the replicated paramagnet has over the generic RS phase [34], thus resulting in the degeneracy of three different masses of the RS phase: replicon, anomalous and longitudinal [5, 36].

The *true* spin glass transition, i.e. the AT transition, has a single critical mass, namely the replicon one m_R, and only the two fully replicon cubic couplings g_1 and g_2 are different from zero (see Eq. (4.18)). The first-order RG for this three-parameter model was worked out by Bray and Roberts [32] who found no stable fixed point when $d < 6$. As for the case above $d = 6$, the stable Gaussian fixed point has, somewhat unusually, a finite basin of attraction that vanishes as $d \to 6^+$ [37]. Although not specifically examined, this finite basin of attraction may exist in any high d, and physical systems outside of it may then not be attracted by the Gaussian fixed point.

These two parts of the parameter space—the replicated paramagnet and the fully replicon subspace — are closed under the RG iteration, and are both special cases of a more general RG system with three masses and eight cubic couplings (see Eqs. (4.16), (4.17) and (4.18)). The first-order RG equations in this large parameter space were presented for generic n and for $n = 0$ in Ref. [38]. The most important conclusion from this many-parameter RG is that there is a critical AT surface in the crossover region around the zero-field fixed point over a range of dimensions $d \lesssim 6$, $d = 6$, and $d \gtrsim 6$ [39, 40].[b] The existence of the critical AT surface around the $H = 0$

---

[b]Note that all these contributions consider a pure cubic model, which is related to but not equal to the effective field theory proposed here.

fixed point does *not* contradict the lack of a stable AT-like fixed point: runaway trajectories for g_1 and g_2 are expected as the RG iterations push the system toward zero temperature.

4.2.4. *An unfinished story: Transition to the RSB phase*

Stable, strong coupling fixed points Various lines of evidence support the existence of an AT-like transition in short range systems over a wide d range. Examples include the numerical work in $d = 4$ [41], Wilson's perturbative RG around the zero-field fixed point (Sec. 4.2.3), and perturbative corrections to MF theory (Sec. 4.2.2). Nevertheless, a theoretical understanding of the AT critical state is still lacking. The failure to find a stable nontrivial fixed point for $d < 6$ in the one-loop perturbative RG [32] and the runaway RG trajectories may be explained by a possible strong coupling fixed point (which is undetectable at one-loop level). Evidence for such a fixed point (stable over a range of d) has been found at two-loop level in Ref. [42], supplemented by a three-loop calculation and a resummation procedure [43], but the situation remains inconclusive (see Sec. 4.3).

Initial conditions for the RG iteration in $d > 6$ For $d > 6$ the Gaussian fixed point is stable, but its basin of attraction is finite [37]. This assessment refers to the fully replicon subspace, which is closed under the RG flow. Physical systems, however, when they are considered as initial conditions for an RG flow, usually lie outside of this subspace. It is therefore nontrivial to predict the outcome of an RG iteration. In Fig. 4.4 the AT line of the effective field theory, introduced in Sec. 4.2.1, is shown for some $d > 6$ and $1/z \ll 1$; the perturbative study in Sec. 4.2.2 is applied here. Three initial conditions on the AT line (where the exact replicon mass Γ_R is zero) are considered:

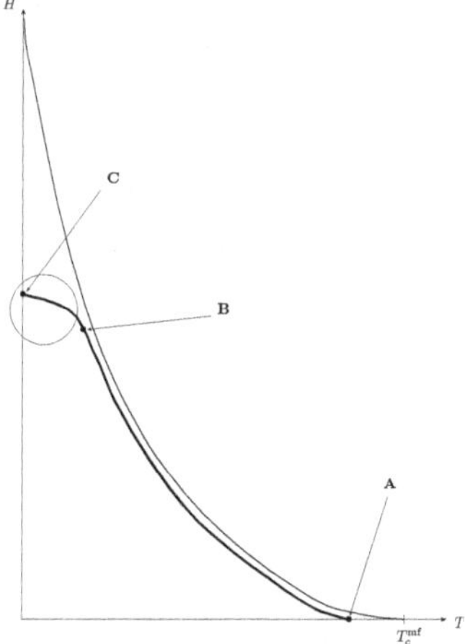

Fig. 4.4.   Phase diagram of the effective field theory in the $H - T$ plane. Three states on the AT line are considered as initial conditions for the RG iteration (see text for details). The encircled region is the nonperturbative part of the RS-to-RSB transition. For comparison, the MF (tree-level) AT line is also displayed (narrow line).

- State A: $H = 0$ endpoint of the AT line, which does not necessarily coincide with the critical point of the replicated paramagnet (see Sec. 4.2.2). This state (and those with $H \gtrsim 0$) is *far* from the fully replicon subspace, because we have (by only showing the leading terms):

$$g_1 = 1, \quad g_3 = -1, \quad g_5 = -1, \quad g_6 = 2, \quad \bar{g}_7 = -\frac{3}{2}, \quad \bar{g}_8 = \frac{1}{4},$$

$$g_2 \sim \frac{1}{z}, \quad \bar{g}_4 \sim \frac{1}{z}, \quad m_R \sim -\frac{1}{z^2}, \quad m_L \sim \frac{1}{z};$$

see Ref. [38] for the definitions of the *bare* couplings which must be used when $n = 0$. Since $g_i/\sqrt{z} \ll 1$ for all i, this state lies inside the perturbative region. From state A, RG iterations move the system toward the fully replicon subspace, driven by the hardening longitudinal mass ($m_L \to \infty$). Decoupling of the RG equations for g_1 and g_2 occurs when $m_L = \infty$. Although Ref. [44] supposed that the RG flow ends at the Gaussian fixed point $g_1 = g_2 = 0$ when $d \gtrsim 6$, it is difficult to see this, and a runaway flow to infinity is also conceivable.

- State B: The low-temperature end of the *perturbative* AT line where $\frac{1}{z} \ll \left(\frac{T}{T_c^{\mathrm{mf}}}\right)^2 \ll 1$. To lighten the notation, let us define $\eta \equiv \left(\frac{T}{T_c^{\mathrm{mf}}}\right)^2 \ll 1$. We have for the couplings:

$$g_1 = g_2 = \frac{4}{5} \eta^{-1/2} \gg 1 \qquad \text{whereas} \qquad g_3, \bar{g}_4, g_5, g_6, \bar{g}_7, \bar{g}_8 \sim \eta^{1/2} \ln \eta \ll 1.$$

Because $g_i/\sqrt{z} \ll 1$ even for $i = 1, 2$, this initial state is still inside the perturbative regime. As for the masses, $m_L = O(1)$ and $m_R \sim -1/\eta z \ll 1$. Although this state is obviously dominated by the replicon mode, it is still somewhat outside the fully replicon subspace.

- State C: The encircled region in Fig. 4.4 shows the nonperturbative part of the AT line where $1/\eta z = O(1)$ (see Sec. 4.2.2). As for the replicon couplings, $g_1/\sqrt{z} = g_2/\sqrt{z}$ are also of order unity and we are out of the range where the perturbative RG is applicable. State C is the zero-temperature limit of the AT line where $1/\eta z \to \infty$. Considering these infinitely large replicon couplings at $T = 0$, one can certainly conclude that, notwithstanding the correct phase diagram with the finite critical field at $T = 0$, the zero-temperature spin glass is not faithfully represented by the effective field theory put forward here. One can speculate that regularization with the replica number $n \gtrsim 0$ may remedy the problem. Alternatively, the loop expansion around the Bethe lattice (instead of the fully connected limit) at $T = 0$ may provide a solution to the problem [45].

4.3. Real-Space RG for Spin Glasses

Maria Chiara Angelini

Dipartimento di Fisica, Sapienza Università di Roma, Rome, Italy
maria.chiara.angelini@roma1.infn.it

As discussed in Sec. 4.1, the standard perturbative RG computation at one loop finds no suitable fixed point (FP) for $d < 6$ to describe the low-T phase [32, 46]. Although the second-order perturbative expansion finds a strong-coupling FP [42, 43], this FP is *nonperturbative*, as it cannot be reached continuously from the Gaussian one from $d_u = 6$. Given that the perturbative analysis is uncontrolled in the strong-coupling regime, the existence and relevance of this FP cannot be confirmed using the approach of Ref. [42]. Real-space RG then seem like a natural methodological choice, because the approach is non-perturbative by construction. In this section we review the real-space RG methods that have been applied to SG, highlighting both their strengths and weaknesses.

4.3.1. *Migdal–Kadanoff RG*

Real-space RG can be viewed as a decimation procedure that reduces a larger system to a smaller one, so as to preserve–or scale appropriately–important physical observables. The partition function is then evaluated iteratively. For each iteration, a block of spins $\{\sigma\}$, described by the Hamiltonian $H(\{\sigma\})$ with couplings $\{J\}$, is replaced by an equivalent system with fewer spins $\{\sigma'\}$ and Hamiltonian $H'(\{\sigma'\})$, with renormalized couplings $\{J'\}$, such that the partition function of the original and the renormalized systems are the same. The study of the resulting transformation of the system couplings can then identify critical points and critical exponents.

While this procedure can be carried out explicitly in $d = 1$ because the Hamiltonian remains of the same form after the reduction of the degrees of freedom, for $d > 1$ new coupling terms arise between distant spins, and the block-spin renormalization cannot be carried out exactly. The Migdal–Kadanoff (MK) approximation aims to overcome the proliferation of couplings [47, 48]. Once the spins in the lattice are divided into blocks, all the couplings internal to the blocks are moved to the spins at the edges of the blocks (see Fig. 4.5(a)). An exact decimation of the spins at the edges, except those on the corners, is then performed. One can demonstrate that the free energy of the system after the bond-moving procedure is a lower bound to the free energy of the original one. The MK procedure applied to a d-dimensional hypercubic lattice consists of replacing it with a hierarchical diamond lattice (HL), for which the MK RG is exact [49]. HL are

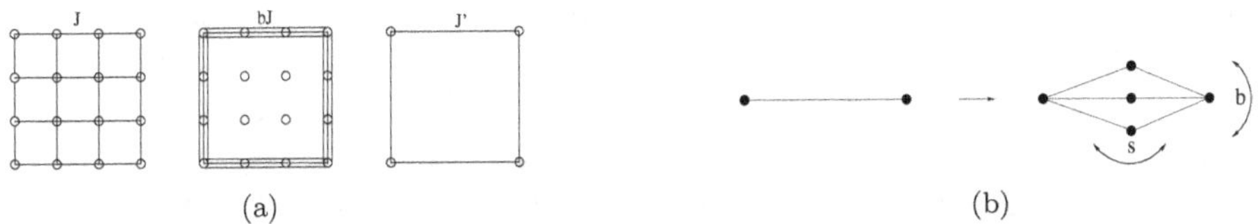

(a)   (b)

Fig. 4.5. (a) Basic step of the MK bond moving procedure to renormalize a $d = 2$ hypercubic lattice. (b) Basic step of the iterative procedure to generate a HL, for which MK RG is exact.

generated iteratively. The procedure starts at step $G = 0$ with two spins connected by a single link. At each step G, for each link of step $G - 1$, b parallel branches, made of s bonds in series each, are added, creating $b \cdot (s - 1)$ new spins. The first step is shown in Fig. 4.5(b). The relationship between the hypercubic lattice and the associated HL is then $d = 1 + \ln(b)/\ln(s)$. The RG procedure is the exact opposite of the iterative procedure to construct the HL. For instance, in step 1, the $b \cdot (s - 1)$ spins generated at the last level are integrated out, generating new effective couplings and fields between the remaining spins.[c] Particular care should be taken when fields are involved [50].

Despite its simplicity, the MK RG can capture highly nontrivial physical features. For example, it accurately describes the $T = 0$ FP of the random field Ising model [51]. However, it becomes less quantitatively accurate as d increases and sometimes even fails qualitatively [52].

The phase diagram for SG with $H = 0$ obtained through MK RG is depicted in Ref. [54]. The model here displays a phase transition from P to SG at $T_c(b)$. Starting at $T > T_c$, the renormalized variance of the coupling distribution v_j decreases, flowing towards the P fixed point $\frac{T}{v_j} = \infty$. Starting at $T < T_c$, the renormalized variance of the coupling distribution increases towards a $T = 0$ FP associated with the SG phase $\frac{T}{v_j} = 0$. At the SG FP, the renormalized variance of the couplings after n iterations grows as $v_J^{(n)} \propto (2^n)^\theta$. Remarkably, the dependence of θ on the effective dimension is well described by $\theta(d) = (d-2.5)/2$, which is consistent with the lower critical dimension $d_L = 2.5$ determined numerically and theoretically [55–57].

In the SG phase, single RG trajectories are chaotic [58], and so is the renormalized couplings dependence on temperature [59].

Let us consider now the contribution of random fields. Suppose that the original fields are extracted from a Gaussian distribution of zero mean and variance v_h. One can show that, for any dimension (any b), the zero temperature SG FP $\frac{T}{v_j} = 0$ becomes unstable, the external field thus corresponding to a relevant perturbation. For small enough d there is no other stable FP associated to the SG phase with field [50]. The transition seems to be destroyed by the field. However, the situation changes as d increases. The renormalization flow projected on the plane $(\frac{T}{v_j}, \frac{v_h}{v_j})$ for $d > 8$ is shown in Fig. 4.6 [53]. Even though the SG-FP is unstable in the presence of an external field, the system then flows toward a new zero-temperature stable fixed point, SGH, which rules the behavior of the SG phase in a field. At high T and/or for strong fields the system flows to the P FP $(\frac{T}{v_j}, \frac{v_h}{v_j}) = (\infty, \infty)$. Therefore, there is necessarily an unstable FP, SGH$_c$, separating the P and the SGH ones. The critical point SGH$_c$ is at $T = 0$ and governs the SG transition in a field. The fact that the critical FP point is a $T = 0$ one implies that there is a third independent critical exponent, in addition to the usual two associated with finite-T FPs. Again, one can compute the new exponent θ_c by looking at how the variance of the couplings increases at the SGH$_c$ FP. The other consequences of a $T = 0$ FP is that, while correlation functions associated to thermal fluctuations decay as $G_{\text{thermal}}(r) \propto \frac{1}{r^{d-2+\eta}}$, correlation functions associated to disorder fluctuations decay as $G_{\text{disorder}}(r) \propto \frac{1}{r^{d-2+\eta-\theta_c}}$ [60]. The MK RG picture is therefore profoundly different from the standard MF description, which predicts a Gaussian FP in $d > d_u$ that is not a $T = 0$

---

[c]In the following we take $s = 2$, which is the value studied in all the works considered.

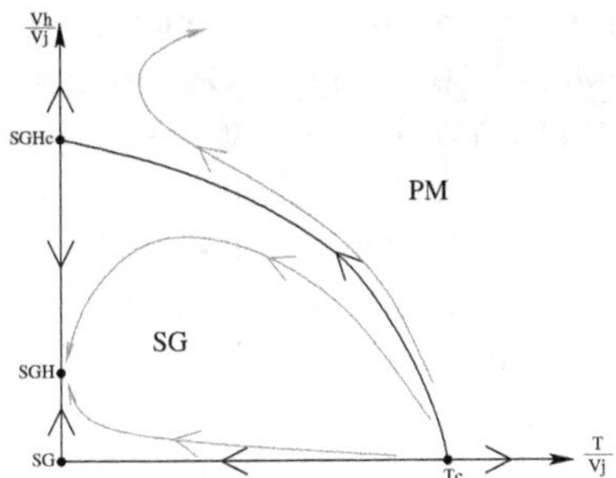

Fig. 4.6.   MK RG flow in the plane $(\frac{T}{v_j}, \frac{v_h}{v_j})$ for $d > 8$ [53]. Reprinted figure with permission from M. C. Angelini and G. Biroli. Phys. Rev. Lett. 114, 095701 (2015). ©(2015) American Physical Society.

one (see Secs. 4.1 and 4.2). For $d \to \infty$, however, the transition found through MK RG loses its $T = 0$ character because $\theta_c \to 0$. MK RG predicts a lower critical dimension $d_L = 8$, below which a stable FP cannot be found when the field is present. The same MK RG method has also been applied to models of glasses for which the microscopic degrees of freedom can take q values. Although the ensuing RG flow is similar to that in Fig. 4.6, the presence of a critical line ending on a $T = 0$ critical FP, and the low-temperature phase governed by another $T = 0$ FP, the lower critical dimension then decreases with increasing q, e.g., $d_L(q = 2) = 8$ but $d_L(q = \infty) \simeq 4$ [61, 62].

The curse of MK RG is that it assumes from the outset that the system is replica symmetric. As was shown by Gardner [63], it cannot include RSB, because it reduces the operative space to a finite, discrete space. To understand if the finite-dimensional world exhibits RSB, then different RG methods are needed.

4.3.2. *Ensemble RG*

At each iteration, MK RG maps a single sample of size N to a smaller one. Given an ensemble of systems of size N, a transformation is applied to each of them to obtain an ensemble of smaller systems. However, a different approach is to establish a direct mapping between the entire probability distributions of couplings in larger and smaller systems, such that the average over such distributions of important observables remains the same. Obviously, in models for which the RG transformation is exact, the two approaches should provide the same answer, but when approximations are made, the latter could lead to better results. In particular, for models with strong disorder (such as SGs), sample-to-sample fluctuations may dominate thermal ones. Following the latter approach, in Ref. [64] the Ensemble RG (ERG), was formulated.

In principle, ERG can be applied to any disordered system. However, it has so far only been applied to the hierarchical model (HM), which is a specific $d = 1$ long-range model, whose Hamiltonian for $N = 2^n$ spins can be constructed iteratively as follows:

$$H_{n+1}(s_1, ..., s_{2^{n+1}}) = H_n(s_1, ..., s_{2^n}) + H_n(s_{2^n+1}, ..., s_{2^{n+1}})$$

$$+ c^{n+1} \sum_{i<j=1}^{2^{n+1}} J_{ij} s_i s_j + \text{const.}$$

In practice, H_n is the sum of interactions at n different levels. HM was introduced by Dyson in its ferromagnetic version [65, 66], and its SG version was proposed in Ref. [67]. By properly tuning the factor c that controls how fast the coupling intensity decays with distance, HM can emulate a d-dimensional short-ranged (SR) model: $c \simeq 2^{-1-2/d}$ for the ferromagnetic model, $c \simeq 2^{(-1-2/d)/2}$ for the SG version (see also Refs. [68, 69]). Because decimation of HM by a standard block-spin transformation does not give rise to any multispin terms (unlike for finite-d lattices), considering pairwise interactions alone in the RG is not an approximation.

ERG assumes that couplings remain independent. They can nevertheless have a different probability distribution $P_k(J)$ at each level $k \in \{1, 2, ..., n\}$. Each coupling distribution is then parameterized by K numbers, otherwise the RG becomes untractable. For SG with a field, one can assume the distribution of couplings and fields to be two independent Gaussians, thus giving $K = 2$ parameters, which are their associated variances. ERG for an ensemble of systems with n levels works as follows:

(1) Compute $(n-1)K$ observables $\langle O_j \rangle$, $j \in \{K+1, ..., Kn\}$ in the larger systems extracted from the original coupling distribution.
(2) Determine the new $(n-1)K$ parameters of the P' distributions by requiring that $\langle O'_i \rangle_{P'} = \langle O_{i+K} \rangle_P$ for any $i \in 1, 2, ..., (n-1)K$.
(3) Build a new ensemble of systems of the original size by joining with random couplings extracted from the original distribution $P_n(J)$ two smaller systems with couplings extracted from $P'_k(J')$, $k \in \{1, 2, ..., (n-1)\}$ found in step (2).

Primed quantities refer to the smaller systems. The first two steps are the true renormalization steps, while the last step is required to obtain a final system size that allows for iterating the method until convergence. The observables used to fix the variances in the SG ERG are normalized SG correlations at different levels. The ERG analysis of SG with $H = 0$ found a SG transition below a critical temperature for (effective) $d \simeq 3$ [64]. The method, which has been assessed by comparing with simulation results, reproduces the proper scaling of the ν exponent, which, for long-range systems, shows a minimum at the upper critical value of c. ERG therefore correctly identifies d_u. The ERG analysis for SG in a field obtained results in perfect agreement with what was found by MK RG [53]. The qualitative phase diagram is as in Fig. 4.6, and below $d_L \simeq 8$ ERG is unable to identify a SG phase.

4.3.3. *Strong disorder RG*

The Strong Disorder RG (SDRG) is a $T = 0$ scheme to construct an approximate SG ground state [70]. It considers the local field of each spin S_i, which is given by $h_i^{\mathrm{loc}} = \sum_j J_{ij} S_j$. Once its largest coupling (in absolute value) is computed, corresponding to some index $j_{\max}(i)$, $\max_j(|J_{ij}|) \equiv |J_{i,j_{\max}(i)}|$, one would like to identify the spins for which the local field

$$h_i^{\mathrm{loc}} = J_{i,j_{\max}(i)} S_{j_{\max}(i)} + \sum_{j \neq j_{\max}(i)} J_{ij} S_j$$

is dominated by the first term. The second term could be approximated by a sum of random terms of absolute values J_{ij} and of random signs. It is therefore reasonable to use

$$\Omega_i \equiv |J_{i,j_{\max}(i)}| - \sqrt{\sum_{j \neq j_{\max}(i)} |J_{ij}|^2}$$

as an indicator of the relative dominance of the maximal coupling in the local field. SDRG is based on the variable Ω_i defined by the following elementary decimation scheme

(1) For each spin i, compute the associated variable Ω_i;
(2) Find the spin i_0 with the maximal Ω_i;
(3) Eliminate the spin S_{i_0}, fixing it to

$$S_{i_0} = S_{j_{\max}(i_0)} \mathrm{sgn}(J_{i_0 j_{\max}(i_0)});$$

(4) Transfer all its couplings $J_{i_0,j}$ with $j \neq j_{\max}(i_0)$ to the spin $S_{j_{\max}(i_0)}$ via the renormalization rule;

$$J^R_{j_{\max}(i_0),j} = J_{j_{\max}(i_0),j} + J_{i_0,j} \mathrm{sgn}(J_{i_0 j_{\max}(i_0)}). \tag{4.20}$$

The procedure is repeated $N - 1$ times; leaving a single spin S_{last} at the end, with $S_{\mathrm{last}} = \pm 1$ labeling the two ground states related by a global flip of all the spins. From $S_{\mathrm{last}} = +1$, one may reconstruct all the values of the decimated spins via the rule described in step 3, and thus approximate the energy of the ground state.

SDRG has been used to assess the validity of the Droplet Picture (DP) or Replica Symmetry Breaking (RSB) description of SG models, depending on d. In the DP, there exists a RS low-T phase with properties determined by the excitation of droplets of fractal dimension $d_s < d$ with a free-energy cost that grows as L^θ for a length scale L. In the RSB picture, there exist system-spanning excitations which have a free-energy cost of $O(1)$ and which are space-filling, i.e., have $d_s = d$. Thus, by investigating the value of d_s of interfaces in the low-T phase, it is possible to determine whether RSB or DP best describes the physics.

In SDRG, θ and d_s are obtained by considering–for each disordered sample — the two ground states associated with two different boundary conditions. Periodic (P) and Anti-Periodic (AP) conditions, in particular, are obtained by flipping the sign of the bonds crossing a hyperplane of the lattice. The difference between the two ground states defines a system-spanning domain wall. The scaling of its energy gives θ, and the scaling of its surface gives d_s.

SDRG values for θ and d_s were first obtained for $d = 2$ and 3 [70]. While the values of d_s by SDRG are in good agreement with those obtained by numerical methods both in $d = 2$ [71] and in $d = 3$ [72], θ is not well captured, giving $\theta(d = 2) \simeq 0$. The scheme thus appears to give the opposite of MKRG, which correctly predicts θ, but misses the value of d_s which is fixed to the trivial $d_s^{MK} = d - 1$. The SDRG value of d_s up to $d = 6$, were later obtained using a greedy algorithm as well [73]. The two estimates appear to merge and give $d_s = d$ in $d = 6$, thus suggesting that RSB could be valid above $d = 6$, while DP could describe the model for $d < 6$.

The key problem of SDRG is that while the approach appears to be accurate for the early iterations, where there exist spins with positive (and large) Ω_i, all Ω_i eventually turn negative, a sign of a failure. As suggested by Monthus [70], it could be that the fractal dimension d_s is dominated by the early iterations, which correspond to long length scales, and for this reason, the SDGR then correctly captures its value.

4.3.4. *M-Layer expansion around the Bethe lattice solution*

We finish with a recently developed expansion around a different soluble MF model: the Bethe lattice (BL) (or, equivalently, a random regular graph of finite connectivity z). A BL model is essentially MF because of the (local) tree structure of the lattice; the contribution of finite-length loops vanishes in the thermodynamic limit. The probability distribution of a spin is therefore independent of the probability of a nearest neighboring spin if the direct edge between them is cut. The idea of an expansion around the BL was originally introduced by Efetov [74] and revived by different authors [75, 76]. Reference [77] formalized the approach through the M-layer construction: one introduces M copies of the original finite-dimensional lattice and generates a new lattice through a local random rewiring of the links. In the $M \to \infty$ limit, the M-layer lattice is locally BL-like in that it presents a tree-like local structure without loops of finite length. (For $M = 1$, one recovers the original lattice.) Using the small parameter $1/M$, one can perform an expansion for a generic multi-point observable. The critical series is expressed as a sum of topological Feynman diagrams with the same numerical pre-factors as in field theories. The only difference is that the contribution of a given diagram must not be evaluated by associating bare propagators to its lines, as is usual; instead, one computes the observable on the corresponding topological loop diagram, thought as manually inserted in a BL. To leading order, one recovers the BL solution with no spatial loops, but upon lowering d spatial loops grow more important. They are therefore present at higher orders in the BL expansion. The perturbative nature of the BL expansion is particularly helpful in keeping computations under control. In addition, it permits following the well-threaded path of standard perturbative RG. BLRG, however, also includes non-perturbative features compared to the standard expansion. The BL solution is exact in one dimension, thus including the resummation of all the non-perturbative effects. Finite connectivity is already encoded at the 0th order of the expansion, and, consequently also accounts for important properties, such as local fluctuation of observables and heterogeneity, at variance with the expansion around the fully-connected MF solution where such effects are construed as non-perturbative effects. The M-layer expansion around BL for a SG in a field in the limit of large connectivity $z \to \infty$ (for $T > 0$) [78] recovers the standard expansion results [32, 46].

In previous sections, we have seen that non-perturbative RG schemes, such as MKRG and ERG, find a critical zero-temperature fixed point for the SG with field, for high enough d (see Fig. 4.4). In the fully connected model, the transition line in the temperature-field $(T - H)$ plane diverges at $T = 0$. There are no zero-temperature fixed points around which one could expand. By contrast, the BL presents such a transition at a finite field h_c [79], around which one can perform an expansion using the M-layer formalism. While setting the temperature straight to 0 is impossible in the Lagrangian approach of the fully connected expansion, $T = 0$ computations can be easily performed in the context of the BL expansion [80]. The zero-loop two-point correlation functions and the first one-loop corrections at $T = 0$ and finite z [45] have found loop corrections not to be negligible for $d < d_u^{\mathrm{BL}} = 8$. The upper critical dimension predicted by the BL expansion is therefore different from $d_u = 6$ predicted by standard field theory. Given that the large z results agree with the standard expansion, finite connectivity is understood to be a crucial ingredient. In other words, the limits $z \to \infty$ and $T \to 0$ do not commute.

The natural next step is to compute three-point correlation functions associated with the cubic vertex at zero- and one-loop order for the BL expansion, to see if, by standard RG field theoretical methods, one can find a non-trivial FP of the RG equations, for $d < d_u^{\mathrm{BL}}$. This program is currently underway.

Acknowledgments

T.L.: I am eternally grateful to have had Brooks Harris as a colleague, collaborator, and part-time mentor during the 1970s and 1980s. I am also grateful for early support from the Office of Naval Research (ONR) and for continuous support of the National Science Foundation.

T.T. acknowledges financial support from the Hungarian Science Found (OTKA), No. K125171.

References

[1] A. Harris, T. Lubensky, and J.-H. Chen, *Phys. Rev. Lett.* **36**, 415, (1976).

[2] K. G. Wilson, *Phys. Rev. B.* **4**(9), 3174, (1971).

[3] K. G. Wilson, *Phys. Rev. B.* **4**, 3184, (1971).

[4] K. G. Wilson and J. Kogut, *Phys. Rep.* **12C**, 75, (1974).

[5] A. J. Bray and M. A. Moore, *J. Phys. C.* **12**, 79–104, (1979).

[6] T. Temesvari, C. De Dominicis, and I. R. Pimentel, *Eur. Phys. J. B.* **25**(3), 361–372, (2002).

[7] J.-H. Chen and T. Lubensky, *Phys. Rev. B.* **16**, 2106, (1977).

[8] P. Chaikin and T. Lubensky, *Principles of Condensed Matter Physics.* (Cambridge University Press, 2000).

[9] N. Goldenfeld, *Lectures Phase Transitions and the Renormalization Group.* (Addison-Wesley, 1972).

[10] J. A. Hertz, *Phys. Rev. B.* **14**, 1165–1184, (1976).

[11] S. Sachdev, *Quantum Phase Transitions.* (Cambridge University Press, 2011).

[12] P.-G. de Gennes, *Scaling concepts in Polymer Physics.* (Cornell University Press, 1979).

[13] P. W. Kasteleyn and C. M. Fortuin, *J. Phys. Soc. Jpn Suppl.* **26**, (1969).

[14] A. B. Harris, T. C. Lubensky, W. K. Holcomb, and C. Dasgupta, *Phys. Rev. Lett.* **35**(6), 327–330, (1975).

[15] T. C. Lubensky and J. Isaacson, *Phys. Rev. Lett.* **41**(12), 829–832, (1978).

[16] T. C. Lubensky and J. Isaacson, *Phys. Rev. A.* **20**(5), 2130–2146, (1979).

[17] M. Mézard, G. Parisi, and M. A. Virasoro, *Spin Glasses and Beyond.* (World Scientific 1987).

[18] J. R. L. de Almeida and D. J. Thouless, *J. Phys. A.* **11**, 983, (1978).

[19] J. R. L. de Almeida, R. C. Jones, J. M. Kosterlitz, and D. J. Thouless, *J. Phys. C.* **11**, L871–L875, (1978).

[20] S. F. Edwards and P. W. Anderson, *J. Phys. F.* **5**, 965–974, (1975).

[21] S. F. Edwards and P. W. Anderson, *J. Phys. F.* **6**, 1927–1937, (1976).

[22] V. J. Emery, *Phys. Rev. B.* **11**, 239–247, (1975).

[23] G. Grinstein and A. Luther, *Phys. Rev. B.* **13**, 1329–1343, (1976).

[24] D. Sherrington and S. Kirkpatrick, *Phys. Rev. Lett.* **35**, 1792–1796, (1975).

[25] S. Kirkpatrick and D. Sherrington, *Phys. Rev. B.* **17**, 4384–4403, (1978).

[26] A. J. Bray and M. A. Moore, *Phys. Rev. Lett.* **41**, 1068–1072, (1978).

[27] A. J. Bray and M. A. Moore, *J. Phys. C.* **12**, 1349–1361, (1979).

[28] S. Fishman and A. Aharony, *Phys. Rev. B.* **21**, 280–295, (1980).

[29] J. H. Chen and T. C. Lubensky, *Phys. Rev. B.* **16**, 2106–2114, (1977).

[30] D. Sherrington and S. Kirkpatrick, *Phys. Rev. Lett.* **35**, 1792, (1975).

[31] I. Kondor, *J. Phys. A.* **16**, L127, (1983).

[32] A. J. Bray and S. A. Roberts, *J. Phys. C.* **13**, 5405, (1980).

[33] T. Temesvári, C. De Dominicis, and I. R. Pimentel, *Eur. Phys. J. B.* **25**, 361, (2002).

[34] T. Temesvári, *Nucl. Phys. B.* **772**(3), 340–370, (2007).

[35] J. E. Green, *J. Phys. A.* **17**, L43, (1985).

[36] E. Pytte and J. Rudnick, *Phys. Rev. B.* **19**, 3603, (1979).

[37] M. Moore and A. Bray, *Phys. Rev. B.* **83**, 224408, (2011).

[38] I. R. Pimentel, T. Temesvári, and C. De Dominicis, *Phys. Rev. B.* **65**, 224420, (2002).

[39] G. Parisi and T. Temesvári, *Nucl. Phys. B.* **858**, 293–316, (2012).

[40] T. Temesvári, *Phys. Rev. B.* **96**, 024411, (2017).

[41] R. A. Banos, A. Cruz, L. A. Fernandez, J. M. Gil-Narvion, A. Gordillo-Guerrero, M. Guidetti, D. Iniguez, A. Maiorano, , E. Marinari, V. Martin-Mayor, J. Monforte-Garcia, A. M. Sudupe, D. Navarro, G. Parisi, S. Perez-Gaviro, J. J. Ruiz-Lorenzo, S. F. Schifano, B. Seoane, A. Tarancon, P. Tellez, R. Tripiccione, and D. Yllanes (Janus Collaboration), *Proc. Nat. Acad. Sci. U.S.A.* **109**, 6452–6456, (2012).

[42] P. Charbonneau and S. Yaida, *Phys. Rev. Lett.* **118**, 215701, (2017).

[43] P. Charbonneau, Y. Hu, A. Raju, J. P. Sethna, and S. Yaida, *Phys. Rev. E.* **99**, 022132, (2019).

[44] M. Moore and N. Read, *Phys. Rev. Lett.* **120**, 130602, (2018).

[45] M. C. Angelini, C. Lucibello, G. Parisi, G. Perrupato, F. Ricci-Tersenghi, and T. Rizzo, *Phys. Rev. Lett.* **128**, 075702, (2022).

[46] I. R. Pimentel, T. Temesvári, and C. De Dominicis, *Phys. Rev. B.* **65**(22), 224420, (2002).

[47] L. P. Kadanoff, *Phys. Rev. Lett.* **34**(16), 1005, (1975).

[48] A. A. Migdal, *J. Exp. Theor. Phys.* **42**, 743, (1976).

[49] A. N. Berker and S. Ostlund, *J. Phys. C.* **12**(22), 4961, (1979).

[50] B. Drossel, H. Bokil, and M. A. Moore, *Phys. Rev. E.* **62**(6), 7690, (2000).

[51] M. S. Cao and J. Machta, *Phys. Rev. B.* **48**(5), 3177, (1993).

[52] F. Antenucci, A. Crisanti, and L. Leuzzi, *J. Stat. Phys.* **155**(5), 909–931, (2014).

[53] M. C. Angelini and G. Biroli, *Phys. Rev. Lett.* **114**(9), 095701, (2015).

[54] B. W. Southern and A. P. Young, *J. Phys. C.* **10**(12), 2179, (1977).

[55] S. Franz, G. Parisi, and M. A. Virasoro, *J. Phys. I (France).* **4**(11), 1657–1667, (1994).

[56] S. Boettcher, *Phys. Rev. Lett.* **95**, 197205, (2005).

[57] A. Maiorano and G. Parisi, *Proc. Nat. Acad. Sci. U.S.A.* **115**(20), 5129–5134, (2018).

[58] S. R. McKay, A. N. Berker, and S. Kirkpatrick, *Phys. Rev. Lett.* **48**(11), 767, (1982).

[59] M. Nifle and H. J. Hilhorst, *Phys. Rev. Lett.* **68**(20), 2992, (1992).

[60] A. J. Bray and M. A. Moore, *J. Phys. C.* **18**(28), L927, (1985).

[61] M. C. Angelini and G. Biroli, *Proc. Nat. Acad. Sci. U.S.A.* **114**(13), 3328–3333, (2017).

[62] M. C. Angelini and G. Biroli, *J. Stat. Phys.* **167**(3), 476–498, (2017).

[63] E. Gardner, *J. Phys. (France).* **45**(11), 1755–1763, (1984).

[64] M. C. Angelini, G. Parisi, and F. Ricci-Tersenghi, *Phys. Rev. B.* **87**(13), 134201, (2013).

[65] F. J. Dyson, *Commun. Math. Phys.* **12**(2), 91–107, (1969).

[66] Y. Meurice, *J. Phys. A.* **40**(23), R39, (2007).

[67] S. Franz, T. Jörg, and G. Parisi, *J. Stat. Mech.* **2009**(02), P02002, (2009).

[68] M. C. Angelini, G. Parisi, and F. Ricci-Tersenghi, *Phys. Rev. E.* **89**(6), 062120, (2014).

[69] R. A. Banos, L. A. Fernandez, V. Martin-Mayor, and A. P. Young, *Phys. Rev. B.* **86**(13), 134416, (2012).

[70] C. Monthus, *Fractals.* **23**(04), 1550042, (2015).

[71] H. Khoshbakht and M. Weigel, *Phys. Rev. B.* **97**(6), 064410, (2018).

[72] W. Wang, J. Machta, H. Munoz-Bauza, and H. G. Katzgraber, *Phys. Rev. B.* **96**(18), 184417, (2017).

[73] W. Wang, M. Moore, and H. G. Katzgraber, *Phys. Rev. E.* **97**(3), 032104, (2018).

[74] K. Efetov, *Physica A.* **167**(1), 119–131, (1990).

[75] G. Parisi and F. Slanina, *J. Stat. Mech.* **2006**(02), L02003, (2006).

[76] V. E. Sacksteder, *Phys. Rev. D.* **76**, 105032, (2007).

[77] A. Altieri, M. C. Angelini, C. Lucibello, G. Parisi, F. Ricci-Tersenghi, and T. Rizzo, *J. Stat. Mech.* **2017**(11), 113303, (2017).

[78] M. C. Angelini, G. Parisi, and F. Ricci-Tersenghi, *EPL.* **121**(2), 27001, (2018).

[79] G. Parisi, F. Ricci-Tersenghi, and T. Rizzo, *J. Stat. Mech.* **2014**(4), P04013, (2014).

[80] M. C. Angelini, C. Lucibello, G. Parisi, F. Ricci-Tersenghi, and T. Rizzo, *Proc. Nat. Acad. Sci. U.S.A.* **117**(5), 2268–2274, (2020).

Chapter 5

Numerical Simulations and Replica Symmetry Breaking

Víctor Martín-Mayor[*], Juan J. Ruiz-Lorenzo[†], Beatriz Seoane[‡] and A. Peter Young[§]

[*],[‡]*Departamento de Física Teórica, Universidad Complutense de Madrid,
Madrid, Spain, and Université Paris-Saclay, CNRS, INRIA Tau team, LISN, 91190,
Gif-sur-Yvette, France*
[*]vicmarti@ucm.es
[‡]beseoane@ucm.es
[†]*Departamento de Física and Instituto de Computación Científica de Extremadura
(ICCAEx), Universidad de Extremadura, Badajoz, Spain*
ruiz@unex.es
[§]*Department of Physics, University of California, Santa Cruz, California, USA*
petery@ucsc.edu

Use of dedicated computers in spin glass simulations allows one to equilibrate very
large samples (of size as large as $L = 32$) and to carry out *computer experiments* that
can be compared to (and analyzed in combination with) laboratory experiments on
spin-glass samples. In the absence of a magnetic field, the most economic conclusion
of the combined analysis of equilibrium and non-equilibrium simulations is that an
RSB spin glass phase is present in three spatial dimensions. However, in the presence
of a field, the lower critical dimension for the de Almeida–Thouless transition seems
to be larger than three.

5.1. Introduction

Equilibrium numerical simulations have been an important tool used by the scientific
community to decide the theoretical controversy regarding the main features of the spin
glass phase (SG) at low temperatures $T < T_c$ (T_c being the critical temperature). On
one side of this polemic, Parisi's solution of the SG in the mean field approximation [1]
has evolved into the replica symmetry breaking (RSB) theory [2] according to which
the spin-glass phase has many pure states. It can be regarded as a critical phase for all
$T < T_c$ in which the surfaces of the magnetic domains are space filling. On the other
side, according to the droplet theory [3–6] there are only two pure states (in zero field)
and the surfaces of magnetic domains (droplets) have a fractal dimension less than the
space dimension D. It corresponds to the Migdal–Kadanoff approximation [7]. There
is also an intermediate picture [8, 9] called TNT for "trivial-non trivial".

However, the emphasis has changed somewhat in recent times. Recent numerical
work has mostly focused on out-of-equilibrium simulations (a choice partly motivated
by the fact that experimental work in spin glasses is carried out under non-equilibrium

conditions). The so-called static-dynamic equivalence allows one to quantitatively relate quantities computed in equilibrium with out-of-equilibrium analogues (see e.g. Ref. [10–16]). Dedicated computers, see Sec. 5.2, have had an important role in this shift of focus that has allowed for a new level of collaboration between simulations and experiments in spin-glass physics. Indeed, it has become possible nowadays to subject experimental and numerical data to a parallel analysis (see Refs. [17–19] and Sec. 5.5). From this new perspective, the situation about the droplet/RSB polemic takes a different light depending on the presence (or absence) of an external magnetic field:

- In the absence of a magnetic field, the latest results, both in equilibrium (see Sec. 5.3) and out-of-equilibrium (Sec. 5.5), find an RSB phase for $T < T_c$ and space dimension $D = 3$. The droplet scenario still remains a logical possibility, but only if one is willing to accept that current simulations and experiments are *entirely* carried out far from the asymptotic regime.[a]
- In the presence of a magnetic field, however, finding a spin-glass phase in $D = 3$ has turned out to be extremely difficult. There is, however, evidence for a spin glass phase in a field in large D, see Sec. 5.4.

Due to space limitations, we shall restrict ourselves to the case of Ising spins ($S_x = \pm 1$), even though Heisenberg and XY spin glass models are also interesting. For Heisenberg and XY spin glasses, the transition temperature is surprisingly low, the asymptotic scaling behavior has probably not been obtained accurately, and there is controversy as to whether there is a separate transition involving chiralities, with Kawamura arguing in favor of a separate transition [20–24], and other authors disagreeing [25–27]. Nevertheless, universality arguments suggest that the unavoidable residual anisotropies in the spin interactions cause the distinction between Ising and Heisenberg spin glasses to be asymptotically irrelevant [28, 29]. Unfortunately, the situation is not yet clear. On the one hand, maybe due to the difficulties in probing the asymptotic scaling regime, critical exponents do not seem to match. For instance, the exponent γ for the non-linear susceptibility is approximately 5.5 from simulations for the Ising spin-glass universality class [30], while experiments on Heisenberg spin glasses get lower values around 2 and 3 [31]. On the other hand, the quantitative agreement in the non-equilibrium dynamics in the spin glass phase between experiments in CuMn samples and Ising–Edwards–Anderson simulations, see Refs. [17–19] and Sec. 5.5, seems to support the choice of modeling spin glasses with an Ising Hamiltonian.

The remaining part of this chapter is organized as follows. We recall the standard model of spin-glasses in Sec. 5.1.1, define the main observables considered in equilibrium simulations in Sec. 5.1.2, and review finite-size scaling methods in Sec. 5.1.3. The need for dedicated computers is explained in Sec. 5.2. Important results obtained in equilibrium simulations in the absence of a magnetic field are recalled in Sec. 5.3. Equilibrium simulations in a field are reviewed in Sec. 5.4. Next, out-of-equilibrium simulations are reviewed in Sec. 5.5, and finally, our conclusions are summarized in Sec. 5.6.

---

[a] A difficulty common to both simulations and experiments is that new behavior might emerge for larger lattice sizes or larger spin-glass coherence lengths.

5.1.1. *The Edwards–Anderson model and its gauge symmetry*

We shall be considering two geometries, namely (hyper) cubic lattices in D-dimensions and $1D$ models with long-range interactions. In the cubic geometry, the spins lie on the nodes of a (hyper)cubic lattice, whose linear size is denoted by L, so the number of spins is $N = L^D$. Periodic boundary conditions are usually taken and interactions are typically restricted to lattice nearest neighbors. The models with long-range interactions are in one dimension and the strength of the interactions falls off as a power of the distance between the spins. Varying this power is argued to be equivalent (at least roughly) to varying the dimension of the short-range model.

For both geometries, we consider the Edwards–Anderson (EA) Hamiltonian:

$$\mathcal{H} = -\sum_{\langle x,y \rangle} J_{xy} S_x S_y - \sum_x h_x S_x, \tag{5.1}$$

where $\langle x, y \rangle$ indicates that the sum is taken over all pairs of interacting spins (e.g. nearest-neighbors for the typical cubic geometry). It would be natural to use a uniform external magnetic field $h_x = h$, but the gauge symmetry (see below) makes it advisable to retain a site-dependence for the magnetic fields h_x. Spin glass models have quenched disorder (see e.g. Ref. [32]) in which the coupling constants J_{xy} (and sometimes also the magnetic fields h_x) are randomly extracted from a probability distribution and held fixed once and for all. We call a particular realization of the $\{J_{xy}, h_x\}$ a *sample*. Thermal averages, denoted by $\langle \ldots \rangle$, are first computed for every sample. The subsequent average over samples of the thermal mean-values is denoted by $[\langle \ldots \rangle]$.

The couplings in Eq. (5.1) are independent, identically distributed random variables. The most popular choices for the probability distributions in a cubic geometry are the bimodal distribution (in which J_{xy} is ± 1 with 50% probability) and a Gaussian distribution with zero mean and unit variance. In the case of the long-range geometry, one usually takes a Gaussian distribution.

The crucial role of the Z_2 Gauge symmetry of the Hamiltonian (5.1) was soon realized [33]. If one chooses $\epsilon_x = \pm 1$ randomly at every lattice site x, the energy remains invariant under the transformation

$$S_x \to \epsilon_x S_x, \quad J_{xy} \to \epsilon_x J_{xy} \epsilon_y, \quad h_x \to \epsilon_x h_x. \tag{5.2}$$

For all the standard choices of coupling distributions, one finds that the original choice $\{J_{xy}, h_x\}$ and its gauge-transformed values $\{\epsilon_x J_{xy} \epsilon_y, \epsilon_x h_x\}$ occur with the same probability. Therefore, the sample-average $[\langle \ldots \rangle]$ effectively averages over all possible choices for the gauge parameters $\epsilon_x = \pm 1$. All quantities that we focus on are invariant under the gauge transformation (5.2), see Secs. 5.1.2, 5.5.1.

5.1.2. *Observables (equilibrium)*

A key quantity in our discussion will be the total overlap per spin defined by:

$$q \equiv q_{1,2} = \frac{1}{N} \sum_x S_x^{(1)} S_x^{(2)}, \tag{5.3}$$

where $S^{(1)}$ and $S^{(2)}$ are two real replicas of the system with the same disorder. Its associated probability density function (pdf) averaged over the disorder can be written as

$$P(q) = \left[\left\langle \delta \left(q - \frac{1}{N} \sum_{\boldsymbol{x}} S_{\boldsymbol{x}}^{(1)} S_{\boldsymbol{x}}^{(2)} \right) \right\rangle \right]. \tag{5.4}$$

It will also be useful to define the link overlap by

$$Q_{\text{link}} = \frac{1}{N_{\text{link}}} \sum_{\langle \boldsymbol{x}, \boldsymbol{y} \rangle} S_{\boldsymbol{x}}^{(1)} S_{\boldsymbol{y}}^{(1)} S_{\boldsymbol{x}}^{(2)} S_{\boldsymbol{y}}^{(2)}, \tag{5.5}$$

where the sum extends over all pairs of interacting lattice sites (also known as *links*), whose number is N_{link}. In a D-dimensional cubic lattice with periodic boundary conditions $N_{\text{link}} = DN$, but for a long-range model N_{link} may be as large as $N(N-1)/2$. In mean field theory the link overlap is trivially related to the spin overlap by $Q_{\text{link}} = q^2$.

Both q and Q_{link} are adequate for a mean-field treatment, but to go beyond this limit we also need to consider the crucial role of fluctuations, characterized by correlation functions. In the presence of a magnetic field, where individual spins have a non-zero average magnetization, several different correlation functions can be defined [34, 35]. Specializing here only to the most divergent correlations [36, 37], we define the "replicon" propagator in real and Fourier space by

$$G(\boldsymbol{r}) = \frac{1}{N} \sum_{\boldsymbol{x}} \left[\left(\langle S_{\boldsymbol{x}} S_{\boldsymbol{x}+r} \rangle - \langle S_{\boldsymbol{x}} \rangle \langle S_{\boldsymbol{x}+r} \rangle \right)^2 \right], \quad \hat{G}(\boldsymbol{k}) = \sum_{r} \mathrm{e}^{-i\boldsymbol{k}\cdot\boldsymbol{r}} G(\boldsymbol{r}). \tag{5.6}$$

In particular, the spin-glass susceptibility is

$$\chi_{SG} \equiv \hat{G}\big(\boldsymbol{k} = (0, 0, \ldots, 0)\big) = \frac{1}{N} \sum_{\boldsymbol{x}, \boldsymbol{y}} \left[\left(\langle S_{\boldsymbol{x}} S_{\boldsymbol{y}} \rangle - \langle S_{\boldsymbol{x}} \rangle \langle S_{\boldsymbol{y}} \rangle \right)^2 \right]. \tag{5.7}$$

In the absence of a field, $\langle S_{\boldsymbol{x}} \rangle = 0$ for all sites $\boldsymbol{x}$ and Eq. (5.7) simplifies to $\chi_{SG} = N\big[\langle q^2 \rangle\big]$.

A quantity related to χ_{SG} is the second-moment correlation length (see e.g. [38]) that in a (hyper)cubic lattice with periodic boundary conditions is

$$\xi_2 = \frac{1}{2 \sin(\pi/L)} \sqrt{\frac{\chi_{SG}}{\hat{G}(\boldsymbol{k}_1)} - 1}, \tag{5.8}$$

where $\boldsymbol{k}_1$ is the minimal non-vanishing wavevector allowed by the boundary conditions (namely, $\boldsymbol{k}_1 = (2\pi/L, 0, 0, \ldots, 0)$ and permutations). Interestingly, ξ_2 was instrumental in showing that there is a second order spin glass phase transition in zero field in space dimension $D = 3$ [39, 40]. A different definition of the correlation length, more appropriate for out-of-equilibrium simulations, will be discussed in Sec. 5.5.1.

Let us conclude this subsection by recalling the most important quantity, namely the Edwards-Anderson order parameter (q_{EA}), which is the maximum overlap. For mean-field models (such as the Sherrington-Kirkpatrick (SK) model), q_{EA} is given by

$$q_{\text{EA}} = \frac{1}{N} \sum_{\boldsymbol{x}} \left[\langle S_{\boldsymbol{x}} \rangle_\alpha^2 \right]. \tag{5.9}$$

where $\langle\!\langle(\cdots)\rangle\!\rangle_\alpha$ is the average constrained to the state α and is independent of the choice of state. Unfortunately, the definition of a *state* beyond the mean-field approximation is quite subtle (see Chapter 33).

5.1.3. *Finite size scaling*

The theory of finite-size scaling, see e.g. [38], explains how critical divergences are rounded in a finite-system of linear size L. Let $T_{\rm c}(h)$ be the critical temperature, in which we have allowed a dependency on the magnetic field h, and let O be a quantity diverging in the thermodynamic limit as $[\langle O\rangle] \propto 1/(T - T_{\rm c}(h))^{x_0}$. (We refer only to the dominant divergence given by the critical exponent x_0; there might be subleading terms.) If the space dimension D is smaller than the upper critical dimension D_u (the dimension above which the mean-field approximation gives exact values for critical exponents) then, according to finite-size scaling,

$$[\langle O\rangle](L,T) = L^{x_0/\nu} f_O(L^{1/\nu}t) + \ldots, \quad t = \frac{T - T_{\rm c}(h)}{T_{\rm c}(h)}, \tag{5.10}$$

where ν is the thermal critical exponent and the dots stand for subleading scaling corrections.

Of particular importance in this context are dimensionless quantities such as the second-moment correlation length ξ_2, defined in Eq. (5.8), in units of the system-size

$$\xi_2/L = f_\xi(L^{1/\nu}t) + \ldots. \tag{5.11}$$

Dimensionless quantities are extremely useful to locate the critical point. See, for instance, Ref. [40]. An example of this use of Eq. (5.11) is explained in Sec. 5.4 and Fig. 5.5.

Some authors, working with $1D$ models with long-range interactions, have found that, in the presence of an external magnetic field, the propagator behaves anomalously, but only for the $\boldsymbol{k} = 0$ mode [41]. This observation suggests trading ξ_2/L for another universal, renormalization-group invariant quantity named R_{12} [42], defined by

$$R_{12} = \frac{\hat{G}(\boldsymbol{k}_1)}{\hat{G}(\boldsymbol{k}_2)}, \tag{5.12}$$

where $\boldsymbol{k}_1$ and $\boldsymbol{k}_2$ are the smallest non-zero momenta compatible with the periodic boundary conditions. For example, for $D=4$, $\boldsymbol{k}_1=(2\pi/L,0,0,0)$ and $\boldsymbol{k}_2=(2\pi/L,\pm 2\pi/L,0,0)$ (and permutations). The generalization to other space dimensions is trivial.

5.2. Why It is So Difficult to Simulate Spin Glasses? The Role of Dedicated Computers

Numerical simulation of spin glasses in equilibrium entails two major difficulties:

(1) The variability between different samples is quite significant (see, for instance, Sec. 5.3.3), which means that one needs to simulate a large number of samples in order to obtain an accurate sample average.

(2) The simulation time needed to equilibrate each sample is very significant. This is to be expected at zero temperature, because finding the ground state is an NP-complete problem [43]. The problem remains difficult at finite temperatures. The most efficient Monte Carlo algorithm for spin glasses seems to be parallel tempering [44, 45], also called "replica exchange Monte Carlo". Unfortunately there is no known, highly-efficient cluster algorithm of general applicability to spin glasses which corresponds to Swendsen and Wang's [46] cluster algorithm for unfrustrated systems. In separate work, Swendsen and Wang [47] developed a cluster-replica approach to spin glasses which works well in two dimensions [48]. In higher dimensions, though, this approach effectively becomes equivalent to parallel tempering. A cluster, replica algorithm for $D = 2$ spin glasses has also been developed by Houdayer [49]. Since $T_c = 0$ for two-dimensional spin glasses, so there is no low-temperature phase, the most efficient algorithm for the spin glass state below T_c seems to be parallel tempering, as noted above. Even with the help of parallel tempering, some samples need an unusually large equilibration time [25]. The underlying physical mechanism that hampers equilibration, even when using parallel tempering, seems to be temperature chaos [50, 51].[b]

For out-of-equilibrium simulations, one uses very large samples to ensure that the slowly growing, time-dependent coherence length $\xi(t)$ is much less than the system size L. One then needs fewer samples than for equilibrium simulations because one can think of a macroscopic sample as being composed of $(L/\xi(t))^D$ equilibrated regions that are more or less independent of each other, so one large sample effectively averages over $(L/\xi(t))^D$ "samples" of size $L_{\mathrm{eff}} \approx \xi(t)$. If one could simulate a truly macroscopic system then only one sample would be needed. This is, of course, the experimental situation.

Another difficulty in out-of-equilibrium simulations is that one has to mimic natural dynamics using, for instance, the Metropolis algorithm. One is not allowed to use accelerated dynamics like parallel tempering. Unfortunately, natural dynamics is very slow at and below T_c (see e.g. Fig. 5.11). Hence, it is clear that one needs to carry out very long simulations in order to reach reasonably large values of $\xi(t)$. This topic is further elaborated in Sec. 5.5.

Given these difficulties, a possible way forward is to build computers specifically designed for spin-glass simulations. Several such computers have been built over the years, such as the Ogielski machine [53], SUE [54], and the Janus supercomputers [55, 56]. The Janus II is currently the most powerful computer for spin glass simulations.

5.3. Equilibrium Numerical Studies of the Overlap

RSB makes many predictions regarding the order parameter in spin glasses. In this section we will focus on a small number of them: (i) its density probability function

---

[b]It is remarkable that temperature chaos seems as well to be a major limiting factor for the performance of a quantum annealer [52].

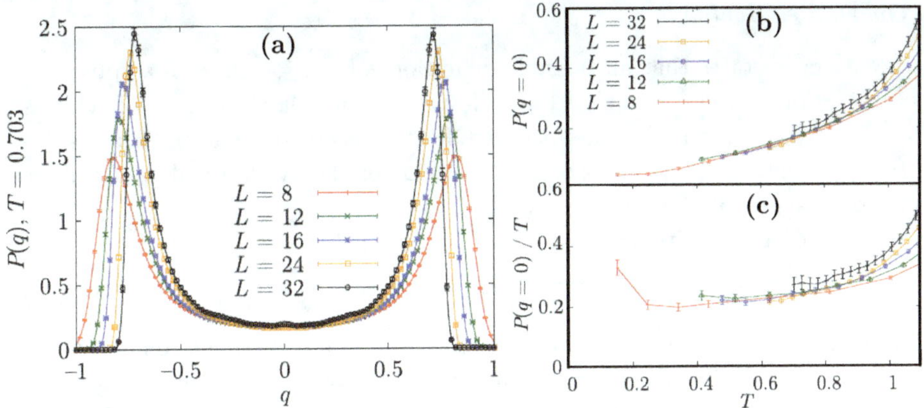

Fig. 5.1. (a) Overlap density distribution function $P(q)$, see Eq. (5.4), as computed for the $3D$ EA model with binary couplings at $T = 0.703 \approx 0.64 T_{\rm c}$ for different lattice sizes L. (b) $P(q = 0)$ and (c) $P(q = 0)/T$ versus temperature T, as computed in $3D$ for several system sizes. We observe an envelope curve with a linear behavior, as expected from RSB. Figure adapted from [57].

$P(q)$, (ii) overlap equivalence, i.e. all possible definitions of an overlap in the model encode the same physics and (iii) stochastic stability (which is used to show Guerra's relations) and ultrametricity.

5.3.1. *Structure of the equilibrium $P(q)$*

One manifestation of the infinite number of pure states predicted by RSB theory is a non trivial pdf of the order parameter, $P(q)$, see Fig. 5.1(a). In contrast, the droplet model predicts a trivial $P(q)$ in the thermodynamic limit, in the sense that it consists, for $h = 0$, of two Dirac-delta functions at $q = \pm q_{\rm EA}$, where $q_{\rm EA}$ is the Edwards–Anderson overlap. Instead, in RSB, $P(q)$ has, in addition to these two delta functions, a continuous function in between which is non-zero in the thermodynamic limit (see the sketch in Fig. 5.9). In the droplet picture the continuous part of the distribution vanishes slowly with linear system size L like $L^{-\theta_S}$ where θ_S is a stiffness exponent whose value is around 0.24 [58] for $D = 3$.

Over the years there have been many studies [57, 59–65] of the weight of $P(q)$ around $q = 0$ and these consistently find a value independent, or nearly independent, of size, in agreement with RSB theory.

We show some recent results in $3D$ [57] for $P(q)$, Fig 5.1(a), $P(0)$, Fig 5.1(b), and $P(0)/T$, Fig 5.1(c), as a function of the temperature deep in the spin glass phase. We recall that $T_c = 1.1019(29)$ [30]. This data supports the RSB predictions that $P(0)$ is independent of L, and is proportional to T at low T. A different analysis of the $P(q)$ behavior comes to the same conclusions [65]. The behavior of $P(q=0)$ could be modified by the presence of interfaces, so it was proposed to compute $P(q)$ in small boxes in order to avoid their effects. This analysis was performed in Ref. [66], which found the same behavior as that obtained from the overlap computed over the whole lattice.

5.3.2. *Overlap equivalence*

Overlap equivalence states that all possible definitions of new overlaps in a spin glass must be a function of the overlap q. Equivalently, we can classify a pair of replicas using their overlap and argue that no finer classification is possible (separability). This implies that fluctuations of all reasonable definitions of the overlap will vanish if we work in a fixed q ensemble.

The variance of a q-conditioned observable O is defined by

$$\mathrm{Var}(O|q=c) = \mathrm{E}(O^2|q=c) - \mathrm{E}(O|q=c)^2, \qquad (5.13)$$

where the symbol $\mathrm{E}(\cdot)$ denotes (i) the average in a given sample over the configurations which satisfy the constraint ($q=c$), and then (ii) the average over disorder.

In this subsection we address the behavior of $\mathrm{Var}(Q_{\text{link}}|q)$. RSB predicts that this conditioned variance should go to zero in the limit of large lattices, due to the existence of a relation between Q_{link} and q. In the droplet model the only possible value of q is q_{EA}, so Q_{link} will be defined only for this value of the overlap (in the infinite volume limit). Therefore, the droplet model predicts as well a vanishing conditioned variance.

Indeed, Fig. 5.2 shows that this conditioned variance goes to zero in the limit of large L [57]. Moreover, Ref. [67] reaches the same conclusion from a different analysis. The good scaling of the conditioned variance of Q_{link} near $q=0$ extends to q_{EA} for the larger lattices ($L=24$ and $L=32$). This scaling supports the RSB picture and not the droplet model, because in the latter droplet picture it would be natural to expect completely different finite size effects for $q=q_{\text{EA}}$ and for $q < q_{\text{EA}}$ (and in particular for $q=0$).

Another interesting quantity is $\mathrm{dE}(Q_{\text{link}}|q)/\mathrm{d}q^2$. In the droplet model, at variance with the RSB picture, this derivative should be zero. Numerically, the derivative is nonzero, although its size decreases with L. Therefore, the analysis based on this observable is not conclusive [57]. Nevertheless the results of Ref. [67], provides numerical evidence that $\mathrm{E}(Q_{\text{link}}|q^2)$ is an increasing one-to-one function of q^2 in the thermodynamic limit. This fact, when combined with a vanishing conditioned variance of Q_{link}, rules out the TNT description of the spin-glass phase.

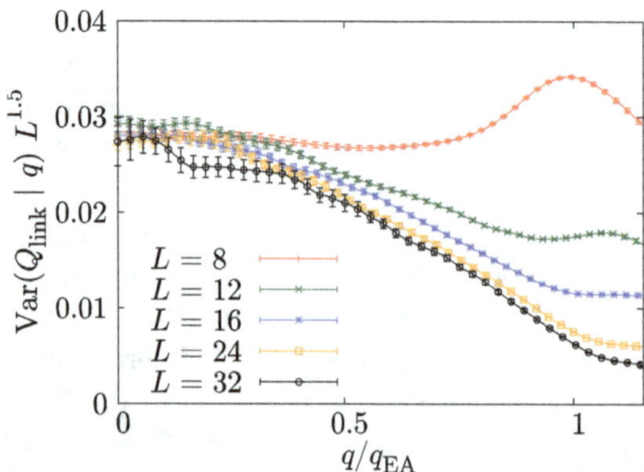

Fig. 5.2.   Plot of the conditional variance at fixed q of Q_{link}, see Eq. (5.13), rescaled by appropriate powers of L in $3D$ at $T = 0.703$ (we chose exponents that provided a good scaling at $q = 0$). The abscissa corresponds to q in units of $q_{\text{EA}}(L, T = 0.703)$. Figure taken from [57].

5.3.3. *Stochastic stability*

Stochastic stability[c] has been proved in the SK model by Guerra [68, 69] and by Aizenman and Contucci [70]. In this section we present numerical evidence supporting stochastic stability in finite-dimensional models, which, in turn, provides evidence that RSB applies in those systems.

Using stochastic stability is possible to write the following relation,

$$R_{\text{link}} = \frac{\left[\langle Q_{\text{link}}^2 \rangle - \langle Q_{\text{link}} \rangle^2\right]}{\left[\langle Q_{\text{link}}^2 \rangle\right] - \left[\langle Q_{\text{link}} \rangle\right]^2} = \frac{2}{3} \qquad (\text{RSB}, L \to \infty, T < T_c). \tag{5.14}$$

Note the difference in the placement of the square in the subtracted terms in the numerator and denominator. In the droplet or TNT pictures both the numerator and denominator vanish in the thermodynamic limit.

Another analogous observable with the same RSB behavior is R_{q^2} (using the mean-field correspondence $Q_{\text{link}} \to q^2$):

$$R_{q^2} = \frac{\left[\langle q^4 \rangle - \langle q^2 \rangle^2\right]}{\left[\langle q^4 \rangle\right] - \left[\langle q^2 \rangle\right]^2} = \frac{2}{3} \qquad (\text{RSB}, L \to \infty, T < T_c). \tag{5.15}$$

In Fig. 5.3 we show the behavior of R_{link} and R_{q^2} as a function of temperature in $3D$ for different lattice sizes. The convergence of both observables to the mean field limit, $2/3$, is very good below the critical temperature. For additional analysis, see Ref. [67].

Finally, we briefly discuss the issue of ultrametricity. It is possible to show that overlap equivalence and stochastic stability imply ultrametricity [71]. In addition, using some of Guerra's relations [68, 69] and assuming the existence of ultrametricity in finite space dimension D, one finds that ultrametricity at finite D should have the same properties as one finds for $D = \infty$ (i.e. a quarter of the triangles are equilateral,

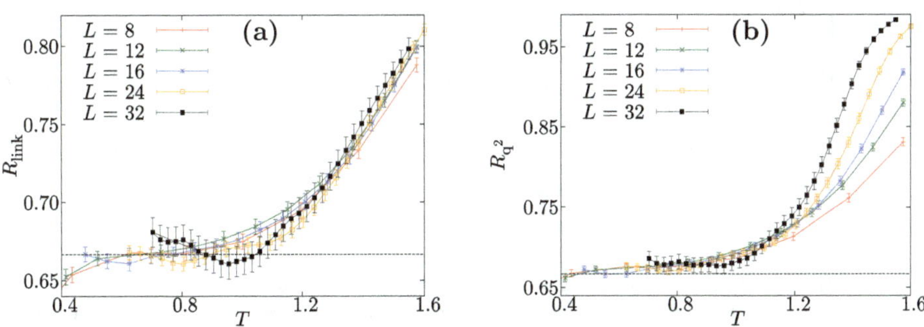

Fig. 5.3.   The ratios R_{link}, Eq. (5.14), (a) and R_{q^2}, Eq. (5.15), (b) versus T for the different system sizes in $3D$. Stochastic stability implies that, in an RSB system below T_c, $R^{\text{link}} = R_{q^2} = 2/3$ in the large-L limit. Recall that $T_c \approx 1.1$. Figure taken from [57].

---

[c]The Parisi matrix Q_{ab} satisfies the condition that $\sum_b f(Q_{ab})$ is independent of the replica index a. Stochastic stability states the invariance of the distribution of the free energies under independent random increments of the interactions. Stochastic stability implies replica invariance but is more general.

otherwise they are isosceles) [72]. Furthermore, Panchenko has shown that ultrametricity follows from stochastic stability without additional assumptions [73]. Hence, the results already presented in this section indicate that ultrametricity should exist in three dimensions with the same properties as in mean field theory. However, direct detection of ultrametricity in $3D$ spin glasses remains elusive [74, 75].

5.4. Results in a Magnetic Field

One of the most striking predictions of the RSB solution of the SK model [76] is a line of transitions in a magnetic field terminating in the zero field transition point, T_c, see Fig. 5.4(a). This was first found by de Almeida and Thouless [34] and so is known as the dAT line.[d] Below the dAT line, the SK model is described by the RSB solution of Parisi [77–79], while above the dAT line the replica symmetric solution is valid. According to RSB theory, there is also a dAT line in short-range models. If there is no dAT line, then there is simply a line of transitions along the zero field axis, terminating at T_c, as shown in Fig. 5.4(b). This is the prediction of the droplet theory.

While the zero field transition has a spontaneously broken symmetry, as usual, the transition in a field on the dAT line is *unusual* in having no broken symmetry, since spin-inversion symmetry is already broken by the magnetic field. While the dAT transition definitely occurs in the SK model, there is controversy as to whether it also occurs in models which do not have infinite-range interactions. According to RSB theory there is a dAT line in short-range models, whereas according to the droplet theory the dAT line is an artefact of the infinite-range nature of the SK model and does not occur in short-range models in *any* dimension.

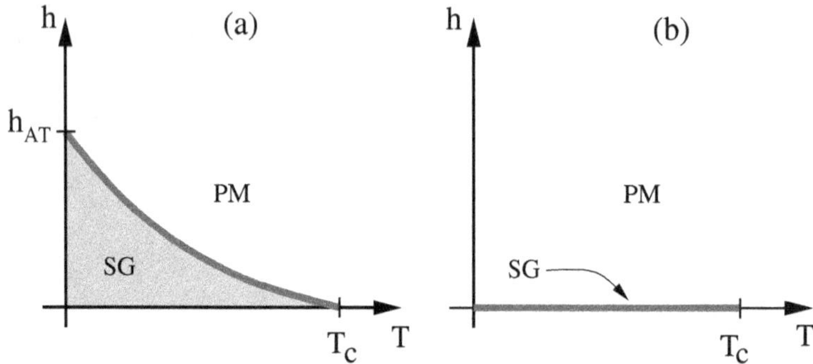

Fig. 5.4.   Schematic representation of the magnetic-field, temperature, (h, T), phase diagram for a spin-glass former. According to RSB theory, the phase diagram depends strongly on the space dimension. (**a**) If the space dimension is larger than the lower critical dimension (in a field) $D > D_\ell^h$, there is a spin-glass phase (SG) for $T < T_c(h)$. For $T > T_c(h)$ the system is in the paramagnetic phase (PM). The critical line separating both phases, $T = T_c(h)$, is called the de Almeida–Thouless (dAT) line [34]. The value of the critical field at $T = 0$ is called h_{AT}. (**b**) Instead, for spatial dimension $D < D_\ell^h$, a spin-glass phase exists only for $h = 0$. According to the droplet picture, figure (b) applies in all dimensions, which corresponds to $D_\ell^h = \infty$.

---

[d] Frequently this has been referred to as the AT line, but here we indicate correctly the initials of the first author.

In critical phenomena, we are familiar with the fact that fluctuations destroy a transition in dimension D at (or below) a "lower critical dimension", D_ℓ, where $D_\ell = 1$ for the Ising ferromagnet (see e.g. Ref. [80]), and $D_\ell \approx 2.5$ for the Ising spin-glass [58, 81, 82]. What about a spin glass in a magnetic field? The gauge symmetry in Eq. (5.2) implies that even a uniform magnetic field in a spin glass is effectively a random field as far as the spin glass ordering is concerned. This observation reminds us immediately of the random field Ising model (RFIM, see e.g. [83]).

When random fields are switched on, they energetically favor spin configurations which are completely unrelated to the ferromagnetic (or spin-glass) ordered configurations that one finds in the absence of a field. The outcome of this competition crucially depends on the space dimension. If $D > D_\ell^h$, the low-temperature ordered phase survives in the presence of small random-fields, while if $D < D_\ell^h$, the slightest random field destabilizes the ordered phase, see Fig. 5.4(b). Clearly $D_\ell^h \geq D_\ell$ and indeed for the RFIM, $D_\ell^h = 2$, which is greater than $D_\ell = 1$. Unfortunately, a consensus has not yet emerged about the value of D_ℓ^h for the spin glass. Here, we will discuss some numerical attempts to determine it.

De Almeida and Thouless [34] computed the stability of the replica symmetric solution of the SK model, finding that an eigenvalue went negative (indicating instability) below the dAT line. Fortunately, this instability can be located in simulations because the unstable ("replicon") eigenvalue is the inverse of the spin glass susceptibility χ_{SG} in the presence of a magnetic field, recall Eq. (5.7).

Hence the goal is to locate a divergence in χ_{SG}. Of course no divergence occurs in the finite systems which are simulated, so we need to locate the dAT line by finite-size scaling (FSS), recall Sec. 5.1.3. This is most straightforward using a dimensionless quantity such as ξ_2/L where ξ_2 is the correlation length of a finite system (second-moment correlation length), defined in Eq. (5.8). Now we recall Eq. (5.11), which indicates that the data for ξ_2/L for different sizes intersect at the transition and splays out again on the low temperature side. We therefore look for intersections in the data.

Early studies did not find a spin glass transition in a field in $D = 3$ using standard FSS methods [84, 86], see Fig. 5.5(a). It is difficult to directly simulate spin glasses in high dimensions, because the number of sites $N = L^D$ increases so fast with linear size L, that one can not equilibrate enough values of L to perform FSS. Instead, it has been proposed to study models in $1D$ with long-range interactions which fall off as a power σ, and, for each value of the power, the model serves as a proxy for a short-range model in a dimension D which depends on σ. Figure 5.5(b) shows a plot from data in Ref. [85] for the long-range model parameters corresponding to a short-range model for $D > 6$. Intersections are clearly seen indicating a dAT line in this region. Varying the power σ, the data of Ref. [85] shows intersections for models corresponding to $D > 6$ but not for $D < 6$.

As pointed out in Ref. [42], a difficulty in applying FSS to spin glasses is that extrapolating the inverse of the wave-vector dependent propagator, Eq. (5.6), to $\boldsymbol{k} = 0$ gives a different value from $1/\chi_{\mathrm{SG}}$ (which is the inverse of the propagator evaluated directly at $\boldsymbol{k} = 0$), even away from the transition. The usual computation of the correlation length ξ_2 involves the $\boldsymbol{k} = 0$ value as well as a $\boldsymbol{k} \neq 0$ value.

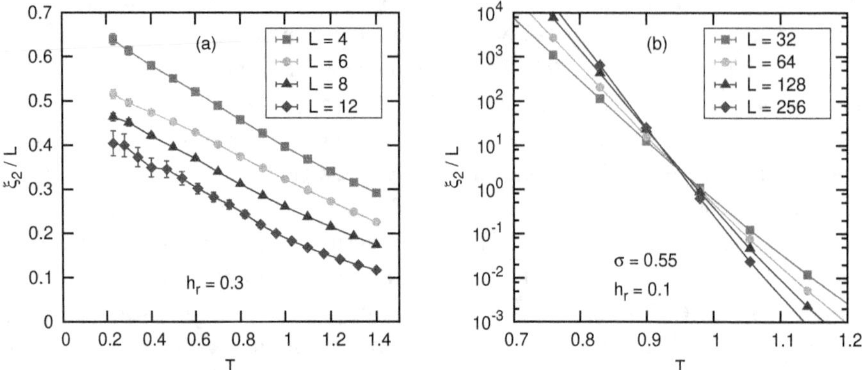

Fig. 5.5.   **(a)**: Temperature dependence of the second-moment correlation length in units of the lattice size, ξ_2/L, as computed in spatial dimension $D=3$ for cubic samples of linear size L. The computation was carried out for Gaussian-distributed couplings and random fields, with zero mean and standard deviations $\sigma_J=1$ (this actually sets the energy units) and $\sigma_h=h_{\rm r}=0.3$. The lack of intersections down to the lowest temperature $T=0.23$ suggests that $D=3$ lies below the lower-critical dimension in a field, recall Fig. 5.4. The figure is adapted from Ref. [84]. **(b)**: Second moment correlation length for a model with long-range power-law interactions for parameters corresponding to a short-range model in dimension D greater than 6, which is the "upper critical dimension" for the spin glass in zero field. The intersections suggest that there *is* a dAT line in this region. Adapted from Ref. [85].

In $D=4$, Ref. [42] used both standard FSS to compute ξ_2 and a non-standard approach to compute a different dimensionless quantity R_{12}, defined in Eq. (5.12), which does not involve the $\boldsymbol{k}=0$ data point. The data for ξ_2/L does not show a transition while that for R_{12} does, see Fig. 5.6–left panel. This may indicate a dAT line in $D=4$, but it is disappointing that two methods, which should give the same result in the asymptotic limit, give different results for the sizes that can be simulated. It has been argued [41] that it is preferable to avoid $\boldsymbol{k}=0$ because it has large corrections to FSS coming from the the negative-q region of $P(q)$. On the other hand the $\boldsymbol{k}=0$ point is the most divergent, which one would therefore *normally* like to include, so at present there is not a general consensus in the community on whether or not a phase transition occurs in a field in $D=4$.

In $D=3$, even avoiding the anomaly in the propagator did not result in any evidence for a phase transition in the presence of a field, see Ref. [87] and Fig. 5.6–right panel.

To conclude this section, despite a huge computational effort and careful analysis, the range of dimensions in which there is a dAT line has not been demonstrated convincingly. The problem is that corrections to FSS are large and not adequately understood.[e] In zero field, the work of Refs. [30, 88] determined the exponent for the largest correction to scaling and the amplitude of those correction terms. One is then confident that the data is in the asymptotic scaling region. However, it has not been possible to identify, and hence compensate for, corrections to scaling.

---

[e]We have already noted the discrepancy between $\lim_{\boldsymbol{k}\to0}\hat{G}_{\rm SG}^{-1}(\boldsymbol{k})$ and $\chi_{\rm SG}^{-1}$.

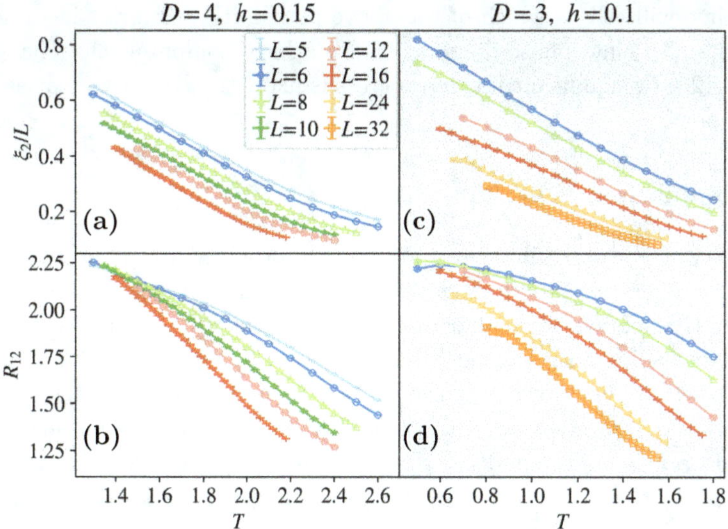

Fig. 5.6. Data for $D = 4$ taken from Ref. [42], and $D = 3$, from Ref. [87]. Top: a plot of ξ_2/L as a function of temperature for $D = 4$ and $h = 0.15$ (**a**), and $D = 3$ and $h = 0.1$ (**c**). According to leading-order finite-size scaling, the curves for different sizes should intersect at the phase transition point, so one would. We conclude that there is no phase transition in this system. Bottom: Plot of the dimensionless ratio R_{12}, Eq. (5.12), for the same parameters [(**b**): $D = 4$, (**d**): $D = 3$] , which should have the same leading-order scaling as ξ_2/L. Unlike the correlation length, however, R_{12} does exhibit intersections in $D = 4$, which suggests that there is a phase transition in a field. In $D = 3$ the only intersection is for the smallest sizes. It is not known if there would be intersections at larger sizes and lower temperatures than can be simulated.

Several interpretations of the numerical results on spin glasses in a field are possible:

- One possibility is that $3 < D_\ell^h < 4$. In fact, some RSB computations suggest [89] that $D_\ell^h < 6$. Unfortunately, these analytic computations do not provide a precise estimate for D_ℓ^h.
- Other analytic computations suggest that $D_\ell^h = 6$ [90]. From this point of view, the observation of scale invariance in some of the $D = 4$ simulation results is attributed to a correlation length which is enormous, but finite, in the thermodynamic limit [91]. A possible piece of evidence in favor of this hypothesis is that a renormalization group calculation of Bray and Roberts [92] found a fixed point for the dAT line in $D > 6$ but not in $D < 6$.[f]
- A more exotic possibility is that $D_\ell^h \approx 3$, but the phase-transition in a field is hidden by truly dramatic statistical fluctuations [87, 94].
- Another possibility is that of a quasi-first order transition [95] (which, thinking in retrospect, would explain naturally many of the dynamic findings in a $D = 3$ simulation [96]). Yet, equilibrium data in the $D = 4$ scaling region do not seem to conform to this expectation [37].

---

[f]This means that the upper critical dimensions of the model is also $D_u^h = 6$. However a recent analytical computation claims that $D_u^h = 8$ [93].

We hope that time will tell us which of the above possibilities (if any!) is an accurate description of the spin-glass phase diagram. Since a huge computer effort has *already* been expended [42, 87], significant future progress is likely to need new ideas as well as more computer power.

5.5. Out-of-Equilibrium

Numerical studies of out-of-equilibrium behavior are designed to mimic experiments, and have the advantage over experiments that they can track the microscopic evolution of the system. In this section, we shall consider the simplest aging experiment, in which a very large system is instantly cooled from $T = \infty$ to $T < T_c$,[g] and its microscopic evolution is followed as function of t_w, the waiting time elapsed after the quench. In some cases, in order to reproduce an experimental protocol, a small magnetic field $h > 0$ will be switched on at time t_w, and the system's response to the field measured at a later time $t + t_w$. In these simulations and experiments, the magnetic field is viewed *only* as probe of the $h = 0$ spin-glass state.

In this context, and at variance with equilibrium studies, one is interested in the evolution of an $L \to \infty$ system, at finite times t_w and t, so the limit $L \to \infty$ must be taken *before* t_w and t get large. Recent simulations explore a time range going from the equivalent of picoseconds to tenths of a second, while the time range in experiments goes from seconds to of order 24 hours. Unfortunately, neat theoretical predictions apply only in the limit of very long t_w. We emphasize that the real control variable is not time, but the size of the glassy domains, which we quantify through the spin-glass coherence length $\xi(t)$, see Eq. (5.19) below.

5.5.1. *Observables (out-of-equilibrium)*

An important and striking observation is that the older a spin glass is (i.e. the longer it has waited in the low-temperature phase), the slower its subsequent relaxation becomes. This is called *aging*. Aging can be studied with the two-time spin correlation function, see Fig. 5.7(a),

$$C(t + t_w, t_w) = [\langle S(\boldsymbol{x}, t + t_w) S(\boldsymbol{x}, t_w) \rangle_T], \tag{5.16}$$

where the thermal noise average $\langle \cdots \rangle_T$ represents an average over independent thermal histories at temperature T.

Aging dynamics is directly related to the sluggish growth of glassy order with t_w, see Fig. 5.7(b). The size of spin glass domains at t_w, namely the coherence length, $\xi(t_w)$, is extracted with high precision (see Fig. 5.7) in simulations from the decay of the spatial autocorrelation function of the overlap field,

$$C_4(\boldsymbol{r}, t_w) = \left[\left\langle q^{(a,b)}(\boldsymbol{x}, t_w) q^{(a,b)}(\boldsymbol{x} + \boldsymbol{r}, t_w) \right\rangle_T \right], \tag{5.17}$$

where

$$q^{(a,b)}(\boldsymbol{x}, t_w) = S^{(a)}(\boldsymbol{x}, t_w) S^{(b)}(\boldsymbol{x}, t_w). \tag{5.18}$$

---

[g]L should be much larger than the growing spin glass coherence length $\xi(t)$, in order to avoid finite-size effects.

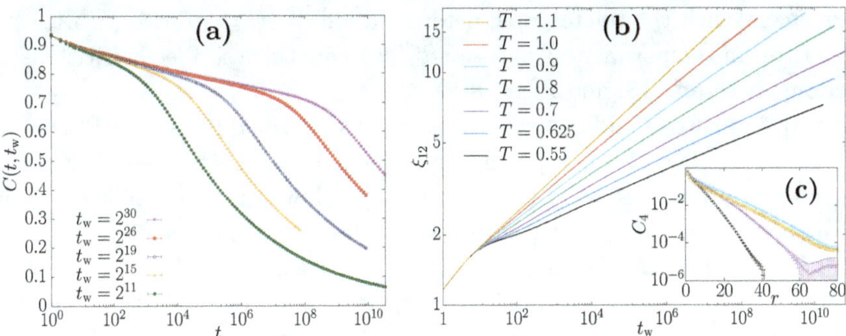

Fig. 5.7.   Aging dynamics for the $3D$ EA model with couplings $J = \pm 1$. (**a**) Decay of the two-time spin correlation function $C(t + t_{\mathrm{w}}, t_{\mathrm{w}})$, see Eq. (5.16), for five different values of t_{w} ranging from 2048 up to 10^8 Monte Carlo sweeps, at $T = 0.7$ (data taken from [15]). (**b**) Size of the glassy domains, as quantified by the spin-glass coherence length $\xi(t_{\mathrm{w}})$, as function of t_{w}, for different temperatures T. For comparison, the critical temperature for this model is $T_{\mathrm{c}} = 1.1019(29)$ [30]. (**c**) Autocorrelation function $C_4(r, t_{\mathrm{w}})$, see Eq. (5.17), as a function of distance r, as computed for the longest t_{w} for each temperature (T color key as in main panel). Note that C_4 varies by six orders of magnitude in this computation. Figure taken from [97].

$C_4(r, t_{\mathrm{w}})$ displays scaling behavior at long distances,

$$C_4(r, t_{\mathrm{w}}) = r^{-\theta} f\big(r/\xi(t_{\mathrm{w}})\big), \tag{5.19}$$

from which one can determine $\xi(t_{\mathrm{w}})$ and the "replicon" exponent θ. The problem of extracting $\xi(t_{\mathrm{w}})$ without knowing the precise form of the scaling function f has been circumvented using integral estimators (see e.g. [12] and the supplemental material for Ref. [97]). However, $\xi(t_{\mathrm{w}})$ is only directly accessible in simulations. In order to estimate it from experiments we need to take an indirect route by perturbing the system with a magnetic field.

In the *zero-field cooled* protocol, the only one considered here, the field is switched-on at time t_{w} and the magnetization density $m(t + t_{\mathrm{w}}) = \sum_{\boldsymbol{x}} S_{\boldsymbol{x}}(t + t_{\mathrm{w}})/N$ is studied as function of h, t and t_{w} with the initial condition $m(t_{\mathrm{w}}) = 0$. We have

$$m(t + t_{\mathrm{w}}) = \chi(t + t_{\mathrm{w}}, t_{\mathrm{w}})h \; - \; \chi_3(t + t_{\mathrm{w}}, t_{\mathrm{w}})\frac{h^3}{3!} + \dots \tag{5.20}$$

$$S(t, t_{\mathrm{w}}; h) = \frac{1}{h}\frac{\partial m(t + t_{\mathrm{w}})}{\partial \log t}, \tag{5.21}$$

which defines the linear (χ), and non-linear (χ_3, χ_5, etc.) susceptibilities, as well as the response function $S(t, t_{\mathrm{w}}; h)$. In equilibrium, the fluctuation dissipation theorem (FDT) relates χ to the two-time correlation function $C(t + t_{\mathrm{w}}, t_{\mathrm{w}})$ by $T\chi = 1 - C$. Out-of-equilibrium, the relationship between χ and C is even more interesting (see Sec. 5.5.3).

The size of the glassy domains is experimentally accessed through the relaxation function $S(t, t_{\mathrm{w}}; h)$, see Eq. (5.21), that peaks at an effective time $t^{\mathrm{eff}}(h)$. The effective time gets shorter when the magnetic field increases, due to the Zeeman effect lowering the free-energy barriers. The Zeeman effect gets stronger as $\xi(t)$ grows, which can be used to experimentally measure $\xi(t_{\mathrm{w}})$. See [98] for details. Interestingly, this experimental set-up for determining $\xi(t_{\mathrm{w}})$ has been reproduced in simulations and found to yield values in agreement with the microscopic determination of $\xi(t_{\mathrm{w}})$ from Eq. (5.19) [99]. In fact, numerical and experimental data for $t^{\mathrm{eff}}(h)$ can be described with the same scaling functions. See Ref. [18] and Fig. 5.8(b).

According to simulations and experiments, $\xi(t_{\mathrm{w}})$ varies roughly as a small power of t_{w}, i.e. $\xi(t_{\mathrm{w}}) \propto t_{\mathrm{w}}^{1/z(T)}$, with an exponent that depends on the temperature $z(T) \simeq z(T_{\mathrm{c}})T_{\mathrm{c}}/T$ (see Fig. 5.7 and Refs. [12, 98, 100–105]). However, this behaviour is not exact and, for the range of $\xi(t_{\mathrm{w}})$ that can be studied, the exponent z is found to depend slightly on t_{w} [17, 97, 106] as well as on T. As we will discuss in Secs. 5.5.3 and 5.5.4, this slowly growing $\xi(t_{\mathrm{w}})$ allows us to build a quantitative *statics-dynamics dictionary*, relating non-equilibrium dynamics of infinite systems at finite time t_{w} with equilibrium properties of finite systems of size $L \sim \xi(t_{\mathrm{w}})$. Hence experiments, which are inevitably out of equilibrium, can be described by the equilibrium physics of systems of size of order $\xi(t_{\mathrm{w}})$, which is not much larger than those explored in recent simulations.

5.5.2. *The replicon exponent*

The droplet and RSB theories disagree about the exponent in the algebraic prefactor of Eq. (5.19), θ, which is called the *replicon exponent*.[h] Droplet theory expects coarsening behavior, so $\theta = 0$, while RSB expects $\theta > 0$. Early simulations found $\theta = 0.50(2)$ [101]. More recent and accurate numerical simulations find θ in the range $0.35 - 0.4$ [12, 97]. From the perspective of droplet theory, see e.g. [107], it has been argued that the non-vanishing value of θ is due to a transient effect in which the system feels the effects of the renormalization group fixed point at T_{c}, rather than the asymptotic fixed point at $T = 0$.

In fact, the crossover between the T_{c} and $T = 0$ fixed points can be studied systematically through the ratio of the Josephson length, $\ell_{\mathrm{J}}(T) \propto (T_{\mathrm{c}} - T)^{-\nu}$, to $\xi(t_{\mathrm{w}})$. The asymptotic value of θ is obtained when the ratio $x = \ell_{\mathrm{J}}(T)/\xi(t_{\mathrm{w}})$ goes to zero. In fact, as shown in Fig. 5.8(a), the ratio x seems to be the controlling variable for θ, which shows a decreasing trend when x goes to zero. The data are compatible with both a vanishing (droplet) and non-vanishing (RSB) extrapolation to $x = 0$. The crucial point however, is that neither simulations nor experiments are carried out at $\xi = \infty$ (i.e. $x = 0$). Rather, representative values for extrapolations to the experimental scale are shown in Fig. 5.8(a): even the droplet scaling predicts $\theta > 0.25$ at those x. In fact, several successful extrapolations of simulation results to the experimental scale have been carried out recently [17, 18, 97] [see also Figs. 5.8(b) and 5.11], all of them with $\theta > 0$. Hence, current simulations *and* experiments are all carried out in an RSB-like regime.

5.5.3. *Generalization of the fluctuation-dissipation theorem*

The generalization of the FDT to the out-of-equilibrium regime for the SK model [108] opened the possibility of checking some of the predictions of RSB. This generalization of FDT was numerically tested in the $3D$ EA model [109, 110] and was finally proven

---

[h]It is unfortunate that the stiffness exponent, θ_{S}, is sometimes also called θ, which may cause confusion.

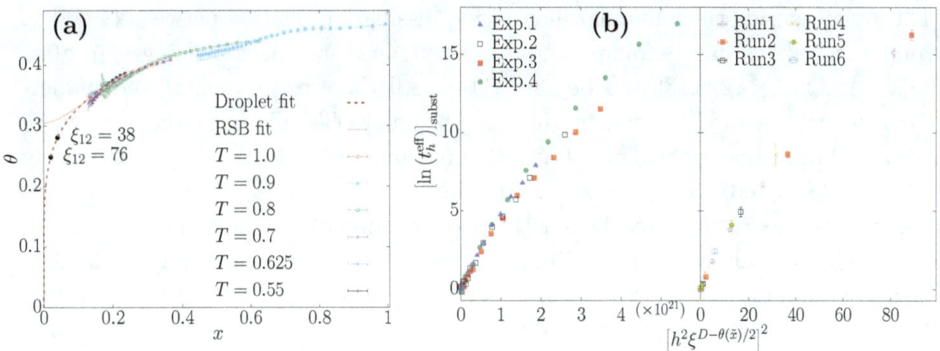

Fig. 5.8.　(**a**) When represented as a function of $x = \ell_J(T)/\xi(t_w, T)$, the replicon exponent θ obtained for several temperatures fall on a single curve. In addition we show a droplet extrapolation [dashed line, $\theta(x \to 0) = 0$] and an RSB extrapolation [full line, $\theta(x \to 0) > 0$]. Even the droplet extrapolation, which has $\theta(x) \to 0$ as $x \to 0$, predicts sizeable values of θ for the values of x relevant to experiments (black dots). Figure adapted from [97]. (**b**) After a proper subtraction [18], the logarithm of the effective time [the time at which the response function (5.21) peaks] obeys the same scaling for CuMn (left) and the Ising–Edwards–Anderson model (right). Figure taken from [18].

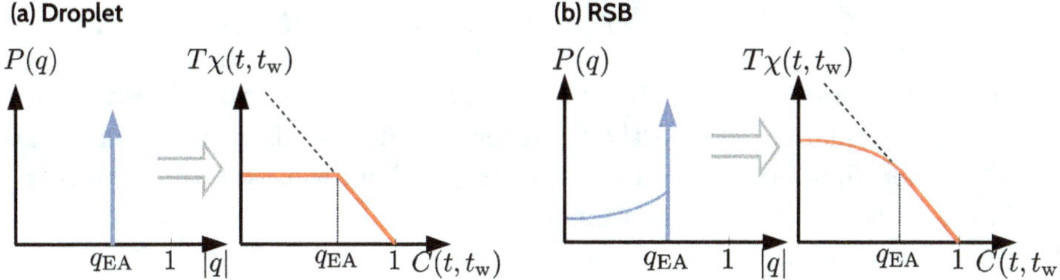

Fig. 5.9.　Sketch of the shape of the expected modification of the FDT according to the droplet and RSB theories in the double limit of $t_w, t \to \infty$.

for finite dimensional systems assuming stochastic stability [10] (see Sec. 5.3.3). The generalized fluctuation-dissipation relation (GFDR) reads[i]

$$T\chi(t + t_w, t_w) = S(C(t + t_w, t_w)),\tag{5.22}$$

where $S(C)$ is a function which can be shown [10, 108–110] to be related, in the limit of $t_w, t \to \infty$, to a double integral of $P(q)$, the equilibrium pdf of the overlap, see Sec. 5.3.1.[j] In equilibrium, $S(C) = 1 - C$, which is the FDT.

From Eq. (5.22), we see that the droplet and RSB theories give very different predictions about how the FDT should be modified, as sketched in Fig. 5.9. This important result allows one to determine the pdf of the overlap experimentally, despite the impossibility of measuring it directly. Such an experiment was conducted by Hérisson and

---

[i]Assuming a dependence of the magnetic field with time as $h(t) = h_0 \theta(t - t_w)$.

[j]This surprising result can be understood using stochastic stability. In equilibrium the system explores the region of lower free energies whereas in the out-of-equilibrium regime it wanders in the region of high free-energy. But stochastic stability tells us that the structure (maxima and minima) of the higher and lower regions of free energy is similar.

Ocio [111] by measuring the nonlinear fluctuation-dissipation relation between C and χ. Many numerical works have explored these relations in simulations of Ising spin glass models [10, 15, 110, 112, 113] and beyond [114]. All these experimental and numerical works describe a modification of the equilibrium FDT similar to that shown in Fig. 5.10(a) (obtained with the Janus I and II supercomputers [15]), which is extremely similar to the RSB prediction sketched in Fig. 5.9(b).

However it is important to recall that the connection between the equilibrium $P(q)$, and $S[C(t + t_\mathrm{w}, t_\mathrm{w})]$ only holds in the limit $t_\mathrm{w}, t \to \infty$. It is also clear from Fig. 5.10(a) that the current data is in a pre-asymptotic regime, because the data for different values of t_w do not superimpose, so one cannot distinguish unambiguously between the droplet and RSB theories in the $t_\mathrm{w} \to \infty$ limit. The same applies to the experimental data. This means that, as discussed above, short t_w aging simulations and experiments are consistent with RSB, but cannot rule out the possibility that the droplet model describes the experimentally unachievable $t_\mathrm{w} \to \infty$ limit.

However, it has been observed that the expected relation between S and the equilibrium $P(q)$ still holds at finite t_w, replacing $P(q)$ by $P(q, L)$, the equilibrium pdf of the overlap in a finite system of size L [15]. Indeed, Fig. 5.10(b) shows

$$S(C, L) = \int_C^1 \mathrm{d}\, C'\, x(C', L), \qquad \text{where}\ \ x(C, L) = \int_0^C \mathrm{d}q\, 2P(q, L) \qquad (5.23)$$

obtained using the numerical equilibrium data of $P(q, L)$ (already discussed in Fig. 5.1), for different L. The similarity between the two panels of Fig. 5.10 is striking since the left panel is for a non-equilibrium situation on a large system, while the right panel is for equilibrium behavior on fairly small systems.

This discussion can be made more quantitative if we now bring into play $\xi(t_\mathrm{w})$, the size of the glassy domains in the non-equilibrium system that grows with time as the system ages. One can use the known growth of $\xi(t_\mathrm{w})$ (shown in Fig. 5.7), to predict the observed data from the equilibrium $S(C, L_\mathrm{eff})$ with $L_\mathrm{eff}(t + t_\mathrm{w}; t_\mathrm{w})$ being a function of $\xi(t_\mathrm{w})$ and $\xi(t + t_\mathrm{w})$. This prediction is shown by the lines in Fig. 5.10(a) and the agreement with the original data (dots) is very good.

5.5.4. *Statics-dynamics dictionary and relation to experiments*

We have argued above that there is a quantitative equivalence between the relaxation and response of an infinite system at finite t_w [and coherence length $\xi(t_\mathrm{w})$] and the equilibrium properties of a system of finite size L. Moreover, it is possible to show that $L \sim k\xi(t_\mathrm{w})$, with $k \sim 4$ [15].[k]

The existence of such a dictionary between equilibrium and non-equilibrium physics had also been explored and confirmed in previous works [11, 13, 57, 115], and tells us that the key to describing real experiments may not be in the physics of $L \to \infty$ equilibrium systems, but in that of much more modest sizes.

The question that naturally comes to mind is how much $\xi(t_\mathrm{w})$ differs in simulations and experiments. The answer is not very much. The current experimental record for

---

[k]The actual proportionality factor k will depend on the details of the definition of ξ [12]. If t considerably exceeds t_w then $\xi(t_\mathrm{w})$ should be replaced by $\xi(t + t_\mathrm{w})$.

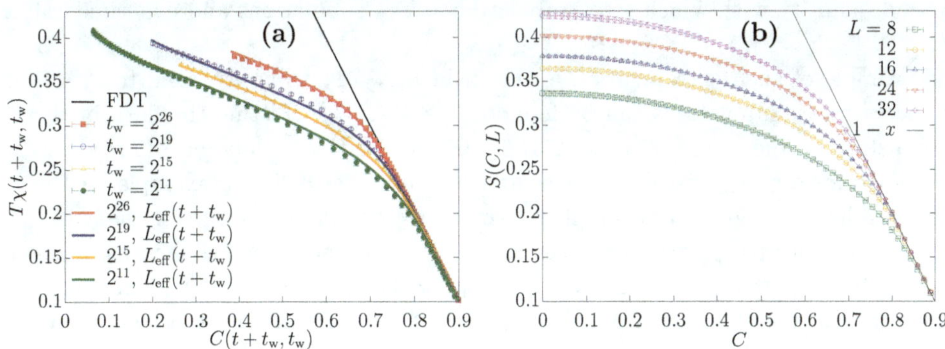

Fig. 5.10. (a) The dots show the response function $T\chi(t+t_{\mathrm{w}},t_{\mathrm{w}})$ versus $C(t+t_{\mathrm{w}},t_{\mathrm{w}})$ at $T=0.7$ for different fixed t_{w}. Upon relaxing at fixed t_{w}, $C(t+t_{\mathrm{w}},t_{\mathrm{w}})$ monotonically decreases from $C=1$ at $t=0$ to $C=0$ at $t=\infty$. In (b) we show the *equilibrium* $S(C,L)$ versus C for different system sizes obtained using Eq. (5.23) and $P(q,L)$ extracted in independent equilibrium studies. These lines are guides to the eye. In (a) the lines are obtained by plotting the $S(C,L_{\mathrm{eff}})$ shown in (b) for an effective size, $L_{\mathrm{eff}}=\xi(t+t_{\mathrm{w}},t_{\mathrm{w}})g\left(\xi(t+t_{\mathrm{w}},t_{\mathrm{w}})/\xi(t_{\mathrm{w}})\right)$, where $g(\cdot)$ is an ansatz function that controls the crossover between the $\xi(t_{\mathrm{w}})$ and $\xi(t+t_{\mathrm{w}})$ dominated regimes. Figures adapted from [15].

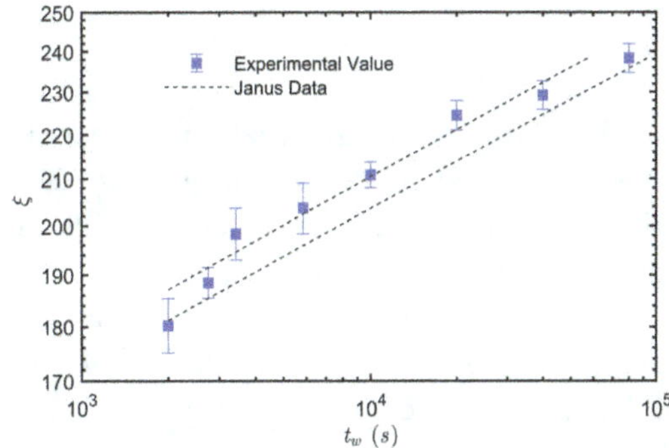

Fig. 5.11. Coherence length $\xi(t_{\mathrm{w}})$ in units of the average distance between magnetic moments (0.64 nm) versus waiting time t_{w}, as measured in a CuMn single crystal at $T\approx0.89T_{\mathrm{c}}$. The extrapolation from Janus II data at smaller $\xi(t_{\mathrm{w}})$ is enclosed by the two dashed lines (the separation between the lines is the uncertainty in the extrapolation). Figure taken from Ref. [17].

the largest $\xi(t_{\mathrm{w}})$, see Fig. 5.11, is larger than the numerical one in Fig. 5.7(b) by a factor[l] $\simeq 15$. Thus the extrapolations needed to compare experiments with current simulations, if expressed in terms of $\xi(t_{\mathrm{w}})$ rather than time, are quite mild.

In fact there is an even better quantity than $\xi(t_{\mathrm{w}})$ to study when extrapolating from simulations to experiment. Roughly speaking we have[m] $\xi(t_{\mathrm{w}})=At_{\mathrm{w}}^{T/(T_{\mathrm{c}}z_{\mathrm{c}})}$. However, the data does not actually fit a power law well so it is more convenient to consider the slope on a log-log plot, which is called the aging rate, $z_{\mathrm{c}}(T,\xi)=(T/T_{\mathrm{c}})\mathrm{d}\log t_{\mathrm{w}}/\mathrm{d}\log\xi$. It is found that z_{c} is not constant but increases as $\xi(t_{\mathrm{w}})$ increases. Nonetheless, it is the

---

[l]Part of the factor of 15 comes from the larger values of t_{w} in experiment, up to order 10^5 seconds as opposed to tenths of a second in simulations, and part comes from the amplitude of the growth of $\xi(t_{\mathrm{w}})$ being larger in the experiments on CuMn than in the simulations.

[m]It is convenient to incorporate the factor of T/T_{c}.

most useful quantity with which to extrapolate between simulations and experimental results.

One example of such extrapolation is shown in Fig. 5.11 which is taken from [17] (other successful extrapolations can be found in [18, 19, 97]). Fitting the data in the figure to a straight line gives [17] $z_c = 12.37 \pm 1.07$. Simulation results for $z_c(T, \xi)$ have been obtained for a range of waiting times and temperatures [97]. For example, at the smallest correlation length, $z_c \simeq 6.7$. By fitting these simulation results as described in Ref. [17] one can extrapolate the values for z_c to the larger coherence lengths in experiment, getting $z_c(180.26a_0) = 11.94 \pm 0.08$, $z_c(238.34a_0) = 12.76 \pm 0.08$, which is in excellent agreement with values from the experimental data itself. Furthermore, combining the extrapolated aging-rate with an additional input from experiment, namely $\xi(t_w = 2750\,\mathrm{s})$, the curve $\xi(t_w)$ could be predicted [the two dashed lines in Fig. 5.11 encompass the experimental error for $\xi(t_w = 2750\,\mathrm{s})$].

In summary, the statics-dynamics dictionary tells us that the dynamics of experimental spin glasses is described by the equilibrium properties of systems of size $L \sim 100$ lattice spacings. Hence the droplet-RSB dispute is irrelevant in this context since it applies to $L = \infty$. At the length scales that *are* relevant to experiments the data is better described by RSB theory.

5.6. Conclusions

The aim of this chapter has been to summarize what numerical simulations tell us concerning the applicability of RSB to short-range spin glasses, most particularly to $D = 3$. We have seen that the situation is somewhat complicated because it appears to depend on whether or not an external magnetic field is applied.

In zero field, large-scale simulations with a dedicated processor find behavior in $D = 3$ which is well described by RSB, both in equilibrium and out-of-equilibrium situations. The out-of-equilibrium simulations are found to be consistent with recent experiments on single crystals.

While the droplet picture cannot be excluded as a description of spin glasses in the thermodynamic limit, if this is the case it can only apply on length and time scales far beyond the reach of simulations and experiments.

In a field, RSB predicts a spin glass phase and a dAT line, see Fig. 5.4, whereas the droplet picture predicts no dAT line. Numerically it has been hard to find evidence for a dAT line in $D = 3$, and the situation is ambiguous in $D = 4$. Numerics does, however, indicate the presence of a dAT line in high dimension. A possible explanation of these results is that D_ℓ^h, the lower critical dimension, the dimension below which there is no transition, is greater than 3 in the presence of a magnetic field, which is different from the case of zero field where $D_\ell \simeq 2.5$.

Acknowledgments

This work was partly supported grants No. PID2021-125506NA-I00, PID2020-112936GB-I00, PID2019-103939RB-I00 and No. PGC2018-094684-B-C21 funded by MCIN/AEI/10.13039/501100011033 by "ERDF A way of making Europe" and by the "European Union" and Fondo Europeo de Desarrollo Regional (FEDER), the Banco Santander and the UCM (grant PR44/21-29937), by grants No. GR21014 and No. IB20079 (partially funded by FEDER) funded by Junta the Extremadura (Spain), and by the Atracción de Talento program (Ref. 2019-T1/TIC-12776) funded by Comunidad de Madrid and Universidad Complutense de Madrid (Spain).

References

[1] M. Mézard, G. Parisi, and M. Virasoro, *Spin-Glass Theory and Beyond.* (World Scientific, 1987).

[2] E. Marinari, G. Parisi, F. Ricci-Tersenghi, J. J. Ruiz-Lorenzo, and F. Zuliani, *J. Stat. Phys.* **98**, 973, (2000).

[3] W. L. McMillan, Scaling theory of Ising spin glasses, *J. Phys. C* **17**, 3179, (1984).

[4] A. J. Bray and M. A. Moore. In eds. J. L. van Hemmen and I. Morgenstern, *Heidelberg Colloquium on Glassy Dynamics*, number 275 in Lecture Notes in Physics. Springer, Berlin, (1987).

[5] D. S. Fisher and D. A. Huse, *Phys. Rev. Lett.* **56**, 1601 (1986).

[6] D. S. Fisher and D. A. Huse, *Phys. Rev. B.* **38**, 373–385 (1988).

[7] Gardner, E., *J. Phys. (France).* **45**(11), 1755–1763, (1984).

[8] F. Krzakala and O. C. Martin, *Phys. Rev. Lett.* **85**, 3013, (2000).

[9] M. Palassini and A. P. Young, *Phys. Rev. Lett.* **85**, 3017–3020 (2000).

[10] S. Franz, M. Mézard, G. Parisi, and L. Peliti, *Phys. Rev. Lett.* **81**, 1758–1761 (1998).

[11] F. Belletti, M. Cotallo, A. Cruz, L. A. Fernandez, A. Gordillo-Guerrero, M. Guidetti, A. Maiorano, F. Mantovani, E. Marinari, V. Martín-Mayor, A. M. Sudupe, D. Navarro, G. Parisi, S. Perez-Gaviro, J. J. Ruiz-Lorenzo, S. F. Schifano, D. Sciretti, A. Tarancon, R. Tripiccione, J. L. Velasco, and D. Yllanes, *Phys. Rev. Lett.* **101**, 157201, (2008).

[12] F. Belletti, A. Cruz, L. Fernandez, A. Gordillo-Guerrero, M. Guidetti, A. Maiorano, F. Mantovani, E. Marinari, V. Martin-Mayor, J. Monforte, et al., *J. Stat. Phys.* **135**(5), 1121–1158, (2009).

[13] R. Alvarez Baños, A. Cruz, L. A. Fernandez, J. M. Gil-Narvion, A. Gordillo-Guerrero, M. Guidetti, A. Maiorano, F. Mantovani, E. Marinari, V. Martín-Mayor, J. Monforte-Garcia, A. Muñoz Sudupe, D. Navarro, G. Parisi, S. Perez-Gaviro, J. J. Ruiz-Lorenzo, S. F. Schifano, B. Seoane, A. Tarancon, R. Tripiccione, and D. Yllanes, *Phys. Rev. Lett.* **105**, 177202, (2010).

[14] M. Wittmann and A. P. Young, *J. Stat. Mech. Theory Exp.* **2016**(1), 013301, (2016).

[15] M. Baity-Jesi, E. Calore, A. Cruz, L. A. Fernandez, J. M. Gil-Narvión, A. Gordillo-Guerrero, D. Iñiguez, A. Maiorano, E. Marinari, V. Martin-Mayor, J. Monforte-Garcia, A. Muñoz Sudupe, D. Navarro, G. Parisi, S. Perez-Gaviro, F. Ricci-Tersenghi, J. J. Ruiz-Lorenzo, S. F. Schifano, B. Seoane, A. Tarancón, R. Tripiccione, and D. Yllanes, *Proc. Natl. Acad. Sci. U.S.A..* **114**(8), 1838–1843, (2017).

[16] M. Baity-Jesi, E. Calore, A. Cruz, L. A. Fernandez, J. M. Gil-Narvion, I. Gonzalez-Adalid Pemartin, A. Gordillo-Guerrero, D. Iñiguez, A. Maiorano, E. Marinari, V. Martin-Mayor, J. Moreno-Gordo, A. Muñoz Sudupe, D. Navarro, I. Paga, G. Parisi, S. Perez-Gaviro, F. Ricci-Tersenghi, J. J. Ruiz-Lorenzo, S. F. Schifano, B. Seoane, A. Tarancon, R. Tripiccione, and D. Yllanes, *Commun. Phys..* **4**(1), 74, (2021). ISSN 2399-3650.

[17] Q. Zhai, V. Martin-Mayor, D. L. Schlagel, G. G. Kenning, and R. L. Orbach, *Phys. Rev. B.* **100**, 094202 (2019).

[18] Q. Zhai, I. Paga, M. Baity-Jesi, E. Calore, A. Cruz, L. A. Fernandez, J. M. Gil-Narvion, I. Gonzalez-Adalid Pemartin, A. Gordillo-Guerrero, D. Iñiguez, A. Maiorano, E. Marinari, V. Martin-Mayor, J. Moreno-Gordo, A. Muñoz Sudupe, D. Navarro, R. L. Orbach,

G. Parisi, S. Perez-Gaviro, F. Ricci-Tersenghi, J. J. Ruiz-Lorenzo, S. F. Schifano, D. L. Schlagel, B. Seoane, A. Tarancon, R. Tripiccione, and D. Yllanes, *Phys. Rev. Lett.* **125**, 237202 (2020).

[19] I. Paga, Q. Zhai, M. Baity-Jesi, E. Calore, A. Cruz, L. A. Fernandez, J. M. Gil-Narvion, I. Gonzalez-Adalid Pemartin, A. Gordillo-Guerrero, D. Iñiguez, A. Maiorano, E. Marinari, V. Martin-Mayor, J. Moreno-Gordo, A. Muñoz-Sudupe, D. Navarro, R. L. Orbach, G. Parisi, S. Perez-Gaviro, F. Ricci-Tersenghi, J. J. Ruiz-Lorenzo, S. F. Schifano, D. L. Schlagel, B. Seoane, A. Tarancon, R. Tripiccione, and D. Yllanes, *J. Stat. Mech. Theory Exp.*. **2021**(3), 033301 (2021).

[20] H. Kawamura, *Phys. Rev. Lett.* **68**, 3785–3788 (1992).

[21] H. Kawamura, *Phys. Rev. Lett.* **80**, 5421–5424 (1998).

[22] H. Kawamura and M. S. Li, *Phys. Rev. Lett.* **87**, 187204 (2001).

[23] H. Kawamura, *Phys. Rev. Lett.* **90**, 237201 (2003).

[24] T. Ogawa, K. Uematsu, and H. Kawamura, *Phys. Rev. B.* **101**, 014434 (2020).

[25] L. A. Fernandez, V. Martín-Mayor, S. Perez-Gaviro, A. Tarancon, and A. P. Young, *Phys. Rev. B.* **80**, 024422, (2009).

[26] I. Campos, M. Cotallo-Aban, V. Martin-Mayor, S. Perez-Gaviro, and A. Tarancon, *Phys. Rev. Lett.* **97**, 217204 (2006).

[27] L. W. Lee and A. P. Young, *Phys. Rev. Lett.* **90**, 227203 (2003).

[28] A. J. Bray and M. A. Moore, *J. Phys. C.* **15**, 3897, (1982).

[29] M. Baity-Jesi, L. A. Fernandez, V. Martín-Mayor, and J. M. Sanz, *Phys. Rev.* **89**, 014202, (2014).

[30] M. Baity-Jesi, R. A. Baños, A. Cruz, L. A. Fernandez, J. M. Gil-Narvion, A. Gordillo-Guerrero, D. Iniguez, A. Maiorano, F. Mantovani, E. Marinari, V. Martín-Mayor, J. Monforte-Garcia, A. Muñoz Sudupe, D. Navarro, G. Parisi, S. Perez-Gaviro, M. Pivanti, F. Ricci-Tersenghi, J. J. Ruiz-Lorenzo, S. F. Schifano, B. Seoane, A. Tarancon, R. Tripiccione, and D. Yllanes, *Phys. Rev. B.* **88**, 224416, (2013).

[31] Bouchiat, H., *J. Phys. (France).* **47**(1), 71–88, (1986).

[32] G. Parisi, *Field Theory, Disorder and Simulations.* (World Scientific, 1994).

[33] G. Toulouse, Theory of the frustration effect in spin glasses, *Commun. Phys.* **2**, 115, (1977).

[34] J. R. L. de Almeida and D. J. Thouless, *J. Phys. A.* **11**, 983, (1978).

[35] C. de Dominicis and I. Giardina, *Random Fields and Spin Glasses: a field theory approach.* (Cambridge University Press, 2006).

[36] G. Parisi and T. Rizzo, *Phys. Rev. E.* **87**, 012101 (2013).

[37] L. A. Fernandez, I. Gonzalez-Adalid Pemartin, V. Martin-Mayor, G. Parisi, F. Ricci-Tersenghi, T. Rizzo, J. J. Ruiz-Lorenzo, and M. Veca, *Phys. Rev. E.* **105**, 054106 (2022).

[38] D. J. Amit and V. Martín-Mayor, *Field Theory, the Renormalization Group and Critical Phenomena.* (World Scientific, 2005), third edition.

[39] M. Palassini and S. Caracciolo, *Phys. Rev. Lett.* **82**, 5128–5131, (1999).

[40] H. G. Ballesteros, A. Cruz, L. A. Fernandez, V. Martín-Mayor, J. Pech, J. J. Ruiz-Lorenzo, A. Tarancon, P. Tellez, C. L. Ullod, and C. Ungil, *Phys. Rev. B.* **62**, 14237–14245, (2000).

[41] L. Leuzzi, G. Parisi, F. Ricci-Tersenghi, and J. J. Ruiz-Lorenzo, *Phys. Rev. Lett.* **103**, 267201, (2009).

[42] R. A. Baños, A. Cruz, L. A. Fernandez, J. M. Gil-Narvion, A. Gordillo-Guerrero, M. Guidetti, D. Iniguez, A. Maiorano, E. Marinari, V. Martín-Mayor, J. Monforte-Garcia, A. Muñoz Sudupe, D. Navarro, G. Parisi, S. Perez-Gaviro, J. J. Ruiz-Lorenzo, S. F. Schifano, B. Seoane, A. Tarancon, P. Tellez, R. Tripiccione, and D. Yllanes, *Proc. Natl. Acad. Sci. U.S.A.* **109**, 6452, (2012).

[43] F. Barahona, *J. Phys. A.* **15**(10), 3241, (1982).

[44] K. Hukushima and K. Nemoto, *J. Phys. Soc. Japan.* **65**, 1604, (1996).

[45] E. Marinari. In eds. J. Kerstész and I. Kondor, *Advances in Computer Simulation.* Springer-Verlag, (1998).

[46] R. H. Swendsen and J.-S. Wang, *Phys. Rev. Lett.* **58**, 86–88 (1987).

[47] R. H. Swendsen and J.-S. Wang, *Phys. Rev. Lett.* **57**, 2607–2609 (1986).

[48] J.-S. Wang and R. Swendsen, *Prog. Theo. Phys. Supplement.* **157**, 317, (2005).

[49] J. Houdayer, *EPJ B.* **22**, 479, (2001).

[50] L. A. Fernandez, V. Martín-Mayor, G. Parisi, and B. Seoane, *EPL.* **103**(6), 67003, (2013).

[51] A. Billoire, L. A. Fernandez, A. Maiorano, E. Marinari, V. Martin-Mayor, J. Moreno-Gordo, G. Parisi, F. Ricci-Tersenghi, and J. J. Ruiz-Lorenzo, *J. Stat. Mech. Theory Exp.* **2018**(3), 033302, (2018).

[52] V. Martín-Mayor and I. Hen, *Sci. Rep.* **5**, 15324 (2015).

[53] A. T. Ogielski, *Phys. Rev. B.* **32**, 7384, (1985).

[54] A. Cruz, J. Pech, A. Tarancon, P. Tellez, C. L. Ullod, and C. Ungil, *Comp. Phys. Comm.* **133**, 165–176, (2001).

[55] F. Belletti, M. Cotallo, A. Cruz, L. A. Fernandez, A. Gordillo, A. Maiorano, F. Mantovani, E. Marinari, V. Martín-Mayor, A. Muñoz Sudupe, D. Navarro, S. Perez-Gaviro, J. J. Ruiz-Lorenzo, S. F. Schifano, D. Sciretti, A. Tarancon, R. Tripiccione, and J. L. Velasco, *Comp. Phys. Comm.* **178**, 208–216, (2008).

[56] M. Baity-Jesi, R. A. Baños, A. Cruz, L. A. Fernandez, J. M. Gil-Narvion, A. Gordillo-Guerrero, D. Iniguez, A. Maiorano, F. Mantovani, E. Marinari, V. Martín-Mayor, J. Monforte-Garcia, A. Muñoz Sudupe, D. Navarro, G. Parisi, S. Perez-Gaviro, M. Pivanti, F. Ricci-Tersenghi, J. J. Ruiz-Lorenzo, S. F. Schifano, B. Seoane, A. Tarancon, R. Tripiccione, and D. Yllanes, *Comp. Phys. Comm.* **185**, 550–559, (2014).

[57] R. Alvarez Baños, A. Cruz, L. A. Fernandez, J. M. Gil-Narvion, A. Gordillo-Guerrero, M. Guidetti, A. Maiorano, F. Mantovani, E. Marinari, V. Martín-Mayor, J. Monforte-Garcia, A. Muñoz Sudupe, D. Navarro, G. Parisi, S. Perez-Gaviro, J. J. Ruiz-Lorenzo, S. F. Schifano, B. Seoane, A. Tarancon, R. Tripiccione, and D. Yllanes, *J. Stat. Mech.* **2010**, P06026, (2010).

[58] S. Boettcher, *Phys. Rev. Lett.* **95**, 197205 (2005).

[59] J. D. Reger, R. N. Bhatt, and A. P. Young, *Phys. Rev. Lett.* **64**, 1859–1862 (1990).

[60] B. A. Berg and W. Janke, *Phys. Rev. Lett.* **80**, 4771–4774 (1998).

[61] E. Marinari, G. Parisi, and J. J. Ruiz-Lorenzo, *Phys. Rev. B.* **58**, 14852–14863 (1998).

[62] H. G. Katzgraber, M. Palassini, and A. P. Young, *Phys. Rev. B.* **63**, 184422 (2001).

[63] H. G. Katzgraber and A. P. Young, *Phys. Rev. B.* **65**, 214402 (2002).

[64] B. A. Berg, A. Billoire, and W. Janke, *Phys. Rev. E.* **66**, 046122 (2002).

[65] W. Wang, M. Wallin, and J. Lidmar, *Phys. Rev. Research.* **2**, 043241 (2020).

[66] E. Marinari, G. Parisi, F. Ricci-Tersenghi, and J. J. Ruiz-Lorenzo, *J. Phys. A* **31**, L481, (1998).

[67] P. Contucci, C. Giardinà, C. Giberti, and C. Vernia, *Phys. Rev. Lett.* **96**, 217204 (2006).

[68] F. Guerra, *Int. J. Mod. Phys. B.* **10**, 1675, (1996).

[69] S. Ghirlanda and F. Guerra, *J. Phys. A.* **31**(46), 9149–9155 (1998).

[70] M. Aizenman and P. Contucci, *J. Stat. Phys.* **92**, 765, (1998).

[71] G. Parisi and F. Ricci-Tersenghi, *J. Phys. A* **33**, 113, (2000).

[72] D. Iñiguez, G. Parisi, and J. J. Ruiz-Lorenzo, *J. Phys. A* **29**, 4337, (1996).

[73] G. Parisi, *Ann. Prob.* **41**, 1315, (2013).

[74] G. Hed, A. P. Young, and E. Domany, *Phys. Rev. Lett.* **92**, 157201 (2004).

[75] R. A. Baños, A. Cruz, L. A. Fernandez, J. M. Gil-Narvion, A. Gordillo-Guerrero, M. Guidetti, D. Iñiguez, A. Maiorano, F. Mantovani, E. Marinari, V. Martín-Mayor, J. Monforte-Garcia, A. Muñoz Sudupe, D. Navarro, G. Parisi, S. Perez-Gaviro, F. Ricci-Tersenghi, J. J. Ruiz-Lorenzo, S. F. Schifano, B. Seoane, A. Tarancón, R. Tripiccione, and D. Yllanes, *Phys. Rev. B.* **84**, 174209 (2011).

[76] D. Sherrington and S. Kirkpatrick, *Phys. Rev. Lett.* **35**, 1792–1796 (1975).

[77] G. Parisi, *Phys. Rev. Lett.* **43**, 1754–1756 (1979).

[78] G. Parisi, *J. Phys. A.* **13**, 1101, (1980).

[79] G. Parisi, Order parameter for spin-glasses, *Phys. Rev. Lett.* **50**, 1946–1948 (1983).

[80] G. Parisi, *Statistical Field Theory.* (Addison-Wesley, 1988).

[81] S. Franz, G. Parisi, and M. Virasoro, *J. Phys. (France).* **4**, 1657, (1994).

[82] A. Maiorano and G. Parisi, *Proc. Natl. Acad. Sci. U.S.A.* **115**(20), 5129–5134, (2018). ISSN 0027-8424.

[83] T. Nattermann. In ed. A. P. Young, *Spin glasses and random fields.* World Scientific, (1998).

[84] A. P. Young and H. G. Katzgraber, *Phys. Rev. Lett.* **93**, 207203 (2004).

[85] H. G. Katzgraber and A. P. Young, *Phys. Rev. B.* **72**, 184416 (2005).

[86] T. Jörg, H. G. Katzgraber, and F. Krzakala, *Phys. Rev. Lett.* **100**, 197202, (2008).

[87] M. Baity-Jesi, R. A. Baños, A. Cruz, L. A. Fernandez, J. M. Gil-Narvion, A. Gordillo-Guerrero, D. Iniguez, A. Maiorano, M. F., E. Marinari, V. Martín-Mayor, J. Monforte-Garcia, A. Muñoz Sudupe, D. Navarro, G. Parisi, S. Perez-Gaviro, M. Pivanti, F. Ricci-Tersenghi, J. J. Ruiz-Lorenzo, S. F. Schifano, B. Seoane, A. Tarancon, R. Tripiccione, and D. Yllanes, *J. Stat. Mech.* **2014**, P05014, (2014).

[88] M. Hasenbusch, A. Pelissetto, and E. Vicari, *Phys. Rev. B.* **78**, 214205 (2008).

[89] G. Parisi and T. Temesvári, *Nucl. Phys. B.* **858**, 293, (2012).

[90] J. Yeo and M. A. Moore, *Phys. Rev. B.* **91**, 104432 (2015).

[91] T. Aspelmeier, H. G. Katzgraber, D. Larson, M. A. Moore, M. Wittmann, and J. Yeo, *Phys. Rev. E.* **93**, 032123 (2016).

[92] A. J. Bray and S. A. Roberts, *J. Phys. C.* **13**, 5405, (1980).

[93] M. C. Angelini, C. Lucibello, G. Parisi, G. Perrupato, F. Ricci-Tersenghi, and T. Rizzo, *Phys. Rev. Lett.* **128**, 075702 (2022).

[94] G. Parisi and F. Ricci-Tersenghi, *Phil. Mag.* **92**, 341, (2012).

[95] J. Höller and N. Read, *Phys. Rev. E.* **101**, 042114 (2020).

[96] M. Baity-Jesi, R. A. Baños, A. Cruz, L. A. Fernandez, J. M. Gil-Narvion, A. Gordillo-Guerrero, D. Iñiguez, A. Maiorano, F. Mantovani, E. Marinari, V. Martin-Mayor, J. Monforte-Garcia, A. Muñoz Sudupe, D. Navarro, G. Parisi, S. Perez-Gaviro, M. Pivanti, F. Ricci-Tersenghi, J. J. Ruiz-Lorenzo, S. F. Schifano, B. Seoane, A. Tarancon, R. Tripiccione, and D. Yllanes, *Phys. Rev. E.* **89**, 032140 (2014).

[97] M. Baity-Jesi, E. Calore, A. Cruz, L. A. Fernandez, J. M. Gil-Narvion, A. Gordillo-Guerrero, D. Iñiguez, A. Maiorano, E. Marinari, V. Martin-Mayor, J. Moreno-Gordo, A. Muñoz Sudupe, D. Navarro, G. Parisi, S. Perez-Gaviro, F. Ricci-Tersenghi, J. J. Ruiz-Lorenzo, S. F. Schifano, B. Seoane, A. Tarancon, R. Tripiccione, and D. Yllanes, *Phys. Rev. Lett.* **120**, 267203 (2018).

[98] Y. G. Joh, R. Orbach, G. G. Wood, J. Hammann, and E. Vincent, *Phys. Rev. Lett.* **82**, 438–441 (1999).

[99] M. Baity-Jesi, E. Calore, A. Cruz, L. A. Fernandez, J. M. Gil-Narvion, A. Gordillo-Guerrero, D. Iñiguez, A. Maiorano, E. Marinari, V. Martin-Mayor, J. Monforte-Garcia, A. Muñoz Sudupe, D. Navarro, G. Parisi, S. Perez-Gaviro, F. Ricci-Tersenghi, J. J. Ruiz-Lorenzo, S. F. Schifano, B. Seoane, A. Tarancon, R. Tripiccione, and D. Yllanes, *Phys. Rev. Lett.* **118**, 157202 (2017).

[100] H. Rieger. In ed. D. Stauffer, *Annual Reviews of Computational Physics II.* World Scientific, (1995).

[101] E. Marinari, G. Parisi, J. Ruiz-Lorenzo, and F. Ritort, *Phys. Rev. Lett.* **76**, 843–846 (1996).

[102] E. Marinari, G. Parisi, F. Ricci-Tersenghi, and Ruiz-Lorenzo, *J. Phys. A* **33**, 2373, (2000).

[103] L. Berthier and J.-P. Bouchaud, *Phys. Rev. B.* **66**(5), 054404, (2002).

[104] L. A. Fernández and V. Martín-Mayor, *Phys. Rev. B.* **91**, 174202 (2015).

[105] S. Nakamae, C. Crauste-Thibierge, D. L'Hôte, E. Vincent, E. Dubois, V. Dupuis, and R. Perzynski, *Appl. Phys. Lett.* **101**(24), 242409, (2012).

[106] Q. Zhai, D. C. Harrison, D. Tennant, E. D. Dahlberg, G. G. Kenning, and R. L. Orbach, *Phys. Rev. B.* **95**, 054304 (2017).

[107] M. A. Moore, *Phys. Rev. E.* **103**, 062111 (2021).

[108] L. F. Cugliandolo and J. Kurchan, *Phys. Rev. Lett.* **71**, 173–176 (1993).

[109] S. Franz and H. Rieger, *J. Stat. Phys..* **79**(3), 749–758, (1995).

[110] E. Marinari, G. Parisi, F. Ricci-Tersenghi, and J. J. Ruiz-Lorenzo, *J. Phys. A.* **31**(11), 2611, (1998).

[111] D. Hérisson and M. Ocio, *Phys. Rev. Lett.* **88**, 257202 (2002).

[112] A. Cruz, L. A. Fernández, S. Jiménez, J. J. Ruiz-Lorenzo, and A. Tarancón, *Phys. Rev. B.* **67**, 214425 (2003).

[113] F. Ricci-Tersenghi, *Phys. Rev. E.* **68**, 065104 (2003).

[114] A. Crisanti and F. Ritort, *J. Phys. A.* **36**(21), R181, (2003).

[115] A. Barrat and L. Berthier, *Phys. Rev. Lett.* **87**, 087204 (2001).

Chapter 6

The High-dimensional Landscape Paradigm: Spin-Glasses, and Beyond

Valentina Ros* and Yan V. Fyodorov[†]

*Université Paris–Saclay, CNRS, LPTMS, 91405, Orsay, France
valentina.ros@universite-paris-saclay.fr
[†]Department of Mathematics, King's College London, United Kingdom
yan.fyorodov@kcl.ac.uk

In this chapter we review recent developments on the characterization of random landscapes in high dimension. We focus in particular on the problem of characterizing the landscape topology and geometry, discussing techniques to count and classify its stationary points and stressing connections with the statistical physics of disordered systems and with random matrix theory.

The idea of corrugated landscapes was ubiquitous in many sciences, however it was not easy to put all these things together and to produce a theory for these kind of phenomena [1]. As G. Parisi recalls in his Nobel lecture, the study of glasses has been instrumental in providing such a theory, allowing to put into a quantitative framework what was up to then regarded mostly as a 'useful metaphor' [2]. In an attempt to characterise metastability and slow dynamics in glasses, several tools to count and classify the stationary points (local minima, maxima and saddles) of complicated, very non-convex (free)-energy landscapes have been conceived and developed. Given that corrugated landscapes are ubiquitous, these techniques are expected to play a relevant role in other contexts involving rugged landscapes to optimize, being them fitness landscapes in biology [3, 4], utility functions in economics [5], cost functions in constraint satisfaction or inference problems [6–8], loss landscapes in supervised learning [9], and obviously energy landscapes in condensed and soft matter physics [10], but also string theory and cosmology [11, 12]. Most of these settings are naturally high-dimensional: for instance, the space of genotypes over which fitness landscapes are defined is combinatorially large; in the same vein, training huge artificial neural networks like those used in current deep learning applications requires to find good minima of loss landscapes depending on an extremely large number of parameters. Therefore, techniques developed in the context of the mean-field study of glasses [13], where this high-dimensional limit is built in, are potentially useful to tackle also newly-emergent problems in biology, computer science and so on. In addition, the complexity of the landscapes and the proliferating number of local attractors of optimization algorithms (local minima or, in the language of glasses, metastable states) makes it reasonable to adopt a statistical framework. In fact, in several fields it is customary to model these landscapes by means of random functions, and to seek a statistical description of their properties. The problem is also of great mathematical interest, lying at the intersection between statistics, probability and differential geometry [14]. In this chapter, we aim to briefly summarise the efforts made to substantiate this landscape paradigm, with a particular focus on more recent developments and applications. We will not discuss dynamics, for which we refer the reader to the other chapters of this book.

6.1. Modelling Complex Landscapes: High-dimensional Random Fields

Complex high-dimensional landscapes are usually modelled as random scalar fields $\mathcal{V}(s)$ defined on configuration spaces $\mathcal{C}_N$ of high dimensionality $N \gg 1$, $s = (s_1, \ldots, s_N) \in \mathcal{C}_N$. The variables s_i (representing the state of a spin, particle, neuronal connection, gene, agent, and so on) are either discrete, e.g. $s_i = \pm 1$, or continuous, e.g. $s_i \in \mathbb{R}$. In the following we denote with $\|s - s'\|$ the Hamming or Euclidean distance between two configurations, and we refer to the normalized scalar product $s \cdot s'/N$ as their *overlap*. The landscape is random in the sense that the field $\mathcal{V}(s)$ at each configuration s depends explicitly on the *disorder*, i.e. on certain random variables. We denote $\mathbb{E}\,[\cdot]$ the average over this randomness. The interest lies in characterizing the structure of the landscape statistically, and in particular in capturing *typical* properties which occur with probability converging to one as $N \to \infty$, as well as *atypical* properties, that in the large-N limit are captured by large-deviation theory. To do so in a quantitative way, it is necessary to make some assumptions on the fluctuations of $\mathcal{V}(s)$.

We focus mostly on the simplest and most ubiquitous case, that of *isotropic Gaussian random fields*: $\mathcal{V}(s)$ is thus assumed to have Gaussian fluctuations, with correlations between the field at two different configurations s and s' that depend only on the distance between them in $\mathcal{C}_N$,

$$\mathbb{E}\,[\mathcal{V}(s)\mathcal{V}(s')] - \mathbb{E}\,[\mathcal{V}(s)]\,\mathbb{E}\,[\mathcal{V}(s')] = N F_2\left(\frac{\|s - s'\|^2}{2N}\right). \tag{6.1}$$

Notable members of this class of random fields are obtained with the following parametrization:

$$\mathcal{V}_{\mathbf{J}}(s) = \sum_{p=2}^{\infty} \frac{\alpha_p}{N^{\frac{p-1}{2}}} \sum_{i_1, i_2, \cdots, i_p} J_{i_1 i_2 \cdots i_p} s_{i_1} \cdots s_{i_p}, \tag{6.2}$$

where for any p the parameters $J_{i_1 i_2 \cdots i_p}$ are independent, centered Gaussian variables with unit variance, and the configuration space $\mathcal{C}_N$ is either a discrete hypercube $\{\pm 1\}^{\otimes N}$, or the surface $\mathcal{S}_N$ of the N-dimensional hypersphere $\mathcal{S}_N = \left\{s : \sum_{i=1}^{N} s_i^2 = N\right\}$. In the latter case, the constraint $\sum_p 2^p \alpha_p < \infty$ guarantees that the field is smooth and Morse almost surely, meaning that all its stationary points are non-degenerate [15]. It is straightforward to see that the covariance of (6.2) is isotropic:

$$\mathbb{E}\,[\mathcal{V}_{\mathbf{J}}(s)\mathcal{V}_{\mathbf{J}}(s')] = N \sum_{p=2}^{\infty} \alpha_p^2 \left(\frac{s \cdot s'}{N}\right)^p \tag{6.3}$$

and thus (6.1) holds with $F_2(x) = \sum_p \alpha_p^2 (1 - x)^p$. In the physics literature, random functions of the form (6.2) go under the name of *(spherical) p-spin Hamiltonians*: the spherical ones (when $\mathcal{C}_N = \mathcal{S}_N$) have been introduced in [16, 17] as a generalization to continuous variables of the standard spin-glass models defined for binary variables $s_i = \pm 1$, such as the Sherrington–Kirkpatrick model [18]. When $\alpha_{p'} = \delta_{p,p'}$ for a fixed p, the model is referred to as *pure* (as opposed to *mixed*) in physics, or as *random Gaussian monomial* in mathematics. Notice also that given that $s \cdot s'/N \leqslant 1$, when $p \to \infty$ the covariance (6.3) vanishes, and the landscape reduces to that of the 'simplest spin-glass', the *random energy model* [19], which is uncorrelated at each point in configuration space.

Landscapes of the form (6.2) are centered; in many cases of interest, however, it makes sense to tilt the isotropic Gaussian field $\mathcal{V}(s)$ with non-random functions of s, such as:

$$\mathcal{F}(s; r) = \mathcal{V}(s) - rN f\left(\frac{s \cdot s_*}{N}\right), \tag{6.4}$$

where s_* is some special configuration in $\mathcal{C}_N$, and f some (usually convex) function. These types of models emerge very naturally in inference settings [7, 20], where the special configuration s_* is a *signal* embedded in the *noise* represented by the fluctuating part of the field. They appear also in the theoretical biology literature [21], the special configuration s_* representing some preferred genotypic configuration, or the native conformation in the landscape associated to proteins [22]. When f is linear, the tilting function simply represents a magnetic field aligned with the direction s_*. Deterministic terms of this form break the statistical isotropy, but 'weakly': the statistics depends on s only through its overlap (or the distance) to the special configuration s_*. Tuning r, which measures the strength of the deterministic contribution with respect to the fluctuating ones, can generate transitions in the structure of the landscape (see below). In a somehow similar vein, one may consider soft variables $s_i \in [a, b] \subseteq \mathbb{R}$ and replace the spherical constraint with a confining potential [23]:

$$\mathcal{F}(s; \mu) = \mathcal{V}(s) + \frac{\mu}{2} s \cdot s, \tag{6.5}$$

with μ some positive mass parameter. We remark that the case of anisotropic mass $\mu \to \mu_i$ with μ_i following a certain distribution has also attracted attention recently [24–27]. Functions like (6.5) can also be thought of as the simplest incarnation of a wider class of models involving random *functionals* rather then functions, such as:

$$\mathcal{F}[s(x); \kappa, \mu] = \int d\,x \left(\mathcal{V}[s(x), x] + \frac{\kappa}{2} (\nabla s(x))^2 + \frac{\mu}{2} s(x)^2\right) \tag{6.6}$$

where now $s(x)$ is an N-dimensional vector field depending on some internal d-dimensional state x, the term proportional to κ is an elastic term, $\mathcal{V}[s(x), x]$ is again a centered Gaussian field and isotropy now takes the form:

$$\mathbb{E}\left[\mathcal{V}[s(x), x]\, \mathcal{V}[s'(y), y]\right] = N\,\delta(x - y)\, F_2\left(\frac{\|s(x) - s'(x)\|^2}{2N}\right). \tag{6.7}$$

Of course, for $d \to 0$ this reduces to (6.5). The landscape (6.6), often referred to as the *random elastic manifold* energy landscape, actually appears in a broad variety of optimization problems (see for instance [28]), in which a random potential favouring configurations supported in the spots where $\mathcal{V}[s(x), x]$ is lower, competes with elastic terms which instead promote smoother and flatter configurations.

It is worth mentioning another class of Gaussian random functions with a different parametrization with respect to that of (6.2):

$$\mathcal{V}_{\mathbf{J}}(s; \alpha) = \frac{1}{\alpha N} \sum_{\mu=1}^{\alpha N} \phi\left(\mathbf{J}^\mu \cdot s\right), \qquad (6.8)$$

where ϕ is a (non-linear) function, $\alpha \in (0, 1]$ and the randomness is encoded in the vectors $\mathbf{J}^\mu \in \mathbb{R}^N$, which in most applications are assumed to be independent Gaussian vectors. These types of functions have been extensively studied in statistical physics and in the statistical theory of learning [29–32]. An analog version of (6.4) now reads:

$$\mathcal{V}(s; \alpha) = \frac{1}{2\alpha N} \sum_{\mu=1}^{\alpha N} \left[\phi\left(\mathbf{J}^\mu \cdot s\right) - \phi\left(\mathbf{J}^\mu \cdot s^*\right)\right]^2, \qquad (6.9)$$

which can be seen as a toy model to study problems of *generalization* in machine learning in an inference-like setup [33].

In the following, we denote the landscape generically with $\mathcal{F}(s)$ and we mostly focus on continuous spaces $\mathcal{C}_N$, for which methods relying on continuous differential calculus (see Sec. 6.3.3) apply. Let us stress however that the landscapes (6.3) on discrete spaces are paradigmatic mean-field (fully-connected) models of energy functions, to which one can associate an *averaged* free-energy function, the so-called Thouless–Anderson–Palmer or *TAP free-energy* [34], which depends on continuous variables — the local magnetization. Techniques similar to those discussed in Sec. 6.3.3 can then be (and have been very extensively) applied to study properties of these functions, too [35–38].

6.2. The Questions: Optimization, Topology and Geometry

The *landscape paradigm* is motivated by the problem of understanding the time evolution of complex systems, whenever such evolution can be thought of as some effective optimization process: either the minimization of an energy or cost, or the maximization of a fitness or utility. Typical optimization algorithms update the system configuration using the local gradient of the function to optimize $\mathcal{F}(s)$, sometimes combined with stochastic terms $\epsilon(t)$ which are unbiased with respect to the landscape,

$$\frac{\mathrm{d}\,s(t)}{\mathrm{d}\,t} = -\nabla \mathcal{F}(s) + \epsilon(t). \qquad (6.10)$$

Gradient descent, Langevin dynamics and (in some broader sense) stochastic gradient descent algorithms used in current machine learning applications [39–41] are of this form. In physics, $\epsilon(t)$ is interpreted as an effective term resulting from interactions with a thermal bath, and it is usually chosen as a centered Gaussian process with equal-time variance proportional to the temperature. The information of interest to understand these algorithms is frequently associated not only with the property of the global attractor of (6.10), the global minimum, but also with the number and position of other stationary points s_{st} (minima, maxima and saddle points) on the landscape surface, defined by $\nabla \mathcal{F}(s_{\mathrm{st}}) = 0$. For clarity, we classify the landscape properties related to their distribution into *topological* and *geometrical* properties.

6.2.1. *Landscape's topology*

Loosely speaking, the landscape topology has to do with the total number of stationary points. The word topology in this context is motivated by Morse theory, which allows to relate the topological properties of a manifold to the property of the stationary points of differentiable functions defined on it. Some questions of interest in this context are:

The complexity of level sets. Random landscapes in general display plenty of local minima connected by saddles. To interpret the system's dynamical evolution it is crucial to know the number $\mathcal{N}_N(f; k)$ of stationary points belonging to specific level sets of the landscape, i.e. such that $\lim_{N \to \infty} N^{-1} \mathcal{F}(s_{\mathrm{st}}) = f \in \mathbb{R}$, and having a certain stability index $k \in \{0, \ldots, N\}$ counting the number of independent directions in $\mathcal{C}_N$ along which the landscape has a negative curvature ($k = 0$ for minima, $k = N$ for maxima, and all other values correspond to saddles). In the limit $N \gg 1$, the number $\mathcal{N}_N(f, k)$ typically diverges exponentially, defining an entropy Σ called *the landscape complexity*:

$$\Sigma(f, k) \equiv \lim_{N \to \infty} \frac{\log \mathcal{N}_N(f; k)}{N}. \tag{6.11}$$

The complexity (6.11) gives information, for instance, on how deep the system can descend in the landscape without encountering local minima, and thus at which level sets one expects metastability to matter and to slow down the optimization dynamics.

Topology trivialization transitions. Landscapes depending on external parameters, such as r in (6.4) or μ in (6.5), can undergo transitions when tuning these parameters between regimes where $\Sigma > 0$ and regimes where the complexity vanishes and the number of stationary points is thus sub-exponential. These transitions are known in the literature as topology trivialization transitions [42], and have a natural interpretation in terms of optimization, which is expected to be a *hard task* (hindered by metastability) when $\Sigma > 0$, and to become *easy* when $\Sigma = 0$.

6.2.2. *Landscape's geometry*

We call geometrical properties the landscape's features that have to do with how stationary points are distributed in the space $\mathcal{C}_N$. The word geometrical is motivated by the fact that these features involve notions of distance and position in $\mathcal{C}_N$. Questions of interest in this context are:

Correlations between stationary points. Stationary points of Morse functions are isolated, and one may be interested in understanding what is the typical distance (or overlap) between them or, given some reference configuration s_*, what is the number of minima, saddles and maxima that are at fixed overlap from it. We use for the reference configuration the same notation as for the special configuration in the models (6.4) and

(6.9) since in these cases it would be a natural choice, but more generally s_* may be a stationary point (e.g. the global minimum of the landscape). Questions of this type can be addressed by computing a geometrically-constrained complexity $\Sigma(f, k; q)$ as a function of an additional parameter, the overlap:

$$q = \lim_{N \to \infty} \frac{s_{\mathrm{st}} \cdot s_*}{N}. \tag{6.12}$$

Having this refined geometrical knowledge is relevant to understand 'how badly' metastability affects the underlying optimization problem, i.e. whether the local minima trapping the system under the dynamics (6.10) are similar to (*magnetized towards*) the global minimum, or the signal or any other sought configuration s_* (i.e. $q > 0$), or whether they are far away and uncorrelated to it (i.e. $q = 0$). In the first case, in the inference setting the term *partial recovery* is used, to signify that minimization algorithms are likely to converge to local attractors that are at least partially informative on the signal configuration s_*, being at non-zero overlap with it.

Distribution of barriers. Ruggedness implies that moving from one local minimum to another requires climbing up in the landscape: local minima are separated by landscape barriers, which correspond to saddles that are nearby the minima in $\mathcal{C}_N$, but located at higher level sets. When the landscape is highly non-convex, the number of (low-index) saddles surrounding a given local minimum may be exponentially large, and thus associated with a complexity providing information on the distribution of barriers. Determining the statistics of barriers is a non-trivial task, as it requires to control of both geometrical properties (one wants to target only stationary points that are in the vicinity of a certain local minimum), and stability properties; in fact, one is looking for saddles, but not arbitrary ones: such saddles must be *connected* to the reference minimum in $\mathcal{C}_N$, meaning that following the unstable direction of the saddle one should move in the direction of the minimum. This non-trivial task is very relevant for understanding stochastic dynamics in regimes in which (weak) noise terms (such as $\epsilon(t)$ in (6.10)) contrast the gradient and allow the system to climb up and escape from trapping local minima via *activated jumps*. The resulting dynamics (which corresponds to a high-dimensional version of the well-known Kramer's escape problem) is slow, dominated by rare events (jumps between different minima) in which the configuration of the system changes substantially, and it is very challenging to describe quantitatively in the high-dimensional setting.

6.2.3. *Dealing with the randomness: Average vs typical*

The above properties can be understood for fixed realizations of $\mathcal{F}(s)$, but the main interest lies in characterizing it statistically. Quantities like $\mathcal{N}_N$ are random variables, and one needs to give a statistical meaning to the complexity. The first non-trivial quantity of interest is the first moment of $\mathcal{N}_N$, the asymptotics of which defines the so-called *annealed complexity*:

$$\Sigma_{\mathrm{ann}} \equiv \lim_{N \to \infty} \frac{\log \mathbb{E}[\mathcal{N}_N]}{N}. \tag{6.13}$$

As it often happens in disordered systems, however, the average of quantities fluctuating exponentially in $N \gg 1$ like $\mathcal{N}_N$ is in general much larger than the typical value, and the two remain different when $N \to \infty$. In other words, $\mathcal{N}_N$ is not self-averaging [43]. One would like then to describe *typical realizations* of $\mathcal{F}(s)$, and thus to compute the asymptotics of the typical value of $\mathcal{N}_N$ given by the *quenched complexity*:

$$\Sigma_{\text{que}} \equiv \lim_{N \to \infty} \mathbb{E} \left[\frac{\log \mathcal{N}_N}{N} \right]. \tag{6.14}$$

Thus, one needs to compute averages of logarithms. The same problem obviously appears when dealing with equilibrium properties: one is in general not interested in getting the average of the partition function

$$\mathcal{Z}_{\beta,\mathbf{J}} = \int_{\mathcal{C}_N} \mathrm{d}\, s \; \mathrm{e}^{-\beta \mathcal{E}_\mathbf{J}(s)}, \tag{6.15}$$

but rather of the free-energy, which is self-averaging:

$$F(\beta) = - \lim_{N \to \infty} \mathbb{E} \left[\frac{1}{N\beta} \log \mathcal{Z}_{\beta,\mathbf{J}} \right]. \tag{6.16}$$

Replicas have been introduced [44, 45] precisely as a trick to extract the expectation value of the logarithm from higher moments of the random variable, via the identity:

$$\log \mathcal{N}_N = \lim_{n \to 0} \frac{\mathcal{N}_N^n - 1}{n}. \tag{6.17}$$

The quenched complexities discussed below are computed by making use of this trick; this requires making some hypothesis on the structure (symmetric or not) of the correlations (overlaps) between different stationary points, similarly to what has to be done in the equilibrium setting [13]; in some fortunate cases, this structure takes a simple form and quenched and annealed complexities match (see Sec. 6.4 for an example) and can be computed in a mathematically rigorous way. In general though, the use of the replica trick forces one to give up the benefit of mathematical rigor, disclosing in exchange a universe of fascinating properties of the underlying complex systems, as testified by the other chapters of this book.

6.3. Techniques for Non-Convex Landscapes

We now give a brief summary of the techniques that have been developed to gain information on stationary points of random landscapes. To facilitate the reading, we begin with a few comments to clarify our terminology.

6.3.1. *(Free)-energies, equilibrium, metastability*

Optimizing a complex, high-dimensional landscape means seeking its global minimum. Of course, when the landscape is very non-convex local algorithms of the form (6.10) fail in locating such configuration(s), as they get trapped into local minima located at higher level-sets of the landscape. In the literature on spin-glasses, the random functions (6.2) are effective energy functions and the optimal configuration(s), the system's ground state(s), correspond to the *equilibrium state* at infinite inverse temperature $\beta \to \infty$, i.e. the configuration on which the Boltzmann measure

$$\nu_{\beta,\mathbf{J}}(\boldsymbol{s}) \equiv \frac{e^{-\beta \mathcal{E}_{\mathbf{J}}(\boldsymbol{s})}}{\mathcal{Z}_{\beta,\mathbf{J}}} d\boldsymbol{s}, \qquad \mathcal{Z}_{\beta,\mathbf{J}} = \int_{\mathcal{C}_N} d\boldsymbol{s} \; e^{-\beta \mathcal{E}_{\mathbf{J}}(\boldsymbol{s})} \tag{6.18}$$

concentrates in that limit. In glassy systems, the above statements generalize to a full range of β: stochastic Langevin dynamics initialized randomly is unable to converge to the equilibrium states identified by the Boltzmann measure at the temperature corresponding to the noise strength, as it gets attracted by metastable states having an intensive free-energy f higher than the equilibrium one (6.16). These metastable states appear to be exponentially numerous, and thus associated to a *configurational complexity* $\Sigma(f, \beta)$, which reduces to the complexity of local minima of the energy landscape when $\beta \to \infty$. Moreover, the Boltzmann measure itself appears to fracture into an exponential multiplicity $\Sigma(f_{\mathrm{eq}}, \beta)$ of *equilibrium states*, whose internal free energy f_{eq} is related to (6.16) by $F(\beta) = f_{\mathrm{eq}} - \beta^{-1}\Sigma(f_{\mathrm{eq}}, \beta)$. In mean-field models, these equilibrium and metastable states can be identified with *stable* stationary points of the TAP free-energy functionals (see Sec. 6.1) in a statistical sense, once averaging over the couplings $\mathbf{J}$ is performed.

6.3.2. *Probing metastability within equilibrium formalisms*

Characterizing metastable states is a purely dynamical problem [46]. However, in the literature on mean-field glasses techniques have been developed to extract information on metastability via (suitably modified) thermodynamic calculations involving *real replicas* [47] or *copies* [48] or *clones* [49] of the system. The basic idea is that the structure of complex free-energy landscapes can be probed considering copies of the system that evolve in the same landscape and are weakly coupled to each others. We briefly review these approaches in the following, without entering into any technicality.

Legendre transforms, or the Monasson method. It is shown in [48] that $\Sigma(f, \beta)$ is related via a Legendre transform to the free-energy of several (say m) copies of the system interacting via an infinitesimal coupling term. The coupling is assumed to be strong enough to force the copies to explore the same metastable state, but weak enough so that they can be considered as independent within the state. Under this assumption, a standard thermodynamic calculation shows that the intensive free-energy $F(m, \beta)$ of the coupled system is given by:

$$F(m, \beta) = \inf_f \left[fm - \frac{1}{\beta}\Sigma(f, \beta) \right]. \tag{6.19}$$

Introducing

$$f_*(m, \beta) = \arg\inf_f \left[fm - \frac{1}{\beta}\Sigma(f, \beta) \right], \tag{6.20}$$

we see how the simple equality (6.19) allows to get $\Sigma(f, \beta)$ parametrically in the conjugate variable m, if the free energy $F(m, \beta)$ is known: it suffices to fix m, determine the corresponding $f_*(m, \beta) = \partial_m F(m, \beta) \to f$, and get the associated entropy from $\Sigma(f, \beta) = \beta f m - \beta F(m, \beta)$ evaluated at the corresponding m. The complexity curve is thus reconstructed by tuning m; for $m \to 1$, one gets the complexity of the equilibrium states and their internal free energy. This method boils down to computing the free-energy of a (slightly complicated) disordered system, which can be done by exploiting the machinery (namely, replica theory) developed in the study of the thermodynamics of glasses. As such, it has been used extensively in the physics literature to explore metastability, for instance in more realistic models of glasses involving particles in high-dimension [50, 51], and even beyond the field of glasses [52].

Large deviations, or the Franz–Parisi potential. The Franz–Parisi potential $V_{\mathrm{FP}}(q)$ is a large deviation function that measures the free-energy cost to keep one copy s of the system at fixed overlap q from another copy s_0, where both of them are weighted with a Bolzmann measure (6.18) with two (in general different) inverse temperatures. Explicitly,

$$V_{\mathrm{FP}}(q) = -\lim_{N \to \infty} \frac{1}{N\beta} \mathbb{E}\left[\frac{1}{\mathcal{Z}_{\beta_0,\mathbf{J}}} \int_{\mathcal{C}_N} \nu_{\beta_0,\mathbf{J}}(s_0) \left(\log \mathcal{Z}_{\beta,\mathbf{J}}(s_0; q) + F(\beta)\right)\right], \qquad (6.21)$$

where $F(\beta)$ is as in (6.16) and

$$\mathcal{Z}_{\beta,\mathbf{J}}(s_0; q) = \int_{\mathcal{C}_N} \nu_{\beta,\mathbf{J}}(s)\delta\left(q - \frac{s \cdot s_0}{N}\right). \qquad (6.22)$$

As shown in detail in [53, 54] and subsequent literature, in presence of metastability the potential $V_{\mathrm{FP}}(q)$ is non-monotonic. When $\beta = \beta_0$ and one local minimum is present as some value of $q = q_{\mathrm{EA}}$, one has $\beta V_{\mathrm{FP}}(q_{\mathrm{EA}}) = \Sigma(f_{\mathrm{eq}}, \beta)$, i.e. the potential gives the complexity of the equilibrium states. Indeed, $e^{-N\beta V_{\mathrm{FP}}(q_{\mathrm{EA}})}$ measures the (exponentially small) probability to find two copies of the system in the same equilibrium state, which can be thought of as being proportional to the inverse of the number of such states, $e^{-N\Sigma(f_{\mathrm{eq}}, \beta)}$. The Franz–Parisi potential or variations of it have become a standard tool in physics [55–59], mathematics [60, 61] and computer science [62], not only to compute complexities but also to study the relationship between equilibrium states at different temperatures via the so-called *state following* procedure. Recently, its large deviations have been studied as well [63].

These methods are very insightful but they are tailored to track stable states or local minima; in general, they need to be adapted to count states or minima that are only *marginally stable*, and it seems very hard to generalize them to count unstable stationary points and thus to get information on saddles and landscape's barriers. For these aims, direct counting techniques (see the following section) seem to be more suitable.

6.3.3. *Direct counting methods: the Kac–Rice formalism*

The landscape problem, as we have formulated it so far, is a bare counting problem: one wants to determine the number of distinct configurations s_{st} that satisfy $\nabla \mathcal{F}(s_{\mathrm{st}}) = 0$.

For $s \in \mathcal{C}_N = \mathbb{R}^N$ this amounts to finding all solutions of the simultaneous conditions

$$f_i(s) = \frac{\partial}{\partial s_i} \mathcal{F}(s) = 0 \qquad i = 1, \ldots, N. \tag{6.23}$$

For general manifolds $\mathcal{C}_N$, the functions $f_i(s)$ may take a more general form: on the sphere $\mathcal{C}_N = \mathcal{S}_N$, the gradient $\nabla \mathcal{F}(s)$ lies in the tangent plane to the sphere at s, and thus the $f_i(s)$ are the projections of $\partial_{s_k} \mathcal{F}(s)$ on the tangent plane (equivalently, the spherical constraint can be encoded in f_i with a Lagrange multiplier). The Kac formula [64] for the number $\mathcal{N}_N$ of isolated solutions of (6.23) reads:

$$\mathcal{N}_N = \int_{\mathcal{C}_N} \mathrm{d}s \, \delta(f_1) \cdots \delta(f_N) \left| \det \left(\frac{\partial f_i}{\partial s_j} \right) \right|, \tag{6.24}$$

where $\delta(f)$ stands for the Dirac delta-function, and appropriate smoothness of the functions $f_i(\mathbf{s})$ is assumed. One can recognize in the determinant in (6.24) a Jacobian of a change of variables in the delta-function: for $f_i(s) = \partial_{s_i} \mathcal{F}(s)$, the matrix is nothing but the *Hessian matrix*, whose eigenvalues give the curvature of the landscape in the vicinity of the stationary point, and thus control its linear stability. For f_i containing random Gaussian terms, Rice [65, 66] (see also [67]) derived an expression for the *average* of $\mathcal{N}_N$, which we write here as:

$$\mathbb{E}\left[\mathcal{N}_N\right] = \int_{\mathcal{C}_N} \mathrm{d}s \, P_{\mathbf{f}(\mathbf{s})}(\mathbf{0}) \, \mathbb{E}\left[\left| \det \left(\frac{\partial f_i}{\partial s_j} \right) \right| \, \Big| \, f_i(s) = 0 \, \forall i \right], \tag{6.25}$$

where $P_{\mathbf{f}(\mathbf{s})}(\mathbf{0})$ is the joint density of the variables $f_i(\mathbf{s})$ evaluated at 0, and $\mathbb{E}\left[\cdot|\cdot\right]$ a conditional expectation value. For $f_i(s) = \partial_{s_i} \mathcal{F}(s)$, the mean number of stationary points can thus simply be written as $\mathbb{E}\left[\mathcal{N}_N\right] = \int_{\mathcal{C}_N} \mathrm{d}s \, \rho_{\mathrm{st}}(s)$, with $\rho_{\mathrm{st}}(s)$ being the corresponding mean density

$$\rho_{\mathrm{st}}(s) = \mathbb{E}\left[| \det \left(\partial^2_{s_i s_j} \mathcal{F}(s) \right) | \prod_{i=1}^{N} \delta(\partial_{s_i} \mathcal{F}(s)) \right]. \tag{6.26}$$

The Eq. (6.25) is the simplest instance of a *Kac–Rice (KR) formula*. A nice review of the history of this formula can be found in [68] and in references therein; its applications to the high-dimensional setting are discussed in Ref. [69], see also [15, 70] for a mathematical exposition. The formula can be generalized to count stationary points satisfying specific constraints (belonging to a certain level set or having a certain index) by inserting in the expectation value (6.26) characteristic functions enforcing these conditions.

It is clear from (6.13) that to get the *annealed complexity* of the landscape or of any of its level sets, it suffices to get the large-N asymptotics of (6.24). The *quenched complexity* (6.14), however, requires going beyond the computation of the first moment. To this aim, one has to introduce Kac–Rice formulas for the higher moments of $\mathcal{N}_N$ [71] or *replicated Kac–Rice* in the language of Ref. [72], which in the notation used above can be written as:

$$\mathbb{E}\left[\mathcal{N}_N^n\right] = \int_{\mathcal{C}_N} \prod_{a=1}^{n} \mathrm{d}s^a \, P_{\mathbf{f}(s^a)}(\mathbf{0}) \, \mathbb{E}\left[\left| \prod_{a=1}^{n} \det \left(\frac{\partial f_i(s^a)}{\partial s_j^a} \right) \right| \, \Big| \, f_i(s^a) = 0 \, \forall i, a \right], \tag{6.27}$$

where now the conditioning to $f_i(\boldsymbol{s}^a) = 0$ has to be imposed for all $a = 1, \ldots, n$, and $P_{\mathbf{f}(\boldsymbol{s}^a)}(\mathbf{0})$ is the joint probability density associated to this event. To determine the asymptotics of (6.25) or (6.27) one has to deal with the conditional expectation of the determinant. In much of the spin-glass literature this term is dealt with approximately; it is only in more recent years that it was realized that random matrix theory allows to treat it exactly, and thus to get a more thorough comprehension of the stability properties of the stationary points one is counting.

Dealing with determinants, approximately: integral representations. The absolute value in (6.25) is not an innocent detail: as it follows from Morse theory [15], omitting it would give a topological invariant (the Euler characteristics of $\mathcal{C}_N$) rather than $\mathcal{N}_N$. Despite being well aware of this fact [73], early works in the physics litera-ture succeeded nevertheless to count minima of energy or TAP free-energy landscapes by largely omitting the modulus, and by introducing integral representations of the determinant (with its own sign) in terms of commuting [35] or anti-commuting (Grass-mann) variables [74, 75]. This was justified by the expectation that in the large-N limit the bottom of the landscape is dominated by minima all having strictly positive determinant; thus, when restricting the counting problem to level sets corresponding to low values of the (free)-energy, the absolute value can be safely dropped. This is in fact the case for models such as the spherical *pure p-spin* model: below a certain *threshold* value of the energy the number of stable local minima is exponentially (in N) larger than the number of saddles, and the calculation of the total complexity (with no constraint on the index) of stationary points of low energy performed in this way [17] reproduces correctly the complexity of local minima [76]. However, the situ-ation becomes complicated when the dominant stationary points are only *marginally stable* (i.e. such that some eigenvalue of the Hessian vanishes and the states are very fragile under external perturbations), as it is the case for the models (6.2) defined on discrete spaces $s_i = \pm 1$, including the Sherrington–Kirkpatrick model [77–79]. The cal-culation of the TAP complexity in these cases proved to be particularly challenging and sometimes not easily interpretable: an illustration of this is the extensive debate one finds in the physical literature [35, 80–86] on the connection between marginality and the breaking of the BRST supersymmetry [87] — a symmetry between the commut-ing and the anticommuting variables introduced with the integral representation of the determinant.

Dealing with determinants, exactly: random matrix theory. The paper [42] was seemingly the first one in which it was observed that the application of the Kac–Rice formula to a certain class of random Gaussian landscapes (in that work, model (6.5)) can be conveniently cast into a Random Matrix Theory (RMT) problem. The random matrices in question are obviously the Hessian matrices: the approach of [42] consists in determining their distribution directly, instead of giving integral representations of their determinant. The condition (6.1) is then crucial, as it translates into properties of invariance of the corresponding random matrix ensembles, allowing one to perform explicit calculations. Indeed, one easily sees that (6.1) implies for a centered Gaussian field $\mathcal{V}(s)$:

$$\mathbb{E}\left[\partial^2_{s_l s_i}\mathcal{V}(s)\partial^2_{s'_j s'_k}\mathcal{V}(s')\right] = N\partial^2_{s_l s_i}\partial^2_{s'_j s'_k}F_2\left(\frac{\|s-s'\|^2}{2N}\right)$$

$$= \frac{1}{N}F_2''\left(\frac{\|s-s'\|^2}{2N}\right)[\delta_{ki}\delta_{jl}+\delta_{ji}\delta_{kl}+\delta_{jk}\delta_{li}]$$

$$+ \frac{1}{N^2}F_2'''\left(\frac{\|s-s'\|^2}{2N}\right)g_1(s,s') + \frac{1}{N^3}F_2''''\left(\frac{\|s-s'\|^2}{2N}\right)g_2(s,s')$$

$$\tag{6.28}$$

where

$$g_1(s,s') = \delta_{kl}(s_j-s'_j)(s_i-s'_i) + \delta_{jl}(s_k-s'_k)(s_i-s'_i) + \delta_{il}(s_j-s'_j)(s_k-s'_k)$$
$$+ \delta_{kj}(s_l-s'_l)(s_i-s'_i) \tag{6.29}$$
$$g_2(s,s') = (s_k-s'_k)(s_i-s'_i)(s_j-s'_j)(s_l-s'_l).$$

Therefore, the correlations between entries of the Hessian matrix, obtained setting $s = s'$, simply read:

$$\mathbb{E}\left[\partial^2_{s_l s_i}\mathcal{V}(s)\partial^2_{s_j s_k}\mathcal{V}(s)\right] = \frac{1}{N}F_2''(0)\left[\delta_{ki}\delta_{jl} + \delta_{ji}\delta_{kl} + \delta_{jk}\delta_{li}\right], \tag{6.30}$$

implying GOE-like statistics. Similarly, one can deduce that the matrix elements of the Hessian and the first derivatives $\partial_{s_i}\mathcal{V}(s)$ at the same point in $\mathcal{C}_N$ are independent, thus the conditioning in the expectation value (6.25) is immaterial, rendering the calculation of the first moment particularly simple. This mapping to RMT has been extended and developed in [88–91], culminating in the works [14, 92] that considerably advanced RMT-based techniques for counting stationary points with a fixed index and conditioned on the value of the landscape (for (6.2) on the sphere $\mathcal{S}_N$).

Computing the higher moments (6.27) is more challenging, as correlations enter into play. Indeed, one has to determine the joint expectation of the product of determinants at different configurations, which as it follows from (6.28) are correlated to each others; moreover, the Hessian at one configuration s is correlated to the derivatives of the random field at another configuration s', and therefore the conditioning in (6.27) is no longer immaterial. However, such calculation can be carried out explicitly for isotropic Gaussian fields [72, 93]; crucial ingredients are the facts that (i) the conditioning modifies the invariant Hessian statistics (6.30) by means of *finite-rank perturbations*, the effect of which on the Hessian spectrum can be studied explicitly with RMT techniques, (ii) the correlations between the Hessian matrices at different configurations is negligible when computing the joint expectation value of the determinants to leading order in N (see also [94] for a rigorous proof of this statement for $n = 2$).

The RMT approach is thus fully controllable and it allows one to determine annealed landscape complexities within a mathematically rigorous framework. It can be extended to quenched complexities embedding the replica trick in the formalism. In particular, the RMT setup is essential to characterize the Hessian statistics well beyond the leading order contribution of the determinant, allowing one to study the emergence of *isolated eigenvalues* in the spectrum and thus to control in detail the stability of the stationary points one is counting; this is fundamental to address the questions related to the landscape geometry and the distribution of barriers, as we hint at in the following section.

6.4. Recent Results on Random Landscapes: A Short Summary

In this section we give an overview of recent results, organizing the presentation around the questions introduced in Sec. 6.2 and focusing mostly on recent developments involving KR formulas and RMT.

On the complexity of level sets. The spherical *pure p-spin model* (6.2) with $\alpha_{p'} = \delta_{p,p'}$, $p \geqslant 3$ and $\mathcal{C}_N = \mathcal{S}_N$ has quickly become one of the most paradigmatic models in the theoretical literature on glasses [95], as well as the favorite playground to test and compare the approaches mentioned in Sec. 6.3, which all give consistent results for this model. The expression for the annealed complexity $\Sigma(f)$ of the stationary points at intensive energy f has been proven rigorously in [14, 92] using KR. It was known from replica calculations [17] that in the pure model quenched and annealed complexities coincide, a statement made rigorous in [94] by means of the second moment method. The works [14, 92] go beyond the calculation of the total complexity by determining the explicit expression of the annealed complexity $\Sigma(f, k)$ of stationary points at fixed index k. The calculation is elegantly framed in the RMT setting: the complexity of saddles of index k is obtained from the large deviation function of the smallest eigenvalues of a GOE matrix [96]. The resulting picture is that of an energy landscape that is hierarchically organized at its bottom (below the *threshold energy* mentioned in Sec. 6.3.3): at fixed f the complexity curves are ordered in the index k, the highest one being that of minima ($k = 0$), followed by that of saddles of index $1, 2, 3, \ldots$. The curves never cross, meaning that at low energy densities saddles are exponentially numerous, but exponentially less numerous than minima (the suppression in their number is precisely due to the large deviation cost mentioned above). The equivalence between quenched and annealed complexity extends to the fixed index case [97]. It should be mentioned that for this model, the curves $\Sigma(f, k)$ were already obtained in [76] within the approximations of Sec. 6.3.3, which are effective here in part thanks to the lacking of crossings between the $\Sigma(f, k)$ for different k (and thus different Hessians sign). Another fortunate property of the pure model is the fact that no *temperature chaos* is present, implying that results on the complexity of the energy landscape can be extended *adiabatically* to the free-energy landscape at low temperature. This is due to the fact that the energy function is homogeneous (a polynomial of fixed degree), and temperature enters as a global rescaling factor [98]. A lot of progress on this topic has been made recently on the mathematical side [99–103].

These simple features of the pure model are quite fragile: already adding a deterministic field breaks the identity between quenched and annealed complexity [104], and the two remain in general different for mixed models. In the latter case the landscape structure becomes more intricate (see [105, 106] for the calculation of the annealed complexity of a $p + k$ *model* with the techniques of Sec. 6.3.3). The interest in these models has reignited recently [107] partly due to the discovery of new forms of ergodicity breaking in the Langevin dynamics associated with these systems [58], and partly due to their emergence in problems of inference [108], and non-linear optics [109]. Recent mathematical work on the free energy of mixed models [110] also elucidated the mechanisms behind the Parisi replica symmetry breaking, complementing approaches based on a direct analysis of Parisi measures [111]. Intriguing features of the complexity of stationary points of the pure model defined on complex configuration spaces $\mathcal{C}_N \subseteq \mathbb{C}^N$ are discussed in [112, 113].

On topology trivialization transitions. Topology trivialization transitions have been identified and discussed in the recent works [42, 69, 89, 90, 114]: they occur when a control parameter, like the signal-to-noise ratio r in (6.4) or the curvature μ in (6.5), exceeds a critical value set by the variance of the local Hessian, $F_2''(0)$ in (6.30). Such critical values are exactly those where zero-temperature replica symmetry breaking mechanisms cease to be operative [89], reflecting the change in the nature of the landscape from supporting exponentially many stationary points to only a few. The transition is further accompanied by the change in the Hessian spectrum at the global minimum of the associated landscape [115]. In the trivial phase $\Sigma_{\text{que}} = \Sigma_{\text{ann}} = 0$, and in some cases more precise asymptotics of $\mathcal{N}_N$ can be determined [116, 117]. A particularly interesting example is provided by the model (6.6) in presence of a force term, where the topology trivialization transition corresponds to the so-called *depinning* dynamical transition [118–120]. Annealed complexities in that case have been rigorously and elegantly computed in [25] using advanced RMT insights into the properties of expectations of random determinants obtained by the same authors in an accompanying paper [25]. For further discussion of topology trivialization (or lack of it) for different types of random landscapes see [8, 121].

On the correlations between stationary points. The models (6.4) are prototypical examples of landscapes where deterministic, convex contributions compete with fluctuating terms, giving rise to a variety of transitions in both the topology and geometry of the landscape. The geometry of a variation of the $p + k$ *model* obtained choosing $\mathcal{V}(s)$ to be a pure p-spin model and $f(x) = x^k/k$ has been studied in [93] (see [122] for the study of the equilibrium properties) by means of the computation of a quenched constrained complexity $\Sigma(f, k; q)$. This study has unveiled the occurrence of three different transitions as a function of r: (i) a transition related to recovery, occurring when the deepest minimum of the landscape becomes correlated with s_* and thus informative on its position in $\mathcal{C}_N$, implying that partial information on s_* could be recovered by an effective landscape minimization; (ii) a geometrical transition occurring when the landscape in the vicinity of the global minimum ceases to be rugged, implying that optimization algorithms initialized with a bias towards the direction of s_* are able to converge to the global minimum; (iii) a topology trivialization transition occurring when the whole landscape becomes convex, even far away from s_*. In this model, the trivialization of the landscape is induced by the low rank perturbations to the Hessian matrices at the stationary points, which generate an isolated eigenvalue that becomes negative, signalling that the local minima develop an instability (a direction of negative curvature) towards s_*. In a certain regime of parameters, the landscape is dominated by marginally stable states with a single zero mode of the Hessian, similarly to what happens in other models [38, 105]: in [93] the functional dependence of this special eigenvalue on f, r and on the overlap q is obtained within a quenched formalism combined with RMT. Based on this analysis, a classification of tilted random landscapes emerges: for $k = 1$ (p-spin in a field) the landscape is very sensitive to the presence of s_* and the exponential majority of local minima are informative — the quenched complexity of this model was computed in [104]. For $k = 2$, a topology trivialization transition occurs for values of $r \sim O(N^0)$ thanks to the weak instability given by the isolated eigenvalue, while for $k = 3$ the transition occurs for $r \sim O(N^\alpha)$ with $\alpha > 0$. This classification emerges with a broader generality when studying the performance of optimization dynamics [39]. We stress that the case $k \geqslant 3$ is particularly interesting in the inference setting, as it includes the so-called *spiked-tensor problem* (when $p = k$) that has attracted a lot of attention in recent literature as a prototypical problem with a *statistical-to-algorithmic gap* [20, 123–126].

On the distribution of barriers.   The recent advances on the KR formalism allow one to revisit the question on the distribution of barriers [127, 128], identified here with the difference between the values of $\mathcal{F}(s)$ at one minimum and that at a nearby, connected saddle. To extract this information, it is necessary to study the landscape locally, i.e. to determine the distribution of stationarity points in the vicinity of any arbitrary local minimum chosen as a reference point, and to study their stability. For large N, this is in essence a large deviation calculation. Early attempts to address this problem for the spherical, pure p-spin model have been made in [129] by means of a variation of the Franz–Parisi potential, and in [130] computing a constrained complexity in the annealed framework. The quenched calculation has been done in [72], and the analysis of the Hessian statistics has revealed a crossing between a population of dominating rank-1 saddles sufficiently close to the reference minimum, and a population of minima dominating far-away in configuration space. It is also shown that the local maximum of the Franz–Parisi potential, which gives an upper bound to the dynamical barrier [98], actually likely corresponds to a local minimum in the landscape rather than a saddle. The complexity of low-rank connected saddles in the region dominated by minima has been determined in [131] via a mapping to a large deviation problem for the smallest eigenvalue *and eigenvector* of a random matrix perturbed by additive and multiplicative finite-rank perturbations, generalizing the RMT results in [132]. Combining this refined knowledge on the landscape structure with the direct study of activated dynamics for the pure p-spin model is an ongoing research direction [133–136]. Recent progress has been made also in the study of free-energy barriers of the Sherrington–Kirkpatrick model with Ising variables [137], that (at variance with the p-spin case) are not scaling linearly in N. This has been made possible by a careful study of the scaling of the coefficients of the expansion of the TAP free energy around a minimum.

6.5. Open Challenges: Landscape Paradigm, and Beyond

High-dimensional landscapes have been first introduced long ago as a visual aid for the dynamical evolution of complicated systems. It is within the field of glasses that this turned into an established theory, with the development of tools to capture and characterize statistically the complexity arising in the high-dimensional limit. Recently these tools are gaining an ever-increasing importance, boosted by the impressive growth of available data on complex systems that are inherently high-dimensional (organisms, neuronal systems, ecosystems, deep networks) and whose evolution can be interpreted as a landscape optimization. We can thus talk about a *high-dimensional landscape paradigm*; nonetheless, substantial work still has to be done to advance the landscape program.

First, even though one might expect that isotropic Gaussian fields are justified by some sort of central limit theory arising in high-dimensional, it would be desirable to export the tools described in this chapter to settings in which standard spin-glass functions are not suitable landscape models. Problems of supervised learning are a playground for this, and indeed in recent years there has been a continuously evolving effort to study different models mimicking loss landscapes emerging in realistic machine learning applications [138, 139]. Similarly, problems of reconstruction of encrypted signals give rise to optimization landscapes that are non-Gaussian, given for example by a sum of squared Gaussian terms [140] (see also [141] for applications of similar models to confluent tissues): understanding the landscape structure in this case is certainly an open direction worth to explore. Within the Kac–Rice formalism, giving up Gaussianity implies that the conditioning of the statistics of the Hessian becomes a more challenging problem: an example of this is discussed in [142], where landscapes of the form (6.8), (6.9) are considered and the complexity problem (within the annealed approximation) is rephrased in terms of a variational problem for the spectral density of the Hessian. The recognition of random-matrix theory as a crucial ingredient for complexity calculations is promising in this respect, as one might hope to derive general (universal) results without needing to restrict from the start to standard invariant ensembles [143, 144].

Methodologically, the replicated Kac–Rice formalism for the quenched complexity has been used so far only within simple replica symmetry-breaking schemes, and it would be interesting to use it e.g. in contexts in which full replica-symmetry-breaking occurs [145]. In particular, studying the finite-rank perturbations to the Hessian statistics induced by this structure is an interesting problem, which might clarify some of the questions related to the stability of minima in models where marginality is relevant. From the mathematical perspective, it remains a huge open problem how to derive quenched complexities without needing to invoke the replica trick.

It is also worth mentioning that Kac–Rice methods can be used to address properties of complex high-dimensional systems beyond the landscape paradigm, by counting statistics of equilibrium points of *non-gradient* autonomous dynamics. The motivations for such studies come from applications in fields ranging from neural networks to ecology, economics, and nonlinear wave scattering. Progress in this direction has been made in [146–152] for the calculation on the annealed complexity of the equilibria of the associated systems of equations, and in [153] for the quenched complexity. Understanding how the properties of a conservative system change under non-gradient perturbations is certainly a question with a huge theoretical interest and a broad range of applications.

Finally, we find it appropriate to conclude this chapter by recalling that getting a refined information on the landscape topology and geometry can hopefully shade light and guide us into the comprehension of the dynamical evolution of the complex systems associated to it: establishing quantitatively this connection between landscape and dynamics is the underlying goal of the landscape program, and thus the most relevant perspective.

Acknowledgments

The authors thank their collaborators, in particular Gérard Ben Arous for the many enlightening discussions on the topic of this chapter. VR acknowledges funding by the "Investissements d'Avenir" LabEx PALM (ANR-10-LABX-0039-PALM). YVF acknowledges the support by the EPSRC Grant EP/V002473/1 "Random Hessians and Jacobians: theory and applications".

References

[1] G. Parisi, *NobelPrize.org. Nobel Prize Outreach AB 2022. Wed. 13 Jul. 2022.* (2022).

[2] S. Wright. In *Proceedings of the Sixth Annual Congress of Genetics*, vol. 1, (1932).

[3] P. G. Wolynes, *Proc. Am. Philos. Soc.* **145**(4), 555–563, (2001).

[4] R. H. Austin. In *Quantitative Biology: From Molecular to Cellular Systems*, pp. 1–21. CRC Press, (2012).

[5] P. Krugman, *Am. Econ. Rev.* **84**(2), 412–416, (1994).

[6] A. Montanari, F. Ricci-Tersenghi, and G. Semerjian, *J. Stat. Mech.: Theory Exp.* **2008**(04), P04004, (2008).

[7] M. Mezard and A. Montanari, *Information, physics, and computation.* (Oxford University Press, 2009).

[8] Y. V. Fyodorov and R. Tublin, *J. Phys. A.* **55**(24), 244008, (2022).

[9] A. Choromanska, M. Henaff, M. Mathieu, G. B. Arous, and Y. LeCun. In *Artificial intelligence and statistics*, pp. 192–204. PMLR, (2015).

[10] M. Goldstein, *J. Chem. Phys.* **51**(9), 3728–3739, (1969).

[11] A. Masoumi, A. Vilenkin, and M. Yamada, *J. Cosmol. Astropart. Phys.* **2017**(12), 035, (2017).

[12] L. L. Feng, S. Hotchkiss, and R. Easther, *J. Cosmol. Astropart. Phys.* **2021**(01), 029, (2021).

[13] M. Mézard, G. Parisi, and M. A. Virasoro, *Spin glass theory and beyond: An Introduction to the Replica Method and Its Applications.* vol. 9, (World Scientific Publishing Company, 1987).

[14] A. Auffinger, G. B. Arous, and J. Černý, *Commun. Pure Appl. Math.* **66**(2), 165–201, (2013).

[15] R. J. Adler and J. E. Taylor, *Random fields and geometry.* vol. 80, (Springer, 2007).

[16] D. J. Gross and M. Mézard, *Nucl. Phys. B.* **240**(4), 431–452, (1984).

[17] A. Crisanti and H.-J. Sommers, *J. Physique I.* **5**(7), 805–813, (1995).

[18] D. Sherrington and S. Kirkpatrick, *Phys. Rev. Lett.* **35**(26), 1792, (1975).

[19] B. Derrida, *Phys. Rev. Lett.* **45**(2), 79, (1980).

[20] E. Richard and A. Montanari, *NeurIPS.* **27**, (2014).

[21] J. Neidhart, I. G. Szendro, and J. Krug, *Genetics.* **198**(2), 699–721, (2014).

[22] J. N. Onuchic, Z. Luthey-Schulten, and P. G. Wolynes, *Annu. Rev. Phys. Chem.* **48**(1), 545–600, (1997).

[23] Y. V. Fyodorov and H.-J. Sommers, *Nucl. Phys. B.* **764**(3), 128–167, (2007).

[24] E. Bouchbinder, E. Lerner, C. Rainone, P. Urbani, and F. Zamponi, *Phys. Rev. B.* **103**(17), 174202, (2021).

[25] G. Ben Arous, P. Bourgade, and B. McKenna, *Probab. Math. Phys.* **3**(4), 731–789, (2022).

[26] P. Mergny and S. N. Majumdar, *J. Stat. Mech.: Theory Exp.* **2021**(12), 123301, (2021).

[27] I. Gershenzon, O. Raz, E. Subag, O. Zeitouni, et al., *arxiv:2206.10554.* (2022).

[28] P. Urbani, *J. Phys. A.* **54**(32), 324001, (2021).

[29] R. Dietrich, M. Opper, and H. Sompolinsky, *Phys. Rev. Lett.* **82**(14), 2975, (1999).

[30] A. Engel and C. Van den Broeck, *Statistical mechanics of learning.* (Cambridge University Press, 2001).

[31] E. Gardner, *J. Phys. A.* **21**(1), 257, (1988).

[32] S. Franz and G. Parisi, *J. Phys. A.* **49**(14), 145001, (2016).

[33] L. Zdeborová and F. Krzakala, *Adv. Phys.* **65**(5), 453–552, (2016).

[34] D. J. Thouless, P. W. Anderson, and R. G. Palmer, *Philos. Mag.* **35**(3), 593–601, (1977).

[35] A. J. Bray and M. A. Moore, *J. Phys. C.* **13**(19), L469, (1980).

[36] A. Bray and M. Moore, *J. Phys. A.* **14**(9), L377, (1981).

[37] A. Cavagna, I. Giardina, and G. Parisi, *Phys. Rev. Lett.* **92**(12), 120603, (2004).

[38] T. Aspelmeier, A. Bray, and M. Moore, *Phys. Rev. Lett.* **92**(8), 087203, (2004).

[39] G. Ben Arous, R. Gheissari, and A. Jagannath, *J. Mach. Learn. Res.* **22**, 106–1, (2021).

[40] G. Ben Arous, R. Gheissari, and A. Jagannath, *NeurIPS* **35**, 25349–25362, (2022).

[41] F. Mignacco and P. Urbani, *J. Stat. Mech.: Theory Exp.* **2022**, 083405, (2022).

[42] Y. V. Fyodorov, *Phys. Rev. Lett.* **92**(24), 240601, (2004).

[43] B. Derrida, *Physica D.* **107**(2-4), 186–198, (1997).

[44] M. Kac. In *Arkiv for Der Fysiske Seminar i Trondheim*, vol. 11, (1968).

[45] S. F. Edwards and P. W. Anderson, *J. Phys. F.* **5**(5), 965, (1975).

[46] J. Kurchan, in Les Houches Summer School, vol. 90, Oxford University Press, (2010).

[47] S. Franz, G. Parisi, and M. A. Virasoro, *J. Physique I.* **2**(10), 1869–1880, (1992).

[48] R. Monasson, *Phys. Rev. Lett.* **75**(15), 2847, (1995).

[49] M. Mézard, *Physica A.* **265**(3-4), 352–369, (1999).

[50] P. Charbonneau, J. Kurchan, G. Parisi, P. Urbani, and F. Zamponi, *Annu. Rev. Condens. Matter Phys.* **8**, 1–26, (2017).

[51] G. Parisi, P. Urbani, and F. Zamponi, *Theory of simple glasses: exact solutions in infinite dimensions.* (Cambridge University Press, 2020).

[52] E. De Giuli and A. Zee, *EPL.* **133**(2), 20008, (2021).

[53] S. Franz and G. Parisi, *J. Physique I.* **5**(11), 1401–1415, (1995).

[54] S. Franz and G. Parisi, *Physica A.* **261**(3-4), 317–339, (1998).

[55] A. Barrat, S. Franz, and G. Parisi, *J. Phys. A.* **30**(16), 5593, (1997).

[56] F. Krzakala and L. Zdeborová, *EPL.* **90**(6), 66002, (2010).

[57] C. Rainone, P. Urbani, H. Yoshino, and F. Zamponi, *Phys. Rev. Lett.* **114**(1), 015701, (2015).

[58] G. Folena, S. Franz, and F. Ricci-Tersenghi, *Phys. Rev. X.* **10**(3), 031045, (2020).

[59] F. Ricci-Tersenghi and G. Semerjian, *J. Stat. Mech.: Theory Exp.* **2009**(09), P09001, (2009).

[60] D. Panchenko, *Ann. Probab.* **46**(2), 865–896, (2018).

[61] G. Ben Arous and A. Jagannath, *Commun. Math. Phys.* **361**(1), 1–52, (2018).

[62] A. S. Bandeira, A. El Alaoui, S. B. Hopkins, T. Schramm, A. S. Wein, and I. Zadik, *NeurIPS* **35**, 33831–33844, (2022).

[63] S. Franz and J. Rocchi, *J. Phys. A.* **53**(48), 485002, (2020).

[64] M. Kac, *Bull. Am. Math. Soc.* **49**(4), 314–320, (1943).

[65] S. Rice, *Bell Syst. tech. j.* **23**, 1–114, (1943).

[66] S. O. Rice, *Bell Syst. tech. j.* **24**(1), 46–156, (1945).

[67] K. Ito, *J. Math. Kyoto Univ.* **3**(2), 207–216, (1963).

[68] C. Berzin, A. Latour, and J. León, *arXiv:2205.08742*. (2022).

[69] Y. V. Fyodorov, *Markov Proc. Rel. Fields.* **21**(3), 483–518, (2015).

[70] J.-M. Azaïs and M. Wschebor, *Level sets and extrema of random processes and fields.* (John Wiley & Sons, 2009).

[71] H. Cramér and M. R. Leadbetter, *Stationary and related stochastic processes: Sample function properties and their applications.* (Courier Corporation, 2013).

[72] V. Ros, G. Biroli, and C. Cammarota, *EPL.* **126**(2), 20003, (2019).

[73] J. Kurchan, *J. Phys. A.* **24**(21), 4969, (1991).

[74] K. Efetov, *Supersymmetry in disorder and chaos.* (Cambridge University Press, 1999).

[75] G. Parisi and N. Sourlas, *Nucl. Phys. B.* **206**(2), 321–332, (1982).

[76] A. Cavagna, I. Giardina, and G. Parisi, *Phys. Rev. B.* **57**(18), 11251, (1998).

[77] A. J. Bray and M. A. Moore, *J. Phys. C.* **12**(11), L441, (1979).

[78] G. Parisi and M. Potters, *Europhys. Lett.* **32**(1), 13, (1995).

[79] M. Müller, L. Leuzzi, and A. Crisanti, *Phys. Rev. B.* **74**(13), 134431, (2006).

[80] A. Cavagna, I. Giardina, G. Parisi, and M. Mézard, *J. Phys. A.* **36**(5), 1175, (2003).

[81] A. Annibale, A. Cavagna, I. Giardina, and G. Parisi, *Phys. Rev. E.* **68**(6), 061103, (2003).

[82] A. Crisanti, L. Leuzzi, G. Parisi, and T. Rizzo, *Phys. Rev. B.* **68**(17), 174401, (2003).

[83] A. Crisanti, L. Leuzzi, G. Parisi, and T. Rizzo, *Phys. Rev. B.* **70**(6), 064423, (2004).

[84] T. Rizzo, *J. Phys. A.* **38**(15), 3287, (2005).

[85] A. Crisanti, L. Leuzzi, and T. Rizzo, *Phys. Rev. B.* **71**(9), 094202, (2005).

[86] G. Parisi, in Les Houches Session LXXXIII, Elsevier, Amsterdam (2005).

[87] C. Becchi, A. Rouet, and R. Stora, *Commun. Math. Phys.* **42**(2), 127–162, (1975).

[88] A. J. Bray and D. S. Dean, *Phys. Rev. Lett.* **98**(15), 150201, (2007).

[89] Y. V. Fyodorov and I. Williams, *J. Stat. Phys.* **129**(5), 1081–1116, (2007).

[90] Y. V. Fyodorov and C. Nadal, *Phys. Rev. Lett.* **109**(16), 167203, (2012).

[91] J. Grela and B. A. Khoruzhenko, *J. Phys. A.* **55**(15), 154001, (2022).

[92] A. Auffinger and G. Ben Arous, *Ann. Probab.* **41**(6), 4214–4247, (2013).

[93] V. Ros, G. Ben Arous, G. Biroli, and C. Cammarota, *Phys. Rev. X.* **9**(1), 011003, (2019).

[94] E. Subag, *Ann. Probab.* **45**(5), 3385–3450, (2017).

[95] T. R. Kirkpatrick and D. Thirumalai, *Phys. Rev. B.* **36**(10), 5388, (1987).

[96] G. B. Arous and A. Guionnet, *Probab. Theory Relat. Fields.* **108**(4), 517–542, (1997).

[97] A. Auffinger and J. Gold, *arXiv:2007.09269*. (2020).

[98] J. Kurchan, G. Parisi, and M. A. Virasoro, *J. Physique I.* **3**(8), 1819–1838, (1993).

[99] G. B. Arous, E. Subag, and O. Zeitouni, *Commun. Pure Appl. Math.* **73**(8), 1732–1828, (2020).

[100] E. Subag, *Invent. Math.* **210**(1), 135–209, (2017).

[101] E. Subag, *arXiv:2101.04352*. (2021).

[102] E. Subag and O. Zeitouni, *Probab. Theory Relat. Fields.* **168**(3), 773–820, (2017).

[103] E. Subag and O. Zeitouni, *J. Math. Phys.* **62**(12), 123301, (2021).

[104] A. Cavagna, J. P. Garrahan, and I. Giardina, *J. Phys. A.* **32**(5), 711, (1999).

[105] A. Annibale, G. Gualdi, and A. Cavagna, *J. Phys. A.* **37**(47), 11311, (2004).

[106] A. Crisanti and L. Leuzzi, *Phys. Rev. Lett.* **93**(21), 217203, (2004).

[107] D. Barbier and L. F. Cugliandolo, *J. Stat. Mech.: Theory Exp.* **2020**(6), 063207, (2020).

[108] S. Sarao Mannelli, F. Krzakala, P. Urbani, and L. Zdeborova. In *ICML*, pp. 4333–4342. PMLR, (2019).

[109] F. Antenucci, A. Crisanti, and L. Leuzzi, *Phys. Rev. A.* **91**(5), 053816, (2015).

[110] E. Subag, *arxiv:1804.10576*. (2018).

[111] A. Auffinger and W.-K. Chen, *Adv. Math.* **330**, 553–588, (2018).

[112] J. Kent-Dobias and J. Kurchan, *Phys. Rev. Research.* **3**(2), 023064, (2021).

[113] J. Kent-Dobias and J. Kurchan, *J. Phys. A.* **55**, 434006, (2022).

[114] Y. V. Fyodorov and P. Le Doussal, *J. Stat. Phys.* **154**(1), 466–490, (2014).

[115] Y. V. Fyodorov and P. Le Doussal, *J. Phys. A.* **51**(47), 474002, (2018).

[116] D. Belius, J. Černỳ, S. Nakajima, and M. A. Schmidt, *J. Stat. Phys.* **186**(1), 1–34, (2022).

[117] A. Auffinger, G. Ben Arous, and Z. Li, *J. Math. Phys.* **63**(4), 043303, (2022).

[118] Y. V. Fyodorov, P. Le Doussal, A. Rosso, and C. Texier, *Ann. Phys. (N.Y.).* **397**, 1–64, (2018).

[119] Y. V. Fyodorov and P. Le Doussal, *J. Stat. Phys.* **179**(1), 176–215, (2020).

[120] Y. V. Fyodorov and P. Le Doussal, *Phys. Rev. E.* **101**(2), 020101, (2020).

[121] B. Lacroix-A-Chez-Toine, S. Belga Fedeli, and Y. Fyodorov, *J. Math. Phys.* **63**, 093301, (2022).

[122] P. Gillin and D. Sherrington, *J. Phys. A.* **33**(16), 3081, (2000).

[123] A. Perry, A. S. Wein, and A. S. Bandeira. In *Ann. I. H. Poincaré Pr.*, vol. 56, pp. 230–264. Institut Henri Poincaré, (2020).

[124] G. Ben Arous, S. Mei, A. Montanari, and M. Nica, *Commun. Pure Appl. Math.* **72**(11), 2282–2330, (2019).

[125] G. Ben Arous, R. Gheissari, and A. Jagannath, *Ann. Probab.* **48**(4), 2052–2087, (2020).

[126] J. H. de Morais Goulart, R. Couillet, and P. Comon, *stat.* **1050**, 15, (2022).

[127] G. Rodgers and M. Moore, *J. Phys. A.* **22**(8), 1085, (1989).

[128] A. Lopatin and L. Ioffe, *Phys. Rev. Lett.* **84**(18), 4208, (2000).

[129] A. Cavagna, I. Giardina, and G. Parisi, *J. Phys. A.* **30**(13), 4449, (1997).

[130] A. Cavagna, I. Giardina, and G. Parisi, *J. Phys. A.* **30**(20), 7021, (1997).

[131] V. Ros, *J. Phys. A.* **53**(12), 125002, (2020).

[132] G. Biroli and A. Guionnet, *Electron. Commun. Probab.* **25**, 1–13, (2020).

[133] V. Ros, G. Biroli, and C. Cammarota, *SciPost Physics.* **10**(1), 002, (2021).

[134] T. Rizzo, *Phys. Rev. B.* **104**(9), 094203, (2021).

[135] D. A. Stariolo and L. F. Cugliandolo, *Phys. Rev. E.* **102**(2), 022126, (2020).

[136] M. R. Carbone and M. Baity-Jesi, *Phys. Rev. E.* **106**, 024603, (2022).

[137] T. Aspelmeier and M. Moore, *Phys. Rev. E.* **105**(3), 034138, (2022).

[138] N. P. Baskerville, J. P. Keating, F. Mezzadri, and J. Najnudel, *J. Stat. Phys.* **186**(2), 1–45, (2022).

[139] N. P. Baskerville, J. P. Keating, F. Mezzadri, and J. Najnudel, *J. Stat. Mech.: Theory Exp.* **2021**(6), 064001, (2021).

[140] Y. V. Fyodorov, *J. Stat. Phys.* **175**(5), 789–818, (2019).

[141] P. Urbani, *arxiv:2208.11730.* (2022).

[142] A. Maillard, G. B. Arous, and G. Biroli. In *MSML*, pp. 287–327. PMLR, (2020).

[143] J. Ipsen and P. Forrester, *J. Phys. A.* **51**(47), 474003, (2018).

[144] N. P. Baskerville, J. P. Keating, F. Mezzadri, J. Najnudel, and D. Granzio, *J. Phys. A.* **55**, 494002, (2022).

[145] J. Kent-Dobias and J. Kurchan, *arXiv:2207.06161.* (2022).

[146] G. Wainrib and J. Touboul, *Phys. Rev. Lett.* **110**(11), 118101, (2013).

[147] Y. V. Fyodorov and B. A. Khoruzhenko, *Proc. Natl. Acad. Sci. USA.* **113**(25), 6827–6832, (2016).

[148] Y. V. Fyodorov, *J. Stat. Mech.: Theory Exp.* **2016**(12), 124003, (2016).

[149] J. R. Ipsen, *J. Stat. Mech.: Theory Exp.* **2017**(9), 093209, (2017).

[150] G. Ben Arous, Y. V. Fyodorov, and B. A. Khoruzhenko, *Proc. Natl. Acad. Sci. USA.* **118**(34), e2023719118, (2021).

[151] S. B. Fedeli, Y. V. Fyodorov, and J. Ipsen, *Phys. Rev. E.* **103**(2), 022201, (2021).

[152] B. Lacroix-A-Chez-Toine and Y. V. Fyodorov, *J. Phys. A.* **55**(14), 144001, (2022).

[153] V. Ros, F. Roy, G. Biroli, G. Bunin, and A. M. Turner, arXiv:2212.01837 (2022).

Chapter 7

Universal Aspects of the Structural Glass Transition from Density Functional Theory

Theodore R. Kirkpatrick[*] and Dave Thirumalai[†]

Institute for Physical Science and Technology, University of Maryland, USA

†*Department of Chemistry, University of Texas at Austin, USA*

The random first order transition (RFOT) theory of the structural glass transition (SGT) can be formulated as a density functional theory (DFT). An important feature of the complete RFOT theory is that it has at least two distinct transition temperatures, one of which is a dynamical transition signaling loss of effective ergodicity, and the other is an equilibrium ideal glass transition. The dynamical transition exists only in mean-field-like theories and becomes a rounded transition when activated transport processes become prominent. Using scaling and renormalization group (RG) ideas, universal aspects of both of these transitions are discussed. Particular attention is paid to the coherence, or correlation, length associated with these transitions in the RFOT picture. We also derive universal scaling relations for several experimentally measurable quantities that are valid near the ideal glass transition. In particular, activated scaling ideas are used to obtain a scaling equation for the non-linear structural glass susceptibility as the ideal glass transition is approached. Important finite size corrections to the ideal glass transition temperature are also discussed. Our work provides additional criteria for assessing the validity of RFOT theory of the liquid to glass transition, and provides a firm theoretical foundation for analyzing experimental data on the temperature dependence of the relaxation times.

7.1. Introduction

When undercooled rapidly almost all liquids undergo a transition to a glassy state, characterized by a dramatic increase in viscosity over a narrow temperature range. Because of the central importance of this phenomenon in condensed matter physics, material science, and biology there has been considerable interest in understanding the characteristics of the structural glass transition (SGT) [1–6]. In the late 1980s, we along with Wolynes developed the random first order phase transition (RFOT) [7] theory of the glass transition [8–12] to explain many the unique aspects of the structural glass transition (SGT) problem. Although initially motivated by precise solutions of a class of infinite range spin glass models (see [1] for a short review), we subsequently used a density functional approach and established that the generic aspects of RFOT can be found in systems even without quenched disorder [13]. It was further argued that the structural glass transition is an example of a RFOT. The emergence of RFOT ideas in a theory without quenched disorder is an important development because it showed that liquid state theories could form the basis for describing glassy states. Indeed, the

115

RFOT has been much discussed in this context and in many ways clarified and further extended [14–17].

There are necessarily at least two [8, 9] distinct transitions within the RFOT theory in the mean-field limit. When the temperature is decreased, the liquid undergoes the so-called dynamical transition at a temperature, T_d. This transition is, in general, not a true equilibrium phase transition, although it is related to the topology of the state space of an equilibrium system in that at T_d there is a breakdown in effective ergodicity. Technically, it can be described by using either an equilibrium approach [13, 18, 19], or a dynamical approach [11, 20–22]. The dynamical approach is consistent with the mode coupling theory of the glass transition [20, 21, 23] in that both the theories show that the nature of relaxation dynamics changes at T_d. The dynamical order parameter of the theory is a freezing of the density fluctuations. To further characterize the nature of the transition at T_d, we introduced [24] a non-linear susceptivity or four point correlation function ($\chi_{NL}(t)$ where t is time), which is the natural susceptibility for this transition [17, 24, 25]. We showed that $\chi_{NL}(t)$ at T_d is also a measure of broken ergodicity — a finding that has been confirmed in computer simulation studies [26]. A number of studies have also shown that $\chi_{NL}(t)$ also gives information on the dynamical heterogeneity in glassy liquids [27–29].

The second transition within RFOT theory is a true equilibrium phase transition occurring at a lower temperature denoted by T_K, for historical reasons. The transition at T_K is a new type of equilibrium phase transition, where the order parameter is both random and, in a technical sense, discontinuous at T_K, and one that has a unique and different coherence or correlation length exponent associated with it compared to other well-studied phase transitions.

In [7] (see also [10]) it was argued that in realistic, non-mean-field, systems the transport for $T < T_d$ is activated and that the driving force is entropic. The eventual freezing at the ideal glass transition occurs because the entropic driving force vanishes at T_K. This and various scaling arguments were the final ideas in the original [7] RFOT theory.

More recently [30–32], there has been an enormous amount of work on liquid systems that can be exactly solved in the high-dimension limit ($d \to \infty$) and that undergo a SGT. As in earlier work, these theories find two transitions; (i) an ergodicity breaking dynamical transition and (ii) a true equilibrium ideal glass transition. The universal features of these transitions are the same as in the original RFOT of the SGT. It is interesting, and possibly relevant, to note that the fundamental variables in these theories are all related to particle displacements, and not directly to density fluctuations (see however [33]).

In recent years there has also been a lot of work on the thermodynamics of metastable or non-equilibrium states within RFOT. This is motivated by the fact that on a restricted time scale, that gets longer and longer further into the glassy phase, these states are almost like equilibrium states. This enlarges the parts of phase space that can be probed by theoretically compressing a fluid. Among other things, this has led to a connection between the glass transition and the so-called jamming transition [32, 34]. This work has emphasized that the existence of a Kauzmann temperature is not central to what is referred to as the Gardner transition [35, 36] and the subsequent jamming transition.

The importance of T_d was already anticipated by Goldstein [37] (see also [38]), who argued that below a certain temperature transport in liquids is determined by activated transitions. Since then there is overwhelming evidence from theoretical, simulation [26], and experimental [39] studies that there is a material-dependent special temperature, T_d, or temperature region, below which ergodicity breaking, dynamical heterogeneity, aging effects play an important role. This temperature, T_d, is generally well above what is conventionally called the glass transition temperature T_g, defined roughly when the viscosity reaches a value of 10^{13} poise. The existence of an ideal glass transition at T_K in RFOT is perhaps debatable. It is difficult to unequivocally probe the existence of T_K experimentally because below T_g ($> T_K$) the equilibration times vastly exceed the observation times. Here, we assume that it does exist, and given that it does, we determine some of the universal properties associated with this transition.

The contents of this contribution are as follows. In Sec. 7.2 we discuss the important characteristics of a RFOT, with an eye towards the DFT of the SGT and on the two distinct (dynamical and equilibrium) transitions within RFOT. Using scaling and RG ideas we obtain previously unnoticed scaling relations and scaling predictions for the SGT. Activated dynamical scaling ideas are used to predict a number of effects that should occur as T_K is approached. Important finite size corrections to the ideal glass transition temperature are also discussed. In Sec. 7.3, we compare a RFOT transition with more conventional phase transition theories for the structural glass transition. In this section we also make a general argument for a correlation exponent inequality. We conclude in Sec. 7.4 with a discussion.

7.2. Characteristics of the RFOT Theory of the SGT

7.2.1. *The order parameter and state degeneracy*

The glassy state may be visualized as a frozen liquid state with elastic properties. To describe a glassy state, we introduce two key ideas. First, we imagine an order parameter description in terms of frozen density fluctuations, $\delta n = n - n_l$, where n is a local number density, and n_l is the spatially average density that is identical to the liquid state density. Other order parameters can be imagined, but frozen density fluctuations are the simplest, and are most directly related to an important characteristic of a solid: elastic properties and a nonzero Debye–Waller factor. Because the glassy phase is amorphous or has random characteristics, the frozen density order parameter is specified by a functional probability measure $DP[\delta n]$ [13, 14, 40].

The second key idea in the formulation of RFOT is that, in general, one expects a large number of distinct metastable glassy states as the dynamics starts to become sluggish. If the number of low free energy metastable states is large enough, this in turn leads to two distinct transitions. The physical arguments leading to this conclusion proceed as follows. We denote a particular glassy state by the label s, with the frozen density in that state, $n_s = n_l + \delta n_s$, and the free energy in that state being equal to F_s. The first two moments of the order parameter are,

$$\overline{\delta n_s(\mathbf{x})} = \int DP[\delta n]\delta n_s(\mathbf{x}) = \frac{1}{V} \int d\mathbf{x}\delta n_s(\mathbf{x}) = 0, \tag{7.1}$$

and

$$q_{ss'} = \int DP[\delta n]\delta n_s(\mathbf{x})\delta n_{s'}(\mathbf{x}) = \frac{1}{V}\int d\mathbf{x}\delta n_s(\mathbf{x})\delta n_{s'}(\mathbf{x}). \qquad (7.2)$$

The final equalities in these equations assume self-averaging. From Eq. (7.2) it follows that the zero in Eq. (7.1) is a term of $O(V^{-1/2})$ with V the system volume and the bulk limit is always taken.

Exact calculation for some infinite range spin-glass models as well as for infinite dimensional liquid models [32] show that below a temperature T_d, there are an extensive number (the number of states scales like $\exp[\alpha N]$ for a N-particle system) of global statistically similar incongruent metastable glassy states [41]. In the RFOT, it is assumed that, in a restricted sense (cf below), this feature also holds in realistic structural glass systems. Statistically similar states have the same spatially averaged correlation functions, and incongruent states have zero overlap,

$$q_{ss'} = \delta_{ss'}q. \qquad (7.3)$$

Because the states are statistically similar one cannot simply use an external field to pick out a particular state, as could be done in a regular Ising model for example. The canonical free energy, F_c, is then given by the partition function via

$$Z = \exp[-\beta F_c] = Tr\exp[-\beta H] = \sum_s \exp[-\beta F_s]. \qquad (7.4)$$

In the STG, there are two important cases when F_c is not the physical free energy. First, if the barrier between states is actually infinite then F_c cannot be a physically meaningful free energy. Second, if the barriers are finite but the experimental time scale is too short for fluctuations to probe the various states, then it is also not a physical free energy. These considerations also apply to cases where there is a multiplicity of long-lived metastable states in any system.

A component averaged free energy can be defined by

$$\overline{F} = \sum_s P_s F_s \qquad (7.5)$$

with P_s the probability to be in the state s,

$$P_s = \frac{1}{Z}\exp[-\beta F_s]. \qquad (7.6)$$

F_c and $\overline{F}$ are related by

$$F_c = \overline{F} + T\sum_s P_s \ln P_s \equiv \overline{F} - TS_s. \qquad (7.7)$$

Here, S_s is the state entropy (sometimes called the complexity, I), which is bounded from above by what is usually meant by the configurational entropy, S_c, in non-mean-field models where there will be transitions between the various states. In general, S_s is related to the solution degeneracy and is extensive (and $F_c \neq \overline{F}$) if there are an exponentially large number of states. Note that in infinite range models with a RFOT and a nonzero S_s the physical free energy is $\overline{F}$ because the S_s in Eq. (7.7) is an entropy term which is a measure of parts of state space not explored in a finite amount of time.

Since a physical entropy should only be associated with accessible configurations, it follows that F_c is not a physically meaningful free energy.

The scenario for the two transitions in the RFOT theory is obtained as follows. For $T > T_d$ transport is not collective, and the topology of state space is trivial. However, as $T \to T_d^+$ the dynamics slows down because at T_d an extensive number of statistically similar, incongruent globally glassy metastable states emerge. If activated transport is neglected, these states are infinitely long lived. The liquid state free energy, F_l is lower than the physical glassy state free energy, $\overline{F}$, but it is equal to the canonical free energy, F_c. Because there is a multiplicity of glassy states, a liquid with unit probability will get stuck in one of the metastable glassy states at temperatures below T_d. If activated transport is ignored, it will remain in that state for all times. For infinite range models with an RFOT, exact dynamical calculations show a continuous slowing down and freezing occurs as $T \to T_d^+$. The same result is also found for some approximate, mean-field like, calculations of dynamics in realistic liquid state models even in the absence of quenched randomness [13]. The transition at T_d is also closely related to the temperature at which the mode coupling theory of the glass transition predicts a power law divergence of the relaxation times.

In realistic systems, with particles interacting with short-range interactions, activated transport does take place at $T < T_d$. The change from diffusive transport to sluggish dynamics, which occurs at surprisingly low viscosities, is the reason T_d is associated with a dynamical transition. It is a sharp transition only in infinite range models, but in general it sets a temperature at which the dynamics becomes glassy like. In support of this interpretation, whose origins in retrospect can be traced to the insightful arguments given by Goldstein [37], there is considerable experimental evidence that at T_d the nature of transport changes from being diffusive to activated [39]. As a result, it is our view, that theories (for example [42]) in which the analogue of T_d does not naturally emerge cannot describe the STG.

The driving force for the activated transport in the RFOT theory for temperatures less than T_d is entropic, and is given by the state or configurational entropy, S_s, Eq. (7.7). At a lower temperature denoted by T_K, after the so-called Kauzmann temperature, the configurational entropy vanishes, and transport ceases. In other words, the second transition at T_K is the ideal or equilibrium glass transition temperature. Fits to viscosity data for an extremely wide class of materials point to the existence of non-zero T_K (for a compilation of experimental data see Ref. [43]).

7.2.2. *The dynamic transition and the associated correlation length*

We characterize the dynamical transition as follows. Consider the dynamical order parameter,

$$q(\mathbf{x} - \mathbf{y}, t_1 - t_2) = \langle \hat{q}(\mathbf{x}, \mathbf{y}, t_1, t_2) \rangle = \langle \delta n(\mathbf{x}, t_1) \delta n(\mathbf{y}, t_2) \rangle. \tag{7.8}$$

Above T_d, this correlation decays as $t \to \infty$ but as $T \to T_d^+$ the decay gets slower and slower in a power law fashion. At T_d it no longer decays, (except in non-mean-field models) on the longest time scale. Effectively, it is the Edwards–Anderson order parameter for the glass transition:

$$q_{EA} = \lim_{t \to \infty} q(\mathbf{0}, t). \tag{7.9}$$

Because the order parameter involves the square of the density fluctuations it is clear that the susceptibility will be non-linear involving higher order correlations [24],

$$\chi_{NL}(\mathbf{x} - \mathbf{y}, t_1 - t_3, t_4 - t_2, t = t_4 - t_1) = \langle \hat{q}(\mathbf{x}, \mathbf{y}, t_1, t_2) \hat{q}(\mathbf{y}, \mathbf{x}, t_3, t_4) \rangle_c, \tag{7.10}$$

where $\langle \rangle_c$ denotes cumulant average where all pairwise density correlations are subtracted out. In an exactly soluble spin-glass model we have previously shown [24] that the 'static' susceptibility for the glass transition at T_d is

$$\chi_{NL}(k, t < \tau_c) = \int d(t_1 - t_3) d(t_4 - t_2) d(\mathbf{x} - \mathbf{y}) \exp(-i\mathbf{k} \cdot (\mathbf{x} - \mathbf{y}))$$

$$\times \chi_{NL}(\mathbf{x} - \mathbf{y}, t_1 - t_3, t_4 - t_2, t = t_4 - t_1 < \tau_c), \tag{7.11}$$

where τ_c is the time that the plateau exists in $q(t)$ (it diverges at T_d in the mean-field limit). As $r = T/T_d - 1 \to 0^+$, the homogeneous static susceptibility, $\chi_{NL} = \chi_{NL}(k \to \mathbf{0})$, in a mean-field like theory, diverges as [24],

$$\chi_{NL} \sim 1/\sqrt{r}, \tag{7.12}$$

and at finite and small wavenumber,

$$\chi_{NL}(\mathrm{k}) \sim 1/[k^2 + \xi_o^{-2}\sqrt{r}] \tag{7.13}$$

with ξ_o a microscopic (correlation) length. This in turn defines a divergent length scale as $T \to T_d^+$ given by,

$$\xi \sim \xi_o/r^{1/4}. \tag{7.14}$$

This is the same divergence seen at a mean-field spinodal point. These same results with $r \to |r|$ were obtained [10] in an exactly soluble spin-glass model for $r = T/T_d - 1 \to 0^-$.

The limiting procedure implied by Eq. (7.11) is crucial to obtain the correct diverging non-linear susceptibility result [24]. In [24] it was suggested that this is a reasonable definition of an ergodic to non-ergodic transition.

7.2.3. *The equilibrium transition and its correlation length*

According to RFOT, the ideal glass transition at T_K is a discontinuous transition. Hence, care must be taken in defining and interpreting a correlation or coherence length. For ordinary first order phase transitions (liquid to a periodic crystal for example) Fisher and Berker (FB) [44] have formally described the meaning of such a length scale. They conclude that there are two distinct interpretations of a divergent length, referred to as coherence or persistent length for a first order transition. The first, using a scaling analysis and the observation that the definition of long range order is consistent with a correlation length exponent given by $\nu_H = 1/d$, with d being the spatial dimension. The second is via a finite-size scaling analysis and the divergent length is the length scale where the sharp first order phase transition becomes rounded in a finite system. This correlation length exponent is also given by $\tilde{\nu} = 1/d$.

Here, we generalize the arguments of FB to a RFOT, further elaborating on our previous study [7]. We use the density order parameter discussed in Sec. 7.2.1. For the conjugate field we use a chemical potential $h = \mu(T,p) - \mu(T_K, p_K)$, allowing for the location of the glass transition to depend on both temperature and pressure.

We then give two further distinct arguments for the exponent characterizing the divergence of the correlation length. The first is an exact calculation for an infinite range spin-glass model with a RFOT that gives an identical result. The final argument that gives the same exponent is a partly dynamical/nucleation-like one and is presented in Sec. 7.2.5. All together there are four separate arguments that give the same result.

A. Scaling analysis

If we define a renormalization group (RG) length rescaling factor by b then the conjugate field h should be associated with the largest RG eigenvalue, b^λ, and therefore should scale as,

$$h' = b^\lambda h \tag{7.15}$$

while the free energy density will scale like,

$$f(h) = b^{-d} f(h'). \tag{7.16}$$

In addition, the scaling of the correlation length should by definition follow,

$$\xi(h) = b\xi(h'). \tag{7.17}$$

If we choose $b = h^{-1/\lambda}$ then we formally obtain,

$$f(h) = h^{d/\lambda} f(1), \tag{7.18}$$

and

$$\xi(h) = h^{-1/\lambda}\xi(1). \tag{7.19}$$

Now, the order parameter q is related to the second derivative of f with respect to h or,

$$q \sim h^{d/\lambda - 2}. \tag{7.20}$$

At the RFOT, q is discontinuous which gives $\lambda = d/2$. Equation (7.19), on the other hand implies that the correlation length exponent is $\nu_h = 1/\lambda$, or

$$\nu_h = 2/d. \tag{7.21}$$

These considerations establish, rather rigorously, that as long as FB type scaling holds near a first order transition it is inevitable that the correlation length should diverge at T_K with an exponent $2/d$ at RFOT. The difference in the values of the correlation length exponent is due to the differing nature of the order parameter describing RFOT and first order transitions. In a first order transition density itself is discontinuous whereas in RFOT at T_K it is the square of the density (EA parameter) that changes abruptly.

B. Finite size effects

Next we consider a system with finite size, L, and do a finite size scaling argument. We postulate that the scaling part of the free energy behaves as,

$$f(h, L) \sim L^{-\zeta} f(L/\widetilde{\xi}) \equiv L^{-\zeta} Y(hL^{1/\widetilde{\nu}}) \tag{7.22}$$

where $\xi \sim h^{-\widetilde{\nu}}$ is the (finite-size correlation or coherence) length scale where finite size rounding of the RFOT takes place at T_K. By noting that the order parameter q is related to the second derivative of f with respect to h, we find,

$$q \sim L^{2/\widetilde{\nu}-\zeta} Y''(hL^{1/\widetilde{\nu}}). \tag{7.23}$$

The discontinuous nature of the transition gives,

$$\zeta = 2/\widetilde{\nu} \tag{7.24}$$

Note that if we used dimensional analysis to obtain $\zeta = d$ then it immediately follows that

$$\widetilde{\nu} = 2/d. \tag{7.25}$$

As an alternative, we follow the FB treatment, and examine the susceptibility, χ, for this transition. Because the order parameter for the transition already involves two density fluctuations, the susceptibility, as used in Sec. 7.2.2, will involve four density fields. Accordingly, it is related to the fourth derivative of f with respect to h. The finite size scaling relation will then be something like,

$$\chi(h, L) \sim L^{2/\widetilde{\nu}} Y''''(hL^{1/\widetilde{\nu}}). \tag{7.26}$$

One can then argue that χ will attain a maximum value at $h = 0$, and will scale as $\sim L^d$. This in turn again gives $\widetilde{\nu} = 2/d$. The inescapable conclusion is that the arguments leading to $\widetilde{\nu} = 2/d$ are robust, and theoretically well-founded.

C. Exact results for an infinite range model

Finally, there is an exact calculation for an infinite range p-state ($p > 4$) Potts spin glass model with a RFOT [10, 11] that gives a length scale that diverges with a correlation length exponent of $\nu = 2/d$ as the transition is approached. In particular, it has been shown that as T_K is approached from above the complexity or state entropy (which here and below we denote by the configurational entropy, S_c) behaves as,

$$S_c \sim N\epsilon \tag{7.27}$$

with N the number of lattice sites ($N \to \infty$) and $\epsilon = 1 - T/T_K$ the dimensionless distance from the RFOT. On the other hand, as T_K is approached from below one finds [10] that S_c diverges as,

$$S_c \sim 1/|\epsilon|. \tag{7.28}$$

If we identify N with a system volume $\sim L^d$ then these two equations give a length scale where even below T_K the system behaves as though it was not frozen. Defining a correlation length, ξ, in this way gives,

$$\xi \sim 1/|\epsilon|^{2/d} \qquad \text{or,} \qquad \nu = 2/d. \tag{7.29}$$

Notice that this definition of a correlation length is closely related to a finite size correlation length.

D. Finite size shift in the glass transition temperature

Understanding glassy physics in a finite geometry is technologically important, and is needed to analyze results from computer simulations. From a phase transition perspective, many authors starting with the pioneering studies by Ferdinand and Fisher [45] have stressed that there are two important finite size effects at any phase transition. The first is the rounding of the transition as described in Sec. 7.2.3B above. The second distinct effect is the finite size shift in the transition temperature. Naturally, we expect them both to be relevant near RFOTs.

Physically, the ϵ (or h) in the above expressions should be replaced by $\check{\epsilon} = \epsilon - \Delta\epsilon(L)$, where $\Delta\epsilon(L)$ measures the shift in the glass transition temperature due to the finite size. We give two distinct arguments for the L dependence of $\Delta\epsilon(L)$. The first uses that the free energy difference between two coexisting states at the RFOT is of order $\sim T_K L^{d/2}$. The temperature difference, ΔT, where the system cannot distinguish between the two states is the total free energy difference, which is proportional to $\sim L^d \Delta T$. Equating these two free energies we obtain,

$$\Delta\epsilon(L) \sim \frac{1}{L^{d/2}}. \tag{7.30}$$

The second argument hinges on an old result of Imry [46] who suggested that at an ordinary first order phase transition the finite size shift in the transition temperature is given by,

$$\Delta T \sim \frac{1}{L^d s} \tag{7.31}$$

where s is the latent heat associated with the transition. At an RFOT, though, the latent heat vanishes as the configurational entropy or, $s \sim \xi^{-1/\nu} \sim L^{-d/2}$ in a finite system. Using this we recover the first argument for $\Delta\epsilon(L)$.

If the predicted L-dependent shift in the ideal glass transition temperature can be systematically studied then measuring the above exponent would be an important verification of the RFOT theory. Recent important developments in computer simulations probing the equilibrium glass transition by random pinning of a fraction of particles [47] as L is varied could be a way of verifying Eq. (7.30).

7.2.4. *The specific heat at the equilibrium RFOT transition*

First order phase transitions are associated with strong coupling RG fixed points [44]. As a result, dangerous irrelevant variables are not expected to play any role, which in turn implies that hyperscaling is valid in all dimensions. If the same applies to random first order phase transitions, then the standard hyperscaling relation for the specific heat exponent,

$$\alpha = 2 - \nu d \tag{7.32}$$

should always hold. With $\nu = 2/d$ one then finds that $\alpha = 0$ at a RFOT. This scaling result for the specific heat is also consistent with exact calculations for infinite range models with an RFOT. For structural glasses, this result presumably implies a discontinuity in the specific heat, as is always observed experimentally. It is worth emphasizing at this juncture that the Adams–Gibbs theory would predict $\alpha = 1$ (a latent heat) if hyperscaling is assumed because in the AG theory $\nu = 1/d$.

7.2.5. *Transport near the equilibrium RFOT*

An important characteristic of a glass transition is the occurrence of extremely long time scales associated with transport below T_d. The critical slowing down at an ordinary transition means that the time scale grows as a power of the correlation length, $\tau \sim \xi^z$ with z being the dynamical scaling exponent. In sharp contrast, at a glass transition the critical time scale grows exponentially with ξ,

$$\ln(\tau/\tau_m) \sim \xi^\psi \tag{7.33}$$

with τ_m a microscopic time scale, and ψ a generalized dynamical scaling exponent. Effectively, this implies $z = \infty$. As a result of such extreme slowing down, the equilibrium behavior of the system near T_K becomes inaccessible for all practical purposes. In other words, the experimentally accessible time scales are not sufficient for the system to reach equilibrium. It is in this sense that the glassy system falls out of equilibrium.

Activated scaling, as described by Eq. (7.33), follows from a barrier crossing picture of the system's free energy landscape. In the context of the STG, it is related to cooperative motions [42] involving particles within a length scale that continues to grow as $T \to T_K$. In the temperature range, $T_d > T > T_K$, there is an entropic driving force that causes a compact, glassy state of size ξ^d to make a transition to a different glassy state, with approximately the same free energy, also of size ξ^d. The physical picture that results is a system that looks like a patchwork, of different glassy regions separated by diffuse or fuzzy interfaces slowly making a transition to yet other glassy states. This is also called the mosaic state. For the uncorrelated states that exist above T_K, the law of large numbers is consistent with a barrier that scale like $\sim \xi^{d/2}$. This is also consistent with scaling and an entropic driving force $\epsilon \xi^d \sim \xi^{d-1/\nu}$, if $\nu = 2/d$. Thus, the driving force and the free energy barrier scale in the same way, if and only if $\nu = 2/d$. Activated transport with the barriers scaling as $\sim \xi^{d/2}$ was also recently argued by Langer [48].

In the original RFOT paper, we modified a wetting argument first given by Villain [49] for the random field Ising model and applied it to the structural glass problem which also led to barriers scaling like $\xi^{d/2}$. Here, we give a different but related argument. We first imagine a putative compact glassy state of size L^d. There will be in general two distinct driving forces that can cause it to make a transition to another glassy state: an entropic one scaling like $\sim \epsilon L^d$ and a free energy one $\sim L^{d/2}$ because there are states that typically have a lower free energy by this amount. Opposing the transition is a barrier that naively scales like a surface tension term $\sim \sigma L^{d-1}$. Now assume a bump (or an excitation) of scale also $\sim L$ (another scale can be introduced but the final result is not altered) forms on the interface because of the free energy driving force. The free energy change due to the creation of the bump is,

$$\delta F \sim -L^{d/2} + \sigma L^{d-1}. \tag{7.34}$$

The physical effect of the bump forming is that the surface tension is reduced compared to its naive value. The scale dependent surface tension can be obtained by minimizing δF with respect to r with the result,

$$\sigma(L) \sim L^{-(d-2)/2}. \tag{7.35}$$

The barriers to transport therefore scale as $\sim \sigma(L)L^{d-1} = L^{d/2}$.

All of these arguments in turn imply a Vogel–Fulcher law for relaxation as the glass transition is approached,

$$\tau \sim \tau_m \exp\left[\frac{D}{T/T_K - 1}\right] \tag{7.36}$$

with D a positive constant.

Note that the barriers scaling like $\xi^{d/2}$ implies there is really no interface between two of the statistically similar glassy states. Rather, to go from one state to another, roughly $N^{1/2}$ of the N particles in a correlated volume must be rearranged, as noted earlier by Bouchaud and Biroli [16].

7.2.6. Rare regions near the glass transition

The existence of dynamical heterogeneity suggests that in a very viscous liquid the longest time decay of any time correlation function will be determined by the large rare regions or anomalous clusters of particles of some linear dimension L [6]. These large clusters are fluidized and can relax to a more typical configuration of particles in some characteristic time $\tau(L)$. For this argument to be sensible, L must be larger than a molecular scale. To estimate the effect of these large rare regions on a typical time correlation function an average over L must be performed.

Since the large clusters are rare, we assume that their probability distribution is controlled by Poisson statistics so that the tail probability of an unusual cluster of size L is

$$P(L) \propto \exp(-cL^d). \tag{7.37}$$

We consider a diffusive correlation function, $C(k,t) \propto \exp(-Dk^2t)$, and we assume the relevant wavenumber scales as $k \propto 1/L$, and a scale dependent diffusion coefficient $D(L)$. That is, we consider,

$$C(L,t) \propto \exp(-t/\tau_D(L)), \tag{7.38}$$

with $\tau_D(L) = L^2/D(L)$ the diffusive time scale. Since $D(L)$ has units of *length²/time* we take τ_D to be proportional to the RFOT time scale,

$$\tau_D(L) \propto \tau_{RFOT}(L) = \tau_m \exp(aL^{d/2}), \tag{7.39}$$

with τ_m a microscopic time and a a positive constant.

Using all this the average correlation function deep in the supercooled region then decays for long times as [5, 6],

$$C(t) \propto \int dL\, P(L) \exp(-(t/\tau_m)e^{-aL^{d/2}})$$

$$\propto \exp[-A(\ln t/\tau_m)^2], \tag{7.40}$$

with A a positive constant. We conclude that for long times $C(t)$ decays faster than any power law, but slower than any exponential. Note that the saddle point evaluation gives the characteristic length scale $L(t) \propto (\ln t)^{2/d}$.

Finally if we define a distribution of relaxation times, $P(\tau)$, by

$$C(t) \propto \int d\tau\, P(\tau) \exp(-t/\tau), \tag{7.41}$$

then,

$$P(\tau \to \infty) \propto \exp[-c(\ln \tau/\tau_m)^2], \tag{7.42}$$

again, slower than any exponential.

7.2.7. *Activated scaling as T approaches T_K*

Activated scaling was developed to understand finite dimensional (i.e., three dimensional) spin glasses and random field magnets where the dynamics is controlled by large, possibly divergent, free energy barriers [50]. Similar ideas can be applied to the structural glass problem, also in three dimensions.

Here we examine the behavior of the glass transition susceptibility, introduced in Sec. 7.2.3 using activated scaling ideas [50] as the ideal glass transition is approached. First we define a slightly different non-linear susceptibility (see Eqs. (7.10) and (7.11)),

$$\tilde{\chi}_{NL}(k,t) = \int d(\mathbf{x} - \mathbf{y}) \exp(-i\mathbf{k} \cdot (\mathbf{x} - \mathbf{y}))\chi_{NL}(\mathbf{x} - \mathbf{y}, t, t, 0). \tag{7.43}$$

We then start with the observation, discussed in Sec. 7.2.4, that the scale dimension of $q(\mathbf{x}, t)$ is zero. This and the activated scaling ansatz implies that the wavenumber and time dependent glass transition susceptibility will satisfy the scaling law [6],

$$\tilde{\chi}_{NL}(\epsilon, k, t) = b^d F_\chi \left[\epsilon b^{1/\nu}, bk, \frac{b^{d/2}}{\ln(t/\tau_m)} \right] \tag{7.44}$$

where $\epsilon = T/T_K - 1$ is the dimensionless distance from the ideal glass transition, τ_m is some microscopic time scale, and F_χ is a scaling function. Note that we have used here that the barrier height scales as $b^{d/2} \sim \xi^{d/2}$. This equation implies a number of non-trivial results. For example, at zero wavenumber, and at the ideal glass transition temperature we can choose $b = [\ln(t/\tau_m)]^{2/d}$ to obtain,

$$\tilde{\chi}_{NL}(0, 0, t \to \infty) \sim [\ln(t/\tau_m)]^2. \tag{7.45}$$

This dynamic scaling result is valid as long as $\epsilon \ln(t/\tau_m) < 1$. This also defines a dynamic crossover ϵ being given by,

$$\epsilon_x \sim 1/[\ln(t/\tau_m)]. \tag{7.46}$$

Physically this means that the large correlations that exist at T_K can be measured by examining the slow growth in time of the glass transition susceptibility around $k = 0$. This should be experimentally relevant. If the exponent of 2 in Eq. (7.45) can be experimentally demonstrated then that would be very strong evidence for the validity of the RFOT theory of the SGT.

The frequency dependent glass transition susceptibility defined by Eq. (7.45) can similarly be expressed as a scaling function. In general the ϵ_x given by Eq. (7.46) will give the scale distinguishing static critical behavior from dynamical critical behavior for all quantities as $T \to T_K$.

Although not as rigorously founded as the scaling law for $\tilde{\chi}_{NL}$, we can also give a scaling law for the frequency dependent shear viscosity, $\eta(\epsilon, \omega)$, if we assume that because it is related to a time integral of a time correlation function its static value is proportional to τ given by Eq. (7.36). We then obtain [6],

$$\eta(\epsilon, \omega) = \exp(b^{d/2}) F_\eta \left[\epsilon b^{1/\nu}, \frac{b^{d/2}}{\ln(1/\tau_m \omega)} \right], \tag{7.47}$$

with F_η a scaling function. The static or zero frequency shear viscosity then behaves as τ but for $\epsilon < 1/\ln(1/\tau_m \omega)$ it behaves as [6]

$$\eta[\epsilon \ln(1/\tau_m \omega) < 1] \sim \frac{1}{\tau_m \omega}. \tag{7.48}$$

Again, the important physical and experimental point is that ϵ_x given by Eq. (7.46) sets the crossover scale in either time or frequency $(t \to 1/\omega)$ space. Note that η being simply proportional to τ in Eq. (7.47) is needed to obtain Eq. (7.48), which in turn is required for the proper stress/strain relation in the glassy phase. Also note that Eq. (7.48) in the Navier–Stokes equation will lead to shear waves in this frequency range, which is certainly the correct physical result for frequencies not too small near the glass transition. The crucial result from activated scaling is that $\epsilon < 1/\ln(1/\tau_m \omega)$ sets the frequency scale where shear waves should be observed in the supercooled liquid phase.

7.3. Comparison to Other Phase Transition Theories for the Glass Transition and an Inequality

In this section, we compare and contrast the RFOT theory with conventional first and second order phase transitions, with particular focus on the SGT.

7.3.1. *First order phase transition theory for the glass transition*

An earlier DFT of the SGT, advanced in the mid-eighties [51, 52], was based on the approximate Ramakrishnan-Yussouff [53] theory of the liquid to crystal transition and modified it for the SGT. By generating random sites of a large system to describe the amorphous state (viewed as an aperiodic solid instead of periodic crystal characterizing an ordered solid) it was shown numerically that the RY free energy functional has a metastable solution, which presumably corresponds to a static description of the glassy state. The transition to such an aperiodic state was deemed to be first order, occurring at a density below the putative crystallization density.

Although such a description might capture aspects of the amorphous state it differs qualitatively from the RFOT in two important aspects: (1) The transition to the aperiodic state is first order with density itself exhibiting a discontinuity, whereas in RFOT it is the analogue of the EA parameter describing density fluctuations, Eq. (7.2), that has a jump at T_K. A regular first order transition would also have a latent heat, and exhibit something that resembles a discontinuity in the specific heat. In contrast, RFOT theory predicts an absence of latent heat at T_K. It is also unclear if the identified freezing density is close to the analogue of T_K. (2) The RY theory was not used to identify a dynamical transition temperature or density. More importantly, the link between T_d and T_K requiring the emergence of exponentially large number of low free energy metastable glassy states, which is the most important aspect of the RFOT theory was not demonstrated. (3) Finally, if one were to associate a divergent length scale or exponent with an ordinary first order phase transition then it would be the Berker–Fisher value $\nu = 1/d$ discussed in Sec. 7.2.4. Such a value is inconsistent with the equality found using the RFOT theory (further discussed in Sec. 7.3.3), nor is it in accord with recent simulation results [54, 55].

7.3.2. *Second order phase transition theory for the SGT*

Over the years there have been numerous theories of the SGT that can be classified as standard second order or continuous phase transitions. The earliest ones were the Adam–Gibbs (AG) [42] and Gibbs–DiMarzio (GDM) theories of the SGT and rubber transitions in polymer systems [56]. A scenario along these lines has been postulated by Tanaka [55, 57] based on computer simulations, which has been further discussed by Langer [48]. It is worth remarking that these theories do not consider consequences of the change in the nature of transport at $T \approx T_d$.

We first remark that it is hard to imagine how any equilibrium order parameter description of a liquid to glass transition would not generically have a discontinuous character, at least according to Landau theory. At isolated critical points, a continuous transition is possible. In fact, within RFOT this has been discussed by others, and related to a critical point for a random field problem [58]. Second, in a second order transition the concept of a metastable state is not obvious. As a consequence it is difficult to see how such transitions can have a temperature crossover scale (in RFOT, it is T_d) and also a true equilibrium transition temperature (in RFOT, it is T_K) at lower temperatures. The existence of two distinct temperatures in supercooled liquids seems to be well confirmed both numerically, as well as experimentally. The existence of the temperature scale T_d at which loss of ergodicity starts to manifest itself [59] also tidily explains dynamic heterogeneity and aging. Technically, the problem with a second order phase transition scenario is that by definition there is only one temperature where the system becomes unstable to infinitesimal fluctuations everywhere.

7.3.3. *Self-generated quenched disorder implies $\nu \geq 2/d$*

For systems with quenched disorder, the correlation length exponent at any phase transition must satisfy the inequality $\nu \geq 2/d$. For the structural glass problem, there is effectively quenched disorder that is self generated. Here, we argue that self-generated quenched randomness in the structural glass problem also leads to the inequality $\nu \geq 2/d$.

We begin by noting that below T_d (technically close to T_K) the glassy state can be partitioned into clusters of particles of size ξ. Because the observation time is much greater than the relaxation time for particles in two clusters to interchange, the motion of particles in one cluster is essentially isolated from another. Since ξ is sufficiently large each cooperatively rearranging region (CRR) will have differing thermodynamic properties, which clearly is a violation of the law of large numbers. In particular, we expect fluctuations of the ideal glass transition temperature, δT_K, in the various clusters to scale as $\sqrt{(\delta T_K)^2} \sim 1/\xi^{d/2}$. In order for the ideal glass transition to exist, this fluctuation must be smaller than the distance to the ideal glass transition, $\epsilon \sim 1/\xi^{1/\nu}$. Consequently, ν must satisfy $\nu \geq 2/d$.

7.4. Discussion

The RFOT theory provides a coherent picture of the liquid state as it is cooled and supercooled. We have given physical arguments, rooted in theory, that there are two relevant temperatures, one attributable to change in transport at T_d and the other in which a genuine equilibrium transition occurs at T_K with both first and second order characteristics. Both these temperatures emerge from a single static theory. By expanding on our prior works [7, 8, 24] we obtained a number of results. (1) We give a variety of arguments to show that a characteristic length diverges at T_K with an exponent $\nu = 2/d$. In many ways this makes rigorous our earlier predictions [7], and this finding is an important corner stone of RFOT. (2) We predict that there are large finite size effects at T_K. The theory predicts a specific rounding of the transition, as well as a specific shift in the location of T_K, due to finite size effects. This implies that there will be variations in the value of T_K depending on the system size. This prediction is amenable to test by computer simulations using the random pinning method [47, 60, 61]. (3) Using ideas based on activated scaling [50], we predict that the non-linear susceptibility near T_K on long length scales diverges as $\sim [\ln(t/\tau_m)]^2$. We have also obtained the cross-over scale that distinguishes between dynamical critical effects and static critical effects as T_K is approached. This is especially relevant for the shear viscosity.

The equilibrium transition in the RFOT theory is a novel type of transition and as such, it has certain universal properties. The implication is that most of the features of the ideal glass transition discussed here are independent of the Kauzmann-like interpretation of T_K. For example, the order parameter definition given by Eqs. (7.1) and (7.2) does not hinge on an entropy or state solution like crisis, rather it is motivated by a glass being characterized by a frozen and random density order parameter. Physically this seems necessary to obtain the elastic behavior of a glass. Any field theory, or Landau theory, for such a transition will necessarily have a first order nature because general symmetry allows for a cubic term in the theory. This implies in general, that if an ideal glass transition exists with such an order parameter it will be a RFOT with some sort of divergent length scale, characterized by an exponent of $\nu = 2/d$. Given this, results like the specific heat behavior discussed in Sec. 7.2.5 will be equally generic. The inequality $\nu \geq 2/d$ also seems generic. To discuss transport near an ideal glass transition we have largely used many state type arguments to obtain free energy barriers that scale like $\xi^{d/2}$. However, this result too seems to go beyond an entropy crisis picture: it only depends on local particle rearrangements to go from two uncorrelated single glassy configurations. The law of large numbers suggests that if the volume in question contains N-particles then this sort of fluctuation will scale as $N^{1/2} \sim \xi^{d/2}$ [13, 62]. The fundamental conclusion from this sort of reasoning is that results like Eq. (7.36), Eq. (7.44) and Eq. (7.45) should hold even if the mechanism for an ideal glass transition is not precisely a Kauzmann-like transition.

In deriving the universal aspects of RFOT at T_K we have assumed that the equilibrium ideal glass transition exist. The temperature dependence of viscosity of a large class of glass forming materials have been analyzed using the VFT law with non-zero T_K [43]. More recently, computer simulations point to the existence of an equilibrium transition below T_d [60]. Among them the most notable ones are those which have observed a phase transition in model glass forming systems by randomly pinning a fraction of particles at low temperatures [47, 60, 61]. This procedure, which apparently allows one to probe equilibrium behavior, clearly shows that an equilibrium transition with characteristics predicted by the RFOT theory does occur. Although the wealth of experimental data as well as computer simulations provides strong evidence that $T_K \neq 0$, additional tests of universal behavior predicted here for RFOT are needed before fully validating all the aspects of the RFOT theory of the SGT.

Historically, the Adam–Gibbs (AG) theory [42] was the first to propose an explanation for the possible divergence of relaxation times at T_K based on vanishing of configurational entropy. The predictions based on the more *ad hoc* AG mechanism is distinct from the RFOT theory in at least two ways. First, in the AG theory there is no analogue of T_d giving the impression that the character of transport changes only at T_K or at all temperatures. This would be inconsistent with many observations suggesting that at T_d, particle transport changes character, and theoretically with numerous exact dynamical solutions in high dimensions [30–32]. Indeed, there are innumerable computer simulations that support this picture. More importantly, by analyzing data for a number of glass forming materials Novikov and Sokolov have proposed that there may be a near "universal" value of 10^{-7}s [39] (larger than the estimate by Goldstein [37]) for relaxation, which sets the boundary between diffusive transport and onset of activated transitions. Of course, the value of T_d at which relaxation exceeds 10^{-7}s is clearly material dependent. Several computer simulations have noted that the nature of transport (non-Gaussian behavior in van Hove correlation functions and evidence for hopping mechanism [26, 63, 64]) changes even before T_d is reached, further supporting the accepted view that the dynamical transition is avoided. We surmise that theories, such as the AG theory, which cannot describe the dynamical changes at T_d may not be suitable for describing the glass transition. Second, RFOT predicts a much stronger growth of the correlation length than the AG theory. Interestingly, recent computer simulation studies support the predictions of RFOT theory first by identifying the existence of T_K (or equivalently density [65]), and second by confirming that $\nu = 2/d$ [54, 55].

Universal aspects of mode coupling theory have been remarkably successful in describing the change in the character of relaxation of undercooled liquids in the neighborhood of T_d. However, because MCT predicts that relaxation times only grow as power law as temperature is decreased it cannot account for activated transitions. As a result MCT cannot describe transport deep into the supercooled regime.

In our view, currently RFOT theory encompassing both T_d and T_K, appears to be the only theory that accounts for changes in phase space structure, break down of effective ergodicity, emergence of dynamical heterogeneity as a consequence of violation of law of large numbers, and growth of ξ. Most importantly, both the equilibrium and dynamical aspects at T_d and T_K emerge naturally without having to treat the physics at these temperatures separately as done by mode coupling theory or the AG theory. The result of the RFOT theory is that analysis of experimental relaxation data must be done in two steps. For $T \geq T_d$ the relaxation time should be analyzed using a power law. In the temperature range, $T_K \leq T \leq T_d$ the temperature dependence of the relaxation data should follow the VFT law. Attempts to fit the data over the entire range by activated dynamics could lead to inconsistent values of the parameters. Finally, we stress that all of this in accord with large dimensionality exact solution of liquid state systems [30–32].

Acknowledgments

This work was supported by the National Science Foundation under Grant Nos PHY 17-08128 and CHE 19-00033, and Welch Foundation (F-0019).

References

[1]　T. Kirkpatrick and D. Thirumalai, *Transp. Theor. and Stat. Phys.* **24**, 927–945, (1995).
[2]　A. Cavagna, *Phys. Rep.* **476**, 51–124, (2009).
[3]　G. Parisi and F. Zamponi, *Rev. Mod. Phys.* **82**, 789–845, (2010).
[4]　L. Berthier and G. Biroli, *Rev. Mod. Phys.* **83**, 587–645, (2011).
[5]　G. Biroli and J. Bouchaud. In eds. V. Lubchenko and P. Wolynes, *Structural glasses and supercooled liquids: theory, experiment and applications*, pp. 31–114. John Wiley & Sons, (2012).
[6]　T. R. Kirkpatrick and D. Thirumalai, *Rev. Mod. Phys.* **87**, 183–209, (2015).
[7]　T. R. Kirkpatrick, D. Thirumalai, and P. G. Wolynes, *Phys. Rev. A.* **40**, 1045–1054, (1989).
[8]　T. R. Kirkpatrick and D. Thirumalai, *Phys. Rev. Lett.* **58**, 2091–2094, (1987).
[9]　T. R. Kirkpatrick and D. Thirumalai, *Phys. Rev. B.* **36**, 5388–5397, (1987).
[10]　T. R. Kirkpatrick and P. G. Wolynes, *Phys. Rev. B.* **36**, 8552–8564, (1987).
[11]　T. R. Kirkpatrick and D. Thirumalai, *Phys. Rev. B.* **37**, 5342–5350, (1988).
[12]　T. R. Kirkpatrick and D. Thirumalai, *J. de Physique I.* **5**, 777–786, (1995).

[13] T. R. Kirkpatrick and D. Thirumalai, *J. Phys. A.* **22**, L149–L155, (1989).

[14] M. Mezard and G. Parisi, *J. Phys. A.* **29**, 6515–6524, (1996).

[15] M. Mezard and G. Parisi, *J. Phys. Cond. Matt.* **12**, 6655–6673 (2000).

[16] J. Bouchaud and G. Biroli, *J. Chem. Phys.* **121**, 7347–7354, (2004).

[17] C. Toninelli, M. Wyart, L. Berthier, G. Biroli, and J.-P. Bouchaud, *Phys. Rev. E.* **71**, 041505, (2005).

[18] S. Franz, H. Jacquin, G. Parisi, P. Urbani, and F. Zamponi, *Proc. Natl. acad. Sci.* **109**, 18725–18730, (2012).

[19] S. Franz, H. Jacquin, G. Parisi, P. Urbani, and F. Zamponi, *J. Chem. Phys.* **138**, 12A540, (2013).

[20] E. Leutheusser, *Phys. Rev. A.* **29**(5), 2765–2773, (1984).

[21] U. Bengtzelius, W. Goetze, and A. Sjolander, *J. Phys. C.* **17**, 5915–5934, (1984).

[22] D. Thirumalai and T. R. Kirkpatrick, *Phys. Rev. B.* **38**, 4881–4892, (1988).

[23] S. Das, *Rev. Mod. Phys.* **76**, 785–851, (2004).

[24] T. R. Kirkpatrick and D. Thirumalai, *Phys. Rev. A.* **37**, 4439–4448, (1988).

[25] C. Donati, S. Franz, S. C. Glotzer, and G. Parisi, *J. Non-Cryst. Solids.* **307**, 215–224, (2002).

[26] D. Thirumalai and R. D. Mountain, *Phys. Rev. E.* **47**, 479–489, (1993).

[27] E. Flenner and G. Szamel, *Phys. Rev. Lett.* **105**, 217801, (2010).

[28] E. Flenner, M. Zhang, and G. Szamel, *Phys. Rev. E.* **83**, 051501, (2011).

[29] S. C. Glotzer, V. N. Novikov, and T. B. Schroder, *The Journal of Chemical Physics.* **112**, 509–512, (2000).

[30] T. Maimbourg, J. Kurchan, and F. Zamponi, *Phys. Rev. Lett.* **116**, 015902, (2016).

[31] J. Kurchan, T. Maimbourg, and F. Zamponi, *Journal of Statistical Mechanics: Theory and Experiment.* **2016**, 033210, (2016).

[32] G. Parisi, P. Urbani, and F. Zamponi, *Theory of simple glasses:exact solutions in infinite dimension.* (Cambridge University Press, 2020).

[33] G. Szamel, *arXiv:2203.09543.* (2022).

[34] P. Charbonneau, J. Kurchan, G. Parisi, P. Urbani, and F. Zamponi, *Ann. Rev. Cond. Mat. Phys.* **8**, 265–288, (2017).

[35] E. Gardner, *Nuc. Phys. B.* **257**, 747–765, (1985).

[36] J. Kurchan, G. Parisi, P. Urbani, and F. Zamponi, *J. Phys. Chem. B.* **117**, 12979–12994, (2013).

[37] M. Goldstein, *J. Chem. Phys.* **51**, 3728–3729, (1969).

[38] M. Goldstein, *J. Chem. Phys.* p. 041104, (2010).

[39] V. Novikov and A. Sokolov, *Phys. Rev. E.* **67**, 031507, (2003).

[40] R. Monasson, *Phys. Rev. Lett.* **75**, 2847–2850, (1995).

[41] D. Huse and D. Fisher, *J. Phys. A.* **20**(15), L997–L1003, (1987).

[42] G. Adam and J. Gibbs, *J. Chem. Phys.* **43**, 139–146, (1965).

[43] S. Capaccioli, G. Ruocco, and F. Zamponi, *J. Phys. Chem. B.* **112**, 10652–10658, (2008).

[44] M. Fisher and A. Berker, *Phys. Rev. B.* **26**(5), 2507–2513, (1982).

[45] A. Ferdinand and M. Fisher, *Phys. Rev.* **185**(2), 832–846, (1969).

[46] Y. Imry, *Phys. Rev. B.* **21**, 2042–2043, (1980).

[47] L. Berthier and W. Kob, *Phys. Rev. E.* **85**, 011102, (2012).

[48] J. S. Langer, *Phys. Rev. E.* **88**, 012122, (2013).

[49] J. Villain, *J. de. Physique.* **46**(11), 1843–1852, (1985).

[50] D. Fisher and D. Huse, *Phys. Rev. B.* **38**, 373–385, (1988).

[51] Y. Singh, J. Stoessel, and P. Wolynes, *Phys. Rev. Lett.* **54**, 1059–1062, (1985).

[52] C. Dasgupta and O. Valls, *Phys. Rev. E.* **59**, 3123–3134, (1999).

[53] T. Ramakrishnan and M. Yussouff, *Phys. Rev. B.* **19**, 2775–2794, (1979).

[54] M. Mosayebi, E. Del Gado, P. Ilg, and H. C. Ottinger, *Phys. Rev. Lett.* **104**, 205704, (2010).

[55] H. Tanaka, T. Kawasaki, H. Shintani, and K. Watanabe, *Nat. Mater.* **9**, 324–331, (2010).

[56] J. Gibbs and E. Dimarzio, *J. Chem. Phys.* **28**(3), 373–383, (1958).

[57] H. Tanaka, *J. Non-Cryst. Solids:X.* **13**, 100076, (2022).

[58] S. Franz, G. Parisi, F. Ricci-Tersenghi, and T. Rizzo, *Eur. Phys. J. E.* **34**, 102, (2011).

[59] D. Thirumalai, R. D. Mountain, and T. R. Kirkpatrick, *Phys. Rev. A.* **39**, 3563–3574, (1989).

[60] W. Kob and L. Berthier, *Phys. Rev. Lett.* **110**, 245702, (2013).

[61] S. Karmakar and G. Parisi, *Proc. Natl. Acad. Sci.* **110**, 2752–2757, (2013).

[62] D. Thirumalai, *J. Phys. I (Fr.).* **5**, 1457–1467, (1995).

[63] H. Miyagawa, Y. Hiwatari, B. Bernu, and J. Hansen, *J. Chem. Phys.* **88**, 3879–3886, (1988).

[64] W. Kob and H. Andersen, *Phys. Rev. E.* **51**, 4626–4641, (1995).

[65] H. Kang, T. R. Kirkpatrick, and D. Thirumalai, *Phys. Rev. E.* **88**, 042308, (2013).

Chapter 8

Non-Perturbative Processes in Glasses

This chapter reviews non-perturbative processes in glasses, which play an extremely important role in their dynamics.

In a first contribution (Sec. 8.1), **P. Wolynes** shows how the Random First Order Transition theory of glasses can take into account spatial and temporal fluctuations, via a variety of non-perturbative instantonic processes. This description is applied to the study of the supercooled liquid dynamics in the vicinity of the glass transition, but also to the plasticity and yielding of the amorphous solid.

In a second contribution (Sec. 8.2), **T. Rizzo** reviews a systematic expansion around dynamical mean field theory, that can be used to study how the mode-coupling dynamical arrest is avoided in finite-dimensional glasses. A stochastic beta-relaxation equation is derived, and used to describe the crossover from diffusive to activated dynamics of the supercooled liquid. The approach is demonstrated for the paradigmatic Ising p-spin glass model, by comparing theoretical predictions and numerical simulation data.

8.1. The Random First Order Transition Theory of Glasses in Real Space-Time: Instantons, Strings, Flames and Flows

Peter G. Wolynes

Rice University, Departments of Chemistry and Physics,
and Center for Theoretical Biological Physics,
6100 Main Street, Houston, Texas 77005, USA
pwolynes@rice.edu

Understanding structural glasses using the Random First Order Transition theory requires a description in both real space and in time, taking into account sample history. A variety of nonlinear objects enter this description when there is replica symmetry breaking: instantons, strings, flames and flows. We use this real space description to describe the crossover to the energy landscape regime, dynamical heterogeneity, aging and the formation of shear bands in glasses under stress.

8.1.1. *Introduction*

Water, Air, Earth, and Fire. Many ancient thinkers recognized these as the elementary aspects of the Natural World, explaining the phenomena they observed as involving their interchange. Arguably, much of modern theoretical physics, in using field theories, adopts the same stance, albeit employing thousands of years of increasing mathematical sophistication. Other ancient thinkers conceived of natural phenomena as universally arising from the motions of ultimately small constituents, atoms. Reconciling these two views comprises a big part of the business of modern statistical physics.

The ancients' view of the relationship between Air and Water involved their interchange through the processes of rarefaction and densification [1]. Van der Waals's theory of the continuity of the gas and liquid phases provided a quantitative basis for this old notion [2]. The density, a single number, then distinguishes the two forms through a scalar field which may vary in space. The fluctuations of this field in space provide the mechanism of interconversion through nucleation of the gas to the liquid through forming droplets of the high-density form within the lower density form [3] and the reverse process of forming low density bubbles in the high-density form [4].

The ancients were more puzzled by the relationship of Earth to Air and Water which differed merely by density. Atomists suggested the essential connection had to do with the shapes of the atoms, arguing that some shapes of atoms, when put together at sufficiently high density, would ineluctably form a rigid body. In more modern times, Kepler articulated a more sophisticated view in his monograph *De Nive Sexangula* [5]. He suggested that the atoms themselves need not have complex shapes, but that even spheres would arrange themselves (like piles of cannonballs) in a highly symmetric fashion (what we now call a face-centered cubic close packing). Rearranging this nearly unique structure would require elaborate motions of many atoms to retain the symmetry, so a snowflake must move as a rigid object, in contrast to what happens for gases or a liquid, which can flow in complex ways. The symmetry of the packing, thus, not only explained the six-sidedness of snowflakes, but the solid form's rigidity. Twentieth century physicists would call this situation a "broken symmetry" because the six-sided shape of a snowflake is not as symmetrical as a sphere, the usual shape of a liquid drop. Anderson, Landau, and de Gennes have emphasized "broken symmetry" as the origin of rigidity throughout the zoo of forms of condensed matter, superconductors, liquid crystals, and magnets [6–8]. Members of the condensed matter zoo then are described through the interactions of several fields (each one possibly more complex than a scalar), allowing one to still use the concept and its powerful field theory mathematics. A puzzle remains: macroscopically, not all matter that appears to be rigid shows the faceting that is characteristic of the snowflake. There are solid spherical glass beads, as well as, still more elaborately shaped glassy materials that are rigid. One partial resolution of this puzzle led to the deep ideas of modern metallurgy: real solids, even if crystalline, are not usually single crystals, but instead are jumbles of small crystallites (each crystallite containing still very many atoms, making them act rigidly), which contain spatially localized defects that do allow such solids to be deformed, albeit with greater difficulty than a liquid or a glass, allowing them to be made into a variety of useful shapes. The resulting beautiful theory of grain boundaries, disclinations, and dislocations [9–12] thus preserves the idea of broken symmetry as the origin of rigidity, but provides mechanisms for structural variety and interconversion of macroscopic forms. The defects of real crystalline solids represent atomic level near singularities in otherwise smooth fields describing the symmetries. Glasses challenge this harmonious paradigm of traditional metallurgy and solid state physics: at the shortest length scales, to the extent that we can probe them, the structures of glasses are so varied that it is very hard to make an assignment of a few broken symmetry fields to characterize their structures. This is not to say that making such symmetry assignments is completely impossible: many ideas for locally broken symmetries in glasses such as the presence of icosahedral order have been put forward [13, 14]. Also, recently, people have been trying to use the tools of artificial intelligence and machine learning to try to identify local order parameters in simulated liquids and glasses. It appears the number of broken symmetries then must be large.

The Random First Order Transition Theory (RFOT) of glasses avoids trying to force the description of amorphous structure into the straightjacket of traditional field theory, which uses only a small number of fields. Instead, the RFOT theory starts from the assumption that there is a statistically large number of possible arrangements of even the simplest (spherical) atoms that are, nonetheless, mechanically stable. Each of these structures can be effectively rigid since they represent local minima of the energy. This idea goes back at least to Descartes [15]. It was made most concrete in modern times by J. D. Bernal [16] who showed such "random" structures can explain x-ray diffraction from liquids. Recently, the existence of statistically large numbers of fields has emerged self-consistently in systems without quenched disorder in studies of hard spheres assemblies in very high dimension [17, 18]. In these mean field theories, which are based on the statistics of the patterns one finds the emergence of a multiplicity of metastable states. Each one of these states is rigid, and could last forever in the absence of thermal motion, like a cold amorphous snowflake. This phenomenon is called Replica Symmetry Breaking [19]. It took some time for the mathematical apparatus of the replica symmetry breaking solution to be understood in physical terms [19], but this analysis provides a firm place to start to study real glasses.

Like the theory of real crystalline solids, understanding laboratory glasses requires going beyond the mean field theory, which treats problems of stability globally. One must describe the local motions of the atoms in real space and time to achieve a description of glasses in finite dimensions. Here, we will describe the dynamics of glasses and glass forming systems using extensions of replica symmetry breaking ideas that allow the statistics of the atomic arrangements to vary in space and time and to have locally near singular behavior: these variations are described using the ideas of instantons, strings, flames, and flows. While far from mathematically rigorous, this development of replica symmetry breaking that is inhomogeneous in space and time provides a reasonably simple framework that explains a wide range of phenomena seen in glasses. It also explains several quantitative regularities that connect the thermodynamics and the kinetics of processes in the liquid state as the liquid transforms into a rigid glassy state [20, 21]. The limitations of space in this chapter force us to be telegraphic both as to the mathematical details of this complex of theoretical developments (for which we refer the reader to a more complete yet still pedagogical review [20]) as well as to displaying the detailed comparisons of the dynamical theory with experiments (see a recent review [22]).

8.1.2. *Self-generated randomness and the local landscape*

Aperiodic energy minima, reflecting locally stable structures, have been generated in several ways. Bernal literally jammed hard spherical balls into a balloon and by sucking the air out, compressed the packed balloon into a high-density conglomeration that was sensibly rigid [16]. By deconstructing by hand the resulting assembly, he was able to characterize many statistical aspects of such a locally stable, albeit, finite structure, including the statistics of the number of close contacts and the extent of local icosahedral order [23]. In a more systematic fashion, Stillinger and Weber used computational quenching by steepest descent on the potential energy surface to create aperiodic structures that are minima of the potential energy. Each one of the minima generated in this way is near to a simulated liquid configuration that was sampled in an equilibrated molecular dynamics run [24]. By doing this, the energy landscape can be fully tiled with basins of attraction. The assemblies generated in all these various ways seem to be as mechanically stable as Kepler's periodically stacked cannon balls were. These studies thus established that aperiodic "crystallites" of quite large size are stable in the absence of thermal motion.

The local stability of these constructed aperiodic assemblies to thermal fluctuations can be assessed using the same tools that have been used to study the local stability of periodic crystals (e.g. self-consistent phonon theory [25] and density functional theory [26]) in the context of freezing into periodic structures. This establishes that there are not only energy minima, but also that there are many local minima of a free energy functional each of which corresponds to an aperiodic density pattern.

The existence of local free energy minima that are not periodic does not guarantee that any such structure can ever be a global minimum of the free energy – almost certainly, for molecules with the simplest shapes, instead, periodic density waves corresponding to the stable crystals will be lower in free energy. According to thermodynamics and ergodicity, such systems, while being aperiodic, will ultimately crystallize, so the observed phenomena of glasses must involve only metastable free energy minima [27]. Furthermore, in general, a single individual aperiodic density pattern cannot be more stable than the entire set of all such aperiodic patterns, which are thermodynamically extensive in number, unless some sort of an ideal glass transition is reached at very low energy. A single aperiodic structure always thermodynamically resembles a superheated "crystal", in that each aperiodic crystal is only metastable with respect to the liquid, which corresponds with an average of such structures, having a uniform density $\rho(\underline{r}) = \bar{\rho}$. The dynamics in the vicinity of a given local free energy minimum can thus be monitored using a local scalar field that measures the similarity of a given aperiodic density pattern to the density wave pattern that describes the closest local minimum. In the theory of spin glasses, this quantity is called an overlap order parameter. The corresponding quantity for a structural glass can actually be experimentally monitored globally through the time delayed structure function $\langle \delta\rho(\underline{r}, t)\delta\rho(\underline{r}', t + \tau)\rangle$. In deeply supercooled liquids, the time delayed structure function has a long plateau for large, but intermediate values of the delay time, τ. The value of this plateau level plays the role of the Edwards–Anderson order parameter in spin glasses, which are systems that have quenched disorder in the interactions, for which the plateau can last forever.

The free energy as a function of the plateau value q if it were assumed to be uniform is sketched in Fig. 8.1. This free energy profile computed for a uniform value of the overlap order parameter resembles what we would find for an ordinary first order transition like the formation of periodic density waves in a crystal. At high temperatures, there will be a large entropic cost for localizing the system near to this initial state, that

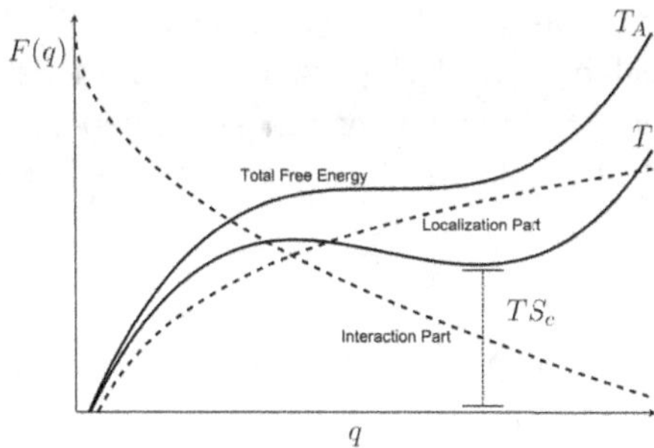

Fig. 8.1. Schematic diagram of the free energy as a function of the structural overlap parameter q. There are two contributions: one coming from the entropy cost of localizing particles on an aperiodic lattice, the other coming from the stabilization arising from particles avoiding each other on that lattice. At the temperature T_A, a metastable minimum begins to appear which becomes more stable upon cooling. It is still less stable than the uniform system, owing to the configurational entropy of the uniform liquid state.

is partially overcome by the fact that the initial density wave pattern avoids repulsive conflicts between molecules. The gain of stability from having localized the atoms, preventing excursions into high energy steric conflict, allows the aperiodic crystal to be metastable. Escaping this metastable minimum then will require activated dynamics, just as a superheated liquid needs bubbles to boil. If all the atoms had to disorder at once, the free energy barrier to escape would be extensive in N. The temperature at which metastability appears and where a secondary metastable minimum appears at finite q is called T_A.

Mode coupling arguments, which are perturbative, lead to a finite value of q, just as the free energy analysis does. Mode coupling theory and density functional approaches are two sides of the same coin [28].

T_A represents a spinodal temperature for stabilizing a metastable basin. On further cooling, the entropic advantage continues further to overcome the localization entropy cost. At some point, the two minima on the free energy profile could actually come close to coinciding in free energy. If such a point were to be reached, a given metastable minimum would remain stable forever. It would be an "ideal glass". The transition temperature, where there would be no extensive configurational entropy advantage to being able to sample other structures, is called the Kauzmann temperature, T_K.

Because of the necessity to extrapolate data to very low temperatures, the actual existence of this ideal glass transition enjoys some controversy. This concern, however, does not in any way undermine RFOT arguments, which depend only on the existence of many metastable glassy states, not their global stability.

At this level, the final escape from the structure function plateau in which the system has been trapped near a metastable configuration proceeds exactly like the melting of a superheated crystal. Access to the other possible arrangements of atoms occurs by nucleating these alternate arrangements at specific points in space. A small region will cooperatively rearrange, so as to resemble one of the other global metastable structures. Because this motion takes place only locally, the free energy barrier for rearrangement in glasses is not extensive.

Within the RFOT picture, glassy dynamics, then occurs by localized excitations or droplets. If the plateau value q or overlap, which in mean field theory is a global order parameter, is "promoted" to being a time and space dependent field, this droplet corresponds to a saddle point of a field theoretical free energy functional

$$\mathcal{F}[\{q(\underline{r})\}] = \int d^3\underline{r} \left(F(q) + \frac{\kappa}{2}[\nabla q(\underline{r})]^2 \right) \tag{8.1}$$

if we assume q varies only slowly in space. This saddle point solution is described by a nonlinear partial differential equation

$$\kappa \nabla^2 q = -\frac{\partial F}{\partial q}. \tag{8.2}$$

The square gradient term in the functional represents the free energy cost of allowing q to vary in space. The inhomogeneity costs reflect the fact that the intermolecular forces in real glasses are fairly short range. An instanton solution of the partial differential equation [29–31] then will be made up of a central core where q is nearly equal to 0. In this core region, the system accesses a set of possible states to which the initial configuration has very significantly rearranged. This core region can be called a local library of states [32, 33]. There will also be an outer region that has not yet transformed. This region will still have a large q for a time, since the original structure started out globally rigid. Between the core and its surroundings, q changes, allowing vestiges of the initial configuration to remain, but where a variety of similar states are being accessed.

Much below the crossover temperature T_A, the interface between the rearranged and unrearranged region will become quite narrow and at the same time the surface energy cost will go up. Simultaneously, per unit volume the entropy gain achieved by rearranging a fixed number of particles goes down. This implies the droplet or instanton size will grow as the temperature is lowered below T_A. The size of the central region of the instanton becomes a decent reaction coordinate for describing an activated transition of escape from the original trapped state. If there are N particles in the rearranging core region, then the free energy cost as a function of this reaction coordinate becomes

$$F(N) = -TS_c N + \gamma N^{2/3}. \tag{8.3}$$

The driving force in the first bulk term involves the configurational entropy per particle S_c, reflecting a growing multiplicity of rearranged aperiodic states as the core grows in size. Particles in the interface have, however, had to compromise between losing their vibrational entropy and stabilization energy or losing their configurational entropy. The surface term is called the "mismatch energy". Xia and Wolynes showed how to estimate this mismatch free energy from density functional theory for molecular systems [34]. The magnitude they predicted depends on the vibrational freedom in the metastable state and turns out to agree well with simulations [35]. The droplet argument implies that a rearranged region of size $N^{\ddagger} = \left(\frac{2\gamma}{3TS_c}\right)^3$ will correspond with a thermodynamically accessible saddle point of the free energy and the free energy cost for reaching this saddle point grows as the configurational entropy density decreases upon cooling: $F^{\ddagger} = \frac{4}{27}\frac{\gamma^3}{(TS_c)^2}$.

8.1.3. *The heterogeneous aperiodic crystal and the random field magnet*

The overlap order parameter field corresponding to a self-generated random periodic structure will intrinsically be spatially inhomogeneous, even before any rearrangement has occurred. The plateau value q should vary from place to place as the local packing structures, bonding patterns, etc. change spatially. Recent machine learning schemes try to describe such variations using terms like "softness" [36–38]. It has been shown that short molecular dynamics runs indeed do show variations in the local Debye–Waller factor throughout the sample. Owing to these variations in the initial values of order parameter, the corresponding gains in the configurational entropy from rearranging regions will also fluctuate as one scans across a locally metastable configuration.

Since the free energy that would be released by reconfiguring a region varies randomly in space, nucleation of new configurations somewhere in the glass initially resembles the heterogeneous nucleation of a bubble on a dirty surface with random quenched disorder. Escapes from metastable initial configurations resemble the activated transitions of a magnet with random frozen fields acting on each site. The corresponding random field Ising magnet (RFM) is still metastable, because we are examining dynamics above the Kauzmann temperature, where there is a substantial free energy gain that comes from exploring more states. The spatial heterogeneity has several direct consequences, which we describe below.

The instantons for a random field magnet are not precisely spherical. Instead, they vary in shape in different parts of liquid. In this way, they can take advantage of favorable fluctuations in the field. The interfaces between the rearranged material and the surroundings, therefore, will broaden a bit to take advantage of the driving force fluctuations that come from the self-generated randomness of the initial configuration. Owing to this broadening, the apparent surface tension is not a constant, but will decrease as the radius of curvature of the instanton droplet grows. The mismatch energy cost scales in the same way with size as do the fluctuations in the driving force. The mismatch cost varies like $\gamma N^{1/2}$. Redoing the standard smooth instanton calculation for the free energy cost with this slower scaling with core size gives

$$N^{\ddagger} = \left(\frac{\gamma}{2TS_c}\right)^2 \text{ and } F^{\ddagger} = \frac{\gamma^2}{TS_c}. \tag{8.4}$$

The correlation length or size of the droplets now grows like $S_c^{-2/d}$. A correlation length that scales in this way restores consistency with hyperscaling, if we assume a heat capacity discontinuity at the ideal glass transition, which fits the behavior at T_K, if we were to extrapolate the changes of the experimental heat capacities measured calorimetrically at the laboratory glass transition.

The predicted barrier scaling, as T_K is approached, exactly coincides with the empirical Vogel–Fulcher–Tammann relation that has been used so often for fitting data for supercooled liquid viscosity,

$$\log \tau = \log \tau_0 + \frac{DT_K}{T - T_K}. \tag{8.5}$$

This barrier scaling was also predicted by Adam and Gibbs. The random instanton argument, however, is quite distinct from theirs [39]. They made the reasonable, but arbitrary assumption that a reconfiguring region must have available to it, some fixed minimum threshold number of configurations, before it can rearrange. This assumption implies the rearranging region grows upon cooling, but the predicted size would still actually be quite small at the laboratory glass transition, a few molecules. In contrast, the random instanton argument shows the reconfiguring region must have available to it a larger and larger number of configurations as the Kauzmann temperature T_K is approached. Consistent with bounds based on experimentally measured nonlinear responses [40], the sizes predicted by the RFOT theory agree quite well both with direct observations of rearranging regions using microscopy at the surface of glasses [41] and inferences of the sizes from local relaxation measurements by Israeloff [42] and a host of fluctuation spectroscopies in bulk.

The heterogeneity of the initial aperiodic configuration leads to a very much more dramatic qualitative effect on the dynamics of glasses: the free energy cost of an instanton varies in different parts of the system, which then relax at different rates. This is called dynamical heterogeneity. This explains the well-known non-exponential character of the relaxation processes in glasses and supercooled liquids, a principal hallmark of glassy physics.

The fluctuations in the barrier size can be estimated to first order just by using the fluctuations of the configurational entropy driving force for regions having the typical size $N^\ddagger$. One finds that the typical fluctuations in the barrier depend on the configurational heat capacity:

$$\frac{\delta F^\ddagger}{F^\ddagger} = \frac{\delta S_c}{S_c} = \frac{1}{S_c}\sqrt{\frac{k_\mathrm{B}\Delta C_p}{N^\ddagger}}. \tag{8.6}$$

Substances with the large ΔC_p characteristic of "fragile liquid" have both very non-Arrhenius kinetics and very strongly nonexponential relaxations, while if ΔC_p is small (as it is for so-called, "strong liquids"), the relaxation time distribution will be narrower and the relaxation rates have nearly Arrhenius temperature dependence. Xia and Wolynes found a simple quantitative relation between the exponent β in the relaxation function $\exp[-(t/\tau)^\beta]$ and the rate at which the average barrier grows on cooling through the coefficient D in the dimensionless form of the Vogel–Fulcher law Eq. (8.5) [43], which is reasonably well satisfied by the experimental data.

The effects of inhomogeneity that we have just described have been formally addressed by using an explicit mapping of the free energy functional of a molecular fluid, onto the random field energy Ising magnet with an additional average field [44]. This mapping starts from Monasson's two real replica approach to one-step replica symmetry breaking [45]. Using Monasson's starting point, Stevenson, Walczak, Hall and Wolynes mapped the density functional for an aperiodic minimum to a random Ising magnet, where the analog spins live on a lattice, which is itself random. The spins are located on the aperiodic lattice of the initial atomic configurations. In this explicit mapping, heterogeneous magnetic couplings were also generated, as well, and their magnitude could be estimated. Real space renormalization group calculations on the analog system, with both randomness in the interactions and in the fields, show the randomness in the fields is the dominant contributor, at least for molecular fluids. This random field Ising analogy has also been developed further by Biroli, Tarjus and their coworkers using field theoretic approaches [46, 47].

The effects of heterogeneity on activated events have also been studied analytically in a different way, using the two-replica tool [30, 31]. This approach yields only a finite renormalization of the mismatch cost interface surface tension. Interestingly, the interface region of the fields theoretic replica instanton shows continuous replica symmetry breaking reminiscent of the Gardner transition. The replica instanton calculations also allow computing the fluctuations in barrier height, showing again that nonexponentiality depends on the configurational heat capacity.

8.1.4. *Strings or filamentous instantons*

Despite the spinodal being a crossover, understanding the dynamics of glasses at this border between activated dynamics and mode coupling theories is simultaneously interesting and conceptually important [48]. This part of the phase diagram is the easiest part to access via computer simulation at reasonable computational cost, so it is important to understand this regime if we are to make proper inferences from such simulations about the asymptotic behavior on the longer time scales characteristic of laboratory glasses. Molecular systems enter this crossover region when their relaxation times have reached about a microsecond at normal temperatures. Colloidal glasses, on the other hand, are often prepared in this regime in the laboratory, again on, say, the one-hour time scale: the slowness of the motion of the individual colloid particles immersed in solvent, in comparison to small molecules, means they start out 10^6 times slower at the microscopic scale. This regime is also relevant for biological soft matter, such as the cytoskeleton [49], again, because of the large size of the constituents. While the spinodal crossover between activated and collisional motions in glasses can be approached by tuning temperature alone, it can also be accessed by imposing external mechanical forces. This is the origin of shear bands within RFOT theory [50]. The stress-tuned spinodal explains the immense strength of glasses [51] and many aspects of the unusual rheology and fluid mechanics of glassy systems.

The magnetic analogy we have discussed, allows us to study the crossover by exploiting the droplet theory of metastable magnets due to Michael Fisher [52], who used it to approximate critical exponents, and more explicitly, its extension to the spinodal by Klein and his collaborators [53]. This theory explicitly accounts for the complex shapes of droplets as the spinodal is approached where they become "stringy", as has been seen in computer simulations [48].

The droplet theory suggests that near T_A the interfacial region becomes wider. The rearranging region becomes ever more filamentous as the crossover is approached from below. The free energy cost of rearranging a filamentous region has several contributions. There is a driving force proportional to the number of rearranging units, N, which depends on the bulk configurational entropy, again $-TS_cN$. Because of the large surface of a filamentous object, however, the mismatch free energy cost scales also like N, rather than with a fractional power, as RFOT predicts for the compact clusters. The coefficient of this mismatch energy term also will be somewhat larger than for the smoother interfaces of the more compact droplets, $F = \gamma'N$. Because $\gamma' > \gamma$, of course, at lower temperatures the compact rearranging regions eventually dominate.

The filamentous shapes are very much more numerous, favoring them entropically at high temperatures over compact clusters. The shape entropies of either one-dimensional strings or percolation clusters, both of which approximate the lattice animals of the droplet theory, scale linearly with their size. Thus, for filamentous rearranging regions, the free energy profile, $F(N) = -TS_cN + \gamma'N - TS_{\text{shape}}N$, becomes linear in N: the average free energy profile either monotonically increases with N or monotonically decreases with N (if we leave out fluctuations of the driving force). The border between these two regions determines the spinodal crossover temperature, T_c, which, thus, satisfies the condition $T_c(S_c + S_{\text{shape}}) = \gamma'$.

Using microscopic estimates of S_{shape} and γ', Stevenson, Schmalian and Wolynes showed that this criterion gives a good estimate of the crossover temperatures of molecular fluids that had been inferred directly from mode coupling fits to experimental data [48]. More or less uniformly, the crossover for molecular systems is predicted to occur when the relaxation times reach about 10^{-7} seconds, so clearly activated dynamics and mode coupling physics coexist in this regime, where true glassy behavior begins to take over. Interestingly, the crossover in this picture is mathematically equivalent to the Hagedorn transition in string theories of elementary particles [54, 55].

Heterogeneity, which broadens the free energy barriers for compact rearranging regions, also favors filamentous rearrangements. The fluctuations for stringy excitations give rise to a low free energy tail to the barrier distribution. Stevenson and Wolynes show that many features of the so-called "secondary relaxations" in molecular glasses can be accounted for by assuming that these subdominant relaxations arise from such stringy instantons [55]. Their typical activation energy does not grow as fast upon cooling as the main part of the relaxation time distribution.

8.1.5. *Aging, rejuvenation, and flames in glasses*

So far, we have actually been discussing the nature of the activated events and relaxation processes in equilibrated systems, but glasses are not at equilibrium, but are kinetically nearly frozen. Glasses still change after they have been initially prepared. They are said to "age" [29]. A simple scenario, by Lubchenko and Wolynes, provides a good account of what is observed in glassy systems with finite range interactions [32]. In their picture, the new minima are accessed not by further global mean field replica symmetry breaking, but by having only some of the local regions rearrange to new nearly equilibrated parts of the landscape. The glass becomes a mosaic of aperiodic crystallites of different energies.

The aging theory uses the local library construction introduced by Lubchenko and Wolynes [32]. A similar local energy landscape library view was also developed by Biroli and Bouchaud [33]. In this picture, when the glass is first prepared, the glass is caught in a high energy state, one characteristic of equilibrium at the temperature at which it began to have trouble equilibrating. The temperature at which the glass fell out of equilibrium is called the fictive temperature T_f. Upon further cooling then, the newly rearranged regions will dominantly be at the low temperature, but the starting state is no longer in equilibrium with the ambient temperature T. By being able to access lower temperature states, the core of either a compact droplet or filamentous string in the nonequilibrium glass acquires an additional driving force per particle $\Delta\epsilon \equiv \epsilon(T_f) - \epsilon(T)$. The free energy profile for compact rearranging regions becomes

$$F(N) = (-TS_c - \Delta\epsilon)N + \gamma N^{1/2}. \tag{8.7}$$

Because this additional driving force remains nearly fixed as the system cools, once the glass has fallen out of equilibrium, the rearranging regions do not grow much in size as the system is further cooled and the activation free energy barrier only grows slightly upon cooling.

Since further aging in the glass is very nearly an Arrhenius process, thermal aging of a glass phenomenologically resembles an ordinary chemical reaction. Nevertheless, the total free energy barrier does not decrease from what it was at T_g, so aging is quite slow and occurs on time scales much longer than the glass preparation time. Likewise, the distribution of barrier heights does not change much from what it was at the fictive temperature, where the glass initially fell out of equilibrium, so the process remains nonexponential. Both of these predicted features agree with experimental observations. The RFOT theory also predicts that the activation enthalpy in the frozen glass at temperature T is nearly proportional to what the activation free energy was at T_f. This connection implies that relaxation times, at the lower temperature, grow, as a power law of the time scale of preparing the sample, which is sometimes called the "waiting time".

Because of the local nature of the individual activated transitions in the aging glass, the description of the glass by a global fictive temperature can only be approximate. After some aging, the glass will have acquired a new source of spatial heterogeneity, the variations of the local fictive temperatures of those regions that have already taken advantage of the chance to re-equilibrate.

The addition of a local fictive temperature field implies the properties of nonequilibrium glass can be manipulated in many ways and are quite complex. To parody Tolstoy, while all equilibrium supercooled liquids are alike, nonequilibrium glasses are each nonequilibrium in their own way, depending on their history. This complexity is most clearly seen in the phenomenon of "rejuvenation". Upon heating an aged glass, the glass does not retrace the energetic history, versus ambient temperature, it had when it was cooled. Instead, the energy content of the glass first lags behind its cooling curve for a while, and then rapidly overshoots, as the aged regions of the glass that have been stabilized by rearranging when held at their lowest temperatures must wait to reach a still higher ambient temperature to re-equilibrate to the higher ambient temperature, than when they were first energetically trapped and were less stable. These features are recapitulated by the spatially inhomogeneous field theoretic version of the RFOT theory [56–58], which combines a description of the activated events with mode coupling theory to describe the interactions between instantons.

In this account, so far, we have focused on the heterogeneity effects, but locality implies instantons couple, so that there is also an effect called "facilitation", which comes from instanton interaction effects. Facilitation arises in the local RFOT picture because once a particular region has rearranged, its neighboring regions now see a new environment, one more energetically suitable to the overturned region. This means the mismatch energy of the neighbors has changed and likely decreased, allowing a faster activation of the neighboring regions. This effect was described by Bhattacharyya, Bagchi and Wolynes. Their extended mode coupling theory (which we call inhomogeneous RFOT/MCT), never fully freezes (as does traditional MCT), but instead goes over to the activated behavior of droplet/instantons at low temperature. This approach is necessary because the instantons themselves are nonperturbative, just as in semiclassical quantum theory and quantum chromodynamics [59].

The spatially averaged BBW equation on long time scales becomes a self-consistent nonlinear integrodifferential equation for the mobility μ (which normally contains the full correlation function). Just as the static theory promoted the plateau value of the time delayed structure function q to a spatially varying field, we can, on this longer time scale, promote the mobility to being a spatiotemporally varying quantity $\mu(\underline{r}, t)$, along with allowing the fictive temperature to vary also in space and time. If we can make the additional approximation that the mobility field varies slowly in space and time, this simplification results in a nonlinear partial differential equation,

$$\frac{\partial \mu}{\partial t} = \mu \xi_1^2 \nabla^2 \mu + \xi_2 (\nabla \mu)^2 - \mu(\mu - \bar{\mu}), \tag{8.8}$$

where ξ_1 and ξ_2 depend on the dynamical correlation length and $\bar{\mu}$ is the self-consistent result that would be obtained from the spatially averaged BBW theory. This input mobility, $\bar{\mu}$, arises primarily from the activated events and has a very strong dependence on both the ambient temperature T and the fictive temperature T_f, so it also varies in space and time $\bar{\mu}(T_f, T)$. The fictive temperature field locally equilibrates to the ambient temperature, through the mobility field, at a rate that depends on the local mobility

$$\frac{\partial T_f}{\partial t} = -\mu(T_f - T). \tag{8.9}$$

Owing to the strong fictive temperature dependence of $\bar{\mu}$, the dynamics arising from the coupling between these two nonlinear equations resembles what happens in the theory of ordinary chemical flames, where the diffusion of heat and combustible

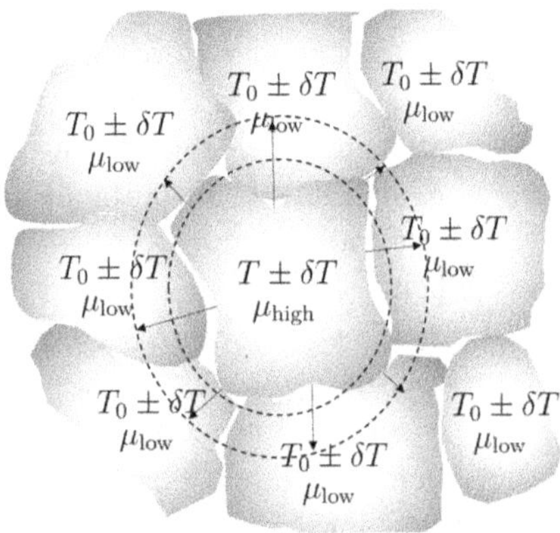

Fig. 8.2.   A cooperatively rearranging region once mobilized releases constraints on its neighbors, thus facilitating their rearrangement. Upon heating or rejuvenation of a glass, this leads to the propagation of mobility fronts.

materials couples to the production of heat, through an exothermic reaction, whose rate, in turn, depends strongly on the local temperature. Much as flames do not form by cooling, the effects of facilitation on the cooling dynamics are very mild. In contrast, on rejuvenation by heating, the autocatalytic feedback between T_f and μ, as in combustion, leads to propagating fronts emanating from the reconfiguring regions [58]. This front propagation phenomenon was discovered by Ediger in his experiments on the calorimetry of ultrastable glasses [22].

Vapor deposition leads to glasses with very low fictive temperatures, because glass dynamics near the free surface of the glass during the layered deposition process occurs much more rapidly than in the bulk [60]. Upon heating such a glass, the surface again reconfigures more rapidly. The mobilized surface region upon heating, therefore, ignites a propagating front that penetrates the sample. For samples thicker than a few microns, this front will finally be intercepted by fronts that have started from reconfiguring regions that started in the bulk, but this leads to the surprisingly large length scale in the microns, not nanometers, which is the scale of the rearranging regions themselves. The velocity of the propagating mobility fronts quantitatively predicted by the inhomogeneous RFOT-MCT theory is roughly independent of the fictive temperature of the glass, but depends strongly on the relaxation rate in the mobilized region, in agreement with experiments [60].

8.1.6. *Glass rigidity, strength and shear bands*

On short time scales, a piece of glass is rigid. As such, a glass object can sustain a shear stress for a time. A modest degree of shear stress will distort the aperiodic lattice, and by compressing or stretching the local bonds, will increase the free energy of the glass. On the longer time scales, where thermally activated transitions will finally occur, the glass will eventually flow, like a liquid. These transitions will locally restore the aperiodic lattice to a non-stressed state. Thus, like the stored energy in the glass that was preserved after quenching, the stress energy in the strained aperiodic lattice acts as an additional driving force for aging, hence, catalyzing the rearrangement and flow [51]. On the longest times, the nonequilibrium stressed glass will flow faster than a glass that has only been cooled, but not stressed.

The strain energy that is released when N particles are allowed to relax to a locally strain free aperiodic crystal scales with N

$$\Delta E_{\text{strain}} = \frac{\kappa \sigma^2}{2G} N v. \tag{8.10}$$

In this expression, σ is the imposed shear stress, which is assumed to be uniform at large distance from the rearranging region, and v is the volume of an atomic unit. G is the elastic modulus. Owing to the long-range nature of elastic force interactions (which resemble elastic quadrupoles), the coefficient κ depends on the shape of the region of N particles. For compact spherical regions this shape dependent coefficient is given by $\kappa = 3 - \frac{6}{7-5\nu}$, where ν is the Poisson ratio that determines the ratio of the bulk and shear moduli.

Both compact rearrangements and filamentous stringy rearrangements are catalyzed by imposed stress. The catalysis of stringy rearrangements implies that the spinodal threshold is shifted by the release of the imposed stress. RFOT theory, thus, puts a limit on the strength of glasses, when sufficient stress is applied to reach the spinodal. Using this idea, Wisitsorasak and Wolynes have shown that at the ideal glass transition point, the strength of glass essentially matches the venerable estimate of maximum material strength of periodic materials [51], made by Frenkel a century ago. Ordinarily polycrystalline metals are much less strong than this Frenkel limit (by a factor of one hundred), owing to the existence of dislocations and grain boundaries. Indeed it was the discrepancy between Frenkel's estimate and experimental measurements of strength that led to the idea of these defects. The RFOT analysis shows that ordinary glasses with a typical T_g can easily achieve $1/3$ of the Frenkel maximum strength, in agreement with experiments. Glasses are, in fact, very strong, which is why they are used to make thinner (and cheaper!) objects than polycrystalline substances like ordinary metals.

This large strength of glasses with respect to deformation means that when glasses are stressed to their limit, they may even break catastrophically by accessing new routes to dissipate stress. For example, with high stress, it is possible to create a small void, owing to the stored stress energy being sufficient to vaporize material. This is the reason we tend to think of the glass objects that we encounter around us as being breakable and easy to shatter.

If a sample of glass is able to remain intact and not shatter, but, nevertheless, nears the limiting stress, the glass can deform and flow, but it does so in an unusual inhomogeneous way: unlike an ordinary liquid, shear bands, where the displacements are concentrated, form [50, 61]. Wisitsorasak and Wolynes have described shear band formation by coupling viscoelastic equations for the strain fields with the mobility transport and mobility production equations that we have just described as giving mobility fronts.

The flame-like propagation described previously leads to the spreading of mobility from the initially reconfiguring regions, which have been catalyzed by stress, producing a mobile band, where the displacements are concentrated. A shear band is mathematically a flame that has been ignited by stress. Failure by shear band formation is characteristic of metallic glasses.

8.2. Stochastic Equations and Dynamics Beyond Mean-Field Theory

Tommaso Rizzo

*Institute of Complex Systems (ISC) — CNR and Dipartimento di Fisica,
Sapienza University of Rome, Rome, Italy*
tommaso.rizzo@cnr.it

The idea that there is a deep connection between structural glasses and spin glasses (SG) with one step of Parisi's replica symmetry breaking (1RSB) was put forward more than thirty years ago and has proven to be very influential [62–64]. Mean-field SG models with 1RSB display a dynamical transition temperature T_d where the Gibbs measure splits into an exponential number of equilibrium states, i.e. there is a finite configurational complexity. This is often followed by a second (static) transition at T_s where the configurational entropy vanishes. The static transition naturally evokes the Kauzmann temperature of supercooled liquids, while the dynamical transition turns out to have the same qualitative features of the mode-coupling theory (MCT) transition [65].

While the existence of the Kauzmann temperature is controversial, the MCT transition temperature is a very popular concept with both experimentalists and theorists, which captures many *qualitative* features of the physics of liquids upon supercooling, notably a two-step relaxation and a stretched exponential decay of time-dependent correlations. Furthermore it agrees *quantitatively* with numerical simulations [66–69]. Its main flaw is that in experiments one does not observe the sharp transition predicted by MCT but rather a crossover from power-law to exponential increase of the relaxation time. Many authors believe that it should be possible to fix this flaw of MCT in some way, although there is no agreement on how to do it.

In the context of mean-field (MF) 1RSB SG one easily recognizes that the transition at T_d is spurious due to their their mean-field nature and expects that ergodicity between T_d and T_s must be restored in finite dimensions by some activated processes: in practice one needs to go beyond mean-field dynamics. On the other hand it seems that the nature of the problem is different for temperatures close to T_d or deep in the MF glassy phase between T_d and T_s. In the following we will solely discuss progress made recently for temperature close to T_d, and we refer the reader to [70] for recent work in the MF glassy phase.

In order to go beyond MF and restore ergodicity one has to include fluctuations neglected at the MF level. In 1RSB SG one sees that the dynamical transition has the features of a second-order phase transition [71] and it is thus to be expected that the fluctuations are naturally described by a simple effective theory. Due to certain non-trivial features of the corresponding theory, it turns out that the effective theory is equivalent to a set of dynamical stochastic equations called stochastic-β-relaxation (SBR) equations [72, 73]. In the following we will demonstrate the validity of SBR in 1RSB SG by comparing its predictions with numerical simulations for the paradigmatic Ising p-spin model.

We consider a system of N spins each of which interacts with a fixed number $c = 6$ of p-spin interactions with $p = 3$. The (random) lattice is such that in the large N limit loops are increasingly rare and it tends to the corresponding $c = 6$ and $p = 3$ Bethe lattice, so that many thermodynamics quantities can be computed analytically by means of the cavity method.[a] The p-spin interactions are chosen randomly with values $J_{ijk} = \pm 1$ in the annealed ensemble. Instead of the standard white average, this corresponds to weighting each disorder instance with a factor proportional to the partition function of the model. This is convenient for numerical studies because the averages over the interactions and the configurations can be exchanged, in particular one can choose a random configuration and then generate the J's accordingly [71, 76, 77].

---

[a]For convenience reasons, instead of a random regular graph we generate the lattice by applying the M-layer construction [74, 75] to a triangular lattice with an interaction for each plaquette.

The order parameter is the correlation with the initial condition:

$$C(t) = \frac{1}{N} \sum_i s_i(t) s_i(0). \tag{8.11}$$

In the thermodynamic limit, the model displays a dynamical transition at a temperature T_d, and the correlation with the initial equilibrium configuration $C(t)$ approaches a plateau value q_d with a power law

$$\langle C(t) \rangle \approx q_d + \frac{1}{(t/t_0)^a}, \tag{8.12}$$

where the angle brackets indicate an average with respect to both the disorder and different thermal trajectories starting from the same initial configuration [71]. At finite N, one observes instead that even at $T = T_d$ the correlation deviates from the above mean-field expression and crosses the plateau value at a finite time that increases with the system size. In order to describe this phenomenon we must compute corrections to mean-field theory. Following the arguments and computations of [72, 73] one can argue that close to T_d the fluctuations of $g(t)$, defined as

$$g(t) \equiv C(t) - q_d, \tag{8.13}$$

are described by SBR, meaning that the generic K-point average obeys for $1 \ll N < \infty$:

$$\langle g(t_1) \dots g(t_K) \rangle \approx [\hat{g}(t_1) \dots \hat{g}(t_K)], \tag{8.14}$$

where $\hat{g}(x,t)$ in the RHS is the solution of the SBR equations:

$$\sigma + s = -\lambda \hat{g}^2(t) + \frac{d}{dt} \int_0^t \hat{g}(t-s)\hat{g}(s)ds. \tag{8.15}$$

The separation parameter σ measures the distance from the critical point and vanishes at $T = T_d$. The square brackets mean average with respect to the random variable s that represents a quenched Gaussian random fluctuation of σ:

$$[s] = 0, \qquad [s^2] = \Delta \sigma^2. \tag{8.16}$$

The SBR equations have to be solved with the short-time condition $\lim_{t \to 0} \hat{g}(t)(t/t_0)^a = 1$ where λ and a are related by the MCT relationship $\lambda = \frac{\Gamma^2(1-a)}{\Gamma(1-2a)}$. In practice, for times smaller than a Ginzburg time $t_G \approx N^{1/(4a)}$ the observables on the LHS of Eq. (8.14) can be accurately approximated with the values they have on the Bethe lattice, while on times of order t_G they are described by the RHS [75]. This leads to the initial conditions of the SBR equations: the *short-time* behavior on times $O(t_G)$ matches the *long-time* behavior for times $1 \ll t \ll t_G$, i.e. the mean-field result given by Eq. (8.12).

Note that on the LHS of Eq. (8.14) we have a model with a complex microscopic dynamics for which no analytic treatment of dynamics is available (not even in the fully connected case), while on the RHS we have a (numerically) solvable set of equations that were derived in [72, 73] starting from symmetry considerations (essentially the detailed balance property of the dynamics) but *without* reference to any specific microscopic model. The microscopic details however determine the actual values of the five SBR parameters a, t_0, $\Delta \sigma$ and σ that are needed to get quantitative predictions. In order to obtain parameter-free predictions, these model-dependent parameters have been computed analytically using existing [78–82] and novel techniques based on the mean-field cavity method on the glassy side of the transition. For the Bethe lattice with 3-spin interactions $J = \pm 1$ and connectivity $c = 6$ we have thus obtained (both in the annealed and quenched ensemble)

$$T_d = 1.087815, \quad q_d = 0.78184, \quad a = 0.31228, \quad \Delta\sigma^2 = \frac{0.02176}{N}. \tag{8.17}$$

The microscopic timescale t_0 depends on the actual microscopic dynamics and therefore cannot be estimated by the static cavity method. This is the only parameter that had to be extracted once and for all by fitting numerical data in the mean-field limit (i.e. at very large N) with the MF Eq. (8.12), leading to $t_0 = 0.00866$.

Within SBR, mean-field theory is recovered setting $\Delta\sigma^2 = 0$. In this case one recovers the critical MCT equation [65], in particular for $\sigma \geq 0$ $(T < T_d)$ $C(t)$ never goes below the plateau value. At finite N there is instead a finite but small $\Delta\sigma$ so that the MCT transition is avoided and $C(t)$ crosses the plateau at a finite time for all values of σ. In Fig. 8.3 we compare numerical data at $T = T_d$ $(\sigma = 0)$ with the SBR predictions that were obtained solving Eq. (8.15) numerically (by time discretization) for many instances of s. From the figure we note that the quality of the SBR predictions increases with N and is excellent for $N = 1.8 \times 10^6$, especially considering that there is *no single fitting parameter* as even t_0 is estimated through an independent procedure.

SBR provides not only the average correlation but, according to Eq. (8.14), also its *fluctuations of all orders*. To demonstrate this, in Fig. 8.4 we compare data and theory for the $\chi_4(t)$ function that yields the fluctuations of the correlation:

$$\chi_4(t) \equiv N \left(\langle C^2(t) \rangle - \langle C(t) \rangle^2 \right). \tag{8.18}$$

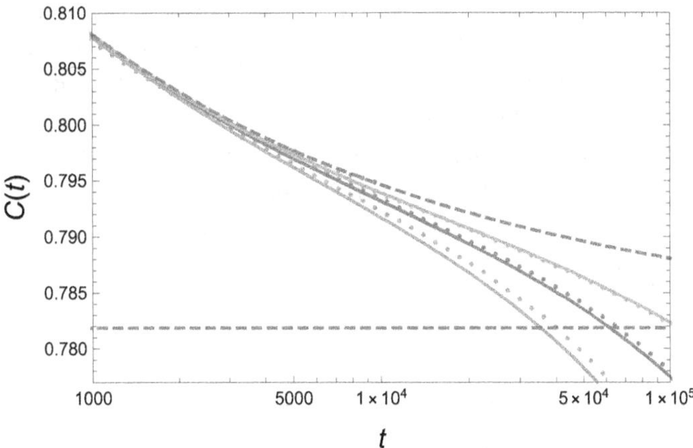

Fig. 8.3. Ising p-spin glass model on fixed connectivity lattice: average correlation with the initial equilibrium condition vs time at $T = T_d$. Points from bottom to top: numerical data for $N = 4.5 \times 10^5$, $N = 9 \times 10^5$, $N = 1.8 \times 10^6$ (sample numbers are respectively 9554, 8048, 7701, error bars are negligible on the scale of the plot). The data follow the Bethe lattice $N = \infty$ curve (dashed line) at initial times and deviate from it at later times increasing with N, eventually crossing the plateau value $q_d = 0.78184$. The solid lines are the corresponding SBR predictions describing the data when they start to deviate from the mean-field curve.

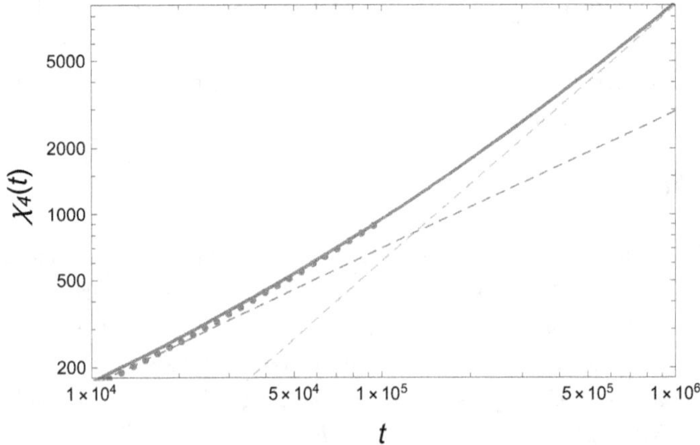

Fig. 8.4.   Ising p-spin glass model on fixed connectivity lattice: $\chi_4(t)$ vs time. Points: numerical data for $N = 1.8 \times 10^6$ (sample number is 7701). The data follow the mean-field asymptote t^{2a} (dashed dark grey) at initial times and deviate from it at later times. Solid line: SBR prediction describing the data when they start to deviate from the mean-field short times asymptote t^{2a} (dashed dark grey). SBR predicts a large times asymptote t^{2b} (dashed light grey).

Within MF theory, at $T = T_d$, $\chi_4(t)$ should diverge with time as t^{2a} [75]. Instead, on the Ginzburg time scale t_G over which $C(t)$ deviates from MF and reaches the plateau value q_d, $\chi_4(t)$ deviates from the MF law and in the late β regime follows a more pronounced t^{2b} growth where b is related to a by $\Gamma^2(1 + b)/\Gamma(1 + 2b) = \Gamma^2(1 - a)/\Gamma(1 - 2a)$.

Our aim here was to demonstrate *quantitatively* that the theory is correct for 1RSB SG and we refer instead the reader to [83, 84] for a discussion of the rich phenomenology displayed *qualitatively* by SBR when considering the case of finite dimensions (in which $g(t)$ is promoted to a field $g(x, t)$) and the case of temperature slightly above and below T_d. Overall, SBR predicts not only that the transition at T_d is avoided as shown by Fig. 8.3 or that the fluctuations deviate from mean-field theory as in Fig. 8.4, but also that there is an essential qualitative change in the structure of the fluctuations with the appearance of dynamical heterogeneities. The excellent agreement between numerical data and the parameter-free predictions is reassuring because SBR is the natural theory for 1RSB SG, but it can also be obtained solely from the symmetries of the original dynamical problem: this implies that the same description is potentially valid also for different models, including notably supercooled liquids. In [75] its validity has been demonstrated in a class of kinetically-constrained-models along the lines discussed here, by first computing analytically the coefficients of the theory and then comparing with numerical simulations. Establishing the relevance of the theory and computing its parameters for actual supercooled liquids is a promising open problem.

Acknowledgments

P. G. Wolynes would like to acknowledge the support for the work described in the chapter over many years from the NSF, most recently through the Center for Theoretical Biological Physics, sponsored by NSF grant PHY-2019745. The support from the Welch Foundation through the Bullard-Welch Chair at Rice University C-0016 is also acknowledged. Wolynes has enjoyed fruitful collaborations with many coworkers over the years, as can be seen in the references, and appreciates sharing this adventure with them. He would also single out Vas Lubchenko for many helpful discussions about glasses in recent years that particularly informed the framework of this chapter, and also thanks Susan Merz for help with finalizing the manuscript and, for the thoughtful preparation of figures, Dr. Andrei G. Gasic.

References

[1] E. Schrödinger, *Nature and the Greeks.* (Cambridge University Press, 1954).
[2] J. D. Van Der Waals and J. S. Rowlinson, *On the continuity of the gaseous and liquid states.* (Courier Corporation, 2004).
[3] Y. B. Zeldovich, *Selected Works of Yakov Borisovich Zeldovich, Volume I: Chemical Physics and Hydrodynamics.* vol. 140, (Princeton University Press, 1993).
[4] K. G. Wilson, *Rev. Mod. Phys.* **55**(3), 583, (1983).
[5] J. Kepler, *Strena Seu de Niue Sexangula.* (Gottfried Tampach, 1611).
[6] P. W. Anderson, *Concepts in solids: lectures on the theory of solids.* vol. 58, (World Scientific, 1997).
[7] P.-G. de Gennes, *Angew. Chem.* **31**(7), 842–845, (1992).
[8] V. L. Ginzburg, *Rev. Mod. Phys.* **76**(3), 981, (2004).
[9] G. I. Taylor, *Proc. R. Soc. Lond. A.* **145**(855), 362–387, (1934).
[10] M. Polanyi, *Z. Phys.* **89**(9), 660–664, (1934).
[11] E. Orowan, *Proc. Phys. Soc. (1926-1948).* **52**(1), 8, (1940).
[12] W. T. Read and W. Shockley, *Phys. Rev.* **78**(3), 275, (1950).
[13] P. J. Steinhardt, D. R. Nelson, and M. Ronchetti, *Phys. Rev. Lett.* **47**(18), 1297, (1981).
[14] S. Sachdev and D. R. Nelson, *Phys. Rev. B.* **32**(7), 4592, (1985).
[15] R. Descartes, *Descartes: The world and other writings.* (Cambridge University Press, 1998).
[16] J. D. Bernal, *Proc. R. Soc. Lond. A.* **280**(1382), 299–322, (1964).
[17] T. R. Kirkpatrick and P. G. Wolynes, *Phys. Rev. A.* **35**(7), 3072–3080, (1987).
[18] G. Parisi, P. Urbani, and F. Zamponi, *Theory of simple glasses: exact solutions in infinite dimensions.* (Cambridge University Press, 2020).
[19] M. Mézard, G. Parisi, and M. A. Virasoro, *Spin glass theory and beyond: An Introduction to the Replica Method and Its Applications.* vol. 9, (World Scientific, 1987).
[20] V. Lubchenko, *Adv. Phys.* **64**(3), 283–443, (2015).
[21] V. Lubchenko and P. G. Wolynes, *Annu. Rev. Phys. Chem.* **58**(1), 235–266, (2007).
[22] M. D. Ediger, M. Gruebele, V. Lubchenko, and P. G. Wolynes, *J. Phys. Chem. B.* **125**(32), 9052–9068, (2021).
[23] C. H. Bennett, *J. Appl. Phys.* **43**(6), 2727–2734, (1972).
[24] F. H. Stillinger and T. A. Weber, *Phys. Rev. A.* **25**(2), 978, (1982).
[25] J. P. Stoessel and P. G. Wolynes, *J. Chem. Phys.* **80**(9), 4502–4512, (1984).
[26] Y. Singh, J. P. Stoessel, and P. G. Wolynes, *Phys. Rev. Lett.* **54**(10), 1059–1062, (1985).
[27] P. G. Wolynes, *J. Non-Cryst. Solids.* **75**(1-3), 443–448, (1985).
[28] P. G. Wolynes. In *AIP Conf. Proc.*, vol. 180, pp. 39–65. AIP, (1988).
[29] T. R. Kirkpatrick and P. G. Wolynes, *Phys. Rev. B.* **36**(16), 8552–8564, (1987).
[30] M. Dzero, J. Schmalian, and P. G. Wolynes, *Phys. Rev. B.* **72**(10), 100201, (2005).
[31] M. Dzero, J. Schmalian, and P. G. Wolynes, *Phys. Rev. B.* **80**(2), 024204, (2009).
[32] V. Lubchenko and P. G. Wolynes, *J. Chem. Phys.* **121**(7), 2852–2865, (2004).
[33] J.-P. Bouchaud and G. Biroli, *J. Chem. Phys.* **121**(15), 7347–7354, (2004).
[34] X. Xia and P. G. Wolynes, *Proc. Natl. Acad. Sci. U.S.A.* **97**(7), 2990–2994, (2000).

[35] G. Biroli, J.-P. Bouchaud, A. Cavagna, T. S. Grigera, and P. Verrocchio, *Nat. Phys.* **4**(10), 771–775, (2008).

[36] X. Liu, F. Li, and Y. Yang, *Sci. China Mater.* **62**(2), 154–160, (2019).

[37] I. Tah, S. A. Ridout, and A. J. Liu, *arXiv:2205.07187.* (2022).

[38] E. D. Cubuk, R. Ivancic, S. S. Schoenholz, D. Strickland, A. Basu, Z. Davidson, J. Fontaine, J. L. Hor, Y.-R. Huang, Y. Jiang, et al., *Science.* **358**(6366), 1033–1037, (2017).

[39] G. Adam and J. H. Gibbs, *J. Chem. Phys.* **43**(1), 139–146, (1965).

[40] L. Berthier, G. Biroli, J.-P. Bouchaud, L. Cipelletti, D. E. Masri, D. L'Hôte, F. Ladieu, and M. Pierno, *Science.* **310**(5755), 1797–1800, (2005).

[41] S. Ashtekar, G. Scott, J. Lyding, and M. Gruebele, *J. Phys. Chem. Lett.* **1**(13), 1941–1945, (2010).

[42] E. Vidal Russell and N. Israeloff, *Nature.* **408**(6813), 695–698, (2000).

[43] X. Xia and P. G. Wolynes, *Phys. Rev. Lett.* **86**(24), 5526, (2001).

[44] J. D. Stevenson, A. M. Walczak, R. W. Hall, and P. G. Wolynes, *J. Chem. Phys.* **129**(19), 194505, (2008).

[45] R. Monasson, *Phys. Rev. Lett.* **75**(15), 2847, (1995).

[46] G. Biroli, C. Cammarota, G. Tarjus, and M. Tarzia, *Phys. Rev. B.* **98**(17), 174205, (2018).

[47] G. Biroli, C. Cammarota, G. Tarjus, and M. Tarzia, *Phys. Rev. B.* **98**(17), 174206, (2018).

[48] J. D. Stevenson, J. Schmalian, and P. G. Wolynes, *Nat. Phys.* **2**(4), 268–274, (2006).

[49] S. Wang and P. G. Wolynes, *J. Chem. Phys.* **138**(12), 12A521, (2013).

[50] A. Wisitsorasak and P. G. Wolynes, *Proc. Natl. Acad. Sci. U.S.A.* **114**(6), 1287–1292, (2017).

[51] A. Wisitsorasak and P. G. Wolynes, *Proc. Natl. Acad. Sci. U.S.A.* **109**(40), 16068–16072, (2012).

[52] M. E. Fisher, *Phys. Phys. Fiz.* **3**(5), 255, (1967).

[53] C. Unger and W. Klein, *Phys. Rev. B.* **29**(5), 2698, (1984).

[54] R. Hagedorn, *Nuovo Cim., Suppl.* **3**(CERN-TH-520), 147–186, (1965).

[55] J. D. Stevenson and P. G. Wolynes, *Nat. Phys.* **6**(1), 62–68, (2010).

[56] S. M. Bhattacharyya, B. Bagchi, and P. G. Wolynes, *Proc. Natl. Acad. Sci. U.S.A.* **105**(42), 16077–16082, (2008).

[57] S. M. Bhattacharyya, B. Bagchi, and P. G. Wolynes, *J. Chem. Phys.* **132**(10), 104503, (2010).

[58] P. G. Wolynes, *Proc. Natl. Acad. Sci. U.S.A.* **106**(5), 1353–1358, (2009).

[59] T. Schäfer and E. V. Shuryak, *Rev. Mod. Phys.* **70**(2), 323, (1998).

[60] A. Wisitsorasak and P. G. Wolynes, *Phys. Rev. E.* **88**(2), 022308, (2013).

[61] A. Wisitsorasak and P. G. Wolynes, *J. Phys. Chem. B.* **118**(28), 7835–7847, (2014).

[62] T. Kirkpatrick and D. Thirumalai, *Phys. Rev. B.* **36**(10), 5388, (1987).

[63] G. Biroli and J. P. Garrahan, *J. Chem. Phys.* **138**(12), 12A301, (2013).

[64] P. G. Wolynes and V. Lubchenko, *Structural glasses and supercooled liquids: Theory, experiment, and applications.* (John Wiley & Sons, 2012).

[65] W. Götze, *Complex dynamics of glass-forming liquids: A mode-coupling theory.* vol. 143, (Oxford University Press, 2008).

[66] M. Nauroth and W. Kob, *Phys. Rev. E.* **55**(1), 657, (1997).

[67] W. Kob, *J. Phys. Condens. Matter.* **11**(10), R85, (1999).

[68] F. Sciortino and W. Kob, *Phys. Rev. Lett.* **86**(4), 648, (2001).

[69] F. Weysser, A. M. Puertas, M. Fuchs, and T. Voigtmann, *Phys. Rev. E.* **82**(1), 011504, (2010).

[70] T. Rizzo, *Phys. Rev. B.* **104**(9), 094203, (2021).

[71] S. Franz, G. Parisi, F. Ricci-Tersenghi, and T. Rizzo, *Eur. Phys. J. E.* **34**(9), 102, (2011).

[72] T. Rizzo, *EPL.* **106**(5), 56003, (2014).

[73] T. Rizzo, *Phys. Rev. B.* **94**(1), 014202, (2016).

[74] A. Altieri, M. C. Angelini, C. Lucibello, G. Parisi, F. Ricci-Tersenghi, and T. Rizzo, *J. Stat. Mech. Theory Exp.* **2017**(11), 113303, (2017).

[75] T. Rizzo and T. Voigtmann, *Phys. Rev. Lett.* **124**(19), 195501, (2020).

[76] F. Krzakala and L. Zdeborová, *J. Chem. Phys.* **134**(3), 034512, (2011).

[77] F. Krzakala and L. Zdeborová, *J. Chem. Phys.* **134**(3), 034513, (2011).

[78] S. Franz, M. Leone, F. Ricci-Tersenghi, and R. Zecchina, *Phys. Rev. Lett.* **87**(12), 127209, (2001).

[79] F. Caltagirone, U. Ferrari, L. Leuzzi, G. Parisi, F. Ricci-Tersenghi, and T. Rizzo, *Phys. Rev. Lett.* **108**(8), 085702, (2012).

[80] G. Parisi and T. Rizzo, *Phys. Rev. E.* **87**(1), 012101, (2013).

[81] G. Parisi, F. Ricci-Tersenghi, and T. Rizzo, *J. Stat. Mech. Theory Exp.* **2014**(4), P04013, (2014).

[82] C. Lucibello, F. Morone, and T. Rizzo, *Phys. Rev. E.* **90**(1), 012140, (2014).

[83] T. Rizzo and T. Voigtmann, *arXiv:1504.06263.* (2015).

[84] T. Rizzo and T. Voigtmann, *EPL.* **111**(5), 56008, (2015).

Chapter 9

Dynamical Mean-Field Theory and the Aging Dynamics

The study of the equilibrium and the out-of-equilibrium dynamics of spin glasses is crucial to understand some of the characterizing properties of disordered systems, including slow relaxation times and aging. The current chapter focuses on recent developments on this relevant topic.

In the first part of the chapter, **Andrea Crisanti** discusses the relation between the equilibrium dynamics of mean-field spin glasses and RSB, briefly reviewing the pioneering ideas of Sommers and Sompolinsky and the subsequent theory by Crisanti, Horner and Sommers. **Jorge Kurchan** and **Silvio Franz** focus on the slow out-of-equilibrium glassy dynamics, in both mean-field models and finite-dimensional models, connecting the RSB scheme of Parisi with the concept of multithermalization. Finally, **Andrea Maiorano** overviews recent results on the presence (and absence) of weak ergodicity breaking in mean-field spin glasses, a pivotal assumption in many theoretical studies focusing on aging.

9.1. Equilibrium Dynamics and Replica Symmetry Breaking in Spin-Glass Systems

Andrea Crisanti

Dipartimento di Fisica, Sapienza University of Rome, Rome, Italy
andrea.crisanti@roma1.infn.it

Replica Symmetry Breaking (RSB) was introduced at the end of 1970s to describe the equilibrium properties of spin glasses within the equilibrium statistical mechanics. However

> equilibrium is a state characterizing the system over a long observation time, and not an instantaneous state. To discuss equilibrium we must consider the approximate length of the observation time [1].

While a great deal of work has been devoted to the off-equilibrium dynamics of glassy systems, the equilibrium dynamics is less known. In this short note, I will review the basic ideas of equilibrium dynamics and its relation with the RSB scheme proposed by Parisi [2].

The Sompolinsky equilibrium dynamics The first attempt to describe the equilibrium properties of spin glasses from dynamics is due to Sommers [3]. Sommers' solution assumes that there are two relevant time scales only: a short one, related to the finite-time part of the motion, and a long one, infinite in the thermodynamic limit,

157

related to the time-persistent part. This scenario was however too restrictive to describe the spin-glass phase where different time scales are involved.

A few years later, Sompolinsky [4] extended Sommers' approach to include many different long time scales. Sompolinsky assumed that there are $R+1$ different time scales t_r, $r = 0, \ldots, R$, all of which diverge in the thermodynamic limit with the prescription $t_r/t_s \to \infty$ if $r < s$. The time scale t_{R+1} is related to the finite-time part of motion and remains finite.

In each time sector $t_{r+1} \ll t \ll t_r$, relaxation processes with characteristic time scales smaller than t_r have all relaxed to equilibrium, whilst those with longer or equal relaxation times have not relaxed yet. Thus introducing the time-ordered limit

$$\mathrm{T}_r\lim_{t\to\infty} \equiv \lim_{t_R\to\infty} \cdots \lim_{t_{r+1}\to\infty} \lim_{t\to\infty} \lim_{t_r\to\infty} \cdots \lim_{t_0\to\infty}, \tag{9.1}$$

in each time sector $t_{r+1} \ll t \ll t_r$

$$\mathrm{T}_r\lim_{t\to\infty} C(t) = q_r, \qquad r = 0, \ldots, R, \tag{9.2}$$

where $C(t)$ is the equilibrium time-translational invariant (auto) correlation function. The overlap q_r measures the time-persistent part of the correlation function over the time interval $t_{r+1} \ll t \ll t_r$, see Fig. 9.1.

In Fourier space $C(\omega)$ acquires a time-persistent part $C(\omega) - \widetilde{C}(\omega) = \sum_{r=0}^{R}(q_r - q_{r-1})\delta_{\epsilon_r}(\omega)$, where $\delta_{\epsilon_r}(\omega)$ is a finite-width representation of the Dirac delta function of width $\epsilon_r = O(1/t_r)$, and $\widetilde{C}(\omega)$ contains the nonsingular contribution. Similarly, the static susceptibility acquires an anomalous contribution and the response function $G(\omega)$ becomes discontinuous at $\omega = 0$. Following Sommers, Sompolinsky writes $G(\omega) - \widetilde{G}(\omega) = -\sum_{r=0}^{R} \dot{\Delta}_r \Delta_{\epsilon_r}(\omega)$, where $\dot{\Delta}_r$ is the anomalous contribution to scale r and $\Delta_\epsilon(\omega)$ is a finite-width representation of the Kronecker delta function of width ϵ. The nonsingular finite-frequency part $\widetilde{G}(\omega)$ is related to $\widetilde{C}(\omega)$ via the Fluctuation

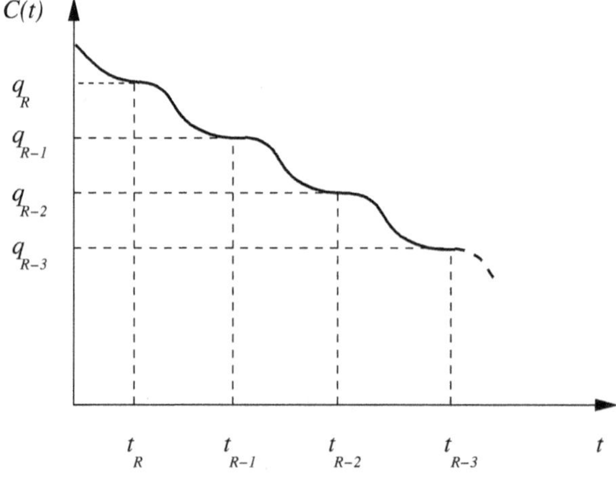

Fig. 9.1.   Schematic form of the correlation function with many relaxation time scales.

Dissipation Theorem (FDT)[a]: $\widetilde{C}(\omega) = (2/\omega)\,\mathrm{Im}\,\widetilde{G}(\omega)$. The product $\delta_\epsilon(\omega)\Delta_\epsilon(\omega)$ is not defined; Sompolinsky assumes that the width of $\delta_\epsilon(\omega)$ is much smaller than that of $\Delta_\epsilon(\omega)$ so that $\delta_\epsilon(\omega)\Delta_\epsilon(\omega) \sim \delta_\epsilon(\omega)$ as $\epsilon \ll 1$. With this assumption the self-consistent equation for the overlap q_r and the anomalous contribution $\dot{\Delta}_r$ can be derived in closed form. Consequences are better discussed in the spherical p-spin model [5], or its generalizations, i.e., infinite-ranged soft spin models with the spherical constraint $\sum_{i=1}^{N} \sigma_i^2 = N$ and Hamiltonian consisting of a sum of one or more terms of the type $\sum_{i_1 < \ldots < i_p} J_{i_1,\ldots,i_p} \sigma_{i_1} \cdots \sigma_{i_p}$ with different $p \geq 2$, where each $J_{i_1,\ldots,i_p}$ is a Gaussian variable distributed around zero. These models present phases described by either discrete RSB (finite R) or continuous RSB ($R \to \infty$). For these models the Sompolinsky theory leads to the self-consistent equations [6]

$$\Lambda(q_r) - \Lambda(q_{r-1}) = \frac{q_r - q_{r-1}}{\chi_r^2}, \quad r = 1,\ldots,R, \tag{9.3}$$

$$\Lambda'(q_r) = \frac{1}{\chi_r \chi_{r+1}}, \tag{9.4}$$

where $\chi_r = 1 - q_R - \sum_{s=r}^{R} \dot{\Delta}_s$ and $\Lambda'(q) = \frac{\mathrm{d}\,\Lambda(q)}{\mathrm{d}\,q}$. For $r = 0$ the first equation reduces to $\Lambda(q_0) = q_0/\chi_0^2$. The function $\Lambda(q)$ is model-specific, for example for the $2+p$ model it reads $\Lambda(q) = \mu_2 q + \mu_p q^{p-1}$ where μ_2 and μ_p are parameters. For comparison the static solution with the Parisi RSB scheme is

$$\Lambda(q_r) - \Lambda(q_{r-1}) = \frac{q_r - q_{r-1}}{\chi_r \chi_{r+1}}, \quad r = 1,\ldots,R, \tag{9.5}$$

$$\Lambda'(q_r) = \frac{1}{\chi_{r+1}^2}, \tag{9.6}$$

with $\chi_r = 1 - q_R + \sum_{s=r}^{R} m_s(q_s - q_{s-1})$, where $0 < m_r < 1$ are the RSB parameters. For $r = 0$ we still have $\Lambda(q_0) = q_0/\chi_0^2$. For any finite R the Sompolinsky solution cannot be reduced to the Parisi solution, not even fixing the "Parisi gauge" $\dot{\Delta}_r = -m_r(q_r - q_{r-1})$ [4]. When, instead, $R \to \infty$, the Sompolinsky solution can formally be reduced to the Parisi solution setting $\mathrm{d}\,\Delta(x) = -x\,\mathrm{d}\,q(x)$, where $\mathrm{d}\,\Delta(x) = \dot{\Delta}(x)\,\mathrm{d}\,x$ and $q(x)$ are the limiting functions of $\dot{\Delta}_r$ and q_r as $R \to \infty$.

This result raises the question about which solution, Sompolinsky's or Parisi's, gives the correct description. Sompolinsky's solution can be obtained from equilibrium statistical mechanics using the de Dominicis–Gabay–Orland (DGO) RSB breaking scheme [7]. It turns out that while the Parisi RSB leads to a stable RSB solution, the DGO RSB scheme, on the contrary, produces an unstable RSB solution. The instability occurs in the Longitudinal–Anomalous sector and cannot be cured [6]; hence the Sompolinsky theory does not yield a physically consistent static limit.

The CHS equilibrium dynamics The difficulties of Sompolinsky's solution follow from the assumption about the relative width of $\delta_\epsilon(\omega)$ and $\Delta_\epsilon(\omega)$. To overcome this problem, Crisanti, Horner and Sommers (CHS) [8] introduced a different dynamical

---

[a]A factor T^{-1} is absorbed into the definition of the response function, removing the temperature T in the FDT.

description of the equilibrium dynamics of the spherical p-spin model, which presents a stable $R = 1$ RSB low temperature phase. The CHS approach assumes that, in the spirit of multiple-scale analysis, the correlation and response functions depend on a fast variable t and a slow variable $\tau = \epsilon t$, $\epsilon \ll 1$. The fast variable describes the decay of C to a plateau q_1, while the slow variable parametrizes the subsequent decay to the equilibrium value q_0. This picture, appropriate for a 1-RSB phase, was later generalized to account for R steps of RSB [6] by considering R slow variables $\tau_r = \epsilon_r t$, $r = 0, \ldots, R$, with $\epsilon_r^{-1} \ll \epsilon_{r-1}^{-1}$, each τ_r describing the motion in the time sector $\epsilon_r^{-1} \ll t \ll \epsilon_{r-1}^{-1}$. Under the assumption of time separation, $C(t)$ can be represented as $C(t) = \sum_{r=0}^{R} \widetilde{C}_r(\tau_r) + q_0$. Each function $\widetilde{C}_r(\tau_r)$ describes the behavior in the associated time sector, and satisfies the boundary condition $\widetilde{C}_r(\tau_r = 0) = q_{r+1} - q_r$ and $\widetilde{C}_r(\tau_r = \infty) = 0$.

By a similar arguments $G(t) = \sum_{r=0}^{R} \epsilon_r \, G_r(\tau_r)$, where each G_r varies only in the corresponding time sector, where $\tau_r = O(1)$ as $\epsilon_r \to 0$, and vanishes in all sectors $s < r$. The function G_r gives the response of the system to a perturbation in the time sector r, i.e., the response of all degrees of freedom which have not yet equilibrated and are still active. The function G_r cannot be related to the correlation $\widetilde{C}_r$ via FDT because all degrees, equilibrated or not, contribute to $\widetilde{C}_r$; G_r must be reduced with respect to the function $\widetilde{G}_r$ satisfying the FDT relation $\widetilde{C}_r(\omega) = (2/\omega) \operatorname{Im} \widetilde{G}_r(\omega)$. In the CHS approach one then introduces the parameters $m_r \in [0,1]$, with the prescription $m_r > m_s$ for $r > s$ and $m_{R+1} = 1$ and $m_0 = 0$, representing the fraction of degrees of freedom not yet relaxed up to sector $r + 1$, and assume $G_r(\tau) = m_{r+1} \widetilde{G}_r(\tau)$. The equations for the order parameters q_r and m_r are obtained by considering the static limit $\omega \to 0$ separately in each sector. This can be computed by introducing a set of infinitesimal frequencies ω_r, with $\epsilon_{r-1} \ll \omega_r \ll \epsilon_r$ and defining the $\omega \to 0$ limit in the r sector as the ordered limit

$$\lim_{\omega \to 0} f(\omega) \equiv \lim_{\epsilon_{R-1} \to 0} \cdots \lim_{\epsilon_r \to 0} \lim_{\omega \to 0} \lim_{\epsilon_{r-1} \to 0} \cdots \lim_{\epsilon_0 \to 0} f(\omega) = f(\omega_r). \tag{9.7}$$

The equation for q_r can be obtained from the discontinuity of $G(\omega_{r-1}) - G(\omega_r) = m_r(q_r - q_{r-1})$ in passing from one sector to the next, m_r from the stability of the dynamical solution. Dynamical stability requires that the $\omega \to 0$ limit of the generalized damping function $\Gamma(\omega)$ governing the relaxation of the dynamical solution must be nonnegative. To ensure the time scale separation between successive sectors, the dynamics must be marginally stable in each sector and hence $\Gamma(\omega_r)$ must vanish in all sectors but the last one where $\Gamma(\omega_0) > 0$ to ensure global stability.

The CHS theory leads to a static solution that agrees with the static calculation performed using replicas and the Parisi RSB scheme [6]. However it does not reproduce exactly the same static solution for finite values of R; while the equations for q_r are the same, the parameters m_r, fixed by the marginal stability condition $\Gamma(\omega_r) = 0$, in the static calculation are determined by the minimization of the free-energy. Phases described by finite RSB, such as 1-RSB ($R = 1$) states found in p-spin models, possess an extensive number of statistically equivalent metastable states that dominates the dynamics. These states have a free energy larger than the free energy of the static minimum, yet they dominate the dynamics due to the macroscopic number. If the number of metastable states, known as complexity, is taken into account in the static calculation then the two approaches gives the same results. It is interesting to note that the dynamical marginal stability condition corresponds to the requirement of maximal complexity in equilibrium statistical mechanics. The difference disappears for $R \to \infty$.

We have seen that the CHS dynamical solution leads to the Parisi RSB static solution. The CHS approach assumes the modified FDT relation $G_r(\tau) = m_{r+1} \widetilde{G}_r(\tau)$, from which it is easy to see that the static limit of susceptibility in sector r is $m_{r+1}(q_{r+1} - q_r)$. This expression can be derived independently using the equilibrium statistical mechanics [9], thus giving support to the CHS approach.

9.2. The Relation Between Parisi Scheme and Multi-Thermalized Dynamics in Finite Dimensions

Silvio Franz[*] and Jorge Kurchan[†]

*LPTMS, UMR 8626, CNRS, Université Paris-Sud,
Université Paris-Saclay, 91405 Orsay, France
silvio.franz@gmail.com
†LPENS École Normale Supérieure, Paris, France
jorge.kurchan@ens.fr*

A system whose equilibrium measure follows the Parisi scheme [10], commonly known as Replica Symmetry Breaking (RSB), will take an infinite time to reach its equilibrium starting from random configurations, a process called 'aging'. It may also be driven into an out-of-equilibrium steady-state by an infinitesimal drive, such as shear [11, 12], or time-dependence of disorder [13]. If the relaxation times are long, or — in a steady-state — if the drive is weak, the dynamics is slow: this is the regime we are interested in.

The out-of-equilibrium dynamics under these circumstances is a very specific one [13–18]. At given times one may define an effective temperature with a thermodynamic meaning [19], which is the same for all observables. Different temperatures are possible, but in different 'time scales', a notion one has to define. We refer to this situation as 'multithermalization' [20, 21].

In finite-dimensional systems, neither the Parisi scheme nor the multi-thermalization scenario are proven to hold. However, the Parisi kind of ordering appears as the only possible non ergodic state which is stable against small random perturbations in the Hamiltonian.

Moreover, it turns out that Parisi RSB and multi-thermalization are deeply related: one of them holds if and only if the other also does. The temperatures involved in the slow dynamics then relate to the average overlap distribution computed for equilibrium in the Parisi scheme. This double implication may be argued on the basis of a strategy devised by Franz, Mézard, Parisi and Peliti [22, 23] and later generalized in [24] that uses linear response theory and equilibration of bulk quantities to compare dynamical quantities to equilibrium ones. An extra element that is of central importance for the validity of both schemes, as we now realize, is the fact that the slow glassy dynamics is *time-reparametrization soft*: small perturbations dramatically stretch the timescales.

Given the relation described above between static replica theory and slow dynamics, it is natural to search for reparametrization invariances in the Parisi replica context, and indeed questions like these have appeared in the literature. The whole matter deserves further clarification.

9.2.1. *Equilibrium: Ergodicity breaking and the Parisi scheme*

Replica symmetry breaking is ubiquitous in disordered systems with long range interactions [10]. Its successful implementation by Giorgio Parisi dates back to the study of the Sherrington–Kirkpatrick model of a spin glass [25], in the effort of parametrizing a $n \times n$ matrix for $n \to 0$ [2]. It describes the low temperature disordered frozen state with broken ergodicity in systems where ordinary ordering is not possible. For large samples, the Gibbs measure is dominated by a few 'valleys' unrelated by symmetry and in random positions in configuration space. The distances between these valleys have broad distributions, but they are strongly constrained, in fact only isosceles triangles, with the different side being the smallest, are possible in the thermodynamic limit, a property called 'ultrametricity'. The mathematical analysis of long range systems [26, 27] has fully confirmed and considerably enriched the picture coming from the physicist's analysis based on the iconoclastic replica method and the more conventional, but still non rigorous cavity method. The Parisi picture is also a natural candidate to describe ideal thermodynamic glassy phases of systems with short range interactions. However, its validity in three and, more in general, in any finite dimensional systems has been seriously questioned [28, 29]. The best available numerical simulations give strong indications in favor of RSB above a critical dimension that is somewhere above two and below four.

The least one can say is that RSB provides a very good statistical description of samples of finite sizes, or, equivalently, of local properties of infinite samples. Local RSB has indeed been proven to hold in models with large but finite interaction range [30]. But we do not know, with a convincing level of theoretical confidence, and even less of mathematical rigour, if RSB really survives as long range order in the thermodynamic limit. What indeed we know, is that under some rather mild assumptions (see later), if random broken ergodicity holds, the structure of the probability measure on random Gibbs measures, also called metastate, should be qualitatively described by the RSB scenario. In fact, the mathematicians were able to prove that under the hypothesis that the overlap distributions verify the so called Ghirlanda–Guerra identities (GGI) [31] then RSB ultrametric statistics follows [32]. In turn, the GGI follow from the stability of Gibbs measure against small perturbations [31, 33], hypothesis that holds true in mean-field and, we will argue, can be generically accepted in finite dimension. Within mean-field, it soon appeared that the dynamics of RSB systems presents anomalies with respect to the one in ordinary ergodic systems [14, 15]. Recognizing the full fledged off-equilibrium character of these anomalies led to the surprise that aging phenomena, which are commonly observed in laboratory glasses, also appeared in mean-field models, giving rise to a coherent and detailed theory of dynamic ergodicity breaking [16, 17]. This is obtained by the asymptotic analysis of exact Dynamical Mean Field Theory (DMFT) equations, which display a low temperature solution violating basic equilibrium properties as time translation invariance and the relations between responses and correlation implied by the fluctuation-dissipation theorem. It soon appeared that RSB and aging are intertwined phenomena in mean-field. Two classes of models were identified: p-spin like models and SK like models [16, 17]. In the former, one observes a decoupling between equilibrium and dynamics. The low temperature equilibrium measure is typically dominated by metastable states (ergodic components) with high stability, while the dynamics starting from a random configuration, tends to a marginal manifold which has higher energy density with respect to the equilibrium states. In the latter, instead, the states dominating equilibrium are marginally stable, and the asymptotic dynamical solution predicts asymptotic values of extensive observables coinciding with the equilibrium ones. Unfortunately, the results of asymptotic dynamics have been rather elusive to rigorous mathematical analysis. While the Parisi picture for equilibrium has been made fully rigorous by mathematicians, not much has been done in dynamics, where the only progress has been the proof of the validity of the physicist's effective one body dynamical equations and their self-consistent Dynamical Mean Field Theory closure [34, 35]. As far as finite dimension is concerned the situation is similar to the one of equilibrium: the Cugliandolo–Kurchan dynamical scenario provides an excellent description of finite time spin-glass dynamics [36, 37], but we cannot exclude that the aging responses eventually become trivial and the system crosses over to complete thermalization.

Overlap Statistics In the physics of disordered systems in equilibrium a crucial role is played by the statistics of the overlap between replicas induced by the thermal and disorder fluctuations [10]. What we call replicas here are configurations extracted independently from the Boltzmann measure for the same disorder. The overlap $Q[\mathbf{s}, \mathbf{s}']$ between two configurations is usually defined as $Q[\mathbf{s}, \mathbf{s}'] = \frac{1}{N} \sum_{i=1}^{N} s_i s_i'$.

A first characterization of the statistics of the overlap is given by its 'average histogram'

$$P(q) = \mathbb{E}\left(\langle \delta(Q[\mathbf{s}_1, \mathbf{s}_2] - q)\rangle_{12}\right) \tag{9.8}$$

where we denoted as $\langle \cdot \rangle_{12}$ the average over the (product) Gibbs measure of the two replicas, and with $\mathbb{E}$ the average over their common disorder. It was shown by Parisi a long time ago, that a nontrivial $P(q)$ (i.e. different from a single δ function) is associated with breakdown of ergodicity [38]. This is trivially true for example in systems with symmetry breaking in the absence of a source, where it just reflects that the measure is uniform over the different possible phases of the system related to one another by symmetry. In that case, the function can be simply collapsed to a δ by the introduction of an infinitesimal symmetry-breaking source that selects one among the possible phases, and the function $P(q)$ does not play any physically important role in this case. In disordered systems $P(q)$ is not related to any symmetry, and the situation can be much more interesting: a small perturbation unrelated to the original Hamiltonian cannot be expected to project on a single state, and modulo possible removal of accidental degeneracies of the original Hamiltonian, the function $P(q)$ of a perturbed system should stay close to the same function in the unperturbed one. This has deep consequences, since the multiplicity of states will affect the response properties of the system and $P(q)$

can be interpreted as the generating function of the responses to a family of random perturbations.

The method of random perturbations   The study of the overlap statistics requires access to microscopic configurations. This is of course easy in computer studies, but is more problematic in experiments. Fortunately one can use linear response theory (LRT) to give a different characterization of $P(q)$, as the generating function of a family of susceptibilities. Starting from a model with Hamiltonian H, one considers a perturbed system where random p-spin-like Hamiltonian are added to the energy of the system[b]

$$H_{\text{pert}}[\mathbf{s}] = H[\mathbf{s}] + \sum_{p=1}^{\infty} \epsilon_p H_p[\mathbf{s}], \quad \text{where} \quad H_p[\mathbf{s}] = - \sum_{i_1,\dots,i_p} J_{i_1,\dots,i_p} s_{i_1} \dots s_{i_p}. \tag{9.9}$$

The couplings $J_{1_i,\dots,i_p}$ are usually taken as centered i.i.d. Gaussian variables scaled as $\mathbb{E}(J^2_{i_1,\dots,i_p}) = \frac{1}{N^{p-1}}$. If the parameters ϵ_p are chosen to be independent of N, the perturbing Hamiltonian involves extensive energy in equilibrium; it is straightforward to see that

$$I^{(p)} \equiv \frac{1}{N}\mathbb{E}[\langle H_p\rangle] = -T\frac{\partial}{\partial \epsilon_p}\log Z = -N\beta\epsilon_p(1 - \langle q^p\rangle) \tag{9.10}$$

$$\langle q^p\rangle = \int \mathrm{d}q\, P_\epsilon(q)q^p \tag{9.11}$$

that can be readily obtained by integration by parts. Values of ϵ_p vanishing with N, namely $\epsilon_p \sim N^{-a}$ with $0 < a < 1$, have also been considered, where (9.10) continues to hold, but the energy absorbed is sub-extensive. This suggests we define *stochastic stability* as the property that $P_\epsilon(q) \to P_0(q)$ (modulo symmetry or accidental degeneracy of the unperturbed Hamiltonian).

The reader may object that in an experimental system the susceptibilities defined by (9.10) are not more accessible than the microscopic configurations. The crucial point that we discuss later in the paper, moreover, is that these quantities can be related to *dynamical* susceptibilities whose generator function can be in principle measured through response experiments in aging dynamics.

Self-averaging and higher order overlap statistics   Higher-order statistics of the overlaps, where one considers those between more than two replicas, are also important. Their distributions appear when formally considering the quadratic fluctuations of the perturbing terms H_p. For example, it is easy to show that the average square Hamiltonian $\mathbb{E}(\langle H_p[\mathbf{s}]^2\rangle)$ is related to the statistics of two overlaps $P(q_{12},q_{13})$

$$\mathbb{E}(\langle H_p[\mathbf{s}]^2\rangle) = \epsilon_p^2\beta^2 N^2 \left(1 - 2\langle q^p\rangle - \langle q^{2p}\rangle + 2\langle q_{12}^p q_{13}^p\rangle\right). \tag{9.12}$$

But H is a self-averaging quantity, and at order N^2, $\mathbb{E}(\langle H_p[\mathbf{s}]^2\rangle) = (\mathbb{E}(\langle H_p[\mathbf{s}]\rangle))^2$. This implies a strong constraint on $P(q_{12},q_{13})$ which needs to verify

$$P(q_{12},q_{13}) = \frac{1}{2}\delta(q_{12} - q_{13})P(q_{13}) + \frac{1}{2}P(q_{12})P(q_{13}), \tag{9.13}$$

---

[b]The ϵ_p have to decrease fast enough with p in order for the system to be well defined.

A similar analysis can be applied to $\mathbb{E}(\langle H_p[\mathbf{s}]\rangle^2)$, resulting in

$$P(q_{12}, q_{34}) = \frac{1}{3}\delta(q_{12} - q_{34})P(q_{12}) + \frac{2}{3}P(q_{12})P(q_{34}). \tag{9.14}$$

Notice that $P(q_{12}, q_{34})$ represents the average over disorder of the product of the disorder-dependent overlap distributions of four independent replicas. Equation (9.14) tells us that this is different from $P(q_{12})P(q_{34})$: self-averageness of the energy, from which (9.14) is derived, implies that the overlap probability (unless trivial) is instead non-self averaging. Also notice that once $P(q)$ is known, the higher order statistics of two overlaps are fixed.

Triangles Equations (9.13) and (9.14) are examples of the celebrated Ghirlanda–Guerra identities [31] that have played a crucial role in the mathematical analysis of spin glasses. It has been shown by Panchenko [32] that in their most general form they imply ultrametricity for any three states at mutual overlaps q_{12}, q_{23} and q_{13}: with probability one in the thermodynamic limit the two smallest overlaps are equal (all triangles are isosceles) $q_{13} = \min(q_{12}; q_{23})$. Moreover, if we consider the conditional probability [10] we find:

$$P(q_{13}|q_{12}=q_{23}=q)=\frac{P(q_{13},q_{12}=q,q_{23}=q)}{P(q_{12}=q,q_{23}=q)}=\theta(q_{13}-q)P(q_{13})+\delta(q_{13}-q)x(q) \tag{9.15}$$

where $x(q) = \int_0^q \mathrm{d}q'\, P(q')$ is the cumulative probability. Notice that q_{13} is independent of q when it is larger than q, and that, as in the case of the overlap pairs, the triangle probabilities are fully specified by the function $P(q)$, or equivalently by its primitive, $x(q)$. Indeed, this generalizes to an arbitrary number of replicas: thanks to self-averageness, $x(q)$ provides a sufficient statistics for the overlaps.

The picture is rather remarkable: in any system where extensive quantities are self-averaging and the system is stable with respect to small long-range random interactions, the only possibility besides triviality is ergodicity breaking according to the Parisi scheme. Originated in a mathematically unconventional analysis of the famous 0×0 replica matrix, the Parisi RSB scheme has revealed a deep, and inescapable symmetry of nature, transcending the replica trick.

Overlap locking It can be easily realized that if RSB is present in a system, then the overlap between any two random configurations should be homogeneous in space. This is true in long range systems, where by space we mean the complete graph (SK model) or the Bethe lattice (Viana–Bray model), but also, and especially, in any finite dimensional system with short range interaction that could possibly display RSB. Let us specifically refer to this case. Overlap homogeneity means that given two random equilibrium configurations, if one measures the value of the overlap in a given large enough region of space, the same value would be found by an analogous measure in any other region, no matter how far away from the original one. This is a very strong correlation property of equilibrium states.

Suppose you divide the system into two adjacent parts. The surface interaction term could be disconnected, without any appreciable change in the expectation values of bulk quantities. On the other hand, this term is crucial for the overlap statistics: in absence of the surface interaction the overlaps in the two halves are independent variables; in presence of it, the overlaps are locked to take the same values. We can generalize this consideration to more general weakly coupled disordered systems. The locking of the overlaps to identical values in the parts of the same system occurs because of statistical homogeneity of a given sample. An analogous locking however also occurs in absence of homogeneity, whenever we weakly couple systems with RSB. Suppose we have two systems S_1 and S_2, whose overlap statistics is specified by $x_1(q)$ and $x_2(q)$ respectively, not necessarily identical. As before, as long as the systems are not interacting the overlaps are independent. Stability of the RSB state on the other hand requires that as soon as a weak interaction is switched on, the overlaps do lock, and one can define a function $Q_2(q_1)$, which allows one to predict the overlap between two replicas in the system S_2, when the overlap is q_1 in the system S_1. It is clear that this relation should be specified by the condition $P_1(q_1)\,\mathrm{d}\,q_1 = P_2(q_2)\,\mathrm{d}\,q_2$, or equivalently $x_1(q_1) = x_2(Q_2(q_1))$ [39]. The actual functions $P_1(q)$ and $P_2(q)$ on the other hand will be only linearly affected by the coupling, and coincide in a first approximation with the overlap probability distribution in the unperturbed systems. Here we encounter a first instance of 'softness' of the solution: the presence or absence of small, thermodynamically irrelevant terms, leads to a complete rearrangement of the Gibbs weights, without affecting the values of self-averaging quantities. Below we shall find the same property in the context of dynamics.

Marginal stability and stochastic stability in mean-field Within mean-field, two classes of models are known: models with 'full-RSB', as the SK model, where the support $\mathrm{Supp}(P)$ is a continuous interval, say $[q_0, q_1]$ and models where the support has 'holes'. The most common case of this scenario is the case of 'one-step RSB' (1RSB) where only two values of the overlap support the whole probability, this is the case of Potts glasses and p-spin models and for simplicity we will refer to it here. We shall address these support values as 'skeleton' values of the correlations, and discuss how they play an important role in the correspondence between equilibrium and dynamics.

The physical picture between continuous and 1RSB cases is very different: In the first case the glassy phase is only marginally stable. This can be easily understood: the supports of the overlaps distributions are self-averaging [40], implying that it is possible to go from a given state to any other crossing only sub-extensive barriers [41, 42]. Within the replica method one finds families of Hessian zero modes associated to small variations $P(q) \to P(q) + \delta P(q)$ [43, 44], a reparametrization transformation that has a deep dynamical analogue as we will see in the following sections. In the second case, conversely, equilibrium states are absolutely stable and are separated by extensive free-energy barriers. The effect of a small but extensive random perturbation is very different in the two cases. In the 1RSB cases the states are reshuffled: their weight changes but they keep their identity and continue to exist. In the full-RSB case the effect is more dramatic, any $O(N)$ perturbation destabilizes the unperturbed equilibrium states and produce new ones in random positions. A crucial property is that the *probability distribution* of the disorder-dependent Gibbs state is only affected in a regular way by the perturbation (i.e., linearly for small perturbations). This regularity property, called stochastic stability, is very natural and at the same time important: it tells us that the original model is generic, sharing the same physics with a broad class of similar systems.

9.2.2. *Dynamics and Multithermalization*

Slow dynamics In the dynamic approach we consider a system evolving according to local reversible dynamics. To fix the ideas we can consider the Langevin equation

$$-m_i \ddot{s}_i - \frac{\partial H(\mathbf{s})}{\partial s_i} = \underbrace{\Gamma_0 \dot{s}_i - \eta_i}_{\text{bath}} \qquad (9.16)$$

where η_i are uncorrelated Gaussian white noises with variance $2\Gamma_0 T$ and Γ_0 is the strength of the coupling to the 'white' bath. This is guaranteed to reach eventually equilibrium, although in the systems that concern us, in times that may diverge with the system's size N. For the considerations that follow, any stochastic reversible dynamics whose update rule just depends on the force $f_i = -\frac{\partial H(\mathbf{s})}{\partial s_i}$ as e.g. Metropolis or Glauber dynamics would give rise to the same results. We shall be concerned with the limit of slow dynamics, which appears, in glassy systems, in different ways:

- *Aging* [45]. Following a quench of the system from a high to a low temperature, at which the equilibration time is infinite, the system 'ages': it evolves slower and slower as the time since the quench elapses. The two-time correlations never become an exclusive function of time-differences. The large parameter is the smallest 'waiting' time since the quench $t' = t_w$, that modulates the decay at further time $C(t, t') = C(\tau/t_w)$: the older (large t_w) the system, the slower the decay. In such conditions of long time scales local observables depending on configurations at a single time, such as the energy or specific heat, magnetization etc., only undergo small variations, and in what follows we will consider the ideal situation where they can be taken to be essentially equal to their asymptotic values.
- *Driven system* [11, 12]. When the system is subjected to forces not deriving from a potential — shear, for example — it is an experimental fact that aging is interrupted, in the sense that all functions become time-translational invariant, but slow. Their timescale of decay of correlation then is controlled by the driving rate σ, the slower the weaker the drive: $C(t - t') = C(\tau\sigma)$.
- *Time-dependent disorder* [13]. Another way to make a system with disorder time-translational invariant is to change the disorder slowly: the small parameter is the timescale τ_0 of change of disorder: $C(t, t') = C(\tau/\tau_0)$.

In what follows, we refer as *slow dynamics* to the limit of either long waiting times, small shear strains or slow variation of parameters. The latter two cases are stationary, all dependence on history is lost, but quite surprisingly they are *not* equilibrium systems, as we shall see.

In all these systems we consider correlation $C_{AB}(t, t')$ and linear response function $R_{AB}(t, t')$ (here $t \geq t'$), the average response of A at time t to a kick of B at time t'.

In the case of spin variables above, correlation and response functions are given by:

$$C_{ij}(t,t') = \langle s_i(t)s_j(t')\rangle; \qquad R_{ij}(t,t') = \frac{\delta}{\delta h_j(t')}\langle s_i(t)\rangle|_{h=0} \tag{9.17}$$

where $h_i(t)$ is the value at time t of a field conjugated to s_i in the Hamiltonian. One in general is interested in the global correlations and response, defined as $C(t,t') = \frac{1}{N}\sum_i C_{ii}(t,t')$ and $R(t,t') = \frac{1}{N}\sum_i R_{ii}(t,t')$ respectively. It is useful to consider the response function in its integral form:

$$\chi(t,t') = \int_{t'}^{t} R(t,t'')\,\mathrm{d}\,t'' \tag{9.18}$$

representing the response at time t to a field acting on the system from t' to time t.

In an equilibrium situation, we have for all A,B time translation invariance $C_{AB}(t,t') = C_{AB}(t-t')$ and the Fluctuation-Dissipation relation $TR_{AB}(t,t') = \partial_{t'}C_{AB}(t,t')$. Glassy dynamics, even when it is rendered stationary as above, violates these relations. In the spirit of the above, it makes sense to define effective temperatures [19] as:

$$T_{AB}(t,t')R_{AB}(t,t') = \frac{\partial C_{AB}(t,t')}{\partial t'}; \qquad T_{AB}(t,t') = \frac{T}{X_{AB}(t,t')}. \tag{9.19}$$

In equilibrium $X_{AB} \equiv 1$ and $T_{AB}(t,t') = T$, the bath's temperature. It turns out that these effective temperatures are exactly what a thermometer would measure when tuned to respond to the corresponding observables at the corresponding temperatures [19].

Reparametrization softness Glassy dynamics have a remarkable emergent property that has long been recognized: their evolutions may be drastically modified by small perturbations. For example, a static perturbation may dramatically modify the equilibrium distribution and, dynamically, the introduction of a perturbation in a well-aged system leads to rejuvenation, modifying the rhythm of relaxation. Even more dramatically, as we have mentioned above, the presence of a small shear or evolution of disorder leads to interruption of aging and the system is rendered stationary.

All these are highly nonlinear effects on the system's dynamics. Paradoxically, this does not mean that linear response breaks down: in spite of there being a very modified time-dependence, there are families of relations where time is gauged out that are only linearly affected by the perturbations. When one looks more closely at how this happens, it turns out that this 'softness' concerns the *pace* of the dynamics, where two point correlations become modified by a *time reparametrization $t \to h(t)$* as follows:

$$C(t,t') \to C(h(t), h(t')), \qquad R(t,t') \to \dot{h}(t')R(h(t), h(t')). \tag{9.20}$$

Or, in general, for a multi-point average $O(t_1, t_2, \dots) = \langle s_i(t_1)\eta_j(t_2)s_k(t_3)\dots\rangle$ a reparametrization acts on each factor as $s_i(t) \to s_i(h(t))$ and $\eta_i(t) \to \dot{h}(t)\eta_i(h(t))$.

Reparametrization-invariant quantities Reparametrization softness means that small perturbations affect, *the speed of the film,* but leave the mutual relations 'within a scene' invariant. It thus follows that there is a particularly significant sub-ensemble of dynamic quantities: those where time is factored out [17], and thus in the limit of large times they are invariant under reparametrizations $t \to h(t)$ $(t \to \infty)$, with h being any monotonously increasing function of time. The first example is rather trivial, but important for the following: for single time quantities $O(t)$, reparametrization invariance implies that they must become independent of time, i.e., asymptotically close to their infinite time value. More significant are the following examples:

- Given three long, successive times $t_1 < t_2 < t_3$, and the corresponding correlations C_{21}, C_{32}, C_{31}, define for large times $C_{31} = f(C_{21}; C_{32}) = \lim_{t_1 \to \infty} f(C_{21}; C_{32}, t_1)$, a 'triangle relation'.[c] Similarly for the integrated responses: $\chi(C_{31}) = \tilde{f}[\chi(C_{21}); \chi(C_{32})]$, i.e. the triangle relations $\tilde{f}$ and f are isomorphic.
- Given any dynamic parameter $X_{AB}(t, t')$ define for large times $X_{AB}(t, t') \to X_{AB}[C_{AB}(t, t')]$. We shall focus on cases in which this limit is non-trivial $X \neq 1$. This also implies that the integrated response becomes a function of the correlation: $\chi(t, t') \to \chi(C(t, t'))$.
- Given any two correlations of the system $\bar{C}(t, t')$ and $C(t, t')$ we write, again in the large-time limit, $\bar{C} \to g(C)$ for some g.

A way of putting this is as follows: a reparametrization-invariant quantity is a function in which times have been eliminated in favor of a correlation at those times. The particular one used acts as a 'clock' with respect to which all other quantities can be referred.

It is very natural to separate those quantities that are reparametrization-invariant from the reparametrizations themselves. A procedure for this may be implemented numerically [46–51].

Time scales   The reparametrizations we consider are such that they leave the triangle function $C_{13} = f(C_{12}, C_{23})$ invariant. The function f allows us to define, in a natural way, time scales in a reparametrization-invariant way.

The function $f(a, b)$ may be easily seen to be associative. It is possible to classify all associative functions, and it turns out that the correlation has special 'skeleton' values, that for simplicity we write here as a discrete and growing series, $q_1, \ldots, q_k$ that divide the possible correlation in intervals $(q_1, q_2), (q_2, q_3) \ldots (q_{k-1}, q_k)$ with the property that if C_{12} and C_{23} belong to two different intervals then $f(C_{12}, C_{23}) = \min(C_{12}, C_{23})$. If, on the contrary, a and b are in the same interval, another law applies. Each interval corresponds to a time scale, defined in a reparametrization-invariant way. *The correspondence between the Parisi scheme and a dynamic, 'multi-thermalization' scheme (to be defined below) holds at the level of these 'skeleton' values.* Let us see some examples of two, three and infinitely many scales where the set of skeleton values corresponds to a continuous interval.

---

[c]More precisely the relation should be thought to be valid in the large time limit according to $f(C_{21}; C_{32}) = \lim_{\substack{t_1 < t_2 < t_3 \to \infty \\ C(t_2, t_1) = C_{21}; C(t_3, t_2) = C_{32}}} C(t_3, t_1)$ and similarly for the quantities we discuss in what follows.

TWO SCALES   This is the most usual case. An example is when the correlation $0 < C \le 1$ and there is a value q such that for the interval $q \le C \le 1$ the correlation is much faster than for the interval $0 \le C < q$. We have, for example:

- For a stationary case

$$C(t{-}t')=(1{-}q)\bar{A}(t{-}t')+q\bar{B}\Big(\tfrac{t-t'}{H(\tau_0)}\Big),$$

    where H is a growing function of τ_0.

- For an aging case $t > t'$:

$$C(t,t')=(1{-}q)A(t{-}t')+qB\Big(\tfrac{L(t')}{L(t)}\Big)=(1{-}q)A(t{-}t')+qB\Big(e^{h(t)-h(t')}\Big),$$

where $(A, B, \bar{A}, \bar{B})$ are functions decreasing from one to zero as their argument goes from zero to infinity. The time reparametrization $h(t) = \ln L(t)$ brings the aging form into a time-translational invariant form.

THREE SCALES   Again, the correlation $0 < C \le 1$ and there are two values q_0 and q_1 such that for the interval $q_1 \le C \le 1$ the correlation is much faster than for the interval $q_0 \le C < q_1$, itself much faster than $0 \le C < q_0$. We have, for example, for the stationary state

$$C(t{-}t')=(1{-}q_1)\bar{A}(t{-}t')+(q_1{-}q_0)\bar{B}\Big(\tfrac{t-t'}{H(\tau_0)}\Big)+q_0\bar{\bar{B}}\Big(\tfrac{t-t'}{\bar{H}(\tau_0)}\Big),$$

where $\bar{\bar{B}}$ is also decreasing from one to zero as its argument goes from zero to infinity. The timescales are nested as $\tau_0 \to \infty$: $\bar{H}(\tau_0) \gg H(\tau_0) \gg 1$.

    The function f is the function min for correlations in any two different scales.

A CONTINUUM OF SCALES   An important case is when there is a dense set of values of correlation in which for all values of correlation

$$f(C_{21}, C_{32}) = \min[g(C_{21}), g(C_{32})] \tag{9.21}$$

holds. An example is:

$$C(t, t') = \mathcal{C}\left(\frac{\ln(t-t'+t_0)}{\ln \tau_0}\right) \tag{9.22}$$

where t_0 is a constant. This form satisfies (9.21) when $\tau_0 \to \infty$.[d] Note how simply ultrametricity appears in dynamics. The Sherrington–Kirkpatrick model (stationarized by shear or by parameter evolution, see next subsection) follows this law with astonishing precision [21].

Bringing a system to a stationary form   Shear and evolving disorder render a system stationary. It came as a surprise that for a small drive the resulting stationary system is by no means close to an equilibrium one (as in usual systems with small currents) but rather a time-reparametrized version of the aging system. For many technical purposes it is convenient then, at least in numerical computations, to *stationarize* the system. The shear strength or the speed of evolution of the disorder becomes then the control parameter, substituting the self-generated waiting time of the aging situation.

---

[d]Note however that, confusingly, $C(t, t') = \mathcal{C}\left(\frac{\ln t'}{\ln t}\right)$ is only *one* scale!

The Multithermalization scheme Having defined timescales and effective temperatures, we are ready to state the multithermalization scheme. For all observables A, B the long-time response and correlation functions define an effective temperature A, B as $T_{AB}(t, t')$ which we may write using a correlation as a 'clock' $T_{AB}(t, t') \to T_{AB}(C_{AB})$.

- Timescales defined on the basis of the correlation of any pair of observables are the same.
- Effective temperatures are, within a timescale, the same for all pairs of observables.

9.2.3. *Susceptibility Lego*

In this section we discuss naive linear response theory (LRT), and show that both in statics and in dynamics, the non-ergodic order parameter, $x(q)$ and $X(q)$ can be viewed as the generating functions, respectively in equilibrium and in dynamics, of a set of responses to random perturbations to the Hamiltonian. Let us add a to the Hamiltonian a perturbation of the form of a p-spin long range Hamiltonian

$$H \to H + \epsilon_p H_p \quad \text{where} \quad H_p = -\frac{1}{N^{(p-1)/2}} \sum_{i_1, \dots, i_p} h_{i_1, \dots, i_p} s_{i_1} \dots s_{i_p}. \tag{9.23}$$

The perturbations H_p are bulk self-averaging quantities, and we have seen that in equilibrium take values $I_{\text{eq}}^{(p)} = \mathbb{E}(\langle H_p \rangle)/N = -\beta \epsilon_p (1 - \int dq\, P_\epsilon(q) q^p)$.

As usual in linear response theory we can consider the limit of small ϵ, $\chi_{\text{eq}}^{(p)} = \lim_{\epsilon_p \to 0} I^{(p)}/\epsilon_p = T \lim_{\epsilon_p \to 0} \lim_{N \to \infty} \frac{1}{N} \frac{\partial^2}{\partial \epsilon_p^2} \log Z$. If this limit is regular, simple measures of the energy absorbed by the perturbation inform us of the correlations in the unperturbed system. Analogously, in dynamics, we can write for the finite time expected value of H_p

$$I^{(p)}(t) = \mathbb{E}\langle H_p(t) \rangle_{\text{dyn}} = -\epsilon_p \int_0^t ds\, R(t, s) p C(t, s)^{p-1} \tag{9.24}$$

and introducing $\beta X(q) = \lim_{\substack{t, s \to \infty \\ C(t, s) = q}} \frac{R(t, s)}{\partial C(t, s)/\partial s}$ we have

$$\lim_{t \to \infty} I^{(p)}(t) = -\beta \epsilon_p \int dq\, X(q)\, p q^{p-1} \tag{9.25}$$

As in the case of equilibrium X is the generator function of response *in presence of the perturbation* and if its $\epsilon \to 0$ limit is regular, we have information about the response in the unperturbed system.

Triangles One can define higher-order susceptibilities that in equilibrium allow one to reconstruct the probability distribution of several replicas, and in dynamics reflect the relations of correlations at different times. Particularly interesting are the ones associated to the probability of triangles $P(q_{12}, q_{13}, q_{23})$, which within Parisi RSB is concentrated on ultrametric triangles. In [22, 23] the triangle probabilities were reconstructed by considering average values of mixed combinations of the two different H_p, where the tensors defining the interactions are contracted over a subset of indexes, namely, in presence of the perturbations H_{n+m} and H_{n+l} in the Hamiltonian one considers the average value of the observable

$$O_{n;m,l} = \sum_{i_1,\ldots,i_{n+m+l}} J^{(n+m)}_{i_1,\ldots,i_n,j_{n+1},\ldots,j_{n+m}} J^{(n+l)}_{i_1,\ldots,i_n,k_{n+1},\ldots,k_{n+l}} s_{j_{n+1}}\cdots s_{j_{n+m}} s_{k_{n+1}}\cdots s_{k_{n+l}}, \qquad (9.26)$$

where n among the indexes of the two tensors, of rank $n+m$ and $n+l$ respectively, are contracted between them, and the others with the spins of the system.

Straightforward integration by parts allows to see that in equilibrium

$$\frac{1}{N}\mathbb{E}\langle O_{n;m,l}\rangle = \beta^2 \epsilon_{n+m}\epsilon_{n+l}\left(1 - \langle q^{n+m} + q^{m+l} + q^{n+l}\rangle + 2\langle q_{12}^n q_{13}^m q_{23}^l\rangle\right) \qquad (9.27)$$

while in dynamics

$$\frac{1}{N}\mathbb{E}\langle \delta O_{n,m,l}(t)\rangle$$

$$= \epsilon_{n+m}\epsilon_{n+l} \int_0^t dv \int_0^t du ([lC(t,v)^{l-1}R(t,v)][C(v,u)^m][nC(t,u)^{n-1}R(t,u)]$$
$$+ [lC(t,v)^{l-1}R(t,v)][mC(v,u)^{m-1}R(v,u)][C(t,u)n]$$
$$+ [C(t,v)l][mC(u,v)^{m-1}R(u,v)][nC(t,u)^{n-1}R(t,u)]). \qquad (9.28)$$

Since $\langle O_{n;m,l}\rangle$ is not directly a response function (i.e., a derivative of the free-energy) its equilibration was considered plausible, but the relation between triangles was not completely proven within LRT. To remedy to this weakness, in [24] it was shown that in fact the triangular correlations could also be generated as responses to perturbations: it suffices to perturb the Hamiltonian with the following term

$$\delta H_{n,m,l} = (\gamma_{ml}O_{n;m,l} + \gamma_{nl}O_{m;n,l} + \gamma_{nm}O_{l;n,m}) \qquad (9.29)$$

that generates the triangles at the cubic order in the γ's.

9.2.4. *The nucleation argument*

As we have stressed, in the large time limit, even in presence of aging, the values of extensive and local single-time observables should tend to asymptotic values. In mean-field systems with long range interactions these may or may not coincide with the corresponding values in equilibrium. In systems with finite range interactions in finite dimensions, on the other hand, these values should coincide with their Boltzmann–Gibbs equilibrium values. The usual argument is that in finite dimensions there are always local relaxation mechanisms allowing for equilibration. As a consequence, for the bulk free-energy, the infinite-time limit and the thermodynamic limit commute. The same should be generically true for its derivatives, such as internal energy and static responses. Notice that this argument tells that any possible broken ergodicity state should be only marginally stable, since the introduction of a small extensive random perturbation destabilizes the old equilibrium states to the advantage of new ones with a more favorable energetic balance between old and new energy.

This does not of course prevent the practical existence of systems such as structural glasses where the relaxation times at low temperature are so high that the energy density remains off-equilibrium on geological scales. Notwithstanding this, the limiting situation of aging close to equilibrium is a useful conceptualization to understand how glasses explore the configuration space. Whether in actual experimental systems on lab time scale one is close or not to this situation has to be decided case by case, depending on the system, preparation and the external parameters. We believe that this should be the case for spin glasses below, but close enough to the critical temperature. In these systems local equilibrium develops on growing scales $\xi(t)$ and the asymptotic situation may be observed if the growth of this scale is not too slow. We have seen that a possible way to measure $P(q)$ consists in introducing *long range* random perturbations. If one admits that these perturbations indeed equilibrate (at the level ϵ) in off-equilibrium dynamics, then one could reconstruct the Parisi function from simple off-equilibrium measures of the response. Unfortunately, the nucleation argument does not hold in presence of long range interactions, and one could cast doubts that small long range perturbations would induce metastable states with free-energy density $O(\epsilon)$ higher than the equilibrium one. These could trap the off-equilibrium dynamics, thus spoiling the statics-dynamic equivalence. Thinking about what could go wrong, this appears as a very remote possibility for small ϵ. Within mean-field, with a long range unperturbed Hamiltonian, where inducing metastability is certainly easier than in finite dimension, we do not know any case where the introduction of a perturbation induces a difference of order ϵ between the value of the asymptotic dynamical energy and its equilibrium counterpart.

To obviate this problem, however, one can look for local perturbations giving rise to the same correlation functions within Linear Response. In [22, 23] it was suggested that this could be achieved by diluting the p-spin perturbations so that they reduce to finite range interactions.

Let us see how this works for $p = 2$, the generalization to arbitrary p being straightforward (and discussed in detail in [22, 23]). To fix the idea consider a spin system on a D dimensional square lattice of size L, $\Lambda = \{1, \ldots, L\}^D$. One can divide the lattice into two halves, Λ_l and Λ_r, where one of the coordinates, say in direction of the x-axes e, take the values $\{1, \ldots, {}^L\!/_2\}$ and $\{{}^L\!/_2 + 1, \ldots, L\}$ respectively. Let us add to the original Hamiltonian a perturbation of the form $\epsilon_2 H_2$, with

$$H_2 = \sum_{x \in \Lambda_-} h_x s_x s_{T(x)} \tag{9.30}$$

where the h_x are independent Gaussian random variables with unit variance, and $T(x)$ is a translation of x of length $L/2$ in direction e. The thermal expectation value of the perturbation H_2 gives a contribution to the internal energy of the system which is extensive and self-averaging, i.e., independent (in the thermodynamic limit) of the particular realization of the disorder contained in either H or H_2. The interaction H_2, which looks long range, is, in fact, a local perturbation in a different space. Let us rename the spins in the right-hand part so that if $x \in \Lambda_l$ then $T(x) \in \Lambda_r$ and $S_{T(x)} = S'_x$. The total Hamiltonian can now be written as

$$H[\mathbf{s}, \mathbf{s}'] = H_l[\mathbf{s}] + H_r[\mathbf{s}'] + B[\mathbf{s}, \mathbf{s}'] + \epsilon_2 \sum_{x \in \Lambda_-} h_x s_x s'_x \tag{9.31}$$

The Hamiltonian H_l and H_r refer, respectively, to the spins in Λ_l and Λ_r. The term $B[\mathbf{s}, \mathbf{s}']$ is a surface term whose presence does not affect the average of H_2. Dropping it, the Hamiltonian (9.31) characterizes a spin system of size $L/2$ with two spins s_x and s'_x on each site, and a purely local interaction. We have traded the long range interactions with a local coupling among non-interacting or weakly coupled systems with different disorder and equal number of spins. We would like now to show that within LRT H_2 continues to be associated with the second moment of the overlap PDF. Simple integration by parts in equilibrium reveals that

$$\langle H_2/N \rangle = \beta\epsilon_2 \frac{1}{N} \sum_{x \in \Lambda_l} \left[1 - \mathbb{E}\left(\langle s_x s_{T(x)} \rangle_\epsilon^2 \right) \right]. \tag{9.32}$$

In [22, 23] it was argued that the limit for $\epsilon_2 \to 0$ of $\mathbb{E}\left(\langle s_x s_{T(x)} \rangle_\epsilon^2 \right)$ *both in presence or in the absence of the boundary term* $B[\mathbf{s}, \mathbf{s}']$ *should be equal to the value that this correlation function takes for strictly zero coupling* $\epsilon_2 = 0$ *in presence of* $B[\mathbf{s}, \mathbf{s}']$. The small coupling between the systems must have the same locking effect on the overlap as the surface interaction that we have discussed in the introduction.

Overlap equivalence if and only if timescale-separation   The property of overlap equivalence is very natural in the Parisi scheme. One has a distribution of states with their Gibbs weights. One now assumes that two pairs of states (a, b), (c, d) having the same mutual overlap measured with one observable $q_{AA}(a, b) = q_{AA}(c, d) = q$, will have also the same mutual overlap measured with any other observable $q_{BB}(a, b) = q_{BB}(c, d) = \bar{q}$. This means that there is a universal function that gives, for every state, the second overlap if one knows the first:

$$\bar{q} = g(q) \tag{9.33}$$

Clearly, we have $\bar{P}(\bar{q}) \, \mathrm{d}\, \bar{q} = P(g(q)) \, \mathrm{d}\, q \to \bar{P}(\bar{q}) = P(g(q)) \frac{1}{g'(q)}$. We may rewrite this putting $\frac{\mathrm{d}\, x}{\mathrm{d}\, q} = P(q)$ and $\frac{\mathrm{d}\, \bar{x}}{\mathrm{d}\, \bar{q}} = \bar{P}(\bar{q})$ as:

$$x(q) = \bar{x}(\bar{q}) \tag{9.34}$$

The property (9.34) has the dynamic counterpart:

$$X(C) = \bar{X}(\bar{C}) \qquad \to \qquad \bar{T}(\bar{C}(t, t')) = T(C(t, t')) \tag{9.35}$$

i.e., the effective temperature obtained from the fluctuation-dissipation relation of two observables at given times coincide.

This is very striking: a very similar relation arises from two apparently different arguments. And yet, using the second of the generating functions above, we find that there is a complete correspondence between g, X, $\bar{X}$ in the dynamic and in the equilibrium context.

In the dynamic case, we may also prove a strong result [24]: overlap equivalence holds *if and only if* there is a wide separation of timescales associated with two different temperatures for each observable. The proof is not complicated: suppose we have two observables that have the same $X(C) = \bar{X}(\bar{C})$ at all times, but the times for different X's are not really separate. Then, one can show that by coupling the observables one may construct a new correlation $\bar{\bar{C}}$ that does not have $\bar{\bar{X}}$ at the same times. In other words, *multithermalization is only consistent if the timescales of different temperatures are widely separated.*

9.2.5. *Commuting limits*

We have seen that within naive perturbation theory, under the hypothesis of equilibration of bulk quantities, dynamics and equilibrium are in strong correspondence and the study of the dynamical response can be used to reconstruct the equilibrium Parisi function, which is an average over disorder realizations. This is at first sight strange. One has a relation between conceptually different kinds of objects that are relevant in different time regimes (in and out of equilibrium, respectively), when the system explores very different regions of phase-space.

In usual applications of LRT thermodynamic states are supposed to be stable against the introduction of a perturbation. For example if we introduce a small positive magnetic field h in the low temperature Ising model we have

$$\langle s_i \rangle_h = \langle s_i \rangle_+ + h\beta \sum_j (\langle s_i s_j \rangle_+ - \langle s_i \rangle_+ \langle s_j \rangle_+) \tag{9.36}$$

Typical configurations of the perturbed systems are close to the unperturbed ones in the phase chosen by the field.

In disordered systems by contrast, when a random perturbation is introduced this does not hold, the Gibbs state is marginally stable and 'chaotic' [28, 52]: the perturbation implies a complete reorganization of the Gibbs measure, which concentrates on regions with zero overlap with the unperturbed states

$$\frac{1}{N} \sum_{i=1}^{N} \mathbb{E}(\langle s_i \rangle \langle s_i \rangle_0) = 0. \tag{9.37}$$

Yet these regions should correspond to close values of the bulk quantities and similar statistical properties. The marginal stability of the Gibbs state should then correspond to the stochastic stability of the metastate and $P_\epsilon(q) \to P(q)$. In dynamics the situation is similar: the chaotic property implies that no matter how small a perturbation, a perturbed trajectory evolving with the same thermal noise as an unperturbed one, will stay close for a certain time, but will eventually diverge when time in large enough. Moreover, any random perturbation introduced after evolution up to a waiting time t_w leads to a free-energy increase and hence to a rejuvenation of the system. This means that if we consider a field acting from t_w to t, the limit for $h \to 0$ of the magnetization at time t, $\chi(t, t_w) = \lim_{h \to 0} m(t, t_w, h)/h$ is not uniform in time. As in the case of statics, this does not prevent to use LRT. We just have to consider reparameterization invariant quantities (e.g. $\chi_{\text{dyn}}(q) = \int_q^1 dq\, X_\epsilon(q)$), whose limit $\epsilon \to 0$ should be regular as the perturbation tends to zero.

9.2.6. *The correspondence between the Parisi and the multithermalization schemes requires time reparametrization invariance*

All reparametrization-invariant relations between macroscopic quantities should coincide in dynamics and statics, where in statics only the 'skeleton' values are present. Ultrametricity, overlap equivalence and $x(q)$ are three examples. As we have mentioned above, the reciprocal is also true: if there is no timescale separation between *different* temperatures, there is no multithermalization, and no equilibrium overlap equivalence.

There is however a problem. Consider two systems brought into weak contact from the beginning, for example two different lattice models, coupled locally so as to obtain a single model with two sublattices. Assume that at the same times the separate systems have non-coincident temperatures. This is perfectly possible, since the systems are independent. Now, couple weakly the two systems: should we conclude that the coupled system, for which there is no distinction between observables of one or the other system, violates the multithermalization scenario — and, *a fortiori*, the Parisi scheme? If this were so, both would be fragile to the point of irrelevance. The answer is surprising: The timescales of the systems rearrange so that different temperatures happen at different scales: thus, the combined system conforms to the scenario. But this needs to happen even *for infinitesimal coupling*, and it can only be possible if the system is 'soft' with respect to time-rearrangements of each temperature separately: in other words, it has to have independent time-reparametrization invariances in the slow dynamics limit. Such invariances, which we have already described above, were first reported by Sompolinsky and Zippelius [14, 15] some forty years ago, and recently had a crucial role in the interpretation of the SYK model [53] as a toy model of holography [54, 55].

In conclusion, we realize that reparametrization softness is crucial for the consistency of the multi-thermalization scenario. But we have seen here that this scenario is in a one-to-one correspondence with the Parisi construction with replicas, at least in finite dimensions. We are thus led to ask ourselves, how do these reparametrizations appear in a replica treatment, where there is no time? In the next section, we will direct our attention to this question.

9.2.7. *Reparametrization invariance and replica space*

A consequence of ultrametricity   In aging experiments the actual perturbation allowing to measure the function $X(q)$ is just an applied magnetic field. A small magnetic field h acting from time t_w to time t induces a magnetization at time t which is

$$\frac{m(t, t_w)}{h} = \chi^+(t, t_w) = \int_{t_w}^{t} \mathrm{d}\, s\, R(t, s) \xrightarrow[t, t_w \to \infty]{C(t, t_w) = q} \int_{q}^{1} \mathrm{d}\, q' X(q'). \tag{9.38}$$

This suggests in equilibrium to consider the response to a magnetic field of a system S_1 which is kept to a fixed overlap $q \in \mathrm{Supp}(P)$ with a configuration $\mathbf{s}_0$ which is well equilibrated *in absence* of the perturbation.

Namely, considering an external random field term $\delta H = -\epsilon_1 \sum_i h_i s_i$ with $\mathbb{E} h^2 = 1$ we would like to compute

$$\chi^+(q) = \frac{1}{\epsilon_1} \mathbb{E} \sum_{\mathbf{s}_0} \frac{\mathrm{e}^{-\beta H[\mathbf{s}_0]}}{Z} \sum_{\mathbf{s}} \frac{\mathrm{e}^{-\beta(H[\mathbf{s}] + \delta H[\mathbf{s}])} \delta(Q(\mathbf{s}, \mathbf{s}_0) - q) \sum_i h_i s_i}{Z_1[\mathbf{s}_0]} \tag{9.39}$$

It is simple to see that within Linear Response Theory the response is given by

$$\chi^+(q) = \beta \left(1 - \mathbb{E} \left\langle \frac{\langle q_{12} \mathbb{1}_{q_{10} = q_{20} = q} \rangle_{12}}{[\langle \mathbb{1}_{q_{10} = q} \rangle]^2} \right\rangle_0 \right) \tag{9.40}$$

where we have denoted as $\langle \cdot \rangle_{a,\dots}$ the Boltzmann average with respect to the replicas $a, \dots$. Remarkably, using the Ghirlanda–Guerra identities, it is possible to show that this last quantity is equal to

$$\mathbb{E}\left\langle \frac{\langle q_{12}\mathbb{1}_{q_{10}=q_{20}=q}\rangle 12}{[\langle \mathbb{1}_{q_{10}=q}\rangle]^2} \right\rangle_0 = \frac{\mathbb{E}(\langle q_{12}\mathbb{1}_{q_{10}=q_{20}=q}\rangle 012)}{\mathbb{E}\langle [\langle \mathbb{1}_{q_{10}=q}\rangle 1]^2\rangle_0} = \int dq_{12}P(q_{12}|q_{10}=q_{20}=q)q_{12}. \quad (9.41)$$

The conditional probability $P(q_{12}|q_{10} = q_{20} = q)$ is fixed by ultrametricity $P(q_{12}|q_{10} = q_{20} = q) = x(q)\delta(q_{12} - q) + \theta(q_{12} - q)P(q_{12})$, which in turn implies that

$$\chi^+(q) = \beta \int_q^1 d q\, x(q). \quad (9.42)$$

This has to be compared with the dynamical susceptibility at time t to a field acting from time t_w to t, in the long time limit having fixed $C(t, t_w) = q$, namely

$$\chi^+_{\mathrm{dyn}}(q) = \beta \int_q^1 d q\, X(q). \quad (9.43)$$

The identity $X(q) = x(q)$ shows that the dynamical susceptibility tends to the constrained equilibrium susceptibility at large times. The result is simple and it has a clear interpretation. It means that asymptotically, during aging, given the configuration reached at a time t_w, partial equilibrium within the subspace with $C(t, t_w) = q$ is essentially achieved before the system can relax to $q - \delta q$.

This deep property suggests that the reparametrization invariant part of the dynamics can be described through a fictive quasi-equilibrium process where the physical time is completely eliminated. The system is supposed to be in equilibrium on a correlation scale q and to evolve to a scale q^- choosing configurations according to the Gibbs distribution. Formally this corresponds to the Markov chain defined by the following transition matrix

$$M_q(\mathbf{s}'|\mathbf{s}) = \frac{1}{Z_{q^-}[\mathbf{s}]} \exp(-\beta H[\mathbf{s}'])\delta(Q(\mathbf{s}', \mathbf{s}) - q^-) \quad (9.44)$$

where $Z_{q^-}[\mathbf{s}]$ is a restricted partition function normalizing the probability. The chain, that was called Boltzmann pseudo-dynamics in [56, 57], does not correspond to any physical dynamics, it implies macroscopic jumps from one configuration to the next one without solution of continuity. In [56, 57] however it was suggested that in a system with aging if one chooses $q = q_{\mathrm{EA}}$ this fictitious dynamical process provides a coarse-grained reparametrization invariant effective representation of the slow part of the relaxation below q_{EA} of true dynamics: the system fully equilibrates in 'dynamical quasi-states' [58] of amplitude q_{EA} before relaxing below this value; in this relaxation the system explores the configuration space choosing new quasi-states at random with Boltzmann probability *among the available ones*, i.e. those lying at overlap q_{EA}. It is clear from the considerations of the previous section that thanks to ultrametricity we can go further with the effective description and instead of coarse graining only the short times corresponding to q_{EA}, we could choose any arbitrary skeleton value of $q \in \mathrm{Supp}(P)$, and the corresponding pseudo-dynamics (9.44) would just provide a reparametrization invariant representation of the relaxation below q with the same physical content as the true dynamics.

9.2.8. *Two, perhaps three finite-dimensional puzzles*

Is one-step RSB unstable in finite dimensions? As we argued above, a system in finite dimensions must be reparametrization-soft and marginally stable, otherwise two systems with similar timescales and different effective temperatures would be unable to become a two-step RSB when weakly coupled. Analogously, a 1RSB system coupled with a fullRSB one must develop a continuum of effective temperatures and hierarchical time scales to become fullRSB itself.

In the mean-field case, however, the equilibrium of one-step system is not marginal. The situation is analogous to the ferromagnetic case, which is not marginal within mean-field (there is an extensive barrier between minima), while it becomes so in finite dimensions, being unstable with respect to a small uniform field.[e] A hypothetical dynamical 1RSB state in finite dimensions should be at least marginally stable against continuous RSB, a situation that could be called weak fullRSB. Such a situation would seem rather unnatural in a disordered system, by its nature heterogeneous, where the effective temperature would have spatial fluctuations. It is thus natural to conjecture that close to equilibrium, one-step, or more generally discontinuous solutions are unstable against higher RSB, thus leading to a situation where all the values of the correlations except the ones corresponding to the trivial equilibrium regime are 'skeleton' values and full ultrametricity holds.

Dynamic timescales in three and four dimensions The experimental evidence of spin-glasses seems to point to *only two timescales* [59, 60], and a non-trivial $P(q)$ [61] with what appears to be many temperatures — i.e. the χ versus C plot appears to have a curved section. Thus, many temperatures but only two timescales apparently violate the multithermalization. This however should be taken with a grain of salt as it could be a preasymptotic effect. Perhaps a clarifying step would be to see whether the correlation decay in times of hours and days is fitted with the same time-dependence of the one in microseconds, a comparison that has not, to our knowledge, been done. The numerical evidence in three dimensions seems to point to overlap equivalence between site and link overlap [62], although we know that this is not possible if there is only one slow timescale and many temperatures. The probable explanation is that the violation is, however, too small to be observed numerically.

In four dimensions the situation is much more clear: the little evidence we have [63] seems to point more resolutely to dynamic ultrametricity with many scales, just as in the Sherrington–Kirkpatrick model.

Aging strongly far from equilibrium Structural glasses as we know them in the laboratory find themselves in extremely long lived metastable states. The internal energy density, specific volume etc. persist to off-equilibrium values high above the equilibrium ones for at least geological times. Yet these systems slowly age. The response during physical aging in such conditions verifies to an excellent approximation

---

[e]This however does not give rise to divergent susceptibility, as the free-energy has only an essential singularity in $h = 0$, and $m(h) = \mathrm{sgn}(h)m^{+} + h\chi$.

scaling laws with a single effective time scale [64]. Numerical simulations of model glasses indicate that a description in terms of a single effective temperature, reminiscent of mean-field 1RSB systems, is appropriate [36, 65].

One can conjecture that in such conditions, which are formally very far from the asymptotic situation needed to have quasi-equilibrium sampling and reparametrization invariance, the dynamics in the aging regime can still be approximately described in terms of these concepts, as a quasi-equilibrium process where degrees of freedom that evolve on the same scales are in mutual 'multithermalized' equilibrium, and that a quasi-equilibrium process as in [56, 57] with a properly chosen q would still be an appropriate quasi-reparameterization invariant description of the slow dynamics.

9.2.9. *Conclusions*

We have discussed the deep connection between dynamic and equilibrium theoretical constructions as it is realized whenever during slow dynamics bulk expectation values are close to equilibrium, as it should asymptotically be the case in finite dimensional systems. In that case Linear Response Theory allows one to relate dynamical response functions to equilibrium correlations. Linear response in disordered systems is, however, subtle.

The main elements at play are the softness displayed by these systems both in equilibrium and off-equilibrium with respect to random perturbations, and somewhat paradoxically, the stability of appropriately defined responses and correlations with respect to the same perturbations.

It seems fair to say that the evolution of the subject has been from an almost miraculous ansatz to the gradual understanding of the questions it raises on more robust and method-independent properties.

9.2.10. *Acknowledgments*

We wrote this homage to Giorgio Parisi's work with in our minds the memory of Miguel Virasoro (1940–2021). The article is dedicated to these two friends.

The support of the Simons Foundation is acknowledged by S. Franz (Grant No 454941) and J. Kurchan (Grant No 454943).

9.3. Weak Ergodicity Breaking in Mean-Field Spin Glasses

Andrea Maiorano

Dipartimento Biotecnologie, chimica e farmacia, University of Siena, Siena, Italy, and Instituto de Biocomputación y Física de Sistemas Complejos (BIFI), Zaragoza, Spain
andrea.maiorano@unisi.it

All glassy systems age [64, 66]. Out-of-equilibrium dynamics shows unbounded growth of relaxation and correlation timescales. In a typical experiment, the *waiting time* t_w, i.e., the interval between the time at which a system is suddenly brought out of equilibrium at a given temperature (*quench*) and the time at which the observation begins is as relevant a time scale as the observation time t itself; the breakdown of time-translational invariance at all experimental time scales is a general feature, which is related to a rough free energy landscape in a very high-dimensional phase space and a complex interplay between entropy and energy barriers. Such features have been captured and thoroughly studied over the years in the dynamics of mean-field models of disordered magnets [67].

In the dynamics of fully connected spin-glass models[f] the average over the disorder and the node degree diverging with the size both allow reducing the causal dynamical equations [15, 68] to a set of closed relations between the two-time autocorrelation $C(t_w + t, t_w)$ and response $R(t_w + t, t_w)$ functions,[g] which have been studied for both *discontinuous* [8] and *continuous* models[h] [15, 68]. At sufficiently high temperatures, one expects that time translational invariance is recovered after a short transient, and the autocorrelation and response functions $C(t)$, $R(t)$ obey the fluctuation-dissipation theorem [69]; at lower temperatures, down to the spin glass transition, the qualitative behavior of the solutions depends strongly on the thermodynamics and the details of the replica symmetry breakdown (a comprehensive account may be found in [67]).

An approach to finding an asymptotic solution that applies to very large waiting times, in the low temperature phase, was proposed by Cugliandolo and Kurchan and has been shown to be applicable to paradigmatic fully connected models (e.g. the spherical p-spin [16, 70] and the Sherrington–Kirkpatrick (SK) model [17]); it relies on some basic assumptions under the so-called *weak ergodicity breaking* (WEB) scenario, after ideas previously introduced in the context of trap models [71].

At all temperatures below the transition temperature (where $q_{\mathrm{EA}} > 0$ for both classes of models), in the presence of a complex free energy landscape and barriers that diverge with the size of the system, an out-of-equilibrium treatment requires the limit of an infinite number of spins to be taken before any large time limit. The system is non-ergodic due to the large N limit and diverging barriers between states. Nevertheless, the system is allowed to wander in a very large subset of the configuration space, such as an unbounded marginal manifold, and reach the maximum allowable distance from the initial state. As it ages, it discovers deeper minima connected by narrower flat valleys that it takes increasingly longer to explore and leave. Equilibrium within the ergodic component, which is a stable state (infinite lifetime), can only be reached

---

[f]Consider the spin Hamiltonian $H[\{s\}] = H_0[\{s\}] + \sum_i h_i s_i$ for a set of N Ising spin variables s_i on the vertices i of a graph (real variables for the p-spin spherical model and the constraint $\sum_i s_i^2 = N$ is enforced), where H_0 is the sum of p-spins interaction terms $J(i_1, i_2, \ldots, i_p)s_{i_1} s_{i_2} \ldots s_{i_p}$ $(p = 2$ in the Sherrington–Kirkpatrick, Edwards–Anderson and Viana–Bray model, $p \geq 3$ for p-spin spherical) with random quenched couplings $J(\cdot)$ on the edges, with zero mean and variance $p!/(2N^{p-1})$ for SK and p-spin spherical, unit variance in the EA and VB model. The interaction network is fully connected for SK and p-spin spherical, nearest-neighbor hypercubic for EA, a graph in the Erdős–Rényi ensemble for VB; $h_i(t)$ is a site and time dependent field that couples to the spin configuration.
[g]The autocorrelation is $C(t, t') = \sum_i \overline{\langle s_i(t)s_i(t') \rangle}/N$, and the response function is $R(t, t') = \sum_i \overline{\delta \langle s_i \rangle / \delta h_i}/N$, with angular brackets and the overbar representing noise and quenched disorder averages respectively.
[h]The overlap in the paramagnetic state is zero; in continuous models the self-overlap of pure states (the Edwards-Anderson order parameter q_{EA}) grows continuously from a zero value when decreasing the temperature below the transition point, whereas it is already non-zero at the transition temperature for *discontinuous* models.

in infinite time, and the dynamics remains non-stationary at any finite (albeit large) time. The fluctuation-dissipation relation must be generalized accordingly (see [69] for a comprehensive review).

The above picture translates to quantitative requirements on the solutions of the dynamical equations. A first assumption is that for any *finite* waiting time t_w, the autocorrelation function $C(t_w + t, t_w)$ is a non-increasing function of the observation time t and, when no external magnetic field is applied, eventually decays to zero, but only at infinite times: $\lim_{t\to\infty} C(t_w + t, t_w) = 0$.

Moreover, the integrated response (e.g., the magnetization $m(t_w+t, t_w)$) to any small initial perturbation (a small constant magnetic field) that was applied since the quench until a *finite* waiting time must vanish at very long times: $\lim_{t\to\infty} m(t_w + t, t_w) = 0$. This *weak long-term memory* hypothesis implies that the very late dynamics forgets any past perturbation that lasted for any finite time interval; during very (infinitely) long observations, one-time quantities must eventually converge to their equilibrium values.

The above two assumptions allow to decouple two distinct regimes in observation times, *quasi-equilibrium* ($t \ll t_w$) and *aging* (t comparable to t_w); combined with the requirement that the fluctuation-dissipation ratio must depend on time only through its dependence on the autocorrelation function,[i] they have led to the solution of the dynamical equations in the large t_w limit. Among the remarkable predictions of the asymptotic theory for continuous models is the identification between the fluctuation-dissipation ratio and the functional order parameter of the spin glass transition, which also holds for a large class of realistic, finite-dimensional spin glasses [22, 23] and opened the possibility to study equilibrium properties — otherwise inaccessible — by extrapolating out-of-equilibrium measurements in experiments on real samples [61, 72] and numerical simulations [73].

It is not so obvious why a WEB scenario should apply in general. Different spin glass models exhibit radically different phase space structures near and below the transition temperature. The asymptotic solution of the dynamics requires that the thermodynamic limit be assumed a priori. Thus when the barriers between states diverge in the infinite size limit, activation is suppressed. In models that undergo a transition with a discontinuous order parameter, such as the spherical p-spin model, the presence of threshold states below a dynamical transition — just above the thermodynamic transition — prevents the system from being trapped in low free energy states [5, 45, 74]. Recently, a case for *non-weak* ergodicity breaking was found by studying the spherical *mixed* p-spin model [75, 76], for which the energy landscape is more complex, and *aging dynamics with memory* can occur after a quench, depending on the temperature at which the initial configuration was sampled. In models with a continuous phase transition like SK, the situation is completely different. Here we have no threshold states but an exponentially large number of metastable states [77], which can have a wide distribution of lifetimes.

---

[i]For $s > t$ and s, t both very large the fluctuation-dissipation ratio is defined as $X(s,t) = TR(s,t)/\partial_t C(s,t) = X[C(s,t)]$, where T is the temperature of the environment; for continuous and stochastically stable models $X(q)$ is the overlap cumulative distribution function.

Nevertheless, the WEB hypothesis has been supported over the years by numerical evidence from autocorrelation and response functions data obtained by integrating the full causal dynamical equations for the p-spin spherical model [8, 16] and by Monte Carlo simulations of the out-of-equilibrium dynamics of SK [78–80] and, as a matter of fact, WEB is widely considered to be a general scenario for the aging dynamics of mean-field spin glasses and more generally for glassy dynamics (and whenever the relaxation times distributions have power-law tails and metastable states have divergent average lifetimes — see, e.g., [81] and references therein); the resulting asymptotic solution for the dynamics is also the theoretical framework for the interpretation of numerical data for finite-dimensional spin glasses, although the relevance of mean-field theory to realistic models is debated.

In numerical simulations of the dynamics of a spin glass with a fully connected topology, the unit of Monte Carlo time requires computational resources that grow with the square of the size of the sample. Any finite system is small enough that the algorithm eventually converges to sampling equilibrium configurations at some finite times; simulating the dynamics for as long a time as possible after a quench below the transition temperature, of samples large enough to show aging on all simulated time scales, is still (after thirty years) a very resource-demanding task, despite the advances in computer technology; therefore, numerical studies of out-of-equilibrium dynamics have focused primarily on finite-dimensional models, for which the interaction topology is not only sparse but also highly regular. In state-of-the-art numerical simulations of the three-dimensional Edwards–Anderson model, the dynamics were simulated down to $C(t_w + t, t_w) \sim 10^{-3}$ [82]; the data showed no significant residual autocorrelation of the system with a fully magnetized initial configuration $C(t, 0)$ after extrapolation to very long times, which is consistent with experimental measures of the *thermoremanent magnetization* on real samples [60]. The asymptotically vanishing thermoremanent magnetization, which is a long-time response to a *strong* perturbation that lasts for a finite time, is a more specific phenomenon than what is assumed in WEB.

In mean-field models with a sparse topology, such as the Viana–Bray model [83, 84], in which each spin has a finite, size-independent random coordination number z and in particular for its fixed-connectivity version, the spin glass on the random regular graph [85, 86], the computational complexity required for a unit of Monte Carlo time scales linearly with the system size. Of course, the study of the dynamics of such models is motivated by more than a technical advantage. As with any finite-connectivity model, the dynamics of the Viana–Bray spin glass cannot be described by the two-times autocorrelation and response function [87, 88] alone; a full characterization of the asymptotic dynamics (see [89] and references therein) is still an open problem. Nonetheless the SK model is commonly considered to be the high-connectivity, large size limit of the model on a random regular graph, by scaling interactions appropriately with system size. Moreover, models with low fixed connectivity are more closely related to models on finite-dimensional hypercubic lattices [90, 91], and their behavior is expected to better match that of the realistic Edwards–Anderson model.

Recent simulations [92] of a spin glass on a random regular graph with $z = 4$ found a significant signal of small but finite autocorrelation after extrapolation to infinite size and (only after that) from very large to infinite observation times, with fixed finite waiting times; the longer the waiting time, the larger the residual autocorrelation. The amptotic aging dynamics then depends on the early evolution and initial conditions. The system gets confined in configuration space, and the size of the region that it is allowed to wander becomes smaller as the system gets older, but cannot be smaller than a single equilibrium state, which then yields an upper bound $\lim_{t_w \to \infty} \lim_{t \to \infty} C(t_w + t, t_w) < q_{EA}$, where the Edwards–Anderson parameter q_{EA} measures the average size of the states (the larger q_{EA}, the narrower and deeper the respective region in configuration space). The data of [92] do not exclude the possibility that the bound is saturated and $\lim_{t_w \to \infty} C(\infty, t_w) \sim q_{EA}$, and that a *strong* ergodicity breaking scenario might then hold: asymptotically the dynamics becomes bound to a single equilibrium state.

A similar analysis in [92] suggests the possibility of *non-weak* ergodicity breaking also for SK. Although the calculation of the size dependence of the free energy barriers between pure states in the spin glass phase of SK is still an open problem, there is a general consensus that they should diverge with the number of spins in the system as $N^{1/3}$ in thermodynamic limit [93, 94]. Recently, it was suggested in [95] that strong ergodicity breaking can be associated with a non-extensive divergence of typical barriers between all exponentially many states below the transition temperature, including metastable states. Moving only along the "flat" directions in configuration space may not be efficient enough to let the system wander far away from any initial conditions.

The work of [75] and [92] suggests that weak ergodicity breaking may not be the most general scenario in the aging dynamics of mean-field spin glasses. Since relaxation depends strongly on the structure of phase space, one would expect different models to exhibit either weak or strong (or both) asymptotic memory of the early dynamics, depending not only on the details of the free energy landscape, but also on the details of the protocol used to both generate the initial configuration and vary the control parameters. Yet the predictions of the asymptotic dynamical solution have had such an impact on the mathematical development and physical understanding of glassy dynamics and on connecting experimental results to the thermodynamics that its basic assumptions deserve close further study.

References

[1] S. K. Ma, *Statistical Mechanics*. (World Scientific, 1985).

[2] G. Parisi, *Phys. Rev. Lett.* **43**(23), 1754–1756, (1979).

[3] H.-J. Sommers, *Z. Physik B.* **31**, 301–307, (1978).

[4] H. Sompolinsky, *Phys. Rev. Lett.* **47**(13), 935–938, (1981).

[5] A. Crisanti and H.-J. Sommers, *Z. Physik B.* **87**, 341–354, (1992).

[6] A. Crisanti and L. Leuzzi, *Phys. Rev B.* **75**, 144301, (2007).

[7] C. de Dominicis, M. Gabay, and H. Orland, *J. Physique Lett.* **42**(23), 523–526, (1981).

[8] A. Crisanti, H. Horner, and H.-J. Sommers, *Z. Physik B.* **82**, 257–271, (1993).

[9] A. Crisanti and C. de Dominicis, *J. Phys. A.* **44**, 115006, (2011).

[10] M. Mézard, G. Parisi, and M. A. Virasoro, *Spin Glass Theory and Beyond*. (World Scientific, 1987).

[11] F. Thalmann, *Eur. Phys. J. B.* **19**(1), 65–73, (2001).

[12] L. Berthier, J.-L. Barrat, and J. Kurchan, *Phys. Rev. E.* **61**(5), 5464, (2000).

[13] H. Horner, *Z. Phys. B.* **86**(2), 291–308, (1992).

[14] H. Sompolinsky and A. Zippelius, *Phys. Rev. B.* **25**(11), 6860, (1982).

[15] H. Sompolinsky and A. Zippelius, *Phys. Rev. Lett.* **47**, 359–362, (1981).

[16] L. F. Cugliandolo and J. Kurchan, *Phys. Rev. Lett.* **71**, 173–176, (1993).

[17] L. F. Cugliandolo and J. Kurchan, *J. Phys. A.* **27**, 5749–5772, (1994).

[18] S. Franz and M. Mézard, *Europhys. Lett.* **26**(3), 209, (1994).

[19] L. F. Cugliandolo, J. Kurchan, and L. Peliti, *Phys. Rev. E.* **55**, 3898–3914 (1997).

[20] P. Contucci, J. Kurchan, and E. Mingione, *J. Phys. A.* **52**(32), 324001, (2019).

[21] P. Contucci, F. Corberi, J. Kurchan, and E. Mingione, *arXiv:2012.03922.* (2020).

[22] S. Franz, M. Mézard, G. Parisi, and L. Peliti, *Phys. Rev. Lett.* **81**, 1758, (1998).

[23] S. Franz, M. Mézard, G. Parisi, and L. Peliti, *J. Stat. Phys.* **97**, 459–488, (1999).

[24] J. Kurchan, *arXiv:2101.12702.* (2021).

[25] D. Sherrington and S. Kirkpatrick, *Phys. Rev. Lett.* **35**(26), 1792, (1975).

[26] M. Talagrand, *Spin glasses: a challenge for mathematicians.* vol. 46, (Springer Science & Business Media, 2003).

[27] D. Panchenko, *The Sherrington–Kirkpatrick model.* (Springer Science & Business Media, 2013).

[28] D. S. Fisher and D. A. Huse, *Phys. Rev. Lett.* **56**(15), 1601, (1986).

[29] A. J. Bray and M. A. Moore, *Phys. Rev. Lett.* **58**(1), 57, (1987).

[30] S. Franz and F. L. Toninelli, *J. Phys. A.* **37**(30), 7433, (2004).

[31] S. Ghirlanda and F. Guerra, *J. Phys. A.* **31**(46), 9149, (1998).

[32] D. Panchenko, *Ann. Math.* pp. 383–393, (2013).

[33] M. Aizenman and P. Contucci, *J. Stat. Phys.* **92**(5-6), 765–783, (1998).

[34] G. B. Arous and A. Guionnet, *Probab. Theory Relat. Fields.* **102**(4), 455–509, (1995).

[35] G. Ben Arous, A. Dembo, and A. Guionnet, *Probab. Theory Relat. Fields.* **136**(4), 619–660, (2006).

[36] J.-L. Barrat and W. Kob, *Europhys. Lett.* **46**(5), 637, (1999).

[37] L. Berthier, J.-L. Barrat, and J. Kurchan, *Eur. Phys. J. B.* **11**(4), 635–641, (1999).

[38] G. Parisi, *Phys. Rev. Lett.* **50**(24), 1946, (1983).

[39] S. Franz, G. Parisi, and M. Virasoro, *Europhys. Lett.* **17**(1), 5, (1992).

[40] G. Parisi and M. Talagrand, *C. R. Math.* **339**(4), 303–306, (2004).

[41] S. Franz and G. Parisi, *J. Phys. I.* **5**(11), 1401–1415, (1995).

[42] S. Franz and G. Parisi, *Physica A.* **261**(3-4), 317–339, (1998).

[43] T. Temesvári, I. Kondor, and C. De Dominicis, *Eur. Phys. J. B.* **18**(3), 493–500, (2000).

[44] C. De Dominicis and I. Giardina, *Random fields and spin glasses: a field theory approach.* (Cambridge University Press, 2006).

[45] T. Castellani and A. Cavagna, *J. Stat. Mech.: Theory Exp.* **2005**, P5012, (2005).

[46] H. E. Castillo, C. Chamon, L. F. Cugliandolo, and M. P. Kennett, *Phys. Rev. Lett.* **88**, 237201 (2002).

[47] H. E. Castillo, C. Chamon, L. F. Cugliandolo, J. L. Iguain, and M. P. Kennett, *Phys. Rev. B.* **68**, 134442 (2003).

[48] C. Chamon, P. Charbonneau, L. F. Cugliandolo, D. R. Reichman, and M. Sellitto, *J. Chem. Phys.* **121**(20), 10120–10137, (2004).

[49] C. Chamon, M. P. Kennett, H. E. Castillo, and L. F. Cugliandolo, *Phys. Rev. Lett.* **89**, 217201 (2002).

[50] C. Chamon and L. F. Cugliandolo, *J. Stat. Mech.* **2007**(07), P07022, (2007).

[51] C. Chamon, F. Corberi, and L. F. Cugliandolo, *J. Stat. Mech.* **2011**(08), P08015 (2011).

[52] I. Kondor, *J. Phys. A.* **22**(5), L163, (1989).

[53] S. Sachdev and J. Ye, *Phys. Rev. Lett.* **70**, 3339–3342 (1993).

[54] A. Kitaev. URL `http://online.kitp.ucsb.edu/online/entangled15/kitaev/`, `http://online.kitp.ucsb.edu/online/entangled15/kitaev2/`. (2015).

[55] J. Maldacena and D. Stanford, *Phys. Rev. D.* **94**, 106002 (2016).

[56] S. Franz and G. Parisi, *J. Stat. Mech.: Theory Exp.* **2013**(02), P02003, (2013).

[57] S. Franz, G. Parisi, F. Ricci-Tersenghi, and P. Urbani, *J. Stat. Mech.: Theory Exp.* **2015**(10), P10010, (2015).

[58] S. Franz and M. A. Virasoro, *J. Phys. A.* **33**(5), 891, (2000).

[59] L. Berthier, J.-L. Barrat, and J. Kurchan, *Phys. Rev. E.* **63**(1), 016105, (2000).

[60] E. Vincent, J. Hammann, M. Ocio, J.-P. Bouchaud, and L. F. Cugliandolo. In *Complex Behaviour of Glassy Systems*, pp. 184–219. Springer, (1997).

[61] D. Hèrisson and M. Ocio, *Phys. Rev. Lett.* **88**, 257202, (2002).

[62] P. Contucci, C. Giardina, C. Giberti, and C. Vernia, *Phys. Rev. Lett.* **96**(21), 217204, (2006).

[63] D. A. Stariolo, *Europhys. Lett.* **55**(5), 726, (2001).

[64] L. C. E. Struik, *Polym. Eng. Sci.* **17**, 165–173, (1977).

[65] G. Parisi, *Phys. Rev. Lett.* **79**(19), 3660, (1997).

[66] J. A. Mydosh, *Spin glasses; an experimental introduction.* (CRC Press, 1993).

[67] J. P. Bouchaud, L. F. Cugliandolo, J. Kurchan, and M. Mézard. In ed. A. P. Young, *Spin Glasses and Random Fields*, pp. 161–223. World Scientific (1998).

[68] H. Sompolinsky and A. Zippelius, *Phys. Rev. Lett.* **25**, 6860–6875, (1982).

[69] A. Crisanti and F. Ritort, *J. Phys. A.* **36**, R181–R290, (2003).

[70] L. F. Cugliandolo and J. Kurchan, *Philos. Mag. B.* **71**, 501–514, (1995).

[71] J. P. Bouchaud, *J. Phys. I.* **2**, 1705–1713, (1992).

[72] D. Hèrisson and M. Ocio, *Eur. Phys. J. B.* **40**, 283–294, (2004).

[73] M. Baity-Jesi, E. Calore, A. Cruz, L. A. Fernandez, J. M. Gil-Narvión, A. Gordillo Guerrero, D. Iñiguez, A. Maiorano, E. Marinari, V. Martín-Mayor, J. Monforte-Garcia, A. Muñoz Sudupe, D. Navarro, G. Parisi, S. Perez-Gaviro, F. Ricci-Tersenghi, J. J. Ruiz-Lorenzo, S. F. Schifano, B. Seoane, A. Tarancón, R. Tripiccione, and D. Yllanes, *Proc. Natl. Acad. Sci. USA.* **114**, 1838–1843, (2017).

[74] A. Crisanti and H. J. Sommers, *J. Phys. I.* **5**, 805–813, (1995).

[75] G. Folena, S. Franz, and F. Ricci-Tersenghi, *Phys. Rev. X.* **10**, 031045, (2020).

[76] G. Folena, S. Franz, and F. Ricci-Tersenghi, *J. Stat. Mech.: Theory Exp.* **2021**, 033302, (2021).

[77] A. J. Bray and M. A. Moore, *J. Phys. C: Solid State Phys.* **13**, L469–L476, (1980).

[78] L. F. Cugliandolo, J. Kurchan, and F. Ritort, *Phys. Rev. B.* **49**, 6331–6334, (1994).

[79] A. Baldassarri, *Phys. Rev. E.* **58**, 7047–7053, (1998).

[80] E. Marinari, G. Parisi, and D. Rossetti, *Eur. Phys. J. B.* **2**, 495–500, (1998).

[81] S. Burov and E. Barkai, *Phys. Rev. Lett.* **98**, 250601, (2007).

[82] F. Belletti, A. Cruz, L. A. Fernandez, A. Gordillo Guerrero, M. Guidetti, A. Maiorano, F. Mantovani, E. Marinari, V. Martín-Mayor, J. Monforte, A. Muñoz Sudupe, D. Navarro, G. Parisi, S. Perez Gaviro, J. J. Ruiz-Lorenzo, S. F. Schifano, D. Sciretti, A. Tarancon, R. Tripiccione, and D. Yllanes, *J. Stat. Phys.* **135**, 1121–1158, (2009).

[83] L. Viana and A. J. Bray, *J. Phys. C: Solid State Phys.* **18**, 3037–3051, (1985).

[84] G. Parisi, *J. Stat. Phys.* **167**, 515–542, (2017).

[85] M. Mézard and G. Parisi, *Europhys. Lett.* **3**, 1067–1074, (1987).

[86] M. Mézard and G. Parisi, *Eur. Phys. J. B.* **20**, 217–233, (2001).

[87] G. Semerjian, L. F. Cugliandolo, and A. Montanari, *J. Stat. Phys.* **115**, 493–530, (2004).

[88] M. Kiemes and H. Horner, *J. Phys. A.* **41**, 324017, (2008).

[89] E. D. Vázquez, G. D. Ferraro, and F. Ricci-Tersenghi, *J. Stat. Mech.: Theory Exp.* **2017**, 033303, (2017).

[90] C. De Dominicis and Y. Y. Goldschmidt, *J. Phys. A.* **22**, L775–L781, (1989).

[91] S. Katsura, *Prog. Theor. Phys. Supplement.* **87**, 139–154, (1986).

[92] M. Bernaschi, A. Billoire, A. Maiorano, G. Parisi, and F. Ricci-Tersenghi, *Proc. Natl. Acad. Sci. USA.* **117**, 17522–17527, (2020).

[93] G. J. Rodgers and M. A. Moore, *J. Phys. A.* **22**, 1085–1100, (1989).

[94] A. Billoire, *J. Stat. Mech.: Theory Exp.* **2010**, P11034, (2010).

[95] T. Aspelmeier and M. A. Moore, *Phys. Rev. E.* **105**, 034138, (2022).

Chapter 10

Dynamical Heterogeneity in Glass-Forming Liquids

Giulio Biroli[*], Kunimasa Miyazaki[†] and David R. Reichman[‡]

[*]*Laboratoire de Physique de l'Ecole Normale Supérieure, ENS, Université PSL, CNRS, Sorbonne Université, Université de Paris, F-75005 Paris, France*
giulio.biroli@ens.fr
[†]*Department of Physics, Nagoya University, Nagoya 464-8602, Japan*
miyazaki@r.phys.nagoya-u.ac.jp
[‡]*Department of Chemistry, Columbia University, 3000 Broadway, New York, New York 10027, USA*
drr2103@columbia.edu

A well-known puzzle for researchers working on the glass transition problem is that a static snapshot of a supercooled liquid looks very similar to that of a high-temperature liquid. However, these two systems are very different *dynamically*, as their relaxation times can differ by fourteen orders of magnitude. No simple signature of this phenomenon is found in particle configurations.[*] What has been understood in the last thirty years is that a clear signature can instead be found by looking at dynamical correlations or, expressed differently, by observing how the dynamical relaxation process unfolds in space and time.

10.1. Dynamical Correlations in Glassy Dynamics

Dynamical relaxation events are correlated in space, and these spatial correlations grow approaching the glass transition [4]. In order to understand this phenomenon, one must focus on a *mobility field* which measures the instantaneous relaxation that has taken place in a window of time t at a given position $\mathbf{r}$ [5]

$$c(\mathbf{r}; t, 0) = \sum_i c_i(t, 0)\delta(\mathbf{r} - \mathbf{r}_i), \tag{10.1}$$

where the sum is over all particles (indexed by i) and the mobility field $c_i(t, 0)$ is a two-point function that compares the configuration at time 0 with that at time t. For example, to measure relaxation on a length scale $2\pi/q$, one might consider $o_i(q, t) = e^{i\mathbf{q}\cdot\mathbf{r}_i(t)}$ and $c_i(t, 0) = o_i(\mathbf{q}, t)o_i(-\mathbf{q}, 0)$. In this case, $o_i(\mathbf{q}, t)$ is related to a Fourier component of the density of the system, and the average of $c_i(t, 0)$ is the self-part of the so-called intermediate scattering function $F(\mathbf{q}, t)$ [6]. Many other choices have also been used in the literature (see Ref. [4] for other examples).

---

[*]The understanding of this state of affairs has changed in recent years through the discovery of subtle static correlations, see [1].

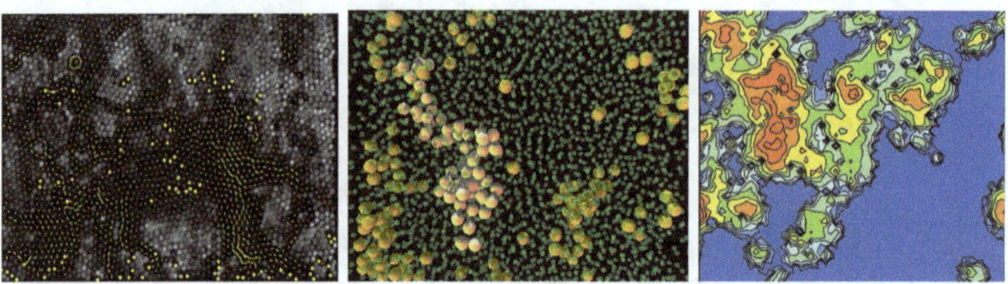

Fig. 10.1. Dynamical heterogeneity in (left) a granular fluid of metallic discs [2], (center) a colloidal hard sphere suspension, and (right) computer simulated two-dimensional system of repulsive disks [3]. In all cases, clusters of high and low mobility are highlighted. (left) Reprinted figure with permission from O. Dauchot, G. Marty, and G. Biroli, Phys. Rev. Lett. 95, 265701 (2005). ©(2005) American Physical Society. (center) Courtesy of Eric R. Weeks and David A. Weitz. (right) Reprinted figure with permission from A. Widmer-Cooper, H. Perry, P. Harrowell, and D. R. Reichman, J. Chem. Phys. 131(19), 194508, (2009). ©(2009) AIP Publishing.

Contrary to its static counterpart, the statistics of the mobility field does show remarkable changes upon supercooling. By considering windows of time of the order of the relaxation time τ_α,[a] one finds that dynamics becomes progressively more heterogeneous and correlated in space. We show in Fig. 10.1 three examples of dynamical heterogeneity for three different kinds of glassy liquids: a granular fluid, a colloidal suspension, and an atomistic simulation. In all cases, one finds that relaxation emerges in correlated clusters of size $\xi(t)$. By studying the t-dependence of dynamical heterogeneity, one finds that such clusters, and accordingly $\xi(t)$, increase with time until occupying a substantial fraction of the system size for $t = \tau_\alpha$.

In order to probe and measure the spatial correlations of the mobility field, two important kinds of correlation functions have been introduced. The first is spatial correlation function [7]

$$G_4(r;t) = \langle c(\mathbf{r};t,0)c(\mathbf{0};t,0)\rangle - \langle c(\mathbf{r};t,0)\rangle^2, \tag{10.2}$$

where brackets denote thermal average over equilibrium dynamics. This expression is the equivalent to the two-point correlation function in critical phenomena. By analyzing its dependence (decrease) on $\mathbf{r}$ one can obtain $\xi(t)$. The second function to have played a very important role in the study of glassy dynamics is the analog of the susceptibility in ordinary phase transitions. Such a function is defined in terms of the fluctuations of a *global* time-dependent correlation function $C(t,0)$ [5]

$$\chi_4(t) = N[\langle C(t,0)^2\rangle - \langle C(t,0)\rangle^2], \tag{10.3}$$

where N is the number of particles in the system. If one thinks of $C(t,0)$ as the order parameter of the glass transition, $\chi_4(t)$ measures its fluctuations (see Sec. 10.2.2 for more details). Note that since $C(t,0)$ is itself a two-point correlation function, as it compares the system at two different times, the function $\chi_4(t)$ is a four-point function.

---

[a]The relaxation time is usually defined as the time t at which a finite fraction of the system, say one half, is relaxed.

Again, as in critical phenomena, one can link the two kinds of correlation functions as

$$\chi_4(t) = \int \mathrm{d}r\, G_4(r;t). \tag{10.4}$$

One therefore expects that if

$$G_4(r;t) \sim \frac{A(t)}{r^p} e^{-r/\xi_4(t)} \tag{10.5}$$

with p a suitable exponent then $\chi_4(t)$ measures the typical number of particles involved in correlated motion (assuming that the prefactor $A(t)$ does not change considerably with t). We show in Fig. 10.2 the behavior of $\chi_4(t)$ in an atomistic simulation for different degrees of supercooling. One indeed finds that $\chi_4(t)$ increases as a function of time at fixed temperature, and that its peak increases when decreasing the temperature.

The realization that glassy dynamics becomes progressively more correlated in space — thanks to the introduction of the above correlation functions — has opened the way to a field-theoretical analysis of the glass transition and to strong connections with replica theory. The aim of this chapter is to briefly review this relationship, the impact that ideas and methods from replica theory have had on the field of dynamical correlations, and discuss future research directions.

Before concluding this introduction, we wish to stress that the dynamical heterogeneity of glassy dynamics encompasses a variety of phenomena that is broader than the one we briefly recalled above [4]. The existence of dynamical correlations is strongly related to the existence of dynamical facilitation; assessing how facilitation influences the space-time correlations associated with dynamical heterogeneity has been a very important topic in the field [8]. Furthermore, the realization that to characterize glassy dynamics one has to focus on high-order dynamical correlation functions has suggested that likewise non-linear response functions should play an important role [9]. This insight has been confirmed, and is now used to characterize spatial properties of glassy dynamics in experiments [10]. We refer to the book [4] for a more thorough introduction to the field of dynamical heterogeneity. We will come back to some of the points discussed above at the end of this chapter when discussing future research directions.

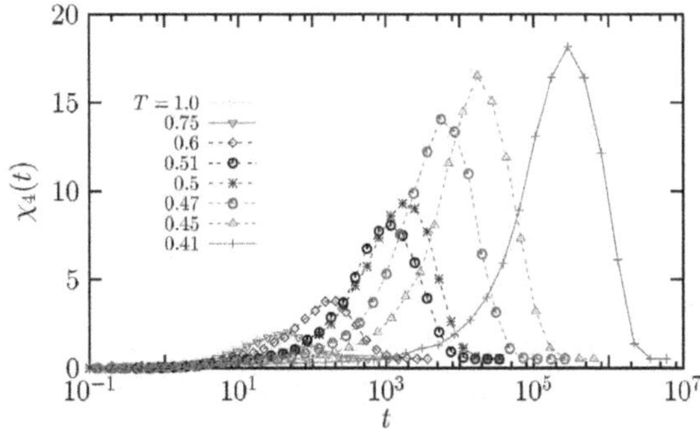

Fig. 10.2. Time dependence of $\chi_4(t)$ obtained using the self-intermediate scattering function for $C(t,0)$ from a molecular dynamics simulation of a Lennard-Jones supercooled liquid.

10.2. *p*-Spin Model and Dynamical Heterogeneity

The theoretical underpinnings of dynamical heterogeneity in supercooled liquids and glasses owe much to simplified models. Perhaps no model has had a larger impact on the study of dynamical heterogeneity, or the glass transition as a whole, than the p-spin spin glass model. In this section, we go over the key physical highlights of that model.

10.2.1. *RSB and metastable states*

The p-spin model was first introduced in the context of the glass transition by Kirkpatrick and Thirumalai in 1987 as an exactly solvable toy model whose dynamical solution coincides precisely with that of the schematic version of the microscopic mode-coupling theory (MCT) of liquid-state dynamics [11]. Specifically, starting from the Hamiltonian

$$H = - \sum_{1 \leq i_1 < i_2 \cdots < i_p \leq N} J_{i_1 i_2 \cdots i_p} s_{i_1} s_{i_2} \cdots s_{i_p} \tag{10.6}$$

with integer p and $p > 2$, Gaussian couplings with zero mean and variance $\frac{p!}{2N^{p-1}}$, and the constraint $\frac{1}{N} \sum_{i=1}^{N} s_i^2 = 1$, one finds the exact dynamical equation for the spin-spin correlation function $C(t) = \frac{1}{N} \sum_{i=1}^{N} \langle s_i(t) s_i(0) \rangle$ (brackets denote average over thermal noise and quenched couplings)

$$\frac{\partial C(t)}{\partial t} + TC(t) + \frac{p}{2T} \int_0^t d\tau \, C^{p-1}(t - \tau) \frac{\partial C(\tau)}{\partial \tau} = 0 \tag{10.7}$$

with $C(0) = 1$ and T the temperature set by the thermal noise. This non-linear integro-differential equation is identical to the schematic equation of motion for the density correlator for $p = 3$ [12, 13]. Although not specifically stated in the original work of Kirkpatrick and Thirumalai, the construction of such an exact equation from an underlying model follows the same logical path taken by Kraichnan decades before in the formulation of the direct interaction approximation (DIA) for the Navier–Stokes equation [14]. In particular, the introduction of quenched randomness exactly renders all diagrams from the field-theoretic solution subleading except for the *melonic* diagrams [15]. In this sense, the original work of Kirkpatrick and Thirumalai amounts to a realizable model for the MCT equations of liquids. The very same considerations are at play in the exact solution to quantum models such as the SYK model [16]. The realizability of the p-spin model means that one can take the model more literally, and explore its properties beyond those afforded by the already known high temperature properties of the schematic MCT equations. These more global properties form a mean-field foundation for the random first-order theory (RFOT) of the glass transition as formulated by Kirkpatrick, Thirumalai and Wolynes two years later [17].

The dynamical properties of the model for $p > 2$ can be divided into two regimes. In the high temperature regime the fluctuation-dissipation theorem (FDT) holds and only the spin-spin correlator, which is a function of time differences only, is required for a complete solution. This quantity decays as a single exponential function in time if temperature is sufficiently high. As the temperature is lowered, a plateau in the relaxation appears. The duration of the plateau grows in time as the temperature is lowered until a sharp transition to a non-ergodic behavior at a temperature T_d occurs. This transition to an arrested state can be viewed as a purely dynamical phenomenon, although as we will discuss below, the transition can be given a thermodynamic-like meaning. Below T_d the FDT is violated and aging behavior sets in. This behavior, which requires the consideration of both the spin-spin correlation function and the associated response function unlike the simpler MCT equation written above, was first exactly solved by Cugliandolo and Kurchan in 1993 [18].

The replica method provides an essentially complete thermodynamic picture of the free energy of the p-spin model at all temperatures [19, 20]. The high temperature regime above T_d corresponds to a replica symmetric solution where the free energy is smooth and contains only one basin corresponding to the ergodic *liquid* state. The transition at T_d is a harbinger of replica symmetry breaking that occurs in one-step (1RSB, by contrast to the infinite step, ∞RSB, that occurs in the Sherrington–Kirkpatrick model [20]). Below T_d the free energy fractures into an extensive number of metastable free energy minima separated by barriers that are infinitely large in the thermodynamic, $N \to \infty$, limit. The configurational entropy, or complexity, counts the number of metastable states in a given energy range. At a temperature $T_K < T_d$, the complexity becomes subextensive in N. This *entropy vanishing* transition, which occurs deep in the glass state, may be viewed as the analog of the empirically-defined Kauzmann transition, where an entropy crisis (the crossing of the configurational entropy associated with the crystal and glass) is envisioned to occur in real materials [21]. It should be noted that in some variants of p-spin and related models, such as the hard-spin (Ising) version of the p-spin model, ∞RSB may occur where the free energy landscape takes on a hierarchical structure [22, 23]. Evidence for this type of transition (the Gardner transition) also appears to find some support in more realistic off-lattice simulation models, although we will not discuss this behavior further [24].

10.2.2. $\chi_4(t)$ *and the dynamical overlap*

The dynamical behavior of the p-spin model is also quite remarkable. One can define a static overlap $Q = \frac{1}{N} \sum_\alpha s_\alpha s'_\alpha$ which measures how similar two different configurations denoted by $\mathbf{s}$ and $\mathbf{s}'$ are. The logarithm of the probability distribution of the static overlap defines an effective potential, called the Franz–Parisi potential, which exhibits non-trivial features as temperature is lowered [25]. In particular, at high temperatures the Franz–Parisi potential exhibits a single minimum centered at $Q = 0$, indicating that the stable phase of the model is a completely disordered *liquid* phase. As temperature is lowered, the function begins to lose convexity, eventually developing a second minimum away from $Q = 0$ below T_d. Within mean-field theory this static behavior has important implications for the dynamics. In particular, it implies that there is a diverging dynamical length scale upon approaching the dynamical transition which is accompanied by dynamically heterogeneous behavior.

To quantify and characterize dynamical heterogeneity, and by analogy the notion of a diverging dynamical length scale, we can generalize the definition of the overlap to consider configurations at different times, $Q(t) = \frac{1}{N} \sum_i s_i(0) s_i(t)$. The measure of fluctuations of this quantity, $\chi_4(t) = N(\langle Q(t)^2 \rangle - \langle Q(t) \rangle^2)$, is the precise analog of the function $\chi_4(t)$ defined in Eq. (10.3). If the system has a dynamical critical point with a diverging length scale, then $\chi_4(t)$ should diverge as $T \to T_d$ from above. Indeed, this is precisely what happens in the p-spin model. Because the model has no spatial scale, any analog of $G_4(r;t)$ is not meaningful, and the diverging length scale must be inferred from the behavior of $\chi_4(t)$ itself. In a physical sense the model is however clearly heterogeneous in the following manner: for a given realization of disorder, the behavior of the local spin-spin correlation function varies from site to site. When averaged over all sites and disorder realizations, the variance of these local dynamical fluctuations diverges at the dynamical critical point.

The arguments leading to the formulation of $\chi_4(t)$ for the p-spin model and the calculation of its growth as T_d is approached were first put forward by Franz and Parisi in 2000 [26]. Technically, Franz and Parisi defined a closely related function, $\chi_{FP}(t)$, which is simpler to calculate directly in the p-spin model, and is closely related to definition of $\chi_{\mathbf{k}}(\mathbf{q}, t)$ within the inhomogeneous MCT (IMCT) formulation discussed in Sec. 10.2.3. This work was influential in motivating the first calculation of $\chi_4(t)$ in molecular dynamics simulations of supercooled liquids by Glotzer and coworkers [27]. It should be noted that a decade prior to the work of Franz and Parisi, Kirkpatrick and Thirumalai outlined the behavior of dynamical overlap fluctuations in Potts glasses, which are in the same 1RSB class as the p-spin model [28]. Kirkpatrick and Thirumalai calculated the behavior of the four-point correlator via the summation of ladder diagrams, noting that the ladder sum diverges at T_d, implying a diverging dynamical length scale at the transition in the model. It is interesting that this mode of calculation is distinct from the approach taken by Franz and Parisi, yet leads to identical conclusions. The summation of ladder diagrams was employed by Bouchaud and Biroli in the first attempt at formulating a microscopic liquid-state theory for $\chi_4(t)$ [29]. Lastly, it has been argued in [30] that the behavior of $\chi_{FP}(t) \sim \chi_4(t)$ should be nearly identical to that of the simpler quantity $\chi_T = \frac{dC(t)}{dT}$ (see Sec. 10.2.3). The behavior of the latter two quantities are illustrated in Fig. 10.3.

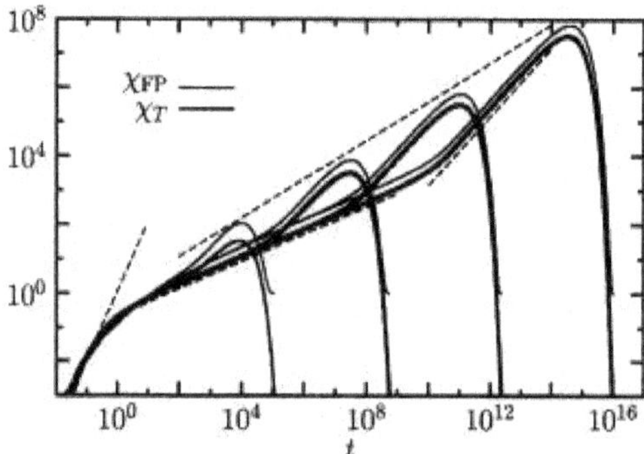

Fig. 10.3.   Growth of $\chi_{FP}(t) \sim \chi_4(t)$ in the p-spin model for $p{=}3$ as the dynamical transition $T_d = 0.612$ is approached from above. Comparison is made to $\chi_T = \frac{dC(t)}{dT}$, which is discussed in Ref. [31]. Reprinted figure with permission from L. Berthier, G. Biroli, J.-P. Bouchaud, W. Kob, K. Miyazaki, and D. R. Reichman, J. Chem. Phys. 126(18), 184504, (2007). ©(2009) AIP Publishing.

It is natural to compare the detailed scaling behavior that emerges from the study of dynamical heterogeneity and $\chi_4(t)$ in the p-spin model to that found in *in silico* studies of supercooled liquids [32]. The scaling behavior in the p-spin model and in liquid-state MCT, where the spatial structure of the associated features of dynamical heterogeneity is more explicit [33], is subtle, and will be explicated in detail below. On a qualitative level, examination of the simulated growth of $\chi_4(t)$ in the p-spin model as illustrated in Fig. 10.3 is quite similar to that seen in computer simulations as shown already in Fig. 10.2. However, on a quantitative level such mean-field approaches do not capture the space-time scaling properties associated with dynamical heterogeneity. The discrepancies between the predicted mean-field behavior and those extracted from liquid-state simulations require care to discern. Using simulations up to $N = 10,000$ particles, Stein and Andersen found scaling exponents in quantitative agreement with those presented in the next section [34]. However, more extensive simulations by Karmakar *et al.* with up to $N = 300,000$ find that, for example, the peak of $\chi_4(t)$ and the dynamical correlation length grows with exponents that differ from those predicted from the IMCT discussed in Sec. 10.2.3 [35]. Given the fact that in three dimensions, mean-field behavior is modified by effects such as local particle hopping and dynamical facilitation [1], these discrepancies are not surprising, and in fact the qualitative agreement between particle-based simulations and mean-field theory provides at least some evidence that the theory provides a reasonable picture of supercooled behavior and a foundation for a more developed understanding of glassy behavior in low spatial dimensions.

10.2.3. *Dynamical heterogeneity and MCT*

As discussed in Sec. 10.2.2, Eq. (10.7) for the p-spin model is mathematically equivalent to the MCT equation for molecular fluids, and the nonlinear susceptibility (either $\chi_4(t)$ or $\chi_{FP}(t)$) for the p-spin model captures features of the simulated $\chi_4(t)$ for the molecular glasses qualitatively, even though the p-spin model is completely blind to the spatial information associated with particle dynamics. Due to this parallel, it is natural to expect that molecular MCT can be extended to the calculation of the non-linear susceptibility for molecular glasses. This extension has indeed been put forward in Refs. [29, 33]. The key idea is to reformulate MCT in the presence of a spatially modulated external field governed by a perturbed Hamiltonian $U_{\text{ext}}(\mathbf{q}) = \lambda \rho_{\mathbf{q}}$, where $\mathbf{q}$ is the wave vector associated with the spatial modulation by the external field. The derivative of the density-density correlation function $F(\mathbf{k}, \mathbf{k} + \mathbf{q}, t)$ with respect to the external perturbation is nothing but the three-point susceptibility $\chi_{\mathbf{k}}(\mathbf{q}, t) \propto \delta F(\mathbf{k}, \mathbf{k} + \mathbf{q}, t)/\delta U_{\text{ext}}(\mathbf{q})$. It captures spatially-dependent dynamical correlations as it probes how much a perturbation at, say, the origin affects the dynamics at a distance r. If one considers the two-point dynamical correlation function as the order parameter of the glass transition, then $\chi_{\mathbf{k}}(\mathbf{q})$ captures the critical behavior, just like the linear susceptibility does in standard second-order phase transitions. The function $\chi_{\mathbf{k}}(\mathbf{q}, t)$ thus conveys the same information as the four-point correlation function $\chi_4(t)$, which measures the fluctuations of the dynamical overlap. Importantly, this function inherently contains information on the length scale associated with the dynamical heterogeneity probed by the spatially modulated field at wave vector $\mathbf{q}$, information that is absent in the counterpart of the

p-spin model. The resulting inhomogeneous MCT (IMCT) equation is

$$\frac{\partial \chi_{\mathbf{k}}(\mathbf{q},t)}{\partial t} + \mu_{\mathbf{k}} \chi_{\mathbf{k}}(\mathbf{q},t) + \int_0^t d\tau \, M_{\mathbf{k}}(t-\tau)\frac{\partial \chi_{\mathbf{k}}(\mathbf{q},\tau)}{\partial \tau}$$

$$+ \int_0^t d\tau \, H_{\mathbf{k}}(\mathbf{q},t-\tau)\frac{\partial F_{|\mathbf{k}+\mathbf{q}|}(\tau)}{\partial \tau} = \mathcal{S}_{\mathbf{k}}(\mathbf{q},t), \tag{10.8}$$

where $\mu_{\mathbf{k}}$ is a diffusion coefficient, $\mathcal{S}_{\mathbf{k}}(\mathbf{q},t)$ is an inhomogeneous source term that does not affect the critical behavior, $M_{\mathbf{k}}(t)$ is the memory kernel of the conventional MCT equation, and $H_{\mathbf{k}}(\mathbf{q},t)$ is given by

$$H_{\mathbf{k}}(\mathbf{q},t) = \frac{2|\mathbf{k}|}{|\mathbf{k}+\mathbf{q}|} \int d\mathbf{k}' V_{\mathbf{k}}(\mathbf{k}',\mathbf{k}-\mathbf{k}')V_{\mathbf{k}+\mathbf{q}}(\mathbf{k}-\mathbf{k}',\mathbf{q}+\mathbf{k}')\chi_{\mathbf{k}'}(\mathbf{q},t)F_{|\mathbf{k}-\mathbf{k}'|}(t) \tag{10.9}$$

with the vertex function of the conventional MCT $V_{\mathbf{q}}(\mathbf{k},\mathbf{k}')$. Equation (10.8) has been analyzed theoretically and solved numerically [33]. The overall behavior of the solution of Eq. (10.8) can be inferred from the scaling behavior of the MCT equation near the dynamical transition point T_d. The β regime, i.e, the time window close to $\tau_\beta \equiv |T - T_d|^{-1/2a}$ (where a is a specified MCT exponent), corresponds to particles largely staying within the cages formed by their neighbors. We then find

$$\chi_{\mathbf{k}}(\mathbf{q},t) = \frac{C_{\mathbf{k}}}{\sqrt{\varepsilon}+\Gamma q^2}g_\beta(\Gamma q^2/\sqrt{\varepsilon},t/\tau_\beta) \tag{10.10}$$

with Γ a constant and C_k a weak function of $k = |\vec{k}|$. $\varepsilon \equiv |1 - T/T_d|$ is the scaled distance from the dynamical transition point. $g_\beta(x,y)$ is a scaling function that ensures the early-β relaxation $g(0,y) \sim y^a$ at $y \to 0$ and the late-β relaxation $\sim y^b$ (where b is another MCT exponent) at $y \to \infty$, which seamlessly converges to the scaling behavior in the α-relaxation regime. By contrast, the scaling in the α regime, in which particles escape their cages, is characterized by $\tau_\alpha = \varepsilon^{-\gamma}$ (with $\gamma = (1/a+1/b)$), which is given by

$$\chi_{\mathbf{k}}(\mathbf{q},t) = \frac{1}{\sqrt{\varepsilon}(\sqrt{\varepsilon}+\Gamma q^2)}f(\Gamma q^2/\sqrt{\varepsilon})g_{\alpha,k}(t/\tau_\alpha), \tag{10.11}$$

where the scaling function $f(x)$ behaves as $\sim 1/x$ at $x \gg 1$, from the condition that the length scale should become independent of ε. Both scalings, Eqs. (10.10) and (10.11), assert that the dynamical length scale should diverge as $\xi \propto \varepsilon^{-\nu}$, with $\nu = 1/4$ rather than $1/2$ as for a Landau theory. These asymptotic scalings can be checked by the full wave vector dependent solution of the IMCT equation. However, integrating Eq. (10.8) numerically is a formidable task due to the coupling of the two wave vectors k and q. From the analogy that the schematic MCT (Eq. (10.7) for the p-spin model) captures the main features of the dynamical behavior of the full k-dependent MCT equation, we simplify the IMCT equation by removing one of the wave vectors, k, which monitors only the static microscopic length of the order of the molecular size. This schematic IMCT equation is numerically integrated and the results for $q = 0$ are shown in Fig. 10.4; the q dependence of various time regimes are shown in Fig. 10.5. The behavior of $\chi(q = 0,t)$ is similar to that of the p-spin model in Fig. 10.3, characterized by the two scalings t^a and t^b for the early-β ($t < \tau_\beta$) and the late-β regimes ($\tau_\beta < t < \tau_\alpha$), respectively, followed by a growing peak $\chi(q = 0, t = \tau_\alpha) \approx \varepsilon^{-1}$ at $t \approx \tau_\alpha$. The q dependence of

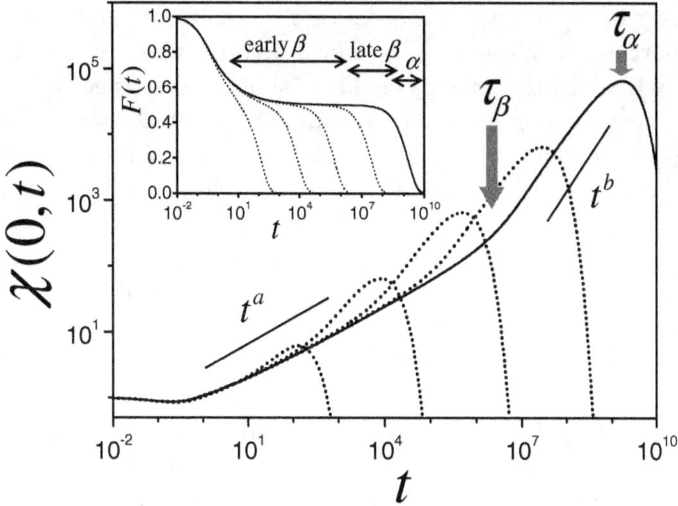

Fig. 10.4. $\chi(q = 0, t)$ for various values of $\varepsilon(= 10^{-1} \sim 10^{-5})$. Note that there are two algebraic growth regimes characterized by t^a and t^b, respectively, below and above τ_β. The peak height at τ_α is scaled as $\chi^* \approx 1/\varepsilon$. The inset reports the density correlation $F(t)$, corresponding to the main panel.

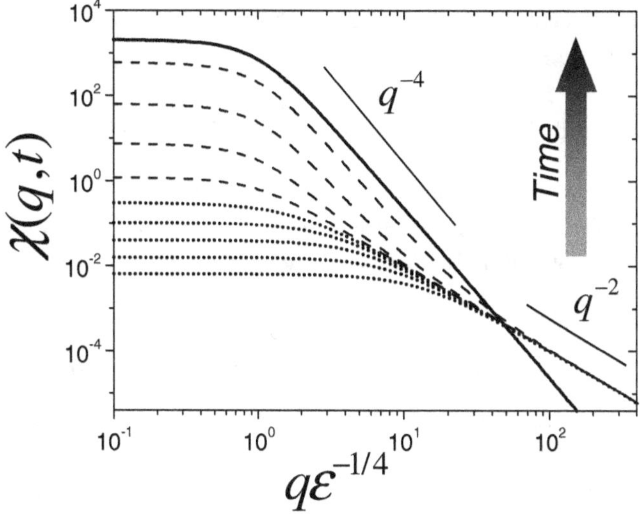

Fig. 10.5. Wave vector q dependence of $\chi(q, t)$ for various t from well below τ_β up to $t \approx \tau_\alpha$. $\varepsilon = |1 - T/T_d|$ is fixed to 10^{-6}. q is scaled by $\varepsilon^{-1/4}$ ($\propto \xi(\tau_\alpha)$). The dotted lines are Lorentzian functions capturing the early-β regime. The solid line marks $t = \tau_\alpha$, where $1/q^4$ at large q. Between τ_β and τ_α (the late-β regime), one observes a crossover from one regime to the other.

$\chi(q, t)$ is interesting as it demonstrates the rich hierarchical growth of the fluctuations. First, in the early-β regime ($t < \tau_\beta$), $\chi(q, t) \approx \xi^2(t)/(1 + q^2 \xi^2(t))$ is characterized by an Ornstein–Zernike form and the dynamical correlation length grows with time as $\xi \propto t^{a/2}$, algebraically characterized by the MCT exponent a. As the system enters the late-β regime, ξ stops growing and is given by $\varepsilon^{-1/4}$ and, concomitantly, the shape of the spectrum develops a tail at large q, which eventually behaves as $1/q^4$ at τ_α. These results imply that the morphology of the dynamical heterogeneity changes non-trivially over time. As time progresses, fluctuations grow, but the shape of dynamically heterogeneous regions are more fractal at the early-β regime and then gradually fatten in the late-β (and early-α) regime, where dynamically heterogeneous regions become compact.

Verifying these results in molecular glass formers by simulations and experiments is a difficult task because MCT, and therefore IMCT, are mean-field descriptions whose *critical* behavior are washed out by thermal hopping and/or facilitation dynamics in finite dimensional systems, especially in the α regime. Results of a recent simulation study, however, show nearly quantitative agreement with IMCT in the β regime. More specifically, these simulations show both the algebraic growth of ξ with t and the power-law $\xi \sim \varepsilon^{-1/4}$ [36]. This behavior is in harmony with the general notion that MCT works best in the β regime, where the collective dynamics of the unstable modes navigating saddles in the energy landscape dominate. Although MCT and IMCT are only capable of describing the moderately supercooled regime above T_d or intermediate time scales shorter than the α regime, it is safe to claim that it is the sole first-principles theory that describes the hierarchically rich dynamics over several decades without a single fitting parameter. A generalization of IMCT to the higher-order glass singularities that are found, for instance, deep in the repulsive-attractive glass-forming regime of certain liquids has also been proposed [37].

10.3. From Mean-Field Theory to Finite Dimensions

In this section, we first present the building blocks of the theory of dynamical fluctuations going from mean-field to finite-dimensions. We then present the numerical results obtained in a three dimensional model of glassy liquids where non-mean field effects are suppressed.

10.3.1. *Breaking up χ_4: Different kinds of dynamical fluctuations*

Section 10.2 focused on dynamical susceptibilities rather than on dynamical correlations. In particular, all χ's (e.g., χ_T) were obtained as the response of a suitable correlation function to changing a control parameter. These susceptibilities were originally thought to scale the same way as χ_4 does. Only later, when considering finite-dimensional fluctuations around MCT, was it realized that this is not the case: a *squaring* effect emerges in χ_4. Its physical origin can be understood by splitting the fluctuations of the dynamical correlation $C(t,0)$ into two parts:

$$\chi_4(t) = \langle (C(t,0) - \langle C(t,0) \rangle_T)^2 \rangle_{T,IC} + \langle (\langle C(t,0) \rangle_T - \langle C(t,0) \rangle_{T,IC})^2 \rangle_{T,IC}. \quad (10.12)$$

The first contribution describes the fluctuations at fixed initial condition (due to thermal noise), while the second describes the fluctuations due to the initial conditions. The latter dominates. This was first realized in terms of a liquid-state diagrammatic field theory in [30, 31], and explicitly demonstrated and further studied in molecular dynamics simulations in [38]. A full understanding was reached after the work [39, 40], which used replica field theory to study dynamical fluctuations in the β regime (first using the analogy between disordered systems and glasses in [39] and then later directly in glassy liquids [40]).

The authors of Ref. [39] showed that the statistics of the overlap fluctuations at the plateau, i.e. in the β regime, are the same as those associated with the spinodal of the random field Ising model (RFIM) [41]. In this mapping, the spinodal is the counterpart of the MCT transition, whereas the disorder is the analog of the initial metastable state, in which the system resides as set by the initial condition.

In terms of scaling, this set of results implies that

$$\chi_4 \sim \chi_T^2, \tag{10.13}$$

where, as mentioned above, $\chi_T = \frac{dC(t)}{dT}$. In other words, the dynamical fluctuations are proportional to the square of the dynamical susceptibility. This scaling can be understood by noticing that some small fluctuations in the initial conditions (the fluctuations related to observables that relax slowly) lead to giant fluctuations of $C(t,0)$. This amplification is governed by the dynamical susceptibilities. For instance, a metastable state with a free energy that is slightly lower than the average has a much longer relaxation time, and hence a correlation function with a much longer plateau. Therefore, there is a component of the fluctuations that can be roughly written as $\delta C(t,0) = \chi_T \frac{dT}{df} \delta f$. It is the square of this contribution which leads to the scaling relation given by Eq. (10.13). Note that this is the same type of argument used to relate connected and disconnected susceptibilities in the RFIM [41].

The mapping between the field theory of the overlap fluctuations and the spinodal of the RFIM has played a very important role in firmly establishing the importance of self-induced disorder fluctuations [42, 43], already highlighted in [44], and in opening the way to a finite dimensional analysis of the MCT transition. This analysis is very intricate, as the spinodal of the RFIM cannot be studied perturbatively [45, 46]. We shall return to this point in the conclusions.

10.3.2. *Gaussian core model*

In finite dimensions, numerical verification of the mean-field description given by MCT has never been satisfactory. Thermally activated dynamics and other mechanisms such as dynamical facilitation, which are generically local, obfuscate the mean-field physics as temperature is lowered. The window over which the MCT power-law divergence of the relaxation quantitatively describes relaxation behavior is narrow in realistic simulations of three-dimensional liquids. Likewise, the agreement between the growing dynamical heterogeneity predicted by IMCT and that of molecular dynamics is largely qualitative. A realistic particle-based model system in finite dimensions, which compellingly verifies the behaviors predicted by MCT and IMCT, has therefore long been sought. The Gaussian core model (GCM) is such a model [47]. This system describes a monatomic fluid whose interaction is pair-wise and Gaussian. Contrary to other monatomic glass models, the nucleation rate of the GCM is extremely small at high densities, and thus the GCM does not crystallize even without size polydispersity. Ikeda and coworkers have found

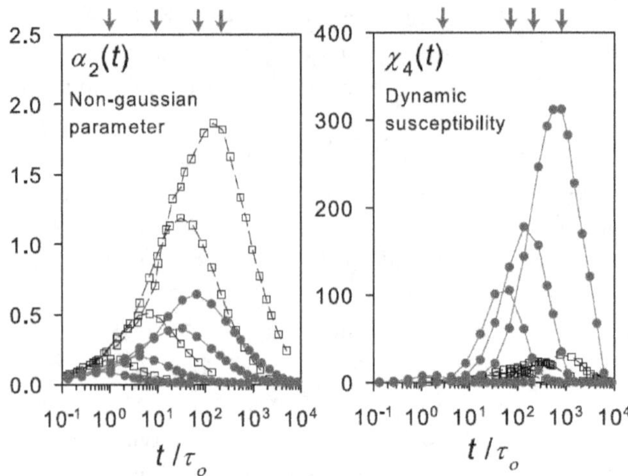

Fig. 10.6. The non-Gaussian parameter $\alpha_2(t)$ (left) and the non-linear susceptibility $\chi_4(t)$ (right) of the GCM (circles) and the KA mixture (empty squares) for several temperatures near their respective dynamic transition points [48]. The time is scaled by the relaxation time at their respective onset temperatures, τ_o. Reprinted figure with permission from D. Coslovich, A. Ikeda, and K. Miyazaki, Phys. Rev. E 93, 042602 (2016). ©(2016) American Physical Society.

that the slow dynamics of the supercooled GCM is described unprecedentedly well by MCT and IMCT [47, 48]. In particular, the dynamical transition temperature T_d is closer to that predicted by MCT and the window of power-law scaling is wider than for any other simulated glass former thus far. In addition, the dynamics are spatially very uniform. For typical glass formers, such as Lennard-Jones binary mixtures, the distribution of particle displacements exhibits clear bimodal structure, thus clearly separating particles into fast and slow groups. This behavior has been believed to be one of the signatures of heterogeneous dynamics. However, the distribution of particle displacements in the GCM is singly-peaked and nearly Gaussian, even in the deeply supercooled regime. More surprising is the fact that dynamical heterogeneity is extremely strong in the GCM despite the near-Gaussian statistics of displacements [48]. Figure 10.6 shows the non-Gaussian parameter $\alpha_2(t)$ and the nonlinear susceptibilities $\chi_4(t)$ for the GCM and the Kob–Andersen binary Lennard-Jones (KA) mixture, respectively. $\alpha_2(t)$, which monitors the deviation of the distribution of particle displacements from a Gaussian, is markedly smaller in the GCM than in the KA mixture at similar degrees of supercooling. For $\chi_4(t)$, the situation is reversed. The peak heights for the GCM are larger by more than an order of magnitude than for the KA mixture. Furthermore, the temperature dependence of the peak height of $\chi_4(t)$ for the GCM is well fitted by

$$\chi_4(t = \tau_\alpha) \sim |T - T_d|^{-2}, \tag{10.14}$$

up to very close to T_d, which is in excellent agreement with the IMCT and mean-field predictions (taking into account the *squaring* effect discussed in Sec. 10.3.1, Eq. (10.13)). This set of agreements is not accidental. The analysis of the modes associated with saddle points on the energy landscape shows that the participation ratio of these modes are more extended than in typical glass formers such as the KA mixture, strongly indicating that unstable modes are delocalized. This is exactly the scenario encoded in MCT, namely that the dynamical transition of MCT is a geometrical transition with a diverging cooperative length scale over unstable saddles, the number of which vanishes as T_d is approached from above [49, 50]. In addition, the average activation energy in the GCM is far higher than in the KA mixture, which implies that thermal activation processes are suppressed. It would be interesting to investigate the q dependence of $\chi_4(q,t)$ for the GCM and verify the scaling behavior of IMCT. Such simulations, however, would be extremely expensive due to the long cutoff length of the Gaussian interaction potential and the large overlaps with the nearest particles at high densities.

10.4. Conclusion and Perspectives

Dynamical heterogeneity is a core aspect of the phenomenology of glass-forming liquids. The replica technique has played an important role in unveiling physical mechanisms behind the emergence of the phenomenon. There are several directions in which it may still prove instrumental.

First, dynamical heterogeneity encompasses a set of phenomena that is broader than just spatial dynamical correlations [4]. Can the replica technique be used to get insights into the full range of these phenomena? As a concrete example, we refer the reader to very recent work based on the large dimensional analysis of the glass transition [51], which provides a new perspective on the emerging non-Gaussian behavior of local dynamical observables. This and related lines of research are ripe for exploration with replica techniques.

The replica technique and its dynamical counterparts have provided a sound platform to explain the development of the spatial and temporal behavior of dynamical correlations approaching the MCT transition. However, in real glass-forming liquids this is only the beginning of the story. In fact, dynamical heterogeneity becomes stronger, more prominent and is characterized by larger length scales approaching T_g, as remarkably shown in very recent work [52]. What can be said about this behavior from replica theory? More specifically, as such behavior is clearly related to that of dynamical facilitation, does replica theory have anything to say about it? Approaches based on RFOT theory addressing some of these issues have been developed in [53] (see also the recent discussion in [54]). An interesting and complementary research direction would consider the non-perturbative corrections based on the mapping to the RFIM, as discussed above. These corrections are different from the non-perturbative ones associated to the growth of a static length-scale connected to growing amorphous order. They are instead related to an avalanche effect in which a region more prone to rearrange induces cascades of rearrangements nearby, as it happens for the spinodal of the RFIM [45]. What remains to be done is to translate these ideas, based on the theory of static fluctuations of the overlap, in a fully fledged dynamical theory. This program is certainly not easy. Except close to T_d and in the β regime [46], this is a fully open problem. It is nevertheless one worth trying, as it would offer a detailed, replica-based theory of dynamical facilitation.

Acknowledgments

We want to deeply thank all our collaborators on the topics covered in this chapter, in particular L. Berthier, J.-P. Bouchaud, D. Coslovich, O. Dauchot, A. Ikeda, F. Ladieu, G. Tarjus, M. Tarzia for many discussions on all these issues over the years. GB, DRR, and KM are members of the Simons Foundation "Cracking the Glass Problem" collaboration. We would like to thank all of our colleagues in this collaboration for many years of stimulating discussions. GB and DRR are partially supported by the Simons Foundation (GB-Grant No. 454935, DRR-Grant No. 454951). KM is financially supported by KAKENHI 20H00128.

References

[1] L. Berthier and G. Biroli, *Rev. Mod. Phys.* **83**, 587–645, (2011).

[2] O. Dauchot, G. Marty, and G. Biroli, *Phys. Rev. Lett.* **95**, 265701, (2005).

[3] A. Widmer-Cooper, H. Perry, P. Harrowell, and D. R. Reichman, *J. Chem. Phys.* **131**(19), 194508, (2009).

[4] L. Berthier, G. Biroli, J.-P. Bouchaud, L. Cipelletti, and W. van Saarloos, *Dynamical heterogeneities in glasses, colloids, and granular media.* vol. 150, (Oxford University Press, 2011).

[5] W. Kob, C. Donati, S. J. Plimpton, P. H. Poole, and S. C. Glotzer, *Phys. Rev. Lett.* **79**, 2827–2830, (1997).

[6] J.-P. Hansen and I. R. McDonald, *Theory of Simple Liquids.* (Academic Press, Amsterdam, 2013), 4th edition.

[7] C. Dasgupta, A. V. Indrani, S. Ramaswamy, and M. K. Phani, *Europhys. Lett.* **15**(3), 307–312, (1991).

[8] G. Biroli and J. P. Garrahan, *J. Chem. Phys.* **138**(12), 12A301, (2013).

[9] J.-P. Bouchaud and G. Biroli, *Phys. Rev. B.* **72**, 064204, (2005).

[10] S. Albert, T. Bauer, M. Michl, G. Biroli, J.-P. Bouchaud, A. Loidl, P. Lunkenheimer, R. Tourbot, C. Wiertel-Gasquet, and F. Ladieu, *Science.* **352**(6291), 1308–1311, (2016).

[11] T. R. Kirkpatrick and D. Thirumalai, *Phys. Rev. B.* **36**, 5388–5397, (1987).

[12] W. Götze, *Complex Dynamics of Glass-Forming Liquids: A Mode-Coupling Theory.* (Oxford University Press, 2009).

[13] D. R. Reichman and P. Charbonneau, *J. Stat. Mech.* **2005**(05), P05013, (2005).

[14] R. H. Kraichnan, *J. Fluid Mech.* **5**(4), 497–543, (1959).

[15] J.-P. Bouchaud, L. Cugliandolo, J. Kurchan, and M. Mézard, *Physica A.* **226**(3), 243–273, (1996).

[16] V. Rosenhaus, *J. Phys. A.* **52**(32), 323001, (2019).

[17] T. R. Kirkpatrick, D. Thirumalai, and P. G. Wolynes, *Phys. Rev. A.* **40**, 1045–1054, (1989).

[18] L. F. Cugliandolo and J. Kurchan, *Phys. Rev. Lett.* **71**, 173–176, (1993).

[19] T. Castellani and A. Cavagna, *J. Stat. Mech.* **2005**(05), P05012, (2005).

[20] M. Mézard, G. Parisi, and M. A. Virasoro, *Spin Glass Theory and Beyond: An Introduction to the Replica Method and Its Applications.* (World Scientific, 1987).

[21] P. Debenedetti, *Metastable Liquids: Concepts and Principles.* (Princeton University Press, Princeton, 1996).

[22] E. Gardner, *Nucl. Phys. B.* **257**, 747–765, (1985).

[23] D. J. Gross, I. Kanter, and H. Sompolinsky, *Phys. Rev. Lett.* **55**, 304–307, (1985).

[24] L. Berthier, G. Biroli, P. Charbonneau, E. I. Corwin, S. Franz, and F. Zamponi, *J. Chem. Phys.* **151**(1), 010901, (2019).

[25] S. Franz and G. Parisi, *J. Physique I.* **5**(11), 1401–1415, (1995).

[26] S. Franz and G. Parisi, *J. Physics.* **12**(29), 6335–6342, (2000).

[27] S. C. Glotzer, V. N. Novikov, and T. B. Schrøder, *J. Chem. Phys.* **112**(2), 509–512, (2000).

[28] T. R. Kirkpatrick and D. Thirumalai, *Phys. Rev. A.* **37**(11), 4439, (1988).

[29] G. Biroli and J.-P. Bouchaud, *Europhys. Lett.* **67**(1), 21–27, (2004).

[30] L. Berthier, G. Biroli, J.-P. Bouchaud, W. Kob, K. Miyazaki, and D. R. Reichman, *J. Chem. Phys.* **126**(18), 184503, (2007).

[31] L. Berthier, G. Biroli, J.-P. Bouchaud, W. Kob, K. Miyazaki, and D. R. Reichman, *J. Chem. Phys.* **126**(18), 184504, (2007).

[32] L. Berthier, *Phys. Rev. E.* **69**, 020201, (2004).

[33] G. Biroli, J.-P. Bouchaud, K. Miyazaki, and D. R. Reichman, *Phys. Rev. Lett.* **97**, 195701, (2006).

[34] R. S. L. Stein and H. C. Andersen, *Phys. Rev. Lett.* **101**, 267802, (2008).

[35] S. Karmakar, C. Dasgupta, and S. Sastry, *Proc. Nat. Acad. Sci. U.S.A.* **106**(10), 3675–3679, (2009).

[36] I. Tah and S. Karmakar, *Phys. Rev. Research.* **2**, 022067, (2020).

[37] S. K. Nandi, G. Biroli, J.-P. Bouchaud, K. Miyazaki, and D. R. Reichman, *Phys. Rev. Lett.* **113**, 245701, (2014).

[38] L. Berthier and R. L. Jack, *Phys. Rev. E.* **76**, 041509, (2007).

[39] S. Franz, G. Parisi, F. Ricci-Tersenghi, and T. Rizzo, *Eur. Phys. J. E.* **34**(9), 1–17, (2011).

[40] S. Franz, H. Jacquin, G. Parisi, P. Urbani, and F. Zamponi, *Proc. Nat. Acad. Sci. U.S.A.* **109**(46), 18725–18730, (2012).

[41] T. Nattermann. In *Spin glasses and random fields*, pp. 277–298. World Scientific (1998).

[42] G. Biroli, C. Cammarota, G. Tarjus, and M. Tarzia, *Phys. Rev. B.* **98**, 174205, (2018).

[43] G. Biroli, C. Cammarota, G. Tarjus, and M. Tarzia, *Phys. Rev. B.* **98**, 174206, (2018).

[44] J. D. Stevenson, A. M. Walczak, R. W. Hall, and P. G. Wolynes, *J. Chem. Phys.* **129**(19), 194505, (2008).

[45] S. K. Nandi, G. Biroli, and G. Tarjus, *Phys. Rev. Lett.* **116**, 145701, (2016).

[46] T. Rizzo, *Phys. Rev. B.* **94**, 014202, (2016).

[47] A. Ikeda and K. Miyazaki, *Phys. Rev. Lett.* **106**, 015701, (2011).

[48] D. Coslovich, A. Ikeda, and K. Miyazaki, *Phys. Rev. E.* **93**, 042602, (2016).

[49] G. Biroli and J.-P. Bouchaud. In eds. P. G. Wolynes and V. Lubchenko, *Structural Glasses and Supercooled Liquids: Theory, Experiment, and Applications*, pp. 31–113. Wiley (2012).

[50] D. Coslovich, A. Ninarello, and L. Berthier, *SciPost Phys.* **7**, 077, (2019).

[51] G. Biroli, P. Charbonneau, G. Folena, Y. Hu, and F. Zamponi, *Phys. Rev. Lett.* **128**, 175501, (2022).

[52] C. Scalliet, B. Guiselin, and L. Berthier, *arXiv:2207.00491.* (2022).

[53] S. M. Bhattacharyya, B. Bagchi, and P. G. Wolynes, *Proc. Nat. Acad. Sci. U.S.A.* **105**(42), 16077–16082, (2008).

[54] G. Biroli and J.-P. Bouchaud, *arXiv:2208.05866.* (2022).

Chapter 11

The Kauzmann Transition to an Ideal Glass Phase

Chiara Cammarota*, Misaki Ozawa[†] and Gilles Tarjus[‡]

*Dipartimento di Fisica, La Sapienza Universitá di Roma, Piazzale Aldo Moro 5,
00185 Rome, Italy
[†]Université Grenoble Alpes, CNRS, LIPhy, 38000 Grenoble, France
[‡]LPTMC, CNRS-UMR 7600, Sorbonne Université, 4 Pl. Jussieu,
F-75005 Paris, France

The idea that a thermodynamic glass transition of some sort underlies the observed glass formation has been highly debated since Kauzmann first stressed the hypothetical entropy crisis that could take place if one were able to equilibrate supercooled liquids below the experimental glass transition temperature T_{g}. This *a priori* unreachable transition at some $T_{\mathrm{K}} < T_{\mathrm{g}}$ has since received a firm theoretical basis as a key feature predicted by the mean-field theory of the glass transition. In this chapter, we assess whether, and in which form, such a transition can survive in finite dimensions, and we review some of the recent computer simulation work addressing the issue in two- and three-dimensional glass-forming liquid models. We also discuss theoretical reasons to focus on an apparently inaccessible singularity.

11.1. Introduction

The existence of a thermodynamic phase transition underlying the experimentally observed glass transformation phenomenon has been a recurring theme in theoretical studies of glass formation. This transition would be between the liquid — most generally a supercooled liquid phase which is metastable with respect to some stabler crystalline phase — and an ideal glass phase. The issue may sound just as futile as arguing over how many angels can dance on the head of a pin because the thermodynamic transition is unreachable due to the very strong slowing down of relaxation that is precisely the phenomenological fingerprint of glass formation. Yet, one can argue that there is some merit to trying to address the problem. One first obvious reason is that despite being unobservable, the putative thermodynamic transition may still control the physics of the glassy slowdown and provide a framework and scaling laws to describe the empirical data. Accordingly, more or less indirect signatures or vestiges of the thermodynamic transition could be probed and would allow for distinguishing the theoretical approaches that do and do not predict such features.

The story of an unreachable transition at some temperature T_K lower than the experimental glass transition (or transformation) temperature T_g begins with Walter Kauzmann's seminal 1948 paper [1]. Addressing the nature of metastability and of the glass transition, Kauzmann collected equilibrium entropy data from various glass-forming materials and plotted the temperature dependence of the entropy difference between the supercooled liquid and the crystal. He noted that this difference decreases sharply with decreasing temperature, more so for molecular glass-forming liquids now known as *fragile* [2], such as glucose or lactic acid, for which the entropy difference drops by a factor of 2 or 3 between the melting point and T_g. At T_g the entropy difference essentially saturates because the liquid falls in a nonequilibrium glass state. However, one may wonder what would happen if the liquid could be equilibrated to still lower temperatures, a point that Kauzmann qualitatively illustrated by extrapolating the experimental curve below T_g. He found that a simple extrapolation leads to an apparent paradox: The entropy difference between the liquid and the crystal vanishes at a nonzero temperature $T_K < T_g$ below which it becomes negative. This temperature T_K is now known as the Kauzmann temperature.

Although Kauzmann himself preferred an interpretation in terms of a pseudo-critical point at (or above) T_K marking the limit of stability of the supercooled liquid with respect to crystal nucleation, T_K has since been associated in many glass studies with a thermodynamic (equilibrium) transition to an ideal glass phase. This view has been pursued by Julian H. Gibbs and his coworkers. Gibbs and DiMarzio found through a mean-field quasi-lattice approach an equilibrium glass transition at which the *configurational entropy* of glass-forming polymers vanishes [3, 4]. Adam and Gibbs later proposed a mechanism to relate the slowdown of relaxation as one lowers temperature to the dearth of available configurations, as quantified by the decrease of that configurational entropy. This mechanism involves cooperatively rearranging regions whose size diverges at the equilibrium glass transition temperature T_K [5].

What gave firmer ground to the notion of a thermodynamic glass transition at some nonzero $T_K < T_g$ is the insight by Ted Kirkpatrick, Dave Thirumalai, and Peter Wolynes that such an entropy-vanishing transition is present in some mean-field spin-glass models, such as Potts glasses and p-spin models [6, 7]. The transition, which in the replica formalism corresponds to a one-step replica symmetry breaking (1RSB) [8], has been dubbed *random first-order transition*, and its scaling extension to finite dimensions has been developed in a series of papers starting with Ref. [9] (see also Chapters 7 and 8). In what follows we will often simply refer to the thermodynamic ideal glass transition as the *Kauzmann transition* to stress the fact that it corresponds to a (configurational) entropy crisis, despite the caveat concerning Kauzmann's own interpretation.

The key step reinforcing the theoretical foundation was the full solution of glass formation for liquids in infinite dimensions that was proven to be associated with the very same 1RSB phenomenology as the above-cited mean-field spin-glass models [10, 11]. The Kauzmann (random first-order) transition is thus a direct prediction of the mean-field theory of glass-forming liquids as obtained in infinite dimensions. This recent result by itself forces one to seriously consider the issue of an underlying thermodynamic glass transition in finite dimensions. In particular, as in the conventional Landau–Ginzburg–Wilson theoretical approach of phase transitions starting from a mean-field description [12], it opens a line of research concerning the role of spatial fluctuations on the transition when moving away from infinite dimensions to reach the physical world of two and three dimensions.

The goal of this chapter is to discuss the nature and the existence of a thermodynamic transition between the liquid and an ideal glass phase in finite-dimensional glass-forming liquids and, considering the fact that it is (at least currently) an essentially inaccessible transition point, to assess the usefulness of the concept for describing the actual glass formation process. In this respect it differs from previous literature reviewing the Kauzmann transition and arguments about its achievability [13, 14].

11.2. Nature of the Kauzmann Transition in Mean-Field and in Finite Dimensions

The core of the mean-field description of glass formation is the existence of a complex free-energy landscape in which equivalent metastable states emerge in an exponentially large (in system size) number below a first critical temperature $T_\mathrm{d} > T_\mathrm{K}$. Below T_d, which corresponds to a purely dynamical transition, ergodicity is broken and the system stays trapped forever in one of the metastable states due to the presence of infinite free-energy barriers. As the temperature is further decreased, the number of metastable states decreases and the configurational entropy per particle, which is defined as the logarithm of the number of typical metastable states divided by the number of molecules, vanishes at the Kauzmann temperature T_K. A bona fide thermodynamic transition to an ideal glass then takes place. Energy, entropy, configurational entropy, and free energy are continuous at the transition but the order parameter, which similarly to spin-glass models can be best chosen as an overlap between configurations and will be discussed in more detail below, has a discontinuity between a low value (characterizing the liquid formed by the superposition of all typical metastable states) and a high value (characterizing the ideal glass). As already mentioned, this phenomenon corresponds to a 1RSB transition in the replica formalism.

This scenario is exactly realized in liquids in infinite dimensions and can be taken as the Landau theory of the glass transition [10, 11]. However, at odds with the treatment of more conventional phase transitions such as the liquid-gas one, extension of this mean-field Landau theory to include spatial fluctuations that are generically present in finite dimensions but absent in infinite dimensions is extremely delicate. One reason is that the very notion of metastability is ill-defined in finite-dimensional statistical mechanics because localized fluctuations destroy it, making the lifetime of metastable states finite in any finite dimension. Strictly speaking, the dynamical transition at T_d cannot persist and/or must be smeared out. On the one hand, the absence of ergodicity breaking at T_d is good news as the liquid is allowed to relax between T_d and T_K through putative activated nucleation processes [9] (see also Chapter 8). On the other hand, the whole theoretical construction, including the central notion of configurational entropy, may completely lose its meaning. The effect of fluctuations, which at this point we do not attempt to better characterize, may indeed be drastic and completely wipe out the mean-field 1RSB scenario. For instance, it is known to be the case for some disordered spin models such as Potts glasses that show no glassiness at all or a continuous (fullRSB) transition in three dimensions [15–18] or for the random Lorentz gas that displays a continuous localization phenomenon associated with a percolation transition in three dimensions [19, 20], both types of systems that nonetheless follow the 1RSB scenario in the fully connected (infinite-dimensional) limit.

What about finite-dimensional glass-forming liquids? In particular, is there an operational way to define a configurational entropy? One line of research that started with Martin Goldstein [21], and was developed into a systematic framework by Frank Stillinger and coworkers [22, 23], considers the potential energy landscape and its multiple minima, also called inherent structures. Contrary to the multiplicity of metastable states in a free-energy landscape at a nonzero temperature, the multiplicity of inherent structures is rigorously defined even in finite dimensions and their number can be used to define a configurational entropy [24]. Stillinger argued that due to the ubiquitous presence of point defects, this configurational entropy cannot vanish at a nonzero T_{K}, thereby preventing the existence of an ideal glass transition [25]. This argument, however, is not conclusive [26, 27] as it only holds when counting potential-energy minima which are much more numerous than metastable free-energy minima in the mean-field limit and are not necessarily relevant for describing the glass transition. We will come back to numerical implementations of this so-defined configurational entropy below.

A substitute for metastable free-energy states based on collections of liquid configurations could be defined in finite dimensions with the help of the dynamics by setting a threshold for the lifetime of these collections. After all, if the lifetime threshold is large compared to the local equilibration time, the system can equilibrate within the metastable state and metastability is thus observable in practice, as it is the case for the *supercooled* liquid phase with respect to the crystalline phase. The case of glassy metastable states is, however, more subtle because in the observable temperature range all timescales (local equilibration time, lifetime, etc.) are expected to be comparable. Moreover, while simple symmetry operations can be used to immediately tell apart, e.g., supercooled liquid from crystalline phase, there are no such symmetry operations allowing one to distinguish one metastable state from another, and the very concept of metastable state lifetime is less sharply defined. Configurations can still in principle be grouped into larger entities, on the basis of their relative distance or the height of the energy barriers separating them. Such entities are sometimes referred to as metabasins [23], but in spite of the pioneering work of Andrea Heuer and coworkers [28], the procedure is hard to implement numerically and has not been used to examine the Kauzmann transition [29].

Another possibility is to restrict the spatial fluctuations so that a nonconvex free-energy landscape with multiple minima can still be defined. This is what happens when considering small system sizes. Long wavelength fluctuations as well as rare localized fluctuations are suppressed by the limited sample size, and some form of metastability can then be studied. A specific protocol of this kind has actually been proposed and implemented to measure a fundamental lengthscale associated with the putative thermodynamic glass transition [30, 31]. By freezing the liquid configuration outside a spherical cavity of radius R and letting the system equilibrate inside the cavity in the presence of the frozen boundary condition, one can extract a crossover length corresponding to the cavity size beyond which the boundary condition no longer fixes the state of the liquid inside. In a schematic adaptation of the mean-field theory to finite dimensions, this length results from the competition between the interfacial cost due to the surface tension between distinct metastable states and the configurational entropy gain resulting from the multiplicity of available states. It diverges at the Kauzmann transition when the configurational entropy vanishes. Importantly, such a lengthscale, ℓ_{PTS}, which is associated with a point-to-set spatial correlation [32], can be probed in finite-dimensional liquids, even if the concept of metastable state is not properly defined in the unconstrained (bulk) liquid. We will also get back to this quantity below.

An alternative approach is to introduce an appropriate order parameter and the associated free energy that can play the role of the Landau effective potential in the mean-field description while being generalizable to finite dimensions. A convenient choice is the so-called Franz–Parisi potential [33, 34]. The first step is to introduce an overlap order parameter Q that measures the similarity between two liquid configurations, or, more properly, between the associated coarse-grained density profiles. Considering two configurations of the liquid, $\mathbf{r}_\alpha^N \equiv \{\mathbf{r}_i^{(\alpha)}\}_{i=1,\ldots,N}$ defined from the particle positions $\mathbf{r}_i^{(\alpha)}$ with $\alpha = 1, 2$, the overlap function between the configurations can be defined as

$$Q_a[\mathbf{r}_1^N, \mathbf{r}_2^N] = \frac{1}{N} \sum_{i,j=1}^{N} w(|\mathbf{r}_i^{(1)} - \mathbf{r}_j^{(2)}|/a), \qquad (11.1)$$

with $w(x) \approx 1$ if $x < 1$ and ≈ 0 otherwise, a being a tolerance associated with the typical amplitude of thermal vibrations in the liquid. As such the overlap function Q_a is small if the configurations are uncorrelated and large if they are strongly correlated, and it can therefore be used to distinguish liquid (low overlap) from glass (high overlap) phases.

The Franz–Parisi potential represents the average cost of maintaining equilibrium liquid configurations $\mathbf{r}^N$ at a global overlap value Q with a reference liquid configuration $\mathbf{r}_0^N$. When all configurations are sampled from the equilibrium measure at the same temperature T, its expression reads

$$V(Q) = -\frac{T}{N} \int d\mathbf{r}_0^N \frac{e^{-\beta \mathcal{H}[\mathbf{r}_0^N]}}{Z} \ln \int d\mathbf{r}^N \frac{e^{-\beta \mathcal{H}[\mathbf{r}^N]}}{Z} \delta(Q - Q_a[\mathbf{r}^N, \mathbf{r}_0^N]), \qquad (11.2)$$

where $\beta = 1/(k_B T)$, $Z \equiv \int d\mathbf{r}^N \exp(-\beta \mathcal{H}[\mathbf{r}^N])$ is a partition function, $\mathcal{H}[\mathbf{r}^N]$ is the liquid Hamiltonian, and $\delta(x)$ is the Dirac delta function.

The mean-field Franz–Parisi potential $V(Q)$ loses convexity at some temperature T_{c} and, below the dynamical transition temperature $T_{\mathrm{d}} < T_{\mathrm{c}}$, a second minimum that is metastable with respect to the stable liquid minimum appears at a high value of the overlap and corresponds to the glass phase. As T further decreases the second minimum becomes deeper and at the Kauzmann temperature T_{K} the two minima have the same free-energy value; this corresponds to a discontinuous transition between the liquid and the ideal glass. Between T_{d} and T_{K} the difference in free-energy between the two minima is exactly the configurational entropy (times the temperature). Note also that below T_{c}, tilting the potential by applying a source term linearly coupled to the overlap, $-\epsilon Q$,

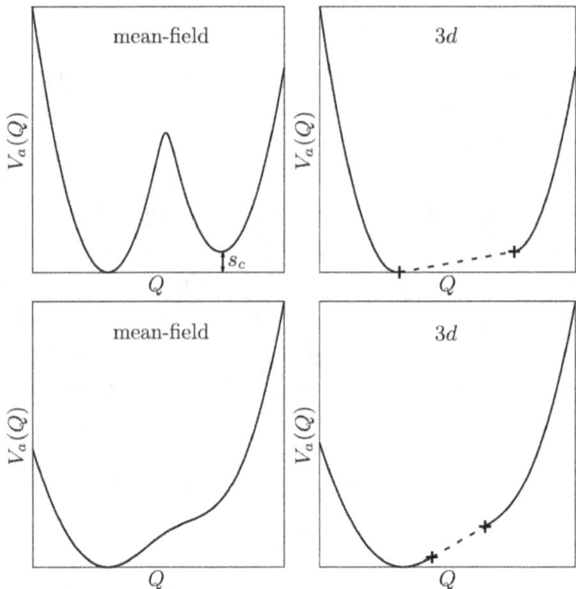

Fig. 11.1.   Sketch of the Franz–Parisi potential $V(Q)$ in the mean-field limit (left panels) and for a three-dimensional glass-former in the thermodynamic limit (right panels) [35]. In the top panels, the temperature is slightly above the Kauzmann temperature T_K. In the bottom panels the temperature is slightly below T_c at which a singular point with $V''(Q) = V'''(Q) = 0$ exists. (Above T_c the potential is convex with $V''(Q) > 0$ everywhere.) Reprinted from B. Guiselin, G. Tarjus, and L. Berthier, J. Chem. Phys. 153, 224502 (2020), with the permission of AIP Publishing.

induces for some $\epsilon^*(T) > 0$ a first-order transition between a low-overlap phase and a high-overlap one [33, 34].

The Franz–Parisi potential $V(Q)$ is well-defined in finite dimensions as well. It should then be convex in the thermodynamic limit but can nonetheless be singular by displaying at low enough temperature a linear segment over a range of Q, as illustrated in Fig. 11.1. If so, a discontinuous transition (associated with a horizontal segment) can still take place at some nonzero T_K. The difference between the values of $V(Q)$ at the high-overlap end of the segment and at the stable liquid minimum corresponds also in finite dimensions to the difference in free-energy of the two phases and operationally defines a configurational entropy, as does in an essentially equivalent way the slope $\epsilon^*(T)$ of the segment. With such definitions, T_K corresponds to a vanishing of the configurational entropy, although the precise link between this configurational entropy and metastable states is blurred in finite dimensions. In any case, one expects that the hypothetical thermodynamic transition would then still be associated with a divergence of the point-to-set correlation length ℓ_{PTS}, as the cavities of the point-to-set construction would then end up having a vanishing free energy gain in changing state at T_K. Although nothing guarantees that the 1RSB nature of the ideal glass phase persists, the divergence of the point-to-set correlation length conveys the idea that the glass phase would have an infinite coherence length. In other words, some form of infinite-range *amorphous order* is present [36] despite the fact that *by the naked eye* nothing in the structure seems to distinguish glass from liquid.

One issue that we will now discuss is whether one indeed finds in $3d$ and $2d$ glass-forming liquids, either in finite-size samples or in the thermodynamic limit, an effective potential that looks like the sketches displayed in Fig. 11.1 and whether the data is compatible with the presence of an equilibrium glass transition at a nonzero T_K.

11.3. Does a Thermodynamic Glass Transition Exist in Two- and Three-Dimensional Liquids?

11.3.1. *The issue of timescale and system size*

As already stressed, the Kauzmann thermodynamic glass transition is inaccessible by simply cooling a liquid. This is the obvious consequence of the slowing down of relaxation that, in practice, prevents equilibration below some temperature $T_g > T_K$. This is true in experiments [37], and even alternative ways of generating ultrastable glasses by physical vapor deposition [14, 38, 39], fall short of reaching the very near vicinity of the extrapolated T_K. The situation is even less favorable for computer simulations that span a less extended timescale domain in equilibrium than experimental techniques. However, computer simulations allow one to access microscopic properties in great detail and, more importantly, to implement protocols and compute quantities, such as the point-to-set correlation length, the statistics of the overlap between configurations, the Franz–Parisi potential, etc., that are hard or impossible to probe experimentally.

Furthermore, advanced simulation techniques such as parallel tempering [40, 41] and swap Monte Carlo [42] that use nonphysical particle moves have tremendously increased the range of temperature over which equilibrium liquid configurations can be numerically prepared [43–45]. In specifically tailored polydisperse glass-forming models, the swap algorithm allows one to sample equilibrium configurations at temperatures below the estimated calorimetric glass transition temperature T_g [44, 46–48]. Yet, as in the case of the experimentally generated ultrastable glasses, the close vicinity of the putative T_K is still not attainable (and studying the equilibrium dynamics via physical particle moves remains, of course, limited). This implies that no *direct* evidence of a thermodynamic glass transition at T_K can be obtained from such numerical studies at present.

Another limitation of computer simulations of glass-forming liquids is the accessible range of system sizes. When dealing with the complex computation of quantities associated with the thermodynamic fluctuations of the overlap between configurations at the lowest temperatures at which equilibration is achievable, no more than a few thousands of particles in three dimensions can be simulated with present-day computer capabilities [49, 50]. The thermodynamic limit can then only be inferred through finite-size scaling analyses. The upside of small system sizes is that metastability can be observed and that an estimate of a (finite-size) configurational entropy can be extracted from the measured Franz–Parisi potential. This process is illustrated in Fig. 11.2 [51]. From simple renormalization-group arguments [52], one expects that such a finite-size configurational entropy is meaningful in terms of metastable states up to sizes of the order of the point-to-set correlation length. For larger system sizes, a configurational entropy can still be operationally defined from the Franz–Parisi

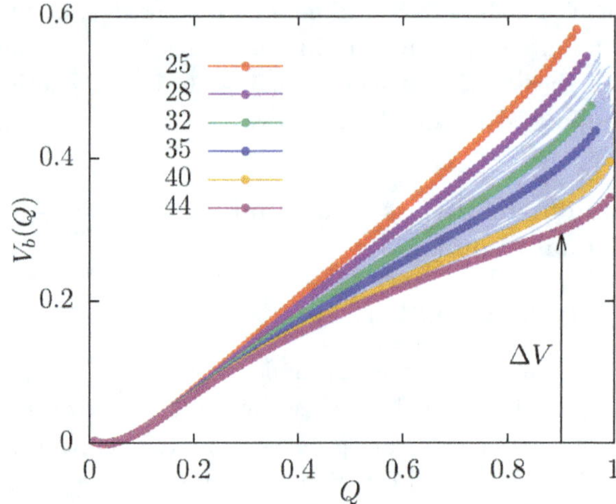

Fig. 11.2.   Evolution with the pressure of the Franz–Parisi potential $V(Q)$ for a $3d$ polydisperse hard-sphere glass-former with $N = 111$ atoms and different pressures P [51]. For $P \gtrsim 28$, the potential is clearly nonconvex, and ΔV can be taken as an ersatz for a finite-size configurational entropy. Reprinted figure with permission from L. Berthier, Phys. Rev. Lett. 127, 088002 (2021). ©(2021) by the American Physical Society.

potential (even in the thermodynamic limit where convexity is restored, see Sec. 11.2 and Fig. 11.1), but we stress again that it lacks a direct interpretation in terms of metastable states.

11.3.2. *Configurational entropy and point-to-set correlation length*

Keeping in mind that the putative Kauzmann transition cannot be directly observed nor very closely approached when decreasing temperature, it is nonetheless worth checking if the behavior of glass-forming liquids is at least compatible with the scenario of glass formation controlled by an underlying thermodynamic glass transition. The two most obvious observables that are relevant for this purpose are the configurational entropy, or rather its different substitutes and estimates, and the point-to-set correlation length extracted from the cavity construction previously discussed.

The configurational entropy has been studied in two- and three-dimensional glass-forming liquid models through both the Franz–Parisi potential and the number of inherent structures in the potential-energy landscape [43, 46, 50, 53]. For the latter, it is, of course, impossible to proceed by brute-force enumeration of the minima except for very small systems [54, 55]. The configurational entropy is instead approximated by the difference between the full thermodynamic entropy and the vibrational entropy, whose calculation is itself nontrivial due to anharmonicity effects and to the mixing entropy present in polydisperse systems [56–58]. As anticipated these complications result in the configurational entropy associated with the potential energy landscape being significantly larger than that estimated from the Franz–Parisi potential [43, 46, 59].

Whatever its definition, the configurational entropy nevertheless decreases with decreasing temperature [24, 60, 61], much like the experimentally determined one [62]

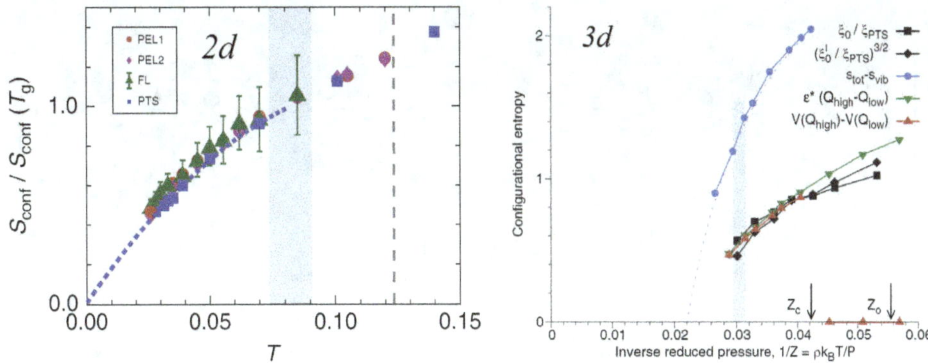

Fig. 11.3. Left: Rescaled configurational entropy obtained through the potential-energy landscape and the point-to-set correlation length (see main text), for a $2d$ polydisperse soft particles as a function of temperature. Figure reproduced from Ref. [59] under CC BY 4.0 license `https://creativecommons.org/licenses/by/4.0/`. Right: Configurational entropy obtained through the potential-energy landscape, the point-to-set correlation length, and the Franz–Parisi potential (see main text) for a $3d$ polydisperse mixture of hard spheres as a function of inverse reduced pressure [46]. Reprinted figure with permission from L. Berthier, P. Charbonneau, D. Coslovich, A. Ninarello, M. Ozawa, and S. Yaida, Proc. Nat. Acad. Sci. U.S.A. 114, 11356–11361 (2017). ©(2017) National Academy of Sciences.

and Kauzmann's original plot [1]. Different behaviors are found for two- and three-dimensional glass-forming liquids, as shown in Fig. 11.3. For three-dimensional liquids, extrapolation of the temperature dependence is compatible with a nonzero Kauzmann temperature [46, 61] whereas for two-dimensional glass-forming liquids, $T_{\mathrm{K}} = 0$ appears to best fit the data [59].

The point-to-set correlation length ℓ_{PTS} has also been measured by several groups and found to increase with decreasing temperature, by a modest factor of $2 - 3$ in $3d$ [31, 46, 63, 64] and of $6 - 7$ in $2d$ [59] over the accessible temperature range. Again, the numerical data do not approach the anticipated singularity at T_{K}, where ℓ_{PTS} should diverge and therefore do not prove the existence of an underlying thermodynamic glass transition, but they do show significant growth, much larger than that observed for any simple (point-to-point) structural correlation length. Furthermore, $\ell_{\mathrm{PTS}}(T)$ behaves as the inverse of the configurational entropy measured from the Franz–Parisi potential [46, 59] as predicted by the mean-field theory (assuming that the surface tension between glassy states essentially does not vary with temperature in the relevant range).

11.3.3. *A necessary condition for the existence of a Kauzmann transition*

As already pointed out, despite the overall consistency between numerical results and mean-field predictions, it is virtually impossible to provide a direct experimental or numerical evidence for the existence of a Kauzmann transition. One may wonder if, conversely, it could be possible to prove that it is absent in finite dimensions. We have already discussed in Sec. 11.2 that *a priori* no rigorous arguments seem to preclude the presence of a random-first-order ideal glass transition at a nonzero temperature.

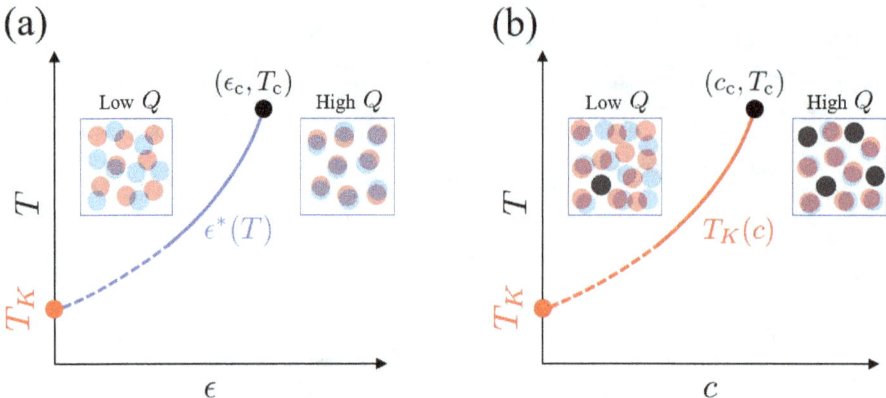

Fig. 11.4.   Schematic plot of the extended phase diagrams of glass-forming liquids obtained by applying a uniform source ϵ biasing the value of the overlap Q (a) or by randomly pinning a fraction c of particles (b), expected for three-dimensional systems. The mean-field theory predicts a line of conventional first-order transition (with latent heat associated with a discontinuous jump of entropy) emerging from the Kauzmann transition in $\epsilon = 0$ and ending at a critical point at (ϵ_c, T_c) in the former case (a) and a line of Kauzmann transition (at which the configurational entropy vanishes and the point-to-set correlation length diverges) also ending in a critical point at (c_c, T_c) in the latter case (b).

An indirect way of addressing the issue is to consider the Franz–Parisi effective potential characterizing the fluctuations of the overlap with a reference liquid configuration and the extended phase diagram obtained by applying a linear uniform source $\epsilon > 0$ to the overlap (see Sec. 11.2). In the ϵ–T phase diagram, the singular behavior of the effective potential, if present, leads to a line of first-order transition ending in a critical point at T_c (and a nonzero ϵ_c). This is sketched in Fig. 11.4(a).

The hypothetical T_K is at the low-temperature limit of the line of first-order transition when $\epsilon = 0$. Clearly, if the line does not exist, and especially if no critical point exists at some $T_c > 0$, no Kauzmann transition can be present. Investigating the critical point and the high-temperature part of the first-order line is numerically very demanding but doable [43, 65, 66]. Computing the Franz–Parisi potential requires sampling a range of large overlap values that correspond to rare occurrences, but this can be achieved by using the large-deviation framework and importance sampling techniques [67]. Furthermore, when studying the existence and the nature of a critical point, one can optimize the calculation by playing with the temperature T_0 at which the reference configurations are sampled [50]. Although the accessible system sizes are limited (see Sec. 11.3.1), a finite-size scaling study has given strong support for the existence of a critical point at a nonzero T_c in a three-dimensional glass-forming liquid and the absence of such a nonzero T_c in a two-dimensional one [50, 68]. As theoretically predicted from field-theoretical arguments [69–71], the results are compatible with the critical point (ϵ_c, T_c) being in the universality class of the equilibrium random-field Ising model (RFIM) (see Ref. [72] for an introduction to the model). In particular, the lower critical dimension of the RFIM below which there is no phase transition is rigorously known to be $d = 2$. The finite-size scaling analysis for the $3d$ case is reproduced in Fig. 11.5.

The above study concerning the extended ϵ–T phase diagram and the associated critical point supports the conclusion that a Kauzmann-like glass transition is precluded

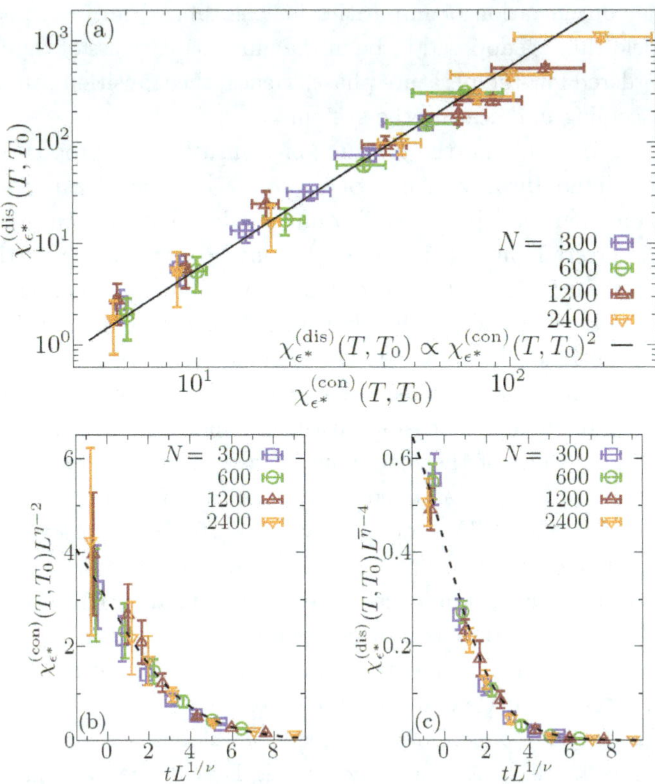

Fig. 11.5. Finite-size scaling analysis of the susceptibilities close to the critical point of a $3d$ glass-forming liquid in the $\epsilon-T$ phase diagram, varying the linear system size $L \propto N^{1/3}$ and the reduced temperature $t = T/T_c - 1$. The so-called connected and disconnected susceptibilities, $\chi_{\epsilon*}^{(con)}$ and $\chi_{\epsilon*}^{(dis)}$, are associated with the overlap fluctuations, and the scaling collapses are obtained with the exponents, $\eta, \bar{\eta}, \nu$, characterizing the universality class of the RFIM. Figure reproduced from Ref. [50] under CC BY 4.0 license `https://creativecommons.org/licenses/by/4.0/`.

in two-dimensional glass-formers while its existence is possible (but not guaranteed) in three dimensions where it may then depend on nonuniversal liquid properties producing the strength of the emergent random field that appears in the effective description (see Ref. [71] and below).

11.3.4. *A thermodynamic glass transition by random pinning*

The Kauzmann transition is not the only inaccessible transition in statistical physics. The equilibrium paramagnetic-to-ferromagnetic transition of the RFIM, which we have already mentioned, is another example. The slowing down of relaxation when approaching the critical point is anomalously strong and has the very same activated character as the glassy slowdown [73, 74]. As a result, it is not possible to reach the vicinity of the transition point by varying the temperature because the system falls off equilibrium at some point where equilibration is no longer achievable in practice. In some experimental realizations of the RFIM, a sufficiently close approach is nonetheless possible to observe a critical scaling behavior [75]. Furthermore, by making use of an additional control parameter, e.g., the concentration of impurities for the diluted anti-ferromagnet in a uniform magnetic field that is supposed to be in the universality class of the RFIM [75], one can access the ordered low-temperature phase. Hence, the transition can in principle be studied by both cooling *and* heating the system.

A similar protocol for studying the Kauzmann transition was proposed for glass-forming systems by Giulio Biroli and one of us [76, 77]. The idea is to choose at random a fraction c of particles in an equilibrium liquid configuration and to freeze them permanently while studying the further evolution of the remaining particles in the presence of the pinned ones [78]. This corresponds to a different boundary condition than the cavity protocol used to access the point-to-set correlation length. The moving particles now form a continuously connected three-dimensional system (in a $3d$ sample, provided that the concentration c of pinned particles is below the percolation threshold), and phase transitions are therefore possible in the thermodynamic limit. The mean-field theory [76] predicts a line of thermodynamic glass transition emerging from the Kauzmann temperature T_K in $c = 0$ and ending in a critical point at some ($c_c > 0, T_c > T_K$), also argued to be in the RFIM universality class [70, 77]. The extended phase diagram in the $c - T$ plane therefore appears similar to that previously considered in the $\epsilon - T$ plane, with one crucial difference: The thermodynamic transition all along the line, except at T_c, now corresponds to a random first-order or Kauzmann-like glass transition, at which the configurational entropy vanishes (yet without replica symmetry breaking). The two extended phase diagrams are sketched in Fig. 11.4.

One advantage of the random pinning protocol or related ones is that it can be realized in experiments [79–81]. A second advantage is that the ideal glass phase is known: When working at constant temperature T by varying the concentration c, the ideal glass phase in the presence of pinned particles corresponds to the initial equilibrium configuration obtained before any particle pinning [82]. Furthermore, it is in principle accessible by following a path in the $c - T$ plane that does not encounter any phase transition.

Notwithstanding these favorable conditions, assessing the presence of a Kauzmann transition with the pinning construction has proven hard numerically due to issues of equilibration time (even in the ideal glass) and of a proper definition of a configurational entropy [83]. Evidence for a glass transition at some $T_K(c)$ has been obtained in rather small systems and without a systematic finite-size scaling analysis [49, 84]. There have been studies of the properties of the ideal glass (or a stable glass) in the presence of pinning, giving a first description of its equilibrium fluctuations [83] and its melting into the liquid through nucleation of the latter phase when temperature is raised [85]. Still, the formation of a glass by nucleation, also predicted by the mean-field theory, has not been observed due to the too large relaxation times involved (while remaining clear of the percolation threshold for the pinned system). Finally, although its properties should be qualitatively similar to those of the (ϵ_c, T_c) critical point recently investigated, a systematic study of the critical endpoint (c_c, T_c) has not yet been attempted. It is anticipated to be very demanding numerically due to its location at the end of a Kauzmann glass transition line, at which the relaxation time is expected to diverge extremely strongly. Establishing the presence of this critical point would nevertheless directly confirm the existence of a Kauzmann glass transition, at least for the pinned system.

11.4. Conclusion and Perspective

To conclude this chapter, we would like to come back to the issue of why one should bother about the existence of an inaccessible phase transition, which, after all, seems a valid question. One lesson learned from studies of the RFIM is that establishing the existence and the properties of the transition via mathematically rigorous methods, the functional renormalization group, or specific (unphysical) algorithms at zero temperature (see Ref. [86] for a review) allows one to rationalize the whole phenomenology observed experimentally and numerically, to cook up adapted observables, and when possible to perform scaling collapses of data. Reaching the same state-of-the-art would clearly be a major step forward for the study of glass-forming liquids.

We have seen that as far as the statics is concerned, the observables devised within the mean-field setting to reflect the properties of the underlying free-energy landscape can be extended to finite dimensions and that they display an overall behavior that is compatible with the existence of a thermodynamic glass transition in three dimensions [46, 49, 68], but not in two dimensions [50, 59]. This, of course, does not prove the existence of a Kauzmann, or random first-order, transition in three-dimensional liquids, but it validates the mean-field scenario as a reasonable starting point for theoretical developments. The concepts of metastable free-energy states and configurational entropy should be bypassed or strongly modified when dealing with finite dimensions. Yet, as discussed above, no fundamental arguments seem to forbid the existence of a thermodynamic glass transition in three dimensions (whereas there are such arguments against the existence of a nonzero T_K in two dimensions). The existence or not of a transition is therefore a nonuniversal feature that may depend on the specific properties of the three-dimensional glass-former. (Indeed, one can construct glass-forming models without a Kauzmann transition [11, 87–89].) This also opens the possibility of finding glass formers with a narrowly avoided thermodynamic glass transition, which for all practical purposes, would play the same role as a true transition. A path to address this issue is via the development of an effective theory taking the overlap between configurations as the fundamental field or variable. Work in this direction suggests that such an effective theory involves *quenched disorder* in the form of a random field and a random coupling [90–92] and that the existence or not of a transition (or how narrowly it is avoided) primarily depends on the relative strength of the random field. Extending the numerical investigation of the global Franz–Parisi potential to that of a local version may then allow one to determine the parameters entering in the effective theory [93]. A similar endeavor could be pursued for the random pinning construction in which quenched disorder plays an important role as well.

More difficult at present is establishing that the dynamical slowdown of relaxation leading to glass transformation is indeed controlled by a thermodynamic glass transition (even a narrowly avoided one). The glassy slowing down prevents an exploration of the asymptotic regime in which scaling about T_K is dominant so that exponents cannot be reliably extracted. Note that this is also partly true in the case of the RFIM, for which the range of dynamical data is not sufficient to accurately determine the exponent characterizing the growth of the activation free-energy barriers when approaching the critical point. However, what is more crucial for glass-forming liquids is that room is left for important if not predominant contributions coming from other dynamical processes unrelated to T_K, such as dynamical facilitation [94], soft modes [95], elasticity [96], or the role of liquid-specific locally preferred atomic arrangements [97, 98]. Establishing the causal relationship between the putative thermodynamic glass transition at T_K and the glassy dynamics beyond the existing empirical but global correlations [99] is therefore the most wanted next stage [100].

References

[1] W. Kauzmann, *Chem. Rev.* **43**(2), 219–256, (1948).

[2] C. A. Angell, *Science.* **267**(5206), 1924–1935, (1995).

[3] J. H. Gibbs, *J. Chem. Phys.* **25**(1), 185–186, (1956).

[4] J. H. Gibbs and E. A. DiMarzio, *J. Chem. Phys.* **28**(3), 373–383, (1958).

[5] G. Adam and J. H. Gibbs, *J. Chem. Phys.* **43**(1), 139–146, (1965).

[6] T. Kirkpatrick and P. Wolynes, *Phys. Rev. A.* **35**(7), 3072, (1987).

[7] T. R. Kirkpatrick and D. Thirumalai, *Phys. Rev. B.* **36**(10), 5388, (1987).

[8] M. Mézard, G. Parisi, and M. A. Virasoro, *Spin glass theory and beyond: An Introduction to the Replica Method and Its Applications.* (World Scientific Publishing Company, 1987).

[9] T. R. Kirkpatrick, D. Thirumalai, and P. G. Wolynes, *Phys. Rev. A.* **40**(2), 1045, (1989).

[10] P. Charbonneau, J. Kurchan, G. Parisi, P. Urbani, and F. Zamponi, *Annu. Rev. Condens. Matter Phys.* **8**, 265–288, (2017).

[11] G. Parisi, P. Urbani, and F. Zamponi, *Theory of simple glasses: exact solutions in infinite dimensions.* (Cambridge University Press, 2020).

[12] J. Zinn-Justin, *Quantum field theory and critical phenomena.* (Oxford University Press, 2021).

[13] C. P. Royall, F. Turci, S. Tatsumi, J. Russo, and J. Robinson, *J. Phys.: Condens. Matter.* **30**(36), 363001, (2018).

[14] M. D. Ediger, *J. Chem. Phys.* **147**(21), 210901, (2017).

[15] C. Brangian, W. Kob, and K. Binder, *J. Phys. A.* **35**(2), 191, (2002).

[16] A. Cruz, L. Fernandez, A. Gordillo-Guerrero, M. Guidetti, A. Maiorano, F. Mantovani, E. Marinari, V. Martin-Mayor, A. M. Sudupe, D. Navarro, et al., *Phys. Rev. B.* **79**(18), 184408, (2009).

[17] C. Cammarota, G. Biroli, M. Tarzia, and G. Tarjus, *Phys. Rev. B.* **87**(6), 064202, (2013).

[18] T. Takahashi and K. Hukushima, *Phys. Rev. E.* **91**(2), 020102, (2015).

[19] G. Biroli, P. Charbonneau, E. I. Corwin, Y. Hu, H. Ikeda, G. Szamel, and F. Zamponi, *Phys. Rev. E.* **103**(3), L030104, (2021).

[20] G. Biroli, P. Charbonneau, Y. Hu, H. Ikeda, G. Szamel, and F. Zamponi, *J. Phys. Chem. B.* **125**(23), 6244–6254, (2021).

[21] M. Goldstein, *J. Chem. Phys.* **51**(9), 3728–3739, (1969).

[22] F. H. Stillinger and T. A. Weber, *Phys. Rev. A.* **25**(2), 978, (1982).

[23] F. H. Stillinger, *Science.* **267**(5206), 1935–1939, (1995).

[24] F. Sciortino, W. Kob, and P. Tartaglia, *Phys. Rev. Lett.* **83**(16), 3214, (1999).

[25] F. H. Stillinger, *J. Chem. Phys.* **88**(12), 7818–7825, (1988).

[26] M. Eastwood and P. Wolynes, *Europhys. Lett.* **60**(4), 587, (2002).

[27] G. Biroli and R. Monasson, *Europhys. Lett.* **50**(2), 155, (2000).

[28] A. Heuer, *J. Phys.: Condens. Matter.* **20**(37), 373101, (2008).

[29] S. Sastry, *J. Phys. Chem. B.* **108**(51), 19698–19702, (2004).

[30] J.-P. Bouchaud and G. Biroli, *J. Chem. Phys.* **121**(15), 7347–7354, (2004).

[31] G. Biroli, J.-P. Bouchaud, A. Cavagna, T. S. Grigera, and P. Verrocchio, *Nat. Phys.* **4**(10), 771–775, (2008).

[32] A. Montanari and G. Semerjian, *J. Stat. Phys.* **125**(1), 23–54, (2006).

[33] S. Franz and G. Parisi, *Journal de Physique I.* **5**(11), 1401–1415, (1995).

[34] S. Franz and G. Parisi, *Phys. Rev. Lett.* **79**(13), 2486, (1997).

[35] B. Guiselin, G. Tarjus, and L. Berthier, *J. Chem. Phys.* **153**(22), 224502, (2020).

[36] J. Kurchan and D. Levine, *J. Phys. A.* **44**(3), 035001, (2010).

[37] M. D. Ediger, C. A. Angell, and S. R. Nagel, *J. Phys. Chem.* **100**(31), 13200–13212, (1996).

[38] S. F. Swallen, K. L. Kearns, M. K. Mapes, Y. S. Kim, R. J. McMahon, M. D. Ediger, T. Wu, L. Yu, and S. Satija, *Science.* **315**(5810), 353–356, (2007).

[39] C. Rodriguez-Tinoco, M. Gonzalez-Silveira, M. A. Ramos, and J. Rodriguez-Viejo, *Riv. del Nuovo Cim.* **45**, 1–82, (2022).

[40] E. Marinari and G. Parisi, *Europhys. Lett.* **19**(6), 451, (1992).

[41] K. Hukushima and K. Nemoto, *J. Phys. Soc. Jpn.* **65**(6), 1604–1608, (1996).

[42] T. S. Grigera and G. Parisi, *Phys. Rev. E.* **63**(4), 045102, (2001).

[43] L. Berthier and D. Coslovich, *Proc. Nat. Acad. Sci. U.S.A.* **111**(32), 11668–11672, (2014).

[44] A. Ninarello, L. Berthier, and D. Coslovich, *Phys. Rev. X.* **7**(2), 021039, (2017).

[45] L. Berthier and D. R. Reichman, *Nat. Rev. Phys.* **5**, 102–116, (2023).

[46] L. Berthier, P. Charbonneau, D. Coslovich, A. Ninarello, M. Ozawa, and S. Yaida, *Proc. Nat. Acad. Sci. U.S.A.* **114**(43), 11356–11361, (2017).

[47] A. D. Parmar, M. Ozawa, and L. Berthier, *Phys. Rev. Lett.* **125**(8), 085505, (2020).

[48] L. Berthier, E. Flenner, C. J. Fullerton, C. Scalliet, and M. Singh, *J. Stat. Mech.* **2019**(6), 064004, (2019).

[49] M. Ozawa, W. Kob, A. Ikeda, and K. Miyazaki, *Proc. Nat. Acad. Sci. U.S.A.* **112**(22), 6914–6919, (2015).

[50] B. Guiselin, L. Berthier, and G. Tarjus, *SciPost Phys.* **12**(3), 091, (2022).

[51] L. Berthier, *Phys. Rev. Lett.* **127**(8), 088002, (2021).

[52] C. Cammarota, G. Biroli, M. Tarzia, and G. Tarjus, *Phys. Rev. Lett.* **106**(11), 115705, (2011).

[53] S. Sengupta, S. Karmakar, C. Dasgupta, and S. Sastry, *Phys. Rev. Lett.* **109**(9), 095705, (2012).

[54] G.-J. Gao, J. Bławzdziewicz, and C. S. O'Hern, *Phys. Rev. E.* **74**(6), 061304, (2006).

[55] D. Wales, *Energy landscapes: Applications to clusters, biomolecules and glasses.* (Cambridge University Press, 2003).

[56] F. Sciortino, *J. Stat. Mech.* **2005**(05), P05015, (2005).

[57] M. Ozawa and L. Berthier, *J. Chem. Phys.* **146**(1), 014502, (2017).

[58] M. Ozawa, G. Parisi, and L. Berthier, *J. Chem. Phys.* **149**(15), 154501, (2018).

[59] L. Berthier, P. Charbonneau, A. Ninarello, M. Ozawa, and S. Yaida, *Nat. Commun.* **10**(1), 1–7, (2019).

[60] S. Sastry, *J. Phys.: Condens. Matter.* **12**(29), 6515, (2000).

[61] L. Berthier, M. Ozawa, and C. Scalliet, *J. Chem. Phys.* **150**(16), 160902, (2019).

[62] S. Tatsumi, S. Aso, and O. Yamamuro, *Phys. Rev. Lett.* **109**(4), 045701, (2012).

[63] G. M. Hocky, T. E. Markland, and D. R. Reichman, *Phys. Rev. Lett.* **108**(22), 225506, (2012).

[64] L. Berthier, P. Charbonneau, and S. Yaida, *J. Chem. Phys.* **144**(2), 024501, (2016).

[65] L. Berthier, *Phys. Rev. E.* **88**(2), 022313, (2013).

[66] L. Berthier and R. L. Jack, *Phys. Rev. Lett.* **114**(20), 205701, (2015).

[67] D. Frenkel and B. Smit, *Understanding molecular simulation: from algorithms to applications.* (Elsevier, 2001).

[68] B. Guiselin, L. Berthier, and G. Tarjus, *Phys. Rev. E.* **102**(4), 042129, (2020).

[69] S. Franz, G. Parisi, and F. Ricci-Tersenghi, *J. Stat. Mech.* **2013**(02), L02001, (2013).

[70] S. Franz and G. Parisi, *J. Stat. Mech.* **2013**(11), P11012, (2013).

[71] G. Biroli, C. Cammarota, G. Tarjus, and M. Tarzia, *Phys. Rev. Lett.* **112**(17), 175701, (2014).

[72] T. Nattermann. In *Spin glasses and random fields*, pp. 277–298. World Scientific, (1998).

[73] J. Villain, *Phys. Rev. Lett.* **52**(17), 1543, (1984).

[74] D. S. Fisher, *Phys. Rev. Lett.* **56**(5), 416, (1986).

[75] D. Belanger. In *Spin glasses and random fields*, pp. 251–275. World Scientific, (1998).

[76] C. Cammarota and G. Biroli, *Proc. Nat. Acad. Sci. U.S.A.* **109**(23), 8850–8855, (2012).

[77] C. Cammarota and G. Biroli, *J. Chem. Phys.* **138**(12), 12A547, (2013).

[78] K. Kim, *Europhys. Lett.* **61**(6), 790, (2003).

[79] S. Gokhale, K. Hima Nagamanasa, R. Ganapathy, and A. Sood, *Nat. Commun.* **5**(1), 1–7, (2014).

[80] G. Kikumoto, N. Torii, C. P. Royall, H. Yao, Y. Saruyama, and S. Tatsumi, *arXiv:2003.06089.* (2020).

[81] R. Das, B. P. Bhowmik, A. B. Puthirath, T. N. Narayanan, and S. Karmakar, *arXiv:2106.06325.* (2021).

[82] P. Scheidler, W. Kob, and K. Binder, *J. Phys. Chem. B.* **108**(21), 6673–6686, (2004).

[83] M. Ozawa, A. Ikeda, K. Miyazaki, and W. Kob, *Phys. Rev. Lett.* **121**(20), 205501, (2018).

[84] W. Kob and L. Berthier, *Phys. Rev. Lett.* **110**(24), 245702, (2013).

[85] G. M. Hocky, L. Berthier, and D. R. Reichman, *J. Chem. Phys.* **141**(22), 224503, (2014).

[86] G. Tarjus and M. Tissier, *The European Physical Journal B.* **93**(3), 1–19, (2020).

[87] A. Moreno, I. Saika-Voivod, E. Zaccarelli, E. La Nave, S. Buldyrev, P. Tartaglia, and F. Sciortino, *J. Chem. Phys.* **124**(20), 204509, (2006).

[88] F. Smallenburg and F. Sciortino, *Nat. Phys.* **9**(9), 554–558, (2013).

[89] W.-S. Xu, J. F. Douglas, and K. F. Freed, *J. Chem. Phys.* **145**(23), 234509, (2016).

[90] J. D. Stevenson, A. M. Walczak, R. W. Hall, and P. G. Wolynes, *J. Chem. Phys.* **129**(19), 194505, (2008).

[91] G. Biroli, C. Cammarota, G. Tarjus, and M. Tarzia, *Phys. Rev. B.* **98**(17), 174205, (2018).

[92] G. Biroli, C. Cammarota, G. Tarjus, and M. Tarzia, *Phys. Rev. B.* **98**(17), 174206, (2018).

[93] B. Guiselin, G. Tarjus, and L. Berthier, *J. Chem. Phys.* **156**(19), 194503, (2022).

[94] D. Chandler and J. P. Garrahan, *Annu. Rev. Phys. Chem.* **61**, 191–217, (2010).

[95] A. Widmer-Cooper, H. Perry, P. Harrowell, and D. R. Reichman, *Nat. Phys.* **4**(9), 711–715, (2008).

[96] J. C. Dyre, *Rev. Mod. Phys.* **78**(3), 953, (2006).

[97] C. P. Royall and S. R. Williams, *Phys. Rep.* **560**, 1–75, (2015).

[98] H. Tanaka, T. Kawasaki, H. Shintani, and K. Watanabe, *Nat. Mater.* **9**(4), 324–331, (2010).

[99] V. Lubchenko and P. G. Wolynes, *Annu. Rev. Phys. Chem.* **58**, 235–266, (2007).

[100] G. Biroli and J.-P. Bouchaud, *arXiv:2208.05866.* (2022).

Chapter 12

The Gardner Glass

The application of the replica method to the analysis of mean-field models of packings of particles has allowed the construction of a theory of amorphous solids in infinite dimensions. In particular, the theory predicts that glassy states can undergo a replica symmetry breaking transition at low temperature. This RSB transition within a glass state is called Gardner transition in analogy with the RSB transition of the ideal glass state in a certain class of mean-field spin glass models and, after the solution of structural glass models in infinite dimensions, it has emerged as a crucial scenario for understanding the low temperature properties of amorphous solids. The chapter focus on recent theoretical and numerical results on this topic. In the first part, **Pierfrancesco Urbani** outlines the ideas that lead to the mean-field theory of the Gardner transition for infinite-dimensional amorphous solids, and the consequent main achievements obtained within such a theory. In the second part, **Yuliang Jin** and **Hajime Yoshino** overview methods and results of the numerical investigations of the nature of the Gardner phase in finite-dimensional packings, and discuss evidences of the validity of some mean-field predictions beyond the infinite-dimensional limit.

12.1. Low Temperature Amorphous Solids: Mean Field Theory and Beyond

Pierfrancesco Urbani

*Université Paris-Saclay, CNRS, CEA, Institut de physique théorique
91191, Gif-sur-Yvette, France
pierfrancesco.urbani@ipht.fr*

12.1.1. *Introduction*

Amorphous solids at low temperature display unusual features that have escaped a clear and unified comprehension since the early seventies when they have been first identified in experiments [1]. In recent years a mean-field theory of amorphous solids constructed in the limit of infinite spatial dimensions has been proposed. We will review what is the outcome of this theory focusing on a specific result: depending on the nature of the microscopic degrees of freedom, their interaction potential and system preparation, amorphous solids may undergo to a so-called Gardner transition under a set of physical conditions (low temperature, high pressure, sufficiently high strain deformation). At this point stable glasses become marginally stable, in the sense that they are very sensitive to external perturbations.

We will review the mean-field theory of the Gardner transition and the nature of the Gardner phase, its connection with spin glasses, and discuss where we stand on the quest for an extension of these results beyond the mean-field limit. We will mainly focus on classical sytems without discussing the effect of quantum fluctuations. We will also restrict the attention to the theoretical picture emerging from the infinite-dimensional limit with very little discussion on how this compares with simulations, experiments and other approaches. The interested reader can look at other chapters in this volume and recent reviews in the literature.

12.1.2. *Theory of glasses in infinite dimensions*

The equilibrium thermodynamic route for rigidity requires symmetry breaking. Cold simple liquids turn into solid crystals when translational symmetry is broken. However, in fact, many solids in nature are amorphous. At the microscopic level the degrees of freedom are arranged in a disordered manner. Glasses are one of the main examples. In this case the route for rigidity goes through an out-of-equilibrium pathway. When cooled down, complex liquids avoid crystallization and get stuck in a metastable branch of their equation of state where they become viscous supercooled liquids. Cooling down further these systems, the viscosity increases of several orders of magnitude in a short interval of temperatures. At some point they become so viscous that they are effectively rigid and form a glass [2–5].

The theoretical description of the glass transition has been very debated and has triggered several different approaches. In the late eighties, in a series of groundbreaking works, it was proposed by T. Kirkpatrick, D. Thirumalai and P. Wolynes, [6–10] that the glass transition was driven by the appearance of an exponential number of metastable glassy states. This picture was built on the fundamental observation that the solution of a class of spin glass models exhibiting a dynamical one-step-replica symmetry breaking (1RSB) transition pathway (notable examples are Potts spin glasses, p-spin glasses with $p > 2$) had essentially the same phenomenology of structural glasses. This connection was completely non-obvious and had extremely far reaching consequences giving birth to the Random First Order Transition theory (RFOT) of the glass transition.

It took a series of fundamental works [11–15], mainly devoted to understand how to adapt the replica method to systems without quenched disorder, to show that the scenario for the glass transition proposed at the beginning was exactly realized in the limit of infinite spatial dimensions [16, 17].

A detailed review of the solution of simple glass models in infinite spatial dimensions can be found in recent works [17, 18]. Here we will describe the main essential steps of the construction.

The simplest approach is to start from the Franz–Parisi construction [11, 19], but alternative ways exist [14].

We consider a system of N interacting degrees of freedom in d-dimensions. The degrees of freedom are the positions of particles and are denoted by $\underline{x}_i = \{x_{i1}, \ldots, x_{id}\}$ with $i = 1, \ldots, N$. They interact through a pairwise interaction potential so that the total Hamiltonian of the system is

$$H[X] = \sum_{i<j}^{N} v(|\underline{x}_i - \underline{x}_j|) \qquad X = \{\underline{x}_i\}_{i=1,\dots,N}. \tag{12.1}$$

We introduce the notation $\hat{H}[X,\underline{c}]$ to denote the generalized Hamiltonian with its dependence on the control parameters $\underline{c}$. For example, if the system is in equilibrium at an inverse temperature $\beta = 1/T$ and density ρ we will denote it by $\hat{H} = \beta H$ and $\underline{c} = \{\beta, \rho\}$. The equilibrium partition function is therefore $Z[\underline{c}] = \int \mathrm{d}X \exp\left[-\hat{H}[X,\underline{c}]\right]$.

As a first approximation, a glass is an arrested phase in which particles are caged by neighbors and cannot diffuse. Defining the mean square displacement between two configurations in phase space as

$$\Delta[X,Y] = \frac{1}{N} \sum_{i=1}^{N} |\underline{x}_i - \underline{y}_i|^2 \tag{12.2}$$

one can consider the following large deviation function, the so-called Franz–Parisi potential, defined as

$$V_{\mathrm{FP}}[\hat{\Delta}, \underline{c}_m, \underline{c}_s] = -\int \mathrm{d}Y \frac{\mathrm{e}^{-\hat{H}[Y,\underline{c}_m]}}{N Z[\underline{c}_m]} \ln \int \mathrm{d}X\, \mathrm{e}^{-\hat{H}[X,\underline{c}_s]} \delta(\hat{\Delta} - \Delta(X,Y)). \tag{12.3}$$

It is useful to call the Y-system as the reference or parent glass, while the X-system is the constrained system. Intuitively, the Franz–Parisi potential looks at the tendency of the constrained system to be closer to the reference one. Practically, the reference system acts as quenched disorder for the constrained one.

We first consider the case where $\underline{c}_s = \underline{c}_m$. To fix ideas we will focus on hard spheres where the only control parameter is the packing fraction ϕ, namely the fraction of space occupied by the spheres. The corresponding interaction potential is formally infinite as soon as spheres overlap and zero otherwise. We underline that all what follows can be repeated for thermal systems by replacing the role of the packing fraction ϕ with the temperature T.

We are interested in looking at the profile of V_{FP} as a function of $\underline{c}_m = \phi$. We can identify three regimes. For sufficiently small packing fraction $\phi < \phi_{\mathrm{d}}$ the Franz–Parisi potential has a global minimum at $\hat{\Delta} \to \infty$. This means that the system is an ergodic liquid because there is no pinning effect of the reference system on the constrained one. When $\phi \in [\phi_{\mathrm{d}}, \phi_{\mathrm{K}}]$ the Franz–Parisi potential develops a metastable minimum at a finite value of $\hat{\Delta} = \hat{\Delta}_r < \infty$. This is the dynamical glass phase and the point ϕ_{d} corresponds to the dynamical/mode-coupling glass transition. In the regime $\phi \in [\phi_{\mathrm{d}}, \phi_{\mathrm{K}}]$, V_{FP} has a local minimum for finite $\hat{\Delta}$ which means that particles in the system are caged. When $\phi = \phi_{\mathrm{K}}$ the local minimum of the Franz–Parisi potential becomes the global one and the system is in the ideal glass state so that ϕ_{K} corresponds to the Kauzmann transition [118]. This dynamical 1RSB phase found in hard spheres coincides with the one of simple mean-field spin glass models as foreseen by Kirkpatrick, Thirumalai and Wolynes and therefore provides a direct evidence that in infinite dimensions the glass transition is realized within the RFOT scenario.

This construction can be generalized to $\underline{c}_m \neq c_s$. When $\underline{c}_m$ is such that the reference system is in a dynamical 1RSB region, this corresponds to selecting an equilibrium glass state and looking at what happens when it is perturbed. In infinite dimensions one can get access to physical perturbation schemes, like cooling, compression, shear deformation. This way, the theory in infinite dimension becomes a tool to understand the behavior of glassy states when, as a first approximation, activation is neglected. This formalism has been pushed forward to obtain a complete theory in $d \to \infty$ of simple colloidal glasses (hard spheres) under compression [20, 21], or simple thermal glasses under cooling [22, 23] and strain deformation [22, 24–27]. This has provided a first principle approach to study low temperature glasses or high pressure colloidal glasses close to the jamming point, and sheared amorphous solids and the corresponding yielding transition.

The computation of the Franz–Parisi potential can be performed in full details in infinite dimensions through the replica method, see [17]. The $d \to \infty$ limit allows to reduce it to a saddle point computation for a set of order parameters. In addition to $\hat{\Delta}$ that minimizes V_{FP} one needs to introduce a mean square displacement matrix Δ_{ab} which encodes for the mean square displacement of $n \to 0$ different replicas of the constrained system all close to the same configuration of the reference one.

This mean square displacement matrix is a generalization of the overlap matrix in spin glasses [28, 29] to particle systems and it represents a measure of similarity between different configurations subjected to the very same quenched disorder.

We will focus on what happens when the parent, reference, glass has control parameters such that it is in the dynamical 1RSB phase. Again we will consider what happens for hard spheres under compression but the same can be repeated in thermal systems by decreasing the temperature.

We will consider a parent glass at a packing fraction $\phi_m \in [\phi_{\mathrm{d}}, \phi_{\mathrm{K}}]$ and compress it by considering a constrained system at $\phi \geq \phi_m$. This can be realized for example by increasing the diameters of the spheres of the constrained system as compared to the reference one. When $\phi = \phi_m$, the solution of the saddle point equations are found within a replica symmetric ansatz. In this case one can parametrize the off-diagonal part of the overlap matrix by a constant $\Delta_{a \neq b} = \Delta_{\mathrm{EA}}$ whose saddle point value coincides with the saddle point one for $\hat{\Delta} = \Delta_r = \Delta_{\mathrm{EA}}$.

We can now consider what happens when the system is compressed. Depending on the parent glass packing fraction ϕ_m, there exist a packing fraction $\phi_{\mathrm{G}}(\phi_m)$, such that the replica symmetric assumption is correct in the interval $\phi \in [\phi_m, \phi_{\mathrm{G}}(\phi_m)]$. Therefore in this case the glass state can be thought as an ergodic metabasin: restricted equilibration within this portion of phase space takes finite time and correlations among degrees of freedom are short ranged.[a] This is the stable glass phase.

However, increasing the pressure above $\phi_{\mathrm{G}}(\phi_m)$, the replica symmetric assumption is no longer correct and one has replica symmetry breaking within a glass basin. This point is the Gardner transition.

---

[a]Note that, as usual in infinite dimensions, instead of correlation functions one can study integrated response functions or susceptibilities. In the stable glass phase the system responds as an amorphous elastic medium.

12.1.3. *The Gardner transition*

The Gardner transition marks the point at which a stable glass enters a phase with broken replica symmetry. This transition was first found in the context of mean field spin glasses in [30, 31]. However in these works it was mainly studied at equilibrium. In this case the ideal glass state, cooled down further undergoes a further replica symmetry breaking. This is different from the construction we have reviewed above, where instead we are looking at perturbed out-of-equilibrium glassy states. In this case one realizes the Gardner transition out-of-equilibrium and, possibly, well above the Kauzmann point.

In the context of structural glass models, the importance of the Gardner transition emerged in [32]. Albeit in a slightly different theoretical framework with respect to the previous section, in this work it was understood that infinite dimensional hard spheres, at sufficiently high pressure, undergo a Gardner transition. It was proposed that this was the essential ingredient to describe the criticality of the jamming transition and the anomalous low temperature properties of glasses. Beyond the Gardner point hard spheres are described by continuous replica symmetry breaking [21, 33, 34]. What was a stable glass has become a metabasin of a hierarchical structure of states. This structure can be described in terms of the probability distribution of the mean square displacement between different typical configurations belonging to the same glass metabasin. This probability distribution can be computed in the infinite dimensional limit.

The formalism needed to compute the properties of the Gardner phase is close to the one found several years before in the context of spin glasses. In a nutshell one has a set of partial differential equations (a non-linear equation of the same form as the one discovered by G. Parisi in his solution of the Sherrington–Kirkpatrick model [35], and another one with a Fokker–Planck structure analogous to what was found in spin glasses [36]). With the addition of a closing equation, this formalism gives access to the cumulative distribution function of the mean square displacement $x(\Delta)$, see [17] for more details.

The appearance of the Gardner transition, as described within the infinite dimensional solution, can be detected looking at a series of observables. On approaching the Gardner point from the stable glass phase, one can look at the relaxation dynamics (Newtonian dynamics or Langevin dynamics) starting from a typical configuration of the glass. While in the stable glass phase the relaxation time is finite, at the Gardner point it diverges. One can focus on the dynamical mean square displacement defined as

$$\Delta(t) = \frac{1}{N} \sum_{i=1}^{N} |\underline{x}_i(t) - \underline{x}_i(0)|^2. \tag{12.4}$$

If $\{\underline{x}_i(0)\}$ denotes a typical configuration of the stable glass at initial time and $\{\underline{x}_i(t)\}$ the resulting configuration at time t, then $\Delta(t)$ relaxes to Δ_{EA} in an exponential way. Approaching the transition point, one finds a divergence of the relaxation time $\tau \sim |\phi - \phi_{\mathrm{G}}|^{-\gamma}$ characterized by a non-universal critical exponent γ. Sitting exactly at the Gardner point the exponential relaxation is replaced by an algebraic one, $\Delta_{\mathrm{EA}} - \Delta(t) \sim t^{-a}$ being a a non-universal dynamical critical exponent [17, 21].

The transition point can be also characterized by looking at diverging susceptibilities. The simplest one is the χ_4 susceptibility defined as $\chi_4 = \lim_{t\to\infty} N(\overline{\Delta(t)^2} - \overline{\Delta(t)}^2)$ and the overline stands for the collective average over the realization of the initial conditions and thermal noise. Approaching the Gardner point one has that $\chi_4 \sim 1/|\phi - \phi_{\mathrm{G}}|$. Other diverging susceptibilities can be defined from the sample-to-sample fluctuations of nonlinear elastic moduli [24]. They imply a breakdown of elastic behavior replaced by plastic responses upon strain deformation. Therefore while in the stable glass phase the response of the glass is elastic and reversible, in the Gardner phase this behavior is replaced by anomalously large responses to small perturbations, typically manifested through avalanche-like phenomenology. Therefore the Gardner phase is said to be marginally stable. Finally, crossing the transition point, zero field cooled and field cooled shear responses start to differ [37] and in the Gardner phase relaxation dynamics is expected to exhibit aging behavior.

It is useful to provide a short overview of which systems, in the infinite-dimensional limit, have been shown to have a Gardner phase and under which circumstances.

Hard spheres under compression always undergo a Gardner transition. Therefore at sufficiently high pressures, any hard sphere glass, including the ideal one, is a Gardner glass [20, 32]. The transition happens sooner the closer the parent glass is to the dynamical glass transition point. The same happens in soft spheres, like harmonic spheres [22] or spheres interacting through a WCA potential [23]. Remarkably, as was found in the latter case, there are situations and interaction potentials for which one can observe a Gardner transition only if the parent glass is sufficiently unstable and close to the mode-coupling point. Harmonic spheres are interesting since they interpolate between the low density hard spheres regime and the high density soft sphere one. At zero temperature and as a function of the density, these two regimes are separated by the jamming transition [38]. This can be seen as the point where zero temperature soft spheres trapped in a glass, cannot be arranged without making them overlap if further compressed. When $d \to \infty$, it is found that the jamming transition is always surrounded by a dome of a marginally stable Gardner phase [23, 24]. Finally the effect of shear strain and combined strain deformation and compression can be also studied [20–22, 25, 27]. Also in this case, if the glass is at sufficiently high pressure and low temperature, once strained it undergoes a Gardner transition.

12.1.4. *Sitting at the bottom of the landscape: Marginal stability and scale invariance*

In the previous section we focused on the Gardner transition and on its characterization. In this section we would like to give a short overview of what are the consequences for extremely low temperature glasses and high pressures granular glasses.

In the infinite pressure limit, hard spheres glasses jam and form rigid random configurations. The outcome of the infinite dimensional analysis, in the jamming limit, is that [33, 34]:

- the Gardner phase, at infinite pressure, gives rise to isostaticity property: the number of contacts between spheres equals the number of degrees of freedom. This property emerges from first principles and it is a direct consequence of the marginal stability of the replica symmetry broken solution (full replica symmetry breaking);
- at jamming one can compute the distribution of contact forces f as well as small gaps h between almost touching spheres. Both distributions are controlled

by two critical exponents. At small argument they respectively behave as $P(f) \sim f^\theta$ and $P(h) \sim h^{-\gamma}$ with $\theta = 0.42311\ldots$ and $\gamma = 0.41269\ldots$;
- on approaching the jamming point from the hard sphere side one can show that the cage size Δ_{EA} (or Debye–Waller factor) decreases to zero with a power law of the pressure p. The critical exponent can be computed as well. One gets that $\Delta_{\mathrm{EA}} \sim p^{-\kappa}$ with $\kappa = 1.41574\ldots$;
- on approaching the jamming point from the jammed phase of harmonic soft spheres, the vibrational density of states displays a plateau at low frequencies and this has been shown using a simplified model for infinite-dimensional harmonic spheres [39].

All these properties were shown to appear in extensive numerical simulations [38, 40–44]. Remarkably, the values of the critical exponents compare well with numerical simulations in finite dimensions, see [45] for the most recent investigations.

The critical exponents (as well as isostaticity) arise in a quite remarkable way from the formalism describing the Gardner phase. In the jamming limit, the equations describing the ultrametric structure of states within the glass metabasin display a scaling regime controlled by a set of critical exponents that imply the ones of forces, gaps and cage size. These exponents can be fully determined by solving numerically the corresponding equations.

This scaling regime can be generalized even beyond jamming. Recently, spheres interacting with a linear ramp potential (and therefore called linear spheres) have been shown to give rise to a full, jamming critical phase [46]. Above jamming if one considers linear spheres at zero temperature, one finds that they sit in local minima of the potential energy landscape that are isostatic (with a more subtle definition of isostaticity) and described by a set of power laws controlling the microstructural properties of these configuration. Again, these power laws can be found within mean field theory [47] and they emerge from a more complicated scaling solution of the equations describing the corresponding Gardner phase. Remarkably, non-trivial algebraic identities imply that the critical exponents arising in this case coincide with the ones at jamming point.

Both at jamming [48] and in mean field models of jammed linear spheres [49], the critical exponents computed from the infinite-dimensional solution can be shown to control the avalanche size distribution of perturbed packings. Finally, the very same critical exponents are found to describe the power law divergence of the shear modulus of hard sphere glasses at very high pressure close to jamming [50].

Away from jamming, in the jammed phase of harmonic soft spheres it was shown through an equivalent simpler model [39] that the Gardner phase can give rise to a vibrational density of states $D(\omega) \sim \omega^2$ populated by delocalized low frequency eigenvectors.

Recently this picture has been challenged by numerical simulations showing that soft glasses sit in local minima that are typically gapless but with a spectrum better described by $D(\omega) \sim \omega^4$ and populated by quasi-localized eigenvectors, see [51] and references therein for a recent review. Therefore in [52–54] a spin glass model having a schematic Gardner phase has been proposed showing that the Gardner phase may give rise to pseudogapped spectrum of quasi-localized modes following an ω^4 law, see [54] for more details. One of the main ingredient of the model is the presence of local heterogeneities that are shown to drive the form of the soft tail of the vibrational density of states. How to incorporate these effects in simple models of structural glasses in infinite dimensions remains to be clarified.

12.1.5. *Beyond mean field theory*

Up to now we have been describing the emergence of the Gardner transition and its consequences within the mean-field limit of infinite spatial dimensions. Here we will give a very short review on what is known beyond mean-field theory.

From a critical phenomena point of view, the Gardner transition is in the same universality class as the spin glass transition in a field [55] since at this point only replica symmetry breaks down. To go beyond mean-field theory one can perform perturbative renormalization group computations at criticality [55] which show that, as for the spin glass problem [56], the Gaussian fixed point of the RG equations looses stability below the upper critical dimension and no other stable fixed point is found. Two-loops renormalization group computations show that a new fixed point can be found below the upper critical dimension but in a non-perturbative region of coupling constants [57]. However, the nature of the low temperature phase cannot be accessed by analyzing the theory at criticality.

It was proposed in [58] that if the spin glass transition in a field arises, it could be controlled by a critical point at zero temperature. Recently it has been shown [54] that, within mean field theory, this transition can be driven by two different mechanisms. On the one hand one can have the appearance of a fat tail ($D(\omega) \sim \omega^2$) of low frequency delocalized eigenmodes in the density of states giving rise a divergence of the spin glass susceptibility. This scenario may not be robust in finite dimensions since getting delocalized excitations at the edge of the spectrum is expected to be hard unless some symmetries are present at long wavelengths (for example translational symmetry giving rise to phonons). On the other hand, in [54] it was shown that one can have a transition driven by the appearance of a finite density of non-linear excitations whose nature is captured by the replica symmetry breaking solution. A field theory analysis focused on this second scenario has been developed recently to go beyond mean field theory [59] and it deserves further investigation.

12.2. Computer Simulations of the Gardner Transition in Structural Glasses

Yuliang Jin[*] and Hajime Yoshino[†]

**Institute of Theoretical Physics, Chinese Academy of Sciences, Beijing, China*
yuliangjin@itp.ac.cn
†Osaka University, Ōsaka, Japan
yoshino@cmc.osaka-u.ac.jp

12.2.1. *Connections between Gardner and spin-glass transitions*

The exact mean-field theory for the simplest glass-forming system — the dense assembly of hard spheres in the large dimensional limit — predicts the existence of a Gardner phase [17, 60]. This transition is characterized by full replica symmetry breaking (RSB) that implies two fascinating physical consequences. (i) A hierarchical free-energy landscape, i.e., the thermal fluctuations are organized hierarchically, meaning that configurations are grouped into meta-basins that are further grouped into meta-meta basins, etc. (ii) marginal stability, i.e., the system responds sensitively to infinitesimal perturbations. Here we discuss recent results of numerical simulations to examine these mean-field predictions in physical dimensions.

From the viewpoint of RSB, the Gardner transition in structural glasses belongs to the same full RSB universality class of the spin-glass transition (see Fig. 12.1(A)). This theoretical ground motivates us to borrow ideas from the extensive research on spin-glasses to study the Gardner transition. To this end, it is useful to review firstly some of the essential results obtained in spin-glass experiments and simulations.

The RSB solution immediately implies a hierarchy of linear responses through the fluctuation-dissipation relation [29]. One expects short-time, intermediate-time, and long-time linear responses associated with thermal fluctuations inside basins, meta-basins, and meta-meta-basins. A remarkable consequence is the "anomaly" that gives a

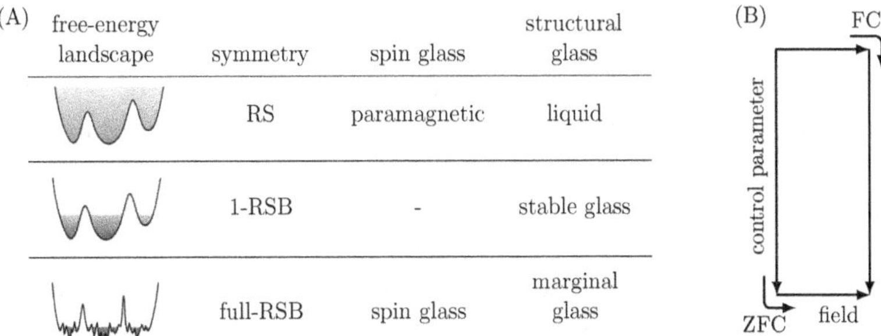

Fig. 12.1. (A) Correspondence between spin and structural glasses. Note that one-step RSB (1-RSB) exists in certain spin-glass models such as the spherical p-spin ($p > 2$) model [63]. (B) Schematic of ZFC/FC protocols. In spin and hard-sphere glasses, the control parameter is the temperature T and the density (volume fraction) φ respectively, and the external field is the magnetic field h and the shear-strain γ respectively.

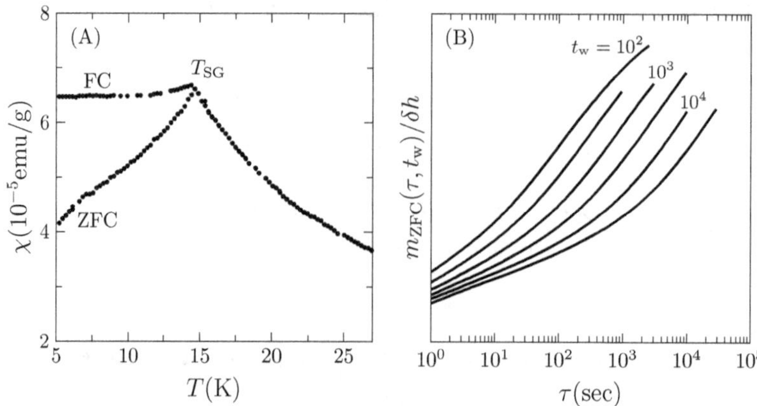

Fig. 12.2.   Experimental results on CuMn spin-glasses. (A) ZFC/FC susceptibilities (adapted from [61]), and (B) the time evolution of $m_{\mathrm{ZFC}}(\tau, t_{\mathrm{w}})/\delta h$ in an aging experiment (adapted from [64]).

natural explanation for the protocol-dependent linear responses observed experimentally [61]. In one protocol called *field cooling* (FC), one measures the magnetization m_{FC} of a spin-glass under cooling from a high temperature T_{max} down to a low temperature T_{min} below the spin-glass transition temperature T_{SG} in the presence of a weak external magnetic field δh; in the other protocol called *zero field cooling* (ZFC), one cools the spin-glass from T_{max} down to T_{min} without the field ($h = 0$), then switches on the magnetic field δh and measures the magnetization m_{ZFC} under heating the spin-glass back to T_{max} (see Fig. 12.1(B)). The two susceptibilities $\chi_{\mathrm{FC}} = m_{\mathrm{FC}}/\delta h$ and $\chi_{\mathrm{ZFC}} = m_{\mathrm{ZFC}}/\delta h$ are the same above T_{SG}, but different ($\chi_{\mathrm{FC}} > \chi_{\mathrm{ZFC}}$) below (see Fig. 12.2(A)). The fact that χ_{FC} and χ_{ZFC} are different in the spin-glass phase is referred to as an "anomaly", because the susceptibility is protocol-independent in standard magnetic systems. The RSB theory gives $\chi_{\mathrm{FC}} - \chi_{\mathrm{ZFC}} = \beta \left[\int_0^1 \mathrm{d}\, q P(q)q - q_{\mathrm{EA}} \right]$, with β the inverse temperature. Here q_{EA} is the Edwards–Anderson (EA) order parameter [62] representing the strength of the thermal fluctuation within lowest-level basins, while $\int_0^1 \mathrm{d}\, q P(q)q$ represents the integral of thermal fluctuations coming from all levels in the hierarchy. In the replica symmetric (RS) solution, $P(q) = \delta(q - q_{\mathrm{EA}})$, so that the anomaly vanishes.

The anomaly is known not to be a transient but a long-time effect, as demonstrated by a series of experiments that reveal aging effects in spin-glasses [64–66]. To study the dynamical effects, one can generalize the ZFC protocol by introducing a waiting time t_{w} before switching on the magnetic field, and a measurement time τ elapsed in the presence of the field. By increasing τ, $m_{\mathrm{ZFC}}(\tau, t_{\mathrm{w}})$ increases passing through m_{ZFC} and heads toward m_{FC} (see Fig. 12.2(B)). However, $m_{\mathrm{ZFC}}(\tau, t_{\mathrm{w}})$ does not reach m_{FC} within finite time, and its time evolution as a function of τ slows down with increasing waiting time t_{w}, manifested by scaling laws depending on τ/t_{w}. These experimental observations are significant because they reveal the out-of-equilibrium nature of spin-glasses. To describe the aging effects and the anomaly from a purely dynamical point of view, a dynamical mean-field theory on spin-glass models is developed [67, 68]. The dynamical theory relates RSB to the notion of effective temperature that characterizes out-of equilibrium glassy dynamics [69, 70]. The numerical evidence of effective temperature [71] and non-zero anomaly in the long-time limit [72] has been indicated by detailed simulations of finite-dimensional spin-glass models.

The marginal stability of the spin-glass phase may account for various complex non-linear responses, such as the effect of static chaos with respect to an infinitesimal change of temperature, or avalanches with respect to an infinitesimal change of magnetic field. Indeed the equilibrium spin configurations at large length scales are completely reshuffled by infinitesimal perturbations, which is predicted first by the droplet theory [73–75], and later by theories based on RSB [48, 76–82]. The rejuvenation-memory effects observed experimentally [83] may be related to such non-linear responses [84, 85].

Once one is aware of the correspondence between spin and structural glasses (see Fig. 12.1(A)), it is natural to use strategies inherited from spin-glass studies to explore the physics of the Gardner phase in structural glasses. For example, in the ZFC/FC protocols, the role of the magnetic field h for spin glasses can be replaced by the shear strain γ for structural glasses (see Fig. 12.1(B)), which only changes the boundary condition and not the thermodynamic properties of the bulk. Indeed, the replica theory of structural glasses predicts a hierarchy of shear moduli reflecting RSB [50, 86, 87]. By adapting the methods developed in spin-glasses, one can examine the aging effects, the protocol-dependent linear responses, and the non-linear responses such as avalanches, in structural glasses with respect to shear deformations. Our discussion focuses on one of the simplest models of structural glasses in three dimensions, hard spheres, where the (reduced) pressure p (or the volume fraction φ) plays the role of temperature T. According to the replica theory [17] that is exact in the large dimensional limit, a Gardner transition occurs in hard spheres under both compression and shear, which is examined by simulations at three dimensions in the following sections. The dynamical mean-field theory for the hard-sphere glass has also been set up [88–91], but a detailed theoretical analysis of the out-of equilibrium dynamics remains challenging. Nonetheless, the analogy to the spin-glass problem outlined above allows us to infer the implications of RSB on the dynamics of hard spheres.

12.2.2. *Gardner transition under compression*

12.2.2.1. *Preparation of ultra-stable glasses*

To study the Gardner transition, we must prepare a glass at first. Experimentally, glasses are obtained by a slow thermal or compression annealing, the rate of which determines the location of the glass transition. It is found that a detailed numerical analysis of the Gardner transition requires the preparation of extremely well-relaxed glasses (corresponding to structural relaxation timescales challenging to simulate in standard algorithms), in order to study vibrational motions of particles without interference from diffusion. Such ultra-stable glasses can be numerically generated by applying a swap Monte Carlo scheme [92, 93] to a simple glass-forming model — a polydisperse mixture of N hard spheres [94].

The annealing procedure contains two steps [94]. First, one produces equilibrated liquid configurations at various densities φ_{g} with the help of the swap algorithm. Second, starting from these liquid configurations, one switches to standard molecular dynamics simulations [95] during which the system is compressed out of equilibrium up to target densities $\varphi > \varphi_g$. In order to obtain thermal and disorder averaging, this procedure is repeated over many samples, each corresponding to different initial equilibrium configurations at φ_g, and over many independent quench realizations for each sample. The independent realizations of the same sample have identical particle positions at φ_g, but are assigned to different initial velocities drawn from the Maxwell–Boltzmann distribution.

The above numerical protocol is analogous to thermal annealing with different cooling rates, which results in different glass transition temperatures. Each glass transition density φ_g selects a particular glass state. The value of φ_g ranges from the mode-coupling theory (MCT) density (or the dynamical glass transition density) φ_d, at which the liquid relaxation is slow but affected by activated α-processes, to $\varphi_g \gg \varphi_d$, where particle diffusion and vibrations are fully separated. For sufficiently large φ_g, the α-relaxation time becomes larger than the simulation time by many orders of magnitude; one thus obtains unimpeded access to the dynamics within the glass state, i.e., the β-relaxation processes [96].

The liquid equation of state (EOS) for the reduced pressure $p = \beta P/\rho$ of the model, where ρ is the number density, and P the system pressure, is well described by the Carnahan-Starling (CS) equation [97]. The dynamical glass transition density $\varphi_d = 0.594(1)$ was estimated following the strategy in Ref. [98]. Note that the dynamical glass transition is only rigorous in large dimensions; it becomes a dynamical crossover in three dimensions (see Chapter 10 for a detailed discussion). The non-equilibrium glass EOSs associated with compression terminate at inherent states (where $p \to \infty$) that correspond to, for hard spheres, jammed configurations at φ_J, and can be captured by a free-volume scaling form, $p_{\text{glass}}(\varphi) \sim (\varphi_J - \varphi)^{-1}$ [99]. Figure 12.3 presents the phase diagram and EOSs of the model.

Along each glass EOS of a given φ_g, a corresponding Gardner transition may exist at density φ_G (or pressure p_G), as predicted by the mean-field theory. For $\varphi_g < \varphi < \varphi_G$,

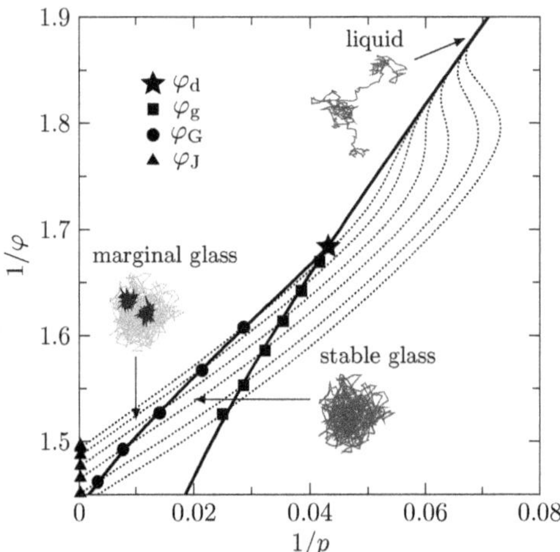

Fig. 12.3.   Phase diagram of a polydisperse hard-sphere glass in three dimensions (adapted from [94]). Solids lines represent the CS liquid EOS and the Gardner line, and dashed lines represent glass EOSs. The insets show typical particle motions in three phases.

the system is in a *stable glass* phase: each glass state is confined in one of the structureless basins on the free-energy landscape (see Fig. 12.1(A)), and is stable in response to small mechanical deformations. On the other hand, the regime $\varphi_G < \varphi < \varphi_J$ corresponds to a *marginal glass* phase, where each simple glass basin splits into a fractal hierarchy of sub-basins and the glass becomes marginally stable to deformations. The Gardner line and the liquid EOS merge around φ_d, suggesting the mixing of dynamical behavior associated to the Gardner transition and to the glass transition — this is why one needs to focus on ultra-stable glasses in order to explore pure Gardner physics.

12.2.2.2. *Key observables and protocols*

In the glass state, particles vibrate inside their cages (see the insets of Fig. 12.3). The first approach to study the Gardner transition is based on the direct analysis of *caging order parameters*, which quantify the caging properties of particles. In the case of stable glasses, the caging order parameter is defined as, $\Delta_{\mathrm{EA}} = \lim_{t\to\infty} \frac{1}{N} \sum_{i=1}^{N} \langle |\vec{r}_i(t) - \vec{r}_i(0)|^2 \rangle$, where $\vec{r}_i(t)$ is the position of particle i at time t. The parameter Δ_{EA}, which decreases with the degree of annealing, corresponds to nothing but the EA parameter q_{EA} in spin glasses.

Similar to the spin-glass transition, the Gardner transition induces the splitting of basins on the free energy landscape and aging effects, which suggests that the order parameter must be generalized: one considers (i) the mean squared displacement (MSD) $\Delta(\tau, t_{\mathrm{w}})$ and (ii) the distance between pairs of independently quenched configurations $\Delta_{AB}(t)$. Here the MSD is defined as, $\Delta(\tau, t_{\mathrm{w}}) = \frac{1}{N} \sum_{i=1}^{N} \langle |\vec{r}_i(\tau+t_{\mathrm{w}}) - \vec{r}_i(t_{\mathrm{w}})|^2 \rangle$, averaged over both thermal fluctuations and disorder, at the target φ reached by compression. A waiting time t_{w} is introduced in order to explicitly examine aging effects (the total time t is the sum of the measurement time τ and t_{w}). On the other hand, $\Delta_{AB}(t) = \frac{1}{N} \sum_{i=1}^{N} \langle |\vec{r}_i^A(t) - \vec{r}_i^B(t)|^2 \rangle$, where the two copies A and B are independent realizations at φ, compressed from the same initial sample at φ_{g}.

The large-time limits of these quantities have important physical meanings. The EA order parameter is defined as $\Delta_{\mathrm{EA}} \equiv \lim_{\tau\to\infty} \lim_{t_{\mathrm{w}}\to\infty} \Delta(\tau, t_{\mathrm{w}})$. Here the order of time limits is crucial [100]: by reversing the order one can define another parameter, $\Delta_{AB} \equiv \lim_{t_{\mathrm{w}}\to\infty} \lim_{\tau\to\infty} \Delta(\tau, t_{\mathrm{w}}) = \lim_{t\to\infty} \Delta_{AB}(t)$. The RSB is signaled by $\Delta_{AB} > \Delta_{\mathrm{EA}}$ (note that $\Delta_{AB} = \Delta_{\mathrm{EA}}$ in stable glasses). In other words, the two large-time limits cannot be interchanged in the Gardner phase, meaning that the aging effects become persistent.

In the second approach, one studies the response of hard-sphere glasses against a shear strain γ, analogous to observing magnetic susceptibilities in spin-glasses. The simple strain γ is applied to the x-coordinates of all particles ($x_i \to x_i + \gamma z_i$) after a waiting time t_{w}, under the constant-volume and Lees–Edwards boundary conditions [101]. The strain is increased slowly with a constant shear rate $\dot{\gamma}$, and the reduced shear stress $\sigma = \beta\Sigma/\rho$ is measured, where Σ is the stress (for convenience, some data are presented with the unitless stress rescaled by pressure, $\tilde{\sigma} = \sigma/p$).

As in the spin-glass case, one can consider two types of protocols, namely *zero field compression* (ZFC) and *field compression* (FC) (see Fig. 12.1 (B)). In the ZFC protocol, one compresses the configuration from φ_{g} to φ, waits for time t_{w} before applying a shear strain $\delta\gamma$ instantaneously, and then measures the stress $\sigma_{\mathrm{ZFC}}(\tau, t_{\mathrm{w}})$ as a function of τ.

In the FC protocol, one applies $\delta\gamma$ at the initial density $\varphi_{\rm g}$, and then measures the stress $\sigma_{\rm FC}(t)$ once the configuration is compressed to φ (t is reset to zero after compression). Similar to the caging order parameters, two large-time limits can be considered: $\sigma_{\rm ZFC} \equiv \lim_{\tau\to\infty}\lim_{t_{\rm w}\to\infty}\sigma_{\rm ZFC}(\tau,t_{\rm w})$ and $\sigma_{\rm FC} \equiv \lim_{t_{\rm w}\to\infty}\lim_{\tau\to\infty}\sigma_{\rm ZFC}(\tau,t_{\rm w})$.

Theories have demonstrated that the above two approaches (more specifically, the caging order parameters Δ and the shear moduli $\mu = \sigma/\delta\gamma$) are intrinsically related [50]: in the large pressure limit, $\mu_{\rm ZFC} \sim 1/\Delta_{\rm EA}$ and $\mu_{\rm FC}/p \sim 1/\Delta_{AB}$. These relationships are the counterpart of the duality between overlapping order parameters and magnetic susceptibilities in spin-glasses.

12.2.2.3. *Aging effects*

In the Gardner phase ($\varphi > \varphi_{\rm G}$), aging effects can be observed in both MSD (without shear deformations) and shear responses. Figure 12.4(A) shows MSD results from simulation MSD. After a short time $\tau_{\rm b} \sim 1$ of ballistic motions, the evolution of $\Delta(\tau,t_{\rm w})$, as a function of τ, exhibits a plateau followed by further growth. The switch from the former to the latter happens at longer times with increasing waiting time $t_{\rm w}$. The height of the short-time plateau gives $\Delta_{\rm EA}$ (practically, we set $\Delta_{\rm EA} = \Delta(\tau = \tau_{\rm b}, t_{\rm w} = 0)$). Figure 12.4(A) also displays $\Delta_{AB}(t)$, which is time-independent and should correspond to a long-time plateau of $\Delta(\tau,t_{\rm w})$ (this plateau is unfortunately beyond the current simulation time window). The clear separation of the two parameters ($\Delta_{AB} > \Delta_{\rm EA}$) is the first numerical evidence of the ergodicity breaking in the Gardner phase [94, 102, 103].

Figure 12.4(B) shows the time-dependent (unitless) shear moduli, $\tilde{\mu}(\tau,t_{\rm w})$, whose behavior is similar to that of MSD. An important feature is that $\tilde{\mu}_{\rm ZFC}(\tau,t_{\rm w})$ exhibits a plateau suggesting the existence of $\tilde{\mu}_{\rm ZFC}$. On the other hand, $\tilde{\mu}_{\rm FC}(t)$ is essentially a constant in time t (for $t > \tau_{\rm b}$), which shall be denoted as $\tilde{\mu}_{\rm FC}$. In the proper order of large-time limits, one expects that $\tilde{\mu}_{\rm ZFC}(\tau,t_{\rm w})$ decays to $\tilde{\mu}_{\rm FC}$, as $\lim_{t_{\rm w}\to\infty}\lim_{\tau\to\infty}\tilde{\mu}_{\rm ZFC}(\tau,t_{\rm w}) = \tilde{\mu}_{\rm FC}$, but the convergence becomes slower as $t_{\rm w}$ increases. Apparently $\tilde{\mu}_{\rm ZFC}$ is larger than $\tilde{\mu}_{\rm FC}$, which parallels $\Delta_{AB} > \Delta_{\rm EA}$.

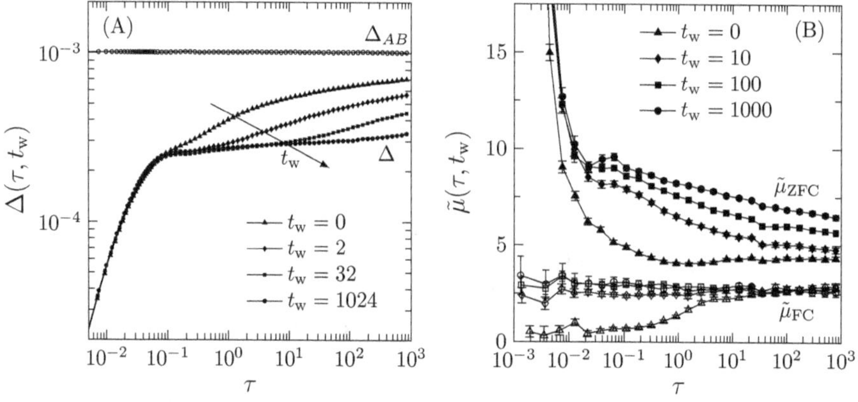

Fig. 12.4.   Time evolutions of (A) caging order parameters (adapted from [94]) and (B) shear moduli (adapted from [37]), in the Gardner phase of the hard-sphere glass model.

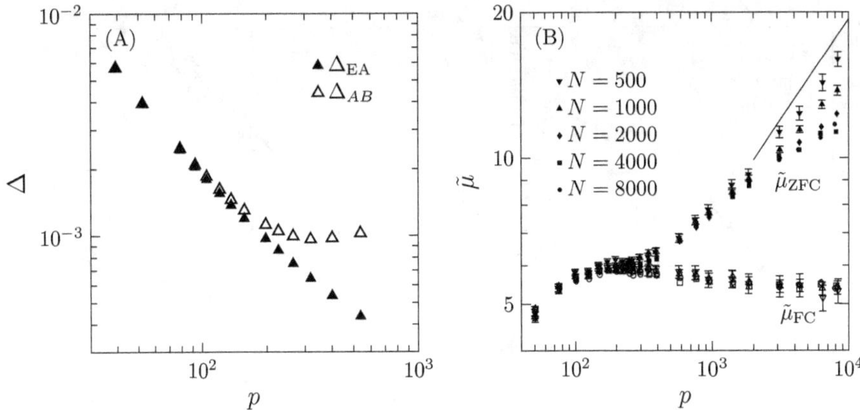

Fig. 12.5.   (A) Bifurcation of caging order parameters Δ_{EA} and Δ_{AB} around the Gardner transition $p_{\mathrm{G}} \approx 2.7 \times 10^2$ (adapted from [94]). (B) Protocol-dependent shear moduli $\tilde{\mu}_{\mathrm{ZFC}}$ and $\tilde{\mu}_{\mathrm{FC}}$ (adapted from [37]). The solid line indicates the scaling $\mu_{\mathrm{ZFC}} \sim p^{1.41574}$ predicted by the mean-field theory [50].

12.2.2.4. *Anomalous order parameters and responses*

Figure 12.5 shows the pressure dependence of caging order parameters (Δ_{EA} and Δ_{AB}) and shear moduli ($\tilde{\mu}_{\mathrm{ZFC}}$ and $\tilde{\mu}_{\mathrm{FC}}$) obtained through the above-mentioned dynamic measurements.   One finds that, in the stable glass phase ($p < p_{\mathrm{G}}$), $\Delta_{\mathrm{EA}} = \Delta_{AB}$ and $\tilde{\mu}_{\mathrm{ZFC}} = \tilde{\mu}_{\mathrm{FC}}$, while in the Gardner phase ($p > p_{\mathrm{G}}$), $\Delta_{\mathrm{EA}} < \Delta_{AB}$ and $\tilde{\mu}_{\mathrm{ZFC}} > \tilde{\mu}_{\mathrm{FC}}$. In the large pressure limit, mean-field theories predict that $\Delta_{\mathrm{EA}} \sim p^{-\kappa}$ [33] and $\mu_{\mathrm{ZFC}} \sim p^{\kappa}$ [50], where $\kappa = 1.41574$. The former is verified by three-dimensional simulations in Ref. [33] and the latter by those in Ref. [37] (see Fig. 12.5(B)). The theories also give large-p predictions $\mu_{\mathrm{FC}}/p \sim 1/\Delta_{AB} \sim$ constant, which are consistent with the simulation results in Fig. 12.5.

12.2.3.   *Gardner transition under shear*

As predicted theoretically [20], a Gardner transition at γ_{G} could occur under shear, before the glass yields at γ_{Y}. Figure 12.6(A) shows the *stability map* of hard-sphere glasses under shear and compression/decompression [27, 104]. The Gardner transition and yielding give rise to three types of behavior in a typical cyclic shear test (see Fig. 12.6(B)). (i) The stress-strain curve is reversible in the stable glass phase ($\gamma < \gamma_{\mathrm{G}}$). (ii) If the shear strain is reversed at a maximum strain γ_{max} between γ_{G} and γ_{Y}, a hysteresis loop emerges, which however disappears below γ_{G}. This partial-reversible phenomenon is a manifestation of the hierarchical free-energy landscape consisting of basins within a common meta-basin. The part of the stress-strain curve in the Gardner phase ($\gamma_{\mathrm{G}} < \gamma < \gamma_{\mathrm{Y}}$) is jerky due to many small avalanches, reflecting the marginal stability. (iii) If $\gamma_{\mathrm{max}} > \gamma_{\mathrm{Y}}$, the cycle becomes strongly irreversible, suggesting the destruction of glass meta-basin after yielding.

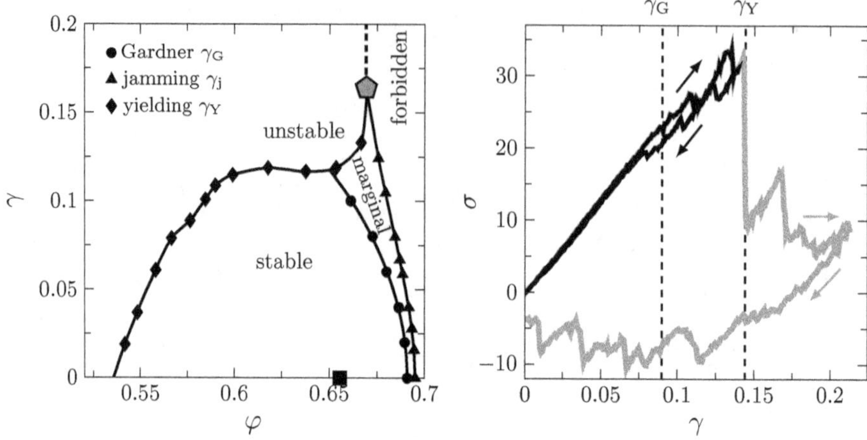

Fig. 12.6. (A) Stability map of hard-sphere glasses, obtained from the initial glass at $\varphi = \varphi_{\mathrm{g}}$ and $\gamma = 0$ (square). (B) Stress-strain curves measured in cyclic shear simulations at a constant $\varphi = 0.66$. Black and gray lines correspond to $\gamma_{\mathrm{G}} < \gamma_{\mathrm{max}} < \gamma_{\mathrm{Y}}$ and $\gamma_{\mathrm{max}} > \gamma_{\mathrm{Y}}$. Adapted from [104, © to the Authors, some rights reserved; exclusive licensee AAAS. Distributed under a Creative Commons Attribution NonCommercial License 4.0 (CC BY-NC)].

12.2.4. *Discussion and outlook*

As a second-order phase transition, the fluctuation of order parameters (or the susceptibility) is expected to diverge at the Gardner transition in the thermodynamic limit. Simulations have shown that the caging susceptibility grows by orders of magnitude approaching the Gardner transition [94]. Furthermore, the spatial correlations between local caging order parameters become long-ranged in the Gardner phase, implying the heterogeneity of vibrational dynamics [94, 105]. However, dynamical activations could possibly turn a mean-field thermodynamic phase transition into a crossover in low dimensions. It remains inconclusive whether a sharp Gardner transition survives in three dimensions, although a renormalization group theory based on loop expansions [57] (see Chapter 4 for details) and a machine-learning facilitated finite-size analysis of simulation data [106] seem to suggest so.

The discussion so far has focused on the hard-sphere model. Hard spheres have a well-defined singularity under compression, the jamming transition, where quantities such as pressure and the length scale of mechanical response diverge (see Chapter 13 for a review on the jamming transition). Because the jamming transition lies in the Gardner phase, the full RSB predictions should also apply to the criticality and marginality of jamming, which are quantified by power-law scalings of weak forces, small interparticle gaps [33] and low-frequency vibrational modes [39]. Remarkably, numerical results seemingly agree with the mean-field exponents even in low dimensions [33, 107, 108]. Evidence for the ultrametricity that characterizes the hierarchical energy landscape, has also been obtained numerically in jammed packings in three dimensions [109].

The Gardner transition seems to emerge as a "precursor" of certain singularities (jamming under compression and yielding under shear) in hard particles. The situation is more complicated in cases without such singularities, e.g., cooling soft spheres under the constant density condition. On the one hand, the mean-field theory universally identifies the existence of the Gardner transition in soft spheres [23], and simulations have reported a rejuvenation-memory effect [110] similar to that found in spin-glasses. On the other hand, however, simulations demonstrate that the Gardner transition could be interfered with by low-dimensional effects such as localized "defects" [111]. Separating the Gardner physics from strong low-dimensional effects in soft spheres remains a challenge in simulations.

Finally, experimental efforts to detect the Gardner transition have shown encouraging progress. The caging order parameter approach is applied to vibrated granular disks, providing evidence of the Gardner phase [112]. In the Gardner phase, one expects a logarithmic growth of the MSD with lag time, which is verified in an experiment of glassy colloidal suspensions [113]. The experimental shear modulus and MSD in a hard-sphere colloidal glass are consistent with the scalings $\mu_{\mathrm{ZFC}} \sim 1/\Delta_{\mathrm{EA}} \sim p^{\kappa}$ [114]. The critical scalings of weak forces and small interparticle gaps have also been verified by precise experimental measurements of jammed photo-elastic disks [115]. The evidence of a Gardner-like transition is reported in a two-dimensional bidisperse granular crystal [116], suggesting that the Gardner physics could be observed with minimum disorder [117, 119]. Examining protocol-dependent shear moduli and complex aging dynamics could provide future directions for the experimental exploration of Gardner physics.

References

[1] R. Zeller and R. Pohl, *Phys. Rev. B.* **4**(6), 2029, (1971).

[2] V. Lubchenko and P. G. Wolynes, *Annu. Rev. Phys. Chem.* **58**, 235–266, (2007).

[3] A. Cavagna, *Phys. Rep.* **476**(4-6), 51–124, (2009).

[4] P. G. Wolynes and V. Lubchenko, *Structural glasses and supercooled liquids: Theory, experiment, and applications.* (John Wiley & Sons, 2012).

[5] L. Leuzzi and T. M. Nieuwenhuizen, *Thermodynamics of the glassy state.* (CRC Press, 2007).

[6] T. R. Kirkpatrick and D. Thirumalai, *Phys. Rev. B.* **36**(10), 5388, (1987).

[7] T. Kirkpatrick and P. Wolynes, *Phys. Rev. B.* **36**(16), 8552, (1987).

[8] T. Kirkpatrick and P. Wolynes, *Phys. Rev. A.* **35**(7), 3072, (1987).

[9] T. R. Kirkpatrick and D. Thirumalai, *Phys. Rev. Lett.* **58**(20), 2091, (1987).

[10] T. R. Kirkpatrick, D. Thirumalai, and P. G. Wolynes, *Phys. Rev. A.* **40**(2), 1045, (1989).

[11] S. Franz and G. Parisi, *J. Phys. I (France).* **5**(11), 1401–1415, (1995).

[12] M. Cardenas, S. Franz, and G. Parisi, *J. Phys. A.* **31**(9), L163, (1998).

[13] M. Cardenas, S. Franz, and G. Parisi, *J. Chem. Phys.* **110**(3), 1726–1734, (1999).

[14] R. Monasson, *Phys. Rev. Lett.* **75**(15), 2847, (1995).

[15] M. Mézard and G. Parisi, *J. Phys. Condens. Matter.* **11**(10A), A157, (1999).

[16] J. Kurchan, G. Parisi, and F. Zamponi, *J. Stat. Mech.: Theory Exp.* **2012**(10), P10012, (2012).

[17] G. Parisi, P. Urbani, and F. Zamponi, *Theory of simple glasses: exact solutions in infinite dimensions.* (Cambridge University Press, 2020).

[18] P. Charbonneau, J. Kurchan, G. Parisi, P. Urbani, and F. Zamponi, *Annu. Rev. Condens. Matter Phys.* **8**, 265–288, (2017).

[19] A. Barrat, S. Franz, and G. Parisi, *J. Phys. A.* **30**(16), 5593, (1997).

[20] C. Rainone, P. Urbani, H. Yoshino, and F. Zamponi, *Phys. Rev. Lett.* **114**(1), 015701, (2015).

[21] C. Rainone and P. Urbani, *J. Stat. Mech.: Theory Exp.* **2016**(5), 053302, (2016).

[22] G. Biroli and P. Urbani, *SciPost Physics.* **4**(4), 020, (2018).

[23] C. Scalliet, L. Berthier, and F. Zamponi, *Phys. Rev. E.* **99**(1), 012107, (2019).

[24] G. Biroli and P. Urbani, *Nat. Phys.* **12**(12), 1130–1133, (2016).

[25] P. Urbani and F. Zamponi, *Phys. Rev. Lett.* **118**(3), 038001, (2017).

[26] A. Altieri, P. Urbani, and F. Zamponi, *Phys. Rev. Lett.* **121**(18), 185503, (2018).

[27] A. Altieri and F. Zamponi, *Phys. Rev. E.* **100**(3), 032140, (2019).

[28] D. Sherrington and S. Kirkpatrick, *Phys. Rev. Lett.* **35**(26), 1792, (1975).

[29] M. Mézard, G. Parisi, and M. A. Virasoro, *Spin glass theory and beyond.* (World Scientific, 1987).

[30] E. Gardner, *Nuclear Physics B.* **257**, 747–765, (1985).

[31] D. J. Gross, I. Kanter, and H. Sompolinsky, *Phys. Rev. Lett.* **55**(3), 304, (1985).

[32] J. Kurchan, G. Parisi, P. Urbani, and F. Zamponi, *J. Phys. Chem. B.* **117**(42), 12979–12994, (2013).

[33] P. Charbonneau, J. Kurchan, G. Parisi, P. Urbani, and F. Zamponi, *Nat. Commun.* **5**(1), 1–6, (2014).

[34] P. Charbonneau, J. Kurchan, G. Parisi, P. Urbani, and F. Zamponi, *J. Stat. Mech.: Theory Exp.* **2014**(10), P10009, (2014).

[35] G. Parisi, *J. Phys. A.* **13**(4), L115, (1980).

[36] H.-J. Sommers and W. Dupont, *J. Phys. C.* **17**(32), 5785, (1984).

[37] Y. Jin and H. Yoshino, *Nat. Commun.* **8**(1), 1–8, (2017).

[38] A. J. Liu and S. R. Nagel, *Annu. Rev. Condens. Matter Phys.* **1**(1), 347–369, (2010).

[39] S. Franz, G. Parisi, P. Urbani, and F. Zamponi, *Proc. Natl. Acad. Sci. U.S.A.* **112**(47), 14539–14544, (2015).

[40] C. S. O'Hern, L. E. Silbert, A. J. Liu, and S. R. Nagel, *Phys. Rev. E.* **68**(1), 011306, (2003).

[41] M. Wyart, L. E. Silbert, S. R. Nagel, and T. A. Witten, *Phys. Rev. E.* **72**(5), 051306, (2005).

[42] C. Brito and M. Wyart, *J. Chem. Phys.* **131**(2), 149, (2009).

[43] E. Lerner, G. Düring, and M. Wyart, *Soft Matter.* **9**(34), 8252–8263, (2013).

[44] P. Charbonneau, E. I. Corwin, G. Parisi, and F. Zamponi, *Phys. Rev. Lett.* **109**(20), 205501, (2012).

[45] P. Charbonneau, E. I. Corwin, R. C. Dennis, R. D. H. Rojas, H. Ikeda, G. Parisi, and F. Ricci-Tersenghi, *Phys. Rev. E.* **104**(1), 014102, (2021).

[46] S. Franz, A. Sclocchi, and P. Urbani, *SciPost Physics.* **9**(1), 012, (2020).

[47] S. Franz, A. Sclocchi, and P. Urbani, *Phys. Rev. Lett.* **123**(11), 115702, (2019).

[48] S. Franz and S. Spigler, *Phys. Rev. E.* **95**(2), 022139, (2017).

[49] S. Franz, A. Sclocchi, and P. Urbani, *J. Stat. Mech.: Theory Exp.* **2021**(2), 023208, (2021).

[50] H. Yoshino and F. Zamponi, *Phys. Rev. E.* **90**(2), 022302, (2014).

[51] E. Lerner and E. Bouchbinder, *J. Chem. Phys.* **155**(20), 200901, (2021).

[52] E. Bouchbinder, E. Lerner, C. Rainone, P. Urbani, and F. Zamponi, *Phys. Rev. B.* **103**(17), 174202, (2021).

[53] C. Rainone, P. Urbani, F. Zamponi, E. Lerner, and E. Bouchbinder, *SciPost Physics Core.* **4**(2), 008, (2021).

[54] G. Folena and P. Urbani, *J. Stat. Mech.: Theory Exp.* **2022**(5), 053301, (2022).

[55] P. Urbani and G. Biroli, *Phys. Rev. B.* **91**(10), 100202, (2015).

[56] A. Bray and S. Roberts, *J. Phys. C.* **13**(29), 5405, (1980).

[57] P. Charbonneau and S. Yaida, *Phys. Rev. Lett.* **118**(21), 215701, (2017).

[58] G. Parisi and T. Temesvári, *Nucl. Phys. B.* **858**(2), 293–316, (2012).

[59] P. Urbani, *J. Phys. A.* **55**(33), 335002, (2022).

[60] L. Berthier, G. Biroli, P. Charbonneau, E. I. Corwin, S. Franz, and F. Zamponi, *J. Chem. Phys.* **151**(1), 010901, (2019).

[61] S. Nagata, P. Keesom, and H. Harrison, *Phys. Rev. B.* **19**(3), 1633, (1979).

[62] S. F. Edwards and P. W. Anderson, *J. Phys. F.* **5**(5), 965, (1975).

[63] T. Castellani and A. Cavagna, *J. Stat. Mech.: Theory Exp.* **2005**(05), P05012, (2005).

[64] P. Granberg, L. Sandlund, P. Nordblad, P. Svedlindh, and L. Lundgren, *Phys. Rev. B.* **38**(10), 7097, (1988).

[65] E. Vincent, J. Hammann, M. Ocio, J.-P. Bouchaud, and L. F. Cugliandolo. In *Complex Behaviour of Glassy Systems*, pp. 184–219. Springer, (1997).

[66] P. Nordblad and P. Svedlindh. In *Spin Glasses and Random Fields*, pp. 1–27. World Scientific, (1998).

[67] L. F. Cugliandolo and J. Kurchan, *Phys. Rev. Lett.* **71**(1), 173, (1993).

[68] L. F. Cugliandolo and J. Kurchan, *J. Phys. A.* **27**(17), 5749, (1994).

[69] L. F. Cugliandolo, J. Kurchan, and L. Peliti, *Phys. Rev. E.* **55**(4), 3898, (1997).

[70] S. Franz, M. Mézard, G. Parisi, and L. Peliti, *Phys. Rev. Lett.* **81**(9), 1758, (1998).

[71] E. Marinari, G. Parisi, F. Ricci-Tersenghi, and J. J. Ruiz-Lorenzo, *J. Phys. A.* **33**(12), 2373, (2000).

[72] H. Yoshino, K. Hukushima, and H. Takayama, *Phys. Rev. B.* **66**(6), 064431, (2002).

[73] A. J. Bray and M. A. Moore, *Phys. Rev. Lett.* **58**(1), 57, (1987).

[74] D. S. Fisher and D. A. Huse, *Phys. Rev. B.* **38**(1), 386, (1988).

[75] D. S. Fisher and D. A. Huse, *Phys. Rev. B.* **38**(1), 373, (1988).

[76] I. Kondor, *J. Phys. A.* **22**(5), L163, (1989).

[77] T. Rizzo and A. Crisanti, *Phys. Rev. Lett.* **90**(13), 137201, (2003).

[78] T. Rizzo and H. Yoshino, *Phys. Rev. B.* **73**(6), 064416, (2006).

[79] H. Yoshino and T. Rizzo, *Phys. Rev. B.* **77**(10), 104429, (2008).

[80] G. Parisi and T. Rizzo, *J. Phys. A.* **43**(23), 235003, (2010).

[81] P. Le Doussal, M. Müller, and K. J. Wiese, *EPL.* **91**(5), 57004, (2010).

[82] P. Le Doussal, M. Müller, and K. J. Wiese, *Phys. Rev. B.* **85**(21), 214402, (2012).

[83] K. Jonason, E. Vincent, J. Hammann, J. Bouchaud, and P. Nordblad, *Phys. Rev. Lett.* **81**(15), 3243, (1998).

[84] H. Yoshino, A. Lemaıtre, and J.-P. Bouchaud, *Eur. Phys. J. B.* **20**(3), 367–395, (2001).

[85] P. Jönsson, R. Mathieu, P. Nordblad, H. Yoshino, H. A. Katori, and A. Ito, *Phys. Rev. B.* **70**(17), 174402, (2004).

[86] H. Yoshino and M. Mézard, *Phys. Rev. Lett.* **105**(1), 015504, (2010).

[87] H. Yoshino, *J. Chem. Phys.* **136**, 214108, (2012).

[88] T. Maimbourg, J. Kurchan, and F. Zamponi, *Phys. Rev. Lett.* **116**(1), 015902, (2016).

[89] J. Kurchan, T. Maimbourg, and F. Zamponi, *J. Stat. Mech.: Theory Exp.* **2016**(3), 033210, (2016).

[90] E. Agoritsas, T. Maimbourg, and F. Zamponi, *J. Phys. A.* **52**(14), 144002, (2019).

[91] E. Agoritsas, T. Maimbourg, and F. Zamponi, *J. Phys. A.* **52**(33), 334001, (2019).

[92] W. Kranendonk and D. Frenkel, *Mol. Phys.* **72**(3), 679–697, (1991).

[93] T. S. Grigera and G. Parisi, *Phys. Rev. E.* **63**(4), 045102, (2001).

[94] L. Berthier, P. Charbonneau, Y. Jin, G. Parisi, B. Seoane, and F. Zamponi, *Proc. Natl. Acad. Sci. U.S.A.* **113**(30), 8397–8401, (2016).

[95] B. D. Lubachevsky and F. H. Stillinger, *J. Stat. Phys.* **60**(5), 561–583, (1990).

[96] M. Goldstein, *J. Chem. Phys.* 132(4):041104, (2010).

[97] T. Boublik, *J. Chem. Phys.* **53**, 471, (1970).

[98] P. Charbonneau, Y. Jin, G. Parisi, and F. Zamponi, *Proc. Natl. Acad. Sci. U.S.A.* **111**(42), 15025–15030, (2014).

[99] A. Donev, S. Torquato, and F. H. Stillinger, *Phys. Rev. E.* **71**(1), 011105, (2005).

[100] J.-P. Bouchaud, L. F. Cugliandolo, J. Kurchan, and M. Mézard. In *Spin glasses and random fields*, vol. 12, p. 161. World Scientific Singapore, (1998).

[101] A. Lees and S. Edwards, *J. Phys. Condens. Matter.* **5**(15), 1921, (1972).

[102] P. Charbonneau, Y. Jin, G. Parisi, C. Rainone, B. Seoane, and F. Zamponi, *Phys. Rev. E.* **92**(1), 012316, (2015).

[103] B. Seoane and F. Zamponi, *Soft Matter.* **14**(25), 5222–5234, (2018).

[104] Y. Jin, P. Urbani, F. Zamponi, and H. Yoshino, *Sci. Adv.* **4**(12), eaat6387, (2018).

[105] Q. Liao and L. Berthier, *Phys. Rev. X.* **9**(1), 011049, (2019).

[106] H. Li, Y. Jin, Y. Jiang, and J. Z. Chen, *Proc. Natl. Acad. Sci. U.S.A.* **118**(11), (2021).

[107] P. Charbonneau, E. I. Corwin, G. Parisi, and F. Zamponi, *Phys. Rev. Lett.* **114**(12), 125504, (2015).

[108] P. Charbonneau, E. I. Corwin, G. Parisi, A. Poncet, and F. Zamponi, *Phys. Rev. Lett.* **117**(4), 045503, (2016).

[109] R. Dennis and E. Corwin, *Phys. Rev. Lett.* **124**(7), 078002, (2020).

[110] C. Scalliet and L. Berthier, *Phys. Rev. Lett.* **122**(25), 255502, (2019).

[111] C. Scalliet, L. Berthier, and F. Zamponi, *Phys. Rev. Lett.* **119**(20), 205501, (2017).

[112] A. Seguin and O. Dauchot, *Phys. Rev. Lett.* **117**(22), 228001, (2016).

[113] A. P. Hammond and E. I. Corwin, *Proc. Natl. Acad. Sci. U.S.A.* **117**(11), 5714–5718, (2020).

[114] R. Zargar, E. DeGiuli, and D. Bonn, *EPL.* **116**(6), 68004, (2017).

[115] Y. Wang, J. Shang, Y. Jin, and J. Zhang, *Proc. Natl. Acad. Sci. U.S.A.* **119**(22), e2204879119, (2022).

[116] L. Kool, P. Charbonneau, and K. E. Daniels, *Phys. Rev. E.* **106**, 054901, (2022).

[117] P. Charbonneau, E. I. Corwin, L. Fu, G. Tsekenis, and M. van Der Naald, *Phys. Rev. E.* **99**(2), 020901, (2019).

[118] W. Kauzmann, *Chem. Rev.* **43**(2), 219–256, (1948).

[119] G. Tsekenis, *EPL.* **135**(3), 36001, (2021).

Chapter 13

The Jamming Transition and the Marginally Stable Solid

Francesco Arceri[*], Eric I. Corwin[†] and Corey S. O'Hern[*, ‡, §]

[*]*Department of Mechanical Engineering and Materials Science, Yale University, New Haven, Connecticut 06511, USA*
[†]*Department of Physics and Materials Science Institute, University of Oregon, Eugene, Oregon 97403, USA*
[‡]*Department of Physics, Yale University, New Haven, Connecticut 06511, USA*
[§]*Department of Applied Physics, Yale University, New Haven, Connecticut 06511, USA*

The jamming transition is one of the physical processes where the mean-field RSB description has been most influential. This chapter presents some of the key highlights of jamming physics and their relationship with the RSB description.

13.1. Introduction

Few things in this world are as common as earth, dirt, and sand. And yet, even as the most exotic, the most distant, and the smallest objects in our universe have fallen prey to human understanding, the nature and origin of the structural and mechanical properties of these materials has been, until recently, surprisingly resistant. It was not for a lack of trying. The *jamming* transition, by which a collection of macroscopic particles goes from flowing to rigid, lies not only at the heart of building practices throughout human history, but is ubiquitous in everyday life. Examples range from grains poured into a container [1], to foams and emulsions in foods such as ice cream and mayonnaise [2], and to sand piles and gravel at the beach and in city parks [3]. The jamming transition from fluid-to-solid behavior in these different systems shares a fundamental feature: the energy scale of the interaction between particles is sufficiently large that thermal fluctuations at room temperature are far too small to affect the dynamics. The control parameters of the jamming transition are therefore the external pressure exerted on the system and the volume in which the system is confined. The first academic study of jamming dates to 1727, when Reverend Steven Hales studied the structures formed by the contacts between dried peas, compressed in an iron pot [4]. Such luminaries as Isaac Newton [5] and James Clerk Maxwell [6] attempted to analytically solve for the properties of jammed packings, but were only able to determine bounds on number of contacts per particle required for mechanical stability. More recently, Bernal connected the amorphous geometric structure of spheres to the properties of the liquid state of matter [7]. However, it was not until nearly the turn of this century that the modern study of jamming was initiated [8–10]. Particularly, Liu and Nagel [11] made the critical realization that athermal jamming could be united with another age old problem: the glass transition. Only within the last decade has a first-principles description of the jamming transition seemed possible, enabled by insights from the mean-field theory of glasses and jamming [12]. Because in this framework the jamming transition takes place within a full replica symmetry breaking (RSB) phase [13], this seemingly simple problem has revealed a world of amazing complexity.

Recent developments in the physics of the glass transition have led to groundbreaking results in the field of jamming. Although the glass transition signals a drastic (and markedly distinct) dynamical slowdown upon cooling, both transitions can be observed in systems of hard particles, which do not deform during collisions. The simple *hard-sphere* model, in particular, has offered theoretical physicists fertile ground for building a mean-field theory of glasses, with jamming occurring in the limit of infinite pressure. Despite the great advances that the hard-sphere model has brought to the field, the fact that it has a discontinuous inter-particle potential represents a major obstacle for computing the mechanical properties in finite-dimensional systems. As a remedy, soft-sphere models, where particle deformations are described by shared volume between particles, have been used in the field as they allow more direct calculations of inter-particle forces. The fact that the jamming transition for frictionless spherical particles can be studied using both the hard- and soft-particle models reflects its geometrical nature. By considering the average number of contacts per particle, z, one finds that the jamming of hard and soft spheres occurs at $z_c = 2d$ [6], i.e., the minimum number of contacts to ensure rigidity [14] (Maxwell's criterion). For soft spheres, which can be compressed beyond the jamming point, the excess number of contacts scales as:

$$\Delta z \equiv z - z_c \sim \Delta\varphi^{1/2}, \tag{13.1}$$

where φ is the packing fraction and the excess packing fraction $\Delta\varphi = \varphi - \varphi_J$ represents the amount of compression above the jamming threshold, which is itself protocol dependent [15, 16]. Further, several studies have shown an exact correspondence in the inter-particle separations between jammed hard-particle and soft-particle packings [16, 17], confirming that accessible configurations of hard and soft spheres are identical near jamming onset [18–20].

13.2. Jamming Criticality

Many numerical studies have documented critical behaviors of bulk quantities near the jamming transition, including observation of power-law scaling [14, 16, 21], scaling collapse of the elastic moduli and excess contact number [22–25], identification of diverging length scales [26–29], and analyses of finite-size scaling [24]. Recent studies have unified these scaling relations in a single theory of jamming using a *scaling ansatz* [30]. This approach borrows ideas from critical phenomena, such as spontaneous magnetization and density-charge waves [31–33], to describe scaling relations for the energy E, pressure p, excess packing fraction $\Delta\varphi$, shear stress s, shear strain ϵ, bulk modulus B, shear modulus G, and number of particles N obtained from a single state function for the elastic energy

$$E(\Delta Z, \Delta \varphi, \epsilon, N) = \Delta Z^\zeta \mathcal{E}_0 \left(\frac{\Delta \varphi}{\Delta Z^{\beta_\varphi}}, \frac{\epsilon}{\Delta Z^{\beta_\epsilon}}, N \Delta Z^\psi \right) \tag{13.2}$$

and its derivatives

$$p \equiv \varphi \frac{dE}{d\Delta\varphi}, \quad s \equiv \epsilon \frac{dE}{d\epsilon}, \quad B \equiv \frac{\varphi^2}{2} \frac{d^2 E}{d\Delta\varphi^2}, \quad G \equiv \frac{d^2 E}{d\epsilon^2}. \tag{13.3}$$

Notice that $\Delta Z = N \Delta z$ is the total number of excess contacts in a jammed soft-sphere system. These relations yield a set of equations that couple the critical exponents. The picture is completed by the addition of the *pressure-shear stress exponent equality*, which dictates that s^2 vanishes in the infinite-size limit as $1/N$.

Although the scaling ansatz offers a description in the $\Delta \varphi \epsilon N$ ensemble, numerical studies are often conducted in the peN or psN ensembles as both pressure and shear stress vanish at the jamming point. The scaling ansatz can be extended to the psN ensemble at finite temperature by defining a new state function for the free energy:

$$F(\Delta Z, p, s, N, T) = \Delta Z^\zeta \mathcal{F}_0 \left(\frac{p}{\Delta Z^{\delta_p}}, \frac{s}{\Delta Z^{\delta_s}}, N \Delta Z^\psi, \frac{T}{\Delta Z^{\delta_T}} \right). \tag{13.4}$$

The new scaling exponent equation, $\delta_T = \zeta = 4$, is consistent with the scaling of the critical temperature, $T^* \simeq \Delta Z^4$, which defines the separation between glass and jamming-like behavior [19, 34]. A scaling theory for thermal systems is nevertheless far from complete due to glassy phenomena, such as aging and dynamical heterogeneity, which stem from the temperature-activated breaking and reformation of particle contacts, that is difficult to capture with simple scaling laws [35, 36].

The scaling ansatz provides a framework that connects the structural and mechanical properties (ΔZ and G) for particle systems above the onset of jamming. The existence of such a framework implies that the jamming transition exhibits scaling invariance, a helpful tool for a renormalization group description. However, recent studies of the shear modulus near the jamming transition have highlighted the limits of the scaling ansatz [37, 38]. In particular, the scaling ansatz cannot explain why the shear modulus G scales linearly with ΔZ, a result which has been numerically tested and theoretically confirmed by effective medium theory [39, 40] as well as by an analytical formalism that accounts for non-affine contributions to the elastic moduli [41]. Interestingly, the inter-particle force law does not play a more important role in determining the shear modulus in jammed packings at non-zero pressure. In addition, the scaling analysis cannot quantify deviations between the ensemble average and the large-system limit, and it does not describe local fluctuations in the elastic moduli, or that the local elastic moduli can become negative [23, 38]. The importance of fluctuations in the elastic moduli suggest that we need to develop a deeper understanding of the energy landscape of jammed packings.

13.3. Marginal Stability

Generically, jammed packings of frictionless, spherical particles with purely repulsive interactions are *isostatic* and marginally stable. In other words, they possess the minimum

     Francesco Arceri, Eric I. Corwin and Corey S. O'Hern

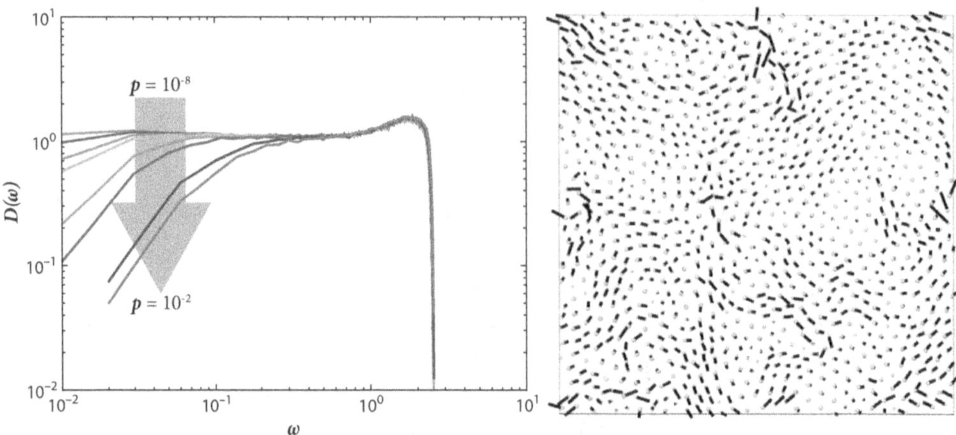

Fig. 13.1. (a) Vibrational density of states $D(\omega)$ plotted as a function of pressure p and (b) the real-space representation of a soft, extended mode. Figures reproduced with permission from Ref. [26] ©(2005) American Physical Society.

number of contacts to ensure mechanical stability and single bond-breaking perturbations can destabilize the entire system [42]. Numerical and experimental studies have characterized marginal stability by measuring the vibrational density of states (VDOS) of jammed solids at finite pressure [43] (Fig. 13.1). In particular, the low-frequency region of the VDOS possesses *soft modes*, i.e., low-frequency normal modes of vibration that are spatially extended and involve a large fraction of particles in the system. Upon decreasing the pressure of jammed soft spheres toward the unjamming transition, the number of force-bearing contacts decreases until it reaches the isostatic value, $N_{iso} = Nz/2$, where the number of contacts equals the number of constraints. Here, the low-frequency region of the VDOS develops a plateau and the frequency of the lowest mode scales as $\omega_c \sim \Delta\varphi^{1/2}$. Finite-size scaling shows that $\omega_c \to 0$ in the large-system limit, in which case, the soft modes correspond to zero-energy modes.

A real-space interpretation of marginal stability is offered by the so-called *cutting argument* introduced by Wyart *et al.* [27]. Imagine removing contacts on the edge between a subsystem of linear size l and the rest of the system. If at this point the system is slightly compressed, the lack of contacts leads to a competition between the overall excess contacts ΔZ created by the compression and the missing contacts at the boundary. If the total number of contacts is equal to the isostatic value N_{iso}, the system possesses soft modes. The number of soft modes N_{soft} corresponds to the difference between the number of contacts at the boundary, which are proportional to l^{d-1}, and the number of extra contacts created by the compression, which scales as $\Delta Z l^d$. Therefore, a critical length $l^* \sim \Delta\varphi^{-1/2}$ exists, below which the system is isostatic and possesses soft modes.

The mean-field theory of glasses provides a theoretical understanding of marginal stability in jammed solids as the jamming transition is viewed as the end-line of the glass phase diagram [12] pictured in Fig. 13.2. Here, compression of an equilibrium liquid composed of hard spheres gives rise to dynamical arrest when the system becomes confined to one of the basins of the complex and hierarchically organized free-energy landscape. Adopting the *state-following formalism* developed by Rainone *et al.* [44],

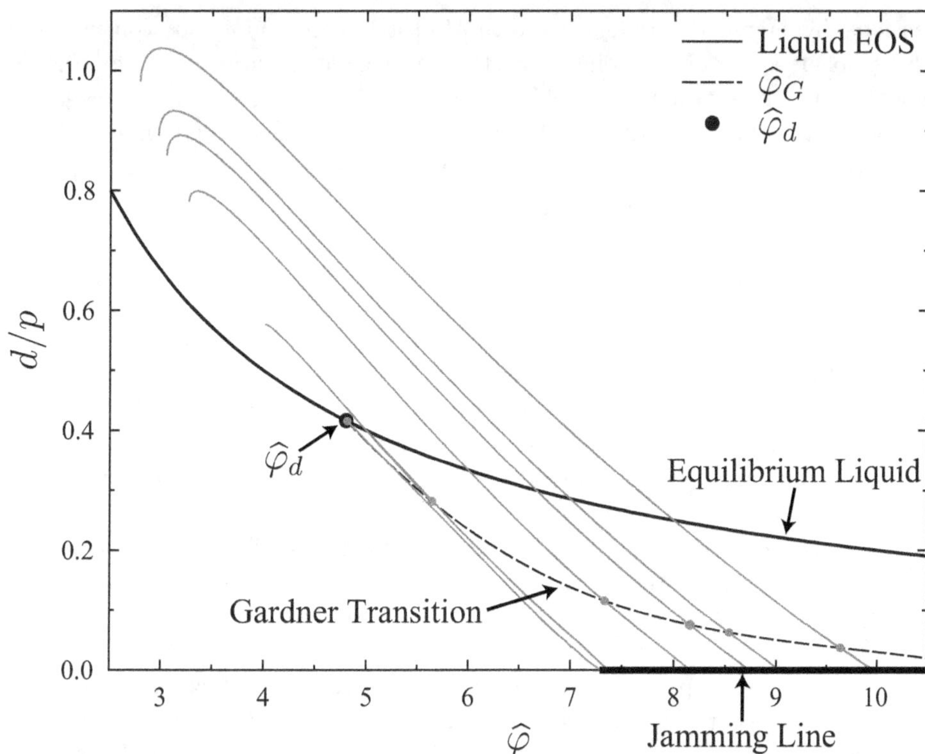

Fig. 13.2.   Glass phase diagram in the d/p versus $\hat{\varphi}$ plane, where $\hat{\varphi} = 2^d \varphi/d$, φ is the packing fraction, and d is the spatial dimension.   In contrast to the *equilibrium liquid* equation of state (thick solid line), each thin solid line represents a state-following compression that starts from a liquid state and evolves toward the glass and RSB glass (dotted line) regions. The end-point of each state-following compression occurs on the jamming line. Figure reproduced with permission from Ref. [44] ©(2016) IOP Publishing.

each glass state undergoes a Gardner transition upon further compression that brings the system to a marginal glass state [45]. Here, the free-energy basins are fragmented into multiple sub-basins that are in turn fractured into sub-sub-basins *ad infinitum*. These marginal glass states are separated by free-energy barriers that grow with system size and link glass formation with marginally stable packings typical of jammed materials. The mean-field theory of glasses also predicts the existence of a *jamming line*, i.e., marginal glass states that cannot be further compressed occur over a range of packing fractions, which depends on the protocol used to produce the initial glass state.

Another connection between jamming and the mean-field theory of glasses is the unjamming transition of soft spheres. Finding configurations of d-dimensional spheres with no inter-particle overlaps is a type of *satisfiability problem* [46–48]. Determining whether collections of spherical particles overlap each other can be cast as a constraint satisfaction problem, where N variables can be adjusted to satisfy M constraints. Several algorithms have been used to solve constraint satisfaction problems, such as gradient descent [49, 50], simulated annealing [51], and the perceptron model [52, 53]. The perceptron model has been successful in describing the high-dimensional energy landscape near the jamming transition [54]. In short, it describes a tracer particle on an

N-dimensional hypersphere of radius $\sqrt{N}$ with M obstacles in random positions placed on the hypersphere surface. The solution for the accessible configurations of the tracer particle maps onto the satisfiability problem of a jammed packing of soft spheres [52]. This theory predicts the same critical behavior of the interparticle gap and force distributions and the same scaling of the coordination number versus the pressure, $\Delta z \sim p^{1/2}$, as those found for jammed packings of spherical particles.

13.4. Numerical Confirmations of the Mean-Field Theory of Jamming

Jammed systems offer a uniquely useful arena to test the predictions of the mean-field theory. Because they are athermal, one can devise experimental and numerical systems to directly measure the particle-scale properties that are predicted by the theory. Over the past decade, fruitful collaborations have emerged between theory, experiment, and numerical simulation to confirm many of the mean-field theoretical predictions in athermal jammed systems.

One of the first, and most striking, confirmations of the mean-field theory has come from the examination of the distribution of inter-particle forces, $P(f)$, in systems at jamming onset [55]. The small-force tail of the force distribution contributes significantly to the mechanical properties of a packing [39]. Both the distribution of small gaps and small forces between particles determine the statistics of contact breaking and formation when a system is mechanically perturbed. The mean-field theory makes a precise prediction about the distribution of small forces. If breaking a weak contact results in a spatially *extended* soft mode, the tail of the force distribution scales as $P(f) \sim f^{\theta_e}$, where $\theta_e \approx 0.42311$. However, if breaking a weak contact results in a spatially *localized* soft mode, a different argument, based on an analysis of marginal mechanical stability, predicts that the tail of the distribution will be distributed as $P(f) \sim f^{\theta_l}$, where $\theta_l \approx 0.17462$ [56]. On the face of it, the decomposition of forces into those associated with *extended* and *localized* excitations is a substantial task. However, it suffices to recognize that the vast majority of localized forces can be associated with *bucklers*, particles that are minimally stable (with only $d+1$ contacts), d of them nearly co-planar, and hence they have only one small contact force. As shown in Fig. 13.3 (which presents the cumulative distribution of forces, $G(f) = \int_0^f df' P(f')$), when the forces are decomposed according to this rule, the mean-field theory predictions for the small force tails are observed in spatial dimensions all the way down to $d = 2$. This surprisingly precise agreement provided strong evidence that the mean-field results are predictive in physically relevant systems.

The strength and validity of the mean-field predictions were further bolstered by a comprehensive study of the finite-size effects on jammed packings [58]. This work showed that the aforementioned force distribution exponents are remarkably precise in low dimensions for systems as small as $N = 256$ particles, showing essentially no finite-size effects.

One unexpectedly fruitful system of interest for studying the implications of the mean-field theory is the so-called *Gardner crystal*, consisting of slightly polydisperse spheres packed into a nearly perfect crystal, as shown in Fig. 13.4. At high temperature or low pressure, the polydispersity is effectively masked by the random motions of the

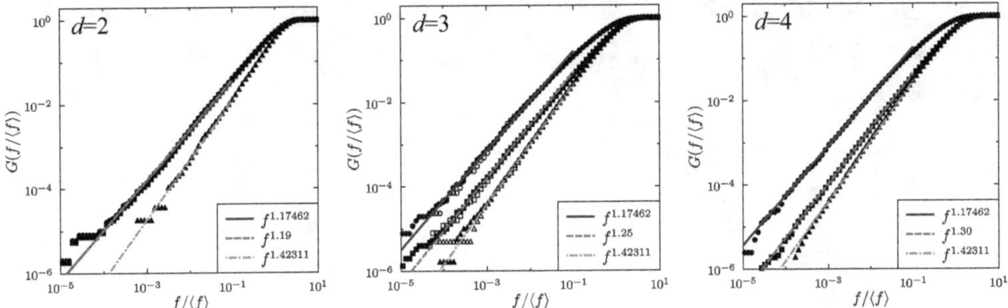

Fig. 13.3.   Cumulative force distributions $G(f)$ for $d=$ 2, 3, and 4, showing power-law distributions at small forces. The overall distribution (with fits shown by the dashed lines) shows evolution with spatial dimension. However, when split into *buckler* and *non-buckler* contacts, $G(f)$ for the former is well-fit by a power-law with exponent $1 + \theta_l$ and $G(f)$ for the latter is well-fit by a power-law with exponent $1 + \theta_e$ in all dimensions, in excellent agreement with the mean-field theory predictions. Figure reproduced with permission from Ref. [55] ©(2015) American Physical Society.

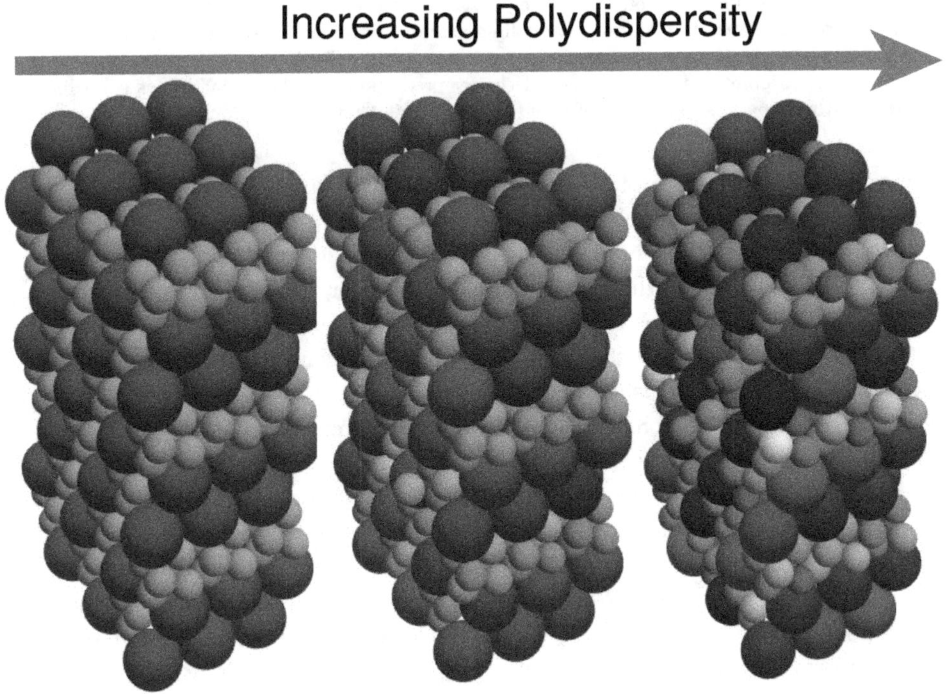

Fig. 13.4.   A crystalline sphere packing with increasing amounts of polydispersity in the particle sizes, from perfectly crystalline on the left to 5% polydispersity on the right. Figure reproduced with permission from Ref. [57] ©(2019) American Physical Society.

particles, resulting in a solid with conventional properties. However, as the temperature is decreased or the pressure is increased, the cages around each particle shrink. Once the gaps between particles become comparable to the scale of the polydispersity, the system is forced to make choices between a hierarchy of different possible configurations, akin to what takes place in an amorphous system [57].

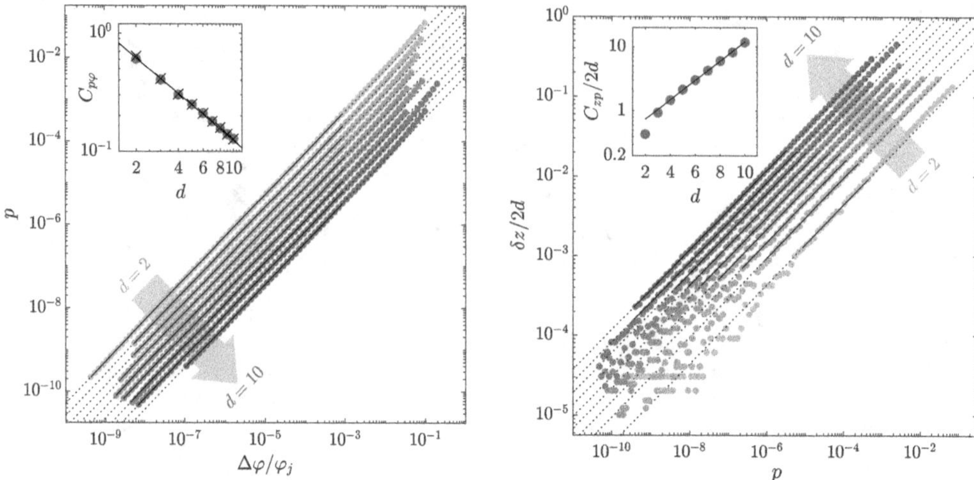

Fig. 13.5. Scaling relations between the pressure, p, and the normalized excess packing fraction, $\Delta\varphi/\varphi_j$, where φ_j is the packing fraction at jamming onset, and the excess contact number, $\delta z \equiv \Delta Z/N$ versus p. The dotted lines are best fits to the scaling relations obtained by the mean-field theory of jamming, as a function of the spatial dimension from $d = 2$ to 10. The insets show the prefactors of the scaling relations as points and the mean-field theory predictions for the prefactors as solid lines. Figure reproduced with permission from Ref. [59] ©(2021) American Physical Society.

Another direct confirmation of the mean-field theory of jamming was obtained in a study of the scaling prefactors relating the pressure, packing fraction, and number of contacts in jammed systems. The mean-field theory provides predictions not only for the scaling exponents relating these quantities, but also for the prefactors themselves, as a function of the spatial dimension of the system [12]. Sartor, Ridout, and Corwin demonstrated through numerical simulations that these prefactor relations hold all the way down to $d = 2$ and 3 [59], as shown in Fig. 13.5.

While the above work demonstrates the predictive powers of the mean-field theory, recent work [60] has also directly confirmed that the energy landscape of jammed systems is consistent with full replica symmetry breaking. As a glassy system undergoes the Gardner transition entering a marginal glass state, the energy landscape results in an "ultrametric" structure for the very large number of marginally stable minima [61]. Through an exhaustive search of the nearby minima in a local region of the energy landscape of jammed packings of finite size, Dennis and Corwin were able to directly measure the degree of ultrametricity of the landscape. They found that, in the large-system limit, this landscape became precisely ultrametric, with the distance to ultrametricity scaling as $N^{-1/2}$. Thus, jammed systems can be viewed as being located deep within the Gardner phase, as described by the mean-field theory.

13.5. Experimental Validations of the Mean-Field Theory of Jamming

Experimental tests of the mean-field theory have chiefly focused on the detection of signatures of the Gardner transition in driven, athermal systems that mimic thermal systems. Seguin and Dauchot [62] constructed a granular system of vibrated disks and used it to explore the fracturing of the energy landscape as pressure is increased. An initial, *high-energy* amorphous configuration was created by confining a system of plastic disks in a fixed volume, and thus at a fixed packing fraction. Energy introduced through vibration allowed the system to make and break inter-particle contacts and explore the local energy landscape. The system was then cyclically quenched to a higher packing fraction (and thus a higher pressure) and then decompressed to the original packing fraction. The mean squared displacement of particles, Δ at the high packing fraction, as well as the mean-squared displacement between cycles, Δ_{AB}, were measured. Figure 13.6(a) shows that these two measurements depart from one another as the quench packing fraction is increased, which is the signature of the Gardner transition in this amorphous 2D system. Xiao, Liu, and Durian made a similar measurement on a dissimilar amorphous system, also observing the clear signature of the Gardner transition [63]. Rather than using vibrated disks, this work instead used a 2D system of air-fluidized rotors, shown in Fig. 13.6(b), constructed with five-fold symmetry to frustrate crystallization. A flexible boundary made of a chain of particles subject to a fixed tension serves to precisely control the pressure of the system, allowing measurements that can be directly compared to the Gardner transition results predicted for thermal systems (see Fig. 13.6(b)).

The aforementioned Gardner crystal provides opportunities for experimental studies of the Gardner transition as well. Kool, Charbonneau, and Daniels constructed a 2D system of photo-elastic disks and were able to track the formation of persistent contacts as the system passed through a Gardner-like transition [64]. This work also showed the characteristic splitting between fluctuations within a system and fluctuations between systems at the Gardner transition (see Fig. 13.6(c)).

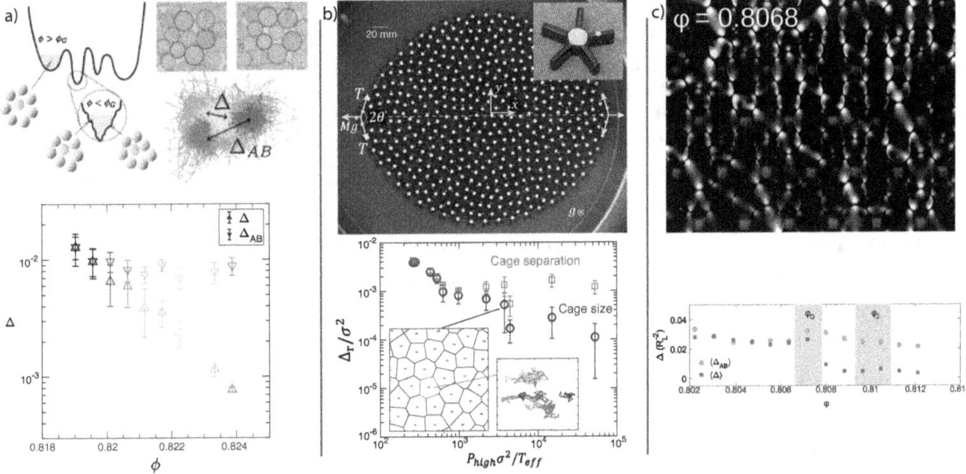

Fig. 13.6. Experimental evidence for the Gardner transition in driven, athermal disk packings, showing the characteristic splitting between Δ and Δ_{AB} at the Gardner packing fraction or pressure. a) Vibrated disk packings. b) Air-fluidized rotors. c) Slightly polydisperse crystalline configuration of photoelastic disks. Figures reproduced with permission from (a) Ref. [62] ©(2016) American Physical Society, (b) Ref. [63] ©(2022) American Physical Society, and (c) Ref. [64] ©(2022) the authors.

13.6. Beyond Sphere Packings

We have presented numerical and experimental confirmations of several predictions from the mean-field theory of jamming in the context of packings of identical frictionless spherical particles, interacting via excluded volume repulsion. However, most of the materials that show jamming transitions are not composed of frictionless, spherical particles–think jelly beans, grains, and rocks. Clogging transitions, which are similar to jamming transitions, also occur in crowds of people and organisms [65]. Moreover, many biological systems are extremely deformable, but can experience jamming transitions, like cells that form confluent tissues [66, 67]. Two additional categories of jamming transitions therefore involve packings of *non-spherical* particles and packings of *deformable* particles.

Experiments [68] and numerical simulations [69] of jamming of non-spherical particles, such as ellipsoids [70], spherocylinders [71], and polyhedra [72], have probed the validity of the Maxwell criterion for determining mechanical stability [73]. Generalized to non-spherical particles, the criterion states that static packings need to possess $z = 2 \times DOF$ contacts per particle to be mechanically stable, where DOF is the number of degrees of freedom per particle [6]. As discussed earlier, the Maxwell criterion holds for sphere packings, where the number of contacts per particle is exactly $2d$ and the number of degrees of freedom per particle is equal to the spatial dimension d. Does the Maxwell criterion hold for non-spherical particles? Consider a packing of spheroids, i.e., an ellipsoid of revolution with one symmetry axis. Two degrees of freedom are required to specify the orientation of a spheroid, and three degrees of freedom are required to specify the position of the center of mass. According to the Maxwell criterion, each spheroid should possess $N_c = 2 \times (3 + 2) = 10$ contacts. However, experiments on spheroid packings clearly show that the number of contacts at jamming onset is always below ten, violating the Maxwell criterion. Therefore, jammed packings of spheroids are *hypostatic*, and possess fewer contacts than the apparent number of degrees of freedom. Subsequent numerical and experimental studies have shown that nearly all jammed packings of non-spherical particles are hypostatic.

Numerical studies have focused on investigating the mechanisms that give rise to hypostaticity in jammed packings of non-spherical particles. These studies reveal that the number of missing contacts is the same as the number of *quartic modes* [74]. Perturbations along these quartic modes give rise to a quartic increase in the potential energy versus the amplitude of the perturbation in the zero-pressure limit [75–78]. Quartic modes are in fact responsible for stabilizing jammed packings of a wide range of non-spherical particles.

The structural properties of jammed packings of non-spherical particles are summarized in Fig. 13.7. Both the packing fraction and coordination number for jammed packings of non-spherical particles show non-trivial dependence on the shape parameter $\mathcal{A}$. In 2D, $\mathcal{A} = p^2/4\pi a$, where p is the perimeter and a is the area of the particles. In 3D, $\mathcal{A} = (4\pi)^{1/3}(3V)^{2/3}/S$, where V and S are the volume and surface area of the particles, respectively. In particular, the average packing fraction and coordination number at jamming onset follow master curves as a function of $\mathcal{A} - 1$. These results suggest

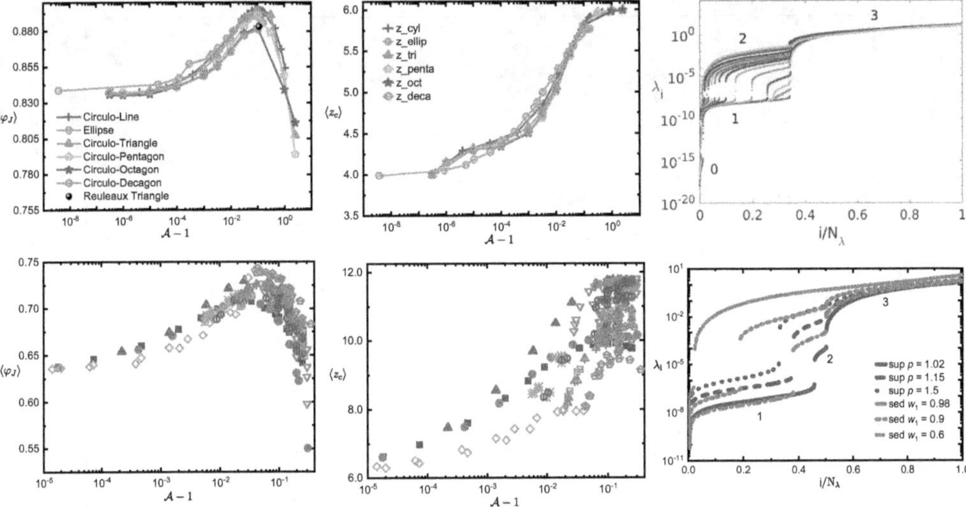

Fig. 13.7.   From left to right: Average packing fraction $\langle \varphi_J \rangle$ and excess contact number $\langle z_c \rangle$ at jamming onset as a function of asphericity $\mathcal{A}-1$ and low-frequency eigenvalues $\lambda = \omega^2$ of the dynamical matrix for jammed packings of non-spherical particles in two (top) and three (bottom) dimensions. The eigenvalues are divided in three branches: (1) quartic modes, (2) rotational modes, and (3) translational modes. Figures reproduced with permission from (top panel) Ref. [77] ©(2018) American Physical Society and (bottom panel) Ref. [79] ©(2019) Royal Society of Chemistry .

that the shape parameter controls the jamming behavior of packings of non-spherical particles.

Using an extension of the perceptron model, Brito *et al.* [78] predicted the scaling of the coordination number versus the pressure and the existence of quartic modes in the VDOS for jammed packings of non-spherical particles [76, 77]. The generalized perceptron model predicts the zero-temperature phase diagram for jammed packings of non-spherical particles in the α-σ plane, where α and σ represent the density and convexity of the obstacles on the hypersphere. (See Fig. 13.8.) The critical behavior in the presence of spherical asymmetry is substantially altered from its counterpart derived for jamming of spherical particles. In particular, different scaling exponents are predicted for the gap and force distributions, and the per-particle coordination number scales as

$$\Delta z \sim c_{\mathcal{A}} p \quad \text{with} \quad c_{\mathcal{A}} \sim \mathcal{A}^{1/2}, \tag{13.5}$$

and consequently the shear modulus follows the scaling $G \sim p/\mathcal{A}^{1/2}$. These results were corroborated by previous numerical studies of jammed packings of non-spherical particles [77, 80], proving the versatility of the mean-field theory for jamming.

Particle shape has also been explored as a tool to incorporate frictional forces into the jamming framework, a direction that requires further experimental investigation [81]. Prior work has investigated jammed packings of particles with circular (in 2D) or spherical (in 3D) asperities on the particle surfaces [75]. These particles have an effective static friction coefficient μ_{eff} and the packing fraction $\phi_J(\mu_{\text{eff}})$ and contact number z_J of

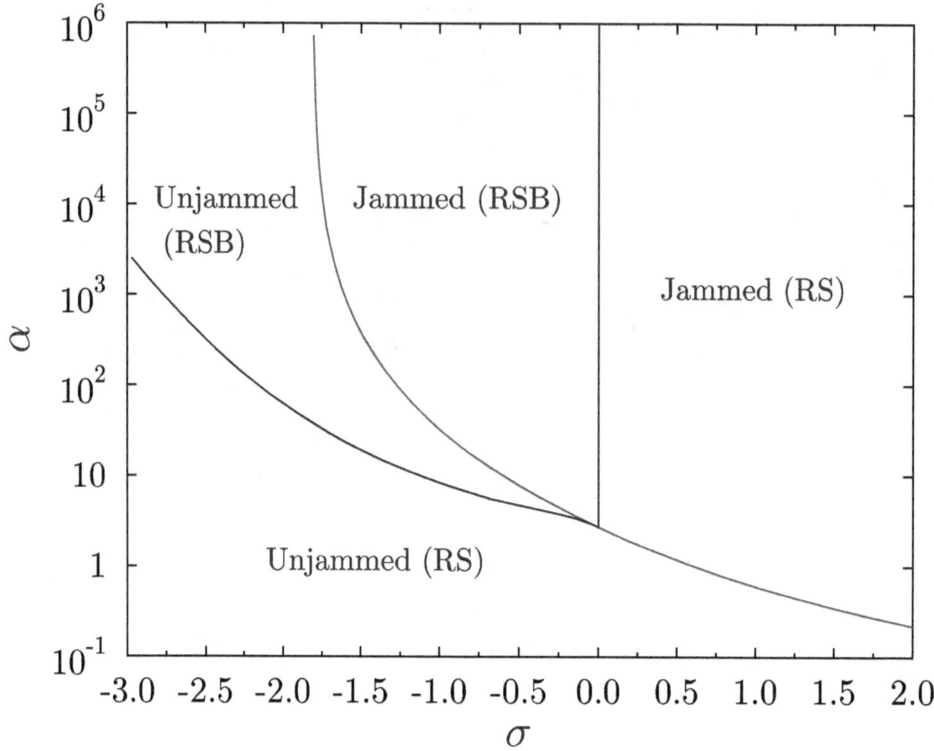

Fig. 13.8. The jamming behavior in the α-σ plane, which quantify the density and convexity of the obstacles on the N-dimensional hypersphere in the generalized perceptron model. Figure reproduced with permission from Ref. [78] ©(2018) National Academy of Sciences of the United States of America.

packings at jamming onset mimic the behavior found for jammed packings of frictional spherical particles using the Cundall–Strack model [82]. However, these packings are isostatic if all contacts between asperities are counted. Other work [83] has also modeled friction by considering rough particle surfaces. In their studies, the amplitude and frequency of the bumps on the disk surface are continuously varied. Although this work shows a clear reduction of the coordination number and packing fraction at jamming onset with increasing static friction coefficient, it is limited to small deviations from smooth spherical shapes and it is not clear how to count contacts at concave surfaces.

The nature of the jamming transition in static packings of soft and deformable particles is much less understood. Experimental studies of aqueous colloidal suspensions have shown that particle deformability plays a crucial role in determining the mechanical properties of colloidal suspensions, leading to glassy behavior with increasing concentration [84]. Colloids with larger deformations resemble strong glass-forming liquids. In contrast, harder colloids display super-Arrhenius increases in viscosity with increasing concentration, typical of fragile glasses. Other studies have shown that the shape parameter of deformable particles plays an important role in determining the onset of rigidity in cell monolayers [85].

Including particle deformability in models of jamming can describe a range of biological phenomena, such as wound healing, development of biological tissues, and macromolecular crowding. The deformable particle model (DPM) studied in 2D [86] and

3D [87], and the elastic polymer ring model [88] in 2D have been developed to describe such systems. In 3D, the shape-energy function includes a volume term that represents particle compressibility, a surface tension term, and a bending energy term that assigns an energy cost to surface deformations. Studies of jammed packings of deformable particles using the DPM have shown that deformable particles possess polyhedral shapes with $\mathcal{A} \sim 1.16$ at confluence, i.e., particles deform until they completely fill all of the available space as observed in epithelia and endothelia [89, 90]. Several other models have also studied the onset of jamming in the context of confluent tissues, such as the vertex [91] and self-propelled Voronoi [85] models. Here, unjamming transitions are strongly influenced by cell activity, which includes cell speed and persistence of the direction of motion. In recent work by Agoritsas [92], activity has been incorporated into a dynamical mean-field theory (DMFT) for a system of infinitely-persistent particles at jamming onset. DMFT represents an important avenue of research for advancing the theory of jamming to driven and active granular systems and it has been recently applied to the perceptron model [93]. While still in its infancy, this direction of research could potentially result in the integration of particle shape degrees of freedom into the mean-field theory of jamming.

Our goal with this chapter was to summarize the predictions of the mean-field theory of jamming that have been confirmed by numerical simulations and experiments. Most of the confirmations have been for mean-field predictions concerning jamming of frictionless, spherical particles, while more recent work has shown confirmations of the mean-field theory of jamming for frictionless, non-spherical particles and frictional, nearly spherical particles. We also present current efforts in expanding the mean-field theory to systems that more closely resemble externally driven granular media, cell aggregates, and active colloidal suspensions. The physics of jamming is far more diverse and rich than the specific topics related to confirmations of the mean-field theory that we presented here. We direct the reader to more detailed review articles for an exhaustive description of numerical and experimental studies of jamming [1, 2, 43] and to the book by Parisi, Urbani and Zamponi for a complete description of the jamming replica theory [12].

Acknowledgments

We would like to thank all of our collaborators in the community without which this work would not have been possible. Particular gratitude goes to our editor Patrick Charbonneau and Elisabeth Agoritsas, Ada Altieri, Bulbul Chakraborty, Cameron Dennis, Andrea Liu, Peter Morse, Sid Nagel, Nidhi Pashine, Mark Shattuck, Pierfrancesco Urbani, Eric Weeks, and Francesco Zamponi. E.C. and F.A. acknowledge funding from the Simons Collaboration on Cracking the Glass Problem via Award No. 454939 and C.S.O. acknowledges funding from NSF Grant No. DMREF-2118988.

References

[1] R. P. Behringer and B. Chakraborty, *Rep. Prog. Phys.* **82**(1), 012601, (2019).
[2] M. van Hecke, *J. Phys.: Condens. Matter.* **22**(3), 033101, (2010).

[3] M. E. Cates, J. P. Wittmer, J.-P. Bouchaud, and P. Claudin, *Phys. Rev. Lett.* **81**(9), 1841–1844, (1998).

[4] S. Hales, S. Gribelin, J. Innys, W. Innys, T. Woodward, W. A. J. Innys, and T. Woodward, *Vegetable Staticks, or, An Account of Some Statical Experiments on the Sap in Vegetables.* (Printed for W. and J. Innys ... :——and T. Woodward, 1727).

[5] I. Newton, *Newton's Principia: The Mathematical Principles of Natural Philosophy.* (D. Adee, 1848).

[6] J. C. Maxwell, *Lond. Edinb. Dublin philos. mag. j. sci.* **27**(182), 294–299, (1864).

[7] J. D. Bernal, *Nature.* **185**(4706), 68–70, (1960).

[8] J. P. Wittmer, P. Claudin, M. E. Cates, and J.-P. Bouchaud, *Nature.* **382**(6589), 336–338, (1996).

[9] P.-G. de Gennes, *Rev. Mod. Phys.* **71**(2), S374–S382, (1999).

[10] A. V. Tkachenko and T. A. Witten, *Phys. Rev. E.* **60**(1), 687–696, (1999).

[11] A. J. Liu and S. R. Nagel, *Nature.* **396**(6706), 21–22, (1998).

[12] G. Parisi, P. Urbani, and F. Zamponi, *Theory of Simple Glasses: Exact Solutions in Infinite Dimensions.* (Cambridge University Press, 2020).

[13] M. Mézard, G. Parisi, N. Sourlas, G. Toulouse, and M. Virasoro, *Phys. Rev. Lett.* **52**(13), 1156–1159, (1984).

[14] C. S. O'Hern, S. A. Langer, A. J. Liu, and S. R. Nagel, *Phys. Rev. Lett.* **88**(7), 075507, (2002).

[15] D. J. Durian, *Phys. Rev. Lett.* **75**(26), 4780–4783, (1995).

[16] C. S. O'Hern, L. E. Silbert, A. J. Liu, and S. R. Nagel, *Phys. Rev. E.* **68**(1), 011306, (2003).

[17] A. Donev, S. Torquato, and F. H. Stillinger, *Phys. Rev. E.* **71**(1), 011105, (2005).

[18] C. Brito and M. Wyart, *Europhys. Lett.* **76**(1), 149–155, (2006).

[19] Q. Wu, T. Bertrand, M. D. Shattuck, and C. S. O'Hern, *Phys. Rev. E.* **96**(6), 062902, (2017).

[20] F. Arceri and E. I. Corwin, *Phys. Rev. Lett.* **124**(23), 238002, (2020).

[21] W. G. Ellenbroek, M. van Hecke, and W. van Saarloos, *Phys. Rev. E.* **80**(6), 061307, (2009).

[22] W. G. Ellenbroek, E. Somfai, M. van Hecke, and W. van Saarloos, *Phys. Rev. Lett.* **97**(25), 258001, (2006).

[23] S. Dagois-Bohy, B. P. Tighe, J. Simon, S. Henkes, and M. van Hecke, *Phys. Rev. Lett.* **109**(9), 095703, (2012).

[24] C. P. Goodrich, S. Dagois-Bohy, B. P. Tighe, M. van Hecke, A. J. Liu, and S. R. Nagel, *Phys. Rev. E.* **90**(2), 022138, (2014).

[25] M. S. van Deen, J. Simon, Z. Zeravcic, S. Dagois-Bohy, B. P. Tighe, and M. van Hecke, *Phys. Rev. E.* **90**(2), 020202, (2014).

[26] L. E. Silbert, A. J. Liu, and S. R. Nagel, *Phys. Rev. Lett.* **95**(9), 098301, (2005).

[27] M. Wyart, S. R. Nagel, and T. A. Witten, *Europhys. Lett.* **72**(3), 486, (2005).

[28] C. P. Goodrich, W. G. Ellenbroek, and A. J. Liu, *Soft Matter.* **9**(46), 10993, (2013).

[29] E. Lerner, E. DeGiuli, G. Düring, and M. Wyart, *Soft Matter.* **10**(28), 5085, (2014).

[30] C. P. Goodrich, A. J. Liu, and J. P. Sethna, *Proc. Nat. Acad. Sci. U.S.A.* **113**(35), 9745–9750, (2016).

[31] B. Widom, *J. Chem. Phys.* **43**(11), 3898–3905, (1965).

[32] A. A. Middleton and D. S. Fisher, *Phys. Rev. B.* **47**(7), 3530–3552, (1993).

[33] F. Pázmándi, R. T. Scalettar, and G. T. Zimányi, *Phys. Rev. Lett.* **79**(25), 4, (1997).

[34] A. Ikeda, L. Berthier, and G. Biroli, *J. Chem. Phys.* **138**(12), 12A507, (2013).

[35] C. Brito and M. Wyart, *J. Chem. Phys.* **131**(2), 024504, (2009).

[36] C. F. Schreck, T. Bertrand, C. S. O'Hern, and M. D. Shattuck, *Phys. Rev. Lett.* **107**(7), 078301, (2011).

[37] K. VanderWerf, A. Boromand, M. D. Shattuck, and C. S. O'Hern, *Phys. Rev. Lett.* **124**(3), 038004, (2020).

[38] P. Wang, S. Zhang, P. Tuckman, N. T. Ouellette, M. D. Shattuck, and C. S. O'Hern, *Phys. Rev. E.* **103**(2), 022902, (2021).

[39] M. Wyart, *EPL.* **89**(6), 64001, (2010).

[40] E. DeGiuli, E. Lerner, and M. Wyart, *J. Chem. Phys.* **142**(16), 164503, (2015).

[41] A. Zaccone and E. Scossa-Romano, *Phys. Rev. B.* **83**, 184205 (2011).

[42] M. Wyart, *Phys. Rev. Lett.* **109**(12), 125502, (2012).

[43] A. J. Liu and S. R. Nagel, *Annu. Rev. Condens. Matter Phys.* **1**(1), 347–369, (2010).

[44] C. Rainone and P. Urbani, *J. Stat. Mech.* **2016**(5), 053302, (2016).

[45] L. Berthier, G. Biroli, P. Charbonneau, E. I. Corwin, S. Franz, and F. Zamponi, *J. Chem. Phys.* **151**(1), 010901, (2019).

[46] A. Biere, M. Heule, and H. van Maaren, *Handbook of Satisfiability.* (IOS Press, 2009).

[47] M. Mézard and A. Montanari, *Information, Physics, and Computation.* (Oxford University Press, 2009).

[48] S. Franz, G. Parisi, M. Sevelev, P. Urbani, and F. Zamponi, *SciPost Phys.* **2**(3), 019, (2017).

[49] F. Aluffi-Pentini, V. Parisi, and F. Zirilli, *ACM Trans. Math. Softw.* **14**(4), 345–365, (1988).

[50] R. N. Chacko, P. Sollich, and S. M. Fielding, *Phys. Rev. Lett.* **123**(10), 108001, (2019).

[51] S. Kirkpatrick, *J. Stat. Phys.* **34**(5-6), 975–986, (1984).

[52] S. Franz and G. Parisi, *J. Phys. A.* **49**(14), 145001, (2016).

[53] A. Altieri, *Phys. Rev. E.* **97**(1), 012103, (2018).

[54] S. Franz, S. Hwang, and P. Urbani, *Phys. Rev. Lett.* **123**(16), 160602, (2019).

[55] P. Charbonneau, E. I. Corwin, G. Parisi, and F. Zamponi, *Phys. Rev. Lett.* **114**(12), 125504, (2015).

[56] E. Lerner, G. Düring, and M. Wyart, *Soft Matter.* **9**(34), 8252–8263, (2013).

[57] P. Charbonneau, E. I. Corwin, L. Fu, G. Tsekenis, and M. van der Naald, *Phys. Rev. E.* **99**(2), 020901, (2019).

[58] P. Charbonneau, E. I. Corwin, R. C. Dennis, R. Díaz Hernández Rojas, H. Ikeda, G. Parisi, and F. Ricci-Tersenghi, *Phys. Rev. E.* **104**(1), 014102, (2021).

[59] J. D. Sartor, S. A. Ridout, and E. I. Corwin, *Phys. Rev. Lett.* **126**(4), 048001, (2021).

[60] R. C. Dennis and E. I. Corwin, *Phys. Rev. Lett.* **124**(7), 078002, (2020).

[61] E. Gardner, *Nuclear Physics B.* **257**, 747–765, (1985).

[62] A. Seguin and O. Dauchot, *Phys. Rev. Lett.* **117**(22), 228001, (2016).

[63] H. Xiao, A. J. Liu, and D. J. Durian, *Phys. Rev. Lett.* **128**(24), 248001, (2022).

[64] L. Kool, P. Charbonneau, and K. E. Daniels, *Phys. Rev. E.* **in press**, (2022).

[65] A. Bunde, J. Kropp, and H. J. Schellnhuber, *The Science of Disasters.* (Springer, 2002).

[66] J.-A. Park, L. Atia, J. A. Mitchel, J. J. Fredberg, and J. P. Butler, *J. Cell Sci.* p. jcs.187922, (2016).

[67] L. Oswald, S. Grosser, D. M. Smith, and J. A. Käs, *J. Phys. D.* **50**(48), 483001, (2017).

[68] G. Lu, R. C. Hidalgo, J. R. Third, and C. R. Müller, *Granular Matter.* **18**(3), 34, (2016).

[69] S. Torquato and F. H. Stillinger, *Rev. Mod. Phys.* **82**(3), 2633–2672, (2010).

[70] S. R. Williams and A. P. Philipse, *Phys. Rev. E.* **67**(5), 051301, (2003).

[71] A. Wouterse, S. R. Williams, and A. P. Philipse, *J. Phys.: Condens. Matter.* **19**(40), 406215, (2007).

[72] E. R. Chen, D. Klotsa, M. Engel, P. F. Damasceno, and S. C. Glotzer, *Phys. Rev. X.* **4**(1), 011024, (2014).

[73] Z. Zeravcic, N. Xu, A. J. Liu, S. R. Nagel, and W. van Saarloos, *EPL.* **87**(2), 26001, (2009).

[74] A. Donev, R. Connelly, F. H. Stillinger, and S. Torquato, *Phys. Rev. E.* **75**(5), 051304, (2007).

[75] S. Papanikolaou, C. S. O'Hern, and M. D. Shattuck, *Phys. Rev. Lett.* **110**(19), 198002, (2013).

[76] C. F. Schreck, M. Mailman, B. Chakraborty, and C. S. O'Hern, *Phys. Rev. E.* **85**(6), 061305, (2012).

[77] K. VanderWerf, W. Jin, M. D. Shattuck, and C. S. O'Hern, *Phys. Rev. E.* **97**(1), 012909, (2018).

[78] C. Brito, H. Ikeda, P. Urbani, M. Wyart, and F. Zamponi, *Proc. Nat. Acad. Sci. U.S.A.* **115**(46), 11736–11741, (2018).

[79] Y. Yuan, K. VanderWerf, M. D. Shattuck, and C. S. O'Hern, *Soft Matter.* **15**(47), 9751–9761, (2019).

[80] C. F. Schreck, N. Xu, and C. S. O'Hern, *Soft Matter.* **6**(13), 2960, (2010).

[81] A. Singh, C. Ness, R. Seto, J. J. de Pablo, and H. M. Jaeger, *Phys. Rev. Lett.* **124**(24), 248005, (2020).

[82] P. A. Cundall and O. D. L. Strack, *Géotechnique.* **29**(1), 47–65, (1979).

[83] H. Ikeda, C. Brito, M. Wyart, and F. Zamponi, *Phys. Rev. Lett.* **124**(20), 208001, (2020).

[84] J. Mattsson, H. M. Wyss, A. Fernandez-Nieves, K. Miyazaki, Z. Hu, D. R. Reichman, and D. A. Weitz, *Nature.* **462**(7269), 83–86, (2009).

[85] D. Bi, X. Yang, M. C. Marchetti, and M. L. Manning, *Phys. Rev. X.* **6**(2), 021011, (2016).

[86] A. Boromand, A. Signoriello, F. Ye, C. S. O'Hern, and M. D. Shattuck, *Phys. Rev. Lett.* **121**(24), 248003, (2018).

[87] D. Wang, J. D. Treado, A. Boromand, B. Norwick, M. P. Murrell, M. D. Shattuck, and C. S. O'Hern, *Soft Matter.* **17**(43), 9901–9915, (2021).

[88] N. Gnan and E. Zaccarelli, *Nat. Phys.* **15**(7), 683–688, (2019).

[89] A. Mongera, P. Rowghanian, H. J. Gustafson, E. Shelton, D. A. Kealhofer, E. K. Carn, F. Serwane, A. A. Lucio, J. Giammona, and O. Campàs, *Nature.* **561**(7723), 401–405, (2018).

[90] O. Ilina, P. G. Gritsenko, S. Syga, J. Lippoldt, C. A. M. La Porta, O. Chepizhko, S. Grosser, M. Vullings, G.-J. Bakker, J. Starruß, P. Bult, S. Zapperi, J. A. Käs, A. Deutsch, and P. Friedl, *Nat. Cell Bio.* **22**(9), 1103–1115, (2020).

[91] D. Bi, J. H. Lopez, J. M. Schwarz, and M. L. Manning, *Soft Matter.* **10**(12), 1885, (2014).

[92] E. Agoritsas, *J. Stat. Mech.* **2021**(3), 033501, (2021).

[93] A. Manacorda and F. Zamponi, *J. Phys. A.* **55**(33), 334001, (2022).

Chapter 14

From Polymers to the KPZ Equation

In the first part of this chapter, **Victor Dotsenko** and **Pierre Le Doussal** analyze the universal statistical properties of one-dimensional directed polymers in a random potential. Through the Cole–Hopf mapping they also give access to the fluctuations of the growth process described by the Kardar–Parisi–Zhang equation. In particular the replica Bethe ansatz technique, which allows to derive the Tracy–Widom distributions of the free energy fluctuations and of the KPZ height, is discussed for various initial and boundary conditions. In the second part of the chapter **Henri Orland**, discusses schematic protein models, with a focus on the analysis of heteropolymers and random heteropolymers. The main models are introduced. The freezing transition of these random heteropolymer models is investigated. The finite dimensional case is also discussed. A replica description of these random heteropolymers that explains qualitatively the swollen coil, the molten globule and the native phase of proteins is discussed.

14.1. Directed Polymers and the Kardar–Parisi–Zhang Equation

Victor Dotsenko* and Pierre Le Doussal[†]

LPTMC, Sorbonne Université, 75252 Paris, France,
victor.dotsenko@sorbonne-universite.fr
[†]*Laboratoire de Physique de l'École Normale Supérieure, ENS, Université PSL,*
CNRS, Sorbonne Université, Université Paris-Cité, 75005 Paris, France
pierre.ledoussal@ens.fr

14.1.1. *Statistical properties of one-dimensional directed polymers in a random potential*

14.1.1.1. *Introduction*

In this chapter we are going to concentrate on the model of directed polymers defined in terms of an elastic string $\phi(\tau)$ directed along the τ-axes within an interval $[0, t]$ which passes through a random medium described by a random potential $V(\phi, \tau)$. The energy of a given polymer's trajectory $\phi(\tau)$ is

$$H[\phi(\tau); V] = \int_0^t d\tau \left\{ \frac{1}{2} \left[\partial_\tau \phi(\tau) \right]^2 + V[\phi(\tau), \tau] \right\}; \tag{14.1}$$

Here the disorder potential $V[\phi, \tau]$ is supposed to be Gaussian distributed with a zero mean $\overline{V(\phi, \tau)} = 0$ and the δ-correlations

$$\overline{V(\phi, \tau)V(\phi', \tau')} = u\delta(\tau - \tau')\delta(\phi - \phi') \tag{14.2}$$

255

where $\overline{(...)}$ denotes the disorder average and the parameter u describes the strength of the random potential. The system defined by the above Hamiltonian (14.1) has been the subject of intense investigations during the past almost three decades (see e.g. [1–11]). Historically, the problem of central interest was the scaling behavior of the polymer mean squared displacement, which in the thermodynamic limit ($t \to \infty$) reveals a universal scaling form $\overline{\langle \phi^2 \rangle}(t) \propto t^{2\zeta}$ (where $\langle \ldots \rangle$ denotes the thermal average), with $\zeta = 2/3$, the so-called wandering exponent.

A more general and more interesting problem is the statistical properties of the free energy of this system. For a given realization of the random potential the partition function of the considered system is defined in terms of the functional integral:

$$Z(x,t) = \int_{\phi(0)=0}^{\phi(t)=x} \mathcal{D}[\phi(\tau)]\ \exp\left\{ -\beta H[\phi(\tau); V] \right\} = \exp\left\{ -\beta F(x,t) \right\} \tag{14.3}$$

where $\beta = 1/T$ is the inverse temperature and the integration goes over all trajectories with fixed boundary conditions $\phi(0) = 0$ and $\phi(t) = x$, and $F(x,t)$ is the (random) free energy. According to the above definition one can easily show that the partition function $Z(x,t)$ satisfies the differential equation

$$\partial_t Z(x,t) = \frac{1}{2\beta} \partial_x^2 Z(x,t) - \beta V(x,t) Z(x,t) \tag{14.4}$$

substituting here $Z(x,t) = \exp\{-\beta F(x,t)\}$ one obtains

$$-\partial_t F(x,t) = \frac{1}{2}\left(\partial_x F(x,t) \right)^2 - \frac{1}{2\beta} \partial_x^2 F(x,t) - V(x,t) \tag{14.5}$$

which is the KPZ equation [12] where the free energy $F(x,t)$ of the original directed polymer problem, Eqs. (14.1)–(14.3), plays now the role of the interface front evolving in time in the presence of quenched random potential $V(x,t)$.

First of all it is evident that in the absence of the random potential the partition function $Z(x,t)$, Eq. (14.4), describes simple thermal diffusion. In other words the typical deviation $\langle \phi(t) \rangle$ of the trajectory due to the *thermal fluctuations* grows as $t^{1/2}$ which is much smaller than the typical value of the trajectory deviations due to the action of the random potentials which scales as $\phi(t) \sim t^{2/3}$. On the other hand, in the presence of the random potential the two terms of the Hamiltonian (14.1) must balance each other. For a given value of the typical deviation $\phi \sim t^{2/3}$ the contribution of the elastic term can be estimated as $\phi^2/t \sim t^{1/3}$. Thus, in the presence of disorder the free energy fluctuations of this system must scale as $t^{1/3}$. In other words, in the limit $t \to \infty$, besides the usual extensive (linear in t) self-averaging part and the elastic term, the total free energy F of the considered systems must contain disorder dependent fluctuating contribution $\sim t^{1/3}$:

$$F = f_0 t + \frac{x^2}{2t} + c t^{1/3} f \tag{14.6}$$

where f_0 is the (non-random) linear free energy density, $x^2/2t$ is the trivial elastic contribution, c is a non-universal parameter, which depends on the temperature and the strength of disorder, and finally $f \sim 1$ is the random quantity which in the thermodynamic limit $t \to \infty$ is expected to be described by a non-trivial universal distribution function $P(f)$. The breakthrough in the studies of the problem defined above took place in 2010 when the exact solution for the free energy probability distribution function (PDF) $P(f)$ for the model with fixed boundary condition was found [13–20] to be given by the Tracy–Widom (TW) distribution of the largest eigenvalue of the Gaussian Unitary Ensemble (GUE) [21].

14.1.1.2. *Replica method*

For the calculation of thermodynamic quantities averaged over quenched disorder parameters (e.g. average free energy) the replica method assumes, first, calculation of the averages of an integer N-th power of the partition function $Z(N)$, and second, analytic continuation of this function in the replica parameter N from integer to arbitrary non-integer values (and in particular, in taking the limit $N \to 0$) [22, 23] (see also [24, 25]). In this section we will consider the application of the replica technique for the directed polymer model (14.1)–(14.2). For simplicity let us consider the situation with the zero boundary conditions: $\phi(0) = \phi(t) = 0$. In this case the partition function of a given sample is (c.f. Eq. (14.3))

$$Z(t) = \int_{\phi(0)=0}^{\phi(t)=0} \mathcal{D}[\phi(\tau)] \, \exp\left\{-\beta H[\phi, V]\right\} \; = \; \exp\left\{-\beta\, F(t)\right\} \tag{14.7}$$

The free energy $F(t)$ is defined for a specific realization of the random potential V and thus represents a random variable. Taking the N-th power of both sides of Eq. (14.7) and performing the averaging over the random potential V we obtain

$$\overline{Z^N(t)} \equiv Z(N;t) = \overline{\exp\left\{-\beta N F\right\}} \tag{14.8}$$

where the quantity $Z(N;t)$ is called the *replica partition function*. The averaging in the rhs of the above equation can be represented in terms of the probability density distribution function $P_t(F)$:

$$Z(N;t) \; = \; \int_{-\infty}^{+\infty} dF \, P_t(F) \, \exp\left\{-\beta N F\right\} \tag{14.9}$$

The free energy of the considered system besides the fluctuating part $\sim t^{1/3} f$ contains also a non-random (self-averaging) contribution $f_0 t$, Eq. (14.6). To extract the probability density distribution function $P_t(f)$ let us redefine $Z(t) \; = \; \tilde{Z}(t) \exp\left\{-\beta f_0 t\right\}$ so that $\tilde{Z}(t) \; = \; \exp\left\{-\lambda(t) f\right\}$ where $\lambda(t) \; = \; \beta c t^{1/3} \propto t^{1/3}$. Correspondingly, for the replica partition function we have $Z(N;t) \; = \; \tilde{Z}(N;t) \exp\left\{-\beta N f_0 t\right\}$. Substituting this relation as well as Eq. (14.6) into Eq. (14.9) we get

$$\tilde{Z}(N;t) \; = \; \int_{-\infty}^{+\infty} df \, P_t(f) \, \exp\left\{-\lambda(t) N f\right\} \tag{14.10}$$

The above equation is the bilateral Laplace transform of the function $P_t(F)$, and at least formally it allows to restore this function via inverse Laplace transform of the replica partition function $\tilde{Z}(N;t)$. In order to do so one has to compute $\tilde{Z}(N;t)$ for an *arbitrary* integer N and then perform the analytical continuation of this function from integer to arbitrary complex values of N.

In an alternative approach, to bypass the problem of the analytic continuation in the replica parameter N to non-integer values, instead of the free energy distribution function $P_t(f)$ one introduces its integral representation

$$W_t(f) = \int_f^\infty df' \, P_t(f') \tag{14.11}$$

Introducing $P_*(f) \equiv \lim_{t\to\infty} P_t(f)$ and $W_*(f) \equiv \lim_{t\to\infty} W_t(f)$ one can easily see that the function $W_*(f)$ can be defined in terms of the replica partition function $\tilde{Z}(N;t)$, Eq. (14.10):

$$W_*(f) = \lim_{t\to\infty} \sum_{N=0}^{\infty} \frac{(-1)^N}{N!} \exp\left\{\lambda(t)Nf\right\} \tilde{Z}(N;t) \tag{14.12}$$

Thus, according to the above relation the probability function $W_*(f)$ can be computed in terms of the replica partition function $\tilde{Z}(N;t)$ by summing over all replica *integers*.

14.1.1.3. *Mapping to quantum bosons*

Explicitly, for the zero boundary conditions ($\phi(0) = \phi(t) = 0$) the replica partition function, Eq. (14.8), of the system described by the Hamiltonian, Eq. (14.1), is

$$Z(N;t) = \prod_{a=1}^{N} \left[\int_{\phi_a(0)=0}^{\phi_a(t)=0} \mathcal{D}\phi_a(\tau) \right] \exp\left\{ -\beta \int_0^t d\tau \sum_{a=1}^{N} \left[\frac{1}{2}[\partial_\tau \phi_a(\tau)]^2 + V[\phi_a(\tau),\tau] \right] \right\} \tag{14.13}$$

Since the random potential $V[\phi,\tau]$ is Gaussian distributed, using Eq. (14.2) one gets

$$Z(N;t) = \prod_{a=1}^{N} \left[\int_{\phi_a(0)=0}^{\phi_a(t)=0} \mathcal{D}\phi_a(\tau) \right] \exp\left\{ -\beta H_N[\phi] \right\} \tag{14.14}$$

where

$$H_N[\phi] = \frac{1}{2} \int_0^t d\tau \left(\sum_{a=1}^{N} [\partial_\tau \phi_a(\tau)]^2 - \beta u \sum_{a\neq b}^{N} \delta\big(\phi_a(\tau) - \phi_b(\tau)\big) \right) \tag{14.15}$$

and $\phi \equiv \{\phi_1, \ldots, \phi_N\}$. It should be noted that the above replica Hamiltonian contains formally divergent contributions proportional to $\delta(0)$ (due to the terms with $a = b$). In fact, this is just an indication that the *continuous* model, Eqs. (14.1)–(14.2), is ill defined at short distances and requires proper lattice regularization. Of course, the corresponding lattice model would contain no divergences, and the terms with $a = b$ would produce just an irrelevant constant $\frac{1}{2}t\beta^2 uN\delta(0)$ (where the lattice version of $\delta(0)$ has a finite value). Since the lattice regularization has no impact on the continuous long distance properties of the considered system, this term is just omitted in Eq. (14.15).

We see that the partition function Eq. (14.14) describes the statistics of N trajectories $\phi_a(\tau)$ with attractive δ-interactions with the boundary conditions: $\phi_a(0) = \phi_a(t) =$

0. In order to map the problem to one-dimensional quantum bosons, let us introduce a more general object

$$\Psi(\mathbf{x};t) = \prod_{a=1}^{N}\left[\int_{\phi_a(0)=0}^{\phi_a(t)=x_a} \mathcal{D}\phi_a(\tau)\right] \exp\left\{-\beta H_N[\phi]\right\} \tag{14.16}$$

which describes N trajectories $\phi_a(\tau)$ all starting at zero ($\phi_a(0) = 0$), but ending at $\tau = t$ in arbitrary given points $\{x_1, ..., x_N\}$. One can easily show that $\Psi(\mathbf{x};t)$ can be obtained as the solution of the linear differential equation

$$\partial_t \Psi(\mathbf{x};t) = \frac{1}{2\beta}\sum_{a=1}^{N}\partial_{x_a}^2\Psi(\mathbf{x};t) + \frac{1}{2}\beta^2 u\sum_{a\neq b}^{N}\delta(x_a - x_b)\Psi(\mathbf{x};t) \tag{14.17}$$

which is the imaginary-time Schrödinger equation that describes N bosonic particles of mass β interacting via the *attractive* two-body potential $-\beta^2 u\delta(x)$. This model is known as the delta Bose gas, or Lieb–Liniger model [26]. The original replica partition function, Eq. (14.14), is then obtained via a particular choice of the final-point coordinates, $Z(N;t) = \Psi(\mathbf{0};t)$. According to the standard procedure, the wave function $\Psi(\mathbf{x};t)$ of the quantum problem, Eq. (14.17), can be represented in terms of the linear combination of the solutions of the corresponding eigenvalue equation

$$-2\beta\, E\, \Psi(\mathbf{x}) = \sum_{a=1}^{N}\partial_{x_a}^2\Psi(\mathbf{x};t) + \kappa\sum_{a\neq b}^{N}\delta(x_a - x_b)\Psi(\mathbf{x};t) \tag{14.18}$$

where $\kappa = \beta^3 u$. A generic eigenstate of such system is described in terms of the so-called *Bethe ansatz* eigenfunctions $\Psi_{\mathbf{Q}}^{(M)}(\mathbf{x})$ and it is characterized by N momenta $\{Q_a\}$ ($a = 1, ..., N$) which split into M ($1 \leq M \leq N$) "clusters" each described by *continuous real* momenta q_α ($\alpha = 1, ..., M$) and by n_α *discrete imaginary* "components" (for details on the Bethe ansatz method see [26–32]): $Q_a \to q_r^\alpha = q_\alpha - i\kappa(n_\alpha + 1 - 2r)/2$ where $r = 1, ..., n_\alpha$; $\alpha = 1, ..., M$ with the global constraint $\sum_{\alpha=1}^{M} n_\alpha = N$. It can be shown that in terms of this *ansatz* the probability function $W_*(f)$, Eq. (14.11), can be expressed in terms of the Fredholm determinant,

$$W_*(f) = \det[1 - \hat{K}_{\mathrm{Ai}}] \equiv F_2(-f/2^{2/3}) \tag{14.19}$$

where $\hat{K}_{\mathrm{Ai}}$ is the integral operator on $[-f/2^{2/3}, \infty)$ with the Airy kernel

$$K_{\mathrm{Ai}}(\omega, \omega') = \frac{\mathrm{Ai}(\omega)\,\mathrm{Ai}'(\omega') - \mathrm{Ai}'(\omega)\,\mathrm{Ai}(\omega')}{\omega - \omega'} \tag{14.20}$$

The function $F_2(s)$ is the GUE Tracy–Widom distribution [21]. It can be shown to admit the following explicit representation:

$$F_2(s) = \exp\left(-\int_s^\infty dt\,(t - s)\,q^2(t)\right) \tag{14.21}$$

where the function $q(t)$ is the solution of the Painlevé II equation, $q'' = tq + 2q^3$ with the boundary condition, $q(t \to +\infty) \sim Ai(t)$ [33, 34]. The shape of the probability density function $P_*(f) = -dW_*(f)/df$ is shown in Fig. 14.1. Note that the asymptotic tails of this function are strongly asymmetric. While its right tail coincides with the Airy function asymptotic $P_*(s \to +\infty) \sim \exp\left[-\frac{4}{3}s^{3/2}\right]$, the left tail exhibits much faster decay $P_*(s \to -\infty) \sim \exp\left[-\frac{1}{12}|s|^3\right]$.

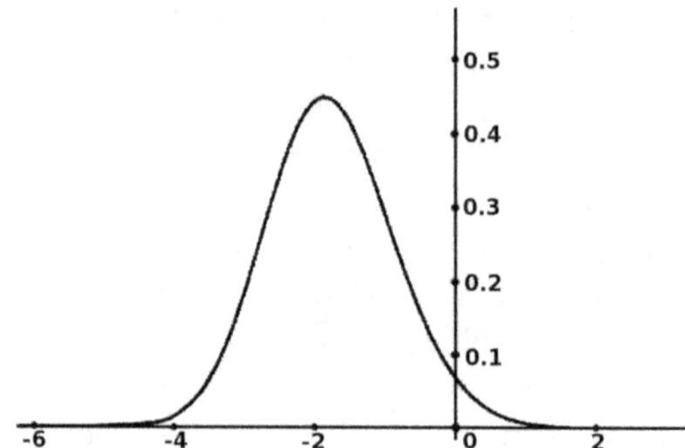

Fig. 14.1. Tracy–Widom distribution function $P_*(f)$.

14.1.2. *More on the KPZ equation*

14.1.2.1. *The KPZ equation with various initial conditions*

In the previous section we have seen that the statistical mechanics of a directed polymer in a random potential, which is an optimisation problem, is related to the Kardar–Parisi–Zhang (KPZ) equation [12] that describes the stochastic growth of an interface. This connection holds in any dimension, i.e. directed polymers in $D = d + 1$ dimension, can be mapped to the growth of a d-dimensional interface. Much analytical progress was achieved for one-dimensional interfaces, i.e. $d = 1$, and we will continue to focus on this case. Let us define $h(x,t)$ the height at time t and position $x \in \mathbb{R}$ of an interface (for instance separating two phases of a liquid crystal as in the experiments [35]). By a choice of units of x, t, h the KPZ equation can always be written as[a]

$$\partial_t h(x,t) = \partial_x^2 h(x,t) + (\partial_x h(x,t))^2 + \sqrt{2}\,\eta(x,t) \tag{14.22}$$

where $\eta(x,t)$ is the noise which drives the growth. Under the Cole–Hopf transformation

$$h(x,t) = \log Z(x,t) \tag{14.23}$$

it is mapped to the so-called stochastic heat equation (SHE)

$$\partial_t Z(x,t) = \partial_x^2 Z(x,t) + \sqrt{2}\,\eta(x,t)Z(x,t) \tag{14.24}$$

where here the noise acts multiplicatively. As explained in the previous section $Z(x,t)$ can be seen as the canonical partition function of a continuum directed polymer in dimension $D = 1 + 1$, with one endpoint at (x,t), and $\eta(x,t)$ is proportional to the random potential. Although other types of noises have been studied [36], we focus here on the case of a standard space-time Gaussian white noise, $\overline{\eta(x,t)\eta(x',t')} = \delta(x - x')\delta(t-t')$, for which exact results can be obtained. Equation (14.24) is then understood in Ito sense, and $\overline{Z(x,t)}$ thus satisfies the standard heat equation.

At this stage we have not specified the initial condition of the KPZ height, $h(x,t = 0)$. Let us denote $Z(x,t|x_0,t_0)$ the solution of the SHE (14.24) with initial condition at $t = t_0$. $Z(x,t_0) = \delta(x - x_0)$. This defines the "point to point" polymer problem

---

[a]Compared to the previous section we define $h = -\beta F$ and $\beta V = -\sqrt{2\bar{c}}\eta$ hence $\beta^2 u = 2\bar{c}$, and we set $\beta = 1/2$, hence $\kappa = \bar{c}$, and finally $\bar{c} = 1$.

discussed in the previous section (with $t_0 = 0$, $x_0 = 0$). This corresponds to the "narrow wedge" initial condition for the KPZ equation, also called the "droplet" initial condition, defined as the limit $w \to 0^+$ of

$$Z(x, t = 0) = \frac{w}{2} e^{-w|x|}, \quad h(x, t = 0) = -w|x| + \log\left(\frac{w}{2}\right) \qquad (14.25)$$

This seems singular but it is not: since at short time one can propagate $Z(x, t)$ with the heat kernel, one sees that this initial condition leads very quickly to a height profile which is "curved" around the origin. One can show that the large time result obtained in the previous section for this very special initial condition, i.e. that the scaled height fluctuates with a GUE Tracy Widom distribution, extends to all initial conditions which exhibit a curved height profile at some intermediate time. For instance (14.25) for any $w > 0$. Even more strikingly, the same large time behavior is observed experimentally when a circular "droplet" of a stable phase is growing into an unstable one [37]. Of course the height fluctuations at finite time differ in all these cases, but the large time one is universal.

A markedly different behavior is observed when the initial condition for $Z(x, t = 0)$ is spatially extended. To handle the case of general initial conditions, one observes that from the linearity of (14.24) one can write

$$Z(x, t) = e^{h(x,t)} = \int_{\mathbb{R}} dx_0\, Z(x, t | x_0, 0) e^{h(x_0, t=0)} \qquad (14.26)$$

This relation connects the boundary conditions of the directed polymer to the initial condition of the KPZ equation. For instance we see that the flat initial condition for the KPZ equation, $h(x, t = 0) = 0$, corresponds to the "point to line" directed polymer problem (the endpoint at (x, t) being fixed, the other at $(x_0, 0)$ can vary along the real line). It turns out that the calculation of the previous section using the replica Bethe ansatz can be extended for the flat initial condition [38–40]. It is much more involved, in parts because one needs to compute integrals of the replica Bethe wavefunctions over space, $\int_{\mathbb{R}^N} d\mathbf{x} \Psi_{\mathbf{Q}}(\mathbf{x})$, introducing regulators since these integrals are not well defined. In practice one solves for a "half-flat" initial profile, $x_0 \in [a, +\infty[$ in (14.26), and takes the limit $a \to -\infty$.

14.1.2.2. *Main classes of large time behaviors*

The results for the various initial conditions can be summarized as follows. The KPZ height behaves at large time as

$$h(0, t) \simeq v_\infty t + t^{1/3} \xi \qquad (14.27)$$

where ξ is a $O(1)$ random variable and v_∞ a non-universal constant. For the flat initial condition it is found that

$$\xi = 2^{-2/3} \chi_1, \quad \text{Prob}(\chi_1 < s) = F_1(s) = \text{Det}[I + P_{s/2} \hat{B} P_{s/2}] \qquad (14.28)$$

where χ_1 is distributed according to the GOE Tracy–Widom distribution whose cumulative distribution is denoted $F_1(s)$. It can be expressed as a Fredholm determinant [41], with the kernel $B(\omega, \omega') = \text{Ai}(\omega + \omega')$ where $P_{s/2}$ is the projector on $[s/2, +\infty[$.

For comparison let us recall from the previous section that for the droplet initial condition $\xi = \chi_2$, where χ_2 is a distributed with the GUE Tracy–Widom distribution, $\mathrm{Prob}(\chi_2 < s) = F_2(s) = \mathrm{Det}[I + P_s K_{\mathrm{Ai}} P_s]$. These two distributions are related via [42]

$$F_1(s) = (F_2(s))^{1/2}\, e^{-\frac{1}{2}\int_s^{+\infty} q(t)dt} \tag{14.29}$$

where $q(t)$ is the solution of the Painlevé II equations, defined above (14.21). Both have random matrix interpretations, as the distribution of the scaled largest eigenvalue of a random hermitian (GUE) or real symmetric (GOE) Gaussian random matrix [43].

It is expected that (14.27) is valid beyond these two special "solvable" initial conditions, and that any profile starting localized (curved, droplet) has $\xi \propto \chi_2$ while any profile starting extended (on both sides of $x = 0$) has $\xi \propto \chi_1$. The boundary between these two behaviors occurs [44] when the initial profile scales as $h(x,0) \sim \sqrt{|x|}$.

This brings us to another "solvable" case, the Brownian initial condition, $h(x,0) = B(x)$ where $B(x)$ is a standard two sided Brownian motion with $B(0) = 0$. It is important since the Brownian is a stationary profile for the KPZ equation (see below). Remarkably this case can also be solved using the replica Bethe ansatz [45]. The initial condition is "random", so one studies height fluctuations with respect to the combination of the space-time noise $\eta(x,t)$ and the Brownian $B(x)$. At large time one obtains

$$h(0,t) \simeq v_\infty t + t^{1/3}\chi_{\mathrm{BR}} \tag{14.30}$$

where the distribution of χ_{BR}, noted $F_0(s)$, was discovered by Baik and Rains [46] in a discrete realization of the directed polymer, equivalent to a discrete growth model called polynuclear growth [47]. It is given by

$$F_0(s) = \frac{d}{ds}\left(F_2(s) \int_{-\infty}^{s} e^{-2\int_s^{+\infty} q(t)dt} \right) \tag{14.31}$$

These three solvable cases represent the main classes of initial conditions, with the three main universal distributions at large time. It is remarquable that all three have been measured in experiments on turbulent liquid crystals [35], more recently in the case of Baik–Rains [48]. One can also consider initial conditions with different behaviors for $x > 0$ and $x < 0$ so that the distribution of $h(x,t)$ "interpolates" between these universal distributions as x increases from $-\infty$ to $+\infty$. This leads to several universal one-parameter families of interpolating distributions [49, 50].

14.1.2.3. *Finite time solutions*

These three special initial conditions are remarkable in that an exact solution can be obtained using the replica Bethe ansatz for any time t. For the droplet initial condition one obtains that the Laplace transform of the distribution of $Z(0,t)$ obeys

$$g_t(s) := \overline{\exp(-e^{-t^{1/3}s}Z(0,t)e^{\frac{t}{12}})} = \mathrm{Det}[I + P_s \hat{K}_t P_s] \tag{14.32}$$

where the "finite time" kernel is

$$K_t(\omega,\omega') = \int_{-\infty}^{+\infty} d\omega'' \frac{\mathrm{Ai}(\omega + \omega'')\mathrm{Ai}(\omega' + \omega'')}{1 + e^{-t^{1/3}\omega''}} \tag{14.33}$$

Because of the apparent "Fermi factor" in this expression one sees that as $t \to +\infty$ this kernel converges to the Airy kernel, hence recovering the GUE-TW distribution. Amazingly, this factor allows to map this problem [51] to the quantum statistics of the rightmost fermion at the edge of a Fermi gas in a trap at a finite temperature $\sim t^{-1/3}$.

A similar formula holds for the flat initial condition, but $g_t(s)$ is now obtained as a Fredholm Pfaffian, i.e. its square is the Fredholm determinant of a 2 by 2 matrix kernel [38, 39]. For Brownian initial conditions one needs to introduce a variant of the generating function $g_t(s)$ in (14.32), which is then shown [45, 52] to equal the Fredholm determinant of an Airy type kernel, deformed by Gamma functions (a cousin of the kernel which occurs in the Baik–BenArous–Péché (BBP) transition [53] for outliers of spiked random matrices).

These finite time formula have interesting applications to study large deviations, in particular at small time. Consider for instance the flat initial condition. At small time h is small and it is reasonable to neglect the non-linear term in the KPZ equation, which leads to the Edwards–Wilkinson (EW) equation [54]. The EW equation being a linear stochastic equation it is straightforward to solve, and one finds that the typical height fluctuations grow as $h \sim t^{1/4}$. A question is: is there any signature of the KPZ non-linearity at short time? The answer is yes, but one should look at the large deviations, i.e. the tails of the height distribution. One shows that they take the form

$$\text{Prob}(h(0,t) = h) \sim \exp\left(-\frac{\Phi(h)}{\sqrt{t}}\right) \tag{14.34}$$

where the rate function $\Phi(h)$ has been computed for the three classes from the exact solutions at finite time mentioned above [55–57]. Note that $\Phi(h) \sim h^2$ as $h \to 0$, consistent with $h \sim t^{1/4}$ for typical fluctuations. However, for very atypical fluctuations $\Phi(h) \sim |h|^{3/2}$ for $h \to +\infty$ and $\Phi(h) \sim |h|^{5/2}$ for $h \to -\infty$, and these anomalous power laws in $|h|$ are found to persist at all times.

14.1.2.4. *Universality*

Although we focus here on the KPZ equation and the directed polymer, both defined in the continuum, a large number of solvable discrete or semi-discrete stochastic models exhibit the same universal large time behavior, referred to as *the KPZ class*. To quote only a few, the polynuclear growth model, interacting particle models such as the asymmetric exclusion process, lattice polymer models such as the log-gamma polymer. In all these models a height field $h(x,t)$ can be defined, e.g. for particle models it is the space integrated density. Upon proper rescaling $h \sim t^{1/3}$, $x \sim t^{2/3}$, its fluctuations at large time are described by the so-called *KPZ fixed point*. The study of these models has led to important developments in mathematics too numerous to review here, see e.g. [9, 58–61]. One remarkable result is the complete characterization of the KPZ fixed point [62], with formula for the multi-space point equal time height distributions for general initial conditions. Note that this is an infinite time result, hence it does not give the finite time behavior. Interestingly, the single space point finite time solutions of the KPZ equation described here, obtained with the replica Bethe ansatz method, have by now been confirmed by rigorous methods.

14.1.2.5. *Two-time correlations and memory*

The joint distribution of the KPZ height at two different times, e.g. of $h(0, t_1)$ and $h(0, t_2)$, with both t_1, t_2 large with a fixed ratio $u = t_2/t_1 > 1$, is believed to be universal, but is notably difficult to calculate using the replica Bethe ansatz [64]. A solution for the tail (when only one of the heights, $h(0, t_1)$, is large), was obtained [65] for droplet initial conditions, and found in good agreement with experiments [66]. The complete solution was obtained [67] by a different method from a discrete polymer model, assuming universality. An interesting quantity is the universal dimensionless ratio $R = \lim_{u \to +\infty} \lim_{t_1 \to +\infty} \mathrm{Cov}(h(0, t_1), h(0, ut_1))/\mathrm{Var}(h(0, t_1))$ which quantifies ergodicity breaking and persitent memory at infinitely separated times. It was obtained analytically for droplet initial conditions in [68], with $R = 0.623$ in agreement with numerics and experiments [37, 66].

14.1.2.6. *Polymer in a half-space and KPZ equation on the half-line*

Consider now a directed polymer of trajectory $(\phi(\tau), \tau)$ constrained to remain in the half-space $\phi(\tau) \geq 0$, with endpoint at $\phi(t) = x \geq 0$. It is described by a partition sum $Z(x, t)$, which still satisfies the SHE (14.24) on the half-line $x > 0$. The Cole–Hopf map $h(x, t) = \log Z(x, t)$ then defines the KPZ equation on the half-line. Consider first the case of "absorbing" boundary conditions $Z(0, t) = 0$, which corresponds to an infinite hard wall at $x = 0$ (the polymer paths cannot touch the wall). The integer moments $\overline{Z^N(x, t)}$ can still be expressed using the delta Bose gas model (14.17) for $x > 0$ with Dirichlet boundary conditions. For these boundary conditions there is again a replica Bethe ansatz solution. The calculation can be performed to the end and for any t in the case of the "droplet" initial condition, i.e. when the polymer starts and ends near the wall. One finds [69] that the height defined (in that case) as $h(0, t) := \log(Z(\epsilon, t | \epsilon, 0)/\epsilon^2)|_{\epsilon=0^+}$ obeys again the large time behavior (14.27), with now

$$\mathrm{Prob}(\xi < s) = \sqrt{\mathrm{Det}(I - P_s K)}, \quad K(\omega, \omega') = K_{\mathrm{Ai}}(\omega, \omega') - \frac{1}{2}\mathrm{Ai}(\omega) \int_0^{+\infty} du\, \mathrm{Ai}(\omega' + u)$$

$$(14.35)$$

This is nothing but the Tracy-Widom distribution of the Gaussian symplectic ensemble (GSE), the last of the three classical Wigner–Dyson ensembles, i.e. $\xi = \chi_4$ with $\mathrm{Prob}(\xi < s) = F_4(s) = \frac{1}{2}(F_1(s) + \frac{F_2(s)}{F_1(s)})$ (using the definition of F_4 in [70]).

The half-space polymer model can be extended [71] to a "soft wall" of parameter A, with the boundary condition $\partial_x Z(x, t)|_{x=0} = AZ(0, t)$. The wall is repulsive for $A > 0$ ($A = +\infty$ being the infinite hard wall) and attractive for $A < 0$. Indeed, for $A < 0$ the delta Bose gas with $N = 1$ has a bound state to the wall, which corresponds to the particular solution $\overline{Z(x, t)} = e^{Ax + A^2 t}$. The replica Bethe ansatz can still be used for any N and indicates that for the quenched problem, i.e. for $\overline{\log Z(x, t)}$ and $N \to 0$, there is a phase transition [71]: for $A < -1/2$ the polymer is bound to the wall, while for $A \geq -1/2$ it wanders in the whole half-space. The structure of the replica bound states for generic A becomes quite complicated [72]. Nevertheless it is possible to obtain a solution for any A. For droplet initial conditions [72–75] it is found that for $A \geq -1/2$ Eq. (14.27) holds, where the scaled height fluctuations ξ are still GSE Tracy–Widom for $A > -1/2$, while at the transition, for $A = 1/2$, they are GOE Tracy–Widom. For $A < -1/2$, in the bound phase, one has $h(0,t) = v'_\infty t + |2A + 1|\omega t^{1/2}$ where ω has a Gaussian distribution. The free energy per unit length of the polymer shows an anomalous behavior $-F/t = v'_\infty - v_\infty = (A + \frac{1}{2})^2$. For flat initial conditions [76] the phase diagram is the same, however the height fluctuations at $x = 0$ are now GUE-TW in the unbound phase $A > -1/2$, and of BBP type at the transition. Remarkably, a similar transition scenario was obtained well before, by totally different methods, in the study of symmetrized random permutations [77], which can indeed be seen as a discrete version of a polymer problem. This is yet another manifestation of the universality of the height distributions obtained at large time for the KPZ equation, here on the half-line. A promising method to observe them in future experiments was proposed [78].

14.1.2.7. *Stationary measures for the KPZ equation*

The KPZ equation describes a growth process and is intrinsically non-equilibrium. Nevertheless, while the height at one point grows linearly in time with non trivial $t^{1/3}$ fluctuations as in (14.27), the *height differences* between any two points, $h(x,t) - h(y,t)$, reaches a stationary distribution at large time. It was noticed long ago [3, 12, 79, 80] that the KPZ equation on the full line admits the Brownian motion $B(x)$ as a stationary measure, i.e. for any given t, $h(x,t) - h(0,t) \equiv B(x)$, i.e. the two processes in x have the same law. This was proved in [81, 82]. With periodic boundary conditions (on the circle) the stationary measure is a Brownian bridge [83]. In the case of the half-line and the interval, the stationary measure is more complicated, not translationally invariant, generically non Gaussian, and was obtained only recently. In fact there is a two-parameter family of such measures. One case is simpler though, and can be inferred using replica from the ground state of the delta Bose gas. Going back to the previous paragraph and the half-line with a soft wall at $x = 0$, one shows [84] that in the bound phase, i.e. for $A < -1/2$, a stationary measure is in law a Brownian motion with drift

$$\frac{Z(x,t)}{Z(0,t)} = e^{h(x,t)-h(0,t)} \equiv e^{B(x)+(A+\frac{1}{2})x} \tag{14.36}$$

for any given t. On the other hand in the bound phase one expects that the large time behavior is dominated by the ground state Ψ_0 of the delta Bose gas. The latter has a simple expression in this geometry [71, 72] and one thus infers that (for $0 \le x_1 \le \cdots \le x_N$)

$$\overline{Z(x_1,t)\ldots Z(x_N,t)} \simeq \overline{Z(0,t)^N} \times \Psi_0(\vec{x}), \quad \Psi_0(\vec{x}) = e^{\sum_{j=1}^{N}(A-j+1)x_j} \tag{14.37}$$

This expression contains a bit more information than the stationary measure (14.36) since it also depends on the correlations between $\log Z(0,t)$ and the ratios $\frac{Z(x,t)}{Z(0,t)}$. One can study the probability distribution of the endpoint $\phi(t) = x$ of a polymer, $p(x,t) = e^{h(x,t)-h(0,t)}/[\int_0^\infty dy e^{h(y,t)-h(0,t)}]$, which becomes stationary for a very long polymer. Remarkably, one finds [85] that (14.36) and (14.37) lead to the same results for the cumulants of $p(x)$, e.g. the noise average (thermal cumulants) $\overline{\langle x^k \rangle^c} = -(-2)^k \psi^{(k)}(-2A - 1)$ where $\psi(z)$ is the digamma function (recovering for $k = 1$ the pioneering result of [71]). Of course the manipulations based on (14.37) involve continuations in N, which are part of the usual magic of the replica method.

For completeness we give the result for the stationary measures on the interval $[0, L]$ with boundary conditions $\partial_x Z(x,t)|_{x=0} = AZ(x,t)$ and $\partial_x Z(x,t)|_{x=L} = -BZ(x,t)$. The stationary measure depends on the parameters $u = A + 1/2$ and $v = B + 1/2$. The stationary height field (omitting the time variable since it is statistically time independent) is such that $h(x) - h(0) = \frac{1}{\sqrt{2}} W(x) + X(x)$ where $W(x)$ is a one-sided Brownian motion ($W(0) = 0$ and $W(L)$ free) and the measure of the process $X(x)$ can be represented by the path-integral

$$\frac{\mathcal{D}X}{\mathcal{Z}_{u,v}} e^{-\int_0^L dx(\frac{dX(s)}{ds})^2} e^{-2vX(L)} \left(\int_0^L dy e^{-2X(y)} \right)^{-(u+v)} \tag{14.38}$$

where $X(0) = 0$ and $X(L)$ is free. This form was obtained in [86] based on the important earlier work [88], see also [87]. There are several applications. One is to study the endpoint distribution $p(x)$ of a very long polymer constrained to remain inside a strip $0 \leq \phi(\tau) \leq L$, which exhibits various unbinding transitions at the two boundaries, as anticipated in [89]. Another application is to take the limit $L \to +\infty$ and obtain the two parameter family of stationary measures on the half-line [86]. This is possible thanks to an earlier work of Hariya and Yor [90] who happened to study measures of the type (14.38) in a quite different context. An explicit expression is obtained [86] and depends on u, the wall parameter, as well as v, the drift at infinity, i.e. $h(x) - h(0) \sim -vx$ as $x \to +\infty$. For $u < 0$ and $u = -v$ the Brownian measure (14.36) is recovered.

14.2. Heteropolymers and Proteins

Henri Orland

*Université de Paris-Saclay, Institut de Physique Théorique, CEA,
CNRS UMR3681, 91191 Gif/Yvette Cedex, France*
henri.orland@ipht.fr

Heteropolymers are polymers made of several kinds of monomers. Typical examples are biopolymers, such as DNA or RNA, made of 4 kinds of nucleotides, or proteins, made of 20 kinds of amino-acids (AA) [91–93]. Their number of monomers is in the range of millions to billions for DNA, and thousands for RNA and proteins. These biopolymers are characterized by some specific sequence which determines their biological properties through their geometric conformation or folding. Upon varying temperature or solvent concentration, these biopolymers may undergo phase transitions, such as denaturation for DNA (unbinding of the two strands), and unfolding for RNA and protein (loss of ground state conformation). In these phases, the biopolymers lose their biological function and behave merely as structureless polymers.

In the following we shall concentrate on protein models. Although in their native state (biologically active state) a sizable amount of proteins are mostly disordered (intrinsically disordered proteins [94, 95]), most proteins in their native state are "folded" in a unique compact native structure which defines their biological function by providing the scaffold for an active site [96]. The amino acids (AA) constituting the building blocks of proteins are complex molecules, made of typically 10 atoms. Some AA are hydrophilic, some are hydrophobic, some are polar and some are not. In addition, several of them are positively or negatively charged. As a result, the effective interaction between the various AA can be attractive or repulsive, depending on their nature. A given protein has a fixed sequence, and to tackle the complexity of its sequence, the simplest way is to model it as a random heteropolymer, with random interactions [97–101]. Given that proteins are not infinitely long and that their sequence is by no means random, such models can provide a qualitative understanding of their phase diagram as the temperature or solvent quality is changed, but in order to reach a quantitative description, one has to resort to computer simulation, using molecular dynamics [102] or even artificial intelligence [103].

In recent years, there has been a renewed interest in the study of synthetic random heteropolymers: indeed, it has been shown that it is possible to use their self-assembly properties to mimic specific environments, biomimetic materials [104, 105], or to enrich them with specific properties [106, 107].

In the following, we will follow the presentation of [108, 109]. We consider a heteropolymer chain made of N beads linked by linkers of size a. Each bead and linker may schematically represent a complex ensemble of atoms, such as a residue or a peptide bond in the case of a protein. As we will assume sequence-dependent interactions between monomers, we write the interaction as

$$\beta V_{ij}(r) = v_0 \delta(r) + \beta v_{ij}(r)$$

where the first term represents the excluded volume (hard core repulsion) between the monomers and the second term is the sequence-dependent interaction. The interaction $v_{ij}(r)$ can be attractive or repulsive, depending on the nature of monomers i and j.

The partition function of the chain is given by

$$Z = \int dr_1 \cdots dr_N \prod_{i=1}^{N-1} g(r_{i+1}, r_i) e^{-\sum_{i<j}(v_0 \delta(r_{ij}) + \beta v_{ij}(r_{ij})) - \frac{w_0}{6} \sum_{i \neq j \neq k} \delta(r_{ij})\delta(r_{jk})}$$

$$(14.39)$$

where $g(r, r')$ enforces the chain constraint, for instance $g(r, r') = \delta(|r - r'| - a)$. We will assume that the monomer interactions are short-ranged, and so we restrict the interactions to the form

$$v_{ij}(r) = w_{ij} \delta(r)$$

where all the sequence dependence is now embedded in the matrix w_{ij} [98]. The 3-body term in (14.39) is added to avoid the collapse of the chain due to attractive interactions between monomers in the sequence.

It is natural to model the complexity of the sequence and of the interactions by randomness. In that case, since the sequence is fixed, one should perform a quenched average over the random interactions.

There are several possible choices for the interaction matrix v_{ij}, depending on the system we want to model. We list here the three most important models.

- *Random hydrophilic-hydrophobic chain*

  If the heteropolymer chain is constituted of hydrophilic and hydrophobic monomers, and it is immersed in water, the interactions of the monomers with the water molecules induce an effective interaction between the monomers. This effective interaction is repulsive between two hydrophilic monomers, less repulsive or even attractive between a hydrophilic and hydrophobic monomer and attractive between two hydrophobic monomers. The Hamiltonian for the system reads

$$w_{ij} = \lambda_i + \lambda_j \tag{14.40}$$

where the λ_i are quenched independent random variables characterizing the hydrophobicity of the monomers [110]. We assume a Gaussian form for the distribution of hydrophobicity as

$$P(\lambda_i) = \frac{1}{\sqrt{2\pi\lambda^2}} \exp\left(-\frac{(\lambda_i - \lambda_0)^2}{2\lambda^2}\right) \tag{14.41}$$

where positive λ_i denote hydrophilic monomers, negative λ_i denote hydrophobic monomers and λ_0 is the average hydrophobicity of the chain.

- *Random chemical sequence*

  In this model, we assume that there are Q types of monomers (for instance the 4 bases of DNA, the 20 amino-acids of proteins, ...), each type being characterized by a set of M parameters $\{q^{(1)}, \ldots, q^{(M)}\}$ (for instance the charge, the hydrophobicity, ...). The sequence of the chain is represented by the series of generalized charges. A simple form for the interaction matrix w_{ij} has been used [99]

$$w_{ij} = -\sum_{p=1}^{M} v_p q_i^{(p)} q_j^{(p)} \tag{14.42}$$

  where the v_p are parameters characterizing the strength of the feature p. Such types of models were introduced in magnetic systems [111] and in neural networks [112]. The generalized charges are taken as independent identically distributed random variables to mimic the complexity of the sequence.

- *Spin-glass model*

  In the spin-glass model [98], similarly to the magnetic spin-glass system, we assume that the variables v_{ij} are random Gaussian independent identically distributed variables with distribution

$$P(w_{ij}) = \frac{1}{\sqrt{2\pi w^2}} e^{-\frac{w_{ij}^2}{2w^2}}$$

The first two models described above display phase transitions which don't involve replica symmetry breaking (RSB). In the following, we will study the spin-glass model which displays a richer complexity.

Since we perform a quenched average over the disordered interactions, we introduce replicas and after averaging we obtain

$$\overline{Z^n} = \int \prod_{i,a} \left[dr_i^{(a)} g(r_i^{(a)}, r_{i+1}^{(a)}) \right] \exp\left(-\tilde{v}_0 \sum_{i<j} \sum_a \delta(r_i^{(a)} - r_j^{(a)})\right)$$

$$\times \exp\left(\frac{\beta^2 w^2}{2} \sum_{a\neq b} \sum_{i<j} \delta(r_i^{(a)} - r_j^{(a)})\delta(r_i^{(b)} - r_j^{(b)})\right)$$

$$\times \exp\left(-\frac{w_0}{6} \sum_{i\neq j\neq k} \sum_a \delta(r_i^{(a)} - r_j^{(a)})\,\delta(r_j^{(a)} - r_k^{(a)})\right) \tag{14.43}$$

with $\tilde{v}_0 = v_0 - \beta^2 \frac{w^2}{2}$ and the superscripts a and b are replica indices running from 1 to $n \to 0$.

Introducing the two order-parameters

$$m_a(r) = \sum_{i=1}^{N} \delta(r - r_i^{(a)})$$

$$q_{ab}(r, r') = \sum_{i=1}^{N} \delta(r - r_i^{(a)}) \delta(r' - r_i^{(b)})$$

the partition function (14.43) can be rewritten as

$$\overline{Z^n} = \int \prod_{a=1}^{n} \mathcal{D}m_a(r)\, \mathcal{D}\hat{m}_a(r)\, \mathcal{D}q_{ab}(r, r')\, \mathcal{D}\hat{q}_{ab}(r, r')$$

$$\times \exp\left(i \sum_{a=1}^{n} \int dr\, m_a(r)\hat{m}_a(r) + i \sum_{a<b} \int drdr'\, q_{ab}(r, r')\hat{q}_{ab}(r, r') \right)$$

$$\times \exp\left(-\frac{\tilde{v}_0}{2} \sum_{a} \int dr\, m_a^2(r) - \frac{w_0}{6} \int dr\, m_a^3(r) \right)$$

$$\times \exp\left(\frac{\beta^2 w^2}{2} \sum_{a<b} \int drdr'\, q_{ab}^2(r, r') + \log Q(\hat{m}_a(r), \hat{q}_{ab}(r, r')) \right) \qquad (14.44)$$

where Q is the partition function

$$Q(m_a(r), q_{ab}(r, r')) = \int \prod_{i,a} \left[dr_i^{(a)} g(r_i^{(a)}, r_{i+1}^{(a)}) \right]$$

$$\times \exp\left(-i \sum_{i} \left(\sum_{a} \hat{m}_a(r_i^{(a)}) + \sum_{a<b} \hat{q}_{ab}(r_i^{(a)}, r_i^{(b)}) \right) \right) (14.45)$$

Within mean-field theory, the equation of state is obtained by minimizing the exponent (effective free energy) with respect to the order parameters. The phase diagram of the chain displays the following properties

- a random coil phase at high temperature, characterized by $m_a(r) = 0$ and $q_{ab}(r, r') = 0$
- a θ (collapse) point to a dense phase if $\tilde{v}_0 < 0$, characterized by $m_a(r) \neq 0$ and $q_{ab}(r, r') = 0$
- a possible low temperature freezing transition due to the $a \neq b$ term of (14.44), characterized by $m_a(r) \neq 0$ and $q_{ab}(r, r') \neq 0$.

To further investigate the freezing transition of the random heteropolymer model, we consider two approximations in the dense phase $m_a(r) \neq 0$

High dimension

To simplify the model, we will assume that the polymer is on a high-dimensional hyper-cubic lattice denoted Ω. In that case, the chain constraint as well as the self-avoidance become irrelevant and we can just ignore it. Since the chain is compact, the number of available sites $|\Omega|$ is taken to be proportional to the number of monomers N of the chain $N = \rho|\Omega|$. The simplified partition function can be written as

$$Z = \sum_{\sigma_i \in \Omega} e^{-\frac{\beta}{2} \sum_{i,j} w_{ij} \delta(\sigma_i, \sigma_j)} \tag{14.46}$$

The energy of a given configuration of the chain is given by

$$E = \sum_{i<j} w_{ij} \delta(\sigma_i, \sigma_j) \tag{14.47}$$

and its average $\bar{E}$ over the disorder is equal to 0. We can similarly compute the correlation of these energies

$$\begin{aligned}
\overline{E.E'} &= \sum_{i<j} \sum_{i'<j'} \overline{w_{ij}.w_{i'j'}} \delta(\sigma_i, \sigma_j) \delta(\sigma'_{i'}, \sigma'_{j'}) \\
&= w^2 \sum_{i<j} \sum_{i'<j'} \delta_{ii'} \delta_{jj'} \delta(\sigma_i, \sigma_j) \delta(\sigma'_{i'}, \sigma'_{j'}) \\
&= w^2 \sum_{i<j} \delta(\sigma_i, \sigma_j) \delta(\sigma'_i, \sigma'_j)
\end{aligned} \tag{14.48}$$

The variance of the energies is given by

$$\begin{aligned}
\overline{E^2} &= w^2 \sum_{i<j} \delta(\sigma_i, \sigma_j) \\
&= \frac{w^2}{2} \sum_{r \in \Omega} m^2(r)
\end{aligned} \tag{14.49}$$

where $m(r)$ is the density of the chain, i.e. $m(r) = \rho = \frac{N}{|\Omega|}$. Therefore

$$\overline{E^2} = \frac{w^2}{2} N\rho \tag{14.50}$$

From Eq. (14.48), the correlation can be written as

$$\overline{E.E'} = \frac{w^2}{2} \sum_{r,r'} q^2(r, r') \tag{14.51}$$

where $q(r, r')$ is the order parameter $q(r, r') = \sum_i \delta(r - \sigma_i)\delta(r' - \sigma'_i)$.

Since $\sum_{r,r'} q(r, r') = N$ and all occupied points are equivalent, we have

$$\begin{aligned}
q(r, r') &= \frac{N}{|\Omega|^2} \\
&= \frac{\rho^2}{N}
\end{aligned} \tag{14.52}$$

and the correlation (14.51) reads

$$\begin{aligned}
\overline{E.E'} &= \frac{w^2}{2} \sum_{r,r'} q^2(r, r') \\
&= \frac{w^2}{2} \rho^2
\end{aligned} \tag{14.53}$$

In the limit of infinite N, the joint probability of the energies is given by

$$\lim_{N\to\infty} P(E,E') = \exp\left(-\frac{E^2 + E'^2}{Nw^2\rho}\right) \tag{14.54}$$

The energies become uncorrelated, and thus the model becomes equivalent to Derrida's random energy model (REM) [113]. As is well known [114], this model can be solved by a one-step replica symmetry breaking scheme. The REM was the basis of the phenomenological model put forward by Bryngelson and Wolynes to describe protein folding [97]. Within the REM phenomenology, the protein chain undergoes a freezing transition at temperature T_c. Above T_c, the system has a finite entropy, and this entropy vanishes at T_c. The system gets frozen in a small number of dominant states which differ by non extensive parts of the free energy. In Ref. [115], it is argued that real biological protein sequences are specifically designed by evolution so that the freezing transition is preempted by a regular transition to a lower energy state, which is the native state of the protein.

Finite dimension

In finite dimension d, the chain constraint cannot be neglected. In order to render the calculation tractable, we use the continuous limit for the polymeric partition function (14.45) and write

$$Q(m_a(r), q_{ab}(r,r')) = \int \prod_a \mathcal{D}r_a(s) \exp\left(-\frac{d}{2a^2}\int_0^N ds\, \dot{r}_a^2(s)\right)$$

$$\times \exp\left(-i\int_0^N ds \left(\sum_a \hat{m}_a(r_a(s)) + \sum_{a<b} \hat{q}_{ab}(r_a(s), r_b(s))\right)\right) \tag{14.55}$$

Using the quantum representation of the Feynman path integral (14.55) (see Ref. [116]), and using the Dirac notation for quantum mechanics, we may write

$$Q = \int dr\, dr' \langle r | e^{-NH} | r' \rangle \tag{14.56}$$

where H denotes the quantum n-body Hamiltonian

$$H = -\frac{a^2}{2d}\sum_a \nabla_a^2 + i\sum_a \hat{m}_a(r_a) + i\sum_{a<b} \hat{q}_{ab}(r_a, r_b) \tag{14.57}$$

To further simplify the calculations, we assume that the number of monomers is large $N \gg 1$. If the Hamiltonian has a gap in its ground state E_0 (which is the case in the compact phase of the chain), we use the ground state dominance approximation [117]

$$Q \underset{N\to\infty}{\sim} e^{-NE_0}\left(\int \prod_a dr\, \Psi_0(r_1, \ldots, r_n)\right)^2 \tag{14.58}$$

where Ψ_0 is the n-body ground state of the Hamiltonian H

$$H|\Psi_0\rangle = E_0|\Psi_0\rangle \tag{14.59}$$

In the limit of large N, the full partition function (14.44) can thus be written as

$$\overline{Z^n} = \int \prod_{a=1}^{n} \mathcal{D}m_a(r)\,\mathcal{D}\hat{m}_a(r)\,\mathcal{D}q_{ab}(r,r')\,\mathcal{D}\hat{q}_{ab}(r,r')$$

$$\times \exp\left(i\sum_{a=1}^{n}\int dr\, m_a(r)\hat{m}_a(r) + i\sum_{a<b}\int drdr' q_{ab}(r,r')\hat{q}_{ab}(r,r') \right)$$

$$\times \exp\left(-\frac{\tilde{v}_0}{2}\sum_a \int dr\, m_a^2(r) - \frac{w_0}{6}\int dr\, m_a^3(r) \right)$$

$$\times \exp\left(\frac{\beta^2 w^2}{2}\sum_{a<b}\int drdr'\, q_{ab}^2(r,r') - NE_0(\hat{m}_a(r),\hat{q}_{ab}(r,r')) \right) \qquad (14.60)$$

where we have neglected the integral term in (14.58) as it does not depend on N.

The ground-state energy E_0 of the Hamiltonian H can be obtained using the Rayleigh–Ritz variational principle [108] as

$$E_0 = \min_{\{\Psi\}}\left[\int dr_1 \ldots dr_n \Psi(r_1 \ldots r_n) H \Psi(r_1 \ldots r_n) \right]$$

$$= \min_{\{\Psi\}}\left[\int dr_1 \ldots dr_n \left(\frac{a^2}{2d}\sum_a (\nabla_a \Psi(r_1 \ldots r_n))^2 \right. \right.$$

$$\left. \left. + i\left(\sum_a \hat{m}_a(r_a) + \sum_{a<b}\hat{q}_{ab}(r_a,r_b) \right)\Psi^2(r_1 \ldots r_n) \right) \right] \qquad (14.61)$$

where $\min_{\{\Psi\}}$ stands for the minimum over all n-body wavefunctions normalized to 1. The mean-field theory is obtained by minimizing the full exponent of (14.60) with respect to $m_a(r), \hat{m}_a(r), q_{ab}(r,r'), \hat{q}_{ab}(r,r')$ and $\Psi(r_1 \ldots r_n)$.

At this stage, the problem still remains untractable due to its many-body nature. To further simplify, it has been proposed to restrict the minimization to Hartree-like wavefunctions [98]

$$\Psi(r_1 \ldots r_n) = \prod_a \phi(r_a) \qquad (14.62)$$

where $\phi(r)$ is normalized to unity. This approximation, which implies full symmetry of the replicas, allows to write a partial differential equation for ϕ. An analysis of this equation shows that the system undergoes a collapse transition at low T, from a swollen coil to a compact globule. This compact globule can be identified with the molten globule phase observed in some proteins [118]. However, within this approximation, there is no freezing-like transition, or any further transition that could be identified with a folding transition.

Using a method proposed by Edwards and Muthukumar [119], Shakhnovitch and Gutin in [100, 101] have proposed another approximation for the wavefunction, which allows for RSB:

$$\Psi(r_1,\ldots,r_n) = \frac{(\det K)^{d/4}}{(2\pi)^{nd/4}}\exp\left(-\frac{1}{4}\sum_{a,b}r_a K_{ab}r_b \right) \qquad (14.63)$$

where K is a $n \times n$ Parisi-like hierarchical matrix (see [120, 121]). The variational free energy is extremized with respect to K. When temperature decreases, there is first a transition from a random coil phase with all order parameters vanishing, to a random globule transition where the monomer concentration is finite, but the off-diagonal terms $K_{ab} = 0$. At lower temperature, within the compact globule phase, there is a freezing transition with RSB, with a non vanishing K_{ab}. The result, for large enough d, is a step function form for $K(x), (x \in [0,1])$, corresponding to a REM type of replica symmetry breaking as seen in the previous subsection. As usual with Parisi-like RSB, there is a large number of conformations which are degenerate for their extensive part, but which differ by their non-extensive part. In addition, there is a dominant state, which is identified as the native state of the protein. This peculiar topology of the phase space implies a slow dynamics, with stretched exponential relaxations [122, 123].

To conclude this section, we have shown that it is possible to give a schematic description of random heteropolymers which explains qualitatively the phases observed in these systems: swollen coil, molten globule and native phase. Due to the complexity of these molecules, however, achieving a quantitative description of these systems requires resorting to molecular dynamics [102] or to machine learning [103].

References

[1] T. Halpin-Healy and Y-C. Zhang, *Phys. Rep.* **254**, 215 (1995).

[2] M. Kardar, *Statistical physics of fields*, Cambridge University Press, (2007)

[3] D.A. Huse, C.L. Henley, and D.S. Fisher, *Phys. Rev. Lett.* **55**, 2924 (1985).

[4] D.A. Huse and C.L. Henley, *Phys. Rev. Lett.* **54**, 2708 (1985).

[5] M. Kardar and Y-C. Zhang, *Phys. Rev. Lett.* **58**, 2087 (1987).

[6] M. Kardar, *Nucl. Phys. B* **290**, 582 (1987).

[7] J. P. Bouchaud and H. Orland, *J. Stat. Phys.* **61**, 877 (1990)

[8] E. Brunet and B. Derrida, *Phys. Rev. E* **61**, 6789 (2000)

[9] K. Johansson, *Comm. Math. Phys.* **209**, 437 (2000)

[10] M. Prahofer and H. Spohn *J. Stat. Phys.* **108**, 1071 (2002)

[11] P. L. Ferrari and H. Spohn, *Comm. Math. Phys.* **265**, 1 (2006)

[12] M. Kardar, G. Parisi, and Y.-C.Zhang, *Phys. Rev. Lett.* **56**, 889 (1986)

[13] T. Sasamoto and H. Spohn, *Phys. Rev. Lett.* **104**, 230602 (2010)

[14] T. Sasamoto and H. Spohn, *Nucl. Phys. B* **834**, 523 (2010)

[15] T. Sasamoto and H. Spohn, *J. Stat. Phys.* **140**, 209 (2010)

[16] P. Calabrese, P. Le Doussal and A. Rosso, *EPL*, **90**, 20002 (2010)

[17] V. Dotsenko, *EPL*, **90**, 20003 (2010)

[18] V. Dotsenko, *J. Stat. Mech.* P07010 (2010)

[19] G. Amir, I. Corwin and J. Quastel, *Comm. Pure Appl. Math.* **64**, 466 (2011)

[20] P. Calabrese, M. Kormos and P. Le Doussal, *EPL* **107** 10011, (2014).

[21] C.A. Tracy and H. Widom, *Commun. Math. Phys.* **159**, 151 (1994)

[22] P.G. De Gennes, *Phys. Lett.* **38A**, 339 (1972)

[23] S.F. Edwards and P.W. Anderson, *J. Phys. F* **5**, 965 (1975)

[24] M. Mezard, G. Parisi and M.A. Virasoro, *Spin Glass Theory and Beyond*, World Scientific, (1987)

[25] Victor Dotsenko, *Introduction to the Replica Theory of Disordered statistical Systems*, Cambridge University Press, (2001)

[26] E.H. Lieb and W. Liniger, *Phys. Rev.* **130**, 1605 (1963)

[27] J.B. McGuire, *J. Math. Phys.* **5**, 622 (1964).

[28] C.N. Yang, *Phys. Rev.* **168**, 1920 (1968)

[29] M. Gaudin, *La fonction d'onde de Bethe*, Paris, Masson, (1983)

[30] V.E. Korepin, N.M. Bogoliubov, and A.G. Izergin, *Quantum inverse scattering method and correlation functions*, Cambridge University Press (1993)

[31] M. Takahashi, *Thermodynamics of one-dimensional solvable models*, Cambridge University Press (1999).

[32] M.L.Mehta, *Random Matrices*, Elsevier, Amsterdam (2004)

[33] P.Panleveé, *Sur les équation différentielles du second ordre et ordre supérieur dont intégrale générale est uniforme*, Acta. Math. **25**, 1 (1902)

[34] P.A.Clarkson, *J. Comp. Appl. Math.* **153**, 127 (2003)

[35] K. A. Takeuchi and M. Sano, *Phys. Rev. Lett.* **104**, 230601 (2010); K. A. Takeuchi, M. Sano, T. Sasamoto, and H. Spohn, *Sci. Rep.* **1**, 34 (2011).

[36] see e.g. S. Chu, M. Kardar *Phys. Rev. E* **94**(1) 010101 (2016).

[37] K. A. Takeuchi, M. Sano, *J. Stat. Phys.* **147**, 853–890 (2012).

[38] P. Calabrese, P. Le Doussal, *Phys. Rev. Lett.* **106**, 250603, (2011)

[39] P. Le Doussal, P. Calabrese, *J. Stat. Mech.* P06001, (2012).

[40] V. Dotsenko, *J. Stat. Mech.* P11014, (2012)

[41] P.L. Ferrari and H. Spohn, *J. Phys. A* **38**, L557 (2005).

[42] C. Tracy and H. Widom, *Comm. Math. Phys.* **177**, 727–754 (1996).

[43] For review see, S. N. Majumdar, G. Schehr, *Journal of Statistical Mechanics: Theory and Experiment*, 2014(1), P01012 (2014).

[44] J. Quastel, D. Remenik, *Trans. Amer. Math. Soc.* **371**, 6047–6085 (2019).

[45] T. Imamura, T. Sasamoto, *Phys. Rev. Lett.* **108**, 190603 (2012); and *J. Stat. Phys.* **150**, 908–939 (2013).

[46] J. Baik and E.M. Rains, *J. Stat. Phys.* **100**, 523–542 (2000).

[47] M. Prahofer and H. Spohn, *Phys. Rev. Lett.* **84**, 4882 (2000).

[48] T. Iwatsuka, Y. T. Fukai, K. A. Takeuchi, *Phys. Rev. Lett.* **124**, 250602 (2020).

[49] A. Borodin, P. L. Ferrari, and T. Sasamoto. *Comm. Pure Appl. Math.* **61**.11 (2008), pp. 1603.

[50] P. Le Doussal, *J. Stat. Mech. Theor. Exp.* P04018, (2014) and *J. Stat. Mech. Theor. Exp.* 053210, (2017)

[51] D.S. Dean, P. Le Doussal, S. N. Majumdar, G. Schehr. *Phys. Rev. Lett.* **114**, no. 11 (2015): 110402.

[52] A. Borodin, I. Corwin, P. L. Ferrari. B. Veto, *Math. Phys. Anal. Geom.* **18**, 20, (2015).

[53] J. Baik, G. Ben Arous, and S. Péché, *Ann. Probab.* **33**, 1643 (2005).

[54] S. F. Edwards and D. R. Wilkinson *Proc. R. Soc. A* **381**, 17–31 (1982).

[55] P. Le Doussal, S. N. Majumdar, A. Rosso, G. Schehr, *Phys. Rev. Lett.* **117**, 070403 (2016).

[56] A. Krajenbrink, P. Le Doussal, *Phys. Rev. E* **96**, 020102, (2017).

[57] N. R. Smith, B. Meerson, *Phys. Rev. E*, **97**(5), p. 052110 (2018).

[58] A. Borodin and I. Corwin, Macdonald processes, *Probab. Theory Rel. Fields* **158**, 225 (2014), arXiv:1111.4408.

[59] I. Corwin, arXiv:1403.6877.

[60] J. Quastel, H. Spohn, *J. Stat. Phys.* **160**, no. 4 (2015): 965–984.

[61] G. Barraquand, A. Borodin, I. Corwin, In Forum of Mathematics, Pi, vol. 8. Cambridge University Press, (2020).

[62] K. Matetski, J. Quastel, D. Remenik, *Acta Math.* **227**, 115–203 (2021).

[63] P. L. Ferrari, H. Spohn, *SIGMA* 12 (2016) 074, arXiv:1602.00486.

[64] V. Dotsenko, *J. Stat. Mech.* P06017 (2013), *J. Stat. Mech.* P06017 (2013), *J. Phys. A.* **49**, 27 (2016),

[65] J. De Nardis, P. Le Doussal, *J. Stat. Mech.* (2017) 053212, and *J. Stat. Mech.* (2018) 093203.

[66] J. De Nardis, P. Le Doussal, K. A. Takeuchi, *Phys. Rev. Lett.* **118**, 125701 (2017),

[67] K. Johansson, *Probab. Theory Relat. Fields* **175**(3), 849–895 (2019).

[68] P. Le Doussal, *Phys. Rev. E* **96**, 060101 (2017).

[69] T. Gueudré, P. Le Doussal, *EPL.* **100**(2), 26006 (2012).

[70] J. Baik, R. Buckingham, and J. DiFranco, *Commun. Math. Phys.* **280**(2), 463–497 (2008).

[71] M. Kardar, *Phys. Rev. Lett.* **55**, 2235 (1985).

[72] J. de Nardis, A. Krajenbrink, P. Le Doussal, T. Thiery, arXiv:1911.06133, (2019).

[73] A. Borodin, A. Bufetov, I. Corwin, *Annals of Physics*, **368**, 191–247, (2016).

[74] A. Krajenbrink, P. Le Doussal, *SciPost Phys.* **8**, 035, (2020).

[75] G. Barraquand, A. Borodin, I. Corwin, M. Wheeler, *Duke Math. J.* **167**(13), 2457–2529, (2018).

[76] G. Barraquand, P. Le Doussal, *Phys. Rev. E* **104**, 024502 (2021).

[77] J. Baik and E. M. Rains, *Math. Sci. Res. Inst. Publ.* **40**, pp. 1–19. Cambridge University Press, (2001).

[78] Y. Ito and K. Takeuchi, *Phys. Rev. E* **97**, 040103(R) (2018)

[79] D. Forster, D.R. Nelson and M.J. Stephen *Phys. Rev. A,* **16** 732 (1977).

[80] G. Parisi, *J. Physique.,* **51** (1990) 1595.

[81] Bertini L. and Giacomin G., *Comm. Math. Phys.,* **183** (1997) 571.

[82] Funaki T. and Quastel J., *Stoch. Partial Diff. Eq.: Anal. Computat.,* **3**, 159 (2015).

[83] Hairer M. and Mattingly J., *Ann. Inst. H. Poincaré Probab. Statist.* **54**(3), 1314–1340 (2018).

[84] G. Barraquand, A. Krajenbrink, P. Le Doussal, *J. Stat. Phys.* **181**, 1149–1203 (2020).

[85] see e.g. Section E in Supp. Mat of G. Barraquand, P. Le Doussal, arXiv:2104.08234.

[86] G. Barraquand and P. Le Doussal, *EPL.* **137**(6), 61003 (2022).

[87] See W. Bryc and A. Kuznetsov, *arXiv:2109.04462* and reference therein.

[88] Corwin I. and Knizel A., *arXiv:2103.12253*, (2021)

[89] Krug J. and Tang L., *Phys. Rev. E,* **50**, 104 (1994).

[90] Y. Hariya, M. Yor M., *Stud. Sci. Math. Hung.,* **41**, 193 (2004).

[91] J. Darnell, H. Lodish and D. Baltimore, *Molecular Cell Biology*, Scientific American Books (1990).

[92] B. Alberts, D. Bray, J. Lewis, M. Raff, K. Roberts and J.D. Watson, *Molecular Biology of the Cell*, Garland Publishing (1983).

[93] T.E. Creighton, *Proteins*, W.H. Freeman, (1984).

[94] A.K. Dunker, J.D. Lawson et al., *J. Mol. Graph. Model.,* **19**, 26–59 (2001).

[95] H.J. Dyson and P.E. Wright, *Nat. Rev. Mol. Cell Biol.,* **6**, 197–208 (2005).

[96] T.E. Creighton (editor), *Protein Folding*, W.H. Freeman, (1992).

[97] Bryngelson J. and P.G. Wolynes, *Proc. Natl. Acad. Sci. USA* **84**, 7524 (1987).

[98] Garel T. and H. Orland, *Europhys. Lett.* **6**, 307 (1988).

[99] T. Garel and H. Orland, *Europhys. Lett.* **6**, 597 (1988).

[100] E.I. Shakhnovich and A.M. Gutin, *Europhys. Lett.* **8**, 327 (1989).

[101] E.I. Shakhnovich and A.M. Gutin, *J. Phys.* **A22**, 1647 (1989).

[102] D.E. Shaw, P. Maragakis, K. Lindorff-Larsen et al., *Science,* **330**, 341–346 (2010).

[103] Jumper, J., Evans, R., Pritzel, A. et al. *Nature* **596**, 583–589 (2021)

[104] B. Panganiban, Baofu Qiao et al. *Science* **359**, 1239–1243 (2018)

[105] S.L. Hilburg, Zhiyuan Ruan, Ting Xu, and A. Alexander-Katz, *Macromolecules* **53**, 9187–9199 (2020)

[106] Tao Jiang, A. Hall et al. *Nature* **577**, 216–220 (2020)

[107] A. Stoddart, *Nat. Rev. Mater.* **5**, 86 (2020)

[108] T. Garel, H. Orland and D. Thirumalai, in *New Developments in Theoretical Studies of Proteins*, R. Elber (ed.), World Scientific, (1996).

[109] T.Garel, H. Orland and E. Pitard, *Spin Glasses and Random Fields*, 387–443, World Scientific, (1997).

[110] T. Garel, L. Leibler and H. Orland, *J. Phys. II (France)*, **4**, 2139 (1994).

[111] D.C. Mattis, *Phys. Lett.*, **56A**, 421 (1976).

[112] J.J Hopfield, *Proc. Natl. Acad. Sci. U.S.A.*, **79**, 2554–2558 (1982).

[113] B.D. Derrida, *Phys. Rev. B*, **24**, 2613 (1981).

[114] D.J. Gross and M. Mézard, *Nuclear Physics B*, **240**, 431–452 (1984).

[115] J.D. Bryngelson, J.N. Onuchic, N.D. Socci and P.G. Wolynes, *Proteins Struct Funct. Genet.*, **21**, 167 (1995).

[116] R. P. Feynman and A.R. Hibbs, *Quantum Mechanics and Path Integrals*, McGraw-Hill, 1965

[117] P.G. de Gennes, *Scaling concepts in polymer physics*, Cornell University Press, Ithaca (1979).

[118] O.B. Ptitsyn, *Adv. Protein. Chem.*, **47**, 83–229 (1995).

[119] S.F. Edwards and M. Muthukumar, *J. Chem. Phys.*, **89**, 2435 (1988)

[120] G. Parisi, *Phys. Rev. Lett.*, **43**, 1754 (1979)

[121] M. Mézard, G. Parisi and M.A. Virasoro, *Spin glass theory and beyond* , World Scientific, (1987).

[122] C. De Dominicis, H. Orland and F. Lainée, *J. Phys. (France)*, **46**, L-463 (1985).

[123] G.J.M. Koper and H.J. Hilhorst, *Europhys. Lett.*, **3**, 1213 (1987).

Chapter 15

Emergent Dynamics in Glasses and Disordered Systems:
Correlations and Avalanches

This chapter reviews some emergent properties of the dynamics of glassy systems, and more generally of a wide class of disordered systems.

In a first contribution (Sec. 15.1), **Zippelius** and **Fuchs** review the emergence of stress propagation upon cooling a glass-forming material. They show that emergent solid elasticity leads to long-ranged stress correlations both in the supercooled liquid and glass phases, having a non-trivial quadrupolar structure of the Eshelby type.

In a second contribution (Sec. 15.2), **Rosso**, **Sethna** and **Wyart** discuss how such long-range stress correlations lead to frustrated interactions between local excitations and the emergence of avalanches in glasses, focusing in particular on the rigid phase at negligible temperature. More generally, they draw an analogy with other avalanche phenomena appearing in a variety of disordered systems, from epidemic models to the depinning transition of elastic interfaces to the jamming transition of granular materials.

15.1. From Viscous Fluids to Elastic Solids: A Perspective on the Glass Transition

Annette Zippelius* and Matthias Fuchs[†]

*University Göttingen, D-37077 Göttingen, Germany
annette@theorie.physik.uni-goettingen.de
[†]University of Konstanz, D-78457 Konstanz, Germany
matthias.fuchs@uni-konstanz.de

A theory for the non-local stress in liquids captures the crossover from viscous to elastic correlations upon supercooling. It explains the emergence of long-ranged stress fields in glass which originate from the coupling of shear stress to transverse deformations. The Goldstone mode in colloidal glass is shown to be diffusive.

15.1.1. *Introduction*

The most prominent distinction between a fluid and a glass is the response to a static shear stress: A fluid continues to flow as long as the shear is applied and hence its response is characterized by a finite shear viscosity. On the other hand, a glass or an amorphous solid displays a finite deformation in response to a small applied shear and is thus characterized by a finite elastic resistivity to shear deformations. One of the first to capture this fundamental difference was Maxwell [1], who suggested that the transition from viscous to elastic behaviour is due to the divergence of a (single) relaxation time τ. He proposed the following simple relation between a shear stress, e.g. σ_{xy}, and the corresponding velocity gradient

$$(\partial_t + 1/\tau)\sigma_{xy} = \mu \, \partial_y v_x \tag{15.1}$$

in terms of the shear modulus, μ, encoding the elasticity. In the solid τ is infinite, implying an elastic response $\sigma_{xy} = \mu \, \partial_y u_x$ in terms of the displacement, u_x, which enters Eq. (15.1) via its time derivative, $v_x = \partial_t u_x$. In the fluid, τ is finite, so that in the hydrodynamic limit $\sigma_{xy} = \eta \partial_y v_x$ with the shear viscosity given by $\eta = \mu\tau$.

What is missing? We know from linear elasticity theory that stresses are long ranged in solids: A localised shear strain, ϵ_{xy}, generates far away stresses according to [2–5]

$$\sigma_{xy}(\mathbf{r}) = 2\mu \int d^3r' G(\mathbf{r} - \mathbf{r}')\epsilon_{xy}(\mathbf{r}') \tag{15.2}$$

$$G(\mathbf{r}) = -\frac{3}{4\pi r^7}\big(r^2(x^2 + y^2) - 10x^2y^2\big) \propto r^{-3}$$

Note that the Green's function, $G(\mathbf{r})$, is not only long-ranged, but also anisotropic, even though we have specialised to isotropic solids, such as glasses or amorphous solids. The basic questions we want to address in this section OR contribution are the following: How do long range stress correlations build up at the glass transition? Are there precursors in the supercooled liquid? Can we formulate a unified hydrodynamic theory of liquids and glasses?

To answer these questions, we have computed the correlations of the *local* shear stress fluctuations [6, 7]

$$C(\mathbf{q}, t) = \frac{n}{k_B T} \langle \sigma_{xy}(-\mathbf{q}, t)\sigma_{xy}(\mathbf{q}) \rangle \tag{15.3}$$

where the homogeneity of the system is conveniently exploited by Fourier transforming. The microscopic stress tensor that enters Eq. (15.3) is taken from Irving and Kirkwood [8] which reads for the potential contribution:

$$\sigma_{\alpha\beta}(\mathbf{r}) = \sum_{\langle j,k \rangle} \frac{\mathbf{r}_{jk}^\alpha \mathbf{r}_{jk}^\beta}{r_{jk}} U'(r_{jk}) \int_0^1 ds\, \delta(\mathbf{r} - \mathbf{r}_k - s\mathbf{r}_{jk}) \tag{15.4}$$

Here the δ-function picks the force contribution from the particle pair j, k through an appropriately chosen small surface-element [9].

The shortcoming of a single relaxation time approximation à la Maxwell is the neglect of slow dynamics in the local stress fluctuations, which cannot be captured by a single relaxation time and which will ultimately give rise to nontrivial stress correlations.

15.1.2. *Emergence of long range stress correlations*

The obvious candidates for slow relaxation in a Newtonian fluid are the conserved densities of particle number, momentum and energy. For simplicity, we consider an incompressible, isothermal system and refer to the literature [7, 10] for the general case. The only conserved field is thus the transverse momentum or velocity, defined as $\mathbf{v}^\perp(\mathbf{q}) = \mathbf{q} \times (\mathbf{q} \times \mathbf{v}(\mathbf{q}))/q^2$ with $\mathbf{v}(\mathbf{q}) = \frac{1}{\sqrt{N}} \sum_{i=1}^{N} e^{i\mathbf{q}\mathbf{r}_i(t)}\mathbf{v}_i$.

In the hydrodynamic limit, its correlation function $\langle \mathbf{v}^\perp(\mathbf{q},t)^* \ \mathbf{v}^\perp(\mathbf{q})\rangle = (1 - \frac{\mathbf{q}\mathbf{q}}{q^2}) \, K_q(t)$ describes diffusive momentum transport at long wavelengths; in the fluid phase the relaxation rate $\propto \eta q^2$ vanishes as the wavenumber goes to zero, reflecting the conservation law. This behaviour is captured in the following representation [11] of the Laplace transform $K_q(s) = \int_0^\infty dt \, e^{-st} K_q(t)$

$$K_q(s) = \frac{k_B T/m}{s + \frac{q^2}{mn} G_0(s)} \tag{15.5}$$

in terms of a generalised shear modulus $G_0(s)$. The main advantage of this representation is that it guarantees the correct treatment of the conservation law and allows for simple approximations of the modulus. For example, a single relaxation time approximation à la Maxwell, $G_0(s) = (\mu\tau)/(1 + s\tau)$, reproduces the diffusion of transverse momentum in the fluid (τ finite) and (undamped) transverse sound modes in the solid (τ infinite).

The conservation of transverse momentum gives rise to a slow component also in the relaxation of the stress correlation [6, 7], which can be isolated with help of the Mori–Zwanzig formalism [12]. A projection operator $\mathcal{P} = \frac{m}{k_B T} \mathbf{v}^\perp(\mathbf{q})\rangle\cdot\langle\mathbf{v}^\perp(\mathbf{q})^*$ captures the overlap between the transverse momentum and a fluctuation of the shear stress. Applying $\mathcal{P}$ to the stress correlation, $C(\mathbf{q})$, yields the desired decomposition [6, 7]

$$C(\mathbf{q},s) = G_0(s) - \left((q_x^2 + q_y^2) - 4\frac{q_x^2 q_y^2}{q^2} \right) \frac{G_0(s)^2}{nk_B T} K_q(s) \tag{15.6}$$

into a hydrodynamic contribution and local dynamics entailed in $G_0(s)$. In a straightforward generalization of the Maxwell model, we use a single relaxation time approximation for $G_0(s) = (\mu\tau)/(1 + s\tau)$, allowing for a divergence of the structural relaxation time τ at the glass transition.

What are the predictions of the generalised Maxwell model? First, the result of Maxwell is reproduced for the global stress in a fluid, $C(\mathbf{q} = \mathbf{0}, s) = G_0(s)$, which reduces to the shear viscosity $\eta = \mu\tau$ in the limit of vanishing frequency, $s\tau \to 0$. Second, stress correlations are strongly *anisotropic* in the isotropic fluid, characterized by finite τ:

$$C(\mathbf{q},s) = \eta - \left(q_x^2 + q_y^2 - \frac{4q_x^2 q_y^2}{q^2} \right) \frac{\eta^2}{nms + \eta q^2}. \tag{15.7}$$

Local stresses do not decay quickly, but display long-lived diffusive behaviour. The distance to the glass transition is controlled by τ, or equivalently η, which is known to increase dramatically as the glass transition is approached. Here, we follow Maxwell and consider an ideal glass transition with a true divergence of τ. The increasingly slow dynamics implies increasingly *long-ranged* stress correlations as the glass transition is approached, i.e. $\tau \to \infty$. The spatial extent of stress correlations is quantified by a correlation length ξ which diverges as the glass transition is approached, $\xi^2 = \mu\tau^2/(mn)$. For high frequencies $s\tau \gg 1$, the fluid supports tranverse sound, as one would expect. Third, the glass (characterized by infinite τ) exhibits a time-persistent part of the stress

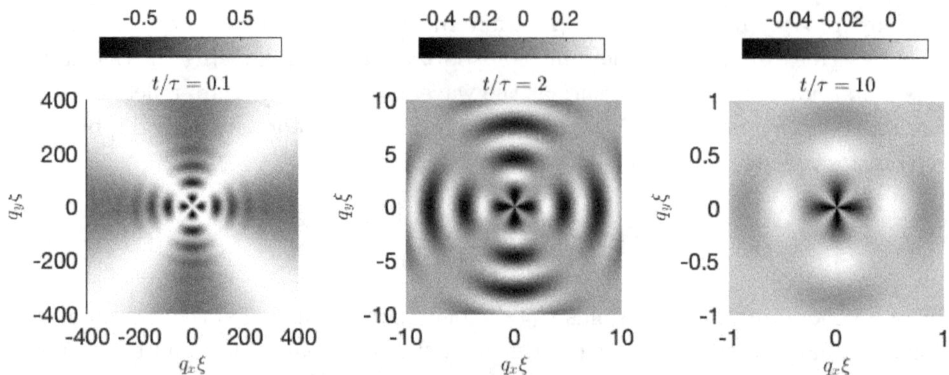

Fig. 15.1.   Shear stress correlations $C(\mathbf{q}, t)/\mu = \mathcal{F}(t/\tau, \mathbf{q}\xi)$ in the generalized Maxwell model for fluid $(t/\tau = 10)$, viscoelastic $(t/\tau = 2)$, and solid $(t/\tau = 0.1)$ state points, from right to left; from Ref. [7].

correlation:

$$\lim_{t \to \infty} C(\mathbf{q}, t) = \lim_{s \to 0} sC(\mathbf{q}, s) = C_\infty(\mathbf{q}) = \frac{4q_x^2 q_y^2 + q_z^2 q^2}{q^4}\mu. \tag{15.8}$$

The glass resists static shear deformations and the above static correlations are equivalent to Eshelby's response function in Eq. (15.2). Shear deformations in the glassy phase are propagating sound modes as reflected in the connected correlation: $C(\mathbf{q}, s) - C_\infty(\mathbf{q}) = \frac{\mu s}{s^2 + q^2 c^2}$ for $q_x = 0$ and with speed of sound $c^2 = \mu/(mn)$. Fourth, with the above definition of the correlation length we can write the stress correlation in scaling form: $C(\mathbf{q}, t) = \mu\mathcal{F}(t/\tau, \mathbf{q}\xi)$, accounting for the stress fluctuations in the fluid, at the glass transition, and in the glassy phase. This scaling function is shown in Fig. 15.1 in the q_x, q_y plane for several values of rescaled time t/τ. The right panel corresponds to a fluid with $t/\tau = 10$, the middle one depicts the transition region with $t/\tau = 2$, and the left panel corresponds to the glassy regime with $t/\tau = 0.1$. The anisotropy is clearly visible in the four-fold symmetric pattern for all three cases. The corrections to the simple Maxwell model vanish along the diagonal $(q_x = q_y = q/\sqrt{2})$. Here the anisotropic terms in Eq. (15.6) vanish and $C(\mathbf{q}, t)$ agrees with the Maxwell modulus $G_0(t)$. Along the axis (either $q_x = 0$ or $q_y = 0$), where force-correlations are tested [13], the deviations from Maxwell are strongest with (undamped) transverse sound modes in the solid.

15.1.3.   *Goldstone modes of a colloidal glass*

The momentum of colloidal particles in suspension is not conserved in contrast to the Newtonian fluid discussed above [14]. The interaction with the solvent is conveniently approximated by a constant friction coefficient ζ_0, ignoring hydrodynamic interactions. Consequently, velocity correlations

$$K_q(s) = \frac{k_B T/m}{s + \frac{q^2}{mn}G_0(s) + \frac{\zeta_0}{m}} \tag{15.9}$$

decay on microscopic timescales in the hydrodynamic regime and, due to symmetry, there are no conserved fields which could give rise to slow shear stress fluctuations. However, we expect that correlations of the transverse displacement, $\mathbf{u}^\perp$, are long ranged also in colloidal glasses. To capture these long-range fluctuations in a unified hydrodynamic theory of supercooled liquids and glasses including suspensions, we separate the dynamics of stress fluctuations into a part in the subspace of $\mathbf{u}^\perp$, or rather its time derivative $\mathbf{v}^\perp = \partial_t \mathbf{u}^\perp$, and the rest. In other words, we use the same decomposition [10] as for the Newtonian case with however different velocity correlations, Eq. (15.9).

The most surprising results of the generalised Maxwell model refer to the (overdamped) colloidal glass. The static elasticity, as described by $C_\infty(\mathbf{q})$, is the same as for the Newtonian model as one would expect. However, frequency dependent transverse deformations propagate diffusively

$$C(\mathbf{q}, s) - C_\infty(\mathbf{q}) = \mu \left(\frac{q_x^2 + q_y^2}{q^2} - 4 \frac{q_x^2 q_y^2}{q^4} \right) \frac{\zeta_0}{s\zeta_0 + q^2 \mu/n} \tag{15.10}$$

We identify this diffusive mode with the Goldstone excitations of an amorphous solid. Localisation of the particles implies a spontaneous breaking of the translational symmetry of the system. In contrast to crystalline systems, the symmetry is restored on a macroscopic level, because the particles are localised at random positions [15]. Nevertheless, a uniform translation of all particles leaves the energy invariant and the energy of an almost uniform translation goes to zero as the wavelength of the perturbation grows. In a phenomenological approach, we start from the elastic free energy $F = \mu/2 \int d^d q \, q^2 \, \mathbf{u}^\perp(\mathbf{q}) \cdot \mathbf{u}^\perp(-\mathbf{q})$ and assume purely relaxational dynamics

$$n\zeta_0 \partial_t \mathbf{u}^\perp(\mathbf{q}) = -\frac{\delta \mathbf{F}}{\delta \mathbf{u}_\perp(-\mathbf{q})} = -\mu \, \mathbf{q}^2 \, \mathbf{u}^\perp(\mathbf{q}).$$

The relaxation of $\mathbf{u}^\perp(\mathbf{q})$ is diffusive in perfect agreement with the diffusive pole $s = -q^2 \mu/(n\zeta_0)$ observed in Eq. (15.10).

Precursors of this diffusive mode can be observed in supercooled colloidal suspensions, which are well described by Eq. (15.10) in the large damping limit, ignoring inertial terms. The frequency dependent spectra are strongly anisotropic in $\mathbf{q}$-space, as already observed for the Newtonian case. Choosing $\mathbf{q}$ along one of the axis, say $\mathbf{q} = (q, 0, 0)$ we find:

$$-i\omega C(\mathbf{q}, s = -i\omega) = C'(\mathbf{q}, \omega) - iC''(\mathbf{q}, \omega)$$

$$C''(q, \omega) = \mu \frac{\omega\tau(1 + q^2\xi^2)}{(q^2\xi^2 + 1)^2 + \omega^2\tau^2} \tag{15.11}$$

$$C'(q, \omega) = \mu \frac{\omega^2\tau^2}{(q^2\xi^2 + 1)^2 + \omega^2\tau^2}$$

Here we have introduced the correlation length $\xi^2 = \mu\tau/(n\zeta_0)$, which diverges as $\xi \propto \sqrt{\tau}$ in contrast to the Newtonian case. For sufficiently large $q\xi > 1$, the peak in the loss spectrum is located at $\omega\tau \sim q^2\xi^2$. Fig. 15.2 shows the evolution of the spectra that agree with the expected rheological moduli of the Maxwell fluid only in the limit $q\xi \to 0$.

15.1.4. *Conclusions*

We have computed the nonlocal stress correlations for both Newtonian as well as colloidal fluids. A generalized Maxwell model connects the emergence of long range stress

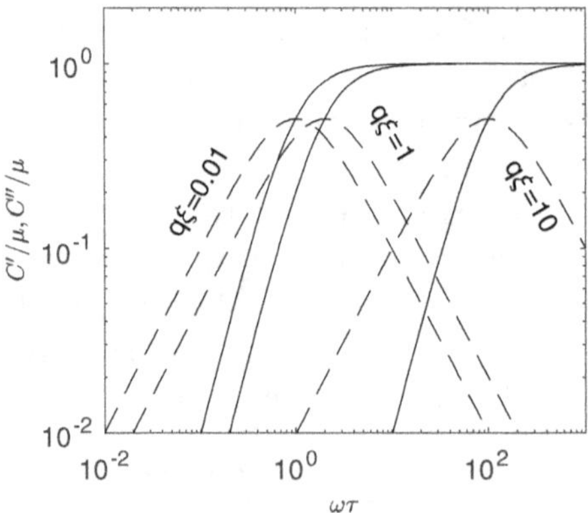

Fig. 15.2. Shear stress spectra, loss C'' (dashed lines) and storage C' (solid lines) terms, are shown as functions of rescaled frequency; from Ref. [10].

correlations in the viscous fluid to the elasticity of glasses. In Newtonian fluids, the range of stress correlations is characterized by a correlation length $\xi \propto \tau$, which grows approaching the glass transition, whereas in colloidal fluids $\xi \propto \sqrt{\tau}$. In the colloidal glass, transverse deformations propagate diffusively in contrast to transverse sound in the Newtonian case.

The nonlocal stress correlations can equivalently be computed from purely hydrodynamic considerations [6, 7, 10, 16], decomposing the flow field into the externally imposed flow and a fluctuating part. The response function to the externally imposed flow is related via the fluctuation-dissipation theorem to the correlation function, as discussed here. Several extensions of the simple model are possible; we have already analyzed compressible systems [7, 10, 17], including longitudinal sound. Another extension refers to a computation of the generalized modulus, going beyond the single relaxation time approximation.

Acknowledgments

All the results presented here were done in collaboration with Manuel Maier and Florian Vogel, whose contributions are gratefully acknowledged.

15.2. Avalanches and Deformation in Glasses and Disordered Systems

Alberto Rosso[*], James P. Sethna[†] and Matthieu Wyart[‡]

Université Paris Saclay, CNRS,LPTMS, 91405, Orsay, France
†*LASSP, Cornell University, Ithaca, NY 14853, USA*
‡*Institute of Physics, École Polytechnique Fédérale de Lausanne (EPFL),*
CH-1015 Lausanne, Switzerland

In this section, we discuss avalanches in glasses and disordered systems, and the macroscopic dynamical behavior that they mediate. We briefly review three classes of systems where avalanches are observed: depinning transition of disordered interfaces, yielding of amorphous materials, and the jamming transition. Without extensive formalism, we discuss results gleaned from theoretical approaches — mean-field theory, scaling and exponent relations, the renormalization group, and a few results from replica theory. We focus both on the remarkably sophisticated physics of avalanches and on relatively new approaches to the macroscopic flow behavior exhibited past the depinning/yielding transition.

15.2.1. *Introduction*

Rigid systems, put under stress, will often respond through a series of avalanches [18–20] with a broad distribution of sizes and durations.[a] Faults in the Earth exhibit earthquakes spanning many decades of size [22–25] when stressed by the motion of tectonic plates. Iron placed in a growing magnetic field will emit Barkhausen crackling noise (both acoustic and electromagnetic) as the internal magnetic domain walls shift between metastable states [26, 27]. Raindrops on your windshield advance in bursts — their leading edges, pinned by dirt, releasing as they grow and merge [28]. Avalanches also arise microscopically in systems that usually are viewed as responding smoothly to an external stress. Your fork, bending irreversibly when you try to cut through a tough piece of meat, responds through many dislocation avalanches with a distribution of sizes — measurable, for example, in experiments where nanopillars of metal are compressed [29–34]. Toothpaste squeezed out of a tube yields above a critical stress through a jerky set of avalanches.

In all these systems an avalanche starts from a weak spot that becomes unstable and slips. This triggers other instabilities nearby that in turn infect other regions — sometimes halting quickly, and sometimes sweeping over vast regions before halting. Some systems exhibit avalanches of all scales (sometimes termed 'crackling noise') only when delicately tuned to balance between stability (only local events) and instability (continuous flow). We shall see that many systems can either *self-organize* to this balancing point, or exhibit *generic scale invariance* — with events of all scales due to long-range non-monotonic (i.e. of varying sign) interactions.

These avalanches are characteristic of systems that have a complex energy landscape (well studied in other chapters of this book). Increasing the stress on the system 'tilts' this landscape, and the avalanches represent transitions from one metastable valley to another. For a sufficiently large tilt, rigidity can be lost and the system flows continuously. We focus on unifying concepts that describe both the avalanche-type response and continuous flows when it occurs, in systems ranging from disordered magnets and granular materials to epidemics, raindrops, and brain activity. We shall explain, without extensive formalism, how *scaling* and *renormalization-group* methods unify all of these systems, and elucidate the important physics that make these systems different from one another.

Our contribution is organized as follows. In Sec. 15.2.2, we introduce a few of the many systems exhibiting collective avalanches and crackling noise: epidemics, depinning of lines and interfaces in random media, yielding in amorphous solids such as glasses

---

[a]Warning: Everyday avalanches in sandpiles, or of snow or rocks on mountains, rarely exhibit the fractal, scale invariant behavior we study here [21].

and foams, and dense granular flows. In the first two cases, system-spanning avalanches occur at a critical point, while in other cases they occur in an entire phase. In Sec. 15.2.3, we explain these facts by introducing the notion of *excitations*, as regions of the material that are about to undergo an instability. If sufficiently long-range interactions are present, requiring stability of the material constrains the density of excitations, which in turn implies a generic scale invariance in the entire rigid phase. In Secs. 15.2.4, 15.2.5 and 15.2.6 we introduce renormalization group results and scaling arguments. They apply but differ in the systems considered, allowing one to both compare these systems and build a detailed understanding of several phenomena, including the shape of avalanches or their connection with stationary flows when rigidity is lost. In Sec. 15.2.7, we conclude by emphasizing key open questions of this field.

15.2.2. *Systems considered*

Avalanches appear in many areas, both in science and engineering and in other fields. In addition to the examples above, avalanche models have been used to describe fracture precursors in quasi-brittle material like bones and seashells [35], bubble avalanches in foams [36], fluids invading porous media [37, 38] (like milk invading puffed rice cereal [39] or coffee soaking into a napkin [40]), vortex avalanches in superconductors [20, Chapter 9] and neutron stars [41], wars [42], neural avalanches in brain tissue [43, 44], noise while tearing paper [45] and while crumpling paper or candy wrappers [46, 47], and clapping after concert performances [48]. In this section, we introduce four phenomena we focus on: the mean-field theory of epidemics, the depinning transition of an elastic manifold in a disordered environment, the plasticity of simple yield stress materials, and the jamming transition in granular systems.

15.2.2.1. *Mean-field pandemic model*

Outbreaks of disease are a public-health manifestation of avalanche behavior. An unlucky person is infected by a bird, pig, or bat, and infects one or more surrounding people. Let R_0 denote the number of infections triggered by each formerly infected person; $R_0 \sim 12$–18 for measles, 2–3 for influenza. For a new disease where nobody is immune, $R_0 < 1$ means that the disease will gradually disappear, $R_0 > 1$ implies that — if not stamped out early — it will cause a global pandemic. Near $R_0 = 1$, there is a phase transition, with avalanches (outbreaks that halt) on all scales for $R_0 \lesssim 1$.

This model is called the Bienaymé–Galton–Watson process [49, 50]. It is a *mean-field* model for avalanches, because there is no notion of space: everyone can infect anyone. It also describes a fully connected Ising model in a disordered material [51], where a spin flips when its external field increases beyond its random threshold, increasing the external 'mean field' on all the other N spins enough to on average flip R_0 neighbors. In some cases, this mean-field aspect is not a realistic assumption: plants do not move, so crop diseases that spread locally have avalanches that are correlated in space.

Consider the number I_{N_R} of infected people at the time when N_R people have stopped being infectious (either recovered or deceased). Each person, before they recover, infects ξ_{N_R} others, where ξ is a random integer chosen from a Poisson distribution of mean $R_0 I_{N_R}$. For simplicity, we assume these infections happen at the time when the person recovers, implying $I_{N_R+1} = I_{N_R} + \xi_{N_R}$. This random walk halts at pandemic size S when I_S first touches zero; its size S is the number of random steps for the first return to the origin. The probability of a pandemic of size S at $R_0 = 1$ thus coincides with the probability that a random walk starting at the origin will have its first return after S steps, which can be calculated to be a power law $P(S) \sim S^{-\tau}$ with $\tau = 3/2$. Let us measure the distance to the critical point as $r = (R_0 - R)/R$. For $r \lesssim 0$ below threshold, the random walk starts positive ($I_1 = 1$) but has a negative drift — it is a biased random walk. For small avalanches near R_c, the accumulated drift $\Delta I = rS$ is negligible compared to the typical random walk distance $I_{\max} \sim S^{1/2}$, but for large avalanches the drift dominates, making large avalanches unusual. Equating the two, we expect the probability distribution of avalanches $P(S, r)$ is cut off at a size $S_{\max} \sim r^{-1/\sigma}$ with $\sigma = 1/2$. More precisely, $P(S, r)$ can be shown to follow

$$P(S, r) \sim S^{-3/2} \exp(-Sr^2/2) \sim S^{-\tau} \mathcal{P}(S^\sigma r) \quad \text{with } \mathcal{P}(X) = \exp(-X^2/2). \quad (15.12)$$

Here τ and σ are universal critical exponents, and $\mathcal{P}$ is a universal scaling function of the invariant scaling ratio $X = S^\sigma r$. Universality signifies that changing our epidemic model to a more realistic stochastic SIR model (a 'compartmental' model discussing the susceptible, infected, and recovered populations), or a model with superspreaders, does not change the values for τ, σ, and $\mathcal{P}$ that describe large epidemics. However, some features like cities can change the behavior away from mean-field in qualitative ways.

Scaling functions arise [52] whenever more than two parameters and properties are involved (here, probability P, depending on size S, and distance r to the critical point). Other examples include avalanche duration versus time as a function of r, scaling depending on the system size L, crossover scaling [26, 53], singular corrections to scaling, etc. In Sec. 15.2.4.2, we shall study a universal scaling function for the average temporal shape of avalanches, which has two properties depending on two parameters.

Finally, note that to obtain avalanches of all scales requires to tune a parameter like R_0 to a critical point. However, in various cases this parameter can spontaneously evolve to that value, a phenomenon called *self-organized criticality* [54]. In our disease outbreak model, imagine we add a term which describes the societal response to widespread illness – wearing masks, getting immunized, avoiding large gatherings. As outbreaks become large and alarming, these responses will tend to reduce the effective interactions, tuning R_0 down until just below the threshold for a pandemic [55].

15.2.2.2. *Depinning transitions*

View Fig. 15.3 as a one-dimensional elastic interface, pushed through a disorder environment by applying a force per unit length f. Examples of this situation abound:[b] it could represent a magnetic film, magnetized 'up' below the jagged interface, and 'down' above the interface with a forcing that depends on the applied magnetic field [27]; or the triple line formed at the edge of a drop on your windshield, forced by gravity [28]. These phenomena are well described as the propagation of a single-valued front $u(r, t)$,

---

[b]One can also view it as a two-dimensional disordered crystal with a jagged dislocation line pinned on impurities, or a polymer pinned on a disordered surface, or an oil-water interface in porous rock [37].

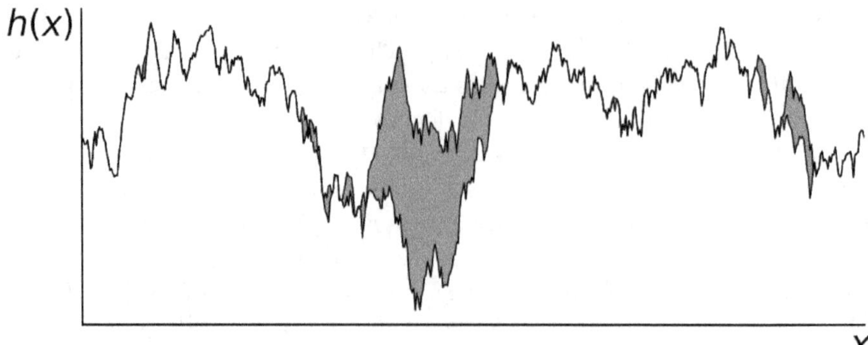

Fig. 15.3. **Depinning** of a one-dimensional manifold in a two dimensional environment. An increasing external field causes the manifold to locally destabilize, moving from one configuration to another in an avalanche (large gray region, of area S). If there are long-range forces in the problem, this event may cause other distant segments to destabilize as well (small gray regions to right).

where r and u are the horizontal and vertical coordinates of the interface. Neglecting inertial effects, the equation of motion of our front might be modeled as a disordered partial differential equation of this class [56, 57]:

$$\partial_t u(r,t) = f_{\text{el}}\left[u\right] + f_{\text{dis}}\left[u(r,t),x\right] + f. \tag{15.13}$$

Here f_{el} is the elastic force trying to restore the straight interface, f_{dis} is the force due to the random potential, and f is the external drive. The solution of this class of equations shows a continuous phase transition with the velocity playing the role of the order parameter and the force acting as the control parameter [58–62]. In particular, below a critical *depinning* force f_c the steady velocity is zero.

Avalanches: If we increase that external field for $f < f_c$, we can destabilize a weakly-pinned region, triggering an avalanche (see Fig. 15.3). Just as in the epidemic model, below f_c these avalanches have a size distribution $P(S,f) \sim S^{-\tau}\mathcal{P}(S(f_c-f)^{1/\sigma})$, becoming scale free when the force approaches $f = f_c$. Individual avalanches smaller than the cutoff $S_{\max} = (f_c - f)^{1/\sigma}$ will spread over a spatial extent $\sim S^{1/d_f}$, where $d_f = 1/(\sigma\nu)$. They will have a duration in time $\sim S^{z/d_f}$ that goes as their spatial extent to the power z. Avalanche distributions have been extensively studied in the literature [63–69].

Flow properties are singular: For $f > f_c$, the interface will begin moving with a mean velocity $v \sim (f-f_c)^{\beta}$ in a jerky fashion, with correlated jumps that mimic the avalanches found just below f_c. Similarly to equilibrium continuous phase transitions, the collective nature of this intermittent dynamics arises from the existence of a correlation length $\xi \sim |f - f_c|^{-\nu}$ that diverges when the force approaches f_c.

Fractal structure: At the depinning threshold, the interface is fractal, with a roughness that is characterized by a typical vertical height change $u(r,t) - u(r',t) \sim (r-r')^{\zeta}$ corresponding to a height-height correlation function $C(r) = \langle(u(r')-u(r'+r))^2\rangle \sim r^{2\zeta}$.

The elastic force f_{el} on a domain wall can involve long-range interactions [70]. This is the case for the triple line of a raindrop on glass [28, 71] (and also of crack fronts propagating in brittle materials [72, 73]). The elastic force on the droplet interface must include the surface tension energy of the wiggly drop shape imposed by the jagged air-water interface $u(r)$, hence $f_{el} \sim \int d^D r'(u(r') - u(r))/(r - r')^{D+\alpha}$, with $\alpha = 1$ and $D = 1$ [71, 72, 74–76]. A second important example is provided by the sliding of frictional interfaces or of localized shear bands in amorphous materials [77–80]. Here, if inertia, velocity weakening or visco-elastic effects can be neglected, the dynamics is depinning-like with $D = 2$ and $\alpha = 1$.

The presence of long-range elasticity does not change the qualitative picture of depinning given above, but for $\alpha < 2$ the values of the exponents β, ζ, τ and σ are modified; for $\alpha \geq 2$ short-range exponents remain correct. Also, long-range interactions can trigger distant weak spots to yield, leading to avalanches with disconnected pieces (see Fig. 15.3), called clusters. Their sizes, distances and extensions display power-law behaviors as for the full avalanche, but with new exponents.

Note that many physical systems self-organize at their depinning transitions – naturally exhibiting an emergent scale invariant avalanche behavior and fractal front geometries. For example, in magnets, the weak but long-range magnetic dipole fields lead to *demagnetizing* forces [20, Sec. 8.2] that decrease the effective driving force as the front advances. Theoretical depinning models add an extra parabolic term to Eq. (15.13) in order to model this self-organization.

In Sec. 15.2.4 we will explain the relationship between avalanches below f_c, stationary flow above f_c, and the fractal structure of the interface at f_c, and how these properties are affected by long-range interactions.

15.2.2.3. *Plasticity in amorphous materials*

Other disordered systems display out-of-equilibrium phase transitions induced by an external drive. For example, a yielding transition is observed in foams, emulsions and metallic glasses when a stress, Σ, is applied. For a small stress these materials deform as solids, but for stresses Σ above a yield stress Σ_c they flow as liquids. In the liquid phase, the strain rate vanishes non-linearly [81, 82], $\dot{\epsilon} \sim (\Sigma - \Sigma_c)^\beta$. This behavior is similar to depinning (albeit with a larger flow exponent β), but here the system exhibits generic scale invariance. Scale-invariant avalanches start well below Σ_c.

In the solid phase one observes plastic instabilities, called shear transformations [83], involving irreversible rearrangements of few bubbles or droplets. As illustrated in Fig. 15.6(c), this local rearrangement induces a large, complex nearby rearrangement and a far-field power-law decay. This stress redistribution then can trigger other shear transformation zones that are kicked above their stability threshold.

Thus, as in depinning, this first instability can be the epicenter of an avalanche [84, 85]. The connection with the depinning transition can be made explicit considering the growth of local strain $\epsilon(r, t)$ at a given stress Σ. Its evolution can be written [86] in the form of Eq. (15.13) for elastic interfaces driven with a force f. A crucial difference between yielding and depinning concerns the far-field kernel, which is of Eshelby type and not only features long range decay, but also[c] is non-monotonic [4, 87]. For example

---

[c]Monotonic, or 'Abelian' interactions, also lead to *no-passing* theorems with fascinating implications [51, 60].

in 2D the elastic kernel can be written as

$$f_{el}[\epsilon(r,t)] \sim \int dr \frac{\cos 4\phi}{r^2} \delta\epsilon \ . \tag{15.14}$$

Here, r is the distance from the shear transformation, ϕ the angle associated to the position $\vec{r}$, and f_{el} is the component of the stress tensor projected on the direction of the applied shear.[d] The presence of the positive and negative interactions from the cosine term is what makes f_{el} non-monotonic [60] — the transition increases the stress for some neighbors, and decreases the stress for others. Indeed, after a plastic instability, the stress redistribution is on average zero: some regions see their stress increase, while in others the stress diminishes. This effect does not occur for the pandemic model or for the depinning transition, where the motion of a region of the interface can only destabilize other regions. For a yielding amorphous material, the stress that a given spot feels in time rises and falls, so that survival without going unstable becomes increasingly unlikely for the particularly weak spots. In Sec. 15.2.3 we will see that the resulting *pseudogap* in the probability of regions ready to yield gives scale-invariant avalanches in the entire yielding solid phase — the system shows generic scale invariance.

15.2.2.4. *Elasto-plastic models of depinning and yielding*

Models of depinning and plastic yielding (Secs. 15.2.2.2 and 15.2.2.3) often involve coupled networks of sites that each slip or jump to new configurations when pushed by one another or an overall stress field. Coupled block-spring models were introduced in the study of earthquakes by Carlson and Langer [89] without explicit disorder. We can model a depinning system with a D-dimensional lattice of blocks connected by springs, moving in a vertical direction u perpendicular to the lattice. We add a force threshold $\sigma_i^y = -f_{\rm dis}(u_i, r_i)$ to each block that depends randomly on its vertical position, and have each block move by one unit, $u_i \to u_i + 1$, when it goes unstable. This produces a kick that can destabilize one or more of its neighbors, triggering an avalanche. Adding longer range springs with strength $G_{ij} \sim r_i - r_j)^{-(1+\alpha)}$ gives us a long-range depinning model, and adding springs $G_{ij} = \cos(4\phi)/(r_i - r_j)^2$ gives us a model of yielding in amorphous materials [4, 87, 90, 91]. We shall return to this class of models again when we discuss mean-field theories of depinning in Secs. 15.2.4.1 and 15.2.5.1.

15.2.2.5. *Jamming transition*

How can a crowded, dense collection of particles manage to move and avoid each other as they are sheared? This question is relevant for the glass transition (when a liquid becomes an amorphous solid), the study of the flow of pedestrians [92] or (unexpectedly) the optimization of neural networks [93]. Initially it was motivated by granular materials, which can be solid or liquid depending on density and shear stress. They present a yield stress Σ_c separating these two phases, which for cohesionless materials must be proportional to the pressure p (the only stress scale in the problem) [94]. From the ratio $\mu_c = \Sigma_c/p$, one obtains the angle of repose $\Theta_c = \arctan \mu_c$, at which a layer

---

[d]A more realistic description of plastic interactions is tensorial [88], yet the scalar approximation described in the main text does not affect critical properties near the transition.

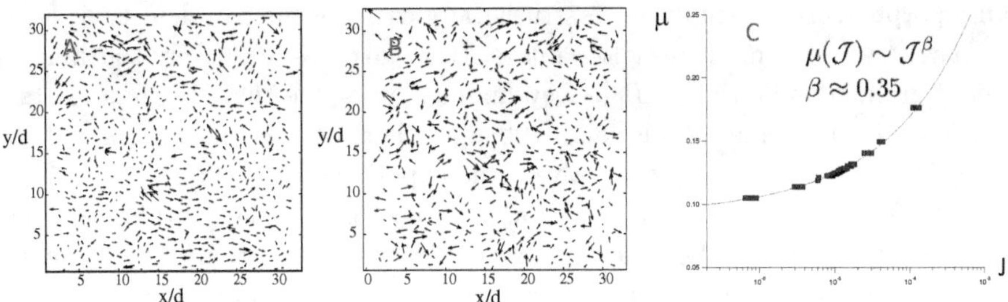

Fig. 15.4. **Jamming:** Critical properties of experimental granular flows. Fluctuating velocity of particles at the free surface of a granular flow in an inclined plane geometry of angle (A) 21° degree close to $\Theta_c = 20°$, showing long-range spatial correlations and (B) far away from it $\Theta = 26°$, where the flow is faster, less dense, and where these correlations are absent. From [100]. (C) Macroscopic friction coefficient μ versus dimensionless shear rate $\mathcal{J}$ for different layer thicknesses h, showing an exponent $\beta \approx 0.35$. This experiment is performed is a drum geometry with short-range electrostatic repulsion between suspensed particles, to ensure that they are effectively frictionless. We shall study the singular flow rates produced by the avalanches for depinning, yielding, and jamming in Secs. 15.2.4, 15.2.5.2, and 15.2.6.2. From [105].

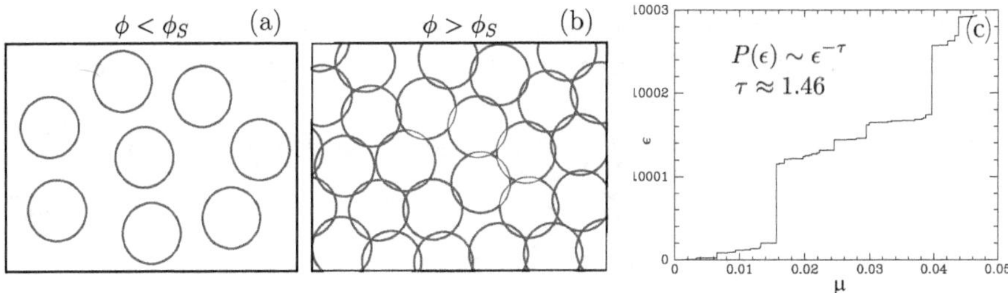

Fig. 15.5. (a) Unjammed assembly of particles at low packing fraction $\phi < \phi_c$ (b) Jammed packing with $\phi > \phi_c$. (c) At ϕ_c, as the stress anisotropy μ is increased, the strain ϵ displays a devil's staircase: there are sequences during which no rearrangements occur (horizontal line) followed by sudden jumps in strain or 'avalanches' that are power-law distributed. We will associate the presence of such a crackling phase with its marginal stability. From Ref. [111].

of sand stops flowing. The stress ratio μ_c and the resulting angle of repose[e] Θ_c determines a critical point. For angles just above Θ_c, flow can occur despite the material being almost as dense as in the solid phase. Yet to avoid each other, the motion of the particles must be very cooperative [100–102] with long-range correlations or 'eddies', as illustrated in Fig. 15.4(A). Also, the flow curve is singular at μ_c [94, 103–105] as illustrated in Fig. 15.4(B). For example in dense suspensions $\mu(\mathcal{J}) - \mu_c \sim \mathcal{J}^{\beta}$, where $\mathcal{J} \equiv \eta_0 \dot{\epsilon}/p$ is a dimensionless ratio of the shear rate $\dot{\epsilon}$, the viscosity η_0 of the suspending fluid, and the particle pressure p (see Sec. 15.2.5.2).

Progress was made by considering an ideal system: frictionless particles with repulsive, finite-range interactions (e.g., slippery rubber balls) [106, 107]. Imagine their positions to be initially random, then moved to locally minimize the energy. As illustrated in Fig. 15.5, for a large enough initial packing fraction of particles, this procedure

---

[e]As mentioned above, sandpiles of frictional particles present two characteristic angles: Θ_c where flow stops, and $\Theta_{\text{start}} > \Theta_c$ where flow starts [20, 21, 95–99].

leads to an amorphous solid, similar to a structural glass. For a small density, it leads to a gas of particles. At some threshold value ϕ_c, the particles are barely touching (a good model of granular materials) [108]. Key findings at ϕ_c are that (i) there exists a $\mu_c \approx 0.05$ below which the material is solid [109, 110]. For $\mu > \mu_c$, flow occurs and the flow curve is singular, capturing quantitatively the experimental results of Fig. 15.4C. (ii) Avalanches are observed for $\mu < \mu_c$, as shown in Fig. 15.5(c) [111]. (iii) Some structural properties display singular behavior. In particular, the distribution $P(f)$ of contact forces f, or the distribution $g(h)$ of interstices between particles, are characterized by non-trivial exponents at small arguments [112]:

$$P(f) \sim f^\theta \quad \text{with } \theta \approx 0.44, \tag{15.15}$$

$$g(h) \sim h^{-\gamma} \quad \text{with } \gamma \approx 0.38. \tag{15.16}$$

15.2.3. *Instability thresholds and stability*

Avalanches are triggered at weak spots, where an abrupt nonlinear response is triggered by an increasing field. More generally, amorphous and disordered materials allow for low-energy local rearrangements that can have a distribution $P(z)$ of excitations whose threshold force is z. It has long been known that systems like Coulomb glasses [113] and spin glasses [114] will excite those rearrangements with the lowest energies to optimize the interaction energies in finding the ground state. This removes many of the lowest energy excitations, leaving a density $P(z)$ of excitations that vanishes as a power law,

$$P(z) \sim z^{\theta_y}, \tag{15.17}$$

as the local excitation energy z goes to zero. Such a vanishing density is called a *pseudo-gap* (to distinguish it from a hard gap with no excitations in a finite energy range). Since then, it was realized that this situation is common, and affects both avalanches and stationary flows when they occur for large forcing.

15.2.3.1. *Nature of excitations in the systems considered*

Excitations correspond to nearly unstable rearrangements of the material. In magnetic systems, they are spins that are weakly polarized [114]. In elastic manifolds, they correspond to small portions of the interface. Here we focus on systems with long-range interactions, in which the notion of excitations turns out to be more crucial.

Amorphous solids: As discussed above, instabilities in that case are shear transformations, illustrated in Fig. 15.6(b). Here z is the increment of shear stress that will trigger an instability of a shear transformation zone, and $P(z)$ is the density of zones with trigger stress z. As briefly mentioned in Sec. 15.2.2.3, the non-monotonicity in the long-range interactions between transformations leads to a local stress history that varies both up and down as the material is plastically deformed, depleting the density of the lowest threshold transformation zones. As in equilibrium systems, sheared amorphous solids are found [115, 116] to displays a pseudo-gap, with $P(z) \sim z^{\theta_y}$. Interestingly, θ_y varies continuously under loading [117]. The condition $\theta_y > 0$ can be obtained form a stability argument [116]. Assume that $\theta_y = 0$ such that $P(x = 0) = P_0 > 0$. Consider a shear transformation occurring at the origin, leading to a kick of stress of order $\Delta\Sigma(r) \sim r^{-d}$

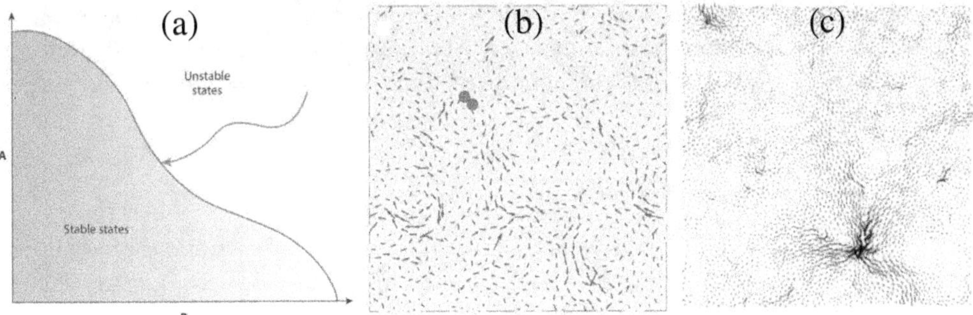

Fig. 15.6.   (a) Schematic stability diagram in configuration space. A and B are observables characterizing the configurations visited. The full black line corresponds to marginal stability: It separates
regions in which excitations are stable and unstable, respectively. The arrow illustrates a dynamical
trajectory of a system that is cooling from an initial high temperature phase by stepwise relaxation
of individual elementary excitations. When the system reaches the marginality line, the excitations
become stable. If these excitations are the main drive of the dynamics, the system slows down very
rapidly as it enters into the stable region and freezes very close to the marginal stability line. There,
low-energy excitations are abundant, and rich dynamics, such as crackling noise, can occur. From
Ref. [118]. (b) Elementary excitation corresponding to the opening of a single contact in a packing of
hard discs. From Ref. [112]. (c) A shear transformation in an amorphous solid made of soft compressed
particles. From Ref. [119].

at a distance r. The probability that a region of unit area displays an instability in
response to this kick is $\sim \Delta\Sigma(r)P_0$. In a system of size L, the total number of new
instabilities R_0 is then obtained by integration: $R_0 \sim P_0 \int_{r<L} \Delta\Sigma(r)r^{d-1}dr \sim \ln(L)$.
This result implies that an individual plastic events always completely destroy the sys-
tem (since $R_0 \gg 1$), with probability one. We know from experience that amorphous
solids are stable to such local perturbations, thus implying $\theta_y > 0$.

Packings of frictionless hard spheres: These systems are *isostatic*: they just
have enough contacts to ensure the stability of the material [120]. Under loading un-
deformable particles, rearrangements can only occur when a contact force goes to zero,
leading to the opening of a contact and to a global motion of all particles called a 'floppy
mode'. An example of such an excitation is shown in Fig. 15.6(b). This motion stops
when a new contact is formed. This process gives a kick of stress in the entire system,
which can in turn trigger the opening of new contacts. The magnitude of the kick can be
shown to be proportional to the displacement along the floppy mode before a new contact is formed, which occurs when a small gap between nearly touching particles closes.
Thus, this distance is controlled by the distribution $g(h) \sim h^\gamma$ of gaps. Furthermore,
the probability that a kick of given magnitude opens a new contact is controlled by the
distribution of small forces $P(f) \sim f^\theta$. Requiring stability, i.e. that the number of new
excitations triggered by a single one does not diverge in the thermodynamic limit (i.e.
$R_0 \leq 1$), can be shown to imply [121]:

$$\gamma \geq 1/(2+\theta). \tag{15.18}$$

As described below, infinite range interactions (independent of distance) imply [118] a
saturation of Eq. (15.18), $\gamma = 1/(2+\theta)$, in agreement with numerical estimates of γ and
θ. A great success of replica theory applied to the jamming transition is the computation

of $\theta \approx 0.42$ and $\gamma \equiv 1/(2 + \theta) \approx 0.41$ in infinite dimensions [122]. These exponents agree well with simulations in finite dimensions [112, 123], as perhaps expected from numerical evidence [124, 125] that the upper critical dimension is $D_{\text{uc}} = 2$ for frictionless jamming.

15.2.3.2. *Pseudo-gaps imply crackling noise*

Stability arguments do not exclude the possibility that the density of excitations presents a hard gap (and strictly no rearrangements for a finite range of loading). Even if gapped configurations exist, they are not found in practice. Figure 15.6(a) gives a pictorial illustration as to why it is so: for some systems and dynamics the system essentially stops as soon as it becomes stable, leading to a gapless marginal state. In mean-field spin glasses for example, it can be shown that finding gapped configurations is a NP complete problem [126].

The existence of a pseudo-gap implies that the rearrangements must be collective — avalanche like, with an initial rearrangement triggering at least some large events, leading usually to what we call crackling noise, without tuning or self-organizing to a critical point. Following [118], consider for example an amorphous solid of volume N, and assume that Eq. (15.17) applies. During an adiabatic loading, there will be periods without plasticity: their magnitude $\delta\Sigma$ is given by z_{min}, the stability of the least stable excitation. Standard extreme value statistics arguments [115, 127] lead to the typical value $z_{min} \sim N^{-1/(1+\theta_y)} \gg \frac{1}{N}$. It implies that the rate of plastic events is sub-extensive: a system twice as large does not display twice as many plastic events. Assume that no crackling occurs: then for local excitations, a plastic event involves $\mathcal{O}(1)$ excitations and thus dissipates an energy $\mathcal{O}(1)$, which is independent of N. For a global change of stress $\Delta\Sigma$, the energy dissipated is thus $\sim \Delta\Sigma/\delta\Sigma \sim N^{1/(1+\theta_y)} \ll N$, i.e. it is sub-extensive. Thus, in the absence of crackling, dissipation per unit volume must vanish in the thermodynamic limit. Plastic materials displaying a finite density of dissipation (which we expect to be the generic situation for disordered materials) must then display crackling. In particular, for dissipation to be extensive, one must have $\langle S \rangle \sim N^{\theta_y/(1+\theta_y)}$.

We return to infinite range interactions (such as frictionless hard spheres in any dimensions, or the SK model of spin glasses). In that case, it can be shown that if inequalities like Eq. (15.18) are not saturated [118], then an excitation has a vanishing probability to trigger a second one in the thermodynamic limit: crackling cannot occur. But we have seen before that crackling noise must occur (to allow for an extensive dissipation), thus our hypothesis is incorrect: we conclude that the bound in Eq. (15.18) must be saturated when infinite-range interactions are present. Note that saturation does not occur for power-law interactions, e.g. in amorphous solids.

Ultimately, this approach leads to a classification of glassy systems based on the range of the interaction of their excitations. If sufficiently long-range and non-monotonic, then a pseudo-gap must be present, and crackling occurs. Instead for short-range interactions, crackling occurs only at a critical point and not in the entire glassy phase. As we shall see below, the pseudo-gap exponent also characterizes the flowing phase, when it exists.

15.2.4. *Theoretical results: Depinning*

15.2.4.1. *Mean-field theory of depinning*

Depinning (see Eq. (15.13)) is characterized by the competition between a decaying elastic force, $f_{\rm el} \sim \int d^D r (u(r') - u(r))/|r - r'|^{D+\alpha}$ that flattens the interface and a disorder force of the $D + 1$ dimensional medium that tries to roughen it. Dimensional analysis can help to determine the result of this competition if we assume that the interface is self-affine, namely that after a dilatation $x \to bx$, its transverse fluctuations grow as $b^\zeta u(x)$. After the dilatation, the elastic force is rescaled as $b^{\zeta - \alpha}$ for $\alpha < 2$ (for shorter-ranged forces it turns out to scale as $b^{\zeta - 2}$) and the short-range disorder force turns out to be rescaled as $b^{D/2 - \zeta/2}$. Using a Flory type of argument one has to balance the two forces in order to estimate the roughness exponent [128, 129]. Thus, the interface results flat ($\zeta = 0$) at the upper critical dimension $D_{\rm uc} = 2\alpha$ for $\alpha < 2$, matching nicely with the value $D_{\rm uc} = 4$ above $\alpha > 2$.

Above $D_{\rm uc}$ disorder is not able to roughen the interface, which turns out to slide with a velocity linear in the force above threshold ($\beta = 1$), and display mean field avalanches ($\tau = 3/2$, $\sigma = 1/2$, and $z = \alpha$), as discussed below. Below $D_{\rm uc} = 2\alpha$, the interfaces are rough ($\zeta > 0$), the velocity grows with a power β less than one, with avalanche exponents τ, σ, and z smaller than those in mean-field.

This Flory argument correctly predicts $D_{\rm uc}$, a result that can be also obtained treating the disorder as a perturbation [58, 130–132]. Unfortunately both arguments fail in predicting the exact value of the exponents below $D_{\rm uc}$. Indeed, for purely linear models, the Flory balance works perfectly at each length scale. However, any nonlinear terms will couple the different length scales, and thus demand a renormalization group approach.[f]

A mean-field theory for depinning can be formed using the block-spring model of Sec. 15.2.2.4, but having every pair of sites x_i and x_j connected by a spring $G_{ij} \equiv G/N$, with N the number of blocks. After each block slips, all blocks receive a kick (force increment) of G/N. Hence, the dynamics are precisely the same as that in the Bienaymé–Galton–Watson process we saw in the pandemic model. The value of the force f controls the parameter R_0, which becomes critical ($R_0 = 1$) at $f = f_c$. Because all of the kicks are in the same direction, the interaction is monotonic, and there is no pseudo-gap. Above f_c a stationary flow is present with a permanent fraction of unstable blocks $\sim |f - f_c|^\beta$, with $\beta = 1$.

15.2.4.2. *Finite dimension and Functional RG*

Table 1 gives a summary of exponents for the depinning of D-dimensional manifolds in $D + 1$ dimensions. The last three rows in the table give a set of scaling relations that allow one to express all the exponents in terms of two, ζ and z, valid below $D_{\rm uc}$. For example, the velocity above threshold can be expressed as the ratio between avalanche displacement and avalanche duration, namely $v \sim \xi^\zeta / \xi^z \sim |f - f_c|^{-\nu(\zeta - z)}$, giving the

---

[f]In systems with 'KPZ'-type nonlinearities Flory's arguments do not work in any dimension. In this case it remains controversial if it exists an upper critical dimension above which interfaces are flat.

Table 1. **Critical exponents and scaling relations** for depinning systems of D dimensional interfaces in $D + 1$ dimensions, assuming no nonlinearities of the qKPZ type and elastic forces $f_{\mathrm{el}} \sim \int d^D r(u(r') - u(r))/|r - r'|^{D+\alpha}$. The last column shows one-loop functional renormalization group calculations [133–136] with $D_{\mathrm{uc}} = \min(2\alpha, 4)$ and $\epsilon = D_{\mathrm{uc}} - D$. Above D_{uc} behavior is mean-field. For $D < D_{\mathrm{uc}}$, exponents are measured numerically with a precision at the second digit. Note that depinning models do not have a pseudo-gap, so $\theta_y = 0$.

Depinning exponent	Observable	$D = 1$ $\alpha = 2$	$D = 1$ $\alpha = 1$	$D = 2$ $\alpha = 2$	FRG $D = D_{\mathrm{uc}} - \epsilon$
z	$t(L) \sim L^z$	1.43	0.77	1.56	$D_{\mathrm{uc}}/2 - 2\epsilon/9$
ζ	$u(x) \sim x^\zeta$	1.25	0.39	0.75	$\epsilon/3$
τ	$P(S) \sim S^{-\tau}$	$\tau = 2 - \alpha/(D + \zeta)$			$3/2 - \epsilon/(3D_{\mathrm{uc}})$
ν	$\xi \sim |f - f_c|^{-\nu}$	$\nu = 1/(\alpha - \zeta)$			$2/D_{\mathrm{uc}} + 4\epsilon/(3D_{\mathrm{uc}}^2)$
β	$v \sim |f - f_c|^\beta$	$\beta = \nu(z - \zeta)$			$1 - \epsilon/(9D_{\mathrm{uc}})$

equation for β. The last column in Table 1 gives one-loop functional RG (FRG) results for the exponents [133–136] close to the upper critical dimension. Two-loop [137–139] and three-loop calculations for the static problem are now available [140, 141].

The RG approach captures the large-scale scale invariant properties of a population of configurations. The traditional RG studies the flow in a space of parameters (field H, temperature T, …) which yield an effective coarse-grained free energy; the free energy encodes the Gibbs weight of different configurations. Here, the weight of the dynamical trajectories is encoded into the Martin–Siggia–Rose action, which averages trajectories over disorder. The resulting RG involves a full function: the force-force disorder correlator, $\Delta(u - u')$, where u, u' are two different positions of the center of mass of the interface. The fixed point Δ^* can be computed by FRG as a perturbation in $\epsilon = D_{\mathrm{uc}} - D$ and has a peculiar cusp at the origin $u = u'$ which has been experimentally measured [142]. Indeed, when an avalanche occurs, much of the interface is left pinned at the same position (same disorder), but the disorder force changes abruptly in the regions which have slipped forward (Fig. 15.3), leading to the cusp.

For physical systems in $D = 1$ and $D = 2$, the best estimation of depinning exponents come from numerical calculations [130, 143–148], summarized in the first two rows of Table 1. The two-loop expansion [137–139, 149], however, settled a *qualitative* question — showing that the interface at thermal equilibrium has a different roughness and universality class from that of the interface at depinning. Even more surprisingly, FRG [131] is also able to describe the thermally activated slow dynamics of magnetic domain walls driven by a magnetic field much smaller than the critical force. Most of the predictions for this creep regime have been tested both experimentally [150, 151] and numerically [152]. See also the FRG results for the avalanche shape in Sec. 15.2.4.3.

Critical exponents are neither the only quantity of interest nor the simplest to observe in experiments [153, 154]. The value of the critical force f_c and its universal fluctuations [155–157] are important for applications. In the following we will see in some details some other important example of such observables.

15.2.4.3. *The average avalanche time series*

A longstanding challenge for the scaling theory of dynamical disordered systems was the rather symmetrical predictions for the average temporal shape [159, 160], which

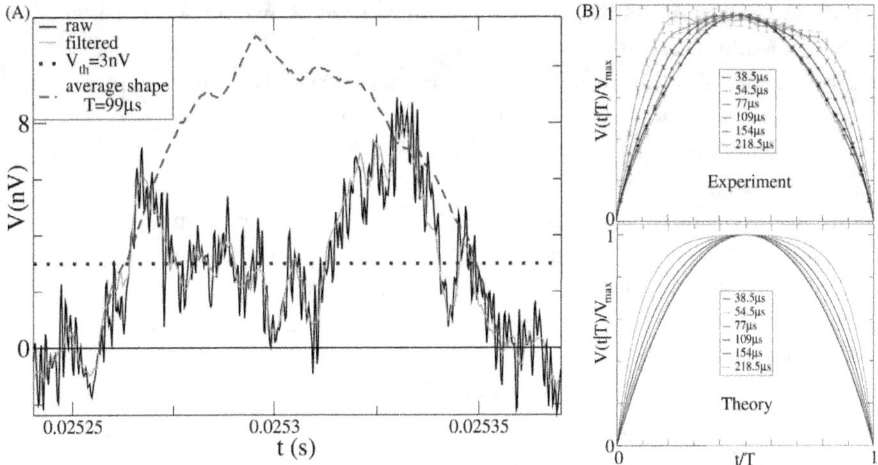

Fig. 15.7. **Avalanche, and average temporal shape,** from Ref. [158]. (A) Experimental signal during an avalanche (jagged), with noise filtered out (wavy), rather than using thresholding (dotted). The dashed line shows the signal $V(t|T)$ averaged over all avalanches of similar duration. (B) Average temporal shape in experiment and predicted by mean-field theory (Eq. (15.19)) for various avalanche durations.

disagreed with a much larger asymmetry in experiments [18]. This eventually was explained as an effect of eddy currents [161]. Figure 15.7(A) shows the time-dependent mean front velocity during a mean-field magnetic avalanche in a thin magnetic film [158], avoiding the effects of eddy currents. Note the characteristic irregular, fractal shape — almost stopping several times. (If it had stopped, it would form a smaller avalanche — big avalanches are just smaller avalanches that did not stop a few times.) Note also the dashed curve — an average $V(t|T)$ over all the experimental avalanches whose durations T were similar to this one. The universal scaling prediction for this average shape is [18, 159]

$$V(t|T,r) = T^{d_f/z-1}\mathcal{V}(t/T, Tr^{z\nu}) = T\mathcal{V}(t/T, Tr).$$ (15.19)

Figure 15.7(B) shows a scaling collapse of average avalanche shapes for different durations (top) and the universal scaling prediction from mean-field theory [158, 162] (bottom). The average shape is an inverted parabola for avalanches small compared to the cutoff $T_{\max} \sim r^{-z\nu} = 1/r$, and has an explicit analytical form for longer durations in mean-field theory (Fig. 15.7(B)).

The same functional RG methods we discussed in Sec. 15.2.4.2, remarkably, have been applied [163] to predict the average temporal shape both at fixed duration and fixed avalanche size for $D \leq D_{uc}$. They predict a slight skewing of the avalanches that nicely fits the measured shapes [160, 164], and also incorporate eddy currents into the scaling predictions [164, 165].

15.2.4.4. *Clusters in avalanches with long-range interactions*

As we saw in Fig. 15.3, avalanches in systems with long-range interactions can be disconnected into *clusters*. It is infeasible in most experiments to visualize avalanches one-by one [166], and naturally impossible to figure out after several avalanches which clusters came from which avalanches — we cannot directly find τ, σ, etc.

At moderate rates of strain, one can measure the statistics of clusters localized in space, which fortunately also display universal scaling [167]. For example their size S_c has a power law probability distribution $P(S_c) \sim S_c^{-\tau_c}$. The other avalanche exponents can be defined for clusters as well. A solid numerical conjecture predicts the value of cluster exponents in terms of the avalanche exponents [168]. For example the relation $\tau_c = 2\tau - 1$ should hold for $\alpha < 2$. One must note, though, that our analytical study of a simple epidemic model with long-range dispersal does not show this behavior [169].

The key to this conjecture is the identification of a Bienaymé–Galton–Watson process describing the statistics of the cluster number [170]. This process has been clearly observed numerically for all $\alpha < 2$, but no proof of its existence yet exists. For $\alpha > 2$ the number of clusters is strongly suppressed; $\tau_c = \tau$ for forces of finite range. It is not yet clear how τ_c behaves for large, but finite values of α. A future challenge is to understand the origin of the Bienaymé–Galton–Watson process describing the cluster statistics.

15.2.5. *Theoretical results: Yielding transition*

15.2.5.1. *Mean field models of yielding*

The mean-field version of the elasto-plastic block-spring models for the yielding transition (Sec. 15.2.2.4) have non-monotonic interaction matrices G_{ij} with both positive and negative values that are randomly chosen with the same distribution and independent of i and j (infinite range). Let us call $z_i = \sigma_i^y - \sigma_i$, where σ_i and σ_i^y are respectively the shear stress and the yield stress of that block. When $z_i < 0$ the block yields, reducing all the other z_j by G_{ij}

In the *Hebraud–Lequeux* model [171], G_{ij} is assumed to follow a Gaussian distribution of variance $\sim N^{-1/2}$, where N is the number of blocks. As a result, each variable z_i is a sum of Gaussian random kicks, where the walk ends when the sum hits zero — a random walk with an absorbing condition at $z = 0$. After yielding, the site is reinserted at some finite positive z_i value. Solving this random walk problem, we find that the distribution $P(z)$ evolves until it vanishes linearly with $\theta_y = 1$. The flow curve is found to be singular at Σ_c, with $\beta = 2$. Interestingly [172], the distribution of avalanche sizes depends on details of how the system is loaded. For realistic loading, $\tau \approx 1$.

In a more realistic mean-field model, the noise is not assumed to be Gaussian. It is still i.i.d. and thus has no spatial correlations, but the distribution of G_{ij} is chosen to satisfy that of the true propagator. For a propagator that vanishes with distance as a power-law, $P(G)$ is then power-law distributed [173]. In that case, z_i follows a *Levy flight* with a Levy coefficient $\mu = 1$. The pseudo-gap is still governed by an absorbing condition: it is found that after a quench at zero stress, $\theta_y = 1/2$ [174]. However, here θ_y continues to evolve as the system is strained; it starts by rapidly decreasing, and then increases. This has been observed in finite dimensional elasto-plastic models [117] and in molecular dynamics of amorphous solids [175, 176]. Flow curves are again singular, with $\beta = 1$ [177]. In this model, aging responses following a quench (a minimization of the energy from some random configuration at $t = 0$) can be computed [178], and are found to be similar to experimental ones.

15.2.5.2. *Scaling theory for yielding*

In this section we will provide a link between the avalanche physics at the mesoscale and the flow curve at the macroscale, for systems with non-monotonic long-range interactions (such as amorphous materials yielding under stress, Sec. 15.2.3).

Stationarity: Consider applying a quasi-static strain in a system of linear size L at the yielding transition. The stress Σ ramps up under increasing strain, and drops abruptly during avalanches. On average, these must cancel out [84, 115, 179]. An avalanche of size S will lead to a stress drop in the system that is proportional to $\delta\Sigma \sim \langle S \rangle / L^d$. The mean avalanche size is $\langle S \rangle \sim \int^{S_{\max}} S \times S^{-\tau} dS \propto S_{\max}^{2-\tau}$, where $S_{\max} \sim L^{d_f}$ is the largest avalanche that can fit into the system. The stress rise between avalanches is determined by the pseudogap in the distribution of threshold stresses. As discussed in Sec. 15.2.3, the weakest site will yield after the stress increases by $\sim L^{-d/(1+\theta_y)}$. Equating the average drop and the average increment, one obtains [86]:

$$\tau = 2 - \frac{\theta_y}{\theta_y + 1}\frac{d}{d_f}. \tag{15.20}$$

Dynamics in the flowing regime: As one approaches the critical stress Σ_c from above in the flowing regime, there is a diverging length scale $\xi \sim (\Sigma - \Sigma_c)^\nu$. Below this length scale, both in depinning transitions [56] and in the yielding transition [86] one can roughly describe the motion as a continuously evolving collection of avalanches of spatial length ξ, covering space. The net strain rate $\dot\epsilon$ is the number of avalanches $\sim 1/\xi^d$ times the strain release $S \sim \xi^{d_f}$ per avalanche divided by the duration $T \sim \xi^z$ of these avalanches, hence $\dot\epsilon = S/(T\xi^d) \sim (\Sigma - \Sigma_c)^{\nu(d-d_f+z)}$. Hence the strain rate $\dot\epsilon \sim (\Sigma - \Sigma_c)^\beta$ grows with an exponent

$$\beta = \nu(d - d_f + z). \tag{15.21}$$

Stress fluctuations: Continuing to view the flow as a superposition of avalanches of size $S_{\max}$ spanning boxes of size $V = \xi^d$, each will lower the stress in its box by an amount $\delta\Sigma \sim S_{\max}/\xi^d \sim (\Sigma - \Sigma_c)^{\nu(d-d_f)}$. Making the common assumption that all quantities with the same units share the same scale near a critical point, we expect that the fluctuations of stress $\delta\Sigma$ on the scale ξ must be of order of the distance to threshold $\Sigma - \Sigma_c$, leading to [86, 179]:

$$\nu = 1/(d - d_f). \tag{15.22}$$

Putting Eqs. (15.22) and (15.21) together, one obtains $\beta = 1 + z/(d - d_f) \geq 1$. Note that the scaling relations in Eqs. (15.20)–(15.22) should work in elasto-plastic models, particle-based models, and real systems, as supported by observations [86, 90]. One must note that elasto-plastic models assume that elastic interactions propagate instantly, and sometimes give an unphysical value of $z < 1$ (leading to avalanche propagation faster than the speed of sound). In this case, we presume that $z = 1$ and the value of β in Eq. (15.21) should thus be larger in physical systems than in elasto-plastic models [177].

These scaling arguments can be extended to non-stationary situations [180] such as the slow creep flows [181] that follows a sudden increase of stress, to non-local phenomena [182] where $\xi \sim |\Sigma - \Sigma_c|^{-\nu}$ is found to characterize the length scale on which an obstacle or interface perturbs flow [183], and to finite temperatures [184, 185] that cause a "thermal rounding" of the flow curves, which becomes smooth near Σ_c.

15.2.6. *Theoretical results: Jamming*

15.2.6.1. *Infinite-dimensional calculations of avalanches*

Avalanches are dynamical phenomena. Yet 'equilibrium avalanches' can be defined, by tilting the energy landscape continuously by adding a force or field, and tracking the position of the global minimum of the system [186]. It then displays jumps, whose statistics can be computed in infinite dimension using replica methods. Right at the jamming transition, this method was successfully used to compute $\tau = (3+\theta)/(1+\theta) \approx 1.41$ [187] in close agreement with numerical experiments for nonequilibrium avalanches in three dimensions [111].[g] The success of the mean-field approach arguably results from the infinite-range nature of excitations in this system [102].

A system of well-compressed particles (packed more densely than at the jamming threshold) should exhibit a yielding behavior as described in Subsec. 15.2.2.3. Replica theory of jamming predicts $\tau = 1$ for the rigid phase [187]. This mean-field result may not hold in three dimensions however, as the length scale of excitations rapidly decreases away from jamming [190], and spatial correlations are then presumably important.

15.2.6.2. *Suspension and granular flows of frictionless particles*

Much of the jamming literature has focused on frictionless particles, both numerically [191–195] and theoretically [196]. Friction is of course important for most of the applications of jamming — from soil engineering to pharmaceuticals to geophysics. It was recently realized that a class of suspensions displaying "shear thickening" display effectively frictionless particles at low stresses, but they become frictional at large stresses [197–200]. Controlled experimental systems with these properties have been designed [96, 105, 201, 202], allowing one to experimentally test scaling theories of flow for frictionless jamming.

Consider a frictionless packing at the critical stress anisotropy $\mu = \Sigma/p = \mu_c$. The first step of the theory consists of estimating the number of contacts δz that open if the stress anisotropy is increased by $\mu - \mu_c$. One finds, by estimating the change of forces in the contacts induced by such a perturbation, and using that the distribution of small force follows $P(f) \sim f^\theta$, that [196]:

$$\delta z \sim (\mu - \mu_c)^{\frac{2+2\theta}{3+\theta}}. \tag{15.23}$$

---

[g]It is known in the random-field Ising model that the universality class of the equilibrium system is different from that of the non-equilibrium, avalanche model at zero temperature. This has been shown in dimensions smaller than about 5.1 using remarkable non-perturbative functional renormalization-group calculations [188], and numerically in two dimensions [189]. Here, however, we are above the upper critical dimension, where non-equilibrium and equilibrium properties should be similar.

Using this, one can use mechanical considerations to compute how an infinitesimal applied strain $\delta\epsilon$ at the boundary moves particles relatively to each other, by some amount δr called the non-affine displacement. Defining $\mathcal{L} \equiv \delta r/\delta\epsilon$, one finds [196]:

$$\mathcal{L} \sim \delta z^{-\frac{2+\theta}{1+\theta}}. \tag{15.24}$$

The overall viscosity of such a suspension is proportional to the dissipated power, which grows as the square of the particle velocities, and is thus proportional to $\mathcal{L}^2$. The viscous number $\mathcal{J}$ is inversely proportional to this viscosity, thus $\mathcal{J} \equiv \eta_0\dot{\epsilon}/p \sim \mathcal{L}^{-2}$. Together with Eqs. (15.23) and (15.24), one obtains the flow curve:

$$\mu - \mu_c \sim \mathcal{J}^{\frac{3+\theta}{8+4\theta}} \approx \mathcal{J}^{0.35}, \tag{15.25}$$

in agreement with experiments, as shown in Fig. 15.4. Several diverging length scales are predicted at the transition [102]; one of these (the divergence of non-local effects) has been favorably tested [105].

Note that this theory is mean-field in nature, as it neglects spatial correlations that could occur e.g. in the structure. Its quantitative agreement with finite-dimensional numerical studies [196] and experiments [105] again underlines the mean-field character of the jamming transition for frictionless particles, where excitations have infinite-range interactions at threshold. This situation does not hold for frictional particles, where other exponents are found [201, 203] and spatial correlations are relevant [204]. An additional complexity is that in the presence of friction, the flow curve is non-monotonic and the transition is first order close to the critical point [96–98, 204].

15.2.7. *Conclusion and open questions*

We have described the closely intertwined physics of avalanches, the stability of the rigid phase, and stationary flows in a variety of disordered systems. Scaling concepts are the key to building such a unifying description. The renormalization group inspires these scaling descriptions, but they are useful even in cases where a RG procedure has not (yet) been developed. We conclude by listing a few open problems in this field:

RG description of the yielding transition: Although the jamming transition of hard particles appears to be mean-field in character, the yielding transition of amorphous materials appears more subtle. Currently, there is no analytical approach to compute exponents in that case (except for avalanche exponents in conditions where a narrow shear band appears, where a mean-field description may apply [77–80]).

Avalanches and first order transitions: Systems often exhibit avalanche precursors before abrupt changes in behavior. The abrupt change in behavior is due to a non-monotonic flow curve: the same force (stress) can lead to different velocities (strain rate). Quasi-brittle materials exhibit power-law fracture precursors under tension [35] before they fracture into two. This also occurs in complex fluids (such as loosely connected colloidal gels) and earthquakes (where frictional forces acting on the fault can decrease with sliding velocity [205]). Inertia can also lead to such flow curves in depinning problems [22, 206] and in amorphous solids [85, 207]. Velocity (or strain-rate) weakening can make the transition between a rigid and flowing phase first order and hysteretic, possibly destroying avalanches. Recent work on frictional interfaces suggests that avalanches persist in that situation (although their statistics change), and act as nucleation centers for system-spanning events [208]. In that view, the avalanche size diverges at some threshold stress, beyond which the rigid material is unstable to the presence of a large nucleus of flowing material. How generic these results are remain to be seen.

Nucleation of failure: This contribution focuses on stationary flow in disordered materials. Another important question is how these materials break as the loading continuously increases. For amorphous solids, this usually occurs by forming a shear-band where plastic strain localizes. Some have argued that the shear band nucleates in a process similar to that of the random field Ising model [176, 209], or fracture [210]; others suggest it is governed by linear stability considerations [211]. Numerical studies [212] report very slowly decaying finite-size effects that remain to be understood.

Yielding at finite temperature T and the glass transition: We focused on the yielding transition at $T = 0$. At finite temperature, the flow curve loses its singular behavior, in a stress interval around Σ_c that vanishes as a power law of T [184, 185]. Such a 'thermal rounding' behavior can be captured by mean-field calculations or scaling arguments [184]. Yet, a spatial description of thermal avalanches triggered by rare activated events is still missing. It may be very relevant to understand the collective dynamics that occurs near the glass transition [213].

References

[1] J. C. Maxwell, *Philos. Trans. R. Soc. A.* **157**, 49, (1867).

[2] L. D. Landau, L. P. Pitaevskii, E. M. Lifshitz, and A. M. Kosevich, *Theory of Elasticity.* (Butterworth-Heinemann, 1986).

[3] J. Eshelby, *Proc. R. Soc. London A.* **241**, 376, (1957).

[4] G. Picard, A. Ajdari, F. Lequeux, and L. Bocquet, *Eur. Phys. Jour. E.* **15**, 371, (2004).

[5] A. Lemaître, *J. Chem. Phys.* **143**, 164515, (2015).

[6] M. Maier, A. Zippelius, and M. Fuchs, *Phys. Rev. Lett.* **119**, 265701, (2017).

[7] M. Maier, A. Zippelius, and M. Fuchs, *J. Chem. Phys.* **149**, 084502, (2018).

[8] J. H. Irving and J. G. Kirkwood, *J. Chem. Phys.* **18**, 817, (1950).

[9] I. Goldhirsch, *Granular Matter.* **12**, 239–252 (2010).

[10] F. Vogel, A. Zippelius, and M. Fuchs, *EPL.* **125**, 68003, (2019).

[11] L. P. Kadanoff and P. C. Martin, *Ann. Phys. (N.Y.).* **24**, 419 (1963).

[12] W. Götze and A. Latz, *J. Phys. Condens. Matter.* **1**, 4169, (1989).

[13] D. Evans, *Phys. Rev. A.* **23**, 2622, (1981).

[14] J. K. G. Dhont, *An Introduction to the dynamics of collois.* (Elsevier, 1996), 1st edition.

[15] S. Mukhopadhyay, P. M. Goldbart, and A. Zippelius, *EPL.* **67**(1), 49, (2004).

[16] F. Vogel and M. Fuchs, *Eur. Phys. J. E.* **43**, 70, (2020).

[17] L. Klochko, J. Baschnagel, J. P. Wittmer, and A. N. Semenov, *Soft Matter.* **14**, 6835, (2018).

[18] J. P. Sethna, K. A. Dahmen, and C. R. Myers, *Nature.* **410**, 242–250, (2001).

[19] J. P. Sethna, K. A. Dahmen, and O. Perković. In *The Science of Hysteresis, Vol. II*, pp. 107–179. Academic Press, (2006).

[20] S. Zapperi, *Crackling noise: Statistical physics of avalanche phenomena.* (Oxford University Press, 2022).

[21] S. R. Nagel, *Rev. Mod. Phys.* **64**, 321–325 (1992).

[22] D. Fisher, K. Dahmen, S. Ramanathan, and Y. Ben-Zion, *Phys. Rev. Lett.* **78**(25), 4885–4888, (1997).

[23] A. P. Mehta, K. A. Dahmen, and Y. Ben-Zion, *Phys. Rev. E.* **73**(5), 056104, (2006).

[24] E. A. Jagla, F. P. Landes, and A. Rosso, *Phys. Rev. Lett.* **112**(17), (2014).

[25] L. de Arcangelis, C. Godano, J. R. Grasso, and E. Lippiello, *Phys. Rep.* **628**, 1–91, (2016).

[26] J. P. Sethna, *Nat. Phys. (News and Views).* **3**, 518–519, (2007).

[27] G. Durin and S. Zapperi. The Science of Hysteresis: Physical Modeling, Micromagnetics and Magnetization Dynamics, vol. II, ch. III (The Barkhausen Effect), (2006).

[28] V. Berejnov and R. E. Thorne, *Phys. Rev. E.* **75**, 066308 (2007).

[29] J. P. Sethna, *Science (Perspective).* **318**, 207–208, (2007).

[30] N. Friedman, A. T. Jennings, G. Tsekenis, J.-Y. Kim, M. Tao, J. T. Uhl, J. R. Greer, and K. A. Dahmen, *Phys. Rev. Lett.* **109**(9), 095507, (2012).

[31] J. P. Sethna, M. K. Bierbaum, K. A. Dahmen, C. P. Goodrich, J. R. Greer, L. X. Hayden, J. P. Kent-Dobias, E. D. Lee, D. B. Liarte, X. Ni, K. N. Quinn, A. Raju, D. Zeb Rocklin, A. Shekhawat, and S. Zapperi, *Annu. Rev. Mater. Res.* **47**, 217–246, (2017).

[32] X. Ni, H. Zhang, D. B. Liarte, L. W. McFaul, K. A. Dahmen, J. P. Sethna, and J. R. Greer, *Phys. Rev. Lett.* **123**, 035501 (2019).

[33] S. Papanikolaou, D. M. Dimiduk, W. Choi, J. P. Sethna, M. D. Uchic, C. F. Woodward, and S. Zapperi, *Nature.* **490**(7421), 517–521 (2012).

[34] F. F. Csikor, C. Motz, D. Weygand, M. Zaiser, and S. Zapperi, *Science.* **318**(5848), 251–254, (2007).

[35] A. Shekhawat, S. Zapperi, and J. P. Sethna, *Phys. Rev. Lett.* **110**, 185505, (2013).

[36] S. Tewari, D. Schiemann, D. J. Durian, C. M. Knobler, S. A. Langer, and A. J. Liu, *Phys. Rev. E.* **60**(4), 4385, (1999).

[37] M. Cieplak and M. O. Robbins, *Phys. Rev. Lett.* **60**(20), 2042, (1988).

[38] J. Ortín and S. Santucci. In eds. E. K. Salje, A. Saxena, and A. Planes, *Avalanches in Functional Materials and Geophysics*, pp. 261–292. Springer International Publishing, (2017).

[39] M. Kuntz, P. Houle, and J. P. Sethna. Crackling noise. `http://SimScience.org/crackling/`, (1998).

[40] M. Alava, M. Dubé, and M. Rost, *Adv. Phys.* **53**(2), 83–175, (2004).

[41] D. Pines, J. Shaham, M. A. Alpar, and P. W. Anderson, *Progress of Theoretical Physics Supplement.* **69**, 376–396 (1980).

[42] E. D. Lee, B. C. Daniels, C. R. Myers, D. C. Krakauer, and J. C. Flack, *Phys. Rev. E.* **102**, 042312 (Oct., 2020).

[43] N. Friedman, S. Ito, B. A. Brinkman, M. Shimono, R. L. DeVille, K. A. Dahmen, J. M. Beggs, and T. C. Butler, *Phys. Rev. Lett.* **108**(20), 208102, (2012).

[44] J. M. Beggs and D. Plenz, *J. Neurosci.* **23**(35), 11167–11177, (2003).

[45] L. Salminen, A. Tolvanen, and M. J. Alava, *Phys. Rev. Lett.* **89**(18), 185503, (2002).

[46] P. A. Houle and J. P. Sethna, *Phys. Rev. E.* **54**, 278–283, (1996).

[47] E. M. Kramer and A. E. Lobkovsky, *Phys. Rev. E.* **53**(2), 1465, (1996).

[48] Q. Michard and J. Bouchaud, *Eur. Phys. J. B.* **47**, 151–159, (2005).

[49] I.-J. Bienaymé, *Oc Philomat Paris Extr. Sér.* **5**(37-39), 4, (1845).

[50] H. W. Watson and F. Galton, *J. R. Anthropol. Inst.* **4**, 138, (1875).

[51] J. P. Sethna, K. Dahmen, S. Kartha, J. A. Krumhansl, B. W. Roberts, and J. D. Shore, *Phys. Rev. Lett.* **70**, 3347–3350, (1993).

[52] J. P. Sethna, *Nat. Rev. Phys.* **4**, 501–503 (July, 2022).

[53] Y.-J. Chen, S. Zapperi, and J. P. Sethna, *Phys. Rev. E.* **92**, 022146, (2015).

[54] P. Bak, C. Tang, and K. Wiesenfeld, *Phys. Rev. Lett.* **59**(4), 381, (1987).

[55] S. Zapperi, K. B. Lauritsen, and H. E. Stanley, *Phys. Rev. Lett.* **75**, 4071–4074 (1995).

[56] D. S. Fisher, *Phys. Rep.* **301**(1-3), 113–150, (1998).

[57] M. Kardar, *Phys. Rep.* **301**(1-3), 85–112, (1998).

[58] A. Larkin, *Sov. Phys. JETP.* **31**, 784, (1970).

[59] D. S. Fisher, *Phys. Rev. B.* **31**(3), 1396–1427, (1985).

[60] A. A. Middleton, *Phys. Rev. Lett.* **68**(5), 670–673, (1992).

[61] T. Giamarchi, A. Kolton, and A. Rosso. In eds. M. C. Miguel and M. Rubi, *Jamming, Yielding, and Irreversible Deformation in Condensed Matter*, vol. 688, pp. 91–108. Springer-Verlag, (2006).

[62] K. J. Wiese, *Rep. Prog. Phys.* **85**(8), 086502, (2022).

[63] B. Alessandro, C. Beatrice, G. Bertotti, and A. Montorsi, *J. Appl. Phys.* **68**(6), 2901–2907, (1990).

[64] F. Colaiori, *Adv. Phys.* **57**(4), 287–359, (2008).

[65] P. Le Doussal and K. J. Wiese, *Phys. Rev. E.* **79**(5), 051105, (2009).

[66] P. Le Doussal and K. J. Wiese, *Phys. Rev. E.* **79**(5), 051106, (2009).

[67] A. Rosso, P. Le Doussal, and K. J. Wiese, *Phys. Rev. B.* **80**(14), 144204, (2009).

[68] P. Le Doussal and K. J. Wiese, *Phys. Rev. E.* **88**(2), 022106, (2013).

[69] M. Delorme, P. Le Doussal, and K. Wiese, *Phys. Rev. E.* **93**, (2016).

[70] A. Zoia, A. Rosso, and M. Kardar, *Phys. Rev. E.* **76**(2), 021116, (2007).

[71] J. F. Joanny and P. G. de Gennes, *J. Chem. Phys.* **81**(1), 552–562, (1984).

[72] H. Gao and J. Rice, *J. Appl. Mech.-Trans. Asme.* **56**, 828–836, (1989).

[73] M. J. Alava, P. K. V. V. Nukala, and S. Zapperi, *Adv. Phys.* **55**(3-4), 349–476, (2006).

[74] D. Bonamy, S. Santucci, and L. Ponson, *Phys. Rev. Lett.* **101**(4), 045501, (2008).

[75] P. Le Doussal, K. J. Wiese, E. Raphael, and R. Golestanian, *Phys. Rev. Lett.* **96**(1), 015702, (2006).

[76] D. Bonamy and E. Bouchaud, *Phys. Rep.* **498**(1), 1–44, (2011).

[77] K. A. Dahmen, Y. Ben-Zion, and J. T. Uhl, *Phys. Rev. Lett.* **102**(17), 175501, (2009).

[78] J. Antonaglia, W. J. Wright, X. Gu, R. R. Byer, T. C. Hufnagel, M. LeBlanc, J. T. Uhl, and K. A. Dahmen, *Phys. Rev. Lett.* **112**(15), 155501, (2014).

[79] W. J. Wright, Y. Liu, X. Gu, K. D. Van Ness, S. L. Robare, X. Liu, J. Antonaglia, M. LeBlanc, J. T. Uhl, T. C. Hufnagel, et al., *J. Appl. Phys.* **119**(8), 084908, (2016).

[80] W. J. Wright, A. A. Long, X. Gu, X. Liu, T. C. Hufnagel, and K. A. Dahmen, *J. Appl. Phys.* **124**(18), 185101, (2018).

[81] W. H. Herschel and R. Bulkley, *Kolloid-Zeitschrift.* **39**(4), 291–300 (1926).

[82] G. Ovarlez, L. Tocquer, F. Bertrand, and P. Coussot, *Soft Matter.* **9**(23), 5540–5549, (2013).

[83] A. Argon, *Acta Metallurgica.* **27**(1), 47 – 58, (1979).

[84] C. Maloney and A. Lemaitre, *Phys. Rev. Lett.* **93**, 016001 (2004).

[85] K. M. Salerno, C. E. Maloney, and M. O. Robbins, *Phys. Rev. Lett.* **109**, 105703, (2012).

[86] J. Lin, E. Lerner, A. Rosso, and M. Wyart, *Proc. Natl. Acad. Sci. U.S.A.* **111**(40), 14382–14387, (2014).

[87] J.-C. Baret, D. Vandembroucq, and S. Roux, *Phys. Rev. Lett.* **89**, 195506 (2002).

[88] Z. Budrikis, D. F. Castellanos, S. Sandfeld, M. Zaiser, and S. Zapperi, *Nat. Commun.* **8**(1), 1–10, (2017).

[89] J. Carlson and J. Langer, *Phys. Rev. A.* **40**(11), 6470, (1989).

[90] A. Nicolas, E. E. Ferrero, K. Martens, and J.-L. Barrat, *Reviews of Modern Physics.* **90**(4), 045006, (2018).

[91] X. Cao, A. Nicolas, D. Trimcev, and A. Rosso, *Soft Matter.* **14**(18), 3640–3651, (2018).

[92] M. Muramatsu, T. Irie, and T. Nagatani, *Physica A.* **267**(3-4), 487–498, (1999).

[93] M. Geiger, L. Petrini, and M. Wyart, *Phys. Rep.* **924**, 1–18, (2021).

[94] B. Andreotti, Y. Forterre, and O. Pouliquen, *Granular media: between fluid and solid.* (Cambridge University Press, 2013).

[95] S. Nowak, A. Samadani, and A. Kudrolli, *Nat. Phys.* **1**(1), 50–52, (2005).

[96] H. Perrin, C. Clavaud, M. Wyart, B. Metzger, and Y. Forterre, *Phys. Rev. X.* **9**(3), 031027, (2019).

[97] J. A. Dijksman, G. H. Wortel, L. T. van Dellen, O. Dauchot, and M. van Hecke, *Phys. Rev. Lett.* **107**(10), 108303, (2011).

[98] S. Mowlavi and K. Kamrin, *Soft Matter.* **17**(31), 7359–7375, (2021).

[99] E. DeGiuli and M. Wyart, *Proc. Natl. Acad. Sci. U.S.A.* **114**(35), 9284–9289, (2017).

[100] O. Pouliquen, *Phys. Rev. Lett.* **93**(24), 248001, (2004).

[101] P. Olsson, *Phys. Rev. E.* **82**(3), 031303 (2010).

[102] G. Düring, E. Lerner, and M. Wyart, *Phys. Rev. E.* **89**(2), 022305, (2014).

[103] P. Olsson and S. Teitel, *Phys. Rev. E.* **83**(3), 030302, (2011).

[104] E. DeGiuli, G. Düring, E. Lerner, and M. Wyart, *arXiv:1410.3535.* (2014).

[105] H. Perrin, M. Wyart, B. Metzger, and Y. Forterre, *Phys. Rev. Lett.* **126**, (2021).

[106] A. J. Liu, S. R. Nagel, W. van Saarloos, and M. Wyart, *The jamming scenario: an introduction and outlook*, In eds. L.Berthier, G. Biroli, J. Bouchaud, L. Cipeletti, and W. van Saarloos, *Dynamical heterogeneities in glasses, colloids, and granular media*, p. 298. Oxford University Press, (2010).

[107] M. van Hecke, *Journal of Physics: Condensed Matter.* **22**(3), 033101–033124, (2010).

[108] C. S. O'Hern, L. E. Silbert, A. J. Liu, and S. R. Nagel, *Phys. Rev. E.* **68**(1), 011306–011324 (2003).

[109] P.-E. Peyneau and J.-N. Roux, *Phys. Rev. E.* **78**(1), 011307, (2008).

[110] R. Lespiat, S. Cohen-Addad, and R. Höhler, *Phys. Rev. Lett.* **106**, 148302 (2011).

[111] G. Combe and J.-N. Roux, *Phys. Rev. Lett.* **85**(17), 3628, (2000).

[112] E. Lerner, G. During, and M. Wyart, *Soft Matter.* **9**, 8252–8263, (2013).

[113] A. L. Efros and B. I. Shklovskii, *J. Phys. C.* **8**(4), L49, (1975).

[114] D. Thouless, P. Anderson, and R. Palmer, *Philo. Mag.* **35**, 593–601 (1977).

[115] S. Karmakar, E. Lerner, and I. Procaccia, *Phys. Rev. E.* **82**, 055103 (2010).

[116] J. Lin, A. Saade, E. Lerner, A. Rosso, and M. Wyart, *EPL.* **105**(2), 26003, (2014).

[117] J. Lin, T. Gueudré, A. Rosso, and M. Wyart, *Phys. Rev. Lett.* **115**, 168001, (2015).

[118] M. Müller and M. Wyart, *Annu. Rev. Condens. Matter Phys.* **6**(1), 177–200, (2015).

[119] C. E. Maloney and A. Lemaître, *Phys. Rev. E.* **74**(1), 016118 (2006).

[120] C. Kane and T. Lubensky, *Nat. Phys.* **10**(1), 39–45, (2014).

[121] M. Wyart, *Phys. Rev. Lett.* **109**, 125502 (2012).

[122] P. Charbonneau, J. Kurchan, G. Parisi, P. Urbani, and F. Zamponi, *Nat. Commun.* **5**(3725), (2014).

[123] P. Charbonneau, E. I. Corwin, G. Parisi, and F. Zamponi, *Phys. Rev. Lett.* **114**(12), 125504, (2015).

[124] C. P. Goodrich, A. J. Liu, and S. R. Nagel, *Phys. Rev. Lett.* **109**, 095704 (2012).

[125] J. D. Sartor, S. A. Ridout, and E. I. Corwin, *Phys. Rev. Lett.* **126**(4), 048001, (2021).

[126] F. Behrens, G. Arpino, Y. Kivva, and L. Zdeborová, *arXiv:2202.10379.* (2022).

[127] A. Lemaître and C. Caroli, *Phys. Rev. E.* **76**(3), 036104, (2007).

[128] T. Nattermann, Y. Shapir, and I. Vilfan, *Phys. Rev. B.* **42**(13), 8577–8586, (1990).

[129] E. Agoritsas, R. García-García, V. Lecomte, L. Truskinovsky, and D. Vandembroucq, *J. Stat. Phys.* **164**(6), 1394–1428, (2016).

[130] A. Tanguy, M. Gounelle, and S. Roux, *Phys. Rev. E.* **58**(2), 1577–1590, (1998).

[131] P. Chauve, T. Giamarchi, and P. Le Doussal, *Phys. Rev. B.* **62**(10), 6241–6267, (2000).

[132] X. Cao, S. Bouzat, A. B. Kolton, and A. Rosso, *Phys. Rev. E.* **97**(2), (2018).

[133] O. Narayan and D. S. Fisher, *Phys. Rev. B.* **46**(18), 11520–11549, (1992).

[134] T. Nattermann and L.-H. Tang, *Phys. Rev. A.* **45**(10), 7156–7161, (1992).

[135] O. Narayan and D. S. Fisher, *Phys. Rev. B.* **48**(10), 7030–7042, (1993).

[136] D. Ertaş and M. Kardar, *Phys. Rev. E.* **49**(4), R2532–R2535, (1994).

[137] P. Chauve, P. Le Doussal, and K. Jörg Wiese, *Phys. Rev. Lett.* **86**(9), 1785–1788, (2001).

[138] P. Le Doussal, K. J. Wiese, and P. Chauve, *Phys. Rev. B.* **66**(17), 174201 (2002).

[139] P. Le Doussal, K. J. Wiese, and P. Chauve, *Phys. Rev. E.* **69**(2), 026112 (2004).

[140] K. J. Wiese, C. Husemann, and P. Le Doussal, *Nucl. Phys. B.* **932**, 540–588, (2018).

[141] C. Husemann and K. J. Wiese, *Nucl. Phys. B.* **932**, 589–618, (2018).

[142] C. ter Burg, G. Durin, and K. J. Wiese, *arXiv:2109.01197.* (2021).

[143] H. Leschhorn, T. Nattermann, S. Stepanow, and L.-H. Tang, *Ann. Phys.* **509**(1), 1–34, (1997).

[144] A. Rosso and W. Krauth, *Phys. Rev. E.* **65**(2), 025101, (2002).

[145] A. Rosso, A. K. Hartmann, and W. Krauth, *Phys. Rev. E.* **67**(2), 021602, (2003).

[146] O. Duemmer and W. Krauth, *Phys. Rev. E.* **71**(6), (2005).

[147] O. Duemmer and W. Krauth, *J. Stat. Mech.: Theory Exp.* **2007**(01), P01019, (2007).

[148] E. E. Ferrero, S. Bustingorry, A. B. Kolton, and A. Rosso, *Comptes Rendus Phys.* **14**(8), 641–650, (2013).

[149] A. Rosso, P. L. Doussal, and K. J. Wiese, *Phys. Rev. B.* **75**(22), 220201, (2007).

[150] S. Lemerle, J. Ferré, C. Chappert, V. Mathet, T. Giamarchi, and P. Le Doussal, *Phys. Rev. Lett.* **80**(4), 849–852, (1998).

[151] N. B. Caballero, E. E. Ferrero, A. B. Kolton, J. Curiale, V. Jeudy, and S. Bustingorry, *Phys. Rev. E.* **97**(6), 062122, (2018).

[152] E. E. Ferrero, L. Foini, T. Giamarchi, A. B. Kolton, and A. Rosso, *arXiv:2001.11464.* (2020).

[153] L. Laurson, X. Illa, and M. J. Alava, *J. Stat. Mech.* **2009**(01), P01019, (2009).

[154] J. Barés, D. Bonamy, and A. Rosso, *Phys. Rev. E.* **100**(2), 023001, (2019).

[155] C. J. Bolech and A. Rosso, *Phys. Rev. Lett.* **93**(12), 125701, (2004).

[156] V. Démery, A. Rosso, and L. Ponson, *EPL.* **105**(3), 34003, (2014).

[157] A. A. Fedorenko, P. Le Doussal, and K. J. Wiese, *Phys. Rev. E.* **74**(4), 041110, (2006).

[158] S. Papanikolaou, F. Bohn, R. L. Sommer, G. Durin, S. Zapperi, and J. P. Sethna, *Nat. Phys.* **7**, 316–320, (2011).

[159] M. C. Kuntz and J. P. Sethna, *Phys. Rev. B.* **62**, 11699–11708, (2000).

[160] A. P. Mehta, A. C. Mills, K. A. Dahmen, and J. P. Sethna, *Phys. Rev. E.* **65**, 046139, (2002).

[161] S. Zapperi, C. Castellano, F. Colaiori, and G. Durin, *Nat. Phys.* **1**(1), 46–49, (2005).

[162] P. Le Doussal and K. J. Wiese, *EPL.* **97**(4), 46004, (2012).

[163] A. Dobrinevski, P. Le Doussal, and K. J. Wiese, *EPL.* **108**(6), 66002, (2015).

[164] G. Durin, F. Bohn, M. A. Corrêa, R. L. Sommer, P. Le Doussal, and K. Wiese, *Phys. Rev. Lett.* **117**(8), 087201, (2016).

[165] A. Dobrinevski, P. Le Doussal, and K. J. Wiese, *Phys. Rev. E.* **88**(3), 032106, (2013).

[166] C. Le Priol, J. Chopin, P. Le Doussal, L. Ponson, and A. Rosso, *Phys. Rev. Lett.* **124**(6), 065501, (2020).

[167] K. J. Måløy, S. Santucci, J. Schmittbuhl, and R. Toussaint, *Phys. Rev. Lett.* **96**(4), 045501, (2006).

[168] L. Laurson, S. Santucci, and S. Zapperi, *Phys. Rev. E.* **81**(4), 046116 (2010).

[169] X. Cao, P. L. Doussal, and A. Rosso, *arXiv:2203.14663.* (2022).

[170] C. Le Priol, P. Le Doussal, and A. Rosso, *Phys. Rev. Lett.* **126**(2), 025702, (2021).

[171] P. Hébraud and F. Lequeux, *Phys. Rev. Lett.* **81**, 2934–2937 (1998).

[172] E. A. Jagla, *Phys. Rev. E.* **92**(4), 042135, (2015).

[173] A. Lemaître and C. Caroli, *arXiv:0705.3122.* (2007).

[174] J. Lin and M. Wyart, *Phys. Rev. X.* **6**(1), 011005, (2016).

[175] W. Ji, M. Popović, T. W. de Geus, E. Lerner, and M. Wyart, *Phys. Rev. E.* **99**(2), 023003, (2019).

[176] M. Ozawa, L. Berthier, G. Biroli, A. Rosso, and G. Tarjus, *Proc. Natl. Acad. Sci. U.S.A.* **115**(26), 6656–6661, (2018).

[177] J. Lin and M. Wyart, *Phys. Rev. E.* **97**(1), 012603, (2018).

[178] J. T. Parley, R. Mandal, and P. Sollich, *Phys. Rev. Mater.* **6**(6), 065601, (2022).

[179] K. M. Salerno and M. O. Robbins, *Phys. Rev. E.* **88**(6), 062206, (2013).

[180] M. Popović, T. W. de Geus, W. Ji, A. Rosso, and M. Wyart, *arXiv:2111.04061.* (2021).

[181] N. J. Balmforth, I. A. Frigaard, and G. Ovarlez, *Annu. Rev. Fluid Mech.* **46**(1), 121–146, (2014).

[182] J. Goyon, A. Colin, and L. Bocquet, *Soft Matter.* **6**(12), 2668–2678, (2010).

[183] T. Gueudré, J. Lin, A. Rosso, and M. Wyart, *Soft Matter.* **13**(20), 3794–3801, (2017).

[184] M. Popović, T. W. de Geus, W. Ji, and M. Wyart, *Phys. Rev. E.* **104**(2), 025010, (2021).

[185] E. E. Ferrero, A. B. Kolton, and E. A. Jagla, *Phys. Rev. Mater.* **5**(11), 115602, (2021).

[186] P. Le Doussal, M. Müller, and K. J. Wiese, *Phys. Rev. B.* **85**, 214402 (2012).

[187] S. Franz and S. Spigler, *Phys. Rev. E.* **95**(2), 022139, (2017).

[188] I. Balog, G. Tarjus, and M. Tissier, *Phys. Rev. B.* **97**, 094204 (2018).

[189] L. X. Hayden, A. Raju, and J. P. Sethna, *Phys. Rev. Research.* **1**, 033060 (2019).

[190] M. Shimada, H. Mizuno, M. Wyart, and A. Ikeda, *Phys. Rev. E.* **98**(6), 060901, (2018).

[191] P. Olsson and S. Teitel, *Phys. Rev. Lett.* **99**, 178001, (2007).

[192] C. Heussinger and J.-L. Barrat, *Phys. Rev. Lett.* **102**, 218303, (2009).

[193] E. Lerner, E. DeGiuli, G. Düring, and M. Wyart, *Soft Matter.* **10**, 5085–5092, (2014).

[194] P. Olsson, *Phys. Rev. Lett.* **122**(10), 108003, (2019).

[195] M. Trulsson, B. Andreotti, and P. Claudin, *Phys. Rev. Lett.* **109**(11), 118305, (2012).

[196] E. DeGiuli, G. Düring, E. Lerner, and M. Wyart, *Phys. Rev. E.* **91**(6), 062206 (2015).

[197] R. Mari, R. Seto, J. F. Morris, and M. M. Denn, *J. Rheol. (1978-present).* **58**(6), 1693–1724, (2014).

[198] M. Wyart and M. Cates, *Phys. Rev. Lett.* **112**(9), 098302, (2014).

[199] C. Clavaud, A. Bérut, B. Metzger, and Y. Forterre, *Proc. Natl. Acad. Sci. U.S.A.* **114**(20), 5147–5152, (2017).

[200] J. Comtet, G. Chatté, A. Niguès, L. Bocquet, A. Siria, and A. Colin, *Nat. Commun.* **8**(1), 1–7, (2017).

[201] M. Ramaswamy, I. Griniasty, D. B. Liarte, A. Shetty, E. Katifori, E. Del Gado, J. P. Sethna, B. Chakraborty, and I. Cohen, *arXiv:2107.13338.* (2021).

[202] M. Ramaswamy, I. Griniasty, J. P. Sethna, B. Chakraborty, and I. Cohen, *arXiv:2205.02184.* (2022).

[203] M. Trulsson, E. DeGiuli, and M. Wyart, *arXiv:1606.07650.* (2016).

[204] E. DeGiuli and M. Wyart, *EPJ Web Conf.* **140**, 01003, (2017).

[205] G. Zheng and J. R. Rice, *Bull. Seismol. Soc. Am.* **88**(6), 1466–1483, (1998).

[206] J. Schwarz and D. Fisher, *Phys. Rev. Lett.* **87**(9), 096107, (2001).

[207] A. Nicolas, J.-L. Barrat, and J. Rottler, *Phys. Rev. Lett.* **116**(5), 058303, (2016).

[208] T. W. de Geus and M. Wyart, *arXiv:2204.02795.* (2022).

[209] M. Ozawa, L. Berthier, G. Biroli, and G. Tarjus, *arXiv:2102.05846.* (2021).

[210] M. Popović, T. W. J. de Geus, and M. Wyart, *Phys. Rev. E.* **98**(4) (2018).

[211] S. M. Fielding, *arXiv:2103.06782.* (2021).

[212] D. Richard, C. Rainone, and E. Lerner, *J. Chem. Phys.* **155**(5), 056101, (2021).

[213] R. N. Chacko, F. P. Landes, G. Biroli, O. Dauchot, A. J. Liu, and D. R. Reichman, *Phys. Rev. Lett.* **127**(4), 048002, (2021).

Chapter 16

Replica Symmetry Breaking in Random Lasers:
Experimental Measurement of the Overlap Distribution

Claudio Conti[*,†], Neda Ghofraniha[†], Luca Leuzzi[*,‡,¶] and Giancarlo Ruocco[*,§]

Physics Department, Sapienza University of Rome,
Piazzale Aldo Moro 5 — 00185, Rome, Italy
†*Institute of Complex Systems, National Research Council of Italy (CNR-ISC),*
Piazzale Aldo Moro 5 — 00185, Rome, Italy
‡*Institute of Nanotechnology, National Research Council of Italy (CNR-NANOTEC),*
Soft and Living matter Lab, Piazzale Aldo Moro 5 — 00185, Rome, Italy
§*Center for Life Nano- & Neuro-Science, Italian Institute of Technology*
(CLN2S@Sapienza, IIT), Viale Regina Elena, 291 — 00161 Rome, Italy

In this chapter we report measurements of the overlap distribution of the replica symmetry breaking solution in complex disordered systems. After a general introduction to the problem of the experimental validation of the Parisi order parameter, we focus on systems where the measurement has been possible for the first time: random lasers. Starting from first principles of light-matter interaction we sketch the main steps leading to the construction of the statistical mechanical model for the dynamics of light modes in a random laser, a spherical multi-p-spin model with complex spins. A new overlap is introduced, the intensity fluctuation overlap, whose probability distribution, under specific assumptions, is equivalent to the Parisi overlap distribution. The experimental protocol for measuring this overlap is based on the possibility of experimentally realizing real replicas. After a description of the first experiment on the random laser made of $T5CO_x$ grains we review and discuss various experiments measuring the overlap distribution, as well as the possible connection with Lévy-like distribution of the intensity of the light modes around the laser threshold, the connection with turbulence in fiber lasers and the role of spatial heterogeneities of light modes in random media.

16.1. Introduction

The theory of replica symmetry breaking (RSB) relies on an order parameter which is not a number or a vector, rather it is a function of a continous variable [1, 2]. This is the main novelty of the theory of Parisi: to conceive and construct an order parameter able to identify a thermodynamic phase of a system with multi-equilibria, a signature for complex disordered systems. The function in question is the probability distribution $P(q)$ of the overlap q between equilibrium states, or its cumulative

$$x(q) = \int^q dq' \, P(q'), \qquad (16.1)$$

¶luca.leuzzi@cnr.it

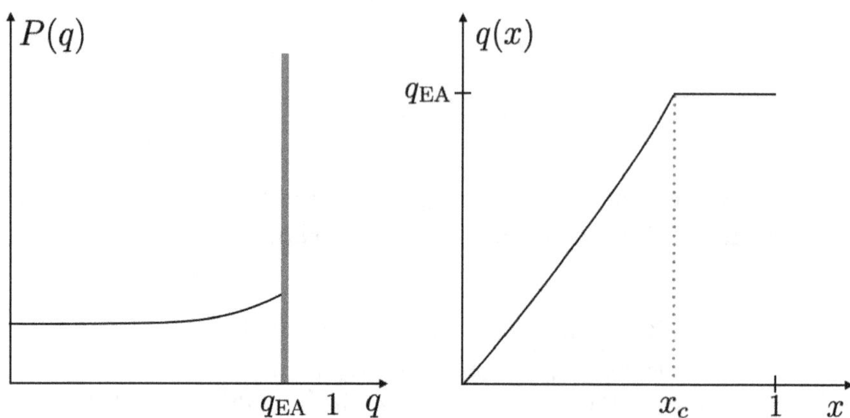

Fig. 16.1. Left: sketch of a full replica symmetry breaking probability distribution of overlaps between states. The Edwards–Anderson parameter $q_{\rm EA}$ denotes the modal of the distribution, its meaning being the overlap of a state with itself. The thick grey bar represents a Dirac delta on $q = q_{\rm EA}$. Right: the functional order parameter $q(x)$, i.e., the inverse of the cumulative distribution (16.1), for a full RSB system. The point x_c of discontinuous derivative is Eq. (16.1) computed at $q = q_{\rm EA}^{-}$.

or, equivalently, the inverse of the cumulative $q(x)$, see Fig. 16.1. Numerous and astonishing are the outcomes of this idea, right in the original replica formalism, as well as in further reformulations, such as the cavity method [3–5]. Though 40 years have passed since the conception of such quantity in spin glasses, the experimental observation of the order parameter in its full functional glory is still a rather difficult and challenging task.

In this chapter, we first explore the early attempts to experimentally expose the inner structure of the organization of states predicted by the RSB theory in complex disordered systems, such as spin glasses and structural glasses. Then we will show how, with some preliminary theoretical work, the distribution of the values of the overlaps between states can be sampled in random lasers [6–12].

A first measurement of a peculiar behavior compatible with the — soon incoming — Parisi picture was performed by Nagata, Keesom and Harrison in 1978 [13] on a spin glass alloy, the cuprate-manganese, CuMn. There, the magnetic susceptibility was carefully measured in static magnetic fields using two procedures. In the first one the system is cooled down at nearly zero magnetic field and, then, at different temperatures the system is perturbed by a magnetic field and the response is acquired. In the second protocol the CuMn is cooled down embedded in a constant uniform magnetic field. Then, at each temperature the field is perturbed and the field cooled susceptibility measured. Both the zero-field-cooled (ZFC) and the field-cooled (FC) susceptibility behaviours, respectively $\chi_{\rm FC}$ and $\chi_{\rm ZFC}$, are qualitatively reproduced by the RSB theory. It holds $\chi_{\rm ZFC} = \beta(1 - q_{\rm EA})$ and $\chi_{\rm FC} = \beta(1 - \langle q \rangle)$, where $q_{\rm EA}$ is the Edwards–Anderson parameter, else called the self-overlap of a state with itself, and $\langle q \rangle$ denotes the average over the distribution $P(q)$. This early kind of experiments on spin glasses provided modal and average values of the distribution.

How to measure the whole distribution? In principle one needs to measure many configurations of spins $\{\sigma\}$ in time, in a well thermalized spin glass. This task is very

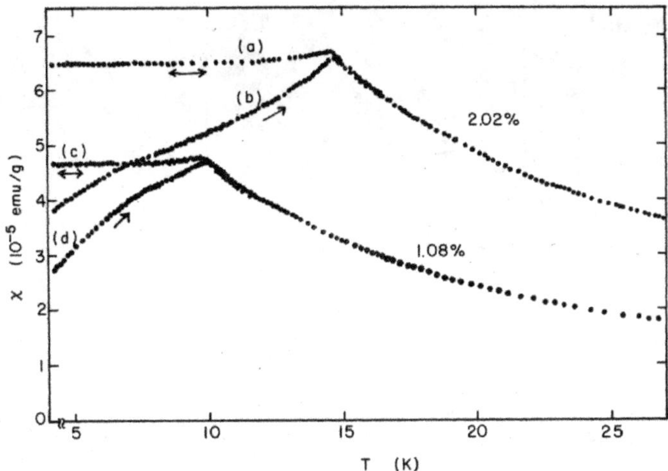

Fig. 16.2. Reproduced from Ref. 13 with permission of the American Physical Society. Magnetic susceptibility of the spin-glass CuMn in the static limit. Curves (b) and (d) are related to measurements taken after zero-field cooling and curves (a) and (c) to measurements after cooling in a field of $5.90G$. The two top curves (a) and (b) are the temperature dependece of the susceptibility of an alloy with 2.02% of Manganese. The two lower curves (c) and (d) are measured on a sample with 1.08% of Mn.

hard, because of the difficulty of measuring several atomic spins at once and because glassy systems hardly reach equilibrium.

Exploiting exactly the slow relaxation dynamics of glassy systems, an alternative procedure circumventing the direct measure of spins configurations was devised in 1998 by Franz, Mézard and Parisi [14]. Under the assumption of stochastic stability they were able to prove that in aging out-of-equilibrium complex disordered systems, in the long time limit of both the waiting and the observation time the ratio between the response and the correlation comes out to be equivalent to the cumulative overlap distribution at equilibrium. In formulas, being the overlap q the asymptotic limit of the two-time self-correlation function,

$$q = \lim_{t \to \infty} C(t, t'),$$

the long-time limit of the fluctuation-dissipation ratio

$$\tilde{X}(q) \equiv \lim_{t,t' \to \infty} \frac{\chi(t, t')}{1 - C(t, t')} \tag{16.2}$$

results to be equal to the cumulative (16.1). Furthermore, under those assumptions the integrated response function depends on t' and t exclusively through the correlation function: $\chi(t, t') = \chi(C(t, t'))$.

To measure such a fluctuation-dissipation ratio in real experiments, though, proved harder than expected. Three impressive experiments were carried out in the last 20 years, [15–18] yielding the behaviours of response vs correlation behavior $\chi(C(t, t'))$ reproduced in Fig. 16.3. We briefly report and comment on outcomes.

The first experiment is on samples of micrometric powder grains of an insulating spin glass $CdCr_{1.7}In_{0.3}S_4$ [15, 16]. Very careful SQUID measurements of magnetic

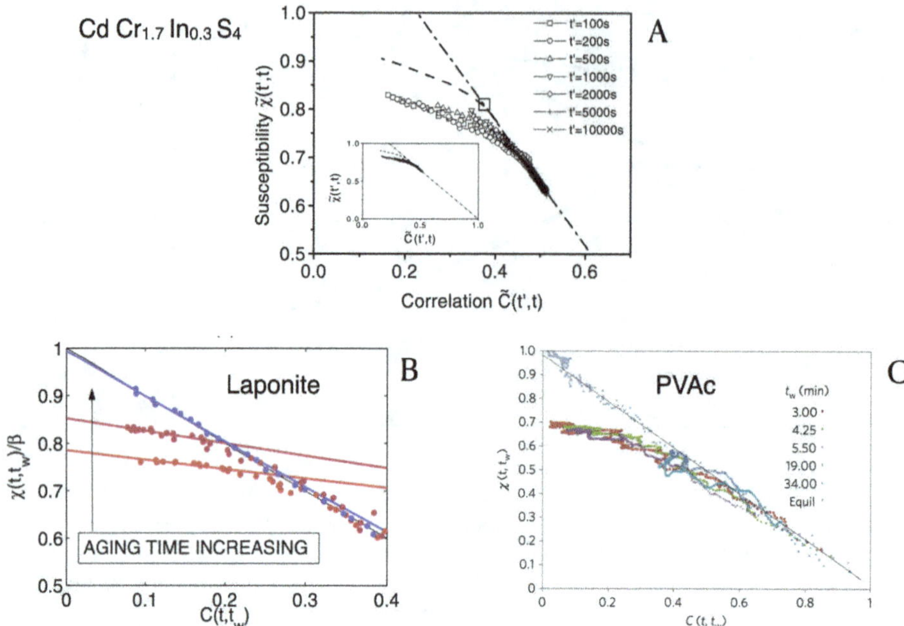

Fig. 16.3. Fluctuation-dissipation ratio on aging systems. (A) the CdCr$_{1.7}$In$_{0.3}$S$_4$ spin glass, reproduced from Ref. 15 with permission from American Physical Society, (B) Laponite clay, reproduced from Ref. 17 with permission from American Physical Society, and (C) polivynil-acetate, reproduced from Ref. 18 with permission from Nature Publishing Group.

fluctuations allowed to provide the $\chi(C)$ function of the correlation function $C(t,t')$ displayed in Fig. 16.3(A). The experiment is very accurate and deals with extremely weak thermodynamic fluctuations. Strict precautions must be taken and kept for the whole duration of the experiment, but very long measurements are required in order to acquire enough statistics. One day of measurements is required to provide data curves with long waiting times and, furthermore, the outcome does not appear clean enough to demostrate the equivalence of (16.1) and (16.2) in the infinite times limit.

In an experiment on the reorientational dynamics of Laponite disks [17], using the orientational correlation functions measured by depolarized dynamic light scattering and the corresponding response function via the electric field induced birefringence, another kind of $\chi(C)$ is obtained. In this case laponite is shown to undergo a glassy transition in density and not in temperature. At high packing density it provides the behavior of a (fragile) structural glass. Therefore, it is expected to be one-step RSB-like in the asymptotic limit, as, actually shown in Fig. 16.3(B), where $\chi(C)$ displays two slopes. In this experiment, though, as the waiting time $t' = t_w$ grows the FDR tends to the equilibrium ratio $1/T$ and the out-of-equilibrium counterpart of the cumulative overlap distribution appears to vanish.

Finally, the nanoscale polarization fluctuations and dielectric responses were measured in polyvinyl acetate (PVAc), [18] also known to be a fragile glass. PVAc displays aging at $T \simeq 0.98\, T_g$ and at such temperature the system is expected to be one-step RSB, i.e., $\chi(C)$ is expected to tend to a function as the one in Fig. 16.3(C), whose derivative is a step function. Instead, according to the analysis with the available data a continuously bending $\chi(C)$ is interpolated, hinting at the occurrence of a continuous RSB, as in the proper spin-glass case, or hinting at the occurrence of strong finite time pre-asymptotic effects.

To sum up, through stochastic stability in out-of-equilibrium dynamics no $P(q)$ has been experimentally demonstrated so far. Experimentally, indeed, things turn out to be different even from the most sophisticated numerical simulations, see [19] for a recent reference.

This is where photonics comes in: unlike single spins in amorphous magnets, or local degrees of freedom (e.g., density, orientational, polarization fluctuations) in structural glasses, single light mode intensities are degrees of freedom accessible to experimental measurements, at least partially. This *partiality* can be dealt with introducing a new overlap, the intensity fluctuation overlap, whose distribution is equivalent to the Parisi overlap distribution (under given conditions that will be discussed in Sec. 16.2.3).

Before showing how $P(q)$ can be acquired in experiments on random lasers and other photonic systems we very briefly recall how and to what extent a random laser is a complex disordered system possibly undergoing a transition to a RSB phase.

16.2. Random Lasers as Complex Disordered Systems

Random lasers are made of an optically active medium and randomly placed scatterers [7, 9–12, 20–27] (sometimes both in one [7]). The first provides the gain, the latter provide the high refraction index and the feedback mechanism needed to lead to amplification by stimulated emission. As opposed to ordered standard multimode lasers, random lasers do not require complicated construction and rigid optical alignment, have omni-directional emission and high operational flexibility. They give rise to a number of promising applications in the field of speckle-free imaging [28, 29], granular matter [25, 30], remote sensing [12, 31, 32], medical diagnostics and biomedical imaging [12, 33–36], optical amplification and optoelectronic devices [12, 37, 38].

Random lasers emission spectra above a pump threshold may show multiple sub-nanometer spectral peaks, as well as single narrow curves with 5-10 nm width. Depending on the material, and its optical and scattering properties, random spectral fluctuations between different pumping shots (i.e., different realizations of the same random laser) may or may not vary significantly. A wide variety of spectral features has been reported [26, 30, 39–41], depending on material compounds and experimental setups. Random lasers can be built in very different ways, can be both solid or liquid, can be 2D or 3D, and the optically active material can be confined or spread all over the volume. Moreover, random lasers are, usually, open systems where light can propagate in any direction rather than being confined between well specified boundaries (mirrors) as in standard lasers and the emission acquisition can be on the whole solid angle.

16.2.1. *The leading model Hamiltonian*

Since the original proposal that a random laser might be described by means of a spin-glass-like Hamiltonian, [42, 43] various derivations have been put forward [44–47] of the leading model

$$\mathcal{H}[a] = -\sum_{k_1,k_2} J^{(2)}_{k_1 k_2} a^*_{k_1} a_{k_2} - \sum_{k_1,k_2,k_3,k_4} J^{(4)}_{k_1 k_2 k_3 k_4} a_{k_1} a^*_{k_2} a_{k_3} a^*_{k_4} + \text{c.c.}, \qquad (16.3)$$

where a's are complex numbers denoting the complex amplitudes of the light modes and the J's denote quenched random mode couplings. The most fundamental derivation is the construction starting from the light-matter interaction between the atoms or molecules of the gain medium, thus displaying an optical gap, and the electromagnetic (e.m.) field of the light. [45] We briefly skecth the basic steps moving from a quantum description of the operator dynamics to a classical Hamiltonian theory for the stationary regime of light amplification by stimulated emission in a disordered medium. The quantum stochastic differential equations describing the interaction of an atom with an optical gap ω_o between two levels $|A\rangle$ and $|B\rangle$, see Fig. 16.4, with the electromagnetic field of frequency ω_λ, represented by the creation and annihilation operators α and $\alpha^\dagger$, are the Jaynes–Cummings equations [48]

$$\dot{\alpha}_\lambda = -\imath\omega_\lambda a_\lambda - \sum_\mu \gamma_{\lambda\mu}\alpha_\mu + \int dr g^\dagger_\lambda(\boldsymbol{r})\,\sigma_-(\boldsymbol{r}) + F_\lambda \qquad (16.4)$$

$$\dot{\sigma}_-(\boldsymbol{r}) = -(\gamma_\perp + \imath\omega_o)\sigma_-(\boldsymbol{r}) + 2\sum_\lambda g_\lambda(\boldsymbol{r})\,\sigma_z(\boldsymbol{r})\,\alpha_\lambda + F_-(\boldsymbol{r}) \qquad (16.5)$$

$$\dot{\sigma}_z(\boldsymbol{r}) = \gamma_\|\left(S\rho(\boldsymbol{r}) - \sigma_z(\boldsymbol{r})\right) - \sum_\lambda \left(g^\dagger_\lambda(\boldsymbol{r})\,\alpha^\dagger_\lambda\sigma_-(\boldsymbol{r}) + \text{h.c.}\right) + F_z(\boldsymbol{r}), \qquad (16.6)$$

where $\sigma_z(\boldsymbol{r}) \equiv |A\rangle\langle A| - |B\rangle\langle B|$ is the population inversion operator, $\sigma_-(\boldsymbol{r}) \equiv |B\rangle\langle A|$ is the lowering operator and $\sigma_+(\boldsymbol{r}) \equiv |A\rangle\langle B|$ the raising operator. The coefficients $g_\lambda(\boldsymbol{r})$ are the atom-field coupling constants, $\gamma_{\mu\nu}$ is the damping matrix and it is associated to the fact that the cavity is open in random lasers and radiative modes are there as well. The coefficients $\gamma_\perp$, $\gamma_\|$ are, respectively, the polarization decay rate and the population inversion rate ($\gamma_\| \equiv (\gamma_A + \gamma_B)/2$, see Fig. 16.4). The atomic density is $\rho(\boldsymbol{r})$ and S represents the intensity of the external optical pumping.

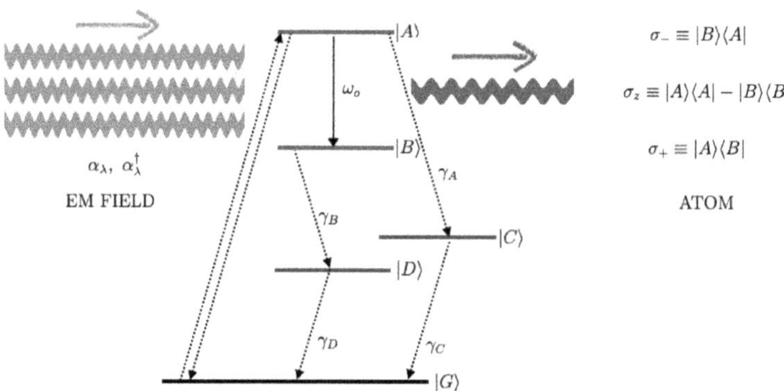

Fig. 16.4. Pictorial representation of the light-matter interaction. The atom here illustrated has five states denoted by letters $|A\rangle$, $|B\rangle$, $|C\rangle$, $|D\rangle$ and $|G\rangle$, the ground state. γ_x, with $x = A, B, C, D$ are the decay rate of the excited states to a state of lower energy. The energy gap between $|A\rangle$ and $|B\rangle$ is $\hbar\omega_o$ where ω_o lies in the optical frequency spectrum and contributes to the laser in the regime of high external pumping, when many atoms coherently emit at once.

Noise terms F_λ, $F_-(\boldsymbol{r})$ and $F_z(\boldsymbol{r})$ are there as well, and they pertain to different stochastic phenomena. The term F_λ is due to the presence of radiative modes in open cavities and the effetive interation between those and the modes inside the cavity. The atomic noise terms $\mathcal{F}_-$ and $\mathcal{F}_z$ arise because of the intercation between the e.m. field and the optically active medium.

Applying perturbation theory the dependence of the atomic operators σ_- and σ_z on the field operator α_λ can be worked out, leading to a single equation for coupled α's. Degrading from quantum operators to complex numbers we are, eventually, left with a single stochastic differential equation for the electromagnetic field modes α in the cavity. These modes, at frequencies ω_λ, are called "cold cavity" or "passive" modes because they are intrinsic to the system and not activated by any external pumping. In presence of external excitation and above the lasing threshold the evolution in the lasing regime is better expressed in the basis $\{E_k(\boldsymbol{r})\}$ of the so-called slow amplitude modes. A slow amplitude mode a_k is a mode that, for long enough time, displays a harmonic oscillating behavior at some given angular frequency ω_k, so that the overall electromagnetic field can be written as

$$E(\boldsymbol{r},t) = \sum_{k=1}^{N} a_k(t)\, E_k(\boldsymbol{r})\, e^{\iota\omega_k t} + \text{c.c.} \tag{16.7}$$

for a system with N modes. The relationship between passive and slow amplitude modes is not unique and can always be expressed in the form

$$\alpha_\lambda(t) = \sum_k M_{\lambda k}\, a_k(t)\, e^{\iota\omega_k t}. \tag{16.8}$$

For a simple case where the relationship between passive and lasing modes can be worked out exactly at the quantum level one can see, e.g., Refs. [49, 50]. It is called slow amplitude approximation because the dynamics of $a_k(t)$ is much slower than the one of the mode oscillation $e^{\iota\omega_k t}$, so that the Fourier transform of $a_k(t)\, e^{\iota\omega_k t}$ tends to a Dirac delta $\delta(\omega - \omega_k)$.

Carrying out this transformation eventually leads to a stochastic differential equation of the potential kind for the slow amplitudes:

$$\dot{a}_k(t) = -\frac{\partial \mathcal{H}[\boldsymbol{a}]}{\partial a_k^*} + F_k(t) \tag{16.9}$$

where the noise $F_k(t)$ can be taken as white noise and the Hamiltonian $\mathcal{H}[\boldsymbol{a}]$ turns out to be

$$\mathcal{H}[\boldsymbol{a}] = -\sum_{\boldsymbol{k}\,|\,\mathrm{FMC(k)}} J^{(2)}_{k_1 k_2} a_{k_1}^* a_{k_2} - \sum_{\boldsymbol{k}\,|\,\mathrm{FMC(k)}} J^{(4)}_{k_1 k_2 k_3 k_4} a_{k_1} a_{k_2}^* a_{k_3} a_{k_4}^* + \text{c.c..} \tag{16.10}$$

In the above Hamiltonian definition a constraint is imposed on the frequencies induced by the slow amplitude condition, which we call the frequency matching condition (FMC). For two and four modes it reads, respectively,

$$|\omega_{k_1} - \omega_{k_2}| \lesssim \gamma \tag{16.11}$$

$$|\omega_{k_1} - \omega_{k_2} + \omega_{k_3} - \omega_{k_4}| \lesssim \gamma, \tag{16.12}$$

where γ is the finite linewidth of the modes. This can only be derived in a quantum theoretical approach, [49] whereas, for what concerns the classical approach, we can include γ as a parameter coherent with experimental observations. In Eq. (16.10) two effective coupling terms appear: a two- and a four-mode coupling, whose expressions are derived as the Hamiltonian is built. In the slow amplitude mode basis they depend on the spatial intersection of the eigenfunctions $E_k(\boldsymbol{r})$ of the modes modulated by the spatial profile of, respectively, the linear $\chi^{(1)}$ and the nonlinear $\chi^{(3)}$ susceptibility of the random medium:

$$J_{k_1 k_2} \propto \int d\boldsymbol{r} \; E_{k_1}(\boldsymbol{r}) \, E_{k_2}(\boldsymbol{r}) \, \chi^{(1)}(\boldsymbol{r}|\omega_{k_1}, \omega_{k_2}) \tag{16.13}$$

$$J_{k_1 k_2 k_3 k_4} \propto \int d\boldsymbol{r} \; E_{k_1}(\boldsymbol{r}) \, E_{k_2}(\boldsymbol{r}) \, E_{k_3}(\boldsymbol{r}) \, E_{k_4}(\boldsymbol{r}) \, \chi^{(3)}(\boldsymbol{r}|\omega_{k_1}, \omega_{k_2}, \omega_{k_3}, \omega_{k_4}). \tag{16.14}$$

One last fundamental ingredient of modes dynamics in a lasing material to be combined in the formulation of the Hamiltonian dynamics is gain saturation.

Gain saturation is fundamental to have a stationary solution at all in the systems under study, that might be represented as a potential, equilibrium-like, solution to the stochastic equations. The most "energetic" phenomenon that can occur in a system of atoms in a laser is when they all are in their excited optical level and they all emit a photon at once. If such an event were to occur, the atoms emission would be soon afterwards depleted because they have to invert their population and that takes time. Therefore, the gain — that is the capability of the material of amplifying light — saturates at a certain level E_{sat}. Its behavior as a function of the total energy $\mathcal{E}$ pumped into the system is usually modeled as [46, 51]

$$g(\mathcal{E}) = \frac{g_0}{1 + \dfrac{\mathcal{E}}{E_{\mathrm{sat}}}}.$$

Even though the external pumping continues the amount of lasing will not increase indefinitely, no matter how strong the pumping is, but it will reach a stationary regime. The overall energy $\mathcal{E}$ shared by the modes in the cavity slowly fluctuates between an upper and a lower bound, but its change is much slower than the one of the single mode intensities. As a further approximation, then, in the spin-glass theory for random lasers we assume that the dynamics of the total energy of N modes is so slow as to be considered as a constant with respect to the dynamics of the single photon emissions at any time t, i.e.,

$$\mathcal{E} = \sum_k |a_k(t)|^2 = \epsilon \, N = \text{const.} \tag{16.15}$$

In Fig. 16.5 we pictorially sketch this approximation in a two-mode case. From the point of view of the phasors $a_k(t)$, whose dynamics is governed by (16.9), Eq. (16.15) is a global contraint for the dynamics of a configuration to be on the $2N$ hyper-sphere of radius $\sqrt{\epsilon N}$. This is the reason why this kind of spins are referred to as "spherical" in the statistical mechanics literature [52]. We will, therefore, call the leading model (16.10) a complex spherical 2+4-spin spin-glass model.

With such a global constraint the stationary regime can be described as if the system were at equilibrium at an effective temperature (a "photonic" temperature T_{ph}) related

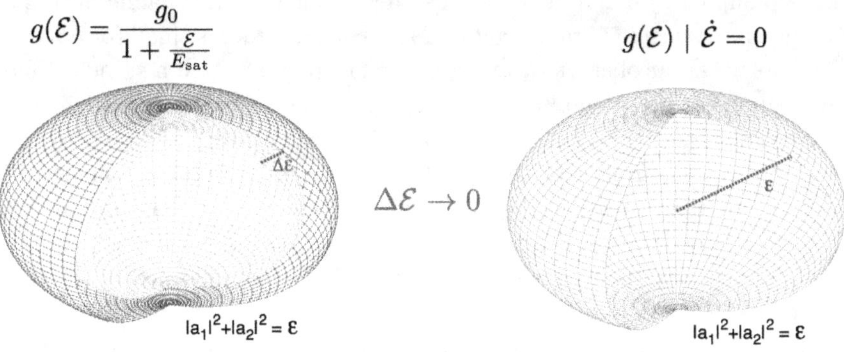

Fig. 16.5.   A sketch of the spherical approximation for the gain saturation.

to the ratio $\mathcal{P}$ between the external pumping rate and the spontaneous emission rate. The latter is proportional to the real heat bath temperature T, whereas the former one is proportional to the energy (16.15) stored into the photonic system. In a formula, the role of the temperature driving the lasing transition is played by the rescaled temperature

$$T_{\text{ph}} = \frac{T}{\epsilon^2} = \frac{1}{\mathcal{P}^2} = \frac{1}{\beta_{\text{ph}}}. \tag{16.16}$$

16.2.2.   *An analytic solution in the narrowband approximation*

The spin-glass model (16.10) in the limit of narrow bandwidth of the random laser spectrum tends to the generalization of the fully connected spherical 2+4-spin spin-glass model [53–56] to complex spins. In the narrowband approximation [51, 57] all resonances have frequencies so close to each other that their difference is of the order of the linewidth γ, so that the conditions (16.11) and (16.12) are always satisfied. Under the further assumption that all modes have a spatial extension on the order of the whole volume of the lasing material, Eqs. (16.13) and (16.14) imply that the interaction network can be taken as fully connected.

The fully connected limit has been extensively studied in the thermodynamic limit in Refs. [45–47, 58] where the couplings (16.13) and (16.14) are chosen to be independent identically distributed Gaussian variables of given mean $\bar{J}/N^\delta$ and variance σ_J^2/N^δ. The exponent is $\delta = 1$ in the two-body term and $\delta = 3$ in the four body term. In this way the magnitude of each coupling decreseas as the number of couplings of a single mode and the Hamiltonian (16.3) on the fully connected graph of interaction is always extensive.

The ratio $R_J \equiv \sigma_J/\bar{J}$ between mean square displacement and mean value represents the degree of disorder of the system.[a] *Glassy* random lasers, i.e., random lasers displaying anomalous shot-to-shot fluctuations of the emission spectra, will generally have a large R_J (even infinite if we take $\bar{J} = 0$). In Fig. 16.6 we reproduce a typical phase

---

[a]The model can be implemented with two different degrees of randomness for the 2- and the 4-body interactions [45] but for the sake of the presentation we consider them equal to each other.

diagram in the pumping rate and degree of disorder. Four thermodynamic phases can occur depending on the degree of randomness R_J. As the disorder is small (or none) the model (16.3) displays an incoherent wave regime at low pumping and a standard mode locking laser regime at high pumping $\mathcal{P}$. This regime also represents random lasers with no glassy features, that is, lasers with random resonances in the spectrum but no anomalous flutucations from shot to shot (the resonances are random but they are always the same). As randomness in the mode-coupling increases a phase-locking wave regime is predicted to occur, that is a regime where the phases of the modes are locked while no resonance occurs in the mode intensities. This phase vanishes as $R_J \to \infty$. Eventually, for large enough randomness a glassy random laser occurs above a certain pumping threshold. This is the regime where the spin-glass theory of multistate systems is necessary in order to deal with the complexity of the spectral behavior.

In the highly (quenched) disordered region the order parameter identifying the random lasing threshold is the probability distribution of the overlap

$$q_{\mathrm{ab}} = \Re\left[\frac{1}{N}\sum_{k=1}^{N}\bar{a}_k^{(\mathrm{a})}a_k^{(\mathrm{b})}\right]. \tag{16.17}$$

between any two replicas a and b.

Some instances of RSB solution in different points of the phase diagram, and the relative $P(q)$'s are reported in Fig. 16.6 (the Parisi distributions are displayed in the rightmost column). For low pumping the incoherent wave regime is described by a replica symmetric solution. Upon increasing the pumping the system undergoes a transition to a glassy random lawer with infinite breakings of the replica symmetry (Full RSB). Increasing $\mathcal{P}$ further moves the laser to a 1-Full RSB phase and, eventually, for very large pumping, where the pairwise (i.e., linear) contribution to (16.3) plays no role anymore, a one-step RSB phase correctly describes the thermodynamic behavior of the glassy random laser.

To measure such an overlap one has to access real and imaginary parts of the complex amplitude of each light mode a_k in each replica. In other words, the intensity and the phase are

$$I_k^{(\mathrm{a})} = \left|a_k^{(\mathrm{a})}\right|^2 \tag{16.18}$$

$$\phi_k^{(\mathrm{a})} = \arg\left(a_k^{(\mathrm{a})}\right). \tag{16.19}$$

As will be discussed in a while, even though the intensities can easily be measured from the emission spectra, the phases in random lasers are hardly accessible experimentally. To overcome such a hindrance it is possible to define an overlap between replica involving intensities alone. Or, better, involving their fluctuations.

16.2.3. *The intensity fluctuation overlap (IFO)*

Let us define the fluctuation between the intensity $I_k^{(\mathrm{a})}$ of a single resonance (a single mode k) in the spectrum of a single replica (a) and its average at equilibrium $\langle I_k^{(\mathrm{a})}\rangle$:

$$\Delta_k^{(\mathrm{a})} = \frac{I_k^{(\mathrm{a})} - \langle I_k^{(\mathrm{a})}\rangle}{2\sqrt{2}\,\epsilon} = \frac{I_k^{(\mathrm{a})} - \langle I_k^{(\mathrm{a})}\rangle}{2\sqrt{2T}}, \tag{16.20}$$

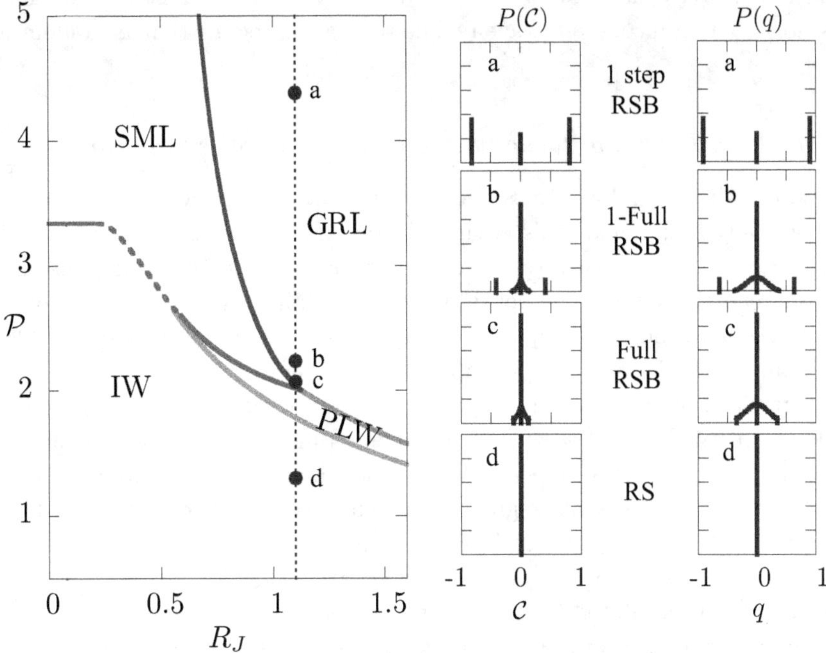

Fig. 16.6.   An instance of a phase diagram of a random laser model (16.3) in the narrowband approximation (left).   Four thermodynamic phases can occur depending on the degree of randomness R_J: incoherent wave (IW) at low $\mathcal{P}$ and low disorder R_J, standard mode locking (SML) at low R_J and high pumping $\mathcal{P}$, phase-locking wave (PLW) in a range of disorder R_J large but not extremely large, glassy random laser (GRL) above a certain pumping threshold for large R_J. The latter is the regime of broken replica symmetry and needs to be analyzed by means of Parisi theory for complex disordered systems. The dotted lines are first order transition lines, that is, above and below those dotted lines a region of phase separation is expected (spinodal lines, and how to computed them, are reported in Ref. 45). On the right the IFO and Parisi overlap distributions $P(\mathcal{C})$ and $P(q)$ are displayed in four points of the phase diagram along a line of increasing pumping for a given degree of disorder. For low pumping the IW regime is described by a replica symmetric solution. Upon increasing $\mathcal{P}$ the system becomes a GRL with a Full RSB. Increasing $\mathcal{P}$ futher moves the laser to a 1-Full RSB phase and, eventually, for very large pumping, the behavior of the GRL is described by a one-step RSB phase. Repoduced from Ref. 59 with permission from Nature Publishing Group.

where the normalization factor $\sqrt{8}$ is a pedantry and simply depends on the coefficients in the definition of (16.3).

We can, then, introduce the overlap between the intensity fluctuations of two replicas a and b:

$$\mathcal{C}_{\mathrm{ab}} \equiv \frac{1}{N} \sum_{k=1}^{N} \Delta_k^{(\mathrm{a})} \Delta_k^{(\mathrm{b})}. \tag{16.21}$$

In the fully connected model with large disorder the distribution of the intensity fluctuation overlap (IFO) is proved to be equivalent to the one of the Parisi overlap (16.17) squared. Indeed, for each couple of replicas the identity holds:

$$\mathcal{C}_{\mathrm{ab}} = q_{\mathrm{ab}}^2, \qquad \mathrm{a} \neq \mathrm{b}. \tag{16.22}$$

In Fig. 16.6 we show some examples of both distributions as the system undergoes a phase transition from an incoherent wave regime to a lasing regime that is random *and* glassy.

16.2.4. *Mode-locked random laser theory and numerical simulations*

Moving to more realistic random lasers one should relax the narrowband assumption. Indeed, the optically active materials composing random lasers have, usually, a wide emission spectrum in which many resonances take place above the lasing threshold. That is, a more realistic system is modeled by Eq. (16.10), implementing the conditions (16.11), (16.12). Such conditions imply a dilution of the interaction network of $\mathcal{O}(N)$ [50, 60] and induce some kind of metrics in the space of the frequencies.[b]

Even though the 2-mode terms are important for the occurrence of a RSB solution of the full kind, in this section we will focus on the 4-mode contribution alone, that is responsible for the onset of a glassy lasing regime, though as a one-step RSB solution. This means that in the lasing regime one should expect a $P(q)$, or $P(C)$, like in Figs. 16.6-d and 16.6-a: a single central peak at high temperature that, as the lasing threshold is overcome, also displays two more side peaks at low T.

To analytically solve a diluted (that is not sparse, nor fully connected) system with a deterministic prescription is still an unsolved problem in replica theory but one can resort to Monte Carlo numerical simulations.[c]

In Fig. 16.7 we report instances of average overlap distributions at various temperatures T for a random laser model of $N = 66$ on a mode-locked graph obtained simulating different replicas with the replica exchange Monte Carlo, or "parallel tempering" algorithm. This exploits the properties of detailed balance in a Markov chain dynamics of the system of spins through different parallel thermal baths in order to drastically reduce the thermalization time in the spin-glass phase. The implementation of the dynamics, moreover, is carried out on GPUs so that both the just mentioned parallel dynamics and the computation of every single energy update can be spread simultaneously on several threads. This is a technical but crucial point in order to have reasonable simulation times in a system that is nondeterministic polynomial-time complete, has continuous variables and a number of interactions growing like N^3. We notice that the IFO distributions, which in the fully connected case are equivalent to the Parisi distributions, on the mode-locked graph appear to have much stronger finite

---

[b]A model with 4-body interaction that represents the fundamental non-linear ingredient to yield lasing at high pumping (low temperature) will, therefore, display $\mathcal{O}(N^3)$ mode-coupling terms in the Hamiltonian (if the modes are spatially extended to a finite fraction of the volume of the lasing material). This also implies that the δ exponent introduced in Sec. 16.2.2 in the average and variance of the random coupling distribution will be descreased by one. The 2-body term will have a sparse structure ($\delta = 0$: each mode has a finite number of connection, whatever N), whereas it will be $\delta = 2$ for the 4-mode couplings.

[c]We also stress that to use a sparse approximation in this case would not allow to use the cavity method because the variables are not locally confined, the "spins" are not $|s|^2 = 1$ as the Ising, the XY [61, 62] or the Heisenberg spins. Instead light mode amplitudes only have an overall constraint (16.15) and locally one or a few of them might condensate the whole power at disposal, $|a|^2 = \mathcal{O}(N)$, leaving nothing for the others. This is a case where the equivalence of the canonical and the microcanonical ensembles break down and cannot be studied in the present form.

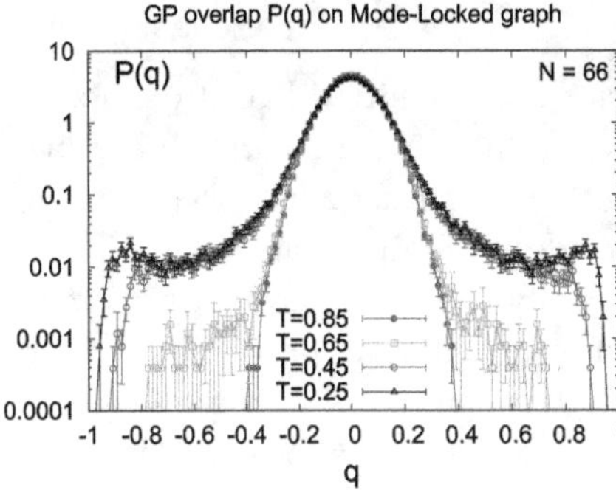

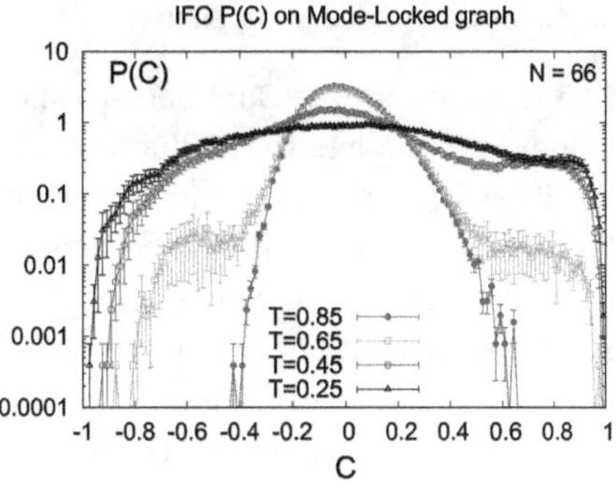

Fig. 16.7. Left: average Parisi overlap distribution $P(q)$ from numerical simulation of the dynamics of the 4-spin complex spherical spin model with $\bar{J} = 0$ ("infinite" degree of randomness R_J), $N = 66$ modes at four different temperatures across the critical point, $T_c = 0.61(3)$ [63]. Right: average distribution $P(\mathcal{C})$ of the Intensity fluctuation overlap, Eq. (16.21), for the same system. In both plots, at each temperature, distributions are averaged over 100 disordered samples. All samples are thermalized, that is the configurations are all at equilibrium and the time average coincides with the ensemble average.

size effects, as analyzed in Ref. 63. On the other hand their signal of a transition to a multi-state phase of nontrivial correlations is much more evident than with the $P(q)$, for which one has to look on a logarithmic scale to appreciate the occurrence of side peaks.

We stress that, even if diluted with the FMC, Eq. (16.12), the thermodynamic solution is expected to be a mean-field one, as in the case of the fully connected model, as confirmed by recent accurate numerical results [63].

When moving from analytical and numerical results to real experiments different aspects have to be taken into account. As in the numerical simulations, in experiments the number of modes is finite as well. However, in experiments on glassy random lasers it is rather difficult to scale the system studying a controlled trend in N and perform finite size scaling as in numerical simulations [64]. Moreover, also the mode resolution is finite and we do not know much about the spatial extension of the modes and, therefore, about the interaction graph, nor about the magnitude and sign of the couplings. As anticipated, when the IFO are introduced in experiments only the mode intensity is acquired and not the mode phase. Moreover, one does not have access to instantaneous emission intensities but only to the integrated intensity emission spectra. It is, thus, rather difficult to directly control equilibration. Notwithstanding it has been possible to obtain clear signatures of RSB across the lasing threshold in experiments on a particular subset of random lasers, having a quenched scattering structure and displaying large shot-to-shot spectral fluctuations.

16.3. Experimental Measurements of the Parisi Order Parameter

In this section we describe and discuss the first experimental demonstration of RSB reported in Ref. 65 and give an overview of the numerous interesting results that have been published after this work. A subsection is dedicated to material requirements for reproducing real replicas in random lasers.

16.3.1. *Experimental procedure*

In Ref. 65 the authors measure shot-to-shot intensity of the emitted light from a suitable random laser, calculate the fluctuation overlap $\mathcal{C}$ of these experimental observables and build its distribution at various input pumping. The resulting $P(\mathcal{C})$ profiles unambiguously reproduce the predictions of RSB theory made by Giorgio Parisi.

The authors use a thiophene (T5OCx) dye chemically treated to have a thick amorphous solid material. When this material is pumped by an external source, above a certain threshold the fluorescence is amplified and a stimulated emission is obtained [66–68]. The amplification is sustained by the multiple light scattering inside the disordered system. A representative confocal image of the sample is depicted in Fig. 16.8(a). For the investigation of emission fluctuations the sample is pumped by an external pulsed laser and at each pulse the emission is collected. A sketch of the pumping and collecting geometry is given in the inset of Fig. 16.8(b).

Figure 16.8(b) shows single shot RL emission spectra taken at identical experimental conditions. The distinct peaks are the activated modes or resonances of the disordered laser. Their configuration changes from shot to shot evidencing that each time the system is pumped the numerous passive modes, characteristic of the material, compete for the available gain, giving rise to several different compositions of the activated spectral peaks [69]. This is also evidenced by the direct visualisation of the sample during pumping, as reported in Fig. 16.9, where four different fluorescence images taken at four single shots exhibit different emission patterns and spectra. From shot to shot the size and the brightness of the luminous spots change showing that also the spatial structure of the modes changes. Such behaviour is strongly dependent on the input energy and it occurs above a pumping threshold that is the RL energy threshold. Below this pumping energy only spontaneous emission (fluorescence) is observed, above this threshold the system becomes a RL with strongly variable emission.

In Fig. 16.10 emission spectra of subsequent 100 shots at two different pump energies are shown. At low energy (Fig. 16.10(a)) only noisy variations of the spontaneous

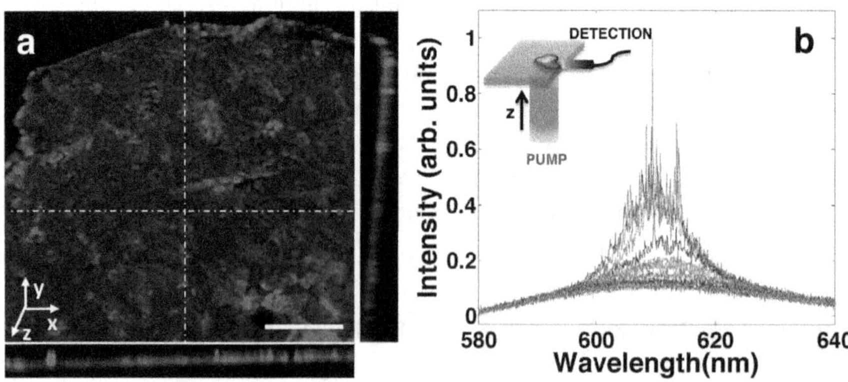

Fig. 16.8.   a) 3D reconstruction of confocal microscopy Z-stack images of a T5OCx solid sample. The right and the bottom panels report the yz- and the xz-sections, respectively. Scale bar: 20μm. b) High resolution single shot spectra taken in the same conditions, 10mJ pump energy. Inset: sketch of the experiment. Reproduced from Ref. 65 with permission from Nature Publishing Group.

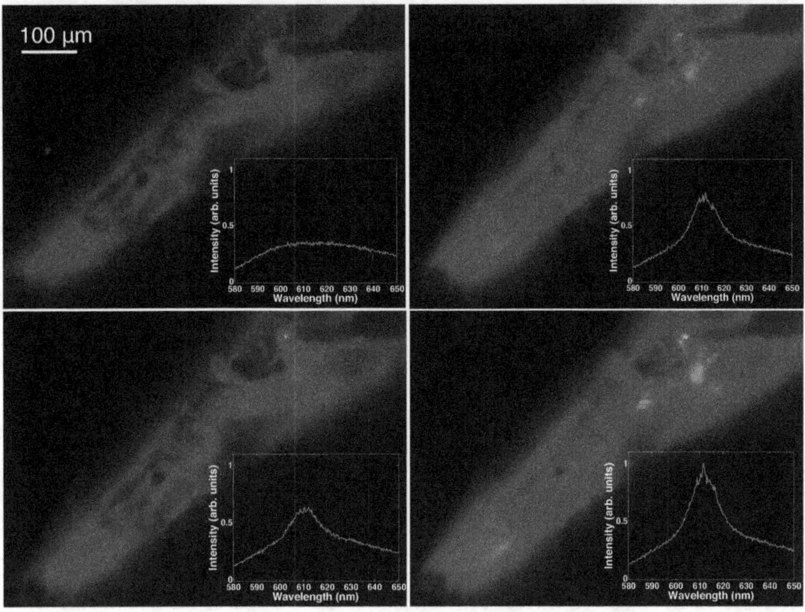

Fig. 16.9.   Snapshots of RL emissions. Single shot optical images and corresponding emission spectra (insets) during the pumping of the sample in the same experimental conditions. The input energy is 10mJ. Reproduced from Ref. 65 with permission from Nature Publishing Group.

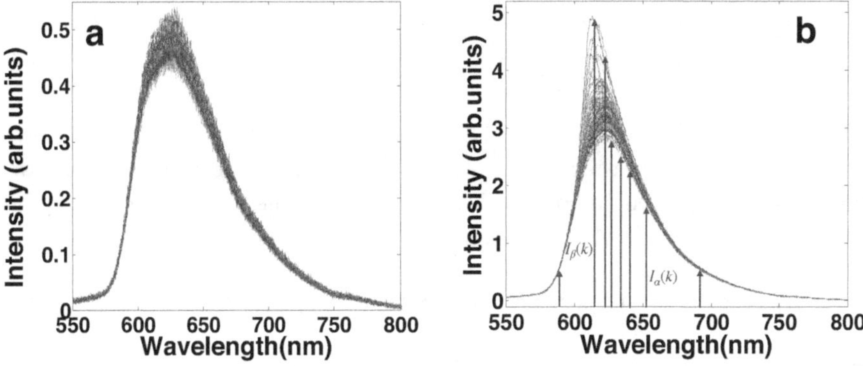

Fig. 16.10.   a–b) Emission spectra at low energy 1mJ (a) and high energy 12mJ with evident fluctuations (b). The experimentally accessible variable, coarse graining the behavior of single modes, is the intensity $I(k)$ at a given wavelength λ_k. In panel b the resonances $I(k)$ for two and for different replicas (spectra), denoted by α (red arrows) and β (blue arrows), are pointed out.

emission are observed, while at high energy (Fig. 16.10(b)) the spectra fluctuate randomly from pulse to pulse. These experimental results can be analyzed in the framework of replica theory. Indeed, the solid property of the material guarantees the reproducibility of the same disordered network of mode interactions from shot to shot. Bond disorder is quenched and real replicas of the same random laser sample are reproduced at each illumination shot. Each spectrum can, thus, be considered as the intensity configuration of a different state of the same thermodynamic glassy phase. Though for the theory, cf. Eqs. (16.3), (16.10), the spins are complex mode amplitudes, the experimentally accessible observables are their intensities (16.18), I_k^{a}, at wavelength λ_k of the shot a: k is the spin index and a is the replica index.

It is important to recall that the effective statistical mechanics Hamiltonian variables are the complex amplitudes a_k, [44, 45, 70] not accessible in the experiments. While, as anticipated in Sec. 16.2.2, their square moduli, the emitted intensities, are easily measurable. In Sec. 16.2.3 we reported that such coarse graining is refined enough to validate the possible breaking of replica symmetry in random lasers and their glass-like behaviour by introducing the IFO parameter $\mathcal{C}$, Eq. (16.21), between pulse-to-pulse intensity fluctuations in different replicas. Now we are considering experimental replicas and the experimental IFO is naturally defined as

$$\mathcal{C}_{\mathrm{ab}} = \frac{1}{\mathcal{N}_{\mathrm{ab}}} \sum_{k=1}^{N} \Delta_k^{(\mathrm{a})} \Delta_k^{(\mathrm{b})}, \tag{16.23}$$

where

$$\Delta_k^{(\mathrm{a})} \equiv I_k^{(\mathrm{a})} - \bar{I}(k) \tag{16.24}$$

with $\bar{I}(k)$ the average over N_s replicas (emission spectra) of each mode intensity

$$\bar{I}_k = \frac{1}{N_s} \sum_{\mathrm{a}=1}^{N_s} I_k^{(\mathrm{a})} \tag{16.25}$$

and where the normalization factor is

$$\mathcal{N}_{\mathrm{ab}} \equiv \sqrt{\sum_{k=1}^{N} \left(\Delta_k^{(\mathrm{a})} \right)^2} \sqrt{\sum_{k=1}^{N} \left(\Delta_k^{(\mathrm{b})} \right)^2}. \tag{16.26}$$

From the N_s measured spectra the set of all $N_s(N_s-1)/2$ values of $\mathcal{C}$ for each different input energy is calculated and their distributions $P(\mathcal{C})$ are depicted in Fig. 16.11 (top).

Six examples are reported in Fig. 16.11, top row of panels, for increasing pump energy. At low energy (Fig. 16.11 left-most plot), all overlaps are centred around the

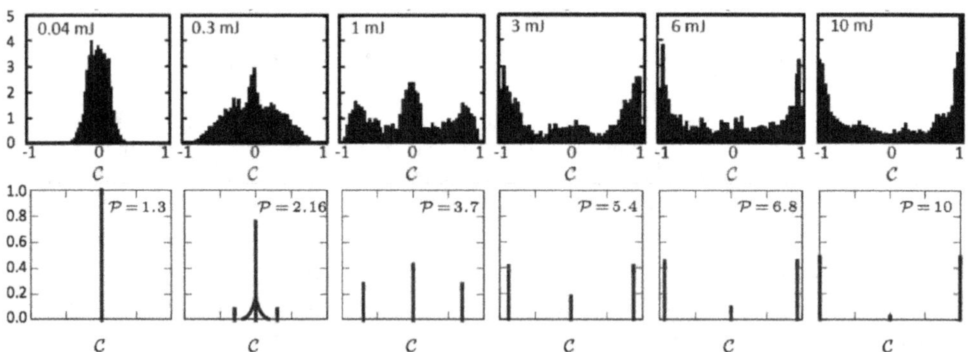

Fig. 16.11. Top line: distribution function of the experimental overlap $P(\mathcal{C})$, Eq. (16.23), showing replica symmetry breaking by increasing pump energy. Bottom line: distribution of the theoretical IFO (16.21) by increasing pumping. Reproduced from Refs. 65 and 59 with permission from Nature Publishing Group.

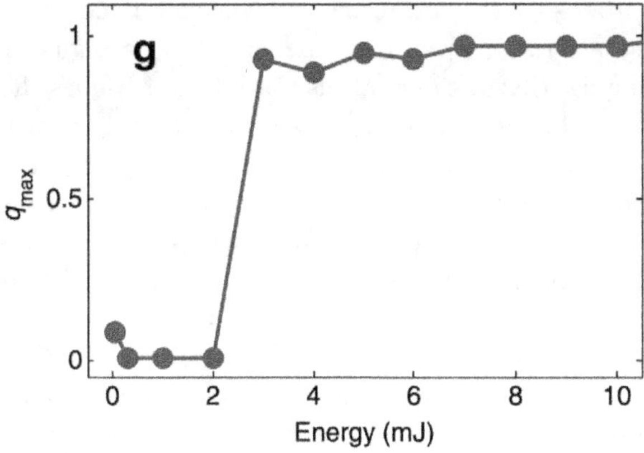

Fig. 16.12.   The value q_{max} corresponding to the position of the maximum of $P(|\mathcal{C}|)$ versus pumping. A sharp transition from 0 to a large value is evidenced. Reproduced from Ref. 65 with permission from Nature Publishing Group.

zero value, meaning that the electromagnetic modes (spins) are independent and not interacting. They are in the paramagnetic regime. By increasing energy, modes are coupled by the nonlinearity and this corresponds to a non-trivial overlap distribution. In the high energy glassy phase, with all modes highly interacting and frustrated by the disorder, $\mathcal{C}$ assumes all possible values in the range $[-1, 1]$. Such behaviour of the $P(\mathcal{C})$ evidences the fact that the correlation between intensity fluctuations in any two replicas depends on the replicas selected. The variety of possible correlations extends to the whole range of values. This is a manifestation of the breaking of the replica symmetry. In the bottom row the analytical results of the fully connected model of Secs. 16.2.2–16.2.3 are reproduced for a heuristic comparison.

In Fig. 16.12 a useful parameter q_{max} corresponding to the position of the maximum of $P(|\mathcal{C}|)$ versus pumping is shown: it changes drastically from 0 to a very large value next to 1 signaling a phase transition at about 3mJ. This is the RL energy threshold. As shown in Figs. (16.6) and (16.7), the onset of the transition to the glassy phase occurs as soon as the $P(\mathcal{C})$ develops non-Gaussian tails. Taking as a reference the full width at half maximum (FWHM) of the low pumping Gaussian distribution one might, therefore, improve the identification of the random lasing threshold as the pumping energy at which the area outside the range of 2 FWHM is sensitively larger than 2%.

These findings besides being a first experimental demonstration of the RSB theory, are also relevant in photonics. The overlap distributions and q_{max} are now used in many works to measure the energy threshold of RLs and are considered a powerful tool to identify the RL behaviour and distinguish it from other emission mechanisms.

16.3.2. *Material requirements for reproducing real replicas*

Before reporting the main results of RSB in other kinds of RL, it is important to stress the concept that not all random lasers show strong emitted intensity fluctuations and consequent breaking of replica symmetry. Reference 65, for instance, shows that RSB is lacking in a RL made of a dyed colloidal dispersion. Indeed, in a fluid sample the particles tend to move from shot to shot during a single experiment and, therefore, the set of possible multiple scattering trajectories experienced by the light pumped into the system changes. This implies that the optical susceptibility, as well as the normal mode profiles in (16.13) and (16.14) change giving rise to a different quenched disordered sample every shot. Under these conditions a RL sample is not replicated but a new RL, with a new random coupling configuration, is realized at every shot, unless the liquid is not stable enough (from the point of view of photonic time scales) to allow the realization of replicas. Within this discussion, we report that RSB has been evidenced in liquid phase RL samples for instance in Ref. 71 and Ref. 72.

In Ref. 71 a dyed sol-gel colloidal suspension with modified amorphous TiO_2 scattering particles, made on purpose to strongly hinder photodegradation and precipitation, shows clear glassy random laser behaviour. The spectra are analysed by following the procedure reported in Sec. 16.3.1 and RSB is evidenced. Although the authors do not expand on the fact that in liquid materials the structural composition changes in time due to the Brownian motion of the particles, they directly test the robustness of their samples against tens of thousand of shots and give evidence that emission spectra from single pump shots can be properly considered as replicas. As pumping increases from the incoherent wave regime across the lasing threshold the $P(\mathcal{C})$ behaviour is, indeed, qualitatively similar to the one reported in Fig. 16.11: a low pumping $P(\mathcal{C})$ with a single Gaussian peak in zero develops long tails around the lasing threshold that become side peaks at larger and larger IFO values upon increasing the pumping.

The opposite approach, pumping energy on a fluid RL whose microscopic scatterer positions certainly change from shot to shot, is followed in Ref. 72. Experimental evidence is provided of the motion of the scattering particles from shot to shot and, looking at the IFO distribution, the robustness of RSB theory also in systems with annealed disorder is claimed. If the statistical mechanical description of glassy random lasers as spin-glass models is to hold, however, one would expect the occurrence of a behavior corresponding to a replica symmetric solution [73]. Our point of view is that in solid systems single shot spectra are considered as replicas because all experimental parameters are quenched and only the strong interaction between modes (spins) at high pumping (low temperature) causes the breaking of their symmetry. In fluid materials whose typical diffusion time scale is shorter than the experimental time (even though possibly longer then the single shot duration) the microscopic matter composition changes from shot to shot. Even though still many modes are randomly activated and interact with quenched disordered couplings at any shot and the system is a random laser it is not possible to look for replica symmetry breaking because real replicas (i.e., identical realizations of the random coupling network) are not there.

Looking at the IFO distributions reported in Ref. 72, indeed, they turn out to have a sharp change from a Gaussian to a purely bimodal distribution across the lasing threshold. A more likely interpretation of this phenomenon might, thus, be the occurrence of bistability, a known phenomenon in standard lasers. Because of randomness (at each shot a different realization of disordered mode couplings is yielded) some samples will be lasing after an illuminating shot, while others might still be in the fluorescent regime. This implies that the average spectrum $\bar{I}_k$ over all emissions will never be similar to any of the single emission spectra: it will be far away from both the fluorescent spectra and the lasing emission spectra. Therefore, no Δ_k in Eq. (16.24) will be small and the only values of the IFO available will be large (positive or negative), inducing a bimodal $P(\mathcal{C})$.

This is also what probably occurs in some other experiments on ordered lasers.

16.3.2.1. *RSB in ordered cavity*

We mention two very bright works where RSB has been claimed to occur in standard ordered cavities. Basak *et al.* in 2016 reported on strong intensity fluctuations in both liquid and solid dye lasers with Fabry–Perot cavities obtained by the cuvette walls in the former and by the interface of polymeric thin slab with air in the latter [74]. The samples were pumped with pulsed lasers and by increasing the pumping energy at laser threshold strong intensity fluctuations were observed. These were analyzed by means of the IFO distribution and RSB was put forward as an explanation of their behaviour.

Actually, the very detailed analysis performed by the authors demostrates the existence of a critical interval of pumping energy where, from shot to shot, a fluorescent or a laser emission takes place. This is a clear indication of bistability, in laser language, corresponding to phase separation in a first order phase transition, in statistical mechanics. It is not unexpected, as the statistical physics model for the ordered (or for the not too disordered) multi-mode laser in a closed cavity corresponds to Eq. (16.3) with only the four-mode coupling part and with small enough R_J for the J's distribution, cf. Fig. 16.6.

Another example is the work of Moura *et al.* in Ref. 75 where the IFO distribution is measured in the spontaneous mode-locking regime of a multimode Q-switched Nd:YAG laser. The authors rightly assert that the observed phenomenon is quite distinct from what has been investigated in random lasers characterized by incoherently oscillating modes. As they display the $P(\mathcal{C})$, calculated via (16.23), (16.24) and (16.26), versus pumping the lasing threshold is identified as the sharp transition from a phase of a single Gaussian peaked $P(\mathcal{C})$ to a clean bimodal $P(\mathcal{C})$.

Since in Ref. 75 the ensemble of spectra from which the $P(\mathcal{C})$ is computed is very instructively displayed, it is possible to see that above threshold only two types of spectra are present: a broad, flat fluorescent one and a narrow, spiky lasing one. Once again, we face bistability. This is expected in the theory transition between model-locking lasers (ordered or slightly random) as reported, for instance, by the dotted line in Fig. 16.6.

From this latter study we also report an interesting phenomenon. As pumping is large enough so that all shots are lasing, strong fluctuations appear to be there in the (narrow) spectra and the $P(\mathcal{C})$ appears to have a more complicated shape, though always basically bimodal, in which overlaps between the side peaks have a finite probability to occur. It would be interesting to understand whether this is due to experimental noise correlated with the strong pumping or to the onset of a glassy phase as, for instance, in Fig. 16.6 for $0.5 < R_J < 1$.

16.3.3. *Evidence of RSB in other different RLs and nonlinear waves*

A completely different class of RLs showing RSB is furnished by erbium-based random fiber lasers (Er-RFL) and widely investigated by A. Gomes and coworkers. A first demonstration is given in Ref. 76, where the authors employ a 30-cm-long Er-RFL, pumped by a continuous wave source. The authors discuss and show that this kind of RFL is a multimode laser with more than 200 longitudinal modes. They analyse emission intensity fluctuation over 1500 acquisition spectra (replicas) for different pumping power and measure the IFO from Eq. (16.23). In Fig. 16.13 the IFO distribution $P(q)$ is depicted together with the parameter q_{max}, at which $P(q)$ assumes its global maximum.[d] It is demonstrated in Fig. 16.13(e) that both sharp line narrowing and q_{max} growth from 0 to 1 occur at the same identical input power interval, that is the laser threshold. This confirms the findings in Ref. 65.

16.3.3.1. *RSB and Lévy flight*

The transition from paramagnetic to glassy states in random lasers has been also analyzed in correspondence to the transition from diffusive to super diffusive (or Lévy flight) regimes of light propagation. Strong emission fluctuations in RLs have been described in the past by using the diffusive model of light and by successfully identifying different statistical regimes for disordered lasers [77, 78]. Recently, the strong emission fluctuations in RLs have been analyzed both in the frameworks of Lévy statistics and spin glass theory. Interesting similarities and differences have been demonstrated.

A first comparison between the two statistical physics properties is reported by Gomes et al. in Ref. 79. In this work the physical origin of the possible correspondence between the Lévy flight statistics of emission intensity and the photonic RSB glassy transition in RLs is both theoretically and experimentally investigated. The RL consists

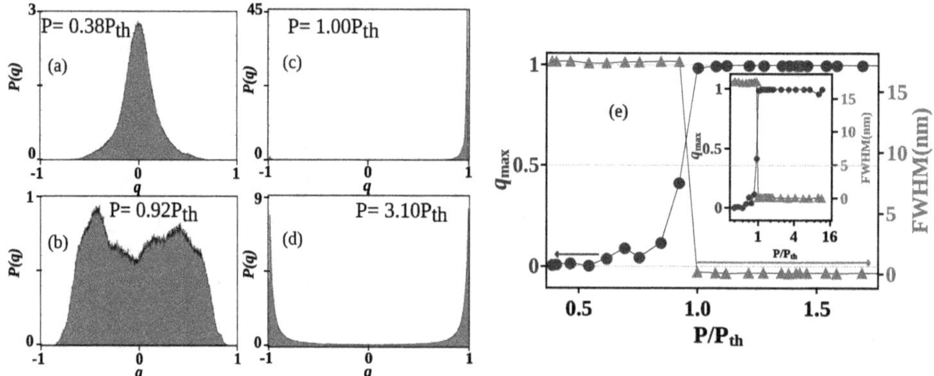

Fig. 16.13.   a–d) IFO distribution $P(q)$ obtained from experimental data at different pump powers (normalized with respect to the threshold power P_{th}). e) q_{max} (circles) versus normalized pump power, together with the FWHM (triangles) for comparison. The inset shows the results for pump powers up to $12P_{th}$. Reproduced from Ref. 76 with permission from American Physical Society.

---

[d]We warn the reader that the symbol q, rather than C, is used here and in the following to denote the intensity fluctuation overlap.

of crystalline powders of Nd^{3+}-doped YBO_3 (Nd:YBO) and pumped by a pulsed laser. The authors for the first time explain the comparison between the RSB transition to the photonic glassy phase and the changes in the statistics of intensity fluctuations in RLs within the same theoretical framework based on the Langevin equations describing the evolution of the mode amplitudes. While such theoretical approach has been introduced and widely used by the spin-glass community [42–44, 70], only recently has it been considered for the statistical distribution of RL intensities [80]. Starting from the Langevin equation the probability density function of emission intensity is obtained. The steady state solution of such equation gives the Lévy-like distribution of intensities. The authors show that, for a given disorder strength, by increasing pumping rate the statistics of emission intensities shifts progressively from an initial Gaussian to a Lévy-like and, then, again to a Gaussian regime, as predicted by the diffusive model of light propagation in random media. The IFO distribution calculated on the same experimental data shows a transition from the spontaneous emission-paramagnetic to the RL glassy behaviour and a recurrence to the paramagnetic regime at higher pumping, similarly to the Lévy statistics results. Once again, this critical behavior is interpreted as a RSB transition, whereas, looking both at the strict bimodal shape of the IFO distribution and at the series of spectra displayed in the work, the transition is probably a first order phase transition with coexistence of fluorescence and (random) laser phases. That is, bistability.

The novelty of these findings lies at higher excitation pulse energy well above the threshold, where fluctuations inside the single spectrum decline considerably with the consequent restoration of the Gaussian diffusive regime for the intensities, but the RL becomes more and more disordered from the point of view of mode coupling and the IFO distribution appears to become non-trivial, hinting at the possible onset of a glassy random laser. In this article the authors do not give any explanation of the existence of a strict causal link between the self-averaged Gaussian regime of intensity fluctuations above the threshold and the observed suppression of the glassy phase, leaving the subject to further studies. The link between the onset of the Lévy statistical regime of intensity fluctuations and the emergence of the RL regime has been reported also in a one dimensional Er-RFL [81].

A different result is shown in Ref. 72, where the authors conclude that the RL transition and the Lévy regime onset may not have a clear causal relation. They claim that the former is strongly related to the threshold and less to the magnitude of the fluctuations, while the latter emerges for large fluctuations and only under strict conditions of the ratio between gain and scattering properties of the material. As a demonstration they report the clear experimental result where the Lévy regime is suppressed while a RSB transition is present. A further study on the matter is probably required, also including the role of bistability in non-glassy random lasers.

16.3.3.2. *RSB and turbulence*

In 2018 Gonzáles *et al.* employ an erbium random fiber laser to demonstrate for the first time the coexistence of turbulence-like and spin-glass-like behavior from the same set of measurements [82].

For the theoretical analysis they introduce the photonic Pearson correlation coefficient that can be considered as a generalized time dependent expression of the spin-glass overlap parameter. If τ is the time of data acquisition, the time dependent IFO between replicas α and β is defined as

$$Q_{\alpha\beta}(\tau) = \frac{\sum_k \Delta_k^{(\alpha)}(\tau)\Delta_k^{(\beta)}(\tau)}{\sqrt{\sum_k \left(\Delta_k^{(\alpha)}(\tau)\right)^2}\sqrt{\sum_k \left(\Delta_k^{(\beta)}(\tau)\right)^2}}, \tag{16.27}$$

with k being the wavelength index in the emission spectra, α and β single shot spectra indexes (replicas). Besides the definition (16.24), for $\tau = 0$, i.e.,

$$\Delta_k^{(\alpha)}(0) \equiv I_k^{(\mathrm{a})}(0) - \bar{I}_k(0),$$

when $\tau > 0$ the time-dependent spectral fluctuation is defined as

$$\Delta_k^{(\alpha)}(\tau) \equiv I_k^{(\alpha)}(\tau) - I_k^{(\alpha)}(0) - \left[\bar{I}_k(\tau) - \bar{I}_k(0)\right].$$

With these notations Eq. (16.27) quantifies the emission intensity fluctuations in time. It is sensitive to both liquid-glass transition and fluid dynamics phenomena such as turbulence. It is demonstrated that above the threshold the distribution of the Pearson coefficient for short times is centered around $Q \sim 0$, leading to the unimodal behaviour of $P(Q)$ in the turbulent-like state. While still above the threshold but at large time scales it assumes a distribution resembling the profile typical of a RSB IFO distributions. In this regime the intermittency vanishes and a crossover to the non-turbulent behavior takes place.

The authors state that, since the overlap parameter considers all separation times between spectra, the statistical weight of the replica overlaps with long times dominates over the short time series. As a consequence, $P(Q(\tau))$ actually appears qualitatively similar to the overlap distribution that characterizes the RSB spin glass phase.

16.3.3.3. *RSB maps*

Recently RSB theory has been applied to obtain real time maps of the laser activity in a heterogeneous RL [83]. The random lasers are made of polymeric ribbon-like and highly porous fibers with evident RL action from separated micrometric domains that alternatively switch on and off by tuning the pumping light intensity. This novel effect is visualised by building for the first time replica symmetry breaking maps of the emitting fibers with micrometric spatial resolution. The overlap parameter is calculated directly from the images. 100 single shot frames are recorded at fixed experimental condition and each one is a replica. Four examples are illustrated in Fig. 16.14, where the variation of the spatial emission from shot to shot is evident. In this work the measurable quantities corresponding to spins are the intensities of the pixels recorded by the camera. The authors calculate the overlap between these observables that are the spatial (transverse) modes while previously only temporal (longitudinal) modes were considered [65].

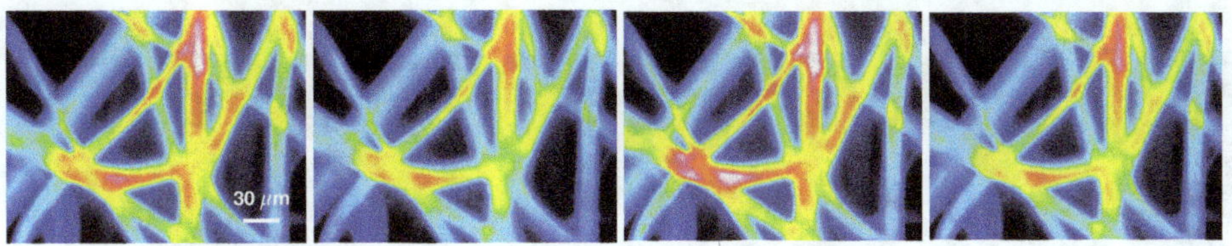

Fig. 16.14.   Four fluorescence images taken under identical experimental situations and regarded as replicas. Reproduced from Ref. 83 with permission from ACS Publications.

Each frame of 1024×1376 pixels is divided into squares of 16×16, named macropixels, and the overlap $q_{\alpha,\beta}^{j}$ for each macropixel j is calculated as:

$$q_{\alpha\beta}^{(j)} = \frac{\sum_{x_k,y_k} \Delta^{(\alpha,j)}(x_k,y_k)\, \Delta^{(\beta,j)}(x_k,y_k)}{\sqrt{\sum_{x_k,y_k}\left(\Delta^{(\alpha,j)}(x_k,y_k)\right)^2}\sqrt{\sum_{x_k,y_k}\left(\Delta^{(\beta,j)}(x_k,y_k)\right)^2}}. \tag{16.28}$$

where α and β are replica indexes, j is the macropixel index, and x_k and y_k are pixel indexes inside one macropixel running from 1 to 16. In Eq. (16.28)

$$\Delta^{(\alpha,j)}(x_k,y_k) \equiv I^{(\alpha,j)}(x_k,y_k) - \overline{I^{(j)}}(x_k,y_k),$$

with $I^{(\alpha,j)}(x_k,y_k)$ being the intensity at the pixel with coordinate (x_k,y_k) of the jth macropixel for the replica α and where

$$\overline{I^{(j)}}(x_k,y_k) \equiv \frac{1}{N_s}\sum_{\alpha=1}^{N_s} I^{(\alpha,j)}(x_k,y_k)$$

is the average intensity over N_s shots for each pixel. With this procedure, from the images one has access to the sets of all $N_s(N_s-1)/2$ values $q^{(j)}$ of $q_{\alpha\beta}^{(j)}$ that determine the distributions $P(q^{(j)})$ for all 64×86 macropixels j. This is done for different pumping energy. Following the previous work, the authors calculate q_{max} for all macropixels and obtain replica symmetry breaking maps at various pumping. The results are shown in Fig. 16.15. Domains with $q_{\text{max}} > 0.5$ are laser-ON and those with $q_{\text{max}} < 0.5$ are laser-OFF.

In this work the mapping of q_{max} allows for the first time the visualisation of heterogeneous RL with switching and variable activity. This procedure is proposed as a robust tool to identify the presence and the spatial extension of RL activity from fluorescence images.

16.3.3.4. *RSB in nonlinear waves*

In 2017 Pierangeli *et al.* [84] report the observation of the breaking of replica symmetry in nonlinear optical propagation. They investigate intensity profiles of a laser beam transmitted from a photorefractive disordered slab waveguide. The nonlinearity of the material is tuned and strong fluctuations of light above a certain threshold are evidenced, as in the intensity map of Fig. 16.16. Differently from previous works, the replica overlap is calculated over the spatial autocorrelation of the intensities $I(x)$, and its distribution undergoes a clear transition into a non-trivial distribution as the nonlinearity exceeds a

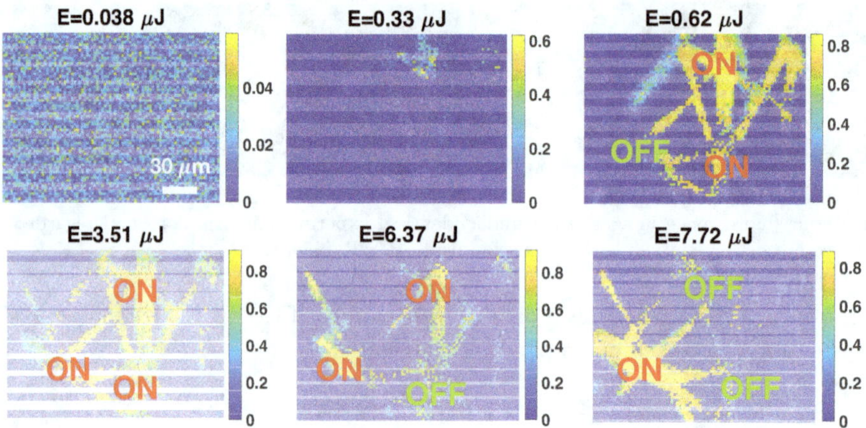

Fig. 16.15.   Replica symmetry breaking maps. Maps of the q_{max} values calculated for each macropixel at different input energies. ON and OFF indicate the activation status of the RL emission.

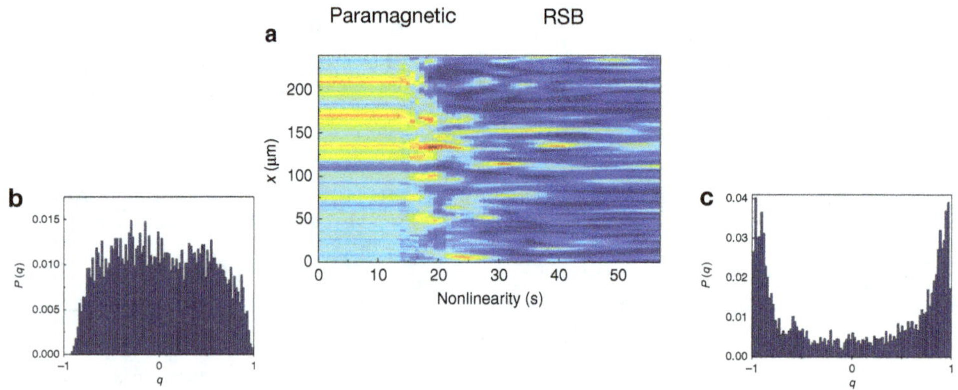

Fig. 16.16.   Transmitted intensity profiles along one direction $I(x)$ by increasing nonlinearity. At high nonlinearity a RSB regime of strong fluctuations is evidenced. The corresponding distribution $P(q)$ in the paramagnetic (left) and glassy (right) regimes are depicted.

threshold value. Results are shown in Fig. 16.16. These findings demonstrate that non-linear propagation can exhibit features typical of spin glasses thanks to the coexistence and interplay of the two main ingredients: disorder and nonlinearity.

16.4. Conclusions and Outlook

In this chapter we have considered the problem of the experimental measure of the functional order parameter for a multi-equilibria phase in complex disordered systems, representing the transition to a replica symmetry broken thermodynamic phase. After a flash introduction of the Parisi overlap distribution we briefly discussed how the outcomes of the RSB theory have soon cast light on peculiar results in early experiments on spin-glass susceptibility. We have, then, been very rapidly reviewing the attempt to reconstruct the equilibrium overlap distribution through measurements of the out-of-equilibrium fluctuation-dissipation ratio in systems satisfying stochastic stability and we did our best to give a state-of-the-art report of the experiments based so far on that approach. Finally, we have diffusively discussed, both theoretically, numerically and experimentally, the approach to the problem by means of complex random photonic systems, the random lasers, and reported the first measurements of the Parisi order parameter through the measurements of light intensity spectral fluctuations and the acquisition of overlaps between fluctuations of different real replicas of the systems.

The study of nonlinear photonics systems by means of statistical mechanics of disordered systems is an inspiring example of a constructive synergy leading to advances in both fields. The idea that random lasers might be described as disordered systems and treated with the tools of statistical physics in order to fully unveil and understand their complex behavior [42–44, 70] has brought about the development of a spin-glass model [45, 58] whose RSB order parameter could finally be accessible to experimental measurements [12, 59, 65, 76, 79].

Furthermore, such synergy has stimulated several new studies on different open issues in photonics in random media. To mention a few, the statistical physics approach has been applied in relation to the onset of a power-law (Lévy-like) distribution of the emission intensity in random laser, [72, 77–81] to the characterization of turbulence in photonic systems, [82] to the spatial distribution of interacting modes [26, 83] and the self-substained nature of mode-locking in random lasers [26, 44] and has led to the study of glassiness in nonlinear photonic systems other than random lasers [84]. Several rather interesting issues remain open in this line of research combining photonics and statistical physics, including the study of a first order critical behavior with phase coexistence and its relationship to the possible occurrence of bistability in random lasers, or the measurement and control of mode phases whose impact would have important consequences in the making and the technological use of random lasers.

Acknowledgments

The authors thank Fabrizio Antenucci, Miguel Ibañez-Berganza, Giacomo Gradenigo, Claudio Maggi, Alessia Marruzzo, Jacopo Niedda and Giorgio Parisi for very many useful scientific exchanges.

We acknowledge the support from the European Research Council (ERC) under the European Union's Horizon 2020 Research and Innovation Program, Project LoTGlasSy (Grant Agreement No. 694925), the support of LazioInnova - Regione Lazio under the program *Gruppi di ricerca 2020* - POR FESR Lazio 2014-2020, Project NanoProbe (Application code A0375-2020-36761).

References

[1] G. Parisi, *J. Phys. A.* **13**, L115, (1980).
[2] G. Parisi, *J. Phys. A.* **13**, 1101, (1980).
[3] M. Mézard, G. Parisi, and M. A. Virasoro, *Europhys. Lett.* **1**(2), 77–82 (1986).

[4] M. Mézard, G. Parisi, and M. Virasoro, *Spin Glass Theory and Beyond.* (World Scientific (Singapore), 1987).

[5] M. Mézard and G. Parisi, Eur. Phys. J. B. **20**, 217, (2001).

[6] D. S. Wiersma, M. P. Vanalbada, and A. Lagendijk, *Nature.* **373**, 203, (1995).

[7] H. Cao, Y. G. Zhao, S. T. Ho, E. W. Seelig, Q. H. Wang, and R. P. H. Chang, *Phys. Rev. Lett.* **82**(11), 2278, (1999).

[8] H. Cao, *Waves in Random and Complex Media.* **13**(3), R1–R39, (2003).

[9] D. S. Wiersma, *Nat. Phys.* **4**, 359, (2008).

[10] J. Andreasen, A. A. Asatryan, L. C. Botten, B. A. Byrne, H. Cao, L. Ge, L. Labonté, P. Sebbah, A. D. Stone, H. E. Türeci, and C. Vanneste, *Adv. Opt. Photonics.* **3**, 88–127, (2011).

[11] I. Viola, L. Leuzzi, C. Conti, and N. Ghofraniha, *Basic Physics and Recent Developments of Organic Random Lasers,* In *Organic Lasers.* Pan Stanford, (2018).

[12] A. S. Gomes, A. L. Moura, C. B. de Araújo, and E. P. Raposo, *Prog. Quantum Electron.* **78**, 100343, (2021).

[13] S. Nagata, P. Keesom, and H. Harrison, *Phys. Rev. B.* **19**, 1633, (1979).

[14] S. Franz, M. Mézard, and G. P. L. Parisi, *Phys. Rev. Lett.* **81**, 1758, (1998).

[15] D. Hérisson and M. Ocio, *Phys. Rev. Lett.* **88**, 257202 (2002).

[16] D. Hérisson and M. Ocio, *Eur. Phys. J. B.* **40**, 283–294, (2004).

[17] C. Maggi, R. Di Leonardo, J. C. Dyre, and G. Ruocco, *Phys. Rev. B.* **81**, 104201, (2010).

[18] H. Oukris and N. Israeloff, *Nat. Phys.* **6**, 135–138, (2010).

[19] M. Baity-Jesi, E. Calore, A. Cruz, L. A. Fernandez, J. M. Gil-Narvión, A. Gordillo-Guerrero, D. Iñiguez, A. Maiorano, E. Marinari, V. Martin-Mayor, J. Monforte-Garcia, A. M. Sudupe, D. Navarro, G. Parisi, S. Perez-Gaviro, F. Ricci-Tersenghi, J. J. Ruiz-Lorenzo, S. F. Schifano, B. Seoane, A. Tarancón, R. Tripiccione, and D. Yllanes, *Proc. Natl. Acad. Sci. U.S.A.* **114**(8), 1838–1843, (2017).

[20] H. Cao, Y. G. Zhao, H. C. Ong, S. T. Ho, J. Y. Dai, J. Y. Wu, and R. P. H. Chang, *Appl. Phys. Lett.* **73**(25), 3656, (1998).

[21] H. Cao, J. Y. Xu, S. H. Chang, and S. T. Ho, *Phys. Rev. E.* **61**, 1985, (2000).

[22] M. Anni, S. Lattante, T. Stomeo, R. Cingolani, G. Gigli, G. Barbarella, and L. Favaretto, *Phys. Rev. B.* **70**, 195216, (2004).

[23] K. L. van der Molen, R. W. Tjerkstra, A. P. Mosk, and A. Lagendijk, *Phys. Rev. Lett.* **98**, 143901, (2007).

[24] A. Tulek, R. C. Polson, and Z. V. Vardeny, *Nat. Phys.* **6**, 303–310, (2010).

[25] V. Folli, A. Puglisi, L. Leuzzi, and C. Conti, *Phys. Rev. Lett.* **108**, 248002, (2012).

[26] F. Antenucci, G. Lerario, B. S. Fernandéz, L. De Marco, M. De Giorgi, D. Ballarini, D. Sanvitto, and L. Leuzzi, *Phys. Rev. Lett.* **126**, 173901 (2021).

[27] Y. Eliezer, S. Mahler, A. A. Friesem, H. Cao, and N. Davidson, *Phys. Rev. Lett.* **128**, 143901 (2022).

[28] B. Redding, A. A. Choma, and H. Cao, *Nature Photon.* **6**, 355–359, (2012).

[29] M. Barredo-Zuriarrain, I. Iparraguirre, J. Fernández, J. Azkargorta, and R. Balda, *Laser Physics Letters.* **14**(10), 106201 (2017).

[30] V. Folli, N. Ghofraniha, A. Puglisi, L. Leuzzi, and C. Conti, *Sci. Rep.* **3**, 2251, (2013).

[31] E. Ignesti, F. Tommasi, L. Fini, F. Martelli, N. Azzali, and S. Cavalieri, *Sci. Rep.* p. 35225, (2016).

[32] Y. Xu, L. Zhang, S. Gao, P. Lu, S. Mihailov, and X. Bao, *Opt. Lett.* **42**(7), 1353–1356 (2017).

[33] R. C. Polson and Z. V. Vardeny, *Appl. Phys. Lett.* **85**, 1289–1291, (2004).

[34] Q. Song, S. Xiao, Z. Xu, J. Liu, X. Sun, V. Drachev, V. M. Shalaev, O. Akkus, and Y. L. Kim, *Opt. Lett.* **35**(9), 1425–1427 (2010).

[35] F. Lahoz, I. R. Martín, M. Urgellés, J. Marrero-Alonso, R. Marín, C. J. Saavedra, A. Boto, and M. Díaz, *Laser Physics Letters.* **12**(4), 045805 (2015).

[36] Y. Wang, Z. Duan, Z. Qiu, P. Zhang, J. Wu, D. Zhang, and T. Xiang, *Sci. Rep.* **7**, 8385, (2017).

[37] D. T. W. Lin, Y. C. Hu, and C. Cheng, *IEEE Sens. J.* **12**(2), 397–403 (2012).

[38] Y.-M. Liao, Y.-C. Lai, P. Perumal, W.-C. Liao, C.-Y. Chang, C.-S. Liao, S.-Y. Lin, and Y.-F. Chen, *Adv. Mat. Technol.* **1**, 1600068, (2016).

[39] S. K. Turitsyn, S. A. Babin, A. E. El-Taher, P. Harper, D. V. Churkin, S. I. Kablukov, J. D. Ania-Castanon, V. Karalekas, and E. V. Podivilov, *Nat. Photon.* **4**, 231–235, (2010).

[40] M. Leonetti, C. Conti, and C. Lopez, *Nat. Photon.* **5**, 615, (2015).

[41] Q. Baudouin, N. Mercadier, V. Guarrera, W. Guerin, and R. Kaiser, *Nat. Phys.* **9**, 357–360, (2013).

[42] L. Angelani, C. Conti, G. Ruocco, and F. Zamponi, *Phys. Rev. Lett.* **96**, 065702, (2006).

[43] L. Angelani, C. Conti, G. Ruocco, and F. Zamponi, *Phys. Rev. B.* **74**, 104207, (2006).

[44] C. Conti and L. Leuzzi, *Phys. Rev. B.* **83**, 134204, (2011).

[45] F. Antenucci, A. Crisanti, and L. Leuzzi, *Phys. Rev. A.* **91**, 053816, (2015).

[46] F. Antenucci, *Statistical physics of wave interactions.* (Springer, 2016).

[47] F. Antenucci, A. Crisanti, M. Ibáñez-Berganza, A. Marruzzo, and L. Leuzzi, *Philos. Mag.* **96**(7-9), 704–731, (2016).

[48] E. T. Jaynes and F. W. Cummings, *Proc. IEEE.* **51**, 89, (1963).

[49] V. Eremeev, S. E. Skipetrov, and M. Orszag, *Phys. Rev. A.* **84**, 023816 (2011).

[50] A. Marruzzo. *Statistical mechanics of continuous spin models and applications to nonlinear optics in disordered media.* PhD thesis, Scuola di Dottorato Vito Volterra, Sapienza Università di Roma, (2015).

[51] A. Gordon and B. Fischer, *Phys. Rev. Lett.* **89**, 103901 (2002).

[52] A. Crisanti and H. Sommers, *Z. Phys. B.* **87**, 341, (1992).

[53] A. Crisanti and L. Leuzzi, *Phys. Rev. Lett.* **93**, 217203, (2004).

[54] A. Crisanti and L. Leuzzi, *Phys. Rev. B.* **73**, 014412, (2006).

[55] A. Crisanti and L. Leuzzi, *Phys. Rev. B.* **75**, 144301, (2007).

[56] A. Crisanti and L. Leuzzi, *Nucl. Phys. B.* **870**, 176–204, (2013).

[57] C. J. Chen, P. K. Wai, and C. R. Menyuk, *Opt. Lett.* **19**, 198, (1994).

[58] F. Antenucci, C. Conti, A. Crisanti, and L. Leuzzi, *Phys. Rev. Lett.* **114**, 043901, (2015).

[59] F. Antenucci, A. Crisanti, and L. Leuzzi, *Sci. Rep.* **5**, 16792, (2015).

[60] A. Marruzzo, P. Tyagi, F. Antenucci, A. Pagnani, and L. Leuzzi, *SciPost Phys.* **5**, 002, (2018).

[61] A. Marruzzo and L. Leuzzi, *Phys. Rev. B.* **91**, 054201, (2015).

[62] A. Marruzzo and L. Leuzzi, *Phys. Rev. B.* **93**, 094206, (2016).

[63] G. Gradenigo, L. Leuzzi, J. Niedda, and G. Parisi. Universality class of the glassy random laser. in preparation, (2022).

[64] G. Gradenigo, F. Antenucci, and L. Leuzzi, *Phys. Rev. Research.* **2**, 023399 (2020).

[65] N. Ghofraniha, I. Viola, F. Dimaria, G. Barbarella, G. Gigli, L. Leuzzi, and C. Conti, *Nat. Comm.* **6**, 6058, (2015).

[66] N. Ghofraniha, I. Viola, F. D. Maria, G. Barbarella, G. Gigli, and C. Conti, *Laser and Photon. Rev.* **7**(3), 432, (2013).

[67] M. Anni, S. Lattante, R. Cingolani, G. Gigli, G. Barbarella, and L. Favaretto, *Appl. Phys. Lett.* **83**, 2754, (2003).

[68] D. Pisignano, M. Anni, G. Gigli, R. Cingolani, M. Zavelani-Rossi, G. Lanzani, G. Barbarella, and L. Favaretto, *Appl. Phys. Lett.* **81**(19), 3534–3536, (2002).

[69] S. Mujumdar, V. Türck, R. Torre, and D. S. Wiersma, *Phys. Rev. A.* **76**, 033807, (2007).

[70] L. Leuzzi, C. Conti, V. Folli, L. Angelani, and G. Ruocco, *Phys. Rev. Lett.* **102**, 083901, (2009).

[71] P. I. R. Pincheira, A. F. Silva, S. I. Fewo, S. J. M. Carreño, A. L. Moura, E. P. Raposo, A. S. L. Gomes, and C. B. de Araújo, *Opt. Lett.* **41**(15), 3459–3462, (2016).

[72] F. Tommasi, E. Ignesti, S. Lepri, and S. Cavalieri, *Sci. Rep.* **6**, 37113, (2016).

[73] W.-K. Chen, H.-W. Hsieh, C.-R. Hwang, and Y.-C. Sheu, *J. Stat. Phys.* **160**, 417–429, (2015).

[74] S. Basak, A. Blanco, and C. López, *Sci. Rep.* **6**, 32134, (2016).

[75] A. L. Moura, P. I. R. Pincheira, A. S. Reyna, E. P. Raposo, A. S. L. Gomes, and C. B. de Araújo, *Phys. Rev. Lett.* **119**, 163902, (2017).

[76] A. S. L. Gomes, B. C. Lima, P. I. R. Pincheira, A. L. Moura, M. Gagné, E. P. Raposo, C. B. de Araújo, and R. Kashyap, *Phys. Rev. A.* **94**, 011801, (2016).

[77] S. Lepri, S. Cavalieri, G. Oppo, and D. Wiersma, *Phys. Rev. A.* **75**, 063820, (2007).

[78] S. Lepri, *Phys. Rev. Lett.* **110**, 230603, (2013).

[79] A. S. L. Gomes, E. P. Raposo, A. L. Moura, S. I. Fewo, P. I. R. Pincheira, V. Jerez, L. J. Q. Maia, and C. B. de Araújo, *Sci. Rep.* **6**, 27987, (2016).

[80] E. P. Raposo and A. S. L. Gomes, *Phys. Rev. A.* **91**, 043827, (2015).

[81] B. C. Lima, A. S. L. Gomes, P. I. R. Pincheira, A. L. Moura, M. Gagné, E. P. Raposo, C. B. de Araújo, and R. Kashyap, *J. Opt. Soc. Am. B.* **34**(2), 293–299, (2017).

[82] I. R. R. González, E. P. Raposo, A. M. Macêdo, L. de S. Menezes, and A. S. Gomes, *Sci. Rep.* **8**, 17046, (2018).

[83] L. M. Massaro, S. Gentilini, A. Portone, A. Camposeo, D. Pisignano, C. Conti, and N. Ghofraniha, *ACS Photonics.* **8**(1), 376–383, (2021).

[84] D. Pierangeli, A. Tavani, F. D. Mei, A. J. Agranat, C. Conti, and E. DelRe, *Nat. Comm.* **8**, 1501, (2017).

Chapter 17

Anderson Localization on the Bethe Lattice

Saverio Pascazio[*], Antonello Scardicchio[†] and Marco Tarzia[‡]

*Dipartimento di Fisica, Università di Bari, I-70126 Bari, Italy
and INFN, Sezione di Bari, I-70125 Bari, Italy
saverio.pascazio@ba.infn.it
†Abdus Salam ICTP, Trieste, Italy
ascardic@ictp.it
‡LPTMC, CNRS-UMR 7600, Sorbonne Université,
4 Place Jussieu, F-75005 Paris, France
and Institut Universitaire de France, 1 rue Descartes,
75231 Paris Cedex 05, France
marco.tarzia@gmail.com

After Anderson's seminal paper in 1958, localization has attracted the interest of many researchers in condensed matter physics and disordered systems. The study of the peculiar nature of this dynamical transition induced by the presence of disorder has required, even in its mean-field formulation, a variety of techniques, from the cavity method to random matrix theory.

In this chapter, **Saverio Pascazio**, **Antonello Scardicchio** and **Marco Tarzia** review this topic covering both some classical results and some more recent advancements, with a particular focus on the problem of Anderson localization on the Bethe lattice.

17.1. A Short Introduction

Anderson localization consists in the suppression of the propagation of waves in a disordered medium. It was first suggested by P. W. Anderson in a seminal article published in 1958 [1, 2], and it is a ubiquitous phenomenon, that applies to waves of very different kinds, both in a classical and quantum mechanical context. Localization has been experimentally confirmed on a number of different physical systems [2–4], although its characteristics are different in different dimensions. While in $D = 1, 2$ spatial dimensions the phenomenon is extremely strong and only special Hamiltonian symmetries can hinder it, in $D \geqslant 3$ the problem is more delicate and a critical value of disorder strength is needed to localize all the spectrum.

Although almost 70 years have passed since the inception of Anderson localization, several issues are still open. For example the critical exponents of the transition are not known exactly in any dimension, and the problem seems resilient to attacks using some kind of perturbation theory (the $\epsilon = D - D_{\text{upper critical}}$ expansion of Wilson comes to mind here). Even a mean-field theory at $D = \infty$, for example by defining the

335

problem on an expander graph such as a Bethe lattice, has proved to be resilient to various numerical and analytical strategies. This is probably due to a twofold set of difficulties. First, the problem has quenched disorder, and second, the transition is not of a thermodynamic nature, but rather of a dynamical one. This means that one has to study the system isolated from the environment. Indeed, as soon as the system is opened to the environment, for example by coupling it to a thermal bath, the localization disappears, to be substituted by a diffusion whose associated constant depends on the temperature of the bath (the so-called Motts variable range hopping conductivity [5]).

Another important problem, tightly related to Anderson localization (AL) is the description of a *many-body* ensemble of electrons, interacting and subject to quenched disorder. This latter line of research (known as many-body localization) took off in the last 15 years thanks to the seminal works of Basko, Aleiner, and Althusler, and those of Huse, Oganesyan, Imbrie, Abanin, Nandkishore, and many others [6–9]. Since preliminary works on the subject [10], many-body localization (MBL) was related to a form of localization in the Fock space of Slater determinants, which play the role of lattice sites in a disordered Anderson tight-binding model. A paradigmatic representation of this transition is indeed Anderson localization of noninteracting "particles" on an expander graph/hierarchical lattice, where the number of sites at distance r grows exponentially with r. Although the analogy between MBL and Anderson localization on hierarchical lattices involves several drastic simplifications (e.g., the correlation between random energies are neglected as well as the specific structure of the Hilbert space), it is very useful to obtain a qualitative understanding of the problem [11–15]. Following the paradigms of statistical physics, hierarchical lattices should represent the mean-field result for a D-dimensional theory, but once it is realized that there are several obscure points in the mean-field theory of Anderson localization (probably due to the fact that the upper critical dimension is infinite [16]), the study of localization on hierarchical lattices has seen a resurgence of interest in the last few years [17–24].

Given the nature of the problem — a ubiquitous physical problem, with quenched disorder and a dynamic transition, that has a rich phenomenology already within the mean-field framework — it is perfectly natural that it would pick Giorgio Parisi's interest. Giorgio's contributions to the field have been multi-faceted and diverse, and we will try to summarize them here quickly.

17.2. Anderson's Tight-Binding Model

Like for all physical phenomena, a thorough discussion requires the analysis of a case-study, namely a model that is able to reproduce the main features of the phenomenon to investigate, without neglecting important physical effects. For the problem at hand, this is provided by the celebrated Anderson tight-binding model, which describes non-interacting electrons in an atomic lattice.

Consider an electron evolving in a regular crystal, according to the Schrödinger equation ($\hbar = 1$)

$$i\frac{\partial \psi}{\partial t} = H\psi, \tag{17.1}$$

where ψ is the wave function of a single electron and H the Hamiltonian. We work in D dimensions and set

$$H = -\frac{1}{2m}\Delta + \sum_k V(x - x_k), \tag{17.2}$$

where Δ is the D-dimensional Laplacian (electron kinetic energy), V a potential, x the position of the electron and x_k the position of the k-th atom in the lattice. For the sake of simplicity we take V to be k-independent (an assumption that can be easily dispensed with).

In the tight-binding approximation, the electron wave function is taken to be a linear superposition of the atomic orbitals ϕ of the single isolated atoms

$$\psi(x) = \sum_j c_j \phi(x - x_j), \tag{17.3}$$

where the summation is over the atoms located at the sites of the crystal lattice $\mathcal{L}$. The Hilbert space is now the space of square-summable sequences of c_j's. The projection of the Hamiltonian on this Hilbert space gives rise to hopping and on-site energies:

$$T_{ij} = \int \mathrm{d}x\, \phi(x - x_i)^* H \phi(x - x_j), \tag{17.4}$$

$$\epsilon_i = \int \mathrm{d}x\, \phi(x - x_i)^* H \phi(x - x_i). \tag{17.5}$$

We can dispense with more than nearest-neighbor hopping, keeping only the nearest neighbor couples (i, j) in the sum. Then in general T_{ij} does have some variation with i, j but we can also dispense with it by substituting $T_{ij} \sim g$, as long as we keep the quenched disorder in ϵ_i, say $\epsilon_i \in [-W/2, W/2]$ for a nonnegative W. We arrive at a simplified model written in first or second quantization

$$\begin{aligned}
H &= \sum_{j \in \mathcal{L}} \epsilon_j |j\rangle\langle j| + g \sum_{(i,j)} (|j\rangle\langle i| + |j\rangle\langle i|) \\
&= \sum_j \epsilon_j c_j^\dagger c_j + g \sum_{\langle i,j\rangle} (c_j^\dagger c_i + c_i^\dagger c_j),
\end{aligned} \tag{17.6}$$

where $|j\rangle$ denotes the state with an electron at site j, and $c_j, c_j^\dagger$ obey fermion anticommutation relations. The Hamiltonian is formally solved to yield

$$H\psi_\alpha(i) = E_\alpha \psi_\alpha(i). \tag{17.7}$$

Note that E_α and $\psi_\alpha(i)$ inherit the randomness of the on-site energies ϵ_i.

Anderson argues that in the limit $g \ll W$, the eigenfunctions should be localized, while in the opposite limit $g \gg W$ the eigenfunctions should be delocalized (akin to a wave). In between, there is a transition. The transition is observed in the return probability, assuming that the particle started as localized on a given site i, but of course, should affect all the conducting properties of the model, in particular the conductivity should drop to zero at sufficiently large disorder.

In fact, Anderson localization manifests itself as a transition in the spectral properties of the eigenvalues E_α and the eigenvectors ψ_α of the Hamiltonian (17.6). In the localized phase, eigenstates close in energy are typically localized around distant points in space and do not overlap: energy levels are thrown as random points on a line and are described by Poisson statistics. Conversely, in the extended phase, nearby delocalized eigenfunctions repel each other and the level statistics corresponds to the eigenvalue statistics of a Gaussian orthogonal ensemble. As explained below, a key observable to characterize the transition is the local density of states (LDoS)

$$\rho_i(E) = \sum_\alpha |\psi_\alpha(i)|^2 \delta(E - E_\alpha), \tag{17.8}$$

which is itself a random variable, from which one can define the average DoS,

$$\langle \rho(E) \rangle = \frac{1}{N} \sum_\alpha \delta(E - E_\alpha) = \frac{1}{N} \sum_{i=1}^N \rho_i(E), \tag{17.9}$$

where N is the number of nodes of the lattice $\mathcal{L}$. Another important observable useful to characterize the transition is the so-called inverse participation ratio, $I_2 = \sum_i |\psi_\alpha(i)|^4$, which is essentially a measure of the inverse of the volume occupied by a wave-function, and allows one to distinguish between extended states (for which $I_2 \propto 1/N$) from localized ones (for which I_2 is of order 1).

We remark here that we are considering a single electron evolving in an atomic lattice. Interactions among different electrons are therefore neglected altogether. This is what is meant by *noninteracting* electrons. The question of what would happen when electron-electron interactions are considered is set aside.

17.3. Resolvent and Propagator

The spectral properties of the model are encoded in the statistics of the elements of the resolvent matrix

$$G = \frac{1}{zI - H}, \tag{17.10}$$

where I is the identity matrix, H the Hamiltonian (17.6), and $z = E + i\eta$, η being an infinitesimal regulator that softens the pole singularities in the denominator and is sent to 0^+ at the end of the calculation. A central role is played by the diagonal elements of the resolvent

$$G_{ii} = \langle i|G|i \rangle. \tag{17.11}$$

A key observation is that the LDoS (17.8) is related to the imaginary part of the diagonal elements (17.11)

$$\rho_i(E) = \frac{1}{\pi} \lim_{\eta \to 0^+} \operatorname{Im} G_{ii}(z) = \frac{1}{\pi} \lim_{\eta \to 0^+} \sum_\alpha |\psi_\alpha(i)|^2 \frac{\eta}{(E - E_\alpha)^2 + \eta^2}. \tag{17.12}$$

Anderson localization can be cast in the framework of spontaneous symmetry breaking, with an order parameter function intimately related to the probability distribution of the LDoS, $P(\rho)$ [25]. In the insulating phase $P(\rho)$ is singular in the $\eta \to 0$ limit, while in the metallic phase, instead, $P(\rho)$ is unstable with respect to the introduction of an arbitrarily small but finite imaginary part, i.e., $P(\rho)$ converges to a non-singular η-independent distribution for $\eta \to 0^+$ (see Figs. 17.4 and 17.5).

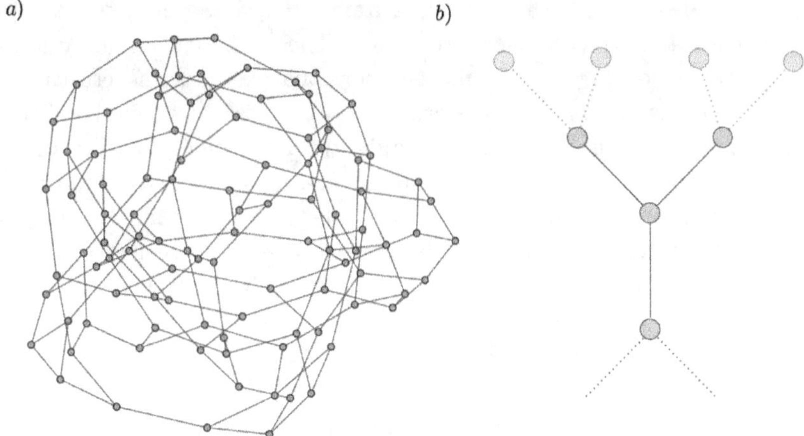

Fig. 17.1.   a) A random regular graph with $N = 100$ vertices and branching $K = 2$. b) Its corresponding local structure: a Bethe lattice.

Similarly, the spectral representation of the IPR of the eigenstates of energy E (which is in fact proportional to the second moment of $P(\rho)$) is

$$I_2 = \lim_{\eta \to 0^+} \frac{1}{\pi\rho(E)N} \sum_{i=1}^{N} |G_{ii}(z)|^2. \tag{17.13}$$

As W is increased from zero value, localization begins from the band edges [1] (which are usually localized for small disorder) and proceeds towards the center, where the density of states is largest. Therefore, to see if all states are localized it is sufficient to look at the center of the band. Hence in the following we will focus only on the central part of the spectrum, $E = 0$, and vary the disorder strength W.

17.4. Bethe Lattice and Random Regular Graphs

As anticipated in the introduction, we will mostly be interested in AL on the Bethe lattice. The most common definition of the Bethe lattice corresponds to the so-called *random regular graph* (RRG). A RRG is defined as a graph chosen uniformly at random among all possible graphs of N nodes such that each node has exactly $K + 1$ edges connecting it to its neighbors (for simplicity, we will fix $K = 2$ in the following). The properties of RRGs have been extensively studied in the latest years (see Ref. [26] for a review). A RRG can be essentially viewed as a tree wrapped onto itself and without boundary. It is known in particular that for large N any finite portion of such a graph is a tree with a probability going to one as $N \to \infty$, and that large loops are present whose typical length scales as $\log N$.

Localization on the Bethe lattice was first studied by Abou-Chacra, Anderson and Thouless [27] and then later by many others, see [19, 28, 29] and references therein. In particular, an exact solution of this model in the thermodynamic limit, which established the transition point and the corresponding critical behavior, was obtained using the supersymmetric formalism [22, 30–41]. Such a framework, however, exhibits a few important differences with respect to the finite D case. These differences mainly concern the critical properties. Contrary to the finite-dimensional case, as the critical value W_c of disorder strength is approached, the critical behavior is not power-law-like but instead exponential, i.e., one finds essential singularities approaching the localization transition from the delocalized regime [36]. This can be understood as a dependence of the critical properties on the diameter of the RRG, $L \sim \ln N / \ln K$. Finite-size corrections are $\propto 1/L$, so critical lengths scale as $\xi \sim |W - W_c|^{-\nu}$, thus turning into essential singularities for the critical volumes $N_c = K^\xi$ [24]. Moreover, the IPR is found to have a discontinuous jump at the transition from an $O(1)$ towards a $1/N$ scaling [36], instead of being continuous at the transition.

17.5. Forward Scattering Approximation on the Bethe Lattice

In the $W \to \infty$ limit the N eigenstates of the Hamiltonian are trivially fully localized on the sites of the lattice, $\psi_i(j) = \delta_{i,j}$, with corresponding eigenvalues ϵ_i, i.e. $G_{ij}(z) = \delta_{ij}/(z - \epsilon_i)$. In the localized phase, for g/W small but finite, the eigenfunctions ψ_i stay roughly localized around i with energy close to ϵ_i. As discussed by Anderson, a very natural way to show the existence of the localized phase is thus to perform a perturbative expansion around the infinite disorder limit in the hopping term of the Hamiltonian, and show that this expansion is convergent. In particular the matrix elements of the resolvent can be formally represented in terms of an infinite series in the hopping, also called *locator expansion* [1]:

$$G_{ij}(z) = \frac{\delta_{ij}}{z - E_i} + \sum_n \sum_{\mathcal{P}_{i \to j}(n)} \prod_{m \in \mathcal{P}} \frac{g}{z - \epsilon_m}, \tag{17.14}$$

where $\mathcal{P}_{i \to j}(n)$ represents all possible paths of length n on the lattice connecting i and j. This object has a very precise physical meaning: $|G_{ij}|^2$ is in fact the spectral representation of the probability that a particle starting in i at $t = 0$ reaches j after infinite time.

Since each term of this series is typically proportional to $(g/W)^n$, in the strong disorder regime, deep into the localized phase, the leading order terms of the expansion yield the most relevant contribution to the Green's function. The so-called *forward scattering approximation* (FSA), therefore, consists in retaining only the leading order term in perturbation theory, which amounts to summing only over the amplitudes of the shortest paths connecting i and j. On the infinite Bethe lattice this expansion becomes particularly simple, due to the fact that the typical size of the loops diverges and there exists a unique directed path connecting two points. One then has:

$$G_{0,r}^{\text{fsa}} = \prod_{i=0}^{r} \frac{g}{z - \epsilon_i} \, .$$

This makes the problem amenable to analytic calculations [27, 42]. We briefly recall some results in the following (we set $z = 0$ for simplicity). $G_{0,r}^{\text{fsa}}$ is obviously broadly distributed and its average over the ϵ_i is infinite. However $\log |G_{0,r}^{\text{fsa}}|$ is a sum of independent and identically distributed random variables with finite variance and its probability distribution can be computed exactly. To this aim, it is convenient to introduce the variable $z = \log(|\epsilon|/g) - \log(W/2g)$. Its probability distribution is then simply given by $P(z) = e^z\,\theta(-z)$, with $\langle z \rangle = -1$ and $\sigma_z^2 = 1$. One thus has:

$$x_r \equiv \frac{\log |G_{0,r}^{\mathrm{fsa}}|}{r} = -\frac{1}{r}\sum_i z_i - \log\left(\frac{W}{2g}\right).$$

One immediately finds that $\langle x_r \rangle = -\log(W/2g\,e)$ and thus:

$$\langle \log |G_{0,r}^{\mathrm{fsa}}|^2 \rangle = -\frac{r}{\xi_{\mathrm{typ}}}, \quad \text{with} \quad \xi_{\mathrm{typ}}^{-1} = 2\log\left(\frac{W}{2g\,e}\right).$$

However ξ_{typ} is not the localization length. Since the average of $|G_{0,r}^{\mathrm{fsa}}|^2$ diverges, the latter must be determined by the decay rate of the maximal amplitude of $|G_{0,r}^{\mathrm{fsa}}|^2$ over the full set of $(K+1)K^{r-1}$ sites at distance r from the origin. In order to do this, we compute the probability distribution of the sum $Z_r = -(1/r)\sum_i z_i$, which can be easily obtained by inverting its characteristic function:

$$P(Z_r) = \frac{r^r Z_r^{r-1}}{\Gamma(r)}\,e^{-rZ_r}\,\theta(Z_r). \tag{17.15}$$

The typical value of the maximal amplitude $2rx_r^\star = 2r[Z_r^\star - \log(W/2g)]$ among K^r paths (which are treated here as independent) is thus given by the solution of

$$K^r \int_{x_r^\star}^\infty P(x_r)\,\mathrm{d}x_r \simeq 1 \implies K^r \frac{\Gamma(r, rZ_r^\star)}{\Gamma(r)} \simeq 1, \tag{17.16}$$

where $\Gamma(z, x) = \int_x^\infty t^{z-1}e^{-t}\mathrm{d}t$ is the incomplete gamma function. In the limit $r \gg 1$ and for $Z_r^\star$ of order one, the asymptotic expansion of the gamma functions gives:

$$\frac{1}{r}\log\left[\frac{\Gamma(r, rZ_r^\star)}{\Gamma(r)}\right] \approx -Z_r^\star + \log(Z_r^\star) + 1 - \frac{\log r}{2r} + \mathcal{O}\left(\frac{1}{r}\right),$$

and hence the condition (17.16) becomes:

$$-Z_r^\star + \log(Z_r^\star\,e\,K) - \frac{\log r}{2r} = 0. \tag{17.17}$$

In the localized phase the correlation functions need to decay with r, i.e. $x_r^\star < 0$, hence the critical disorder must satisfy:

$$Z_r^\star = \log\left(\frac{W_c^{\mathrm{fsa}}}{2g}\right)\left[1 - \frac{\log r}{2r\log\left(\frac{W_c^{\mathrm{fsa}}}{2g\,e}\right)}\right].$$

This condition, together with Eq. (17.17), gives the well-known expression of the critical disorder within the FSA [27]:

$$W_c^{\mathrm{fsa}} = 2g\,e\,K\log\left(\frac{W_c^{\mathrm{fsa}}}{2g}\right).$$

One then also gets the expression of the correlation length within the FSA in the vicinity of the localization transition:

$$\xi_{\mathrm{loc}}^{\mathrm{fsa}} = \frac{1}{2\log(W/W_c^{\mathrm{fsa}})} \approx \frac{W_c^{\mathrm{fsa}}}{2(W - W_c^{\mathrm{fsa}})}.$$

17.6. Cavity Equations

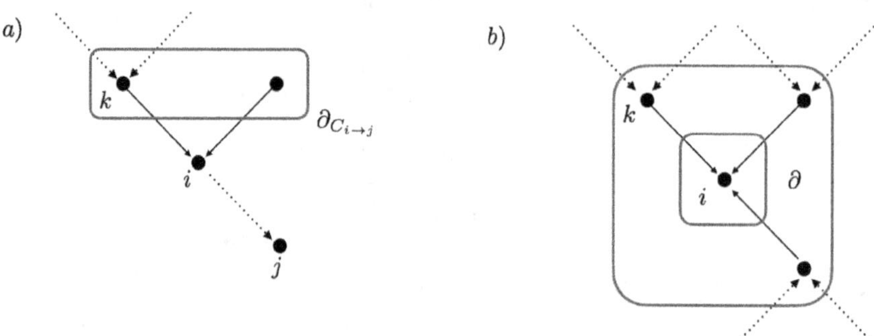

Fig. 17.2. a) Cavity construction and propagators $G_{i\to j}$. b) Same site propagators G_{ii} as a function of the cavity propagators.

As shown by Anderson [1], the sum over all possible paths in the series (17.14) can be rewritten as a sum over self-avoiding walks only. On the infinite Bethe lattice a significant simplification arises due to the absence of closed loops, and one obtains a self-consistent equation for the so-called *cavity Green's functions* [27]

$$G_{i\to j}(z) = \frac{1}{z - \epsilon_i - g^2 \sum_{k\in\partial C_{i\to j}} G_{k\to i}(z)}, \qquad (17.18)$$

where $k \in \partial C_{i\to j}$ indicates that the sum runs over all sites k that are nearest neighbors of i in the cavity: $\partial C_{i\to j}$ stands for "cavity boundary" of i on the path to j, i.e., the subset of all the neighbors of i except j. These equations correspond to the Hamiltonian restricted to the sub-tree rooted in site i, once the link connecting sites i and j is removed.

Once the cavity Green functions are obtained, one can compute the diagonal elements of the Green's function (17.11) [and thus the LDoS according to Eq. (17.12)] as a function of the cavity Green's functions on the $K + 1$ neighbors of i:

$$G_{ii} = \frac{1}{z - \epsilon_i - g^2 \sum_{k\in\partial i} G_{k\to i}}. \qquad (17.19)$$

As discussed before, the order parameter for the Anderson transition is the probability distribution of the local density of states. This can be obtained by looking at the probability distribution of the imaginary part of the propagator G_{ii} (or, equivalently, of the cavity propagator $G_{i\to j}$) with $z = E + i\eta$ when $\eta \to 0^+$. However, an equivalent criterion is the stability of the values of the propagators (both cavity and regular) already at $\eta = 0$, under a small change of the on-site energy. Physically, this should be easy to understand: if the eigenstates are localized, a small change in the Hamiltonian far away from the site under analysis should not affect the observations.

In fact, in the regime in which the imaginary part of the Green's functions are infinitesimally small (and for $\eta \to 0^+$), the recursion equation (17.18) can be linearized as (we set $E = 0$ for simplicity):

$$\mathrm{Re}G_{i \to j} = \frac{1}{-\epsilon_i - g^2 \sum_{k \in \partial C_{i \to j}} \mathrm{Re}G_{k \to i}},$$

$$\mathrm{Im}G_{i \to j} = \frac{g^2 \sum_{k \in \partial C_{i \to j}} \mathrm{Im}G_{k \to i}}{\left(\epsilon_i + g^2 \sum_{k \in \partial C_{i \to j}} \mathrm{Re}G_{k \to i} \right)^2} = g^2 \left| \mathrm{Re}G_{i \to j} \right|^2 \sum_{k \in \partial C_{i \to j}} \mathrm{Im}G_{k \to i}. \tag{17.20}$$

The last recursive equation allows one to identify an integral operator which governs the exponential growth or the exponential decay of the imaginary part of the cavity Green's function under iteration (see Eqs. (17.25)–(17.27) below). Anderson localization thus occurs when the largest eigenvalue of such integral operator becomes larger than $1/K$ [41]. On the other hand, the correlation function $|G_{0r}|^2$ between two points at distance r takes a particularly simple form on the infinite Bethe lattice (again due to the absence of loops):

$$|G_{0r}|^2 = \prod_{i \in \mathcal{P}_{0 \to r}(r)} g^2 \left| G_{i \to i-1} \right|^2,$$

where $\mathcal{P}_{0 \to r}(r)$ denotes the (unique) path of length r joining the nodes 0 and r. As a result, the same integral operator that governs the exponential growth or the exponential decay of the imaginary part of the cavity Green's functions in the linearized regime, Eq. (17.20), also determines the growth or decay rate of the sum of the propagator $|\mathrm{Re}G_{0r}|^2$ over all K^r paths of length r starting from 0, leading to an equivalent susceptibility criterion which is discussed in details in Sec. 17.7.

17.7. Solution with Real Energies

The recursion relation (17.18) is defined for a finite tree geometry, and is expected to become exact in the infinite volume limit. As anticipated in Sec. 17.3 one writes $z = E + i\eta$, and sends $\eta \to 0$ *after* the thermodynamic limit is taken. We follow here an alternative route [43] and consider $\eta \to 0$ first. This is the so-called "inverted thermodynamic limit" [17], considered to deal with the eigenfunction statistics [17, 44, 45]. In this case, the G's are always real. In the following, we assume for simplicity that each site has only $K + 1 = 3$ neighbors, set $E = 0$, and focus on box disorder.

For complex energies (as argument of the propagator), the localized (delocalized) phases are detected by the (lack of) stability of the phase in which $\mathrm{Im}\, G$ is concentrated, close to its limiting value. As we saw in Eq. (17.12), this quantity is related to the LDoS. For real energies, G is also real, and the idea is to look at the stability of a given population, or at the decay of the susceptibility.

In the localized region, the change of an energy level at position i should not affect the dynamics at site j, when the distance between sites i and j, $d(i, j) = L$ is much larger than the localization length $d \gg \xi$. One therefore considers the decay with L of the telescopic identity associated with the shortest (unique) path p from i to j

$$\chi_p = \frac{\partial G_j}{\partial \epsilon_i} = \left(\prod_{k=1}^{L} \frac{\partial G_{k+1}}{\partial G_k} \right) \frac{\partial G_i}{\partial \epsilon_i} \propto \prod_{k=0}^{L} G_k^2, \tag{17.21}$$

where k indexes all the sites on the (unique) path between j and i, with $k = 0$ corresponding to site i and $k = L + 1$ to the end site j.

As explained above, in a RRG, the number of paths going from one site to the other is one for $L \lesssim \ln N / \ln K$ but (quickly) becomes K^L when $L \gtrsim \ln N / \ln K$ [46, 47]. The susceptibility is then obtained by summing (17.21) over K^L paths,

$$\chi_L = \sum_{p=1}^{K^L} \prod_{k \in p} G_k^2. \tag{17.22}$$

Let us define the Lyapunov exponent

$$\Lambda = \lim_{L \to \infty} \frac{1}{L} \ln \chi_L, \tag{17.23}$$

which unlike the susceptibility χ_L, is self-averaging. As explained above, it is not difficult to check that the request $\Lambda < 0$ yields the stability condition of the localized phase [43], Eq. (17.20).

Consider now the distribution $Q(\chi)$ of a single path contribution χ_p (we shall drop henceforth the index p), which can be extracted from its s-th moment,

$$\langle \chi^s \rangle = \int_0^\infty \mathrm{d}\chi\, Q(\chi)\chi^s = \left\langle \prod_{k=1}^L G_k^{2s} \right\rangle = C_L \lambda(s)^L, \tag{17.24}$$

where λ is the largest eigenvalue of the integral equation

$$\int_{-\infty}^\infty \mathrm{d}x\, K_s(y, x)\phi_s(x) = \lambda(s)\phi_s(y). \tag{17.25}$$

This integral equation is the same as the one derived in Ref. [27], its kernel being related to the conditional probability of having two consecutive propagators along a given path [43]

$$P(G_{k+1}|G_k) = \mathbb{E}_{\epsilon,\zeta}\left[\delta\left(G_{k+1} + \frac{1}{\epsilon + \zeta + G_k}\right)\right] \tag{17.26}$$

by the equation

$$K_s(y, x) \equiv x^{2s} P(y|x). \tag{17.27}$$

To see that this is the case, we can write the average in terms of the initial probability distribution of the first term and conditioned probability distributions for the other terms introduced above:

$$\left\langle \prod_{k=1}^L G_k^{2s} \right\rangle = \int \mathrm{d}^L G\, G_L^{2s} P(G_L|G_{L-1})\, G_{L-1}^{2s} P(G_{L-1}|G_{L-2}) \cdots G_1^{2s} P(G_1). \tag{17.28}$$

By renaming the dummy variables we find

$$\left\langle \prod_{k=1}^L G_k^{2s} \right\rangle = \int \mathrm{d}^L x\, K_s(x_L, x_{L-1}) K_s(x_{L-1}, x_{L-2}) K_s(x_{L-2}, x_{L-3}) \cdots \psi_0(x_1)$$

$$\simeq \langle \psi_1 | K^L | \psi_0 \rangle \simeq \lambda(s)^L, \tag{17.29}$$

where K is the operator defined above, $\psi_0(x) = x^{2s}P(x)$ is the starting vector for the iteration and $\psi_1(x) = 1$ is the final vector (one can argue and check a posteriori that both ψ_0 and ψ_1 have an overlap with the eigenvector of K corresponding to the largest eigenvalue λ). In the last equality in (17.24) we have absorbed any exponential dependence in $\lambda(s)$, and thus assumed that C_L grows less than exponentially with L.

We introduce a generalized Lyapunov exponent $\mu(s)$ through the equality $\lambda(s) = e^{\mu(s)}$ and invert the Mellin transform (17.24), getting

$$Q(\chi) = C_L \int_B \frac{\mathrm{d}s}{2\pi i} \chi^{-s-1} e^{L\mu(s)} = C_L \int_B \frac{\mathrm{d}s}{2\pi i} e^{-L((s+1)\theta - \mu(s))}\Big|_{L\theta = \log\chi} \tag{17.30}$$

where B is the Bromwich path, parallel to the imaginary axis. The distribution $Q(\theta)$ of the rescaled variable $\theta = (\ln\chi)/L$ reads

$$Q(\theta) = C_L \int_B \frac{\mathrm{d}s}{2\pi i} e^{-L(s\theta - \mu(s))}. \tag{17.31}$$

This expression enables us to apply the saddle point method for large L, through the (real) saddle point s^*, in a direction parallel to the imaginary axis, yielding

$$Q(\theta) \simeq e^{-L(s^*\theta - \mu(s^*))}. \tag{17.32}$$

where s^* is an implicit function of χ or θ defined by the condition

$$\mu'(s^*) = \theta. \tag{17.33}$$

The value $\theta = 0$ discriminates between an exponentially growing ($\theta > 0$) and decaying ($\theta < 0$) susceptibility along a given path. The typical value of the path susceptibility is defined by

$$\theta_{\text{typ}} = \lim_{s \to 0} \frac{\partial \mu(s)}{\partial s}, \tag{17.34}$$

implying the vanishing of the large-deviation function for θ, see Eq. (17.31).

The transition between the localized and delocalized phases is governed by atypically large fluctuations of the single-path susceptibilities; the typical decay Eq. (17.34) has however been considered in the literature[a]: it appears in a sufficient criterion for delocalization in Ref. [48], and it has been conjectured to be related to the transition between ergodic and non-ergodic phases in the delocalized phase in Ref. [17]. We discuss this more extensively in the next section.

The distribution of the product in the right hand side of (17.22) is fat-tailed, so that the sum is dominated by the largest summand. The typical value of the sum solves the equation $K^L Q(\chi_L^{\text{typ}}) = 1$. The transition corresponds to the typical value becoming equal to one (corresponding to $\Lambda = 0$), and is thus obtained by setting $\theta = 0$ in Eq. (17.32). This is valid iff $s = 1/2$ [27, 49]. The criterion for the transition thus becomes

$$\ln K + \mu(s^*) = 0 \quad \Leftrightarrow \quad \lambda(s^*)K = 1, \tag{17.35}$$

for $s^* = 1/2$, which is the resonant criterion derived in Ref. [50].

---

[a]Notice that these references consider the typical value of the squared susceptibility.

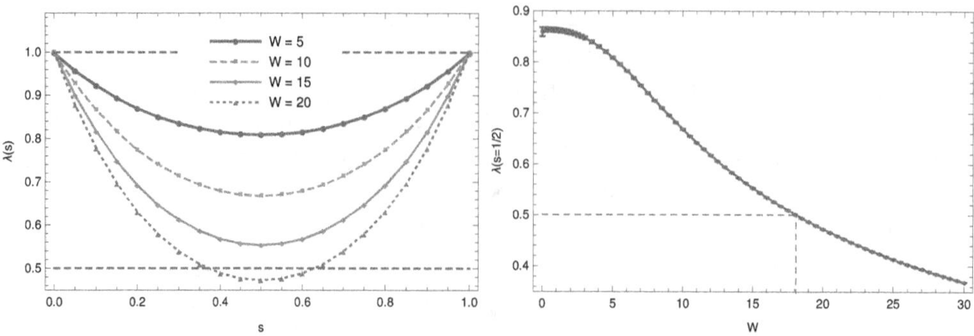

Fig. 17.3. *Left panel.* Largest eigenvalue $\lambda(s)$ as a function of the exponent s in Eq. (17.24), showing the symmetry at $s = 1/2$. *Right panel.* Largest eigenvalue $\lambda(s)$ for $s = 1/2$, as a function of disorder W. The localization transition takes place at $W_c = 18.17 \pm 0.05$.

The largest eigenvalue $\lambda(s)$ as a function of the exponent s is displayed in Fig. 17.3. The minumum $\lambda(s = 1/2)$ is plotted in the right panel as a function of the disorder strength W. The localization transition point takes place at $W_c = 18.17 \pm 0.02$ [24, 41].

Finally, observe that close to the critical point, and for $\chi = O(1)$, one can even write the full probability distribution of χ by noticing that, close to $\theta = 0$, by writing $s^* = 1/2 + \epsilon$ we have $\epsilon = \theta/\mu''(1/2)$, yielding a log-normal distribution

$$
Q(\chi) = \mathrm{e}^{-L\left(\ln K + \frac{3}{2}\theta + \frac{\theta^2}{2\mu''(1/2)}\right)} = \frac{K^{-L}}{\chi^{3/2}}\,\mathrm{e}^{-\frac{(\ln \chi)^2}{2L\mu''(1/2)}} . \tag{17.36}
$$

17.8. Solution with Complex Energies

Equation (17.18) (and hence Eq. (17.19)) can be in principle solved with arbitrary numerical precision on infinite RRGs using a *population dynamics* algorithm, first introduced by Giorgio Parisi and Marc Mézard in the context of spin glasses [51]. This algorithm (also called the pool method) works as follows: The probability distribution of the cavity Green's functions is approximated by the empirical distribution of a large population of M values, in the form $P(G) \simeq \sum_{\alpha=1}^{M} \delta(G - G_\alpha)$; At each iteration step, K instances of G are extracted from the sample and a values of ϵ is taken from the uniform distribution; A new instance of G is generated using Eq. (17.18) and inserted in a random position of the pool, until the process converges to a stationary distribution. From such stationary distribution $P(G)$, one can finally compute the probability distribution of the diagonal elements of the resolvent using Eq. (17.19), and in particular of their imaginary parts associated to the LDoS via Eq. (17.12).

In the following, without loss of generality, we focus on the $K = 2$ case (i.e., total connectivity $K+1 = 3$) and on the center of the spectrum, $E = 0$. Previous studies of the transmission properties and dissipation propagation have attempted to determine the critical value of the disorder at which the localization transition takes place. Hovever, as discussed in [41], the finiteness of the size of the pool produces very pronounced finite-size effects and should be handled with care when studying the critical behavior. The most accurate and precise estimations of W_c in the thermodynamic limit are provided

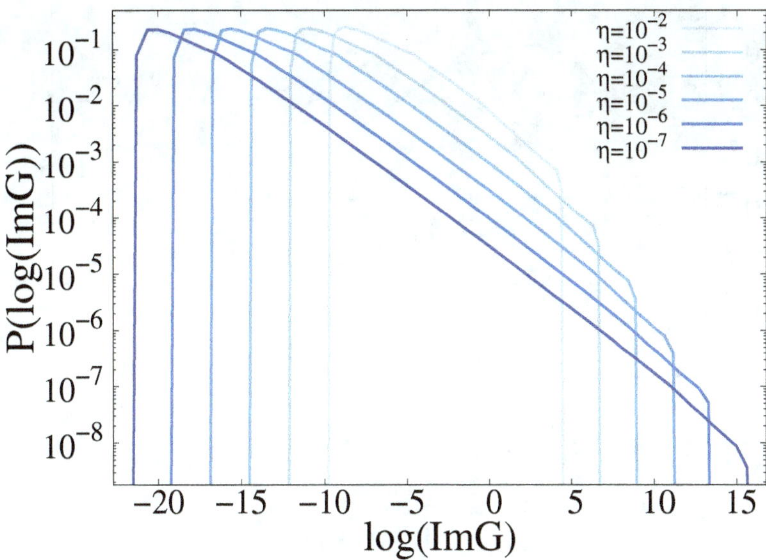

Fig. 17.4. Probability distribution of the logarithm of the imaginary part of the Green's function for $W = 24$, deep into the localized phase, and for several values of η from 10^{-2} to 10^{-7}. The plots are obtained using the population dynamics algorithm with a pool of about 64 millions elements.

by Refs. [41, 43], based on a direct high-precision numerical diagonalization of the integral operator governing the linear stability of the recursive cavity equations for the imaginary part of the self-energy (17.20), yielding $W_c \simeq 18.17 \pm 0.01$ (see also Fig. 17.3 of the previous section).

As explained above, AL can be cast in the framework of spontaneous symmetry breaking. In the insulating phase, $P(\mathrm{Im}G)$ is singular in the $\eta \to 0$ limit. As shown in Fig. 17.4 for $W = 24 > W_c$, $P(\mathrm{Im}G)$ has a maximum in the region $\mathrm{Im}G \sim \eta$ and power-law tails $P(\mathrm{Im}G) \sim \sqrt{\eta}/(\mathrm{Im}G)^{3/2}$ with a cutoff at η^{-1}. Hence the normalization integral of $P(\mathrm{Im}G)$ is dominated by the region $\mathrm{Im}G \sim \eta$ and the typical value of $\mathrm{Im}G$ is of order η, while the main contribution to all moments $\langle (\mathrm{Im}G)^q \rangle$ $(q \geq 1/2)$ comes from the cutoff $\mathrm{Im}G \sim \eta^{-1}$. This behavior reflects the fact that in the localized phase wave-functions are exponentially localized on few $O(1)$ sites where the LDoS ρ_i takes very large values, while the typical value of the LDoS is exponentially small and vanishes in the thermodynamic limit for $\eta \to 0^+$.

In the metallic phase, instead, $P(\mathrm{Im}G)$ is unstable to the introduction of an arbitrary small but finite imaginary part, i.e., $P(\mathrm{Im}G)$ converges to a non-singular η-independent distribution for $\eta \to 0^+$. These probability distributions are illustrated in Fig. 17.5 for several values of W across the delocalized phase. These plots show that upon approaching the critical disorder from below $P(\mathrm{Im}G)$ becomes very broad and asymmetric, and a (large) characteristic scale N_{corr}, playing a role analogous to that of η^{-1} in the localized phase, spontaneously emerges. The probability distribution has a sharp maximum for $\mathrm{Im}G \sim N_{\mathrm{corr}}^{-1}$ followed by a power law decay $P(\mathrm{Im}G) \sim (\mathrm{Im}G)^{-3/2}$ with a cutoff at $\mathrm{Im}G$ of order N_{corr} [40, 52]. Such N_{corr} can be interpreted as the *correlation volume* of typical eigenstates. For $W \lesssim W_c$ the wave-functions have bumps localized in a small region

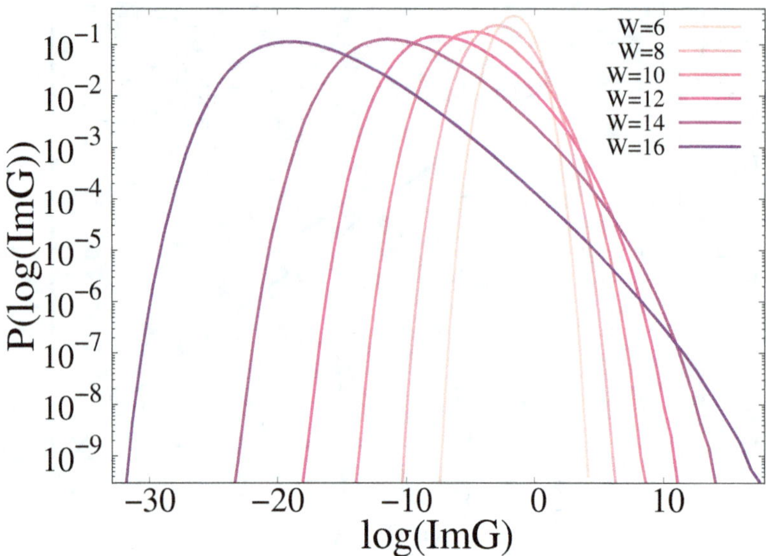

Fig. 17.5. Probability distribution of the logarithm of the imaginary part of the Green's function for several values of the disorder across the delocalized phase in the $\eta \to 0^+$ limit. The plots are obtained using the population dynamics algorithm with a pool of about 64 millions elements.

of the Bethe lattice where the amplitude is of order N_{corr}/N, separated by regions of size $\log N_{\text{corr}}$ where the amplitude is very small. All moments I_q ($q \geq 1/2$) — including the normalization integral, $q = 1$, and the IPR, $q = 2$—are dominated by the bumps of size of $O(1)$, $I_q \sim (N_{\text{corr}}/N)^{q-1}$, while the typical amplitude is dominated by the large regions of size N_{corr} between the bumps.

A numerical estimate of the correlation volume can be obtained by fitting the tails of the distributions $P(\text{Im}G)$, whose asymptotic functional form close to W_c has been predicted analytically within the supersymmetric framework [40]. In order to do this, a new type of advanced large-deviation algorithm that allows one to sample the distributions with very high precision in the tails has been recently introduced [52]. Using such large-deviation approach, probability densities as small as 10^{-50} can be accessed with very high precision, well below any probability reached by a standard population dynamics approach. Applying this procedure one finds that the functional form predicted by Ref. [40] fits remarkably well the tails of the distributions of the imaginary part of the Green's function over dozens of decades down to very small probability density, thereby allowing one to obtain a reliable numerical estimation of the correlation volume. Repeating this procedure for several values of the disorder across the metallic phase, one finds that N_{corr} diverges exponentially at the critical disorder as:

$$N_{\text{corr}} = A \ e^{\frac{c}{(W_c - W)^\nu}}$$

where the exponent ν is consistent with the value predicted by the supersymmetric formalism $\nu = 0.5$ [22, 30–40] and found numerically in Refs. [41, 43] (see Fig. 17.3(left) of Sec. 17.7).

17.9. Relationship with RSB

The relationship between AL on the Bethe lattice and RSB comes from the fact that the recursive relation for the imaginary part of the cavity Green's functions in the linearized regime (17.20) can be formally interpreted as the expression of the partition function of a directed polymer on a tree in presence of quenched and correlated bond disorder $e^{-\omega_{i \to j}} \equiv g^2 |G_{i \to j}|^2$. The partition function associated with this problem is given by the susceptibility defined in Eq. (17.22) and its free-energy (per unit length) is closely related to (minus) the Lyapunov exponent defined in Eq. (17.23). The analogy between the iteration equation for the imaginary part of the propagator and the partition function of directed polymers in random media has been exploited and analyzed by several recent works, both in $2d$ [53] and on the Bethe lattice [13, 17, 54].

The study of directed polymers on the Bethe lattice in presence of quenched i.i.d. random energies was originally introduced by Derrida and Spohn [55], who highlighted the existence of a one-step RSB freezing glass transition, akin to the one of the Random Energy Model [56], separating a high-temperature (or weak disorder) phase, in which the partition function receives a contribution from an exponential number of configurations of the polymers, and a low-temperature (strong disorder) phase in which the partition function only receives a significant contribution from few $O(1)$ specific disorder-dependent paths.

Several recent works indicated the presence of a very broad crossover region at moderately strong disorder, where an apparent freezing-glass transition of the paths contributing to transport and dissipation on the Bethe lattice takes place [13, 17, 18]. In this region resonances are formed only on rare disorder-dependent nodes on very distant generations on the tree. Such a glassy regime, however, is in fact cut-off and replaced by a standard metallic fully ergodic behavior in the thermodynamic limit. This happens on sizes that diverge as the correlation volume as the localization transition is approached. Hence, a genuine transition in the thermodynamic limit only occurs at W_c.

17.10. Concluding Remarks

Giorgio Parisi's work on the Anderson transition focused mostly on the problem which has the highest chance of being amenable to an analytic solution: the Bethe lattice Anderson model. Giorgio was involved in the study of the recursion relations for imaginary energies, and for real energies, where analytic progress is made by reducing the problem of finding the transition point to the solution of an integral equation. Although the integral equation has no explicit analytic solution for cases of interest, its numerical solution can be fully exploited to find the transition point with 4 significant digits. However, even if the solution of the integral equation would be found, it would be informative on the thermodynamic limit only, and many features of the finite-size problems would be still inaccessible. Another line of attack considered by Giorgio for other problems involving random systems on the Bethe lattice (which is not discussed here) concerns $O(1/N)$ corrections to the thermodynamic limit [57, 58]. This line of research is currently being investigated and seems indeed to provide very useful insights to rationalize the peculiar critical behavior of the Anderson model on the Bethe lattice and its finite-size corrections.

We have not discussed the relationship between the Anderson model on RRGs with the problem of many-body localization, which also falls in Giorgio's sphere of interest [59].

Another important contribution made by Giorgio in this context is the extension of the cavity formalism to investigate the statistics of the eigenvalues of H, and in particular the so-called level compressibility [57]. This formalism has been recently applied by some of Giorgio's collaborators to the Anderson model on the Bethe lattice [21], as well as to related random matrix models, leading to valuable insights towards the understanding of how full ergodicity in the level statistics is recovered on the delocalized side of the transition.

Finally, as explained in the introduction, one of the main difficulties arising in the study of the Anderson transition on the BL is that the case $D = \infty$ is a singular point, and plays the role of the upper critical dimension [16, 25], with corrections to the critical exponents of the form $1/D$. In this respect, it is worth mentioning the valuable attempts by Giorgio and his collaborators to develop a renormalization group treatment of Anderson localization on the Dyson hierarchical lattice [60].

We conclude by mentioning that Philip W. Anderson had a great admiration for Giorgio Parisi's groundbreaking results and methods of investigation. It is enjoyable and instructive to read the series of articles that Anderson wrote for the wide audience of Physics Today [61–67]. Besides being a source of inspiration, these articles show how a dominant figure in the Physics of last century perceives the sudden presence of a young genius.

References

[1] P. W. Anderson, *Phys. Rev.* **109**(5), 1492, (1958).
[2] E. Abrahams, *50 years of Anderson Localization.* vol. 24, (World Scientific, 2010).
[3] M. Cutler and N. F. Mott, *Phys. Rev.* **181**(3), 1336, (1969).
[4] G. Modugno, *Rep. Prog. Phys.* **73**(10), 102401, (2010).
[5] R. M. Hill, *Philos. Mag.* **24**(192), 1307–1325, (1971).
[6] D. M. Basko, I. L. Aleiner, and B. L. Altshuler, *Ann. Phys. (N.Y.).* **321**(5), 1126–1205, (2006).
[7] A. Pal and D. A. Huse, *Phys. Rev. b.* **82**(17), 174411, (2010).
[8] D. A. Abanin, E. Altman, I. Bloch, and M. Serbyn, *Rev. Mod. Phys.* **91**(2), 021001, (2019).
[9] J. Z. Imbrie, V. Ros, and A. Scardicchio, *Ann. Phys. (Berlin).* **529**(7), 1600278, (2017).
[10] B. L. Altshuler, Y. Gefen, A. Kamenev, and L. S. Levitov, *Phys. Rev. Lett.* **78**(14), 2803, (1997).
[11] K. S. Tikhonov and A. D. Mirlin, *Ann. Phys. (N.Y.).* **435**, 168525, (2021).
[12] A. De Luca and A. Scardicchio, *EPL.* **101**(3), 37003, (2013).
[13] G. Biroli and M. Tarzia, *Phys. Rev. B.* **102**(6), 064211, (2020).
[14] G. Biroli and M. Tarzia, *Phys. Rev. B.* **96**(20), 201114, (2017).
[15] D. E. Logan and S. Welsh, *Phys. Rev. B.* **99**(4), 045131, (2019).
[16] E. Tarquini, G. Biroli, and M. Tarzia, *Phys. Rev. B.* **95**(9), 094204, (2017).

[17] V. Kravtsov, B. Altshuler, and L. Ioffe, *Ann. Phys. (N.Y.).* **389**, 148–191, (2018).

[18] B. Altshuler, E. Cuevas, L. Ioffe, and V. Kravtsov, *Phys. Rev. Lett.* **117**(15), 156601, (2016).

[19] K. S. Tikhonov, A. D. Mirlin, and M. A. Skvortsov, *Phys. Rev. B.* **94**(22), 220203, (2016).

[20] I. Garcia-Mata, O. Giraud, B. Georgeot, J. Martin, R. Dubertrand, and G. Lemarié, *Phys. Rev. Lett.* **118**(16), 166801, (2017).

[21] F. L. Metz and I. P. Castillo, *Phys. Rev. B.* **96**(6), 064202, (2017).

[22] K. Tikhonov and A. Mirlin, *Phys. Rev. B.* **99**(2), 024202, (2019).

[23] I. García-Mata, J. Martin, R. Dubertrand, O. Giraud, B. Georgeot, and G. Lemarié, *Phys. Rev. Research.* **2**(1), 012020, (2020).

[24] P. Sierant, M. Lewenstein, and A. Scardicchio, *arXiv:2205.14614.* (2022).

[25] A. D. Mirlin and Y. V. Fyodorov, *Phys. Rev. Lett.* **72**(4), 526, (1994).

[26] N. C. Wormald et al., *LMS Lect. Notes Ser.* pp. 239–298, (1999).

[27] R. Abou-Chacra, D. Thouless, and P. Anderson, *J. Phys. C.* **6**(10), 1734, (1973).

[28] A. De Luca, B. Altshuler, V. Kravtsov, and A. Scardicchio, *Phys. Rev. Lett.* **113**(4), 046806, (2014).

[29] G. Biroli, G. Semerjian, and M. Tarzia, *Prog. Theor. Phys. Supplement.* **184**, 187–199, (2010).

[30] K. Efetov, *Zh. Eksp. Teor. Fiz.* **88**, 1032–1052, (1985).

[31] K. Efetov, *Zh. Eksp. Teor. Fiz.* **92**(2), 638–656, (1987).

[32] K. Efetov, *Zh. Eksp. Teor. Fiz.* **93**, 1125–1139, (1987).

[33] M. R. Zirnbauer, *Phys. Rev. B.* **34**(9), 6394, (1986).

[34] M. R. Zirnbauer, *Nucl. Phys. B.* **265**(2), 375–408, (1986).

[35] J. Verbaarschot, *Nucl. Phys. B.* **300**, 263–288, (1988).

[36] A. D. Mirlin and Y. V. Fyodorov, *Nucl. Phys. B.* **366**(3), 507–532, (1991).

[37] A. Mirlin and Y. V. Fyodorov, *J. Phys. A.* **24**(10), 2273, (1991).

[38] Y. V. Fyodorov and A. D. Mirlin, *Phys. Rev. Lett.* **67**(15), 2049, (1991).

[39] Y. V. Fyodorov, A. D. Mirlin, and H.-J. Sommers, *J. Physique I.* **2**(8), 1571–1605, (1992).

[40] A. D. Mirlin and Y. V. Fyodorov, *J. Physique I.* **4**(5), 655–673, (1994).

[41] K. Tikhonov and A. Mirlin, *Phys. Rev. B.* **99**(21), 214202, (2019).

[42] F. Pietracaprina, V. Ros, and A. Scardicchio, *Phys. Rev. B.* **93**(5), 054201, (2016).

[43] G. Parisi, S. Pascazio, F. Pietracaprina, V. Ros, and A. Scardicchio, *J. Phys. A.* **53**(1), 014003, (2019).

[44] K. S. Tikhonov and A. D. Mirlin, *Phys. Rev. B.* **94**(18), 184203, (2016).

[45] A. D. Mirlin, *Physics Reports.* **326**(5-6), 259–382, (2000).

[46] B. Bollobás. In *Modern graph theory*, pp. 215–252. Springer, (1998).

[47] E. Marinari and R. Monasson, *J. Stat. Mech.: Theory Exp.* **2004**(09), P09004, (2004).

[48] M. Aizenman and S. Warzel, *J. Math. Phys.* **53**(9), 095205, (2012).

[49] B. Altshuler and V. Prigodin, *Sov. Phys. JETP.* **68**(1), 198, (1989).

[50] M. Aizenman and S. Warzel, *arXiv:1104.0969.* (2011).

[51] M. Mézard and G. Parisi, *Eur. Phys. J. B.* **20**(2), 217–233, (2001).

[52] G. Biroli, A. K. Hartmann, and M. Tarzia, *Phys. Rev. B.* **105**(9), 094202, (2022).

[53] G. Lemarié, *Phys. Rev. Lett.* **122**(3), 030401, (2019).

[54] C. Monthus and T. Garel, *J. Phys. A.* **42**(7), 075002, (2008).

[55] B. Derrida and H. Spohn, *J. Stat. Phys.* **51**(5), 817–840, (1988).

[56] B. Derrida, *Phys. Rev. B.* **24**(5), 2613, (1981).

[57] F. L. Metz, G. Parisi, and L. Leuzzi, *Phys. Rev. E.* **90**(5), 052109, (2014).

[58] A. Altieri, M. C. Angelini, C. Lucibello, G. Parisi, F. Ricci-Tersenghi, and T. Rizzo, *J. Stat. Mech.: Theory Exp.* **2017**(11), 113303, (2017).

[59] F. Pietracaprina, G. Parisi, A. Mariano, S. Pascazio, and A. Scardicchio, *J. Stat. Mech.: Theory Exp.* **2017**(11), 113102, (2017).

[60] F. Metz, L. Leuzzi, G. Parisi, and V. Sacksteder IV, *Phys. Rev. B.* **88**(4), 045103, (2013).

[61] P. W. Anderson, *Physics Today.* **41**(1), 9–11, (1988).
[62] P. W. Anderson, *Physics Today.* **41**(3), 9, (1988).
[63] P. W. Anderson, *Physics Today.* **41**(6), 9, (1988).
[64] P. W. Anderson, *Physics Today.* **41**(9), 9–11, (1988).
[65] P. W. Anderson, *Physics Today.* **42**(7), 9, (1989).
[66] P. W. Anderson, *Physics Today.* **42**(9), 9, (1989).
[67] P. W. Anderson, *Physics Today.* **43**(3), 9, (1990).

Chapter 18

Quantum Glasses

Leticia F. Cugliandolo[*,†] and Markus Müller[‡]

*Sorbonne Université, Laboratoire de Physique Théorique et Hautes Energies, CNRS
UMR 7589, 4 Place Jussieu, 75252 Paris 05, France
†Institut Universitaire de France, 1 rue Descartes, 75231 Paris 05, France
‡Laboratory for Theoretical and Computational Physics,
Paul Scherrer Institute, Villigen CH-5232, Switzerland

We review recent research on quantum glasses, with a focus on their equilibrium dynamics and the interplay between glassiness and localization phenomena. Interesting relations with the SYK model are discussed.

18.1. Introduction

The interplay of disorder, interactions and quantum mechanics leads to a host of interesting phenomena. A particularly intriguing aspect is the breakdown of ergodicity in a way that differs significantly from that of standard spontaneous symmetry breaking. This can arise as a consequence of quenched disorder, as in spin glasses, or structural disorder, such as amorphous density order. Both quenched and self-generated disorder entail a clustering in phase space associated with glass attributes like memory effects and extremely slow relaxations [1–3]. The replica method allows one to access the phase space structure, and replica symmetry breaking (RSB) signals the existence of a large number of metastable states separated by substantial free energy barriers. Even though barriers may be finite in low dimensions, thus preventing a genuine thermodynamic glass transition, the replica method has proven useful for these cases as well.

As a result of frustration and the competition between many nearly degenerate ordering patterns, the glassy order is often rather soft and gives rise to an unusually high density of low energy excitations. In or close to a quantum glass phase those may have a strong influence on electronic transport and have often been invoked as candidates to explain the non-Fermi liquid behavior of the resistivity of complex materials, such as high temperature superconductors (cuprates), heavy fermion systems, but also systems close to a Mott–Anderson metal-insulator transition.

Apart from this "glassy" route, very slow dynamics and non-ergodicity in quantum systems can be due to other mechanisms too, especially in low dimensions where the effects of disorder are very strong. On the one hand, under a real space renormalization group treatment, disordered quantum spin chains typically flow to fixed points characterized by infinite randomness [4], with extended regions of parameter space where

353

Griffiths–McCoy singularities are very important [5, 6]. Thereby the low frequency response is dominated by nearly isolated degrees of freedom only weakly coupled to others further away.

On the other hand, non-interacting quantum particles in one dimension subject to a disordered potential Anderson localize and stop diffusing on the scale of the elastic mean free path [7, 8]. Its interacting counterpart, many-body localization (MBL) [9–12], relies on the discreteness of non-interacting excitations and the rareness of resonant interactions, which then fail to induce diffusion of energy. Thus, MBL can only occur in isolation, with no coupling to the continuum of a bath which would reinstate transport and ergodicity. In contrast, the above discussed glass phases are stable against a bath, as they rely on the rugged structure of the free-energy landscape. A further difference between quantum glasses and MBL systems is that the latter are highly susceptible to local inclusions where disorder is weak. Those act as sources of dynamical chaos, and it is believed that only in low-dimensional, discrete lattices such nucleation centers of local baths do not destroy MBL [13–15] (although the existence of MBL even in 1d has been questioned recently [16–18]). In contrast, glasses, like standard symmetry broken phases, are stabilized in high dimensions (and RSB is certain to occur above a d_c [19]). In summary, while both quantum glassiness and MBL entail non-ergodicity and impede full thermalization, they do so for fundamentally different reasons.

Other obstructions to full ergodicity exist, e.g., integrable systems with an extensive number of conserved quantities [20], systems hosting many-body scars (a set of eigenstates that violate the eigenstate thermalization hypothesis) [21] or cases with fragmented Hilbert spaces [22]. However, none of these is robust against generic perturbations of the Hamiltonian, as even modest ones reinstate equilibrating dynamics rather quickly. We do not consider them as being quantum glassy and we will not discuss them here. A further way to kill ergodicity is the sufficiently strong coupling to an Ohmic bath of a single quantum degree of freedom, which can get dressed with many bath modes, so as to acquire an infinite mass, and its dynamics freezes out [23, 24]. We will not discuss this effect of non-glassy "local ergodicity breaking" either, except for noting that the coupling of quantum systems to a bath usually results in the reduction of fluctuations, and thus extends the regime of stability of the glass [25, 26].

In this review we focus on quantum glasses that arise in high dimensions, where disorder is so relevant as to produce amorphous order and phase space clusterization, but does not flow to infinite randomness. This structure withstands both thermal *and* quantum fluctuations, which soften the energy landscape and eventually melt the glass. We note though that for certain types of glasses the quantum melting differs drastically from the thermal route.

Since this chapter is part of a book devoted to replica symmetry breaking, we focus the discussion on equilibrium aspects and we structure it as follows. In Sec. 18.2 we overview some general aspects of quantum glassy dynamics. Section 18.3 reminds the gist of the replica treatment of mean field glasses. In Sec. 18.4 we classify different universality classes of (mean field) glasses according to the type of interactions and environments, and discuss their phenomenology, in particular the nature of their low energy collective modes which we obtain both from Landau theory and an effective potential approach in Sec. 18.5. In Sec. 18.6 we discuss whether an isolated quantum glass explores its clusterized phase space by tunneling or rather stays localized. The interplay between the glass and localization routes to non-equilibrium is a multi-faceted topic briefly reviewed in Sec. 18.7. Section 18.8 reviews a few experimental glassy materials and artificial systems and their phenomenology. Finally, in Sec. 18.9 we survey fermionic models closely connected to the paramagnetic phase of Heisenberg spin glasses, *a.k.a.* the Sachdev–Ye–Kitaev (SYK) model, that may fertilize the study of spin glasses via interesting dynamical analogies.

18.2. Dynamics in Quantum Glassy Phases

A particularly interesting aspect of quantum glasses is their dynamics, both in and out of equilibrium. We broadly survey them here and discuss selected questions in more detail in later sections.

18.2.1. *Short-time dynamics*

Distinct quantum aspects of glasses appear on microscopic time scales. The high-frequency dynamics depend crucially on the symmetries of the order parameter and the nature of the quantum fluctuations. In the low-frequency limit, instead, the excitations feel the softness of the glassy landscape, which, in the mean-field limit, exhibits surprisingly universal spectral features whose frequency scaling merely depends on the glass being metallic or insulating. We will review the salient results in Secs. 18.4, 18.5 and 18.9.

18.2.2. *Moderately long-time dynamics*

The intermediate to long-time dynamics of quantum glassy systems are essentially identical to those of their classical counterparts. Indeed, one expects that on time scales $t \gg \hbar/T$ all degrees of freedom decohere and any quantum effects are washed out. After a quench from the disordered phase, the glass hovers over saddles in the free energy landscape and slowly relaxes its energy without ever getting deeply trapped into rare deep minima, in a manner dubbed *weak ergodicity breaking* [27–31]. The response slows down increasingly with time (the glass "ages"). In solvable mean field models, the fluctuation-dissipation relation evaluated on those long time scales takes the classical form, albeit with an effective temperature T_{eff} that exceeds the bath temperature (even at $T = 0$). The latter is formally related to Parisi's order parameter $Q(x)$ as in the classical limit [1]. Moreover, the equations governing the slow evolution of the response and correlation functions are invariant under time reparametrizations, $t \to f(t)$ [32]. Such an invariance also occurs in the large M limit of the $SU(M)$ Heisenberg and the SYK models. Recent progress in this direction will be reviewed in Sec. 18.9. Finally, as in the classical limit, one can tune the initial state to lie within one of the valleys in the free-energy landscape and show that the subsequent dynamics will remain confined to it (at least for times which are not exponentially large in system size).

A short summary of the real-time dynamics of quantum disordered systems on these time scales can be found in Ref. [33]. We will not extend this discussion further here, as we aim to focus mainly on equilibrium properties.

18.2.3. *Extremely long-time dynamics*

On extremely long time scales, crossing over or tunneling under barriers between metastable valleys should be possible. In mean-field models barriers scale with system size and thermal activation over them is exponentially slow. Since the latter is the root cause for the failure of simulated annealing finding the ground state of NP-hard problems, there was hope that quantum annealing could achieve a significant speed-up [34]. The idea was to initialize the system under strong quantum fluctuations (e.g. a transverse field) which induce a simple ground state. Then, by invoking the adiabatic theorem, one should reach the classical ground state upon turning off the fluctuations sufficiently slowly. The caveat is that exponentially slow switch-off rates are required to follow the ground state while it delicately hybridizes distant low-energy valleys in phase space. Still, one may ask which of the exponentially long times (barrier crossing or adiabatic ground state preparation) is more efficient to explore complex landscapes [35], an idea that was explored experimentally in quantum Ising spin glasses [36], cf. Sec. 18.8.1. However, an even bigger obstacle to quantum annealing [37, 38] is posed by the fact that NP-hard problems have quantum first order transitions [39, 40] (see Sec. 18.4.1.2).

A related dynamical question arises for an isolated quantum spin glass — the setting considered in MBL: after preparation in a deep valley, can it tunnel to others or does it remain localized? We discuss this question in Sec. 18.6.

18.3. Replica Treatment of Quantum Mean-Field Glasses

Most theoretical insights on quantum glasses have been obtained from mean-field $SU(M)$ models, where all $i = 1, \ldots, N$ spins interact with all others via random couplings with variance proportional to J^2 and conveniently scaled with N and M. While this looks remote from any real physical glass, long range couplings can be emulated via light-matter coupling in multi-mode cavities, see Sec. 18.8.3. The *equilibrium* properties of such glasses were derived with a replicated imaginary-time path integral formulation of the partition function [41]. A saddle-point evaluation allows one to define the glass order parameter[a]

$$Q_{ab}(\tau) = \frac{1}{NM^2} \sum_i [\langle \mathrm{T}\, \boldsymbol{\sigma}_i^a(\tau) \cdot \boldsymbol{\sigma}_i^b(0)\rangle] \tag{18.1}$$

where $a, b = 1, \ldots, n$ are the replica indices, τ the imaginary time and T the time-ordering operator. Depending on the complexity of the model, the free-energy density can either be just a functional of the saddle-point $Q_{ab}(\tau)$, or the partition function can be transformed into one for a single spin with $Q_{ab}(\tau)$ self-consistently given by the expectation value of its imaginary-time correlations (see, e.g., [42]). In all cases, $Q_{a \neq b}$ are τ-independent, vanish in the disordered phase, and adopt an RSB structure in the glass phase. The diagonal elements $Q_{aa}(\tau) \equiv q_d(\tau)$ are independent of the replica index but depend on time, being $\beta\hbar$ periodic, in the whole phase diagram. In certain cases (typically models in which also the single-spin partition function can be calculated

---

[a]The normalization factor M^2 captures the leading dependence for $M \to \infty$. In general one should naturally divide by the number of spin components $(M^2 - 1)$.

exactly), Q_{ab} satisfies a generic differential equation of the form

$$G_0^{-1}(\tau)_{ac} Q_{cb}(\tau) = \delta_{ab}\delta(\tau) + \int_0^{\beta\hbar} d\tau' \, \Sigma_{ac}(\tau - \tau') Q_{cb}(\tau'), \qquad (18.2)$$

with a sum over repeated indices. G_0^{-1} is a differential operator, typically diagonal in replica indices, and its order (first or second time derivative, further time dependence) depends on the kind of degrees of freedom and whether the system is coupled to a bath (microscopic dynamics). Σ is a self-energy which typically depends on time only *via* Q. Note though that this equation is not causal, and is simpler to solve in frequency space. We will specify G_0^{-1} and Σ in several concrete cases below. The physical properties follow from Q_{ab}. Of special importance is the out-of-phase local susceptibility

$$\chi''_{\text{loc}}(\omega) = \text{Im} \, \tilde{q}_d(\omega + i0^+), \qquad (18.3)$$

with $\tilde{q}_d$ the Fourier transform of q_d. The right-hand side is the analytic continuation to real ω of $\tilde{q}_d(\omega_n)$, with ω_n the Matsubara frequencies. χ''_{loc} contains essential information on the spectrum of collective excitations since

$$\chi''_{\text{loc}}(\omega) = \frac{\pi}{N} \sum_{im} |\langle \psi_m | \sigma_i^1 | \psi_0 \rangle|^2 [\delta(\omega - E_m + E_0) - \delta(\omega + E_m - E_0)],$$

(at $T = 0$) where (ψ_m, E_m) are the many-body eigenstates and energies, with 0 referring to the ground state. A continuous glass transition is identified by the condition $J\chi_{\text{loc}} = 1$, with χ_{loc} the zero frequency limit of the local susceptibility, $\chi_{\text{loc}} = \int_0^{\beta\hbar} d\tau \, q_d(\tau)$.

18.4. Classification of Mean-Field Quantum Glasses

The local degrees of freedom, their interactions and the environment they couple to define different mean-field classes, distinguished by their phase diagrams and properties. We list three distinguishing aspects of spin models and discuss them in turn below.

- The number of spins coupled by typical interaction terms decides on the organization of phase space as elucidated, for instance, by the replica analysis and its symmetry breaking scheme. This distinction drastically affects the nature and the order of the quantum glass transition.
- The symmetry group in spin space is important. It matters whether the various spin-spin interaction terms mutually commute (as in Ising and rotor models) or not (as in Heisenberg systems). In the latter case quantum fluctuations are substantially stronger, entailing a weaker glassy order and softer excitations, both at low and high T.
- The low-frequency dynamics depend on whether the quantum glass is embedded in an insulating, gapped host, or couples to a gapless bath with Ohmic spectrum, as in metallic glasses. For a given environment — insulating or metallic — the dynamically relevant states of all mean-field models, in spite of quantitative differences, display a striking universality in their low-frequency response within the glass phase (Sec. 18.5).

Note that these spin glass models do not cover all possible glassy quantum systems. Some other cases are pinned elastic systems (including vortex lattices in superconductors, Wigner crystals, charge and spin-density waves or disordered liquid crystals) in which frustrating disorder originates, e.g., from substrate impurities [43, 118]. The interested reader may consult Ref. [44]. Nonetheless, once coarse-grained at the collective pinning scale, these systems resemble short-range coupled spin systems in random fields.

18.4.1. *Pair versus multi-spin interactions*

18.4.1.1. *Pair interactions ($p = 2$) — continuous glass transition*

Usually one considers Ising-like interactions when discussing the distinction between pair and multi-spin interactions. Ising-type glasses arise in numerous contexts, as they describe generic interacting two level systems (TLS). The simplest representative is the transverse field Ising model (TFIM)

$$\hat{\mathcal{H}} = -\sum_{ij} J_{ij}\, \hat{\sigma}_i^z \hat{\sigma}_j^z + \sum_i \mathbf{H}_i \cdot \hat{\boldsymbol{\sigma}}_i \tag{18.4}$$

where $\hat{\boldsymbol{\sigma}}_i = (\hat{\sigma}_i^x, \hat{\sigma}_i^y, \hat{\sigma}_i^z)$, with the usual Pauli matrices acting in the Hilbert space of the i'th TLS. In finite dimensions the first sum extends over nearest neighbours of a lattice. The interaction strengths J_{ij} are drawn from a probability distribution, $P(J_{ij})$, typically chosen to be Gaussian with zero mean $[J_{ij}] = 0$ and variance $[J_{ij}^2] = J^2/(2c)$, where J is $O(1)$ and c is the connectivity of the lattice. Mean values over P are indicated with square brackets. The $\mathbf{H}_i$ are local fields. Most often one restricts to a homogeneous transverse field, $\mathbf{H}_i = \Gamma \mathbf{e}_x$. Since the last term does not commute with the first one in the Hamiltonian, it induces non-trivial quantum dynamics. In the absence of longitudinal fields H_i^z, the Hamiltonian possesses an Ising symmetry which is spontaneously broken at sufficiently low T and weak transverse fields $\Gamma < \Gamma_c$. For $H_i^z \neq 0$ (as in many experimental systems of interest) the only potential phase transition is an RSB one, which however occurs only in high enough dimensions.

Allowing each spin to interact with all others, $c \to N - 1$, places the spins on a complete graph. The scaling of the variance, $[J_{ij}^2] \approx J^2/(2N)$, ensures a non-trivial thermodynamic limit, $N \to \infty$. The Hamiltonian becomes the quantum extension [41] of the Sherrington–Kirkpatrick (SK) spin-glass (TFSK), which is tractable with the replica trick. Again, only the replica diagonal, $q_d(\tau) \equiv Q_{aa}(\tau) = [\langle \mathrm{T}\sigma_a^z(\tau)\sigma_a^z(0)\rangle]$ depends on the imaginary time τ, while the RSB structure of the off-diagonal elements remains basically the same as in the classical limit. Glassy freezing is signalled by a finite Edwards–Anderson parameter $q_{\mathrm{EA}} \equiv \lim_{\tau \to \infty} q_d(\tau)$ (at $T = 0$). The resulting single-site problem, with the coupling to the rest encapsulated self-consistently in Q_{ab}, is of similar difficulty as the impurity problems of Dynamical Mean Field Theory [45].

From the stability criterion $1 = J\chi_{\mathrm{loc}}$, a $(T/J, \Gamma/J)$ phase diagram with a second order phase transition between a paramagnetic and a spin-glass phase is predicted [41]. Quantum fluctuations depress the transition temperature but do not destroy the transition. For $\Gamma \to 0$ the classical SK $T_c = J$ is recovered and for $T \to 0$ a quantum critical point at $\Gamma_c = 1.52J$ is found [46]. Order sets in when the entropy loss and/or the loss in transverse field energy are compensated by the gain in interaction energy.

Close to the phase transition both scale like $O(m^2)$, where $m \ll 1$ is a typical ordered moment of a single spin. The glass transition, whether classical or quantum, can thus be viewed as a condensation into the first magnetization mode to become unstable. The glass transition differs crucially from standard ordering phenomena, however, because a large number of modes turn soft almost simultaneously. This entails many local minima with different ordering patterns. Moreover, *throughout* the entire glass phase there are permanently some gapless, critical modes at the verge of condensing.

Interestingly enough, a "static approximation" in which $q_d(\tau)$ is replaced by a τ-independent variational parameter captures the essence of the phase transition. A more detailed dynamical analysis for the Ising case [47] and related rotor models with $M \gg 1$ components [48] shows that the spectral gap closes as $\Delta \sim [(\Gamma - \Gamma_c)/\ln(\Gamma - \Gamma_c)]^{1/2}$ at Γ_c, the spectral function becoming gapless as $\chi''_{\text{loc}}(\omega) \sim \omega$, associated with algebraic decay in imaginary time, $q_d(\tau) \sim 1/\tau^2$.

Determining Q_{ab} and $q_d(\tau)$ deeper in the glass phase requires the solution of a quantum impurity problem in a frozen field whose distribution is controlled by full RSB in the off-diagonal Q_{ab} [49]. The latter ensures marginal stability, which in turn implies a gapless spectrum *everywhere* in the glass phase. Moreover, the limit of small Γ admits a scaling form for the mean field solution. From this it follows that the low-frequency spectral function becomes independent of Γ,

$$\chi''_{\text{loc}}(\omega; \Gamma \ll J) = 0.59\, \omega/J^2, \tag{18.5}$$

which we will interpret physically in Sec. 18.5.

18.4.1.2. $p > 2$ — *discontinuous onset of glassy order*

Models in which $p > 2$ classical spins interact simultaneously are particularly interesting since at the mean field level their dynamics are described by equations identical to those arising in the mode coupling theory of structural glasses. It is therefore believed that they capture the physics of the structural glass transition and the glassy phase [1, 2]. Moreover, such multi-spin Hamiltonians are ubiquitous in combinatorial optimization problems when translated into questions about ground states of statistical mechanics systems. Defined on diluted graphs, the p-spin models are, e.g., closely connected to the K-satisfiability problem [50].

A typical multi-spin Hamiltonian reads [25, 26, 40, 51–53]

$$\hat{\mathcal{H}} = - \sum_{i_1 \neq \cdots \neq i_p} J_{i_1 \ldots i_p}\, \hat{\sigma}^z_{i_1} \cdots \hat{\sigma}^z_{i_p} + \sum_i \Gamma_i \hat{\sigma}^x_i, \tag{18.6}$$

with the parameter p taking any integer value $p \geq 3$. The model is defined on a hypergraph, the sum running over all p-uplets. The couplings are random independent variables with variance $p! J^2/(2N^{p-1})$.

The important difference w.r.t. pairwise interacting models lies in the scaling of the loss of entropy or transverse field energy as compared to the interaction energy gain with a putative small emerging magnetization pattern $m_i = \langle \sigma^z_i \rangle$. The former still scale as $O(m^2)$, but the energy gain is only $O(m^p)$ and cannot compensate for this loss if m is small. The only possibility for a phase transition is that the order parameter, $q_{\rm EA} = 1/N \sum m_i^2$ jumps discontinuously to a finite value at a critical point. Technically, this is reflected by a one-step RSB. Part of the liquid entropy is transferred to configurational entropy without a thermodynamic phase transition (the free energy is smooth). The Gibbs weight distributes over an exponential number of metastable states. When quantum fluctuations are switched on, and temperature is sufficiently low, the transition necessarily has to change nature since the configurational entropy cannot contribute to the free energy. The phase transition thus becomes truly first order [29] and the ground states on the two sides of the transition are essentially unrelated. For this reason quantum annealing is not expected to be useful for $(p > 2)$-spin systems and other systems with a 1-step RSB.

In quantum and classical glasses of this type alike, the proliferation of metastable states affects the dynamics, but does not necessarily change the static observables. Over a finite range of free-energy densities one finds exponentially many local minima, the fewer the lower the free energy. As temperature decreases the Gibbs weight concentrates on lower energy states. A thermodynamic freeze-out transition occurs once the lowest $O(1)$ states dominate. Consequently, the dynamical glassy phase extends beyond the thermodynamic one [27, 28, 54].

The p-spin potential was also used to model a quantum particle in a random potential, in which the interactions are between p-uplets of coordinate positions on an N-dimensional sphere. Conventional kinetic energy is given to the particle. In these cases an equation of the kind of Eq. (18.2) applies with $G_0^{-1}{}_{ab} = (d_\tau^2 + \mu)\delta_{ab}$ with μ a Lagrange multiplier enforcing the spherical constraint and $\Sigma_{ab} = J^2 Q_{ab}^{\bullet(p-1)}$ where $\bullet$ denotes a normal power. Self-energies of this very same kind appear in the SYK model, Sec. 18.9.

18.4.2. *Commuting versus non-commuting interactions*

18.4.2.1. *Commuting interactions*

The disordered quantum rotor model is defined by [48]

$$\hat{\mathcal{H}} = \frac{g}{2M} \sum_i \hat{\mathbb{L}}_i^2 + \frac{M}{\sqrt{N}} \sum_{i<j} J_{ij}\,\hat{\mathbf{n}}_i \cdot \hat{\mathbf{n}}_j \qquad \hat{\mathbf{n}}_i^2 = 1 \;\; \forall i. \tag{18.7}$$

The M components $\hat{n}_i^\mu$ of the ith unit-length rotor $\hat{\mathbf{n}}_i$ commute with each other, unlike the components of quantum spins. As a consequence, all interaction terms mutually commute. $\hat{L}_i^{\mu\nu}$ (with $\mu < \nu$, $\mu,\nu = 1,\ldots,M$) are the $M(M-1)/2$ components of the angular-momentum generator $\hat{\mathbb{L}}_i$ in rotor space, and $[L_i^{\mu\nu}, n_j^\sigma] = i\delta_{ij}(\delta_{\mu\sigma}n_j^\nu - \delta_{\nu\sigma}n_j^\mu)$. The J_{ij} are $O(1)$ randomly distributed uncorrelated exchange constants. As $g \to 0$ the model reduces to the classical, infinite-range, M-component spin glass, the limit $M \to 1$ being very similar to the Ising model.

There is no Berry phase in the real action of the path integral representation of the partition function, and the $O(M)$ symmetric saddle-point [48] in the $M \to \infty$ limit yields a self-consistency equation, Eq. (18.2), with $G_0^{-1}{}_{ab} = g^{-1}(d^2/d\tau^2 + \mu)\delta_{ab}$, where μ enforces the constraint $\hat{\mathbf{n}}_i^2 = 1$, and one has $Q_{ab} = q_d\delta_{ab}$ and $\Sigma_{ab} = Q_{ab}$. In the glass phase the same equation is obeyed by $q_d(\tau) - q_{\rm EA}$, while $Q_{a\neq b} = q_{\rm EA}$ becomes non-zero, without however breaking the replica symmetry. The integro-differential equation is easy to solve in frequency space and yields spectral functions that we will review in Sec. 18.5. The quantum critical behavior was found to be in the TFSK universality class, which was rationalized by showing that $1/M$ corrections do not modify the critical exponents and the low frequency spectrum.

18.4.2.2. *Non-commuting interactions — $SU(M)$ spins*

The most relevant model in this class is the quantum Heisenberg spin glass,

$$\hat{\mathcal{H}} = -\sum_{i \neq j} J_{ij}\, \hat{\boldsymbol{\sigma}}_i \cdot \hat{\boldsymbol{\sigma}}_j. \tag{18.8}$$

A static approximation used to evaluate the instability condition for $S = 1/2$ [41] yields a surprisingly good estimate for $T_g \approx \sqrt{3}/12 \approx 0.14\,J$, obtained with quantum Monte Carlo calculations [55]. The substantial reduction with respect to the classical $T_g = J/4$ is due to quantum fluctuations.

With the static approximation, though, one cannot access the spin dynamics. A crucial step forward was taken in [56] where $SU(2)$ was promoted to $SU(M)$ and a Schwinger boson representation of the spins, with the number of bosons constrained to be $n_b = SM$, was adopted. A first analysis in the (M, S) parameter space was performed in the large M limit. Soon after, a complete solution with $M \to \infty$ and fixed S was derived, and global aspects, some of them also valid for $SU(2)$, discussed [57, 58]. The solution is formulated in terms of the Green functions of the bosons, $G_B^{ab}(\tau) \equiv -M^{-1}\sum_\mu [\langle T\hat{b}_\mu^a(\tau)\hat{b}_\mu^{b\dagger}(0)\rangle]$ and their self-consistency equations are again of the form of Eq. (18.2) with

$$G_{0\ ab}^{-1} = (d_\tau + \mu^a)\delta_{ab}\,, \qquad \Sigma_B^{ab}(\tau) = J^2 G_B^{ab}(\tau)G_B^{ab}(\tau)G_B^{ab}(-\tau). \tag{18.9}$$

μ^a is a chemical potential which fixes $G_B^{aa}(\tau = 0) = -S$. The disorder-averaged spin-spin correlator is obtained from G_B by

$$q_d(\tau) \equiv \frac{1}{M^2}[\langle \hat{\boldsymbol{\sigma}}^a(\tau) \cdot \hat{\boldsymbol{\sigma}}^a(0)\rangle] = G_B^{aa}(\tau)G_B^{aa}(-\tau). \tag{18.10}$$

For large S one finds an essentially classical glass transition at $T_g \sim S^2 J$, where the bosonic spinons condense. The 4-spinon interaction term resembles the $p = 4$-spin problem, and for similar reasons one finds a 1-step RSB transition. This leaves open the choice of the size of replica blocks, which selects the energy of the targeted metastable states. Usually one uses the condition of marginal stability (vanishing of the "replicon" mode), as those are reached dynamically [31] and exhibit a gapless spectrum. Extremization of the free-energy density instead describes dynamically inaccessible states with a gap in $\chi_{\text{loc}}''(\omega)$.

At large S, quantum fluctuations introduce a frequency scale $\sim SJ$, which sets the crossover temperature where collective quantum dynamics emerges. Consistent with the Landau analysis of Sec. 18.5 marginal states are found to have $\chi_{\text{loc}}''(\omega) \sim \omega$ and a low-T specific heat that scales as T^3 [59, 60] (contrary to the linear T dependence originally claimed in [57, 58]).

The case of small $S \ll 1$ exhibits much stronger quantum fluctuations and is thus more interesting. Here, the spin-fluid, paramagnetic regime survives down to much lower temperatures $T \ll J$ and is radically different from the classical paramagnet of the high T and large S limits. Below $T \sim J$, the system enters a gapless, quantum critical regime in which the Green's function assumes long-time tails, $G_B^{aa}(\tau) \sim 1/(J\tau)^{1/2}$, while the melon-bubble self-energy is unusually large, $\Sigma(\omega) \sim (\omega J)^{1/2} \gg \omega$, reflecting the strong scattering among spinons. From the spin-spin correlation $q_d(\tau) \sim 1/(J\tau)$ one extracts a susceptibility very similar to the one of marginal Fermi liquids: $J\chi''_{\mathrm{loc}}(\omega) \simeq \tanh(\hbar\omega/2T)$ implying $\chi'_{\mathrm{loc}} \simeq \ln(J/T)$. One further finds linear in T specific heat and a residual low-temperature entropy. This holds in the paramagnetic regime $T_g < T < J$, for an extended range of S all the way up to $S \simeq 1$. These properties are very similar to those of black holes to which this model and SYK are related.

From Eq. (18.10) one sees that the onset of glassy order modifies the Green functions beyond the time scale $\tau^* = (\omega^*)^{-1} = (q_{\mathrm{EA}}J)^{-1}$ where $G_B(\tau)G_B(-\tau) \sim q_{\mathrm{EA}}$. At that scale the spinons get confined, and $Q(\tau)$ crosses over to $Q(\tau) - q_{\mathrm{EA}} \sim \tau^*/(J\tau^2)$. This corresponds to a linear spectral function $J\chi''_{\mathrm{loc}}(\omega) \sim \omega/(q_{\mathrm{EA}}J)$, as is found in all insulating mean-field glasses, cf. Sec. 18.5. Note, however, that weak glass order implies a potentially large prefactor $\sim 1/q_{\mathrm{EA}}$, reflecting very slow collective modes.

The bosonic representation is *a priori* best suited for large S. Fermionic $SU(M)$ representations are instead believed to better capture the physically most relevant case $S = 1/2$. Such an approach yields essentially identical results for the paramagnetic phase [61], though no glass transition is found at $M = \infty$ in this case [56], since quantum fluctuations are much stronger. Yet, a $1/M$ expansion [62] yields an instability to a glass phase where a fermionic bilinear condenses at $T_g \sim J \exp(-\sqrt{\pi M})$ (now with continuous RSB — as the effective action is quadratic in the emerging order parameter, like in $p = 2$ models). One expects a similar suppression of the order parameter, $q_{\mathrm{EA}} \sim T_g/J$ (which ensures that at $T \sim T_g$ the low-T linear spectral function matches that of the paramagnetic regime). Exact diagonalization for all-to-all coupled $SU(2)$ spins [63, 64] indeed yields $q_{\mathrm{EA}} \approx 0.02$. However, currently accessible system sizes of ~ 20 spins do not allow to disentangle the regime $\omega < \omega^*$ from the broadened peak $\sim q_{\mathrm{EA}}\delta(\omega)$ reflecting static spin glass order. Nonetheless, they do exhibit spectral features as predicted by the fractionalized large M approach for $\omega > \omega^*$.

18.4.2.3. *Heisenberg glasses and many-body localization*

We close this section by remarking that Heisenberg spin chains with coupling J under strong, but random *i.i.d.* local fields $\mathbf{H}_i = H_i^x \mathbf{e}_x$ drawn from a distribution of width $W \gg J$, has become one of the standard models for MBL [10]. Indeed, the typically large mismatch between the local gaps H_i^x cannot be bridged resonantly by the weak couplings J, and thus coherent, bath-free dynamics is expected to remain stuck close to an arbitrary initial state. It is worth pointing out again that MBL is favored by completely opposite ingredients than a spin glass phase: it requires the non-commuting interactions to be weak, and the dimensionality should be low. In contrast, in the parameter range where a glass with non-trivial energy landscape exists, one expects rapid and full thermalization within any local minimum of the energy landscape, independently of the coupling to a bath.

18.4.3. *Insulating versus metallic environment*

Remarkably, all insulating mean-field quantum glasses in their marginally stable glassy states exhibit the same linear scaling $\chi''_{\text{loc}}(\omega) \sim \omega$, albeit with quantitatively different prefactors, and a low-T specific heat $c_V \sim T^3$. This contrasts with a spin glass coupled to a gapless bath, e.g. via Kondo coupling to itinerant conduction band electrons, as in heavy fermion materials [65]. The dissipation due to the low-energy bath degrees of freedom slows down the collective modes and thereby substantially enhances the low-frequency spin spectral function and the spin contribution to the specific heat, as we will review via a Landau approach in the next section.

18.5. Landau Theory and the Low Frequency Spectrum

The Landau expansion was reviewed in [66] and we only sketch it here. The aim is to construct an effective action for the glass order parameter Q_{ab} by integrating out all other degrees of freedom. This approach is expected to succeed for phase transitions in which the spins undergo standard ordering, as e.g. in the TFIM and rotor models. However, in Heisenberg-type models, where at least for $M \gg 1$ the spins fractionalize into deconfined spinons in the paramagnetic phase, it will likely fail to capture the entire dynamical crossover functions correctly. Methods such as the ones for deconfined quantum critical points [67] may instead be required. Still, even in these cases the Landau approach may capture well the glassy phase in its low-frequency, spinon-confined regime.

Considering symmetry restrictions and constraints on the replica structure, and assuming the absence of time-reversal symmetry-breaking fields, the resulting mean-field action close to the quantum glass transition takes the form [68]

$$n\beta\mathcal{F}[\delta Q] = \sum_a \int d\tau \, \mathcal{L}[\delta Q_{aa}] + u \sum_a \int d\tau \, [\delta Q_{aa}(\tau,\tau)]^2$$

$$-c_3 \sum_{abc} \int d\tau_1 d\tau_2 d\tau_3 \delta Q_{ab}(\tau_1,\tau_2)\delta Q_{bc}(\tau_2,\tau_3)\delta Q_{ca}(\tau_3,\tau_1) + O(\delta Q^4),$$

where $\delta Q(\tau,\tau') = Q_{ab}(\tau,\tau') - c\delta_{ab}\delta(\tau - \tau')$, with the constant c fixed to remove the uninteresting and non-universal short-time dynamics. The coefficients are bare correlations of the degrees of freedom coupling to Q, but only in the linear term their time-dependence is relevant. The leading low-frequency dependencies distinguish whether the degrees of freedom are gapped (insulating) or gapless like in a Fermi sea (metallic), and are

$$\begin{aligned}
\mathcal{L}_{\text{ins}}[\delta Q_{aa}] &= (r + \partial_{\tau_1}\partial_{\tau_2})\delta Q_{aa}(\tau_1,\tau_2), \\
\mathcal{L}_{\text{met}}[\delta Q_{aa}] &= \left[r' - (\tau_1 - \tau_2)^{-2}\right]\delta Q_{aa}(\tau_1,\tau_2),
\end{aligned} \tag{18.11}$$

where $\tau_1 - \tau_2 = \tau$. In the metallic case we dropped the subleading time derivatives, obtaining a leading $|\omega_n|$ dependence in Matsubara space, while the coefficient in insulating glasses displays a faster ω_n^2 dependence.

18.5.1. *Insulating glasses*

Minimizing $\mathcal{L}_{\text{ins}}$ with respect to δQ close to the quantum transition at $T = 0$ yields [68] $\delta\tilde{Q}_{aa}(\omega_n) = -\sqrt{\omega_n^2 + \Delta^2}$ (dropping numerical coefficients), which implies the spectral function

$$\chi''_{\text{loc}}(\omega) = \text{sgn}(\omega)\sqrt{\omega^2 - \Delta}\,\Theta(|\omega| - \sqrt{\Delta}). \tag{18.12}$$

The parameter-dependent energy Δ plays the role of a spectral gap, which closes, $\Delta \to 0$, upon approaching the transition from the paramagnetic side. However, remarkably, within the glassy phase the gap remains pinned to zero, $\Delta = 0$, which entails a linear low frequency spectral function:

$$\chi''_{\text{loc}}(\omega) = \omega. \tag{18.13}$$

This dynamical crossover agrees with the exact solution of large M quantum rotors and the critical behavior of the TFIM. Allowing for RSB, one finds marginally stable solutions with a vanishing replicon and gapless spectrum.

Note that, as anticipated above, the high-frequency spectrum predicted by the Landau approach differs qualitatively from the spin susceptibility $\chi''_{\text{loc}}(\omega) \sim \text{sgn}(\omega)$ of the large M limit of Heisenberg models, which hinges on spinon deconfinement.

18.5.2. *Metallic glasses*

Minimizing $\mathcal{L}_{\text{met}}$ close to the transition one finds [65, 69] $\delta Q_{aa}(\omega_n) = -\sqrt{|\omega_n| + \Upsilon}$, whereby the crossover energy Υ vanishes again at the quantum transition, $\Upsilon \to 0$, and stays pinned to $\Upsilon = 0$ in the glassy phase. Here the spectral function is everywhere *gapless* and approaches

$$\chi''_{\text{loc}}(\omega) = \frac{1}{\sqrt{2}}\frac{\omega}{\sqrt{\Upsilon + \sqrt{\omega^2 + \Upsilon^2}}} \xrightarrow{\Upsilon \to 0} \text{sgn}(\omega)\frac{|\omega|^{1/2}}{\sqrt{2}} \tag{18.14}$$

in the glass phase, which, at low frequencies, is substantially stronger than the one of insulating glasses, Eq. (18.13). Again, the Landau approach does not capture the high-frequency features associated with spinon deconfinement [64].

18.5.3. *Physical interpretation of glassy spectral functions*

The low-frequency spectral functions in the glass phase can be interpreted as arising from of set of collective random spin-density modes that behave as either underdamped or overdamped harmonic oscillators.

In the glass phase a local minimum of the free-energy landscape (expressed as a functional of local magnetizations) has a Hessian with positive eigenvalues λ_k which may be interpreted as generalized spring constants. The marginal stability of the relevant glass states assures that their distribution is gapless, and random matrix theory suggests that at small λ, it behaves as $\rho(\lambda) \equiv N^{-1}\sum_k \delta(\lambda - \lambda_k) = c\sqrt{\lambda}$.

In the insulating case one expects the Hessian normal modes to behave as independent harmonic oscillators with an effective mass M, set by the typical microscopic time scale of the spin dynamics. The associated oscillator frequencies then scale as

$\omega_k = \sqrt{\lambda_k/M}$, with a spectral density $\rho(\omega) \sim cM^{3/2}\omega^2$. This correctly predicts the specific heat to scale as $c_V(T) \sim T^3$ at low T, rationalizing the result of [59] (with the notable exception of quantum particles at jamming where $\rho(\lambda) \sim \lambda^{-1/2}$ [70]). The typical mean square displacement of oscillator mode k scales as $\langle x_k^2 \rangle \sim \hbar/M\omega_k \sim \hbar/\sqrt{M\lambda_k}$, and from the Lehmann representation, Eq. (18.3), one expects the spectral function to scale as

$$\chi''_{\text{loc}}(\omega) \sim \rho(\omega) \langle x^2 \rangle_\omega \sim c\sqrt{M}\omega, \qquad (18.15)$$

which rationalizes the linear scaling in Eq. (18.13).

The random oscillator picture is further supported by the scaling of the ratio $\chi''_{\text{loc}}(\omega)/\omega$. Exact calculations for rotors [68] or a particle in a random environment [29] indeed obtained a ratio $\sim \sqrt{M}$. In the TFSK, an effective potential construction yields $c \sim \sqrt{\Gamma}/J^2$ for $\Gamma \ll J$, while one expects $M \sim 1/\Gamma$. This correctly predicts the Γ-independent prefactor in Eq. (18.5).

For metallic environments, the oscillator dynamics is instead expected to be overdamped with a friction coefficient η proportional to the prefactor of $|\omega_n|\tilde{Q}_{aa}$. In this case the characteristic frequency of mode k is given by the relaxation rate, $\omega_k \sim \lambda_k/\eta$, implying a mode density $\rho(\omega) \sim c\eta^{3/2}\omega^{1/2}$ with larger weight at low frequencies. Accordingly, one expects corrections $\delta c_V(T) \sim T^{3/2}$ to the specific heat, as indeed predicted in [65]. The typical oscillator displacement follows from the scaling $\hbar\omega_k \sim \lambda_k x_k^2$, that is, $\langle x_k^2 \rangle \sim \hbar/\eta$, independent of the mode. The spectral function should then scale as

$$\chi''_{\text{loc}}(\omega) \sim \langle x^2 \rangle_\omega \rho(\omega) \sim c\sqrt{\eta\omega}, \qquad (18.16)$$

which again correctly reproduces the result of the Landau theory given in Eq. (18.14), as well as the scaling with η.

Unfortunately, little is known about the collective modes in short-range glasses. Those may play an important role in electronic processes such as hopping transport in insulators, as potential glue for strong-coupling superconductors, or as inelastic scatterers affecting the electrical resistance in metallic glasses.

18.6. Tunneling and Eigenstate Localization

It is interesting to ask whether and how quantum tunneling allows one to explore the clusterized landscape of quantum models with a 1-step RSB pattern. Having initialized a quantum Ising glass in a deep energy valley, tunnelling might not take place, even in the thermodynamic limit, since the remaining discreteness of the eigenstates (within one valley) may prevent resonant intervalley coupling.

This problem was first analyzed for $p > 2$ models [71]. Computing the tunneling amplitude between valleys of equal internal energy E and equating it to the intra-valley level spacing determines a minimal transverse field $\Gamma_c(E)$, below which wavefunctions and thus quantum dynamics, remain valley-localized. This situation is globally non-ergodic, yet delocalized within one valley - an unusual situation, believed to be impossible in finite dimensional models of MBL. The delocalization threshold $\Gamma_c(E)$ was found to lie consistently below the threshold $\Gamma_d(E)$ where glassy dynamics sets in. Indeed, Γ_c only senses the energy barriers in phase space, while dynamics can be exponentially trapped by entropic (*free* energy) barriers, in spite of percolation in the energy landscape.

At finite p, once quantum tunneling resonantly connects different valleys of energy E, the eigenstates hybridize all classical configurations having energy close to E, since the wavefunctions behave ergodically within a valley. This is not so in the strict limit $p \to \infty$ [72–74] where the random energy model results, and each valley contains only one single configuration. In this limit, only states in a very narrow energy shell hybridize, its width being the exponentially small tunneling between those states.

Ref. [35] studied how tunneling under barriers can be exploited for a quantum algorithm to efficiently find other valleys of equal internal energy.

18.7. Interplay of Glassy Order with Localization Phenomena

The interplay of glassy freezing with other quantum phenomena, especially with the localization of fermions or bosons, is a rich subject. Below, we discuss how (fermionic) electron glasses become metals, and how glasses of bosons may become superfluid.

18.7.1. *Quantum electron glasses*

The classical Coulomb glass is a disordered insulator with unscreened Coulomb interactions between localized electrons, realized in e.g. doped semiconductors [75–77]. A standard model is

$$\mathcal{H}_{\mathrm{Cb}} = \sum_i \epsilon_i n_i + \sum_{i<j} \frac{n_i n_j}{r_{ij}} \tag{18.17}$$

with random energy ϵ_i on site i drawn from a box distribution $[-W/2, W/2]$. The local occupation number is $n_i = 0, 1$ and r_{ij} is the distance between sites i and j. The number of electrons is a fixed fraction of the sites, which are arranged on a lattice or at random.

The unscreened, long range $1/r$ interactions between localized electrons enforce the Efros-Shklovskii (ES) Coulomb gap in the single-particle density of states, $\rho(E)$. It has long been conjectured that the stability constraint $\rho(E) \leq \mathrm{const.} \times E^{d-1}/e^{2d}$ (which assures that particle-hole recombinations do not lower the energy) is only marginally satisfied. A mean-field treatment with marginal full RSB predicts this critical property [78–80]. This phenomenon is directly analogous to the appearance of a linear density of local fields in the classical SK model, which is known to saturate similar stability bounds [81].

Upon increasing the density of dopants the hopping t_{ij} between the sites i and j becomes important and a term $\sum_{i<j}(t_{ij}c_j^\dagger c_i + h.c.)$ must be added to $\mathcal{H}_{\mathrm{Cb}}$ in Eq. (18.17). Single-particle eigenfunctions ψ_α now spread over several sites. When written in the basis of ψ_α, the interactions take the generic form $\sum_{\alpha,\beta,\gamma,\delta} U_{\alpha\beta\gamma\delta} c_\alpha^\dagger c_\beta^\dagger c_\gamma c_\delta$, which couples all wavefunctions ψ_α that overlap in real space. Close to the metal-insulator transition this term resembles the fermionic models reviewed in Sec. 18.9.

Eventually localization breaks down and the wavefunctions become extended [82]. At the same time screening sets in, the effective Coulomb interactions become short range and the density of states at the Fermi level becomes finite. Close to criticality the

Coulomb gap suppresses the occurrence of strong resonances for low-energy electrons, so that their wavefunctions concentrate less on rare paths. This results in a larger fractal dimension as compared to the ones of non-interacting critical wavefunctions [83, 84].

Already in the proximity of the insulating state one finds multiple solutions to Hartree-Fock equations. This may signal the emergence of metastability [85, 86], which then extends all the way into the insulating electron glass. Slow relaxation and aging in gated 2d electron gases in silicon [87, 88] at metallic densities was taken as an indication for electron glassy behavior. However, the existence of a genuine glass transition in $d = 3$ remains debated even in the classical limit, as the random potential breaks a potential Ising symmetry so that only the replica symmetry is left to be broken. Numerical simulations have not fully clarified the situation [89, 90].

In Sec. 18.8.3.2 we will review the related case of fermionic atoms with photon-mediated long-range interactions. Interestingly, this case allows for a genuine glass transition (with RSB) already in the metallic phase.

18.7.2. *Superfluidity and glassy density order*

Experiments that had suggested superflow in solid, but possibly amorphous Helium [91] had raised the interesting question whether and how (glassy) density order of bosons could coexist with the a priori competing superfluid order. For models with mean field-like, frustrated density interactions (such as e.g. realized in multimode cavities) and locally hopping bosons, it was indeed found that the two orders can coexist [92], while they try to avoid each other locally: if the local superfluid order parameter is high, the glassy density order is weak, and vice versa [93]. This phase is the bosonic analogue of the metallic glass of fermionic atoms discussed in Sec. 18.8.3.2. For a specific 3d model whose quantum Hamiltonian maps onto the Fokker–Planck equation of Brownian hard spheres, the existence of such a superglass phase could be inferred explicitly, drawing on the knowledge on the classical glass phase of hard spheres [94]. An off-equilibrium super-glass phase based on interaction-blockade of cold atoms was studied in [94b].

18.8. Experimental Realizations of Quantum Glasses

Let us now review a few selected examples of quantum glasses in correlated materials and possible realizations in artificial structures involving light-matter coupling.

18.8.1. *Quantum Ising spin glasses*

For long, $LiY_{1-x}Ho_xF_4$ was considered to be "the" quantum spin-glass realization [95]. The rare earth magnetic ion Holmium (Ho) has an Ising doublet with a large magnetic moment of $5.4\mu_B$ as its crystal field ground state. As the content of Ho is decreased below $x \approx 44\%$, the material turns from a dipolar ferromagnet to a dipolar-interacting Ising spin glass. Quantum fluctuations are introduced by a transverse field H_t, which at second order in perturbation theory hybridizes the two states of the Ho ground-doublet, resulting in an effective transverse field for the Ising doublet $\Gamma \sim H_t^2/\Delta$, where Δ is the gap in the crystal field spectrum.

With decreasing Γ the linear susceptibility for $x = 0.167$ reflects a rather sudden dynamic slowdown and the onset of low frequency $1/f$ noise [96]. However, the non-linear susceptibility does not diverge, ruling out a continuous glass transition. These findings were initially interpreted in terms of a first order transition at low temperatures, which, however, is at odds with the rule of thumb that two-body interactions usually entail continuous transitions. It was later argued [97] that no equilibrium glass transition can occur at large H_t, since the latter induces finite transverse moments whose internal longitudinal fields break the Ising symmetry explicitly. In the absence of a de Almeida–Thouless line, one could thus at best expect a regime of correlated spin clusters, whose size diverges as $\Gamma \to 0$. This might explain the flat maximum in the non-linear susceptibility as a function of Γ, and its decrease with T. However, to fully understand the dynamical response of $LiY_{1-x}Ho_xF_4$, it will be crucial to include the hyper-fine coupling to the Ho nuclear spin, especially in the quantum glassy low T regime [98].

Interestingly, the susceptibility at a given point (Γ, T) in the glassy regime depends strongly on the annealing protocol [36]. Quantum annealing results in significantly faster typical relaxation rates and larger $\chi'(\omega)$ than thermal annealing. Moreover, it results in a nearly Γ-independent dissipation $\chi''(\omega)$ at low ω, which was interpreted to signal a critical state. The authors suggested that faster response in quantum annealed samples implies more complete relaxation than under thermal annealing. However, the opposite conclusion seems equally possible: quantum annealing remains stuck closer to the marginal surface of the rugged energy landscape, leaving more fluctuating regions with small barriers and faster relaxation times. In contrast, the thermally annealed state, in which the system has managed to cross barriers, looks more "aged", being entrenched in deeper and more stable valleys, and thus displaying slower response.

18.8.2. *Quantum Heisenberg spin glasses*

Heisenberg quantum spin glasses attract a lot of interest because of the intriguing SYK-like spectral features they might display in their paramagnetic phase, as well as above a moderate frequency scale – provided the mean-field and large-M predictions survive for $SU(2)$ spins in 3d. A prominent example is the cuprate $La_{2-x}Sr_xCuO_4$ [99] which was recently shown to host spin glass order at low temperatures, all the way up to optimal doping, albeit with strong short-range antiferromagnetic correlations. If critical spectral features as predicted for fully frustrated mean-field Heisenberg glasses also survive in such real materials, they might possibly be at the root of the linear temperature dependence of the resistivity often observed in this type of materials [100].

In heavy fermion compounds, such as *e.g.* $Y_{1-x}U_xPd_3$, the dilute, randomly positioned local moments of U couple to conduction electrons that mediate RKKY interactions. Such materials are promising candidates to find genuine metallic quantum glass phases and quantum glass transitions to a paramagnet, where Kondo screening of the moments dominates. A quantum spin glass phase and interesting non-Fermi liquid behavior at higher temperatures was indeed reported for $0.2 < x < 0.4$ of the above compound [101]. For a more thorough review of quantum glass candidates and their magnetic properties we refer to [102].

18.8.3. *Mean-field quantum glasses in optical cavities*

Random and long-range interactions among cold atoms can be generated via light-matter coupling in multi-mode cavities with sufficiently random mode functions [103, 104]. We distinguish realizations with non-intinerant and itinerant atoms, respectively.

18.8.3.1. *Non-itinerant fermionic atoms*

Laser-trapped, immobile atoms act as local TLS (Ising spins). They are coupled by an effective long range Ising interaction J_{ij} obtained from integrating out the photons of the enclosing optical cavity. In cavities with a large number of modes, the long-ranged J_{ij} are nearly random, owing to the complex structure of the mode amplitudes. Such systems effectively realize a TFSK model, whereby the interaction may assume a non-vanishing mean $[J_{ij}] = J_0$ [105], and can be tuned via the driving parameters of the optical cavity. Upon dialling up the average coupling J_0 a ferromagnetic component of the spin freezing may arise as in classical analogues. Here it essentially realizes Dicke's superradiant phase. Under out-of-equilibrium conditions, as introduced by the driving of the laser cavity and the leakage of photons, the (steady state) phase diagram remains robust, but the critical behavior is modified [106].

18.8.3.2. *Itinerant fermionic atoms*

If the atoms are able to move, an interesting interplay between amorphous charge order and atomic delocalization occurs. In contrast to the case of Coulomb interactions (Sec. 18.7.1), the interactions remain long-ranged across the glass and the localization transitions. This allows for a glassy density order to develop upon decreasing the kinetic energy of the fermions while they are still in a metallic phase. Glassy density order in turn generates increased local disorder which eventually localizes the fermions.

The instability of the ergodic metal to glassy order and the single particle localization threshold are well separated in a lattice model with one fermionic level per site and close to half-filling. Thus, a metallic glass intervenes between the insulator and the ergodic metal [107]. In contrast, for more dilute filling the transition between ergodic metal and glassy insulator becomes first order, and in an extended parameter regime the two phases can coexist. How one phase nucleates out of the less favorable one remains an interesting open question.

18.9. Fermion Models and the Sachdev–Ye–Kitaev Model

Kitaev [108] proposed to use the Majorana fermion system

$$\hat{\mathcal{H}}_{SYK} = \frac{1}{i^{q/2}} \sum_{i_i < i_2 < \cdots < i_q}^{N} J_{i_i i_2 \ldots i_q} \hat{\psi}_{i_1} \hat{\psi}_{i_2} \ldots \hat{\psi}_{i_q}, \tag{18.18}$$

with $\hat{\psi}_i = \hat{\psi}_i^\dagger$, $\{\hat{\psi}_i, \hat{\psi}_j\} = 2\delta_{ij}$, quenched random couplings with zero mean and $[J_{i_1 \ldots i_q}^2] = (q-1)! J^2 / N^{q-1}$, and four fermion ($q = 4$) interactions, as a toy model for near-extremal black holes. Being very similar to the fermionic representation of the

$SU(M \to \infty)$ Heisenberg model, it has no glassy phase. The main reason to propose the connection with gravity is that it becomes approximately conformal in the infrared (dropping time-derivatives, low-frequency limit), with a time-reparametrization symmetry which is broken to SL(2,R), as expected in blackhole theories which develop a nearly AdS$_2$ background [100]. A "Schwarzian action" describes the cost of reparametrizations [109]. Moreover, there is non-zero entropy at $T \to 0$ (taken after $N \to \infty$) and the specific heat is linear in T – thermodynamic properties that are expected in the black hole context as well. Finally, this system is a "maximally chaotic/perfect scrambler" meaning that the bound $\lambda_T \leq 2\pi T/\hbar$ on the Lyapunov exponent (a consequence of the fluctuation-dissipation theorem [110]), defined from the exponential growth of out-of-time-order correlations [111], is saturated.

It was soon realized that Kitaev's proposal is very close to the Sachdev–Ye model, introduced and studied with the aim of describing non-Fermi liquid behavior in condensed matter systems hosting quantum spins (see Sec. 18.4.2.2). The above quenched disordered fermion system (with no glassy phase), subsequently called SYK, thus became a popular model in high-energy theory. Potential experimental realizations were proposed in disordered graphene flakes under strong magnetic fields [112, 113].

In order to make a connection with the formalism we described in the rest of the chapter, the relevant correlator in the SYK model is $Q(\tau) = -[\langle \mathrm{T}\hat{\psi}_i(\tau)\hat{\psi}_j(0)\rangle]$ (the fermionic analogue of G_B of Sec. 18.4.2.2), which satisfies an equation like Eq. (18.2) in its replica-diagonal form (no need of off-diagonal terms here) with

$$G_0^{-1} = d_\tau, \qquad \Sigma(\tau) = J^2 Q^3(\tau). \qquad (18.19)$$

Let us now comment on some interesting properties of the SYK model. Time-reparametrization symmetry also emerges in mean-field glass models, where sigma models for the reparametrizations were phenomenologically proposed (but not derived) [32]. Coupling two (or more) SYKs, popular in high-energy studies to mimic wormholes, is similar to coupling real replicas in disordered systems, a procedure that has long been used in the glass literature to access properties of the free-energy landscape [114]. Moreover, the relation of SYK with tensor models without quenched disorder [115] parallels the ideas of self-generated disorder put forward in the '90s to link p-spin models to the Mode-Coupling Theory for structural glasses [1]. In the SYK context, the trick is to use tensor models such that in a perturbative expansion only melon diagrams for the two-time function, and ladder diagrams for the four-time function, survive. With quenched disorder this structure occurs thanks to the average over randomness.

These results motivated numerous studies of other quantum spin glasses [116, 117], in particular those discussed in Sec. 18.4.1. Let us just mention here the analysis of chaos in the paramagnetic and marginal glassy phases of the spherical p-spin models [117]. Quantum fluctuations were found to make the paramagnetic phase less and the spin glass phase more chaotic. In the classical limit $\hbar \to 0$, a crossover from strong to weak chaos, as marked by a maximum in λ_T, arises well above T_d, concomitant with the onset of two-step slow relaxation.

18.10. Conclusion and Outlook

This short review on quantum glassy systems focuses on the discussion of their equilibrium properties. We have tried to tie connections between the different systems and models presented. On the analytic side, we mostly discussed results obtained in different mean-field limits, where the replica method and replica symmetry breaking schemes can be safely applied. The phenomenology of these disordered and glassy mean-field models is very rich and has a wide scope. Indeed, many applications beyond physics have been exploited, notably to optimization problems, but more recently fruitful connections with unexpected fields, like gravity, have been uncovered too. As usual, finite-dimensional physically relevant problems are not amenable to an exact treatment and much of what is known about them is either phenomenological or numerical.

Putting this summary together we came across a number of open issues which would be interesting to study. We just mention three of them. Revisiting the quantum glass transitions with deconfining spinons, especially in insulating Heisenberg systems, should be within analytic reach. We have only superficially discussed the interplay between glassiness and localization. There are certainly many interesting open questions there: how and when does glassiness set in? How does a localized quantum glass melt into a metal? Finally, it would be welcome to establish deeper connections between SYK insights (such as the treatment of the reparametrization invariance) and glass physics.

References

[1] J.-P. Bouchaud, L. F. Cugliandolo, J. Kurchan, and M. Mezard, *Spin-glasses and random fields*, vol. 12, Chapter Out of equilibrium dynamics in spin-glasses and other glassy systems, p. 161. World Scientific, (1997).

[2] L. Berthier and G. Biroli, *Rev. Mod. Phys.* **83**, 587–645, (2011).

[3] H. Westfahl, J. Schmalian, and P. G. Wolynes, *Phys. Rev. B.* **68**, 134203 (2003).

[4] D. S. Fisher, *Phys. Rev. Lett.* **69**, 534–537, (1992).

[5] H. Rieger and A. P. Young. In *Complex Behaviour of Glassy Systems*, vol. 492, *Lecture Notes in Physics*, p. 256. Springer Verlag, (1997).

[6] F. Iglói and C. Monthus, *Phys. Rep.* **412**, 277–431, (2005).

[7] P. W. Anderson, *Phys. Rev.* **109**, 1492–1505, (1958).

[8] N. F. Mott and W. Twose, *Advances in Physics.* **10**, 107–163, (1961).

[9] D. Basko, B. Altshuler, and I. Aleiner, *Annals of Physics.* **321**, 1126–1205, (2006).

[10] R. Nandkishore and D. A. Huse, *Ann. Rev. Cond. Matt. Phys.* **6**, 15–38, (2015).

[11] F. Alet and N. Laflorencie, *C. R. Physique.* **19**, 498–525, (2018).

[12] D. A. Abanin, E. Altman, I. Bloch, and M. Serbyn, *Rev. Mod. Phys.* **91**, 021001, (2019).

[13] J. Imbrie, *J. Stat. Phys.* **163**, 998–1048, (2016).

[14] W. de Roeck and F. Huveneers, *Phys. Rev. B.* **95**, 155129, (2017).

[15] W. de Roeck, F. Huveneers, M. Müller, and M. Schiulaz, *Phys. Rev. B.* **93**, 014203, (2016).

[16] J. Šuntajs, J. Bonča, T. Prosen, and L. Vidmar, *Phys. Rev. E.* **102**, 062144, (2020).

[17] D. Sels, *Phys. Rev. B.* **106**, L020202 (2022).

[18] M. Kiefer-Emmanouilidis, R. Unanyan, M. Fleischhauer, and J. Sirker, *Phys. Rev. B.* **103**, 024203 (2021).

[19] C. D. Dominicis, I. Kondor, and T. Temesvari, *Spin Glasses and Random Fields*, vol. 12, chapter Beyond the Sherrington-Kirkpatrick Model, p. 119. World Scientific, (1997).

[20] P. Calabrese, F. H. L. Essler, and G. Mussardo, *J. Stat. Mech.* **2016**, 064001, (2016).

[21] C. Turner, A. Michailidis, and D. A. et al., *Nature Phys.* **14**, 745–749, (2018).

[22] S. Moudgalya, B. A. Bernevig, and N. Regnault, *Rep. Prog. Phys.* **85**, 086501 (2022).

[23] A. J. Leggett, S. Chakravarty, A. T. Dorsey, M. P. A. Fisher, A. Garg, and W. Zwerger, *Rev. Mod. Phys.* **59**, 1–85, (1987).

[24] M. Vojta, *Phil. Mag.* **86**, 1807, (2006).

[25] L. F. Cugliandolo, D. R. Grempel, G. S. Lozano, H. Lozza, and C. A. da Silva Santos, *Phys. Rev. B.* **66**, 014444, (2002).

[26] L. F. Cugliandolo, D. R. Grempel, G. S. Lozano, H. Lozza, and C. A. da Silva Santos, *Phys. Rev. B.* **70**, 024422, (2004).

[27] L. F. Cugliandolo and G. S. Lozano, *Phys. Rev. Lett.* **80**, 4979, (1998).

[28] L. F. Cugliandolo and G. S. Lozano, *Phys. Rev. B.* **59**, 915, (1999).

[29] G. Biroli and L. F. Cugliandolo, *Phys. Rev. B.* **64**, 014206, (2001).

[30] M. P. Kennett and C. Chamon, *Phys. Rev. Lett.* **86**, 1622, (2001).

[31] G. Biroli and O. Parcollet, *Phys. Rev. B.* **65**, 094414, (2002).

[32] L. F. Cugliandolo and C. Chamon, *J. Stat. Mech.* **2007**, P07022, (2007).

[33] L. F. Cugliandolo, *Int. J. Mod. Phys. B.* **20**, 2795, (2006).

[34] T. Kadowaki and H. Nishimori, *Phys. Rev. E.* **58**, 5355, (1998).

[35] C. L. Baldwin and C. R. Laumann, *Phys. Rev. B.* **97**, 224201, (2018).

[36] J. Brooke, D. Bitko, T. F. Rosenbaum, and G. Aeppli, *Science.* **284**, 779, (1999).

[37] T. Jörg, F. Krzakala, J. Kurchan, and A. J. Maggs, *Phys. Rev. Lett.* **101**, 147204, (2008).

[38] V. Bapst, L. Foini, F. Krzakala, G. Semerjian, and F. Zamponi, *Phys. Rep.* **52**, 127, (2013).

[39] V. Dobrosavljevic and D. Thirumalai, *J. Phys. A.* **23**(15), L767–L774, (1990).

[40] L. F. Cugliandolo, D. R. Grempel, and C. A. da Silva Santos, *Phys. Rev. Lett.* **85**, 2589, (2000).

[41] A. J. Bray and M. A. Moore, *J. Phys. C.* **13**, L655, (1980).

[42] F. Krzakala, A. Rosso, G. Semerjian, and F. Zamponi, *Phys. Rev. B.* **78**, 134428, (2008).

[43] L. F. Cugliandolo, T. Giamarchi, and P. L. Doussal, *Phys. Rev. Lett.* **96**, 217203, (1996).

[44] T. Giamarchi and P. L. Doussal, *Spin-glasses and random fields*, vol. 12, Chapter Statics and Dynamics of Disordered Elastic Systems, p. 321. World Scientific, (1997).

[45] A. Georges, G. Kotliar, W. Krauth, and M. Rozenberg, *Rev. Mod. Phys.* **68**, 13, (1996).

[46] D. R. Grempel and M. J. Rozenberg, *Phys. Rev. Lett.* **81**, 2550, (1998).

[47] J. Miller and D. Huse, *Phys. Rev. Lett.* **70**, 3147–3150, (1993).

[48] J. Ye, S. Sachdev, and N. Read, *Phys. Rev. Lett.* **70**, 4011, (1993).

[49] A. Andreanov and M. Müller, *Phys. Rev. Lett.* **109**, 177201, (2012).

[50] R. Monasson, R. Zecchina, S. Kirkpatrick, B. Selman, and L. Troyansky, *Nature.* **400**, 133–137, (1999).

[51] Y. Y. Goldschmidt, *Phys. Rev. B.* **41**, 4858, (1990).

[52] T. M. Nieuwenhuizen and F. Ritort, *Physica A.* **250**, 89, (1998).

[53] L. F. Cugliandolo, D. R. Grempel, and C. A. da Silva Santos, *Phys. Rev. B.* **64**, 014403, (2001).

[54] L. F. Cugliandolo and J. Kurchan, *Phys. Rev. Lett.* **71**, 173, (1993).

[55] D. R. Grempel and M. J. Rozenberg, *Phys. Rev. Lett.* **80**, 389–392, (1998).

[56] S. Sachdev and J. Ye, *Phys. Rev. Lett.* **70**, 3339, (1993).

[57] A. Georges, O. Parcollet, and S. Sachdev, *Phys. Rev. Lett.* **85**, 840, (2000).

[58] A. Georges, O. Parcollet, and S. Sachdev, *Phys. Rev. B.* **63**, 134406, (2001).

[59] G. Schehr, T. Giamarchi, and P. L. Doussal, *Europhys. Lett.* **66**, 538, (2004).

[60] G. Schehr, *Phys. Rev. B.* **71**, 184204, (2005).

[61] O. Parcollet and A. Georges, *Phys. Rev. B.* **59**, 5341, (1999).

[62] M. Christos, F. M. Haehl, and S. Sachdev, *Phys. Rev. B.* **105**, 085120, (2022).

[63] L. Arrachea and M. J. Rozenberg, *Phys. Rev. Lett.* **86**, 5172–5175, (2001).

[64] H. Shackleton, A. Wietek, A. Georges, and S. Sachdev, *Phys. Rev. Lett.* **126**, 136602, (2021).

[65] A. M. Sengupta and A. Georges, *Phys. Rev. B.* **52**, 10295, (1995).

[66] N. Read and S. Sachdev, *Phys. Rev. B.* **52**, 384, (1996).

[67] T. Senthil, A. Vishwanath, L. Balents, S. Sachdev, and M. P. A. Fisher, *Science.* **303**, 1490–1494, (2004).

[68] N. Read, S. Sachdev, and J. Ye, *Phys. Rev. B.* **52**, 384–410, (1995).

[69] S. Sachdev, N. Read, and R. Oppermann, *Phys. Rev. B.* **52**, 10286–10294, (1995).

[70] S. Franz, T. Maimbourg, G. Parisi, and A. Scardicchio, *Proc. Nat. Acad. Sc.* **116**, 201820360 (2019).

[71] C. L. Baldwin, C. R. Laumann, A. Pal, and A. Scardicchio, *Phys. Rev. Lett.* **118**, 127201, (2017).

[72] C. L. Baldwin, C. R. Laumann, A. Pal, and A. Scardicchio, *Phys. Rev. B.* **93**, 024202, (2016).

[73] L. Faoro, M. Feigel'man, and L. Ioffe, *Annals of Physics.* **409**, 167916 (2019).

[74] G. Biroli, D. Facoetti, M. Schiró, M. Tarzia, and P. Vivo, *Phys. Rev. B.* **103**, 014204, (2021).

[75] A. L. Efros and B. I. Shklovskii, *J. Phys. C.* **8**, L49, (1975).

[76] A. Vaknin, Z. Ovadyahu, and M. Pollak, *Phys. Rev. Lett.* **84**, 3402–3405 (2000).

[77] A. Vaknin, Z. Ovadyahu, and M. Pollak, *Phys. Rev. B.* **65**, 134208 (2002).

[78] M. Müller and L. B. Ioffe, *Phys. Rev. Lett.* **93**, 256403, (2004).

[79] S. Pankov and V. Dobrosavljević, *Phys. Rev. Lett.* **94**, 046402 (2005).

[80] M. Müller and S. Pankov, *Phys. Rev. B.* **75**, 144201, (2007).

[81] M. Müller and M. Wyart, *Ann. Rev. Cond. Matt. Phys.* pp. 177–200, (2015).

[82] F. Epperlein, M. Schreiber, and T. Vojta, *Phys. Rev. B.* **56**, 5890–5896 (1997).

[83] M. Amini, V. E. Kravtsov, and M. Müller, *New J. Phys.* **16**, 015022 (2014).

[84] I. S. Burmistrov, I. V. Gornyi, and A. D. Mirlin, *Phys. Rev. Lett.* **111**, 066601, (2013).

[85] A. A. Pastor and V. Dobrosavljević, *Phys. Rev. Lett.* **83**, 4642–4645 (1999).

[86] V. Dobrosavljević, D. Tanasković, and A. A. Pastor, *Phys. Rev. Lett.* **90**, 016402 (2003).

[87] S. Bogdanovich and D. Popović, *Phys. Rev. Lett.* **88**, 236401 (2002).

[88] J. Jaroszyński and D. Popović, *Phys. Rev. Lett.* **99**, 046405 (2007).

[89] M. Goethe and M. Palassini, *Phys. Rev. Lett.* **103**, 045702, (2009).

[90] A. Barzegar, J. C. Andersen, M. Schechter, and H. G. Katzgraber, *Phys. Rev. B.* **100**, 104418, (2018).

[91] E. Kim and M. H. W. Chan, *Science.* **305**(5692), 1941–1944, (2004).

[92] G. Carleo, M. Tarzia, and F. Zamponi, *Phys. Rev. Lett.* **103**, 215302, (2009).

[93] X. Yu and M. Müller, *Phys. Rev. B.* **85**, 104205 (2012).

[94] G. Biroli, C. Chamon, and F. Zamponi, *Phys. Rev. B.* **78**, 224306, (2008).

[94b] A. Angelone, F. Mezzacapo, G. Pupillo, *Phys. Rev. Lett.* **116**, 135303 (2016).

[95] W. Wu, B. Ellman, T. F. Rosenbaum, G. Aeppli, and D. H. Reich, *Phys. Rev. Lett.* **67**, 2076, (1991).

[96] W. Wu, D. Bitko, T. F. Rosenbaum, and G. Aeppli, *Phys. Rev. Lett.* **71**, 1919, (1993).

[97] M. Schechter and N. Laflorencie, *Phys. Rev. Lett.* **97**, 137204, (2006).

[98] M. Schechter and P. C. E. Stamp, *Phys. Rev. Lett.* **95**, 267208, (2005).

[99] M. Frachet *et al*, *Nat. Phys.* **16**, 1064–1068, (2020).

[100] D. Chowdhury, A. Georges, O. Parcollet, and S. Sachdev, *Rev. Mod. Phys.* (2022).

[101] D. A. Gajewski, R. Chau, and M. B. Maple, *Phys. Rev. B.* **62**, 5496, (2000).

[102] J. A. Mydosh, *Reports on Progress in Physics.* **78**(5), 052501, (2015).

[103] S. Gopalakrishnan, B. L. Lev, and P. M. Goldbart, *Nature Phys.* **5**, 845, (2009).

[104] S. Gopalakrishnan, B. L. Lev, and P. M. Goldbart, *Phys. Rev. Lett.* **107**, 277201, (2011).

[105] P. Strack and S. Sachdev, *Phys. Rev. Lett.* **107**, 277202 (2011).

[106] M. Buchhold, P. Strack, S. Sachdev, and S. Diehl, *Phys. Rev. A.* **87**, 063622, (2013).

[107] M. Müller, P. Strack, and S. Sachdev, *Phys. Rev. A.* **86**, 023604 (2012).

[108] A. Kitaev. A simple model of quantum holography in *kitp strings seminar and entanglement program*, (2015).

[109] J. Maldacena and D. Stanford, *Phys. Rev. D.* **94**, 106002, (2016).

[110] S. Pappalardi, L. Foini, and J. Kurchan, *SciPost Phys.* **12**, 130, (2022).

[111] J. Maldacena, S. H. Shenker, and D. Stanford, *Journal of High Energy Physics.* **2016**, 106, (2016).

[112] A. Chen, R. Ilan, F. de Juan, D. I. Pikulin, and M. Franz, *Phys. Rev. Lett.* **121**, 036403 (2018).

[113] M. Brzezinska, Y. Guan, O. V. Yazyev, S. Sachdev, and A. Kruchkov, *arXiv:2208.01032.* (2022).

[114] S. Franz and G. Parisi, *Phys. Rev. Lett.* **79**, 248, (1997).

[115] I. R. Klebanov, F. Popov, and G. Tarnopolsky. TASI lectures on large N tensor models PoS TASI2017, (2018).

[116] T. Anous and F. M. Haehl, *J. Stat. Mech.* **2021**, 113101, (2021).

[117] S. Bera, K. Y. V. Lokesh, and S. Banerjee, *Phys. Rev. Lett.* **128**, 115302, (2022).

[118] G. E. Volovik, J. Rysti, J. T. Mäkinen, and V. B. Eltsov, *J. Low Temp. Phys.* **196**, 82, (2019).

Chapter 19

The Cavity Method: From Exact Solutions to Algorithms

Alfredo Braunstein[*] and Guilhem Semerjian[†]

Politecnico di Torino and Italian Institute for Genomic Medicine, Torino, Italy
alfredo.braunstein@polito.it
†*Laboratoire de Physique de l'École Normale Supérieure, ENS, Université PSL,*
CNRS, Sorbonne Université, Université Paris Cité, Paris, France
guilhem.semerjian@lpt.ens.fr

The goal of this chapter is to review the main ideas that underlie the cavity method for disordered models defined on random graphs, as well as present some of its outcomes, focusing on the random constraint satisfaction problems for which it provided both a better understanding of the phase transitions they undergo, and suggestions for the development of algorithms to solve them.

19.1. Introduction

The quest for an analytic solution for the simplest mean-field spin-glass model (the Sherrington–Kirkpatrick (SK) one [1]) led Giorgio Parisi to the invention of the replica method [2]. This method is able to describe and handle the complicated structure of the configuration space of the SK model, with a hierarchical division of the configurations into nested pure states, through the analytical parametrization of matrices of size $n \times n$, in the limit where $n \to 0$, which is, to say the least, a questionable mathematical construction (its predictions have been nevertheless confirmed rigorously later on [3–5]). In the physics literature an alternative method to solve the SK model was proposed in [6], and subsequently dubbed the cavity method. In a nutshell the idea is to consider the effect of the addition of one spin in a large SK model, or equivalently to create a "cavity" by isolating one spin and modeling the influence that the rest of the system has on it in a self-consistent way. The replica and the cavity methods yield the same predictions for the SK model, with complementary insights on its structure, the cavity method bypassing the "analytic continuation" from integer values of n to 0.

Even if the replica and cavity methods have had an impact inside physics, in particular in the context of structural glasses, they have also been very fruitful in fields which at first sight could seem unrelated, and in particular in computer science, information theory and discrete mathematics. Roughly speaking, the reason for their versatility lies in the rather universal character of the structure of the configuration space evoked above, that appears not only in the SK model but in many other problems with a non-physical origin, notably some random constraint satisfaction problems and error correcting codes. It turns out indeed that these problems can be viewed as mean-field spin glasses, but slightly different from the SK one: the degrees of freedom in these problems interact strongly with a finite number of neighbors, whereas in the SK all degrees of freedom interact with each other weakly, in a "fully-connected" manner. The mean-field character of these sparse, or diluted, models arise from the choice of the neighbors, which is done uniformly at random, without the geometrical constraints of an Euclidean space. In physics terms such a network of interaction is called a Bethe lattice, in mathematics a random graph. This type of model appeared in the physics literature relatively shortly after the fully-connected ones [7], but it became quickly clear that they were much more challenging to solve, some simplifications of the diverging connectivity (of a central limit theorem flavor) being absent in this case. A line of research extended the replica method to this sparse setting, see in particular [8, 9] and references therein, at the price of a rather complicated order parameter. It turned out that the cavity method is a more convenient framework than the replica one for these problems, the complex configuration space encoded by the replica symmetry breaking being formulated in a more transparent manner through the cavity approach, as first discussed in [10]; in addition the formalism of the cavity method can be used to develop algorithms that provide informations on a single sample of mean-field spin-glasses, not only on average thermodynamic quantities.

The goal of this chapter is to review the main ideas that underlie the cavity method for models defined on random graphs, as well as present some of its outcomes, focusing on the random constraint satisfaction problems for which it provided both a better understanding of the phase transitions they undergo, and suggestions for the development of algorithms to solve them. It is organized as follows; Sec. 19.2 focuses on the analytic aspects of the method. It contains an introduction to models defined on random graphs (in Sec. 19.2.1), then the equations of the cavity method at the so-called replica symmetric (RS) level and one step of replica symmetry breaking (1RSB) are presented in Sec. 19.2.2 and 19.2.3, before reviewing in Sec. 19.2.4 their outcomes concerning the phase diagram of random constraint satisfaction problems. Algorithmic consequences of this approach are detailed in Sec. 19.3.

19.2. The Cavity Method for Sparse Mean-Field Models

19.2.1. *Models on random graphs*

We shall consider systems made of N elementary degrees of freedom (spins) σ_i, which take values in some finite alphabet χ, and whose global configuration will be denoted $\underline{\sigma} = (\sigma_1, \ldots, \sigma_N) \in \chi^N$. They interact through an energy function (also called Hamiltonian, or cost function), that we decompose as

$$E(\underline{\sigma}) = \sum_{a=1}^{M} \varepsilon_a(\underline{\sigma}_{\partial a}), \tag{19.1}$$

where the sum runs over the M basic interactions terms ε_a. We denote $\partial a \subset \{1, \ldots, N\}$ the set of variables involved in the a'th constraint, and for a subset S of the variables $\underline{\sigma}_S$ means $\{\sigma_i | i \in S\}$. In what follows we assume that all interactions involves a subset of

k variables, for a given $k \geq 2$. This framework encompasses usual Ising spin-glass models, with $\chi = \{-1, 1\}$, $k = 2$ and $\varepsilon_a(\underline{\sigma}_{\partial a}) = -J_a \sigma_{i_a} \sigma_{j_a}$, J_a being the coupling constant between the spins i_a and j_a. It also allows to deal with Potts spins when $\chi = \{1, \ldots, q\}$ for a number $q \geq 2$ of spin states, also interpreted as colors; in this case a relevant energy function corresponds to pairwise interactions ($k = 2$), with $\varepsilon_a(\underline{\sigma}_{\partial a}) = \delta_{\sigma_{i_a}, \sigma_{j_a}}$. This yields the Hamiltonian of the Potts antiferromagnetic model, corresponding in the perspective of computer science to the q-coloring problem, the cost function counting the number of monochromatic edges among the interacting ones. More generically a constraint satisfaction problem (CSP) corresponds to a cost function of the form (19.1) with ε_a taking values 0 or 1, and being interpreted as the indicator function of the event "the a-th constraint is not satisfied by the configuration of the variables in $\underline{\sigma}_{\partial a}$". In particular the k-SAT and k-XORSAT problems can be described in this way with Ising spins and k-wise interactions. One calls solution of a CSP a configuration $\underline{\sigma}$ satisfying simultaneously all the constraints, i.e. a zero-energy groundstate, and one says that the CSP is satisfiable if and only if it admits at least one solution.

The Gibbs–Boltzmann probability measure associated to this Hamiltonian for an inverse temperature β reads

$$\mu(\underline{\sigma}) = \frac{1}{Z} \prod_{a=1}^{M} w_a(\underline{\sigma}_{\partial a}), \quad Z = \sum_{\underline{\sigma} \in \mathcal{X}^N} \prod_{a=1}^{M} w_a(\underline{\sigma}_{\partial a}), \quad \Phi = \frac{1}{N} \ln Z. \qquad (19.2)$$

where the partition function Z ensures the normalization of the probability law, and $w_a(\underline{\sigma}_{\partial a}) = e^{-\beta \varepsilon_a(\underline{\sigma}_{\partial a})}$. We introduced the thermodynamic potential Φ which we shall call a free entropy, as we did not include the constant $-1/\beta$ that would make it a free energy. This choice allows us to handle the uniform measure over the solutions of a CSP (assumed to be satisfiable), that corresponds to $w_a(\underline{\sigma}_{\partial a}) = (1 - \varepsilon_a(\underline{\sigma}_{\partial a}))$, in which case Z counts the number of solutions and Φ is the associated entropy rate. It amounts to setting formally $\beta = \infty$ in the Gibbs–Boltzmann definition, in other words to work directly at zero temperature.

A convenient representation of a probability measure μ of the form (19.2) is provided by a factor graph [11], see Fig. 19.1 for an example, which is a bipartite graph where each of the N variables σ_i is represented by a circle vertex, while the M weight functions w_a are associated to square vertices. An edge is drawn between a variable i and an interaction a if and only if w_a actually depends on σ_i, i.e. $i \in \partial a$. In a similar way we shall denote ∂i the set of interactions in which σ_i appears, i.e. the graphical neighborhood of i in the factor graph, and call $|\partial i|$ the degree of the i-th variable. One has a natural notion of graph distance between two variable nodes i and j, defined as the minimal number of interaction nodes on a path linking i and j.

Our interest lies in disordered systems, in which the probability measure μ is itself a random object. Suppose indeed that the weight functions w_a are built by drawing, independently for each a, the k-uplet of variables ∂a uniformly at random among the $\binom{N}{k}$ possible choices (and also the coupling constants defining the interaction if necessary). We will denote $\mathbb{E}[\bullet]$ the average with respect to this quenched randomness (let us emphasize that there are two distinct level of probabilities in these systems: the spins $\underline{\sigma}$ are random variables with the probability law μ, and μ is random because of

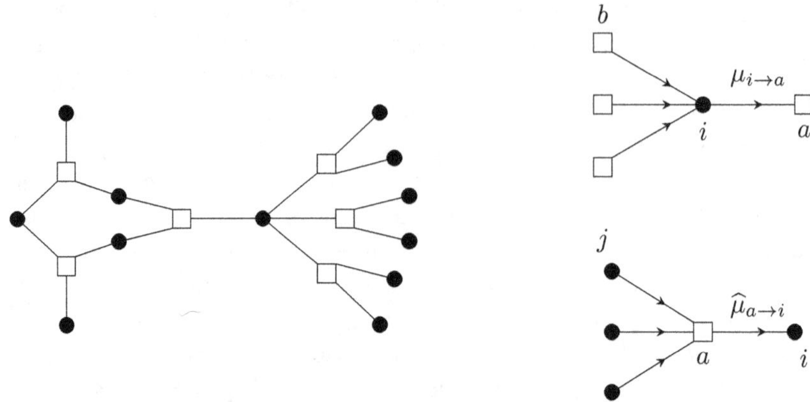

Fig. 19.1.   Left: an example of a factor graph. Right: illustration of Eqs. (19.4), (19.5).

the stochastic choices in the construction of the factor graph.) For $k = 2$ the resulting factor graph is drawn from nothing but the celebrated Erdős–Rényi $G(N, M)$ random graph ensemble, the case $k > 2$ corresponding to its natural hypergraph generalization. The large size (thermodynamic) limit we shall consider corresponds to $N, M \to \infty$, with $\alpha = M/N$ a fixed parameter. Let us recall some elementary properties of these random factor graphs in this limit:

- the probability that a randomly chosen variable i has degree $|\partial i| = d$ is $q_d = e^{-\alpha k}(\alpha k)^d/d!$, the Poisson law of mean αk.
- if one chooses randomly an interaction a, then a variable $i \in \partial a$, the probability that i appears in d interactions *besides* a, i.e. that $|\partial i \setminus a| = d$, is $\widetilde{q}_d = e^{-\alpha k}(\alpha k)^d/d!$.
- the random factor graphs are locally tree-like: choosing at random a vertex i, the subgraph made of all nodes at graph distance from i smaller than some threshold t is, with a probability going to 1 in the thermodynamic limit with t fixed, a tree.

More general ensembles of random factor graphs can be constructed, by fixing a degree distribution q_d and drawing at random from the set of all graphs of size N with $N q_0$ isolated vertices, $N q_1$ vertices of degree 1, and so on and so forth. Then the two distributions q_d and $\widetilde{q}_d$ are different in general, and related through $\widetilde{q}_d = (d + 1)q_{d+1}/\sum_{d'} d' q_{d'}$. An important example in this class corresponds to random regular graphs, where q_d is supported by a single integer.

19.2.2. *The replica symmetric (RS) cavity method*

The goal of the cavity method is to describe the properties of the random measure μ constructed above, for typical samples of the random graph ensemble. The free-entropy Φ is self-averaging in the thermodynamic limit, its typical value concentrates around its average, the quenched free entropy ϕ defined as

$$\phi = \lim_{N\to\infty} \mathbb{E}[\Phi] = \lim_{N\to\infty} \frac{1}{N}\mathbb{E}[\ln Z]. \tag{19.3}$$

The computation of this quantity is thus the objective of the cavity method, along with a local description of the measure μ in terms of its marginal distributions on a finite number of spins.

The cavity method relies crucially on the local convergence of random factor graph models to random trees explained at the end of Sec. 19.2.1. Let us assume momentarily that the factor graph representing the model under study is a finite tree. Then the problem of characterizing the measure (19.2) and computing the associated partition function Z can be solved exactly in a simple, recursive way: one can break the tree into independent subtrees, solve the problems on these substructures, and combine them together to get the solution on the larger problem. This is nothing but a generalization of the transfer matrix method used in physics to solve unidimensional problems, a form of what is known as dynamic programming in computer science. More precisely, for each edge between a variable i and an adjacent interaction a one introduces two directed "messages", $\mu_{i\to a}$ and $\widehat{\mu}_{a\to i}$, which are probability measures on the alphabet χ, that would be the marginal probability of σ_i if, respectively, the interaction a were removed from the graph, or if all interactions around i except a were removed. A moment of thought reveals that these messages obey the following recursive (so-called Belief Propagation (BP)) equations (see the right part of Fig. 19.1 for an illustration),

$$\mu_{i\to a}(\sigma_i) = \frac{1}{z_{i\to a}} \prod_{b\in\partial i\backslash a} \widehat{\mu}_{b\to i}(\sigma_i), \tag{19.4}$$

$$\widehat{\mu}_{a\to i}(\sigma_i) = \frac{1}{\widehat{z}_{a\to i}} \sum_{\underline{\sigma}_{\partial a\backslash i}} w_a(\underline{\sigma}_{\partial a}) \prod_{j\in\partial a\backslash i} \mu_{j\to a}(\sigma_j), \tag{19.5}$$

with $z_{i\to a}$ and $\widehat{z}_{a\to i}$ ensuring the normalization of the laws. On a tree factor graph there exists a single solution of these equations, which is easily determined starting from the leaves of the graph (for which the empty product above is conventionally equal to 1) and sweeping towards the inside of the graph. Once the messages have been determined all local averages with respect to μ can be computed, as well as the partition function, in terms of the solutions of these BP equations. The Belief Propagation algorithm consists in looking for a fixed-point solution of (19.4), (19.5), iteratively, even if the factor graph is not a tree; in this case the formula giving Φ in terms of the messages is only an approximation, known as the Bethe formula for the free-entropy (see for instance [12] for more details on the connections between the stationary points of the Bethe free-entropy and the solutions of the Belief Propagation equations). These equations were discovered independently in Statistical Physics as the Bethe–Peierls approximation, in artificial intelligence as the Belief Propagation algorithm, and in Information Theory as the Sum-Product algorithm [13].

Of course random graphs are only locally tree-like, they do possess loops, even if their lengths typically diverge in the thermodynamic limit. The cavity method amounts thus to a series of prescriptions to handle these long loops and to describe the boundary condition they impose on the local tree neighborhoods inside a large random graph.

The simplest prescription, that goes under the name of replica symmetric (RS) and that is valid for weakly interacting models (i.e. small α and/or large temperature), assumes some spatial correlation decay properties of the probability measure μ. When one removes an interaction a from a factor graph the variables around it become strictly independent if one starts from a tree, and asymptotically independent provided only long enough loops join them in absence of a, and provided the correlation decays fast enough along these loops. To compute the average thermodynamic potential (19.3) it is enough in this case to study the statistics with respect to the quenched disorder of the messages $\mu_{i \to a}$, $\widehat{\mu}_{a \to i}$ on the edges of the random factor graph. In other words the order parameter of the RS cavity method is the law of the random variables η, $\widehat{\eta}$, which are equal to the random messages one obtains by drawing at random a sample, solving the BP equations on it, choosing at random an edge $a - i$, and observing the value of $\mu_{i \to a}$ and $\widehat{\mu}_{a \to i}$. With the assumption of independence underlying the RS cavity method the equations (19.4), (19.5) translate into Recursive Distributional Equations (RDE) of the form:

$$\eta \overset{\mathrm{d}}{=} f(\widehat{\eta}_1, \ldots, \widehat{\eta}_d), \qquad \widehat{\eta} \overset{\mathrm{d}}{=} \widehat{f}(\eta_1, \ldots, \eta_{k-1}). \tag{19.6}$$

In this equation all the η_i's and $\widehat{\eta}_i$'s are independent copies of the random variables η and $\widehat{\eta}$, $\overset{\mathrm{d}}{=}$ denotes the equality in distribution between random variables, d is drawn according to the law $\widetilde{q}_d$, and the functions f and $\widehat{f}$ are defined by the right hand sides of equations (19.4), (19.5) (with possibly an additional random draw of the weight w). The RS prediction for ϕ can then be expressed as the average over random copies of η and $\widehat{\eta}$ of the local free-entropy contributions obtained from the exact computation of the partition function of a finite tree. Note that the equation (19.6), if it has in general no analytic solution, lends itself to a very natural numerical resolution where the law of η is approximately represented as an empirical distribution over a set of representatives η (a population representation) [10, 14].

The exactness of the predictions of the RS cavity method has been proven rigorously for some models which are not too frustrated (e.g. ferromagnetic systems, or matching models), see for instance [15–17]. But in general the correlation decay assumption fails, in this case one has to turn to a more sophisticated version of the cavity method, which will be introduced in the next section.

19.2.3. *Handling the replica symmetry breaking (RSB) with the cavity method*

As a matter of fact for low enough temperature, and high enough density of interactions α, the configuration space of frustrated random models gets fractured in a large number of pure states (or clusters), and the correlation decay hypothesis only holds for the Gibbs measure restricted to one pure state, not for the complete Gibbs measure. In the replica method this phenomenon shows up as a breaking of the equivalence between different replicas, we will now explain how the cavity method is able to handle this structure of the configuration space. It amounts to make further self-consistent hypotheses on the correlated boundary conditions this induces on the tree-like portions of the factor graph. Inside each pure state the RS computation is assumed to hold true, and the RSB computation is then a study of the statistics of the pure states. Let us explain how this is done in practice at the first level of RSB (1RSB cavity method). The partition function is written as a sum over the pure states γ that form a partition of the configuration space, $Z = \sum_\gamma Z_\gamma$, where Z_γ is the partition function restricted to the pure state γ. It can be written in the thermodynamic limit as $Z_\gamma = e^{N f_\gamma}$, with f_γ the internal free-entropy density of a given pure state. One further assumes that the number of pure states with a given value of f is, at the leading exponential order, $e^{N\Sigma(f)}$, with the so-called configuration entropy, or complexity, Σ a concave function of f, positive on the interval $[f_{\min}, f_{\max}]$. In order to compute Σ one introduces a parameter m (called Parisi breaking parameter) conjugated to the internal thermodynamic potential, and the generating function of the Z_γ as $\mathcal{Z}(m) = \sum_\gamma Z_\gamma^m$. In the thermodynamic limit its dominant behavior is captured by the 1RSB potential $\phi_{1\mathrm{RSB}}(m)$,

$$\phi_{1\mathrm{RSB}}(m) = \lim_{N\to\infty} \frac{1}{N} \log \mathcal{Z}(m) = \sup_f \left[\Sigma(f) + mf \right], \tag{19.7}$$

where the last expression is obtained by a saddle-point evaluation of the sum over γ. The complexity function is then accessible via the inverse Legendre transform of $\phi_{1\mathrm{RSB}}(m)$ [18], or in a parametric form

$$f(m) = \phi'_{1\mathrm{RSB}}(m), \qquad \Sigma(f(m)) = \phi_{1\mathrm{RSB}}(m) - m\phi'_{1\mathrm{RSB}}(m), \tag{19.8}$$

where $f(m)$ denotes the point where the supremum is reached in Eq. (19.7). One has $\Sigma'(f(m)) = -m$, i.e. the introduction of the parameter m allows to explore the complexity curve by tuning the tangent slope of the selected point.

The actual computation of $\phi_{1\mathrm{RSB}}(m)$ is done as follows [10]. One introduces on each edge of the factor graph two distributions $P_{i\to a}$ and $\widehat{P}_{i\to a}$ of messages, which are the probability over the different pure states γ, weighted proportionally to Z_γ^m, to observe a given value of $\mu_{i\to a}^\gamma$ and $\widehat{\mu}_{a\to i}^\gamma$ respectively, where $\mu_{i\to a}^\gamma$ and $\widehat{\mu}_{a\to i}^\gamma$ are the messages that appear in Eqs. (19.4), (19.5), for the measure restricted to the pure state γ. Because $P_{i\to a}$ and $\widehat{P}_{a\to i}$ are themselves random objects with respect to the choices in the generation of the instance of the factor graph, the order parameter of the 1RSB cavity method becomes the distributions of $P_{i\to a}$ and $\widehat{P}_{a\to i}$ with respect to the disorder. The latter is solution of a self-consistent functional equation written as

$$P \overset{\mathrm{d}}{=} F(\widehat{P}_1, \ldots, \widehat{P}_d), \qquad \widehat{P} \overset{\mathrm{d}}{=} \widehat{F}(P_1, \ldots, P_{k-1}), \tag{19.9}$$

that parallels the equation (19.6) of the RS cavity method, with again independent copies of the distributions P_i and $\widehat{P}_i$. The right hand sides of these distributional equalities stand for:

$$P(\eta) = \frac{1}{Z} \int \prod_{i=1}^{d} \mathrm{d}\widehat{P}_i(\widehat{\eta}_i) \; \delta(\eta - f(\{\widehat{\eta}_i\})) \; z(\{\widehat{\eta}_i\})^m, \tag{19.10}$$

$$\widehat{P}(\eta) = \frac{1}{\widehat{Z}} \int \prod_{i=1}^{k-1} \mathrm{d}P_i(\eta_i) \; \delta(\widehat{\eta} - \widehat{f}(\{\eta_i\})) \; \widehat{z}(\{\eta_i\})^m, \tag{19.11}$$

with the functions f and $\widehat{f}$ corresponding to the recursion functions at the RS level, see Eqs. (19.4), (19.5), and z and $\widehat{z}$ the associated normalization factors. From the solution of this equation (that again can be found numerically with the population dynamics method [10]) one computes the 1RSB potential $\phi_{1\text{RSB}}(m)$ via an expression similar to the one giving the expression of ϕ at the RS level, but with now averages over random distributions P and $\widehat{P}$.

There are different justifications for the appearance of the "reweighting factors" z^m and $\widehat{z}^m$ in Eqs. (19.10), (19.11). The argument in [10] is based on the exponential distribution of the free entropies Nf_γ of the pure states with respect to some reference value, and on consistency requirements on the evolution of the pure states when the cavity factor graph is modified. One can also study the statistics of the many fixed point solutions of the BP equations (19.4), (19.5) and devise a dual factor graph for the counting of these fixed points [13], the reweighting factor allowing to select the fixed points associated to some internal free-entropy. Another interpretation was proposed in [19], associating the pure states of a large but finite factor graph model to boundary conditions on trees. This interpretation is particularly relevant in the case $m = 1$, for which these boundary conditions are actually drawn from the Gibbs measure itself, and reveals a deep connection between the 1RSB cavity method and the reconstruction on tree problem, as first unveiled in [20], and with the point-to-set correlations of the Gibbs measure [21].

This construction can be generalized to higher levels of replica symmetry breaking [2], with a hierarchical partition of the configuration space into nested pure spaces; the resulting equations for models on sparse random graphs involve a recursive tower of probability distributions over probability distributions, whose numerical resolution becomes extremely challenging beyond 1RSB.

19.2.4. *Some analytic outcomes of the cavity method*

As presented above the cavity method is quite versatile, in the sense that it can address a variety of models defined on random graphs, and it has indeed been applied to several different problems. As an illustration of some of its outcomes we shall now present some results it has provided on the phase diagram of random constraint satisfaction problems (see also Chapter 32), and sketch the connections between this qualitative understanding and the quantitative formalism we have introduced before.

In the case of a constraint satisfaction problem the cost function defined in Eq. (19.1) is made of a sum of indicator functions of events that the a-th constraint is unsatisfied, for instance the number of monochromatic edges in the q-coloring problem. The natural questions in this context are: does an instance of the problem admit at least one solution? if yes, how are the solutions organized in the configuration space? It turns out that the answers to these questions have drastically different answers depending on the value of the density of constraints α, in other words there exist, in the thermodynamic limit, sharp phase transitions for some threshold values of this parameter.

The main transitions that occur for generic ensembles of random CSPs are represented in a schematic way on Fig. 19.2. The squares represent the full configuration space, for four different values of α (obviously the representation of this N-dimensional hypercube on a two-dimensional drawing is only a cartoon), while the black area stands for the solutions. For $\alpha > \alpha_{\text{s}}$, the satisfiability transition, the square is empty, which

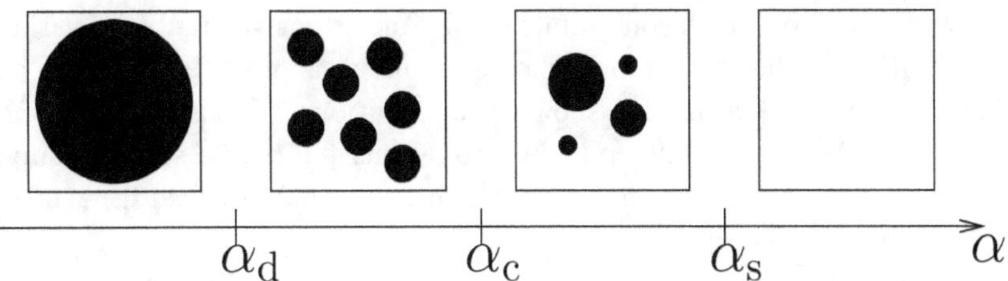

Fig. 19.2.   Schematic representation of the phase transitions in a random CSP ensemble.

translates the absence of solution in typical instances for these density of constraints. The satisfiable regime $\alpha < \alpha_\mathrm{s}$ is further divided in three regions, separated by structural phase transitions at which the organization of the set of solutions changes qualitatively. For $\alpha < \alpha_\mathrm{d}$, the so-called clustering, or dynamic transition, all solutions are somehow close to each other, while in the rest of the satisfiable regime they are broken in clusters of nearby solutions, each cluster being separated from the other ones. The number and size of the relevant clusters further change at the condensation threshold α_c: for $\alpha_\mathrm{d} < \alpha < \alpha_\mathrm{c}$ most solutions are contained in an exponential number of clusters which have all roughly the same size, while in the regime $\alpha_\mathrm{c} < \alpha < \alpha_\mathrm{s}$ most solutions are found in a sub-exponential number of clusters with strongly fluctuating sizes.

These qualitative predictions, along with quantitative numerical values for some definite random CSPs families, have been obtained by the analysis of the solutions of the 1RSB cavity equations, according to the following criteria [19, 22]:

- α_d is the smallest value of α such that the 1RSB equations at $m = 1$ admit a non-trivial solution.
- in the regime $[\alpha_\mathrm{d}, \alpha_\mathrm{c}]$ the configurational entropy, or complexity, associated to the $m = 1$ solution, is positive, whereas it becomes negative for $\alpha > \alpha_\mathrm{c}$.
- the satisfiability transition is marked by the vanishing of the complexity computed at $m = 0$, in the so-called energetic version of the 1RSB cavity method [23], that counts all clusters irrespectively of their sizes.

19.3. Some Algorithmic Outcomes of the Cavity Method

19.3.1. *Algorithmic applications of the cavity method*

As mentioned above the Eqs. (19.4)–(19.5) can be used on a single instance to compute (approximately) several properties of the distribution (19.2), including single-site marginals, joint marginals of variables in a common factor, the free energy and Shannon's entropy. This approach has been applied to Bayesian networks, in the decoding phase of communication codes (syndrome-based decoding, Turbo Codes [24]) and in stereo image reconstruction. More recently, it has found applications in a large variety of fields that we shall now review.

BP applications in notable models   In [25], a Belief Propagation algorithm for CDMA decoding has been presented. Interestingly, it shows how BP can be efficiently applied to dense models (i.e. which constraints involve an extensive number of variables) through an application of the central limit theorem (the basis of a BP derivative called AMP, see Chapter 20), and it is also shown that solutions are also fixed points of the famous Thouless–Anderson–Palmer (TAP) equations [26] while showing superior iterative convergence properties. A similar approach has been employed in [27] for the binary discrete perceptron learning problem.

In [28], the affinity propagation (AP) algorithm was presented. AP is a BP algorithm for variables with an extensive number of states. The AP algorithm solves approximately a clustering problem which is similar in spirit to K-means, but with the important difference of only relying on a distance matrix instead of the original, possibly high-dimensional, data representation. Auxiliary variables with a large number of states can be employed to locally enforce global constraints such as connectivity, by representing in the variables state the discrete time of an underlying dynamics. BP has been applied to the resulting extended model [29].

The dynamic cavity method [30] is an application of BP to study a certain class of out-of equilibrium dynamical models. The method can be understood as an application of BP to an auxiliary model in which a variable consists in a couple of time-dependent quantities: one is a single spin trajectory, the other a local field. Subsequent works showed that a slightly simpler but equivalent representation can be obtained with a pair of spin trajectories. On certain models such as discrete, microscopically irreversible ones (i.e. ones in which a variable can never go back to a visited state, including the Bootstrap percolation model [31], SI or SIR epidemic models [32]), single trajectories can be efficiently represented by the transition times. In other cases, some approximations must be employed [33]. A somehow related variant of the cavity method deals with quantum models, the basic degrees of freedom becoming imaginary-time spin trajectories [34].

Exactness of BP on single instances Some rigorous results have been proven regarding the exactness of BP algorithms. For certain models and sufficiently large temperature, the BP update equation becomes a contractive mapping, guaranteeing the existence and uniqueness of its fixed point and the convergence towards it under iterations thanks to the Banach theorem. Moreover, this condition guarantees exactness in the thermodynamical limit on graphs with large girth [35].

On the other side of the spectrum, some exactness results exist in the small temperature limit as well. Equations to analize models explicitly at zero temperature can be devised by taking the $T \to 0$ limit of the BP equations under an an opportune change of variables, resulting in equations for energy-shifts instead of probabilities. These had been known in coding theory as Max-Sum algorithms. Existing proofs of exactness (on some models) rely on a local optimality condition for BP fixed points. [36–38].

Gaussian BP (GaBP) [39] is an application of BP for a continuous model with positive definite quadratic potential, i.e. a Multivariate Gaussian. It is shown under certain conditions on the precision matrix that the GaBP equations converge and give the correct estimation of the means (but wrong estimation of the variances in general), effectively solving a linear system iteratively, with convergence properties that make the method competitive. Note that due to the fact that the mode is equal to the mean in a Gaussian distribution, this result can be again thought of as the exactness of the computation of the maximum.

Survey Propagations and the RSB Phase   Survey propagation (SP) is the algorithmic counterpart of the 1RSB cavity method. It has seen its first applications to study the k-SAT [40, 41] and q-coloring [42] problems in the replica symmetry broken phase. SP can be thought as BP for the combinatorial problem of solutions of a lower order message passing system (typically max-sum or some coarsened version of it). Such a hierarchical approach can also be employed to analyze problems that possess explicitly such a nested structure, such as the ones coming from (stochastic) control problems (e.g. the stochastic matching problem [43]).

It should also be noted that BP can be used in the RSB phase of constraint satisfaction problems. In [27] BP has been applied successfully to the perceptron learning problem with binary synapses, even in the regime in which it shows a RSB phase. The solution to this conundrum has been clarified in [44], where it was shown that BP describes an exponentially small portion of the solution space that is still exponentially large and has a non-clustered geometry akin to the dominant region of the solution space in the RS phase.

Decimation and reinforcement.   An algorithm estimating marginal distributions such as BP can be employed for sampling, and in particular to find solutions to a constraint satisfaction problem. The main idea is ancestral sampling, i.e. given an arbitrary permutation of variable indices π, one can estimate the marginal distribution $p\left(x_{\pi_1}\right)$ and sample $x^*_{\pi_1}$ from it, then restrict the solution space to solutions with $x_{\pi_1} = x^*_{\pi_1}$ and reiterate, effectively sampling $x^*_{\pi_i} \sim p\left(x_{\pi_i}|x^*_{\pi_1},\ldots,x^*_{\pi_{i-1}}\right)$ for $i = 1,\ldots,n$. As $p\left(\underline{x}\right) = \prod_{i=1}^{n} p\left(x_{\pi_i}|x_{\pi_1},\ldots,x_{\pi_{i-1}}\right)$, this solution provides a fair sample $\underline{x}^*$ if the estimation of the marginals is exact. The analysis of ancestral sampling with BP has been performed in [45–48]. When one is merely interested in finding *any* solution to a contraint satisfaction problem, and remembering that marginal estimations are only approximate, it is convenient to iteratively fix the variable that reduces the solution space the *less,* which corresponds to fixing the most polarized variable in the direction of the largest probability of its marginal. This process is called *decimation.* In practice, decimation corresponds to iteratively selecting the variable with the largest local field and applying an infinite external field to it with the same sign (and then making the equations converge again and reiterating). A soft version of decimation, called reinforcement, can also be conceived, in which a field is applied iteratively to all variables with the same sign of their local field and an intensity that is either a constant [49] or proportional to its magnitude [27, 29]. This dynamics slowly drives the system to one with sufficiently large external fields that becomes trivially polarized on one solution. As an additional twist, a backtracking procedure can be implemented on top of decimation, in which variables are occasional freed from their external field when that choice enlarges the solution space sufficiently. This has been implemented for SP, with excellent results [50].

19.4. Conclusions

The cavity method is a powerful and versatile approach to the description of disordered systems, that has been shown so far to provide the exact asymptotic solution for many models. For given (finite) system instances, its algorithmic counterpart has many practical applications, ranging from a statistical description of the Boltzman–Gibbs distribution to the individuation of single solutions of a CSP. Moreover, at variance with more traditional methods for inference such as MCMC sampling, it can provide an analytical description, given implicitly by the solution(s) of the cavity equations. This fact enables many possibilities, such as its recursive application (SP), and a functional expression of statistical features as a function of the disorder parameters (see for instance Chapter 22 for a discussion of inverse problems).

References

[1] D. Sherrington and S. Kirkpatrick, *Phys. Rev. Lett.* **35**(26), 1792–1796, (1975).
[2] G. Parisi, *J. of Phys. A.* **13**(4), L115, (1980).
[3] F. Guerra and F. L. Toninelli, *Comm. Math. Phys.* **230**, 71–79, (2002).
[4] M. Talagrand, *Ann. Math.* **163**, 221, (2006).
[5] D. Panchenko, *The Sherrington-Kirkpatrick Model.* (Springer, 2013).
[6] M. Mézard, G. Parisi, and M. A. Virasoro, *Europhys. Lett.* **1**(2), 77–82 (1986).
[7] L. Viana and A. Bray, *J. Phys. C.* **18**(15), 3037–3051, (1985).
[8] R. Monasson, *J. Phys. A.* **31**(2), 513–529, (1998).
[9] G. Biroli, R. Monasson, and M. Weigt, *Eur. Phys. J. B.* **14**, 551, (2000).
[10] M. Mézard and G. Parisi, *Eur. Phys. J. B.* **20**, 217, (2001).
[11] F. Kschischang, B. Frey, and H. Loeliger, *IEEE Trans. Inf. Theory.* **47**(2), 498, (2001).
[12] J. S. Yedidia, W. T. Freeman, and Y. Weiss. In *Exploring Artificial Intelligence in the New Millennium*, p. 239, (2003).
[13] M. Mézard and A. Montanari, *Information, Physics and Computation.* (Oxford University Press, 2009).
[14] R. Abou-Chacra, D. Thouless, and P. Anderson, *J. Phys. C.* **6**, 1734, (1973).
[15] A. Dembo and A. Montanari, *Ann. Appl. Probab.* **20**, 565–592, (2010).
[16] C. Bordenave and M. Lelarge, *Random Struct. Algorithms.* **37**(3), 332–352, (2010).
[17] C. Bordenave, M. Lelarge, and J. Salez, *Probab. Theory Relat. Fields.* pp. 1–26, (2012).
[18] R. Monasson, *Phys. Rev. Lett.* **75**, 2847–2850 (1995).
[19] F. Krzakala, A. Montanari, F. Ricci-Tersenghi, G. Semerjian, and L. Zdeborová, *Proc. Natl. Acad. Sci. U.S.A.* **104**(25), 10318–10323, (2007).
[20] M. Mézard and A. Montanari, *J. Stat. Phys.* **124**(6), 1317–1350, (2006).
[21] A. Montanari and G. Semerjian, *J. Stat. Phys.* **125**(1), 23–54, (2006).
[22] M. Mézard and R. Zecchina, *Phys. Rev. E.* **66**(5), 056126 (2002).
[23] M. Mézard and G. Parisi, *J. Stat. Phys.* **111**(1-2), 1–34, (2003).
[24] S. Benedetto, G. Montorsi, D. Divsalar, and F. Pollara, *The Telecommunications and Data Acquisition Report.* (1996).
[25] Y. Kabashima, *J. Phys. A.* **36**(43), 11111–11121 (2003).
[26] D. Thouless, P. Anderson, and R. Palmer, *Philos. Mag.* **35**(3), 593–601, (1977).
[27] A. Braunstein and R. Zecchina, *Phys. Rev. Lett.* **96**(3), (2006).
[28] B. J. Frey and D. Dueck. In *Advances in Neural Information Processing Systems*, vol. 18. MIT Press, (2005).
[29] M. Bayati, C. Borgs, A. Braunstein, J. Chayes, A. Ramezanpour, and R. Zecchina, *Phys. Rev. Lett.* **101**(3), (2008).

[30] I. Neri and D. Bollé, *J. Stat. Mech.: Theory Exp.* **2009**(08), P08009 (2009).

[31] F. Altarelli, A. Braunstein, L. Dall'Asta, and R. Zecchina, *J. Stat. Mech.: Theory Exp.* **2013**(9), (2013).

[32] F. Altarelli, A. Braunstein, L. Dall'Asta, A. Lage-Castellanos, and R. Zecchina, *Phys. Rev. Lett.* **112**(11), (2014).

[33] E. Aurell and H. Mahmoudi, *Phys. Rev. E.* **85**(3), 031119 (2012).

[34] V. Bapst, L. Foini, F. Krzakala, G. Semerjian, and F. Zamponi, *Phys. Rep.* **523**(3), 127–205, (2012).

[35] M. Bayati and C. Nair, *Proc. 44th Allerton Conference* (2006).

[36] M. Bayati, D. Shah, and M. Sharma. In *Proceedings. International Symposium on Information Theory, 2005. ISIT 2005.*, pp. 1763–1767 (2005).

[37] Y. Weiss and W. Freeman, *IEEE Trans. Inf. Theory.* **47**(2), 736–744 (2001).

[38] D. Gamarnik, D. Shah, and Y. Wei, *Oper. Res.* **60**(2), 410–428 (2012).

[39] Y. Weiss and W. T. Freeman, *Neural Computation.* **13**(10), 2173–2200 (2001).

[40] M. Mézard and R. Zecchina, *Phys. Rev. E.* **66**(5), 056126 (2002).

[41] A. Braunstein, M. Mézard, and R. Zecchina, *Random Struct. Algorithms.* **27**(2), 201–226, (2005).

[42] F. Krzakala, A. Pagnani, and M. Weigt, *Phys. Rev. E.* **70**(4), 046705 (2004).

[43] F. Altarelli, A. Braunstein, A. Ramezanpour, and R. Zecchina, *Phys. Rev. Lett.* **106**(19), 190601, (2011).

[44] C. Baldassi, C. Borgs, J. T. Chayes, A. Ingrosso, C. Lucibello, L. Saglietti, and R. Zecchina, *Proc. Natl. Acad. Sci. U.S.A.* **113**(48), E7655–E7662 (2016).

[45] A. Montanari, F. Ricci-Tersenghi, and G. Semerjian, *Proc. 45th Allerton Conference* (2007).

[46] F. Ricci-Tersenghi and G. Semerjian, *J. Stat. Mech.: Theory Exp.* p. P09001, (2009).

[47] A. Coja-Oghlan, *Proc. 22nd SODA.* p. 957, (2011).

[48] A. Coja-Oghlan and A. Y. Pachon-Pinzon, *SIAM J. Discrete Math.* **26**, 1471–1509, (2012).

[49] J. Chavas, C. Furtlehner, M. Mézard, and R. Zecchina, *J. Stat. Mech.: Theory Exp.* **2005**(11), P11016–P11016 (2005).

[50] R. Marino, G. Parisi, and F. Ricci-Tersenghi, *Nat Commun.* **7**(1), 12996 (2016).

Chapter 20

Message Passing and Its Applications

Florent Krzakala[*], Manfred Opper[†] and David Saad[‡]

IdePHICS Laboratory, EPFL, Switzerland
florent.krzakala@epfl.ch
†*Department of Theoretical Computer Science, Technical University of Berlin,*
Germany, and Centre for Systems Modelling and Quantitative Biomedicine,
University of Birmingham, United Kingdom
m.opper@bham.ac.uk
‡*School of Engineering and Applied Science, Aston University,*
Birmingham, United Kingdom
d.saad@aston.ac.uk

This chapter describes the journey of the distributed inference method of message passing over nearly four decades. Message passing algorithms for inferring approximate variable marginal probabilities have been developed independently in a number of disciplines including the statistical physics community, where it was derived to explore the macroscopic properties of disordered systems. Having realized their ability to provide good approximate solutions with a modest computational cost, message passing methods have been used in many application domains. Moreover, only recently, the power of message passing methods has been harnessed also to provide rigorous results for the performance of statistical estimators in general and for investigating models of disorder systems in statistical physics in particular, thus returning to the field where they originated and the questions they were designed to solve.

20.1. Message Passing — A Statistical Physics Perspective

Message passing algorithms provide efficient computations of approximate marginal probabilities for high-dimensional probabilistic models. Such methods have originally been developed independently within the information sciences (for inference in data models) and within the community of statistical physics where they were used to compute local averages for models of disordered systems. The relation between the two fields may not be obvious at first sight, but statistical assumptions about quenched random parameters (the 'disorder') made in statistical physics are structurally similar to those made for models in statistics and machine learning. For the latter, the frozen randomness is a result of the observed random data and/or system topology, representing the interaction between variables. In applications to real data, message passing methods often yield surprisingly accurate approximations compared to other methods.

The corresponding error can even vanish in the large system limit, when specific assumptions about the generation of data are made. Hence, by analysing the the dynamics of message passing one can obtain rigorous results for the performance of statistical estimators and for models of disorder in physics. In this chapter, we will mainly tell the story of message passing from the viewpoint of statistical physics, but will also discuss cross-fertilisations with methods of information sciences as well as applications of message passing algorithms to data problems.

20.1.1. *Probabilistic models with pairwise interactions*

Before we present the details and analysis of such algorithms, we will discuss the implicit approximations behind the resulting fixed points. We will focus on a nontrivial class of probabilistic models which are defined by probability distributions for a vector of random variables $\boldsymbol{x} \doteq (x_1, \ldots, x_N)$ of the form

$$p(\boldsymbol{x}) = \frac{1}{Z} \prod_i f_i(x_i) \exp\left[\frac{1}{2} \sum_{i,j} J_{ij} x_i x_j\right] \tag{20.1}$$

containing single site potentials and pairwise interactions with $J_{ij} = J_{ji}$ and $J_{ii} = 0$. This class contains models relevant for statistical mechanics and for data science: By the choice $f_i(x) = \{\delta(x - 1) + \delta(x + 1)\}e^{\theta_i x}$, we obtain an Ising model with discrete random variables $x_i = \pm 1$, couplings J_{ij} and external fields θ_i. A second example with continuous random variables $\boldsymbol{x}$ describes Bayesian supervised learning [1] of a binary classification task; N binary class labels $y = \pm 1$ are modelled as $y = \mathrm{sign}(\phi(z) + \epsilon_i)$; $\phi(z)$ is an unknown function of an input z which has to be inferred from a set of training input/label pairs $\{z_i, y_i\}_{i=1}^N$; ϵ denotes i.i.d. noise. To encode prior knowledge about the typical smoothness of the unknown function one assumes that $\phi(z)$ is a realisation of a Gaussian process with zero mean and covariance $K(z, z') = E[\phi(z)\phi(z')]$, with a predefined kernel function K. The posterior distribution $p(\boldsymbol{\phi}|\boldsymbol{y})$ of the unobserved function values $\boldsymbol{\phi} = (\phi(z_1), \ldots, \theta(z_N)$ encodes the knowledge about $\phi(z)$ given the training data. Defining $\boldsymbol{K} = \{K(z_i, z_j)\}_{i,j=1}^N$ and applying Bayes rule one finds

$$p(\boldsymbol{\phi}|\boldsymbol{y}) \doteq \frac{1}{Z} e^{-\frac{1}{2}\boldsymbol{\phi}^\top \boldsymbol{K}^{-1} \boldsymbol{\phi}} \prod_{i \leq N} p(y_i|\phi_i) \tag{20.2}$$

where the form of the likelihood $p(y|\phi)$ is derived from the noise distribution. Identifying $\boldsymbol{x} \equiv \boldsymbol{\phi}$ shows that the posterior is of the form (20.1).

20.1.2. *The variational approximation*

A common technique is to approximate intractable distributions $p(\boldsymbol{x})$ such as (20.1) by a member $q(\boldsymbol{x})$ from a family of tractable distributions depending on a set of variational parameters. These are optimised by minimising the *Kullback–Leibler* (KL) divergence $D(q\|p) \doteq \left\langle \ln\left(\frac{q(\boldsymbol{x})}{p(\boldsymbol{x})}\right)\right\rangle_q$ between the approximation q and the exact p. It is nonnegative and zero only when $q \equiv p$. If $p(\boldsymbol{x}) \neq 0$ for all $\boldsymbol{x} \in R^N$ one can e.g. choose q to be a multivariate Gaussian in order to preserve dependencies between the x_i. Unfortunately, this is no longer possible when the support of $p(\boldsymbol{x})$ is constrained or discrete such as for the Ising model. The KL–divergence is infinite for such cases. Hence, one often has to resort to *mean–field* (MF) approximations, where $q(\boldsymbol{x}) = \prod_i q_i(x_i)$, thereby neglecting the dependencies between the x_i. The MF approximation yields the self consistency equations

$$q_i(x) = \frac{f_i(x)}{Z_i} \exp\left[x \sum_j J_{ij}\langle x_j\rangle_q\right] \qquad i = 1, \ldots, N \tag{20.3}$$

which can be solved by the simple algorithm of cycling sequentially through all nodes i multiple times. The performance of MF algorithms is often surpassed in terms of accuracy and speed by message passing methods.

20.1.3. *TAP mean field equations*

To improve on the simple MF approximation, we will first derive an exact expression for the marginal distribution $p_i(x)$. We make use of the fact that the interactions between x_i and the other random variables is mediated via the field $h_i \doteq \sum_j J_{ij}x_j$. We will focus on the so-called cavity approach pioneered by Parisi and Mézard [2] and write

$$p_i(x) = \int d\boldsymbol{x}_{\backslash i}\, p(\boldsymbol{x}) \propto f_i(x) \int dh \exp\left[xh\right] p_{\backslash i}(h) \tag{20.4}$$

where the *cavity field* distribution is defined as

$$p_{\backslash i}(h) = \int d\boldsymbol{x}_{\backslash i}\, \delta\left(h - \sum_j J_{ij}x_j\right) p_{\backslash i}(\boldsymbol{x}_{\backslash i}) \tag{20.5}$$

and where $p_{\backslash i}(\boldsymbol{x}_{\backslash i})$ is the joint distribution of the $N-1$ random variables $\boldsymbol{x}_{\backslash i}$ for a system, where the node x_i together with the couplings J_{ij} to the remaining nodes are *deleted* from the original distribution $p(\boldsymbol{x})$, thereby creating a 'cavity' at x_i. We argue that for many models of interest, the dependencies of the random variables in the cavity system $p_{\backslash i}(\boldsymbol{x}_{\backslash i})$ are sufficiently weak. Take for example, a model, where the graph of nonzero couplings $J_{ij} \neq 0$ forms a tree. In this case, by deleting node i, the dependencies between its neighbours are completely destroyed and we have $p_{\backslash i}(\boldsymbol{x}_{\backslash i}) = \prod_{j\neq i} p_{j\backslash i}(x_j)$. When the graph of couplings is 'tree-like' in the sense that short loops are typically absent we may still neglect such dependencies and derive a sequential computation of the marginals. This leads to the *belief propagation* algorithm discussed in more generality in Sec. 20.2.1.

In a similar way, we may argue that for densely connected models when most couplings J_{ij} are nonzero but sufficiently weak, the dependencies between random variables in the sum $\sum_j J_{ij}S_j$ are small enough to justify the Gaussian approximation $p_{\backslash i}(h) \approx \mathcal{N}(\gamma_i, V_i)$. γ_i and V_i are the cavity mean and cavity variance. This leads to

$$p_i(x) = \frac{f_i(x)}{Z_i} \exp\left[x\gamma_i + \frac{1}{2}V_i x^2\right] \tag{20.6}$$

where for notational convenience, we have replaced the approximation by an equality. In contrast to a variational approximation with a multivariate Gaussian, (20.6) can be applied to both discrete and continuous random variables. To close the system of equations (20.6), we first determine γ_i. Within the Gaussian field approximation, we obtain

$$\sum_j J_{ij}\langle x_j\rangle = \langle h_i\rangle = \frac{\int dh\,dx\, p_{\backslash i}(h)\, f_i(x)\, h\, e^{xh}}{\int dh\,dx\, p_{\backslash i}(h)\, f_i(x)\, e^{xh}} = \gamma_i + V_i\langle x_i\rangle \qquad (20.7)$$

Equation (20.6) reduces to the MF expression when the so-called *Onsager correction* term V_i is neglected. To find a sensible expression for the cavity variances V_i we first discuss a class of statistical physics models, for which the cavity approximation becomes exact in the infinite system limit $N \to \infty$.

20.1.4. *Gaussian random couplings*

We consider a setting well established in the physics of disordered systems where the couplings J_{ij} are drawn independently at random for $i < j$ from a Gaussian density with mean zero and variance $\overline{J_{ij}^2} = J_0/N$. The bar denotes expectation with respect to the distribution of the J_{ij}. For the case of Ising spins, this is the celebrated *Sherrington–Kirkpatrick* (SK) model [3]. We can also assume that V_i does not depend on the node index i and that $V_i \simeq \overline{V}_i \equiv V$ becomes self averaging with respect to the random draws of the J_{ij} for $N \to \infty$. By the independence of the couplings, $p_{\backslash i}(\boldsymbol{S}_{\backslash i})$ is also independent of J_{ik} and J_{ij}. Hence, by averaging the exact expression $V_i \doteq \sum_{jk} J_{ik}J_{ij}\left(\langle x_j x_k\rangle_{\backslash i} - \langle x_j\rangle_{\backslash i}\langle x_k\rangle_{\backslash i}\right)$ over the couplings we get

$$V = \sum_j \overline{J_{ij}^2}\left(\langle x_j^2\rangle - \langle x_j\rangle_{\backslash i}^2\right) \simeq \frac{J_0}{N}\sum_j \left(\langle x_j^2\rangle - \langle x_j\rangle^2\right) \qquad (20.8)$$

In the last line we have neglected the effect of removing a single node for large N. Equations (20.6)–(20.8) form a closed set for approximate local means and variances, known as TAP equations [4] after Thouless, Anderson and Palmer who derived them first for the SK model.

　　For the SK model, it is also easy to obtain order parameters from the cavity approach which characterise the macroscopic behaviour of the model. The magnetization $\overline{\langle x_i\rangle}$ and the *Edwards Anderson parameter* $q \doteq \overline{\langle x_i\rangle^2}$ can be computed from (20.6) using the probability density of the cavity mean γ_i with respect to the distribution of the couplings (since $x_i^2 = 1$, V does not appear in the result). Using the independence of couplings J_{ij} from the cavity distribution $p_{\backslash i}(\boldsymbol{S}_{\backslash i})$, we obtain the Gaussian density $\gamma_i \sim \mathcal{N}(0, J_0 q)$. This agrees with the replica symmetric (RS) result for the SK model, indicating the asymptotic correctness of the cavity results for models with random Gaussian couplings. As we will see in Sec. 20.4.1, a dynamical version of the cavity mean is also Gaussian distributed with respect to the distribution of couplings. This fact allows for a complete analysis of the corresponding message passing algorithm in the thermodynamic limit.

　　We have tacitly assumed so far that model parameters are in a range, where the TAP equations have unique solutions and there is no breaking of replica symmetry (RSB).

For extensions of the TAP equations and message passing to the RSB setting, see Sec. 20.4.2.

20.1.5. *Spherically symmetric ensembles of coupling matrices*

TAP equations with the simple approximation (20.8) for the cavity variance can also be applied to models of statistical inference [5] in machine learning such as (20.2). Nevertheless, the quality of the cavity approximation can be improved by adapting the computation of cavity variances V_i to the empirical distribution of couplings J_{ij} rather than assuming a simple Gaussian statistics. This approach is based on results of Parisi and Potters [6] who derived the TAP equations for Ising models with coupling matrices of the form $\boldsymbol{J} = \boldsymbol{ODO}^\top$ where $\boldsymbol{O}$ is a random Haar matrix (i.e. a random rotation) and $\boldsymbol{D}$ a diagonal matrix. This model class contains independent Gaussian couplings as a special case but gives the flexibility to choose the spectrum of the coupling matrix, but the eigenvectors of $\boldsymbol{J}$ point in 'general directions'. These spherically invariant random matrix ensembles play a significant role as data models in information theory and signal processing [7]. They result in small (of the order $1/\sqrt{N}$) correlations between couplings which yields to an expression for the cavity variance which differs from (20.8). Based on a re–summation of a weak coupling expansion Parisi and Potters concluded that the cavity variance V is a function of the susceptibility $\chi \doteq \frac{1}{N}\sum_i(1 - \langle x_j \rangle^2)$ which is independent of the specific single site potential $f_i(x)$. Hence an exactly solvable *spherical model* which assumes $\sum_j x_j^2 = N$ rather than the Ising condition $x_j^2 = 1$, must lead to the same expression for V. Relaxing the spherical constraint to a soft constraint via a Lagrange multiplier Λ for $N \to \infty$, one obtains the result for V from an equivalent Gaussian model with $f_i(x) = e^{-\frac{\Lambda}{2}x^2 + \theta_i x}$. Comparing the marginal distributions for this Gaussian model with the cavity result (20.6) we get the equality

$$\chi = G(\Lambda) = \frac{1}{\Lambda - V} \tag{20.9}$$

with the Green's function $G(\Lambda) = \frac{1}{N}\mathrm{Tr}\,(\boldsymbol{\Lambda} - \boldsymbol{J})^{-1}$. Thus $V = \Lambda - \frac{1}{\chi} = G^{-1}(\chi) - \frac{1}{\chi} \equiv R(\chi)$, the so-called R-transform of the spectrum. Again, it can be shown that the cavity means are Gaussian distributed with respect to the spherical random coupling ensembles. This result can be extended to the dynamical case and applied to the derivation and analysis of message passing algorithms for these ensembles. In Sec. 20.2.4 we discuss a further generalisation for computing the cavity variance which leads to *adaptive TAP equations* and the corresponding *Expectation Propagation* (EP) algorithm, where no explicit assumptions on the statistics of J_{ij} is made.

20.2. Message Passing Algorithms

Message passing methods or belief propagation have been developed independently in a number of scientific disciplines, in physics [2], computer science [8] and information theory [9] as an approximation for the Maximum A Posteriori (MAP) estimator of variables $\boldsymbol{x}$ from observations or constraints D, $\widehat{\boldsymbol{x}} = \arg\max_{\boldsymbol{x}} P(\boldsymbol{x}|D)$. Since calculating the MAP estimator is generally intractable as the search increases exponentially with the number of variables, an equally difficult alternative, the marginal posterior maximizer (MPM) estimator is being considered,

$$\widehat{x}_i = \arg\max_{x_i} P(x_i|D), \tag{20.10}$$

which converts the maximization to a local operation but requires a global marginalization. The crux behind message-passing based methods is to address the global problem by introducing localized, distributive and scaleable operations, where variable estimates depend on their immediate neighboring variables, with which they interact. The direct link between message passing and statistical physics methodology has been established in [10], linking it to the cavity approach and its microscopic manifestation [2]. At the heart of the method is the *assumption* that variable values are mostly affected by those of their immediate neighbors with which they directly interact, due to the sparsity of the interactions and of the negligible role played by long-range correlations. However, the states of neighboring variables depends on their neighbors and so on. The method is therefore based on passing messages — conditional probabilities — iteratively between interacting variables until they stabilize and then inferring the variable values from the converged messages in their immediate neighborhood.

20.2.1. *Basic message passing*

There are different ways to explain message passing methods [11, 12], through approximate minimization of the Bethe free energy using a variational approach, modeling the joint probability of the system using factorized interactions between variable groups (factors) and many others [12]. The simple explanation provided here is based on a Bayesian probabilistic view and relies on mapping the problem onto a bipartite graph, where variable nodes appear on the left and factor nodes, representing the interaction between them, on the right, as shown in Fig. 20.1. Factors can represent validating a rule (e.g., two neighboring nodes having different colors in the graph coloring problem), observations that depend on the interacting variable values or some probability of the interacting variables to be in a given state. The factors variable j interacts with are denoted by $\mathcal{M}(j)$ and the set of variables interacting through factor a as $\mathcal{L}(a)$. The messages represent conditional probabilities of variable S_j assuming a certain state given all the factors in $\mathcal{M}(j)$ except factor a - $\mu_{x_j \to Z_a}$ and the probability of factor Z_a given that variable x_j is in some state - $\mu_{Z_a \to x_j}$.

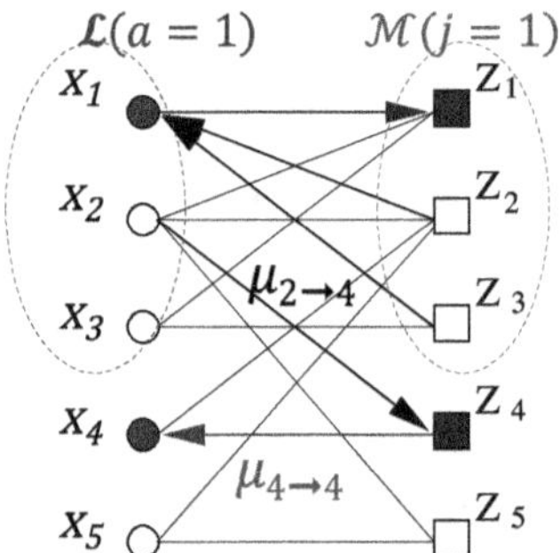

Fig. 20.1.   An example bipartite graph representation, where variable nodes x appear on the left and factor nodes Z, representing the interaction between them, on the right. Lines represent interaction between variables at the factor nodes; arrows are example messages from variable to factor ($\mu_{x_j \to Z_a}$) and vice versa ($\mu_{Z_a \to x_j}$). The neighboring nodes to factor a are marked by $\mathcal{L}(a)$ (in the figure for $a=1$), while the neighboring factors to node j are marked by $\mathcal{M}(j)$ (in the figure for $j=1$).

This gives rise to a closed set of equations representing the conditional probabilities passed between variables and factors (messages)

$$\mu_{x_j \to Z_a} = P(x_j \mid \{Z_b : b \in \mathcal{M}(j) \setminus a\}) = \alpha_{aj}\, p(x_j) P(\{Z_b : b \in \mathcal{M}(j) \setminus a\} \mid x_j)$$

$$\approx \alpha_{aj}\, p(x_j) \prod_{b \in \mathcal{M}(j) \setminus a} \mu_{Z_b \to x_j} \tag{20.11}$$

$$\mu_{Z_a \to x_j} = P(Z_a \mid x_j) = \sum_{\{x_i : i \in \mathcal{L}(a) \setminus j\}} P(Z_a \mid x_j, \{x_i : i \in \mathcal{L}(a) \setminus j\})$$

$$\times P(\{x_i : i \in \mathcal{L}(a) \setminus j\} \mid \{Z_b : b \in \mathcal{M}(j) \setminus a\})$$

$$\approx \sum_{\{x_i : i \in \mathcal{L}(a) \setminus j\}} P(Z_a \mid x_j, \{x_i : i \in \mathcal{L}(a) \setminus j\}) \prod_{i \in \mathcal{L}(a) \setminus j} \mu_{x_i \to Z_a}. \tag{20.12}$$

These messages are iterated until their values stop changing. The coefficient α_{aj} is a normalization factor obtained by summing over all possible x_j values. The derivation is based on simple identities and hinges on the assumption due to the sparse nature of the interactions, the joint probabilities $P(\{Z_b : b \in \mathcal{M}(j) \setminus a\} \mid x_j)$ and $P(\{x_i : i \in \mathcal{L}(a) \setminus j\} \mid \{Z_b : b \in \mathcal{M}(j) \setminus a\}$ can be factorized. *This is exact on trees and works well on locally tree-like graphs away from criticality.* Once the messages have converged, one can calculate the marginal values for the variables

$$P(x_j \mid \{Z_b : b \in \mathcal{M}(j)\}) = \alpha_j\, p(x_j) \prod_{b \in \mathcal{M}(j)} \mu_{Z_b \to x_j}, \tag{20.13}$$

α_j being a normalization coefficient, to infer variable values.

Basic message passing is also commonly known as belief-propagation and the sum-product algorithm. Under the factorized representation it allows one to calculate marginal variable values of individual components. However, on many cases the MAP solution is quite different from the individual MPM estimates. A closely related message-passing variant is the max-sum algorithm [1], aiming to obtain the MAP estimates by obtaining maximal contributions at each step; a version of the algorithm has been originally presented by Viterbi [13] and has been linked to dynamic programming [14].

20.2.2. *Survey propagation and the impact of loops*

The underlying assumption of message factorization for both factors-to-variables and variables-to-factors due to the sparsity of the interaction breaks down as the number of constraints increases and variable values become dependent on decaying messages from non-directly-interacting variables. This results in non-converging messages and inaccurate inference.

A successful method to account for the variability of messages, akin to the replica-symmetry breaking mechanism, is termed survey-propagation [15]. Inspired by insight from the study of spin-glass systems, survey-propagation introduces a distribution of messages that, due to its simplicity, can be formatted in a tractable form [16]. It has been applied successfully to various combinatorial optimization tasks. Alternative message passing approaches that account for graph loops have been presented [17, 18] but mostly account for short loops.

Structured interactions that form short loops, e.g. between pixel groups in image reconstruction, have also been addressed using cluster variation [19] and generalized belief propagation [20], where messages are passed between structures (e.g., pixel groups in image reconstruction) while considering the double-counting of messages originating by variables that participate in a number of sub-structures.

20.2.3. *Messages on densely connected graphs*

As described above, message passing relies on the sparsity of interactions between variables due to the assumption that conditional probabilities can be factorized with respect to factors and variables, and the summation over neighboring variable and factor values is manageable. The factorization assumption is violated in densely connected systems due to the presence of many short loops and summation over the contribution of neighboring variables and factors becomes intractable. However, message passing has been shown to be useful also in this regime, primarily due to the small contribution of individual variables. This leads to the aggregation of messages which is most commonly modeled by a Gaussian that only requires the update of mean and variance values [21]. Variants of message passing methods that deal with densely connected graphs provide a tractable and simple approximation to inference in the case of densely connected networks [22, 23].

20.2.4. *Adaptive TAP and expectation propagation*

For models of type (20.1) a Gaussian parametrization of messages lead to the so-called Approximate Message Passing (AMP) algorithms which converge to the solution of the TAP equations with the simple cavity variance (20.8), neglecting effects of dependencies between different couplings J_{ij} which may be relevant for applications to real data. Generalisations of AMP-style algorithms which converge to TAP equations for the spherical symmetric coupling ensembles of Sec. (20.1.5) were e.g. introduced in [24, 25]. While these algorithms were designed to reproduce the correct statistical physics results for (20.1) in the thermodynamic limit $N \to \infty$, one may look for methods which might improve predictions for finite N and avoid an explicit random matrix model for the couplings. The approach of Parisi and Potters discussed in Sec. (20.1.5) has been generalized [26] by discarding the restriction that the V_i are independent of i. They assume that the functional form of V_i in terms of *local* susceptibilities $\chi_i \doteq \langle x_i^2 \rangle - \langle x_i \rangle^2$ can be derived from an auxiliary model with Gaussian single site potentials $\tilde{f}_i(x) = -\frac{1}{2}\Lambda_i x^2 + \gamma_i x$ which are chosen to agree with a given set of values $\{\chi_j\}_{j=1}^N$. Applied to data models, the accuracy of the *adaptive TAP equations* is often superior to those assuming constant cavity variance V. This approach can be viewed as a method where first and second marginal moments computed from the approximate marginal (20.6) match those of the auxiliary Gaussian model. The method is fairly robust and can e.g. be combined with the replica trick to compute approximate resampling (bootstrap) averages [27] for machine learning algorithms. Working on online algorithms for inference [28] has independently developed the *Expectation Propagation* (EP) framework, which, when applied to models of the type (20.1) sequentially updates an auxiliary Gaussian to achieve the corresponding moment matching. The fixed points of EP message passing was found to coincide with the adaptive TAP equations. EP has become an important and widely applicable inference method in the field of machine learning.

20.2.5. *Real variable values*

Message passing techniques are highly suitable for discrete variables, since in the case of real variables the messages (20.11) and (20.12) become functions and should be represented in by a small number of parameters [29], for instance, by assuming a Gaussian representation [30]. This representation is more accurate when the minimized objective function is convex and for graphs with high degree distribution.

20.2.6. *Message passing in dynamical systems*

Inferring variable values using message passing in dynamical systems poses a different type of challenge, since the whole history of the evolving system should be considered, making the problem intractable. One specific scenario that lends itself to message passing inference is that of unidirectionally evolving systems, such as the case of epidemic spreading processes that progresses sequentially from state to state, since it obviates the need to keep the complete system history. A number of attempts and approximations have been introduced to address inference in dynamical systems using message passing, some are based on representing the or on identifying the transition points from state to state termed Dynamic Message Passing [31]; while others employ belief propagation directly by transforming the loopy variable-based factor graphs into an interaction-based tree-like graph that incorporates infection and recovery time variables and their interaction with the state variables of the system [32]. Both methods have been employed successfully to solve a variety of epidemic spreading problems.

20.3. Applications

While the macroscopic equivalent of message passing techniques, namely the cavity method [2], has been an established method in the physics community since the 1980s, message passing techniques have become highly popular through their use in a variety of applications. These include combinatorial optimization problems in theoretical computer science, decoding error-correcting codes, compressed sensing and group testing in information theory, epidemic spreading processes and various applications in the general area of machine learning.

20.3.1. *Combinatorial optimization*

Message-passing methods have been useful in solving hard combinatorial problems [11]. They work effectively and scale well, typically linearly or quadratically, with respect to the number of free variables, but break down in the hard regime where long-range correlations between variables are formed. Some of the most well known examples is the study of K-Satisfiability, which is arguably the most fundamental NP-complete (non-deterministic polynomial time complete) problem as it can be mapped directly to the Turing machine [33]. The problem is in determining the existence of an N-dimensional Boolean vector $\boldsymbol{x}$ that obeys simultaneously M clauses comprising K elements of $\boldsymbol{x}$ or their negations. Message passing methods in general and survey propagation [15] in particular have been successfully employed for finding valid solutions very close to the critical ratio of M/N (for instance, for 3-SAT the critical ratio beyond which no solutions can be found is $M/N \approx 4.267$ and the survey propagation algorithm successfully find solutions close to $M/N \approx 4.25$, for typical case instances).

Another well-researched NP-complete problem is the graph coloring task of assigning colors to vertices of a random graph such that two vertices with the same color assignment do not share an edge. Solutions close to the critical graph average degree have been obtained using survey propagation [34].

20.3.2. *Inferring a sparse source*

Message passing has been highly successful in problems where the variable values to be inferred are very sparse, e.g., most variable values are zero and one relies on this information to infer values from measurements. Examples include Boolean variable values such as group testing, where samples are mixed at random prior to testing; the test results that identify the existence of a positive sample in the mix are then used to infer the individual Boolean sample values. This allows for a significant reduction in the number of tests, by up to a factor of $H_2(p) = -p \log_2 p$, where p is the prevalence of positive samples in the population [35, 36].

Another prominent example is the use of message passing for decoding in low-density parity-check error correcting codes [37, 38], where noise levels are low, which has facilitated the saturation of Shannon's capacity limit later on [39]. A different problem of similar characteristics is that of compressed sensing, where the sparse real-valued source variables are inferred from measurements that combine them linearly [40]; also here, message passing has allowed to nearly saturate the theoretical limits.

20.3.3. *Non-localized interactions*

Another scenario in which message passing has been employed is the non-localized interaction between routes in a variety of routing scenarios. Routing of vehicles or information on a graph representing the road or communication networks requires an optimization of a chosen objective function (e.g., uniform load or reduced number of active routes) under various constraints. Message passing algorithms have been employed to transform non-localized interactions to localized ones [41] for finding global solutions. Of particular interest to routing in optical communication networks is edge-disjoint routing where two different communications cannot use the same fiber using the same wavelength. Message passing has been successful in introducing a scalable solution in the presence of a large number of communication source-destination pairs and wavelengths [42].

20.4. Rigorous Results and Approximate Message Passing

Over the last two decades, there has been a drastic impact of a different nature for message passing algorithms, especially in the applied mathematics community. This has allowed for new connections to emerge and has been at the center of a message passing renaissance in statistics, signal processing, and probability. The origin of this burst of activity can be traced back to [43], who aimed to study rigorously the convergence of the TAP equation in the SK model. However, the interdisciplinary impact of this work is mainly due to the seminal work of [44, 45]. This approach, dubbed Approximate Message Passing (AMP), is currently leading to a burst of new results, both in mathematics and in applications.

20.4.1. *Approximate message passing and state evolution*

The main idea behind this approach is to seemingly forget the physics or probabilistic motivation and instead consider the iterative algorithm as, well ..., just an algorithm. This leads, surprisingly, to a reformulation of Parisi replica equations in terms of computation on a particular given problem, instead of a description of the equilibrium behavior for an infinite physical system. Let us briefly describe the idea. Consider the following iteration, with a Gaussian matrix A and an arbitrary function $f_t(\mathbf{x})$:

$$\mathbf{x}^{t+1} = A\mathbf{m}^t \tag{20.14}$$
$$\mathbf{m}^t = f_t(\mathbf{x}^t)$$

The question now is, what is the statistics of the vector $\mathbf{x}^t$? Starting from a vector $\mathbf{x}^0$, it is clear that the vector $\mathbf{x}^1$ is asymptotically Gaussian: from the central limit theorem, one can see immediately that it is the weighted random sum of $\mathbf{m}^0$, so that with the proper scaling of A:

$$\mathbf{x}^1 \sim \mathbf{N}(0, \mathbf{I}_n q^0), \ q^0 = \frac{\|\mathbf{m}^0\|_2^2}{N}. \tag{20.15}$$

It is *very tempting* to think that this is actually true *at all times*:

$$\mathbf{x}^{t+1} \sim \mathbf{N}(0, \mathbf{I}_n q^t), \tag{20.16}$$
$$q^t = \mathbb{E}_Z \left[f_t(Z\sqrt{q^{t-1}})^2 \right], \ Z \sim \mathcal{N}(0, 1).$$

As tempting as it is, this is, however, just plain wrong. Indeed, one cannot repeat the argument at time greater than one since $\mathbf{x}^1$ *depends* on the matrix A, so that we cannot use the CLT on $A\mathbf{m}^1$.

It turns out that one can modify the iteration (20.14) in a minimal way, such that the Gaussian assumption remains indeed true at all (finite) time. One just needs to consider, instead the so-called AMP sequence of iterates:

$$\mathbf{x}^{t+1} = A\mathbf{m}^t - b_t\mathbf{m}^{t-1} \tag{20.17}$$
$$\mathbf{m}^t = f_t(\mathbf{x}^t)$$

with initialization at $\mathbf{x}^0$ and with the Onsager term (so named since, indeed, it corresponds to the Onsager term in the TAP equations):

$$b_t = \mathbb{E}\left[\operatorname{div} f_t(\mathbf{Z}^t)\right] \tag{20.18}$$

where $\mathbf{Z}^t \sim \mathbf{N}(0, K_{t,t}\mathbf{I}_n)$.

With this simple modification, one can prove (using a very elegant approach called Bolthausen conditioning [43, 45]) that the AMP iteration can be tracked (for any finite time) as $N \to \infty$ by the recursion Eqs. (20.17), which is called the "state evolution" of the algorithm. Note that we have not yet connected this iteration to any kind of practical problem! This is, so far, just an iterative algorithm for which we have a mathematically rigorous (asymptotic) statement.

20.4.2. *Thouless–Anderson–Palmer revisited*

We can now come back to a physics application. Consider our iteration using the time-dependent function

$$f_t(x) = \tanh(\beta x + h) \tag{20.19}$$

In this case, AMP can be rewritten, starting form the Onsager term as:

$$b_t = \beta(1 - \mathbb{E}[\tanh(\beta \mathbf{x}^t + h)^2]) = \beta(1 - q^t) \tag{20.20}$$

consequently, one obtains

$$\mathbf{x}^{t+1} = \mathbf{A}\mathbf{m}^t - \beta(1 - q^t)\mathbf{m}^{t-1} \tag{20.21}$$
$$\mathbf{m}^{t+1} = \tanh(\beta \mathbf{x}^{t+1} + \beta h).$$

so that

$$\mathbf{m}^{t+1} = \tanh(\beta\left(\mathbf{A}\mathbf{m}^t - \beta(1 - q^t)\mathbf{m}^{t-1}\right) + \beta h). \tag{20.22}$$

At the fixed point, if and when it converges, these are nothing but the TAP equations [4] for the SK model [3]! With this function, AMP is thus (almost) just TAP (while the recursion (20.14) is just the naive mean-field). There are, however, subtle points to notice: First, for the AMP iterates, q^t obeys a state evolution that is nothing but the replica symmetric equation [3] *at all times*:

$$q_t = \mathbb{E}\left[\left(\tanh(\beta\sqrt{q_{t-1}}Z + \beta h)\right)^2\right]. \tag{20.23}$$

What was before an equation describing the equilibrium of a statistical physics model is now an equation describing the behavior of an iteration. Note in particular that this is valid regardless of whether or not the problem is replica symmetric! Even in the replica symmetry broken phase of the SK model, this peculiar AMP iteration follows the RS recursion.

A second remark is that the time indices in Eq. (20.22) are non trivial: the Onsager correction is evaluated *one step behind* the others. This is not a small detail: it is a fundamental change that makes the algorithm converge and follow the state evolution equation.

Finally, [43] also proved that AMP converges to a fixed point if the following condition is satisfied:

$$\mathbb{E}\left[\left(\tanh'(\beta\sqrt{q^*}Z + \beta h)\right)^2\right] \leq 1 \tag{20.24}$$

which is precisely the Almeida–Thouless criterion [46] for the presence of replica symmetry breaking.

To illustrate how rich the AMP formalism — that gives us a theorem for (almost) any arbitrary function f_t — really is, consider the following question: Since the replica symmetric equation is the state evolution of TAP/AMP when the function f is chosen as in eq.(20.19), could it be that Parisi's more generic replica symmetry broken equation [2] be the state evolution of another, different, algorithm? The answer is yes; as shown in [47]. Such constructions thus allowed Parisi's solution of the SK model to be (re-)interpreted as a way to track the iteration of a peculiar algorithm! This is merely an illustration of the richness of the approach, as in fact any TAP-like message passing iteration will obey such a (rigorous) replica-like prediction.

20.4.3. *The impact of the AMP approach*

20.4.3.1. *Algorithms*

This approach has allowed for TAP-like iterations such as those considered in Sec. 20.2.3 to reappear in various settings, with much better convergence properties due to the modified time indices. In particular, AMP was popularized in compressed sensing in a seminal paper [44] and further generalized to slightly more complex systems by [23]. This approach was, in a nutshell, a rigorous and (well time-ordered) reformulation of the much earlier work on the perceptron that appeared in physics literature in [48]. It lead to an explosion of activity on these problems, see e.g. [49–52]. A related work was the "vector" version of the AMP algorithm, or VAMP [25] that also corresponds to revisitng algorithms discussed in physics [6, 12], and in particular in [53]. These are precisely the type of approach discussed in Sec. 20.1.5 (see [54] for a unifying perspective). There have been various extensions of these approaches; for instance the multi-layer version of AMP [55–57], a version of AMP using complex priors (including neural networks) [58, 59] used in fMRI reconstruction [60] or even mini-batch version of AMP [61].

20.4.3.2. *Rigorous proofs of replica predictions*

The rigorous state evolution of AMP is not only a fantastic feature to understand the behavior of the algorithm, it can also be used as a *mathematical tool* to prove open question in spin glass theory, statistics and inference.

Starting from the seminal work on the performance of LASSO in statistics [62], AMP has been used to prove cavity and replica statements in statistics [63, 64], machine learning [65] and optimization of non-convex functions [66, 67]. Recently, it played a fundamental role in a rigorous derivation of the dynamical mean field equation [68, 69].

20.4.3.3. *Revisiting computational complexity*

Finally, the liberty in the choice of f_t allows mathematicians to use AMP approaches to answer deep questions on computational complexity. In particular, it is widely believed that, for a large class of inference problems, the Bayesian version of AMP is the best algorithm among all polynomial ones: if it fails, then a natural conjecture is that no polynomial algorithm will work (see e.g. [50, 70]).

Thanks to AMP and state evolution techniques, a very recent work proved that indeed, AMP is the "best" among all first-order method [71]: this allows to put the AMP conjecture on a rigorous, well-defined, track and is the subject of current efforts and investigations.

Another recent progress has been in the development of an AMP-specific algorithm for spin glasses. Using Parisi's ultrametric solution, it is possible to design an algorithm that provably achieves the ground state energy in the SK model [72], and that finds "best among polynomials" energies in the p-spins models and generic mean-field spin glasses [73, 74].

20.5. Message Passing — Reflection

We have followed the remarkable story of a theoretical method, which was initially developed in statistical physics [2] for analysing spin-glass models, that became an important practical tool for inference and optimization, and finally has been reinvented as a rigorous and powerful tool in statistics and applied mathematics. These developments show that this research direction is alive and well, and is the source of many interdisciplinary results and cross-fertilization between disciplines.

References

[1] C. M. Bishop, *Pattern Recognition and Machine Learning*. Number 4, (Springer, 2006).
[2] M. Mézard, G. Parisi, and M. A. Virasoro, *Spin glass theory and beyond*. (World Scientific, 1987).
[3] D. Sherrington and S. Kirkpatrick, *Phys. Rev. Lett.* **35**(26), 1792, (1975).
[4] D. J. Thouless, P. W. Anderson, and R. G. Palmer, *Philos. Mag.* **35**(3), 593–601, (1977).
[5] M. Opper and O. Winther, *Phys. Rev. Lett.* **76**, 1964–1967, (1996).
[6] G. Parisi and M. Potters, *J. Phys. A.* **28**(18), 5267, (1995).
[7] A. M. Tulino and S. Verdú, *Found. Trends Commun. Inf. Theory.* **1**(1), 1–182, (2004).
[8] J. Pearl. In *AAAI-82*, pp. 133–136. CA: AAAI Press, (1982).
[9] R. Gallager, *IRE Trans. Inf. Theory.* **8**(1), 21–28, (1962).
[10] Y. Kabashima and D. Saad, *Europhys. Lett.* **44**(5), 668–674, (1998).
[11] M. Mézard and A. Montanari, *Information, physics, and computation.* (Oxford University Press, 2009).
[12] M. Opper and D. Saad, Eds., *Advanced mean field methods: theory and practice.* Neural Information Processing, (MIT, 2001).
[13] A. Viterbi, *IEEE Trans. Inf. Theory.* **13**(2), 260–269, (1967).
[14] T. H. Cormen, C. E. Leiserson, R. L. Rivest, and C. Stein, *Introduction to Algorithms.* (The MIT Press, 2009), 3rd edition.
[15] M. Mézard, G. Parisi, and R. Zecchina, *Science.* **297**(5582), 812–815, (2002).
[16] A. Braunstein, M. Mézard, and R. Zecchina, *Random Struct. Algorithms.* **27**, (2005).

[17] G. T. Cantwell and M. E. J. Newman, *Proc. Natl. Acad. Sci. U.S.A.* **116**(47), 23398–23403, (2019).

[18] A. Montanari and T. Rizzo, *J. Stat. Mech.: Theory Exp.* **2005**(10), P10011, (2005).

[19] R. Kikuchi, *Phys. Rev.* **81**, 988–1003, (1951).

[20] J. Yedidia, W. Freeman, and Y. Weiss, *IEEE Trans. Inf. Theory.* **51**(7), 2282–2312, (2005).

[21] Y. Kabashima, *J. Phys. A.* **36**(43), 11111–11121, (2003).

[22] M. Bayati and A. Montanari, *IEEE Trans. Inf. Theory.* **57**, 764–785, (2010).

[23] S. Rangan, *2011 IEEE Int. Symp. Inf. Theory - Proc.* pp. 2168–2172, (2011).

[24] M. Opper, B. Cakmak, and O. Winther, *J. Phys. A.* **49**(11), 114002, (2016).

[25] S. Rangan, P. Schniter, and A. K. Fletcher, *IEEE Trans. Inf. Theory.* **65**(10), 6664–6684, (2019).

[26] M. Opper and O. Winther, *Phys. Rev. Lett.* **86**, 3695–3699, (2001).

[27] D. Malzahn and M. Opper, *JMLR.* **4**, 1151–1173, (2003).

[28] T. P. Minka. In *Proc. of 17th UAI*, p. 362–369, San Francisco, CA, USA, (2001).

[29] S. L. Lauritzen, *Graphical Models.* (Oxford University Press, 1996).

[30] K. M. Wong and D. Saad, *Phys. Rev. E.* **74**(1), 010104, (2006).

[31] A. Y. Lokhov, M. Mézard, and L. Zdeborová, *Phys. Rev. E.* **91**, 012811, (2015).

[32] F. Altarelli, A. Braunstein, L. Dall'Asta, A. Lage-Castellanos, and R. Zecchina, *Phys. Rev. Lett.* **112**, 118701, (2014).

[33] M. R. Garey and D. S. Johnson, *Computers and Intractability: A Guide to the Theory of NP-Completeness.* (W. H. Freeman, 1979).

[34] A. Braunstein, R. Mulet, A. Pagnani, M. Weigt, and R. Zecchina, *Phys. Rev. E.* **68**, 036702, (2003).

[35] M. Mézard, M. Tarzia, and C. Toninelli, *J. Stat. Phys.* **131**, 783–801, (2007).

[36] A. Sakata, *Phys. Rev. E.* **103**, 022110, (2021).

[37] T. Richardson and R. Urbanke, *IEEE Trans. Inf. Theory.* **47**(2), 599–618, (2001).

[38] Y. Kabashima, T. Murayama, and D. Saad, *Phys. Rev. Lett.* **84**, 1355–1358, (2000).

[39] S. Kudekar, T. Richardson, and R. L. Urbanke, *IEEE Trans. Inf. Theory.* **59**(12), 7761–7813, (2013).

[40] F. Krzakala, M. Mézard, F. Sausset, Y. F. Sun, and L. Zdeborová, *Phys. Rev. X.* **2**, 021005, (2012).

[41] C. H. Yeung and D. Saad, *Phys. Rev. Lett.* **108**(20), 208701, (2012).

[42] Y.-Z. Xu, H. F. Po, C. H. Yeung, and D. Saad, *Phys. Rev. E.* **105**, 044316, (2022).

[43] E. Bolthausen, *Commun. Math. Phys.* **325**(1), 333–366, (2014).

[44] D. L. Donoho, A. Maleki, and A. Montanari, *Proc. Natl. Acad. Sci. U.S.A.* **106**(45), 18914–18919, (2009).

[45] M. Bayati and A. Montanari, *IEEE Trans. Inf. Theory.* **57**(2), 764–785, (2011).

[46] J. R. de Almeida and D. J. Thouless, *J. Phys. A.* **11**(5), 983, (1978).

[47] F. Antenucci, F. Krzakala, P. Urbani, and L. Zdeborová, *J. Stat. Mech.: Theory Exp.* **2019**(2), 023401, (2019).

[48] M. Mézard, *J. Phys. A.* **22**(12), 2181, (1989).

[49] A. Maleki. *Approximate message passing algorithms for compressed sensing.* PhD thesis, Stanford University, (2010).

[50] L. Zdeborová and F. Krzakala, *Adv. Phys.* **65**(5), 453–552, (2016).

[51] S. Rangan, P. Schniter, A. K. Fletcher, and S. Sarkar, *IEEE Trans. Inf. Theory.* **65**(9), 5339–5351, (2019).

[52] B. Cakmak, O. Winther, and B. H. Fleury. In *IEEE ITW 2014*, pp. 192–196, (2014).

[53] Y. Kabashima, *J. Phys. Conf. Ser.* **95**(1), 012001, (2008).

[54] A. Maillard, L. Foini, A. L. Castellanos, F. Krzakala, M. Mézard, and L. Zdeborová, *J. Stat. Mech.: Theory Exp.* **2019**(11), 113301, (2019).

[55] A. Manoel, F. Krzakala, M. Mézard, and L. Zdeborová. In *2017 IEEE ISIT*, pp. 2098–2102, (2017).

[56] A. Baker, B. Aubin, F. Krzakala, and L. Zdeborová, (2020).

[57] C. Gerbelot and R. Berthier, *arXiv:2109.11905.* (2021).

[58] P. Schniter, S. Rangan, and A. Fletcher, *arXiv:1611.01376.* (2016).

[59] C. A. Metzler, A. Maleki, and R. G. Baraniuk. In *2015 IEEE ICIP*, pp. 3116–3120, (2015).

[60] E. M. Eksioglu and A. K. Tanc, *SIIMS.* **11**(3), 2090–2109, (2018).

[61] A. Manoel, F. Krzakala, E. W. Tramel, and L. Zdeborová. In *2017 55th Annu. Allerton Conf. Commun. Control Comput.*, pp. 1048–1055. IEEE, (2017).

[62] M. Bayati and A. Montanari, *IEEE Trans. Inf. Theory.* **58**(4), 1997–2017, (2011).

[63] D. Donoho and A. Montanari, *Probab. Theory Relat. Fields.* **166**(3), 935–969, (2016).

[64] C. Gerbelot, A. Abbara, and F. Krzakala, *arXiv:2006.06581.* (2020).

[65] B. Loureiro, G. Sicuro, C. Gerbelot, A. Pacco, F. Krzakala, and L. Zdeborová, *NeurIPS.* **34**, 10144–10157, (2021).

[66] D. L. Donoho, A. Javanmard, and A. Montanari, *IEEE Trans. Inf. Theory.* **59**(11), 7434–7464, (2013).

[67] M. Dia, N. Macris, F. Krzakala, T. Lesieur, L. Zdeborová, et al., *NeurIPS.* **29**, (2016).

[68] L. F. Cugliandolo and J. Kurchan, *J. Phys. A.* **27**(17), 5749, (1994).

[69] M. Celentano, C. Cheng, and A. Montanari, *arXiv:2112.07572.* (2021).

[70] A. S. Bandeira, A. Perry, and A. S. Wein, *Port. Math.* **75**(2), 159–186, (2018).

[71] M. Celentano, A. Montanari, and Y. Wu. In *COLT*, pp. 1078–1141, (2020).

[72] A. Montanari, *SIAM J. Comput.* pp. FOCS19–1, (2021).

[73] E. Subag, *Commun. Pure Appl. Math.* **74**(5), 1021–1044, (2021).

[74] A. El Alaoui, A. Montanari, and M. Sellke, *Ann. Prob.* **49**(6), 2922–2960, (2021).

Chapter 21

Information and Communication

Yoshiyuki Kabashima* and Toshiyuki Tanaka[†]

*Institute for Physics of Intelligence & Department of Physics,
The University of Tokyo, Japan
kaba@phys.s.u-tokyo.ac.jp
[†]Systems Science Course & Data Science Course, Graduate School of Informatics,
Kyoto University, Japan
tt@i.kyoto-u.ac.jp

Some of the most important developments in information theory in the last three decades have deep connections with spin glass theory. In this chapter, **Yoshiyuki Kabashima** and **Toshiyuki Tanaka** illustrate this fascinating scientific convergence by focusing on three main topics: error correcting codes, wireless communication and compressive sensing.

21.1. Introduction

In the 1940s, Claude E. Shannon discovered that the average negative logarithm of the probability of the occurrence of events plays an important role in his mathematical theory of communication. He wondered what to call it, and once decided to name it "uncertainty". However, when he discussed this concept with John von Neumann, von Neumann suggested a better idea. He said, 'You should call it entropy, for two reasons. In the first place your uncertainty function has been used in statistical mechanics under that name, so it already has a name. In the second place, and more important, no one really knows what entropy really is, so in a debate you will always have the advantage' [1].

This episode, whether true or not, vividly represents the fundamental connection between information theory and statistical mechanics. Its recognition remained at a conceptual level for the first 40 years. However, since the 1980s, sequential successful applications of spin glass theory to concrete problems in information and communication have enhanced their connection to a level of practical utility. The replica and cavity methods are now recognized as powerful tools in information theory as well.

This chapter illustrates how spin glass theory can be utilized to address problems in information and communication by three application examples.

21.2. Error Correcting Code

21.2.1. *Communication via noisy channels*

Error correcting codes are coding techniques that facilitate reliable communication in noisy environments. In a general scenario, each of the 2^K messages are encoded to an $N(> K)$-dimensional Boolean vector $\boldsymbol{x} = (x_i) \in \{0,1\}^N$, which is called the *codeword*. The codeword $\boldsymbol{x}$ is transmitted through a noisy channel when the corresponding message is generated, and an N-dimensional degraded vector $\boldsymbol{y} = (y_i)$ is received at the other terminal. Then, the receiver decodes $\boldsymbol{y}$ to retrieve the transmitted message.

The error-correction ability is achieved at the expense of information redundancy. Shannon showed in his seminal work [2] that error-free communication is theoretically possible as $K, N \to \infty$ if and only if the code rate $R = K/N$, which represents the fraction of informative bits in the transmitted codeword, is less than the channel capacity.

The quest for practical codes that saturate the fundamental error-correction limit is a longstanding central goal in information theory. However, in the 1990s, a pre-existing code called *low-density parity-check (LDPC) code*, which was proposed by Gallager in the 1960s [3] but remained largely ignored for 30 years, was experimentally shown to closely approach the channel capacity. Since then, the family of LDPC codes has been the de facto standard error correcting code used in modern digital communications.

21.2.2. *Performance analysis*

Spin glass theory offers useful tools for theoretically examining the typical error-correction performance of LDPC codes.

LDPC code A basic LDPC code is defined by a randomly constructed large parity-check matrix, $H = (H_{\mu i}) \in \{0,1\}^{(N-K) \times N}$, where only $k \sim O(1)$ and $j \sim O(1)$ elements are nonzero (unity) per row and per column, respectively. The code rate is $R = 1 - j/k$. This matrix characterizes codewords using the parity-check equation: $H\boldsymbol{x} = 0 \pmod 2$, which after the "binary-bipolar transform" $s_i = (-1)^{x_i}$ is expressed as the prior distribution of the Ising vector $\boldsymbol{s} = (s_i) \in \{+1, -1\}^N$:

$$p(\boldsymbol{s}) = \prod_{\mu=1}^{N-K} \frac{1 + \prod_{i \in \partial\mu} s_i}{2}. \tag{21.1}$$

Here, $\partial\mu$ denotes the set of indices of nonzero entries in the μ-th row of H.

In the following, we focus on the binary symmetric channel (BSC) in which each transmitted bit $\in \{0,1\}$ is independently flipped to another alphabet with probability p, but the generalization to other memoryless channels is straightforward. In the Ising expression, BSC is modeled as a conditional distribution

$$p(\boldsymbol{\tau} \mid \boldsymbol{s}) = \prod_{i=1}^{N} \frac{e^{F\tau_i s_i}}{2\cosh(F)}, \tag{21.2}$$

where $F = (1/2)\log\left[(1-p)/p\right]$. The degraded vector τ is decoded to retrieve the transmitted vector based on Bayes' theorem

$$
\begin{aligned}
p(s \mid \tau) &= \frac{p(\tau \mid s)p(s)}{p(\tau)} \\
&= \frac{1}{Z(H,\tau)} \prod_{\mu=1}^{N-K} \frac{1 + \prod_{i\in\partial\mu} s_i}{2} \times \prod_{i=1}^{N} \frac{e^{F\tau_i s_i}}{2\cosh(F)},
\end{aligned}
\tag{21.3}
$$

where $Z(H,\tau) = \sum_s \prod_{\mu=1}^{N-K} \frac{1+\prod_{i\in\partial\mu} s_i}{2} \times \prod_{i=1}^{N} \frac{e^{F\tau_i s_i}}{2\cosh(F)}$ plays the role of the partition function in statistical mechanics.

Free entropy   The typical property of (21.3) can be analyzed using the replica method. Under the replica symmetric (RS) ansatz, the replica method yields an expression for the typical free entropy (per bit) as

$$
g := \lim_{n\to 0} \frac{\partial}{\partial n} \lim_{N\to\infty} \frac{1}{N} \log\left[Z^n(H,\tau)\right]_{H,\tau} = \operatorname*{extr}_{\hat{\pi}(\cdot),\pi(\cdot)} \{\mathcal{G}(\hat{\pi}(\cdot),\pi(\cdot))\},
\tag{21.4}
$$

where extr_X and $[\cdots]_X$ denote the extremization and average operations with respect to X, and

$$
\begin{aligned}
\mathcal{G}(\hat{\pi}(\cdot),\pi(\cdot)) := \frac{j}{k} &\int \prod_{i=1}^{k} dh_i \pi(h_i) \log\left(\frac{1 + \prod_{i=1}^{k}\tanh(h_i)}{2}\right) \\
&- j \int dh\pi(h)d\hat{h}\hat{\pi}(\hat{h}) \log\left(\frac{\cosh(h+\hat{h})}{\cosh(h)}\right) - \log 2\cosh(F) \\
&+ \int \prod_{\mu=1}^{j} d\hat{h}_\mu \hat{\pi}(\hat{h}_\mu) \left[\log\left(2\cosh\left(F\tau + \sum_{\mu=1}^{j} \hat{h}_\mu\right)\right)\right]_\tau
\end{aligned}
\tag{21.5}
$$

is a functional of certain probability densities $\pi(h)$ and $\hat{\pi}(\hat{h})$. We assumed that the transmitted codeword is $\mathbf{1} = (1,\ldots,1)^\top$ without loss of generality, which yields $[\cdots]_\tau = \sum_{\tau\in\{+1,-1\}} \frac{(\cdots)e^{F\tau}}{2\cosh(F)}$. The RS ansatz is justified when the true prior and channel models are used for decoding, which corresponds to the Nishimori condition in spin glass theory [4]. One can find the derivation of a result equlvalent to (21.5) in [5].

LDPC code is capacity-approaching   The possibility of correct decoding can be examined by assessing the dominant solution of (21.4). The extremum condition of (21.4) is expressed as

$$
\hat{\pi}(\hat{h}) = \int \prod_{i=1}^{k-1} dh_i \pi(h_i)\delta\left(h - \tanh^{-1}\left(\prod_{i=1}^{k-1}\tanh(h_k)\right)\right),
\tag{21.6}
$$

$$
\pi(h) = \int \prod_{\mu=1}^{j-1} d\hat{h}_\mu \hat{\pi}(\hat{h}_\mu) \left[\delta\left(h - F\tau - \sum_{\mu=1}^{j-1} \hat{h}_j\right)\right]_\tau,
\tag{21.7}
$$

which can be numerically solved using sampling-based methods. The solution offers an overlap between a typical s from (21.3) and the true codeword $\tau = 1$ as

$$m = \frac{1}{N} \left[\mathbf{1} \cdot \langle s \rangle \right]_{H,\tau} = \int \prod_{\mu=1}^{j} d\hat{h}_{\mu} \hat{\pi}(\hat{h}_{\mu}) \left[\tanh \left(F\tau + \sum_{\mu=1}^{j} \hat{h}_{\mu} \right) \right]_{\tau}, \tag{21.8}$$

where $\langle \cdots \rangle$ denotes the average with respect to the posterior (21.3).

For $k \geq 3$, $\hat{\pi}(\hat{h})$ and $\pi(h)$ having unit masses at $\hat{h}, h = +\infty$, respectively, always satisfy (21.6) and (21.7), providing $m = 1$. This solution corresponds to the decoding success, and yields the free entropy as

$$g_{\text{success}} = F \tanh(F) - \log(2 \cosh(F)) = p \log p + (1-p) \log(1-p). \tag{21.9}$$

In addition, $k, j \gg 1$, $\hat{\pi}(\hat{h}) = \delta(\hat{h})$ and $\pi(h) = [\delta(h - F\tau)]_{\tau}$ constitute the only alternative solution that allows for $m = \tanh^2(F) = (1 - 2p)^2$ and

$$g_{\text{failure}} = -\frac{j}{k} \log 2 = -(1 - R) \log 2. \tag{21.10}$$

Of these two, the solution with the larger free entropy dominates (21.4). This indicates that error-free communication is possible if and only if

$$R < 1 + p \log_2 p + (1-p) \log_2(1-p) \tag{21.11}$$

holds, which implies that the LDPC codes with $k, j \gg 1$ saturate the channel capacity of BSC.

For moderate values of $k \geq 3$, we must resort to numerical methods to evaluate the failure solution. The results obtained for several pairs of (k, j) are shown in Table 1, where p_c denotes the critical value of p, below which the successful solution dominates globally. In contrast, p_s denotes the spinodal point, below which the failure solution disappears. For $p < p_s$, practical decoding is easily performed because there is no solution other than the successful solution. p_{Shannon} represents the fundamental decoding limit determined by (21.11). Table 1 implies that larger k, j enhance the error correcting ability, and thus p_c becomes closer to p_{Shannon}, whereas the easily decodable region of $p < p_s$ becomes narrower.

21.2.3. *Practical decoding by belief propagation*

Belief propagation (BP) The optimal decoding is, unfortunately, computationally difficult. Therefore, an approximate algorithm termed the *sum-product algorithm* or,

Table 1. Performance comparison of LDPC codes for several (k, j) pairs.

k	j	R	p_s	p_c	p_{Shannon}
6	3	0.5	0.084	0.997	0.110
8	4	0.5	0.076	0.107	0.110
10	5	0.5	0.068	0.109	0.110
5	3	0.4	0.113	0.137	0.146
6	4	0.333	0.116	0.173	0.174
4	3	0.25	0.167	0.209	0.215

more generally, *belief propagation (BP)* is used for the practical decoding of LDPC codes. Although BP was developed in information science [3, 6], independently of statistical mechanics, it is in agreement with the algorithm that the cavity method of spin glass theory provides. Here, we derive the BP decoding algorithm using the terminology of the cavity method.

Suppose that the distribution of N-dimensional vectors $\boldsymbol{s}$ is expressed as follows:

$$p(\boldsymbol{s}) = \frac{1}{Z} \prod_{\mu=1}^{M} \psi_\mu(\boldsymbol{s}_\mu) \prod_{i=1}^{N} \psi_i(s_i).$$
(21.12)

Here, nonnegative functions $\psi_\mu(\boldsymbol{s}_\mu)$ and $\psi_i(s_i)$ are termed *factors*, where $\boldsymbol{s}_\mu$ denotes the subset of $\boldsymbol{s}$ on which $\psi_\mu(\cdot)$ depends, and Z is the normalization constant. The general goal of BP is to efficiently compute the marginal distributions

$$p_i(s_i) = \sum_{\boldsymbol{s}\backslash s_i} p(\boldsymbol{s}),$$
(21.13)

where $A\backslash a$ generally denotes the exclusion of element a from the set A.

For this purpose, the cavity method focuses on the identity

$$p_i(s_i) = \frac{\sum_{\boldsymbol{s}\backslash s_i} \left(\prod_{\mu\in\partial i} \psi_\mu(\boldsymbol{s}_\mu) \right) p_{\backslash i}(\boldsymbol{s}\backslash s_i) \times \psi_i(s_i)}{\sum_{\boldsymbol{s}} \left(\prod_{\mu\in\partial i} \psi_\mu(\boldsymbol{s}_\mu) \right) p_{\backslash i}(\boldsymbol{s}\backslash s_i) \times \psi_i(s_i)},$$
(21.14)

where ∂i denotes the set of indices of factors that involve s_i as an argument.

$$p_{\backslash i}(\boldsymbol{s}\backslash s_i) = \frac{1}{Z_{\backslash i}} \prod_{\nu\notin\partial i} \psi_\nu(\boldsymbol{s}_\nu) \prod_{j\neq i} \psi_j(s_j),$$
(21.15)

is called a *cavity distribution*, which represents the distribution of a virtual system that is defined by excluding s_i from the original system.

Generally, the assessment of (21.14) is computationally difficult. However, when the variable dependence of $p(\boldsymbol{s})$ is expressed by a cycle-free bipartite graph (Fig. 21.1(a)), the computational cost is drastically reduced since the most time-consuming part is

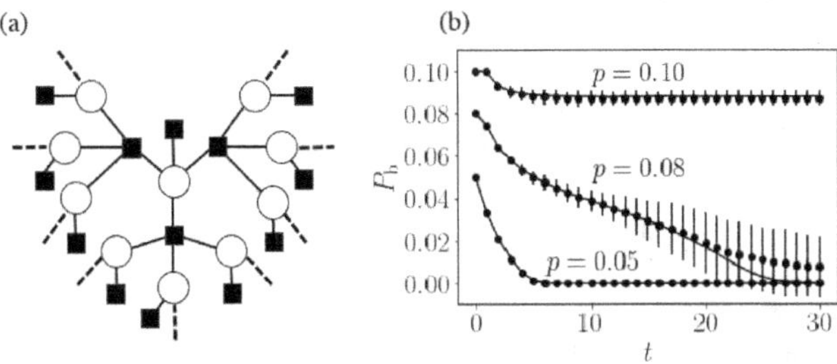

Fig. 21.1. (a) Cycle-free bipartite graph. Circles and squares represent the variables (s_i) and factors ($\psi_\mu(\boldsymbol{s}_\mu)$ or $\psi_i(s_i)$), respectively. (b) Trajectories of bit error rates are compared between BP and DE. BP data (markers) represent the averages assessed from 10 experiments for $(k, j) = (6, 3)$ LDPC codes of $N = 10000$. The error bars denote one standard error. The curves represent trajectories assessed using DE.

computed as

$$\sum_{\boldsymbol{s}\backslash s_i}\left(\prod_{\mu\in\partial i}\psi_\mu(\boldsymbol{s}_\mu)\right)p_{\backslash i}(\boldsymbol{s}\backslash s_i)=\prod_{\mu\in\partial i}\left(\sum_{\boldsymbol{s}_\mu\backslash s_i}\psi_\mu(\boldsymbol{s}_\mu)\prod_{j\in\partial\mu\backslash i}\mathcal{M}_{j\to\mu}(s_j)\right),\qquad(21.16)$$

where *cavity marginal* $\mathcal{M}_{j\to\mu}(s_j)=\sum_{\boldsymbol{s}\backslash s_i,s_j}p_{\backslash i}(\boldsymbol{s}\backslash s_i)$ is determined using a set of recursive updates over the bipartite graph as follows:

$$\mathcal{M}_{\mu\to i}(s_i)=\alpha_{\mu\to i}\sum_{\boldsymbol{s}\backslash s_i}\psi_\mu(\boldsymbol{s}_\mu)\prod_{j\in\partial\mu\backslash i}\mathcal{M}_{j\to\mu}(s_j),\qquad(21.17)$$

$$\mathcal{M}_{i\to\mu}(s_i)=\alpha_{i\to\mu}\psi_i(s_i)\prod_{\nu\in\partial i\backslash\mu}\mathcal{M}_{\nu\to i}(s_i),\qquad(21.18)$$

where $\partial\mu$ denotes a set of variable indices in $\boldsymbol{s}_\mu$. The algorithm composed of (21.17) and (21.18) is generally termed "belief propagation (BP)". Once the cavity marginals are determined, (21.13) is computed as

$$p_i(s_i)=\alpha_i\psi_i(s_i)\prod_{\mu\in\partial i}\mathcal{M}_{\mu\to i}(s_i),\qquad(21.19)$$

using *cavity bias* $\mathcal{M}_{\mu\to i}(s_i)$. In the above, α's represent constants to normalize the integrals of the left-hand side to unity.

BP-based decoding   For cycle-free graphs, BP exactly assesses marginal distributions with $O(N)$ computational cost provided that $|\partial\mu|$ are $O(1)$ in the graphs. Unfortunately, the variable dependence of LDPC codes cannot be expressed by cycle-free graphs. However, the method for constructing H indicates that the expression of LDPC codes results in large and sparse random graphs. This means that the typical lengths of cycles in the graphs scale as $O(\log N)$, which guarantees that BP serves as a good approximation algorithm for $N\gg 1$.

For Ising variables, the distributions can be generally expressed using single parameters as $\mathcal{M}_{\mu\to i}(s_i)=\frac{1+\tanh(h_{\mu\to i})s_i}{2}$ and $\mathcal{M}_{i\to\mu}(s_i)=\frac{1+\tanh(h_{i\to\mu})s_i}{2}$. These allow a compact expression for the BP to be determined for the decoding problem as

$$h_{\mu\to i}=\tanh^{-1}\left(\prod_{j\in\partial\mu\backslash i}\tanh(h_{j\to\mu})\right),\qquad(21.20)$$

$$h_{i\to\mu}=\tanh\left(F\tau_i+\sum_{\nu\in\partial i\backslash\mu}h_{\nu\to i}\right).\qquad(21.21)$$

After these parameters are obtained in an iterative manner, the bitwise optimal estimator $\hat{s}_i$ $(i=1,\ldots,N)$ is assessed as

$$\hat{s}_i=\text{sign}\left(F\tau_i+\sum_{\mu\in\partial i}h_{\mu\to i}\right).\qquad(21.22)$$

Density evolution (DE) For $N \to \infty$, the correspondence between cycle-free and large sparse random graphs guarantees that the behavior of BP can be captured by tracking the evolution of the distributions of $h_{\mu \to i}$ and $h_{i \to \mu}$ in infinitely large cycle-free graphs (Fig. 21.1(b)), which is termed *density evolution* (DE) [7]. DE is described by the forward iterative update of (21.6) and (21.7). This means that the practical error correcting limit of BP decoding is characterized not by the theoretical limit p_{c}, but by the spinodal point p_{s}.

21.2.4. *Notes*

The close relationship between error correcting codes and spin glass models was first highlighted in the seminal work by Sourlas [8], which demonstrated that densely-connected p-body spin glass models saturate Shannon's limit for $R \to +0$. The connection was generalized for finite R by [9]. The relationship between optimal decoding and the Nishimori condition was examined by [10–13]. The equivalence of BP and the cavity method was first highlighted by [14]. Replica-based analysis of LDPC codes was first performed by [15] and [16] for two variations, known as the MN code [17] and the turbo code [18], respectively.

21.3. **Wireless Communication**

21.3.1. *CDMA and multiuser detection*

As wireless communication has become ubiquitous, communications systems are becoming larger and larger in size. Such a trend is making application of spin glass theory to analysis of communications systems more and more reasonable than ever before. In the following we demonstrate it via the example of the analysis of the *code-division multiple-access (CDMA)*.

An *uplink* communication channel in wireless communication (i.e., from end-user devices to a base station or an access point) is called a multiple-access channel, in which the same communication medium is shared by multiple devices. Sharing of a communication medium can be done in several different ways, and CDMA does such sharing via use of *codes*. The sharing in CDMA can be mathematically represented as

$$y = Ax^0 + n, \qquad (21.23)$$

where $x^0 \in \mathbb{R}^N$ consists of information symbols to be sent by N devices, and where $A \in \mathbb{R}^{M \times N}$ is the matrix whose columns are *spreading codes* of the respective devices. That is, in CDMA communication each device converts its scalar information symbol into an M-dimensional vector signal via multiplying the information symbol with its own spreading code, and the received signal $y \in \mathbb{R}^M$ at the receiver (base station or access point) is the sum of the vector signals sent from the N devices as well as a channel noise $n \in \mathbb{R}^M$. One can generalize it a bit further, by regarding each member of y to be conditionally distributed on the respective member of Ax^0, as

$$R_0(y \mid Ax^0) = \prod_{\mu=1}^{M} \rho_0(y_\mu \mid (Ax^0)_\mu), \qquad (21.24)$$

where ρ_0 represents the conditional distribution of y_μ characterizing the channel.

The receiver has to solve the problem of *multiuser detection*, that is to extract information symbols from $\boldsymbol{y}$ and A. This can be done via assuming a signal-generating model, which consists of a postulated probability distribution $p(\boldsymbol{x}) = \prod_{i=1}^{N} p(x_i)$ of the information symbols $\boldsymbol{x} = (x_i)$ and a postulated channel model

$$R(\boldsymbol{y} \mid A\boldsymbol{x}) = \prod_{\mu=1}^{M} \rho(y_\mu \mid (A\boldsymbol{x})_\mu), \tag{21.25}$$

and considering the posterior distribution of $\boldsymbol{x}$ given $\boldsymbol{y}$ and A under this postulated model, which is given by

$$p(\boldsymbol{x} \mid \boldsymbol{y}, A) = \frac{p(\boldsymbol{x})R(\boldsymbol{y} \mid A\boldsymbol{x})}{Z(\boldsymbol{y}, A)}, \tag{21.26}$$

where

$$Z(\boldsymbol{y}, A) = \int d\boldsymbol{x}\, p(\boldsymbol{x})R(\boldsymbol{y} \mid A\boldsymbol{x}) \tag{21.27}$$

is the marginal likelihood, or the evidence, of the postulated model given $\boldsymbol{y}$, and plays the role of the partition function.

21.3.2. *Performance analysis*

The key quantity to analyzing the CDMA channel is the per-signal self-information, or negative free entropy, $-M^{-1}\log Z(\boldsymbol{y}, A)$, averaged over $\boldsymbol{y}$. If the receiver uses the true model, then this quantity corresponds to the per-signal (Shannon) entropy of $\boldsymbol{y}$. The average self-information $-M^{-1}[\log Z(\boldsymbol{y}, A)]_{\boldsymbol{y}}$, however, depends on the spreading codes A as well. In CDMA, (pseudo) random sequences are typically used as the spreading codes, so that further averaging the average self-information with respect to the random spreading codes A is expected to yield results that are typical in this setting. In evaluating $-M^{-1}[\log Z(\boldsymbol{y}, A)]_{\boldsymbol{y},A}$ under the random-spreading setting, one may resort to the replica method, via the identity

$$g := M^{-1}[\log Z(\boldsymbol{y}, A)]_{\boldsymbol{y},A} = \lim_{n \to 0} \frac{\partial}{\partial n} M^{-1}[Z^n(\boldsymbol{y}, A)]_{\boldsymbol{y},A}, \tag{21.28}$$

evaluating the nth moment of $Z(\boldsymbol{y}, A)$ for $n \in \mathbb{N}$ in the thermodynamic limit $M \to \infty$ with the help of the saddle-point method, and then continuating the resulting formula to real n to take the derivative and the limit $n \to 0$.

Assuming the channel pair $\{\rho_0, \rho\}$ and the prior pair $\{p_0(x^0), p(x)\}$ of the information symbols, and the matrix A consisting of independent and identically-distributed (iid) sub-Gaussian zero-mean random elements with variance $1/M$ one has, under the RS ansatz,

$$g = \operatorname*{extr}_{\substack{r,m,q \\ \hat{r},\hat{m},\hat{q}}} \left\{ \int \bar{\rho}_0\left(y \;\middle|\; \sqrt{\frac{\beta m^2}{q}}\,t\right) \log \bar{\rho}(y \mid \sqrt{\beta q}\,t)\, Dt\, dy + \beta\left[-\frac{r\hat{r}}{2} - m\hat{m} + \frac{q\hat{q}}{2}\right.\right.$$
$$\left.\left. -\frac{1}{2}\log\frac{2\pi}{\hat{m}} + \int \left[\mathcal{N}\left(z \;\middle|\; x^0, \frac{\hat{q}}{\hat{m}^2}\right)\right]_{x^0} \log[\mathcal{N}(z \mid x, (\hat{m})^{-1})e^{(\hat{r}-\hat{q}+\hat{m})x^2/2}]_x\, dz\right]\right\}, \tag{21.29}$$

where $Dt = \frac{dt}{\sqrt{2\pi}}e^{-t^2/2}$ and $\beta = N/M$, where $\mathcal{N}(z \mid x, \sigma^2)$ denotes the probability density function of the Gaussian distribution with mean x and variance σ^2, and where

$$\bar{\rho}_0(y \mid v) = \int \rho_0\left(y \;\middle|\; v + \sqrt{\beta\left(r_0 - \frac{m^2}{q}\right)}u\right) Du, \qquad (21.30)$$

$$\bar{\rho}(y \mid v) = \int \rho(y \mid v + \sqrt{\beta(r-q)}u)\, Du, \qquad (21.31)$$

with $r_0 = [(x_i^0)^2]_{x^0}$. One can interpret the formula (21.29) as follows: The average free entropy g is decoupled in the large-system limit under random spreading into two parts, one being the entropy of the per-signal Gaussian-input channel pair $\{\bar{\rho}_0, \bar{\rho}\}$ which are additive white Gaussian noise (AWGN)-degraded version of the original channel pair $\{\rho_0, \rho\}$, and the other being the entropy of the per-symbol AWGN channel pair $\{\mathcal{N}(z \mid x^0, \frac{\hat{q}}{\hat{m}^2}), \mathcal{N}(z \mid x, (\hat{m})^{-1})\}$, with the postulated input symbol distribution proportional to $p(x)e^{(\hat{r}-\hat{q}+\hat{m})x^2/2}$. This decoupling corresponds to the reduction of the original many-body system into a single-body representation in the mean-field framework. It can also be regarded as an asymptotic "single letterization" in information theory.

The values of the parameters governing the decoupled expression are to be determined via the extremization. At the extremum, one has $r = N^{-1}\sum_{i=1}^{N}\langle x_i^2\rangle$, $q = N^{-1}\sum_{i=1}^{N}\langle x_i\rangle^2$, and $m = N^{-1}\sum_{i=1}^{N}x_i^0\langle x_i\rangle$, where $\langle\cdots\rangle$ denotes the posterior average of the per-symbol AWGN channel $\mathcal{N}(z \mid x, (\hat{m})^{-1})$ of x given z, with prior $\propto p(x)e^{(\hat{r}-\hat{q}+\hat{m})x^2/2}$. These parameters characterize the *subshell* that is dominant under the posterior distribution of $\boldsymbol{x}$ derived from the postulated model, so that various performance measures for posterior-based multiuser detectors can be calculated therefrom.

Specializing the above general result to the case where $\rho_0(y \mid u)$ and $\rho(y \mid u)$ are AWGN channels such that $y = u + \sigma_0 n$ and $y = u + \sigma n$ with $n \sim \mathcal{N}(0,1)$, respectively, one has $\hat{r} - \hat{q} + \hat{m} = 0$ at the saddle point, and (21.29) is reduced to

$$g = \mathop{\mathrm{extr}}_{\substack{r,m,q \\ \hat{r},\hat{m},\hat{q}}}\left\{-\frac{1}{2}\frac{\sigma_0^2 + \beta(r_0 - 2m + q)}{\sigma^2 + \beta(r-q)} - \frac{1}{2}\log 2\pi(\sigma^2 + \beta(r-q)) + \beta\left[-\frac{r\hat{r}}{2}\right.\right.$$

$$\left.\left. - m\hat{m} + \frac{q\hat{q}}{2} - \frac{1}{2}\log\frac{2\pi}{\hat{m}} + \int\left[\mathcal{N}\left(z \;\middle|\; x^0, \frac{\hat{q}}{\hat{m}^2}\right)\right]_{x^0}\log[\mathcal{N}(z \mid x, (\hat{m})^{-1})]_x\, dz\right]\right\}.$$

$$(21.32)$$

It should be noted that the RS solution obtained via the extremization is locally unstable against perturbations breaking the replica symmetry when

$$\frac{\beta}{(\sigma^2 + \beta(r-q))^2}\int\left[\mathcal{N}\left(z \;\middle|\; x^0, \frac{\hat{q}}{\hat{m}^2}\right)\right]_{x^0}\left(\langle x^2\rangle - \langle x\rangle^2\right)^2 dz > 1. \qquad (21.33)$$

Performance comparison Assume for simplicity that the information symbols are iid bipolar random variables taking ± 1 with equal probability and the AWGN channels as above. A posterior-based multiuser detector is then defined via taking the componentwise signs of the posterior mean of $\boldsymbol{x}$. The bit-error rate of the multiuser detector is

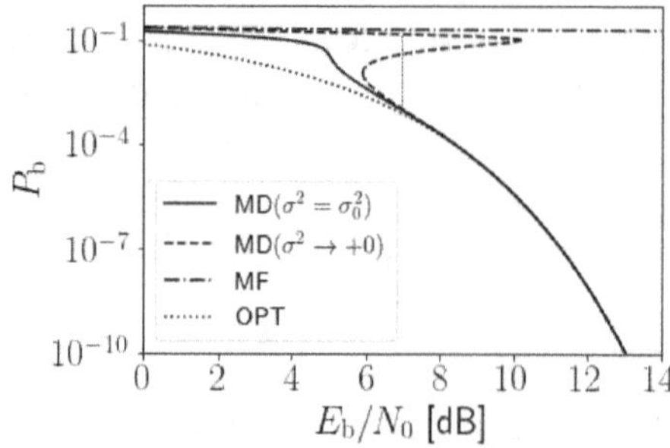

Fig. 21.2. Bit-error rate for various detection schemes in the case $\beta = 1.4$. MD, MF, and OPT stand for the multiuser detector, the matched filter detector, and the single-user bound, respectively.

evaluated as

$$P_{\mathrm{b}}^{\mathrm{MD}} = H\left(\hat{m}/\sqrt{\hat{q}}\right), \tag{21.34}$$

where $H(x) = \int_x^{+\infty} Dz$. Figure 21.2 plots $P_{\mathrm{b}}^{\mathrm{MD}}$ for two conditions of $\sigma^2 = \sigma_0^2$ and $\sigma^2 \to +0$ versus $E_{\mathrm{b}}/N_0 = (2\sigma_0^2)^{-1}$ (in decibel) for the case of $\beta = 1.4$.

A matched-filter detector, defined via taking the component-wise signs of $A^\top y$, has the bit-error rate $P_{\mathrm{b}}^{\mathrm{MF}} = H\left(1/\sqrt{\sigma_0^2 + \beta}\right)$. This, along with the single-user bound $P_{\mathrm{b}}^{\mathrm{OPT}} = H(1/\sigma_0)$, which corresponds to the bit-error rate when there is only one device, is also shown for comparison.

The multiuser detector with $\sigma^2 = \sigma_0^2$, which corresponds to the Bayes-optimal detection, exhibits considerably better performance than the matched-filter detector in the entire region. In particular, it closely approaches the single-user bound $P_{\mathrm{b}}^{\mathrm{OPT}}$ for E_{b}/N_0 greater than ~ 8.0 dB. This solution is locally stable against the replica symmetry breaking (RSB) perturbations. On the other hand, for the multiuser detector with $\sigma^2 \to +0$, there are multiple solutions: one with the bit-error rate almost as small as $P_{\mathrm{b}}^{\mathrm{OPT}}$, and another with larger bit-error rate. The third solution on the intermediate branch is physically unstable and therefore irrelevant. The dominance of the two relevant solutions is switched at the place of the vertical dotted line, whereas achieving the smaller bit-error rate by practical detection algorithms is difficult as long as the solution of the larger bit-error rate exists. However, as the left-hand side of (21.33) diverges in the entire region for both of the relevant solutions, taking RSB into account should be necessary for the accurate assessment of the performance.

21.3.3. *BP-based detection*

BP on dense graphs   Although the multiuser detector with $\sigma^2 = \sigma_0^2$ minimizes the bit-error rate, evaluating the posterior mean of x is computationally difficult. In the previous section, the same difficulty was resolved by BP exploiting the nature of large sparse random graphs on which LDPC codes are defined. Unfortunately, (21.3) is represented by not a sparse but a *dense* (complete) bipartite graph (Figure 21.3(a)). Nevertheless, BP offers a practical solution to the current problem as well.

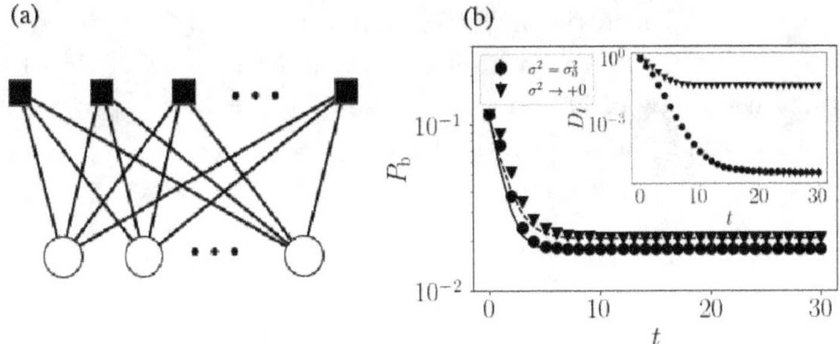

Fig. 21.3. (a): Graphical expression of CDMA multiuser detection. Circles and squares represent variables (x_i) and factors ($\psi_\mu(\boldsymbol{x})$), respectively. (b): Comparison of P_b between BP and DE for $\beta = 1/2$ and $E_\mathrm{b}/N_0 = 4$ [dB]. Markers stand for averages over 10000 experiments for systems of $N = 2000$. Standard errors are smaller than markers. Full and dashed curves represent DE for cases of $\sigma^2 = \sigma_0^2$ and $\sigma^2 \to +0$, respectively. Inset: $D_t = \frac{1}{N}\sum_{k=1}^{N}(m_k^t - m_k^{t-1})^2$ is plotted versus t. Convergence to a finite value for the case of $\sigma^2 \to +0$ signals the instability of the fixed point of BP.

Literally applying BP of (21.17) and (21.18) to the current system yields

$$\mathcal{M}_{\mu \to k}(x_k) = \alpha_{\mu \to k} \sum_{\boldsymbol{x} \backslash x_k} e^{-\frac{1}{2\sigma^2}(y_\mu - \sum_j A_{\mu j} x_j)^2} \prod_{j \neq k} \mathcal{M}_{j \to \mu}(x_j), \tag{21.35}$$

$$\mathcal{M}_{k \to \mu}(x_k) = \alpha_{k \to \mu} \prod_{\nu \neq \mu} \mathcal{M}_{\nu \to k}(x_k). \tag{21.36}$$

The computational difficulty resides in the summation with respect to $\boldsymbol{x} \backslash x_k$ on the right-hand side of (21.35). However, attention to the following property significantly reduces the necessary computational cost of BP.

The summation is regarded as the average of factor $\psi_\mu(\boldsymbol{x}) = e^{-\frac{1}{2\sigma^2}(y_\mu - \sum_j A_{\mu j} x_j)^2}$ with respect to $\boldsymbol{x} \backslash x_k \sim \prod_{j \neq k} \mathcal{M}_{j \to \mu}(x_j)$, a distribution under which the components of $\boldsymbol{x} \backslash x_k$ are independent. Thus the central limit theorem guarantees that $\Delta_{\mu \to k} = \sum_{j \neq k} A_{\mu j} x_j$ in $\psi_\mu(\boldsymbol{x})$ can be regarded as Gaussian $\Delta_{\mu \to k} \sim \mathcal{N}(\langle \Delta_{\mu \to k} \rangle, v_{\mu \to k})$ with

$$\langle \Delta_{\mu \to k} \rangle = \sum_{j \neq k} A_{\mu j} m_{j \to \mu}, \ v_{\mu \to k} = \sum_{j \neq k} A_{\mu j}^2 (1 - m_{j \to \mu}^2), \tag{21.37}$$

and $m_{j \to \mu} = \sum_{x_j \in \{+1,-1\}} x_j \mathcal{M}_{j \to \mu}(x_j)$. This, in conjunction with representing the cavity bias as $\mathcal{M}_{\mu \to k}(x_k) = e^{A_{\mu k} \xi_{\mu \to k} x_k}/(2\cosh(A_{\mu k}\xi_{\mu \to k}))$, yields the following compact expression of BP

$$\xi_{\mu \to k} = \frac{1}{\sigma^2 + v_{\mu \to k}} \left(y_\mu - \sum_{j \neq k} A_{\mu j} m_{j \to \mu} \right), \tag{21.38}$$

$$m_{k \to \mu} = \tanh\left(\sum_{\nu \neq \mu} A_{\nu k} \xi_{\nu \to k} \right), \tag{21.39}$$

whose computational cost per update is $O(M^2 N + M N^2)$.

The smallness of $A_{\mu k}$ allows us to reduce the computational cost further. For this, we define "node variables" $\xi_\mu = \frac{1}{\sigma^2 + v_\mu}(y_\mu - \sum_k A_{\mu k} m_{k \to \mu})$ and $m_k = \tanh(\sum_\mu A_{\mu k} \xi_{\mu \to k})$, and express $\xi_{\mu \to k}$ and $m_{k \to \mu}$ in a perturbative manner as $\xi_{\mu \to k} \simeq \xi_\mu + \frac{A_{\mu k}}{\sigma^2 + v} m_k$ and $m_{k \to \mu} \simeq m_k - A_{\mu k}(1 - m_k^2)\xi_\mu$. Here, we replaced $v_{\mu \to k}$ with $v_\mu = \sum_k A_{\mu k}^2(1 - m_k^2) \simeq v = \beta(1 - q)$ relying on the law of large numbers, and let $q = N^{-1}\sum_k m_k^2$. These lead to the expression of BP using the node variables as

$$\xi_\mu = \frac{1}{\sigma^2 + \beta(1 - q)}\left(y_\mu - \sum_{k=1}^{N} A_{\mu k}m_k + \beta(1 - q)\xi_\mu\right), \tag{21.40}$$

$$m_k = \tanh\left(\sum_{\mu=1}^{N} A_{\mu k}\xi_\mu + \frac{1}{\sigma^2 + \beta(1 - q)}m_k\right), \tag{21.41}$$

which can be carried out with $O(MN)$ computations per update. The estimator of the multiuser detector is assessed as $\hat{b}_k = \text{sign}(m_k)$.

At the fixed point of (21.40) and (21.41), $\xi_\mu = \frac{1}{\sigma^2}(y_\mu - \sum_k A_{\mu k}m_k)$ holds. This offers a closed-form equation with respect to $\boldsymbol{m} = (m_k)$ as

$$m_k = \tanh\left(\frac{1}{\sigma^2}\left(h_k - \sum_{j \neq k} J_{kj}m_j - \frac{\beta(1 - q)}{\sigma^2 + \beta(1 - q)}m_k\right)\right), \tag{21.42}$$

where $h_k = \sum_\mu A_{\mu k}y_\mu$ and $J_{kj} = (1 - \delta_{kj})\sum_\mu A_{\mu k}A_{\mu j}$. This corresponds to the Thouless–Anderson–Palmer equation [19] for the posterior of $\boldsymbol{x}$ given $\boldsymbol{y}$.

DE on dense graphs   As in LDPC codes, the behavior of BP for CDMA can also be captured by DE. In a sense, DE for CDMA is simpler than for LDPC codes because the density is limited to a Gaussian form due to the central limit theorem, and therefore, can be handled in a parametric manner. More specifically, we can assume that $\zeta_{k \to \mu} = \sum_{\nu \neq \mu} A_{\nu k}\xi_{\nu \to k}$ in (21.39) follows a Gaussian, so that we characterize it as $\zeta_{k \to \mu} = \hat{m}x_k + \sqrt{\hat{q}}z_{k \to \mu}$, where $z_{k \to \mu} \sim \mathcal{N}(0, 1)$. The parameters $\hat{m}$ and $\hat{q}$ can be assessed by inserting $m_{k \to \mu} = \tanh(\hat{m}x_k + \sqrt{\hat{q}}z_{k \to \mu})$ and $y_\mu = \sum_k A_{\mu k}x_k + \sigma_0 n_\mu$ $(n_\mu \sim \mathcal{N}(0, 1))$ into (21.38), and taking the average and variance of $x_k\zeta_{k \to \mu} = x_k\sum_{\nu \neq \mu} A_{\nu k}\xi_{\nu \to k}$. This yields

$$\hat{m} = \frac{1}{\sigma^2 + \beta(1 - q)}, \quad \hat{q} = \frac{\sigma_0^2 + \beta(1 - 2m + q)}{(\sigma^2 + \beta(1 - q))^2}, \tag{21.43}$$

$$m = \int Dz\,\tanh(\hat{m} + \sqrt{\hat{q}}z), \qquad q = \int Dz\,\tanh^2(\hat{m} + \sqrt{\hat{q}}z), \tag{21.44}$$

which is DE for CDMA. This is equivalent to the extremum condition of RS free entropy (21.32), which implies that BP for CDMA achieves the performance predicted by the replica method as $M, N \to \infty$ as long as the RS solution is correct.

DE of (21.43) and (21.44) always converges. However, this does not necessarily mean that BP converges microscopically. Examining how the variance of random perturbations around the fixed point of (21.38) and (21.39) develops in BP indicates that the fixed point is unstable if

$$\frac{\beta}{(\sigma^2 + \beta(1 - q))^2} \times \frac{1}{N}\sum_{k=1}^{N}(1 - m_k^2)^2 > 1 \tag{21.45}$$

holds, which statistically agrees with (21.33) thus implying the equivalence between the dynamical instability of BP and the local instability of the RS solution. Figure 21.3(b) shows a comparison between BP and DE. The remarkably good agreement validates our analysis.

21.3.4. *Notes*

The replica analysis of the CDMA multiuser detection problem was first performed by [20, 21]. BP-based detection algorithm, its DE, and the relationship between BP's instability to that of the RS solution were shown by [22]. The CDMA multiuser detection problem falls within what is called the teacher-student scenario, where the student is to estimate hidden variables of the teacher on the basis of signals generated by the teacher. The formulation presented here is quite general, encompassing not only the CDMA multiuser detection, but also MIMO channel capacity [23] and perceptron learning [24, 34, 35], as well as compressive sensing, to be discussed in the next subsection.

21.4. Compressive Sensing

21.4.1. *Signal processing by exploiting sparsity*

Compressive (or compressed) sensing is a signal-processing technique that enables recovery of high-dimensional signals from lower-dimensional measurements by utilizing prior knowledge of the sparsity of the signals [25]. Let us consider a situation in which an N-dimensional continuous signal, $x^0 \in \mathbb{R}^N$, is compressed to a vector of dimension $M = \alpha N$ ($\alpha \in (0,1)$), $y \in \mathbb{R}^M$, using an $M \times N$ measurement matrix $A \in \mathbb{R}^{M \times N}$, as follows:

$$y = Ax^0. \tag{21.46}$$

We also assume that A is known and x^0 is *sparse* in the sense that the number of nonzero components of x^0 is upper bounded by ρN, where $\rho \in (0,1)$. Then, under what conditions can the original signal x^0 be recovered from the compressed expression y?

It is obvious that (21.46) cannot uniquely determine x^0 from y as the number M of conditions associated with y is smaller than the dimension N of x^0. However, the assumption of sparsity of x^0 may facilitate the correct recovery. A popular approach for realizing this is to recover the signal by minimizing a sparsity-inducing cost function under the constraint given in (21.46). In particular, the ℓ_1-recovery, which is formulated as

$$\text{minimize}\{||x||_1\} \text{ subject to } Ax = y, \tag{21.47}$$

has attracted significant attention since it allows sparse solutions with practically feasible computational costs using linear programming, where $||x||_p = \left(\sum_{i=1}^{N} |x_i|^p\right)^{1/p}$ ($p > 0$) generally denotes the ℓ_p-norm of x.

21.4.2. *Performance analysis*

Random setup To theoretically characterize the condition for recovery success by (21.47), we consider the following setup. Each component of the original signal x^0, x_i^0 ($i = 1, \ldots, N$), is independently generated from an identical sparse distribution,

$p_0(x) = (1 - \rho)\delta(x) + \rho f(x)$, where $f(x)$ is a distribution that does not have finite mass at the origin. The compressed expression $\boldsymbol{y}$ is given by $\boldsymbol{y} = A\boldsymbol{x}^0$, where each entry of A, $A_{\mu i}$ ($\mu = 1, \ldots, M$; $i = 1, \ldots, N$), is sampled independently from the Gaussian distribution $\mathcal{N}(0, M^{-1})$.

For analytical convenience, we convert the minimization problem of (21.47) into a posterior distribution with the inverse temperature β as

$$p_\beta(\boldsymbol{x} \mid \boldsymbol{y}, A) = \frac{e^{-\beta\|\boldsymbol{x}\|_1}\delta(A\boldsymbol{x} - \boldsymbol{y})}{Z(\beta; \boldsymbol{y}, A)}, \tag{21.48}$$

where $Z(\beta; \boldsymbol{y}, A) = \int d\boldsymbol{x}\, e^{-\beta\|\boldsymbol{x}\|_1}\delta(A\boldsymbol{x} - \boldsymbol{y})$ denotes a partition function. In the limit $\beta \to \infty$, (21.48) concentrates on the solution to (21.47). Therefore, we can evaluate the performance of the ℓ_1-recovery by examining the macroscopic behavior of (21.48) in the limit of $\beta \to \infty$, for which we can use statistical mechanical methods.

Replica analysis for recovery limit　For this purpose, we use the replica method, which yields an expression for the average free energy density as

$$f := -\lim_{\beta\to\infty}\lim_{n\to 0}\frac{\partial}{\partial n}\lim_{N\to\infty}\frac{1}{\beta N}\log\left[Z^n(\beta; \boldsymbol{y}, A)\right]_{\boldsymbol{x}^0, A}$$

$$= \underset{\substack{Q,m,\chi \\ \hat{Q},\hat{m},\hat{\chi}}}{\mathrm{extr}}\left\{\frac{\alpha(Q - 2m + Q_0)}{2\chi} + \hat{m}m - \frac{\hat{Q}Q}{2} + \frac{\hat{\chi}\chi}{2}\right.$$

$$\left. -\int dx^0 p_0(x^0) Dz\phi\left(\hat{m}x^0 + \sqrt{\hat{\chi}}z; \hat{Q}\right)\right\}. \tag{21.49}$$

Here, we assumed the RS ansatz, which is supported by the uniqueness of the solution of (21.47) owing to its convexity. $\phi(h; \hat{Q}) = (|h| - 1)^2/(2\hat{Q})$ for $|h| > 1$ and 0, otherwise.

The mean squared error of the solution $\hat{\boldsymbol{x}}$ of (21.47) is computed as

$$\mathrm{MSE} = \frac{1}{N}[\|\hat{\boldsymbol{x}} - \boldsymbol{x}^0\|_2^2]_{\boldsymbol{x}^0, A} = Q - 2m + Q_0 \tag{21.50}$$

using the extremum solution of (21.49). When the correct signal $\hat{\boldsymbol{x}} = \boldsymbol{x}^0$ is typically recovered, $Q = m = Q_0$ holds. This indicates that examining its stability yields the conditions for successful recovery. For instance, in the case of $f(x) = \mathcal{N}(x \mid 0, 1)$, the stability analysis yields the following recovery success condition:

$$\alpha > 2(1 - \rho)H\left(\hat{\chi}^{-1/2}\right) + \rho, \tag{21.51}$$

where $\hat{\chi}$ is the solution of

$$\hat{\chi} = \alpha^{-1}\left[2(1-\rho)\left((\hat{\chi} + 1)H\left(\hat{\chi}^{-1/2}\right) - \hat{\chi}^{1/2}\frac{e^{-1/(2\hat{\chi})}}{\sqrt{2\pi}}\right) + \rho(\hat{\chi} + 1)\right]. \tag{21.52}$$

Figure 21.4 shows a heat map of the experimentally assessed recovery success probability together with the critical condition of (21.51). The excellent consistency between the experimental and theoretical results supports our analysis.

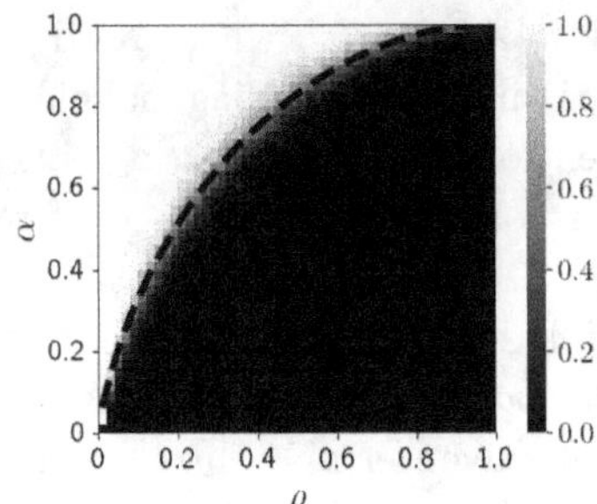

Fig. 21.4. Heat map of recovery success probability for the ℓ_1-recovery. For $f(x) = \mathcal{N}(x \mid 0, 1)$, the probability of each pair of (ρ, α) was assessed in 100 experiments for $N = 100$ systems using a linear programming method. The dashed curve represents the critical condition given by (21.51).

21.4.3. *Signal recovery by approximate message passing*

Approximate message passing The linear programming method is a popular scheme for performing the ℓ_1-recovery. However, solving linear programming problems incurs a much higher computational cost compared with standard linear recovery schemes. The expensive computation required to solve linear programming may reduce the application range of the ℓ_1-recovery.

Approximate message passing (AMP) is a promising approach to performing the ℓ_1-recovery at a lower computational cost. Under the condition that the norm of each column vector of A is normalized to unity, AMP for (21.47) proceeds iteratively according to

$$x_{t+1} = \eta(A^\top z_t + x_t; \hat{\sigma}_t^2), \tag{21.53}$$

$$z_t = y - Ax_t + \frac{1}{\alpha} \left\langle \eta'(A^\top z_{t-1} + x_{t-1}; \hat{\sigma}_{t-1}^2) \right\rangle, \tag{21.54}$$

where the soft-threshold function $\eta(u; \sigma^2) = u - \lambda\sigma\,\mathrm{sign}(u)$ for $|u| \geq \lambda\sigma$ and 0 otherwise, is applied in the component-wise manner. $\lambda(> 0)$ is a threshold control parameter, $\eta'(u; \sigma) = \frac{\partial}{\partial u}\eta(u; \sigma)$ and $\langle u \rangle = N^{-1}\sum_{i=1}^{N} u_i$, for vector $u = (u_1, \ldots, u_N)^\top$. $\hat{\sigma}_t^2$ is an estimate of $N^{-1}\|x_t - x^0\|_2^2$ for the current vector x_t. For instance, setting $\hat{\sigma}_t^2 = N^{-1}\|z_t\|_2^2$ is a practical choice when A and x^0 are statistically independent.

The computational cost required to perform (21.53) and (21.54) is $O(N^2)$ per update. In addition, under the random setup in which each entry of x^0 and A is independently sampled from $p_0(x)$ and $\mathcal{N}(0, M^{-1})$, AMP typically converges after $O(1)$ iterations in the recovery success phase. As the computational cost for linear programming methods grows as $O(N^3)$, this indicates that AMP can find a solution with lower computational cost.

What does AMP do? To show the fast convergence of AMP, we first examine how a simpler algorithm, naive iterative thresholding

$$x_{t+1} = \eta(A^\top z_t + x_t; \hat{\sigma}_t^2), \tag{21.55}$$

$$z_t = y - Ax_t \tag{21.56}$$

proceeds. For a random setup, $W = A^\top A - I_N$, where I_N denotes the $N \times N$ identity matrix, behaves as a random matrix in which the diagonal elements vanish. This allows us to decompose the first argument of (21.55) into $A^\top z_t + x_t = x^0 + n_t$, where $n_t = W(x^0 - x_t)$ can be regarded as a noise vector composed of random entries with zero mean and variance $M^{-1}\|x_t - x^t\|_2^2$. For each update t, the *spatial* correlations among the entries of n_t, $n_{i,t}$, are negligibly small provided that $t \sim O(1)$. However, for each $i \in \{1,\ldots,N\}$, $n_{i,t}$ has strong *temporal* correlations along the update index t, which makes the recovery performance of naive iterative thresholding poor.

These correlations originate from (21.56). To show this explicitly, we rewrite (21.56) in a component-wise manner as follows:

$$
\begin{aligned}
z_{\mu,t} &= y_\mu - \sum_{i=1}^{N} A_{\mu i} x_{i,t} = y_\mu - \sum_{i=1}^{N} A_{\mu i} \eta \left(\sum_{\nu=1}^{M} A_{\nu i} z_{\nu,t-1} + x_{i,t-1}; \hat{\sigma}_{t-1}^2 \right) \\
&\simeq y_\mu - \sum_{i=1}^{N} A_{\mu i} x_{i\backslash\mu,t} - \left(\sum_{i=1}^{N} A_{\mu i}^2 \eta'_{\backslash\mu} \right) z_{\mu,t-1},
\end{aligned}
\tag{21.57}
$$

where we used the abbreviations $x_{i\backslash\mu,t} = \eta \left(\sum_{\nu\neq\mu}^{M} A_{\nu i} z_{\nu,t-1} + x_{i,t-1}; \hat{\sigma}_{t-1}^2 \right)$ and $\eta'_{\backslash\mu} = \eta' \left(\sum_{\nu\neq\mu}^{M} A_{\nu i} z_{\nu,t-1} + x_{i,t-1}, \hat{\sigma}_{t-1}^2 \right)$. This indicates that z_t depends strongly on z_{t-1}, which results in nontrivial temporal correlations of the noise vector $n_t = W(x^0 - x_t)$ through (21.55).

The preceding argument motivates us to modify the naive iterative thresholding to cancel the term that is proportional to $z_{\mu,t-1}$ in the final expression of (21.57). Such treatment would lead to an improvement in the recovery performance, eliminating the temporal correlations of n_t during the iterative updates. This is nothing but AMP. More precisely, the cancellation, in conjunction with the replacement of $x_{i\backslash\mu,t}$ and $\sum_{i=1}^{N} A_{\mu i}^2 \eta'_{\backslash\mu}$ with $x_{i,t}$ and $(N\alpha)^{-1} \sum_{i=1}^{N} \eta' \left(\sum_{\mu=1}^{M} A_{\mu i} z_{\mu,t-1} + x_{i,t-1}, \hat{\sigma}_{t-1}^2 \right)$, respectively, which is justified by the law of large numbers and the statistical independence among the entries of x^0 and A, results in AMP of (21.53) and (21.54).

State evolution The cancellation is not only promising for performance improvement, but is also beneficial for analyzing the behavior of the algorithm. Given that both the spatial and temporal correlations among the entries of $x_t - x^0$, $x_{i,t} - x_i^0$, are negligible, the behavior of AMP can be captured by tracking the evolution of MSE $\sigma_t^2 = N^{-1}\|x_t - x^0\|_2^2$, which is expressed as *state evolution* (SE)

$$
\sigma_{t+1}^2 = \Psi(\sigma_t^2),
\tag{21.58}
$$

where $\Psi(\sigma^2) = \int dx p_0(x) Dz \left\{ \eta \left(x + \frac{\sigma}{\sqrt{\alpha}} z; \sigma^2 \right) - x \right\}^2$.

Figure 21.5 compares the trajectories of σ_t^2 for the AMP, naive iterative thresholding, and SE. The results indicate that the trajectories of AMP and SE exhibit excellent consistency and converge exponentially, whereas that of naive iterative thresholding diverges (inset). Naive AMP that keeps λ fixed does not perform as well as the linear programming method. However, it achieves recovery with a limit determined by (21.51) under a random setup when tuned optimally by controlling λ.

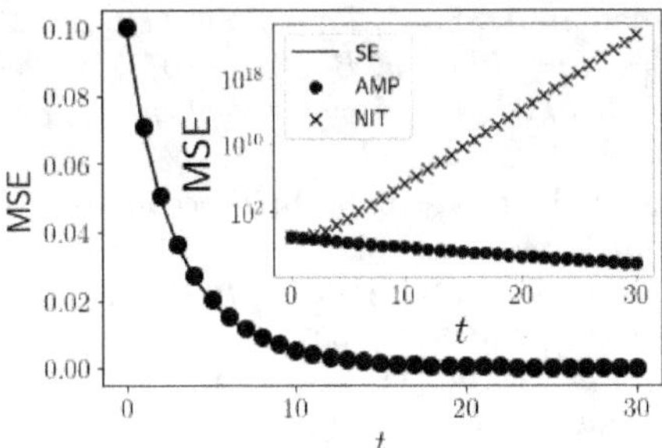

Fig. 21.5. Trajectories of MSE for AMP, naive iterative thresholding, and SE under the condition of $(\alpha, \rho, \lambda) = (0.5, 0.1, 1)$. Markers for AMP and naive iterative thresholding represent the averages assessed from ten experiments for $N = 10000$ systems. The standard errors are smaller than the marker size.

21.4.4. *Notes*

Performance analysis of compressive sensing by using the replica method was introduced by [26] while a condition for the recovery success equivalent to (21.51) had been obtained in a mathematically rigorous manner by [27]. [28] provides yet another rigorous analysis of a general class of models termed the generalized linear models (GLMs), which includes CDMA, perceptron learning, and compressive sensing as special cases. However, the replica-based analysis is still beneficial as it can handle advanced setups such as cases of noisy measurement [29] and advanced matrices [30], for which mathematically rigorous treatment is technically difficult.

AMP was proposed by [31], and later, its validity was mathematically proved by [32, 33]. AMP is quite similar to BP for CDMA shown in Sec. 21.3. Actually, the latter algorithm can be regarded as the earliest example of AMP. However, in a sense, AMP offers a more general framework than BP on dense graphs as it is not necessarily derived from computation of marginals or optimization of cost functions.

References

[1] M. Tribus and E. C. McIrvine, *Sci. Am.* **225**(3), 179–190, (1971).

[2] C. E. Shannon, *Bell Syst. Tech. J.* **27**, 379–423, (1948).

[3] R. Gallager, *IRE Transactions on Information Theory.* **8**(1), 21–28, (1962).

[4] H. Nishimori and D. Sherrington, *AIP Conf. Proc.* **553**(1), 67–72, (2001).

[5] Y. Kabashima and D. Saad, *J. Phys. A.* **37**(6), R1–R43 (2004).

[6] J. Pearl. In *Probabilistic Reasoning in Intelligent Systems*, p. i. Morgan Kaufmann, San Francisco (CA), (1988).

[7] T. Richardson, M. Shokrollahi, and R. Urbanke, *IEEE Trans. Inf. Theor.* **47**(2), 619–637, (2001).

[8] N. Sourlas, *Nature.* **339**(6227), 693–695 (1989).

[9] Y. Kabashima and D. Saad, *Europhys. Lett.* **45**(1), 97–103, (1999).

[10] P. Ruján, *Phys. Rev. Lett.* **70**, 2968–2971 (1993).

[11] H. Nishimori, *J. Phys. Soc. Jpn.* **62**(9), 2973–2975, (1993).

[12] N. Sourlas, *EPL.* **25**(3), 159–164 (1994).

[13] Y. Iba, *J. Phys. A.* **32**(21), 3875–3888 (1999).

[14] Y. Kabashima and D. Saad, *EPL.* **44**(5), 668–674 (1998).

[15] Y. Kabashima, T. Murayama, and D. Saad, *Phys. Rev. Lett.* **84**, 1355–1358 (2000).

[16] A. Montanari and N. Sourlas, *Eur. Phys. J. B.* **18**(1), 107–119 (2000).

[17] D. J. C. MacKay and R. M. Neal. In ed. C. Boyd, *Cryptography and Coding*, pp. 100–111, Springer (1995).

[18] C. Berrou, A. Glavieux, and P. Thitimajshima. In *Proceedings of ICC '93 - IEEE International Conference on Communications*, vol. 2, pp. 1064–1070 vol. 2, (1993).

[19] D. J. Thouless, P. W. Anderson, and R. G. Palmer, *Philos. Mag.* **35**(3), 593–601, (1977).

[20] T. Tanaka, *Europhys. Lett.* **54**(4), 540–546 (2001).

[21] T. Tanaka, *IEEE Trans. Inf. Theor.* **48**(11), 2888–2910, (2002).

[22] Y. Kabashima, *J. Phys. A.* **36**(43), 11111–11121 (2003).

[23] A. L. Moustakas, S. H. Simon, and A. M. Sengupta, *IEEE Trans. Inf. Theor.* **49**(10), 2545–2561, (2003).

[24] H. S. Seung, H. Sompolinsky, and N. Tishby, *Phys. Rev. A.* **45**, 6056–6091 (1992).

[25] E. J. Candes and M. B. Wakin, *IEEE Signal Process. Mag.* **25**(2), 21–30, (2008).

[26] Y. Kabashima, T. Wadayama, and T. Tanaka, *J. Stat. Mech. Theory Exp.* **2009**(09), L09003 (2009).

[27] D. L. Donoho, *Discrete Comput. Geom.* **35**(4), 617–652 (2006).

[28] J. Barbier, F. Krzalaka, N. Macris, L. Miolane, and L. Zdeborová, *Proc. Natl. Acad. Sci. U.S.A.* **116**(12), 5451–5460 (2019).

[29] S. Rangan, A. K. Fletcher, and V. K. Goyal, *IEEE Trans. Inf. Theor.* **58**(3), 1902–1923, (2012).

[30] M. Vehkaperä, Y. Kabashima, and S. Chatterjee, *IEEE Trans. Inf. Theor.* **62**(4), 2100–2124 (2016).

[31] D. L. Donoho, A. Maleki, and A. Montanari, *Proc. Natl. Acad. Sci. U.S.A.* **106**(45), 18914–18919, (2009).

[32] M. Bayati and A. Montanari, *IEEE Trans. Inf. Theor.* **57**(2), 764–785, (2011).

[33] F. Krzakala, M. Mézard, F. Sausset, Y. F. Sun, and L. Zdeborová, *Phys. Rev. X.* **2**, 021005 (2012).

[34] M. Mézard, *J. Phys. A.* **22** (12), 2181–2190, (1989).

[35] Györgyi, Géza, *Phys. Rev. A.* **41** (12), 7097–7100, (1990).

Chapter 22

The Mighty Force: Statistical Inference and High-Dimensional Statistics

Erik Aurell[*], Jean Barbier[†], Aurélien Decelle[‡] and Roberto Mulet[§]

*Department of Computational Science and Technology,
AlbaNova University Center, Sweden
eaurell@kth.se

†International Center for Theoretical Physics, Trieste, Italy
jbarbier@ictp.it

‡Departamento de Física Teorica, Universidad Complutense de Madrid, Spain
adecelle@ucm.es

§Department of Theoretical Physics, University of Havana, Cuba
mulet@fisica.uh.cu

Statistical inference, and high-dimensional statistics, is the tool by which, given a set of data, scientists are able to make predictions taking advantage of the correlations between various events or states living in a large dimensional space. While these methods have been widely used for decades, this chapter focuses on some particular examples where statistical mechanics helped make significant improvement in inverse problems. Through the prism of direct coupling analysis and community detection models, we emphasize how to bring new insights and to shed light on both the inference and learning tasks using a physicist's perspective.

Full well hath Clifford play'd the orator,
Inferring arguments of mighty force.
— *Henry VI*, Part 3, Act II, Scene II.

22.1. Introduction

Inference is an English noun formed on the verb *infer*, from the Latin *inferre*, meaning to carry (fero) in or into (in-) something. That originally concrete meaning can still be felt in the portal quote of this chapter. In modern non-technical use the meaning of inference is more abstract, and rendered either as "A conclusion reached on the basis of evidence and reasoning" or as "The process of reaching such a conclusion" [1]. In scientific language these translate into characteristics of a phenomenon that are not observed directly, but which are arrived at (inferred) from observations with the help of mathematical and/or statistical methods, and those methods themselves. We will discuss three prominent examples of inference in both senses of modern usage, and how they naturally open up new perspectives and possibilities.

423

Statistical physics is played out on the terrain between individual items and distributions over properties of items. The canonical example is the Langevin equation which describes the motion of a Brownian particle interacting with a thermal reservoir, and the Fokker-Planck equation which describes the evolution of the distribution of possible positions and velocities of the particle. In inference the goal can analogously be to reach one conclusion or retrieve one object, or to establish characteristics of a distribution over objects. The second kind of inference is also called *statistical inference*. We will here discuss inference in this sense.

In the "big-data era", statistical inference of different kinds is routinely performed based on data sets containing millions or even billions of samples, which themselves may live in spaces of tremendously large dimensionality. In this realm, classical statistical wisdom and tools fail: new mathematics and algorithms able to tackle the phenomena emerging in this regime are necessary. In the very same way, phase transitions were understood to emerge from the complexity (i.e. high-dimensionality) of physical systems more than a century ago, thanks to the development of statistical mechanics. It turns out that this is more than an analogy as the theory and methods to perform *high-dimensional inference* are directly connected to statistical mechanics as we will see in this chapter (and others in this book). High-dimensional inference itself is part of a broader statistical theory of complex systems, referred to as *high-dimensional statistics*, a very active research field at the crossroads of (statistical) physics, computer science, information theory and machine learning, and which is the powerhouse of modern information processing systems.

Let us now dive in some specific models whose richness, generality and wide applicability make them ideal candidates to showcase modern high-dimensional inference and its links with physics. A canonical example of statistical inference is to retrieve the interaction graph and the parameters of the interactions of an energy function of the Ising or Potts model type. In statistics the first task would be called *model learning* and the second *parameter inference*. All together the task would be referred to as *learning and inference in an exponential family* [2]. The set of Gibbs–Boltzmann distributions with unknown energy function is the model family, which in statistics is called exponential because the energy function appears in the exponent. In statistical physics the term *inverse Ising/Potts model* has been used [3]. We prefer to avoid this term since it is now well established, and discussed in detail in [3], that the best learning and inference procedure is not (or is rarely) to infer model parameters from means and correlations. We will instead use the term *Direct Coupling Analysis* (DCA) introduced in [4] which does not have the same restrictive connotation, and which encompasses several new aspects which have turned out to be very important in applications. Below we will discuss the distinguishing characteristics of DCA, its main methods applied, and successes in biological data analysis.

After DCA we will move towards the problem of *community detection* (COMDEC) — or graph partitioning —, the paradigmatic model of inference from an observed graph. The main focus of COMDEC is to partition a given graph into two or more communities, possibly without prior knowledge on the number of hidden communities or their statistical properties, such as the connectivity among the different communities or their fractions of nodes. In this model, whose study has quickly become a whole field of research [5, 6], one notable success of statistical physics has been to exhibit in the celebrated *stochastic block model (SBM)* the notion of phase where a given graph could not be distinguished by any mean from a purely random structure-less graph despite the fact that it has been built according to a process dependent on hidden communities (i.e. sets of nodes sharing the same property). Of course, this is true in the thermodynamic limit where the number of nodes diverges. Digging deeper in the landscape of solutions of the problem, it has been then demonstrated the presence of interesting regimes such as when the true partition can be recovered information-theoretically, but is impossible in practice to retrieve without prior knowledge [7]. Other approaches from the physics community [8] have also emphasized the presence of retrieval and spin glass phases, suggesting that the design of new methods for clustering should be done with great care. We refer to Chapter 23 for a discussion of phase transitions in high-dimensional inference and learning, and Chapters 1, 19 and 32 for combinatorial optimization.

The Gibbs–Boltzmann distribution which underlies both DCA and COMDEC is the thermodynamic equilibrium of a system which exchanges energy with a thermal reservoir. In the weak-interaction limit this distribution is the fixed point of a stochastic process which satisfies detailed balance, e.g. the Metropolis–Hastings process. The parameters of the distribution are then related to the process rates and can be assimilated to causes, in opposition to correlations, which can be assimilated to effects.[a] Non-equilibrium dynamics which do not obey detailed balance on the other hand typically lead to distributions qualitatively different from Gibbs–Boltzmann, for a famous instance, see [9]. As a third contribution of statistical physics to statistical inference we will review attempts to extend the cavity method in order to describe data which is not generated by a process in detailed balance, and/or where one has access to a time series. This *dynamic cavity method* (DYNCAV) brings specific challenges compared to standard (static) cavity, which we will outline together with some advances and current problems.

To sum up, the purpose of the present chapter is to showcase a selection of contributions from the spin glass community at large to high-dimensional statistics, by focusing on three important "graph-based" models and methodologies having deeply impacted the field: inference *of* graphs (DCA), inference *from* graphs (COMDEC), and inference *from graphs encoding causal relations*, which is one of the motivations of (DYNCAV).

22.2. Direct Coupling Analysis (DCA)

22.2.1. *Definition, under-sampling, and evaluation criteria*

In this chapter we use DCA as the collective term encompassing a wide array of methods to arrive at point estimates of parameters in the exponential family of the Gibbs–Boltzmann distribution of Ising or Potts models. Point estimates means that the outcome of the analysis is one numerical value for each parameter. Ising and Potts

---

[a]This relation is the likely backdrop to "Direct Coupling" in the acronym DCA.

models have pairwise Hamiltonians, which for Ising models are over spins ($s_i = \pm 1$)

$$\mathcal{H}_{\mathbf{J},\mathbf{h}}(\mathbf{s}) = -\sum_i h_i s_i - \sum_{i<j} J_{ij} s_i s_j. \tag{22.1}$$

Up to a re-definition of the parameters, spin variables are equivalent to Boolean variables $b_i \in \{0, 1\}$. Potts models are analogously built on categorical variables $x_i \in \{1, 2, \ldots, q\}$.

In equilibrium statistical mechanics the probability of a configuration $\mathbf{s}$ is the Gibbs–Boltzmann distribution

$$p_{\mathbf{J},\mathbf{h}}(\mathbf{s}) = \frac{1}{\mathcal{Z}(T, \mathbf{J}, \mathbf{h})} \exp\left(-\frac{1}{k_B T} \mathcal{H}_{\mathbf{J},\mathbf{h}}(\mathbf{s}) \right). \tag{22.2}$$

In inference temperature is not relevant as it can always be absorbed in a redefinition of the parameters of the Hamiltonian. We will therefore from now on set $k_B T = 1$. The normalization $\mathcal{Z}$, the partition function, is then a functional of the Hamiltonian only, and given by

$$\mathcal{Z}(\mathbf{J}, \mathbf{h}) = \sum_{\mathbf{s}} \exp\left(-\mathcal{H}_{\mathbf{J},\mathbf{h}}(\mathbf{s}) \right). \tag{22.3}$$

DCA, the basic task: *Let $D = \{\mathbf{s}^{(m)}\}_{m \leq M}$ a set of independent samples of configurations of an Ising or Potts system, the parameters of which are unknown. The basic task of DCA is to infer the parameters from D.*

Obviously one could relax the assumption that the samples are independent. In most applications where DCA has been used successfully, samples have almost surely not been independent. However, dependence between samples is a complication and has been little investigated in the methodological literature, except under the assumption that they have been generated by a dynamics of known type (Glauber model [10, 11] or parallel dynamics [12]). On the other hand, in this setting other methods are available which take advantage of access to time series data *cf.* [13]. We will therefore throughout assume that samples are independent draws from the same probability distribution.

The number of parameters of a general Ising model on N spins is $N(N + 1)/2$, and correspondingly larger for a Potts model. Each of the M samples consists of N Boolean variables (categorical variables for the Potts model). It is easy to imagine that for many data sources, M can be of the order of N, if not less. Such problems are *under-sampled*. Indeed, in the flagship application of DCA to biological data reviewed below in Sec. 22.2.5, a protein typically consists of $10^2 - 10^3$ amino acids (N), a protein family would often consist of $10^4 - 10^5$ proteins (M), and there are 20 amino acids (q), hence $\alpha \equiv qMN/(q^2 N^2) \approx 1$. We find this sufficiently important to state it as

DCA, distinguishing property: *Real-world applications of DCA are usually under-sampled: the amount of data is of the order of the number of parameters, and sometimes less. Any version of DCA intended for practical use hence has to be evaluated in the under-sampled regime.*

If the number of samples M is less than the number of parameters N, it is not possible to infer all parameters. A natural assumption is to then use supplementary conditions. *Sparsity* in general refers to the situation where a fraction of all parameters are known to be zero; if the remaining fraction of non-zero parameters is small enough, it is (in principle) possible to infer them. We here only state the empirical fact that sparsity assumptions and L_1 penalties have (up to now) not been very useful in DCA applications. Usually a much simpler L_2 penalty (which does not enforce sparsity) has given more useful predictions. We posit that the reason is the following:

DCA, importance of criteria: *In real-world applications of DCA one is rarely or never interested in all the parameters. In practice, one is interested in a small subset of leading predictions, typically the inferred parameters of largest numerical value.*

We note that if the task is from the outset formulated as retrieving the k largest parameters where k is much less than N^2 and also less than M, the problem is no longer under-sampled. All successful applications of DCA known to us are in fact of this type. The task of inferring the k largest parameters in the Hamiltonian from M samples with some given inference procedure is a mathematically well-defined problem. Some (not all) of the procedures to be reviewed below are *statistically consistent*, meaning that given an infinite number of samples they will almost surely return the correct value. A problem which has been much less studied is the spread around the correct value given finite number of samples. We formulate this as

DCA, a problem in extreme value statistics: *Given M independent samples from a Gibbs–Boltzmann distribution of an Ising/Potts model and a DCA procedure, find the probability distribution of the k largest inferred model parameters.*

An obvious analogy showing that the problem is not trivial is the Marchenko–Pastur distribution of empirical (sample) correlations from a distribution with given ensemble (model) correlations[b] [14]. An equally obvious complication is that computing correlations is a linear transformation of the data,[c] while all DCA procedures are nonlinear transformations. For the pseudo-likelihood maximization method (PLM, see below) and assuming that the Ising coupling parameters J_{ij} are independent random variables of typical amplitude $N^{-\frac{1}{2}}$, the expected mean square error of the inferred parameters was computed in [15] and [16] using the replica and cavity methods. More recently this analysis was extended to the dilute case [17], i.e. when the known interaction matrix is locally tree-like, again with the use of replica and cavity methods.

The full probability distribution of the retrieved parameters has to our knowledge only been considered theoretically in [18], for J_{ij} distributed as in the Sherrington-Kirkpatrick model, and for an L_2-regularized naive mean-field inference, a DCA procedure which can be implemented as a nonlinear matrix transformation [19]. Some

---

[b]Marchenko–Pastur relates the sample correlation matrix $\mathbf{C}^*$ to the ensemble correlation $\mathbf{C}$ of the underlying probability law. For models of the Ising/Potts type $\mathbf{C}$ is a function of the parameters $\mathbf{J}$ (forward Ising/Potts problem). At the same time, some versions of DCA infer parameters $\mathbf{J}^*$ from $\mathbf{C}^*$ (inverse Ising/Potts problem solved by naive mean-field or TAP). For these versions of DCA Marchenko–Pastur hence implies a complicated but in principle precise probabilistic relation between $\mathbf{J}$ and $\mathbf{J}^*$. More generally, for versions of DCA that do not rely on correlations, e.g. pseudo-likelihood maximization, there should be an analogous though so far imperfectly known probabilistic relation between $\mathbf{J}$ and $\mathbf{J}^*$ which does not go through ensemble and sample correlations.
[c]For simplicity, assume zero means.

numerical results for other and more uneven distributions of interaction parameters were reported in [20]. We believe that the issue merits further attention.

22.2.2. *Thermodynamics, maximum likelihood, and max-entropy*

As we have defined it above, DCA has aspects not germane to equilibrium statistical mechanics. Nevertheless, a relation obviously exists, and has been the source of inspiration for several important versions of DCA. Let us start from the Helmholtz free energy at a conventional value of $k_B T = 1$:

$$\mathcal{F}(\mathbf{J}, \mathbf{h}) = -\log \mathcal{Z}(\mathbf{J}, \mathbf{h}), \tag{22.4}$$

In the forward problem, the first and second order moments are given by derivatives of (22.4):

$$\chi_i = \langle s_i \rangle = -\frac{\partial \mathcal{F}}{\partial h_i}(\mathbf{J}, \mathbf{h}), \qquad \phi_{ij} = \langle s_i s_j \rangle = -\frac{\partial \mathcal{F}}{\partial J_{ij}}(\mathbf{J}, \mathbf{h}). \tag{22.5}$$

The correlation (covariance matrix) is defined by $\chi_{ij} = \phi_{ij} - \chi_i \chi_j$ and can also be expressed as

$$\chi_{ij} = -\frac{\partial^2 \mathcal{F}}{\partial h_i \partial h_j}(\mathbf{J}, \mathbf{h}). \tag{22.6}$$

In inference the roles of the parameters $\mathbf{J}, \mathbf{h}$ and the observables ϕ, χ are reversed: the latter are now fixed, the former to be determined. As noted in [21] one can construct a thermodynamic potential which is a function of the observables, the partial derivatives of which give the parameters. That potential is a Legendre transform of the Helmholtz free energy with respect to both couplings and fields:

$$\mathcal{S}(\phi, \chi) = \min_{\mathbf{J}, \mathbf{h}} \left[-\sum_i h_i \chi_i - \sum_{i<j} J_{ij} \phi_{ij} - \mathcal{F}(\mathbf{J}, \mathbf{h}) \right]. \tag{22.7}$$

It is immediate that this is the entropy of the Gibbs–Boltzmann distribution (22.2) as a function of magnetizations and correlations. Given that $\mathcal{S}$ is a convex function, the Helmholtz free energy is given by a second Legendre function of the entropy functional i.e.

$$\mathcal{F}(\mathbf{J}, \mathbf{h}) = \min_{\phi, \chi} \left[-\sum_i h_i \chi_i - \sum_{i<j} J_{ij} \phi_{ij} - S(\phi, \chi) \right]. \tag{22.8}$$

From this follows a second type of variational equations:

$$J_{ij} = -\frac{\partial \mathcal{S}}{\partial \phi_{ij}}(\phi, \chi), \qquad h_i = -\frac{\partial \mathcal{S}}{\partial \chi_i}(\phi, \chi). \tag{22.9}$$

Let us now assume M independent samples and the maximum likelihood criterion to infer parameters from samples. According to this criterion the best estimate $(\mathbf{J}, \mathbf{h})^{ML}$ based on the available data is given by

$$(\mathbf{J}, \mathbf{h})^{ML} = \arg \max_{(\mathbf{J}, \mathbf{h})} p(x_1, \ldots, x_M \mid (\mathbf{J}, \mathbf{h})). \tag{22.10}$$

For numerical reasons, it is common practice to maximize the average logarithm of the likelihood

$$\mathscr{L}_D(\mathbf{J}, \mathbf{h}) = \frac{1}{M} \log p(x_1, \ldots, x_M \mid \mathbf{J}, \mathbf{h}). \tag{22.11}$$

A penalty (for concreteness here L_2 penalty) in maximizing log-likelihood means to maximize instead

$$\mathscr{L}_D(\mathbf{J}, \mathbf{h})_\lambda = \frac{1}{M} \log p(D \mid \mathbf{J}, \mathbf{h}) - \sum_i \lambda_i |h_i|^2 - \sum_{ij} \lambda_{ij} |J_{ij}|^2. \tag{22.12}$$

Clearly this is the same as maximum likelihood with a modified probability distribution

$$p_{\lambda, D}(\mathbf{J}, \mathbf{h}) \sim \prod_{i=1}^M \exp\left(-\mathscr{H}_{\mathbf{J}, \mathbf{h}}(\mathbf{s}^{(i)}) - \sum_i \lambda_i |h_i|^2 - \sum_{ij} \lambda_{ij} |J_{ij}|^2\right). \tag{22.13}$$

For Ising parameters $\mathbf{J}, \mathbf{h}$ we can write the average log-likelihood more concretely as

$$\mathscr{L}_D(\mathbf{J}, \mathbf{h})_\lambda = \sum_i h_i \langle s_i \rangle_e + \sum_{ij} J_{ij} \langle s_i s_j \rangle_e + \mathcal{F}(\mathbf{J}, \mathbf{h})$$
$$- \sum_i \lambda_i |h_i|^2 - \sum_{ij} \lambda_{ij} |J_{ij}|^2 \tag{22.14}$$

where e stands for empirical expectation value, i.e. $\langle s_i \rangle_e = \frac{1}{M} \sum_{m=1}^M s_i^{(m)}$, etc. Since only empirical expectation values enter in the function to be maximized it follows that the optimal parameter values are determined only by them. This is true both with penalties and without. One says that these empirical expectation values are *sufficient statistics.*

Let us now consider the case without penalties. Maximizing the likelihood (22.14) with respect to $\mathbf{J}$ and $\mathbf{h}$ for given samples $D = \{\mathbf{s}^{(m)}\}_{m \leq M}$ is then the same as the minimization of the right-hand side of (22.7), but where the values of ensemble averages (the parameters in (22.7)) now take the values of the sample averages (the parameters in (22.14)). We state this important fact as

Max-entropy principle: *Maximum-likelihood inference of parameters in an exponential family is equivalent to maximizing the entropy of a probability distribution given empirical expectation values of the functions of the variables multiplying the parameters.*

A large literature starting from Jaynes assigns an independent epistemological importance to the max-entropy principle [22–24]. We rather subscribe to the alternative point of view that the undisputed practical utility of max-entropy is most easily explained by the importance of the maximum-likelihood inference criterion and the ubiquity of probability distributions in exponential families. In statistics this side has been argued in the framework of *information geometry* [25, 26]. An argument formulated in the language of DCA and applications to biological data analysis can be found in [27]. From the point of view of thermodynamics and statistical mechanics the most commonly held point of view is indeed that Gibbs–Boltzmann distributions have objective existence, and are not only expressions of ignorance and/or limits on what empirical averages can be determined. For a discussion with references to the literature on the foundations of statistical mechanics, see [28].

22.2.3. *The two main DCA methods: nMF and PLM*

Naive mean-field inference (nMF), or simply mean-field inference, is a versatile and computationally efficient DCA procedure which can be derived in several different ways. The most straightforward is to say that it treats probability distributions of the Ising/Potts type as if they were Gaussian probability distributions over continuous variables. The matrix of the quadratic form of the Gaussian is the inverse correlation matrix. The naive mean-field inference procedure applied to Ising variables is hence

$$\mathbf{J}_*^{nMF} = -\chi^{-1}, \tag{22.15}$$

where χ is the empirical correlation matrix and $*$ indicates inferred value. When the problem is under-sampled the empirical correlation matrix does not have full rank, and the inverse does not exist. *Regularized* nMF can hence be seen as regularized matrix inverse. L_2-regularized nMF is explicitly so, in that it can be written as as well-defined (and simple) matrix transformation [28]. L_1-regularized nMF was used in the DCA context in [29], and can be computed by convex optimization techniques. The breakthrough paper for DCA in biological applications [30] used a regularization with pseudo-counts which is equivalent to adding a matrix proportional to the identity to the empirical correlation matrix before taking the inverse. The naive mean-field inference formula (22.15) was first obtained in [31]. Other ways to obtain it can be found therein and in the standard methodological reference [3].

Pseudo-Likelihood Maximization (PLM) [32, 33] is computationally more demanding than nMF inference but, however, it has the advantage that it is statistically consistent. It has also proven to be a more accurate predictor in many applications. PLM is an attempt to match parameters not to the full probability distribution but only to the set of conditional probabilities of each variable conditioned on all the others. In the context of exponential models, optimization of the PseudoLikelihood function is particularly simple. The conditioned variables do not intervene in the normalization constant and the parameters related to these variables cancel out. Indeed, for Ising models the conditional probability of s_i under the observation of the other variables $\mathbf{s}_{\backslash i}$ is

$$p(s_i \mid \mathbf{s}_{\backslash i}) = \frac{1}{2}\left[1 + s_i \tanh\left(h_i + \sum_{j:j\neq i} J_{ij}s_j\right)\right] \tag{22.16}$$

which only depends on the field h_i and on the couplings $\{J_{ij}\}_{j:j\neq i}$. From this one can form the log-pseudo-likelihood per sample,

$$\mathscr{L}_D^i(\{J_{ij}\}_{j:j\neq i}, h_i) = \frac{1}{M}\sum_m \log\frac{1}{2}\left[1 + s_i^{(m)} \tanh\left(h_i + \sum_{j:j\neq i} J_{ij}s_j^{(m)}\right)\right] \tag{22.17}$$

which can be optimized over its N parameters. The log-pseudo-likelihood can be regularized in the same manner as log-likelihoods. The authors of [33], an article where the focus was on recovering the sparsity structure, used an L_1 penalty. In most later applications of DCA instead an L_2 penalty was used, following [34, 35].

It follows from above that the outcome of PLM is a set of values $h_{*,i}^{PLM}$, one for each i, and a set $J_{*,ij}^{PLM,i}, J_{*,ij}^{PLM,j}$, two for each pair (ij). The underlying probability distribution on the other hand only contains one parameter J_{ij} for each pair (ij). As part of PLM one therefore needs an output precedure. One possibility is to sum all the log-pseudo-likelihood functions (22.17) and maximize all parameters at the same time. This substitutes N optimization problem on N parameters with one optimization problem on $N(N+1)/2$ parameters. Typically this increases the computational burden. An alternative procedure is to take for the final inferred parameters the averages of the separately inferred values:

$$J_{*,ij}^{PLM} = (J_{*,ij}^{PLM,i} + J_{*,ij}^{PLM,j})/2. \tag{22.18}$$

In practice the second procedure is more used because it is computationally easier, and the first has not led to more accurate predictions.

22.2.4. *Advanced DCA methods*

Naive mean-field inference is built on a mean-field approximation of the thermodynamic potentials. This can be generalized by improving the approximation which has been done by adding an Onsager reaction term. The resulting inference procedure is called Thouless–Anderson–Palmer (TAP) [36] and substitutes the equality in (22.15) with a quadratic transformation [31]. TAP inference has also been derived by methods of information geometry [37, 38].

A second type of generalization is obtained by starting from more complicated trial functions. Considering all pair-wise trial functions together with correlation-response leads to an iterative procedure called *susceptibility propagation* [39]. Later it was shown that the fixed point of susceptibility propagation can be computed in closed form [40, 41]. This gives an inference formula of the same general form as (22.15) involving trancendental functions but still factorized over parameters to be retrieved. For appropriately chosen models all the above methods outperform naive mean-field inference. Still, these methods are limited when the samples are drawn from "clusterized" dataset, such as low-temperature samples from the Ising model [42, 43]. For a unified treatment, see [3].

A major advance in the analysis of PLM and similar DCA algorithms was obtained in [15, 16, 44, 45] building on earlier results in [33] and [46]. In all these papers were proven results of the type that perfect structure recovery is achievable with only $M \sim \log N$ samples when the interaction graph is sparse, that there is a gap between the smallest nonzero coupling and the set of strictly zero couplings, and that successively weakened additional assumptions. In [44] it was shown for the regularized interaction screening estimator (RISE) algorithm that if the goal is to recover top-k predictions a gap is not needed, and in [45] a similar result was shown for PLM (in Sec. S1 of Supplementary Material). The authors of [44] showed that RISE is asymptotically optimal (in a certain sense) and rigorously better than PLM (under certain assumptions). In [15] a further level of optimality was considered when some summary characteristics of the distributions over parameters was assumed known, and the optimum was computed using the replica method. At this time, all these methodological advances are however limited to bounded maximum interaction strength and bounded degree of the interaction graph.

22.2.5. *DCA in computational biology*

The origins of the interest in DCA for biological data analysis can be traced to maximum-entropy arguments advanced in [47]. In the terminology of above, that paper proposed naive mean-field inference of an Ising model. Four years earlier, in a paper never published in a major journal, and therefore for a long time not widely known, it was proposed in [48] that the parameters of a Potts model inferred from protein sequences in a protein family are good predictors of physical proximity. Such amino acid-amino acid spatial contacts (residue-residue contacts) contain important information on protein structure, non-local in the sequence. It can therefore be used (and was later used) as part of a protein structure prediction pipeline. Residue-residue contacts also make sense as an evolutionary mechanism which contributes to the total biological fitness of the organism. The technical term for such non-additive contributions to biological fitness is *epistasis*. The relation between epistasis and DCA was reviewed in [49] and [50].

The flavour of DCA used in [48] was maximum likelihood, computed by an iterative method. The same problem was later addressed for a well-characterized family of bacterial signal transduction pathways [4]. Since for that data it proved possible to predict physical contacts between enzymes in the pathway which could be validated from other points of view, this was an important step forward toward biological relevance. The DCA implemented in [4] was however susceptibility propagation [39] and thus also fairly computationally costly. At the same time residue-residue contacts were derived from tables of sequences by another method not explicitly in the DCA family [51].

The first result using DCA to predict residue-residue contacts in proteins and which had wide resonance used naive mean-field inference [30], with a regularization using pseudo-counts. DCA built on mean-field inference with other regularization schemes were introduced in the same application area in [19, 29, 52]. The second main type of DCA in computational biology has been pseudo-likelihood maximization [34, 35, 53], and has been considered somewhat superior to naive mean-field inference in this application domain [54]. Later versions of DCA on the protein structure prediction problem were meta-algorithms incorporating also other information sources [55–58]; although exhibiting higher performance they (and the earlier undiluted DCA methods) have more recently been overtaken by AI/deep learning methods [59, 60]. For other biological inference tasks with less abundant training data and/or where the goal is to uncover new biology, DCA (usually either mean-field of pseudo-likelihood) remains an important tool *cf.* [61–67].

To end on a forward perspective, we consider human genome data. The human genome contains about $3 \cdot 10^9$ nucleotides out of which about $60 \cdot 10^6$ are in exons (parts of genes that code for proteins). About a decade ago several large meta-studies on the origin of human obesity were published in leading journals where M (total number of patients) was on the order of hundred of thousands or millions [68–70]. Those studies were mainly built on exon sequencing, and with some filtering out of amino acids fixed or almost fixed in the whole human population, the effective number of loci of variability (N) was on the order of millions. The under-sampling ratio ($\sim M/N$) was hence in these studies from order one to order 10^{-2}. We formulate the challenges which pose themselves as

DCA, human-scale genomic data: *To design smart speed-ups yielding interesting predictions and are computationally feasible on the human exome scale ($N \sim 10^6$) and eventually on the human genome scale ($N \sim 10^9$).*

We note that determining the largest elements or set of largest elements of large correlation matrices is known in computer science as "the light bulb problem". The challenge can hence be considered an analogous problem from the perspective of DCA. While the light bulb problem is not computationally hard (the elementary algorithm scales as N^2) it is still not trivial in practice when N is in the range of millions or billions. Advanced algorithms are known to work in sub-quadratic time, but with significant pre-factors, and only appear to become competitive for N as large as 10^5 [71].

22.2.6. *From DCA to Restricted Boltzmann Machines*

While all the previous approaches to DCA are concerned with the inference of pairwise interactions of an underlying statistical model, it is quite natural to consider generalizations that can also adjust for higher moments of the distribution. The most (seemingly) natural way would be to add higher-order terms in the Hamiltonian. However, this seems unreasonable since in order to include all possible terms of n-body interactions, the number of parameters to add is of order $\mathcal{O}(N^n)$. To avoid this issue, it is possible to use hidden-variable models. In these models, it is considered that a subset of nodes is not observed in the dataset but can still help in the modelization of the statistical properties when integrating them out. When integrated, they create effective many-body interactions between the variables to which they are connected. This type of approach has given rise to the celebrated Restricted Boltzmann Machine in the field of Machine Learning [72, 73].

RBM, definition and learning: *To design a practical machine, the Hamiltonian of the model is defined on a bipartite graph. A first layer regroup the variables that are observed (from the dataset), named visible nodes, while the other layer is made of hidden nodes whose role is to induce effective interactions between those in the first layer.*

In its formulation, we usually distinguish the notation between the visible, s_i, and the hidden nodes τ_a, yet both of them takes value in ± 1. This led to the following Hamiltonian:

$$H_{\mathbf{w},\mathbf{h}}(\mathbf{s}, \boldsymbol{\tau}) = -\sum_{ia} w_{ia} s_i \tau_a - \sum_i h_i s_i - \sum_a h_a \tau_a. \tag{22.19}$$

The bipartite structure, the fact that there is no coupling between two visible nodes or two hidden nodes, is a crucial aspect here to make Monte Carlo sampling much easier than in a fully connected model, making it practical to use the maxium likelihood approach in order to learn the parameters $\mathbf{w}, \mathbf{h}$. As one can see from (22.19), the distribution over the set of visible nodes, after integrating the hidden nodes, is no longer an exponential distribution and in particular, can adjust for higher moments of the dataset. This model has been used in the context of proteins [74–76], but has not shown further progress in the contact prediction task, and is thus more dedicated to extract useful features from a given dataset.

22.3. Community Detection: The Art of Inferring Clusters in a Spin Glass World

In the COMDEC problem, rather than inferring the parameters of the model like in DCA, the goal is the following: given a graph and an hypothesis on the nature of the interactions between its nodes, one has to infer the nodes states (i.e. the "community" to which each node belongs to). The two standard hypotheses on the interactions are the *assortative* case, meaning that the graph has been generated in a way that connections are statistically more present between nodes of the same community; this, in turns, make this problem a cousin of the Ising model (or Potts model when there are more than two hidden communities) with ferromagnetic interactions on a random graph. It is relevant to model, e.g. friendships on social networks where people with similar opinions tend to be more friends. In the *disassortative* case it is the opposite: links between members of different communities are favored, relating this model to an anti-ferromagnetic spin model. Ecological networks of predators-preys are of this nature.

To deal with this kind of problem, a successful approach has been to design a generative model that, given certain parameters, generates a graph where communities have been planted by construction. The paradigmatic generative model for graphs encoding community structures is the Stochastic Block Model (SBM) [5, 6, 77]. With the SBM and its parameters in hand, it is then possible to design an inference procedure for the community structure, with the parameters being known. But also a learning algorithm which intend to estimate the values of the parameters given a particular family of models.

The Stochastic Block Model: *The SBM is a generative model of graphs with communities. As is often the case in Bayesian inference, first a generative model is defined before working out the form of the posterior distribution needed in order to estimate the parameters of the model.*

Many heuristic approaches have been considered for COMDEC [78]. For instance simple spectral methods were developed in order to partition a graph using the eigenvectors of variations of the adjacency matrix and/or Laplacian of the graph; later we are going to present state-of-the-art spectral clustering algorithms. But the lack of a proper model for how the graph communities were generated prevented to do much better than these simple approaches. The SBM was designed for that purpose. It is rooted on random graphs with additional ingredients forcing the network to develop a partition in the generation process. The ingredients are:

- the probabilities $\{n_a\}_{a \leq q}$ of a node to belong to the community $a \in \{1, \ldots, q\}$;
- the probability matrix $\{p_{ab}\}_{a,b \leq q}$ to have a link between two randomly chosen nodes, one in community a and the other in b;

- a hidden (or "planted") partition of the nodes into q communities or groups: $\{t_i\}_{i \leq N} \in \{1, \ldots, q\}^N$.

Major differences arise when considering different scaling regimes. In the *dense regime* of the SBM, meaning $p_{ab} = \mathcal{O}(1)$ when $N \to +\infty$, the generated graphs have many $(\mathcal{O}(N^2))$ links, each node being connected to $\mathcal{O}(N)$ other ones. The *logarithmic degree regime* corresponds to $p_{ab} = \mathcal{O}(\ln(N)/N)$ [79]. Finally, in the *sparse regime* $p_{ab} = c_{ab}/N = \mathcal{O}(1/N)$ the generated graphs have $\mathcal{O}(N)$ links and most nodes are connected to a finite number of other ones in the thermodynamic limit, up to few "hubs". In the dense regime, the communities can be read off from the degrees of the nodes, which makes the inference task rather straightforward using standard spectral methods. The real challenge arises in the sparse case, where completely novel ideas are needed, from a conceptual and algorithmic point of views, and where techniques from spin glasses have been particularly fruitful. We will thus focus on this sparse regime.

We now expose the four main algorithmic approaches which have altogether lead to a leap forward in the understanding of the COMDEC problem. We start with the Bayesian inference approach, given that it is in this context that one of the most striking phenomenon in COMDEC/SBM has been discovered: below the *detectability transition*, it is information-theoretically impossible to distinguish a graph generated from the SBM from a purely random one.

22.3.1. *Approach 1: Bayesian inference*

Given the parameters of the SBM and under the assumption that the nodes partition and the observed graph G (parametrized by its edges A_{ij} between nodes i and j) were drawn according to this generative model, it is possible to write down the joint law of G and the partition:

$$P(G = \{A_{ij}\}, \{t_i\} \mid \{n_a\}, \{p_{ab}\}) = P(G \mid \{t_i\}, \{n_a\}, \{p_{ab}\})P(\{t_i\} \mid \{n_a\})$$
$$= \prod_{i<j} p_{t_i t_j}^{A_{ij}} \left(1 - p_{t_i t_j}\right)^{1-A_{ij}} \prod_i n_{t_i}. \tag{22.20}$$

Hence, the probability to put a link between two nodes now depends on the community of each node and the probability to have a link precisely between those two nodes.

Inference of the groups: *Having defined our generative model, we need to decide how to infer the probability that a given node of the graph belongs to one of the possible groups.*

With this generative model it is now theoretically possible to infer the nodes states by computing their marginal probabilities to belong to one of the communities. This can be done using Bayes theorem. Given parameters $\{n_a\}$ and $\{p_{ab}\}$ (in addition to G) the posterior reads

$$P(\{t_i\} \mid G, \{n_a\}, \{p_{ab}\}) = \frac{P(G, \{t_i\} \mid \{n_a\}, \{p_{ab}\})}{\sum_{\{t_i\}} P(G, \{t_i\} \mid \{n_a\}, \{p_{ab}\})}. \tag{22.21}$$

It relates the probability of an assignment to the generative model that we defined in (22.20). This distribution can be rephrased as the Gibbs–Boltzmann distribution of a

Potts model by taking (minus) the log of the un-normalized probability (22.21) (recall that $p_{ab} = c_{ab}/N$):

$$\mathcal{H}(\{t_i\}) = -\sum_i \log n_{t_i} - \sum_{(ij)\in\mathcal{E}} \log p_{t_i t_j} - \sum_{(ij)\notin\mathcal{E}} \log(1 - p_{t_i t_j})$$

$$= -\sum_i \log n_{t_i} - \sum_{(ij)\in\mathcal{E}} \log c_{t_i t_j} + \frac{1}{N} \sum_{(ij)\notin\mathcal{E}} c_{t_i t_j} + C \qquad (22.22)$$

(where the second equality is true up to a negligible $o(N)$ correction) with $\mathcal{E} = \{(ij): A_{ij} = 1\}$ is the set of edges of G, and C is an irrelevant constant. It is possible to write the first term as $-\sum_{i,a} \delta_{a,t_i} \log n_a$, and the second one too using a similar trick with Potts interacting terms δ_{a,t_i} and δ_{b,t_j} living on the interaction graph G. The third term is interesting because it describes an interaction between nodes that do *not* share an edge, which is rather uncommon in typical disordered spin systems.

Both edges and non-edges contain information: *A specific feature of the SBM is that not only an observed edge of G yields information, but also the absence of an edge does so. Each edge results in a $\mathcal{O}(1)$ interaction in the equivalent Potts model, which, e.g. is ferromagnetic in the assortative case; absence of an edge yields a "weak" $\mathcal{O}(1/N)$ interaction term, which overall competes with the "edge" interactions due to their large number.*

Hence, the inference task of computing the marginals in the SBM is equivalent to the estimation of the local mean magnetizations of a peculiar Potts model, with a field generated by the non-edges which prevents the Potts variables to end up in a ferromagnetic state where most have same value. Said differently, this field enforces phase separation, i.e. appearance of separated communities. The standard approach for sampling would be to use Monte Carlo methods, but, as we will see, Belief Propagation (or equivalently the cavity method) can be used in a very efficient way.

The second task is to estimate, or learn, the parameters of the model. Again using the Bayes theorem, we can write a posterior probability distribution but this time on the parameters:

$$P(\{n_a\}, \{p_{ab}\} \mid G) = \frac{P(G \mid \{n_a\}, \{p_{ab}\})P(\{n_a\}, \{p_{ab}\})}{P(G)}. \qquad (22.23)$$

Without being too specific, the simplest case to deal with is by considering the absence of prior on the parameters, and to look only at a (possibly local) maximum of the probability distribution by performing a gradient ascent. The above expression therefore tells us that we need to maximize the free energy $\ln P(\{n_a\}, \{p_{ab}\} \mid G)$ of our SBM with respect to the parameters. Interestingly, this gradient can be expressed in terms of the mean values computed during the inference problem, and using the expectation-maximization method we get the following iterative algorithm:

$$p_{ab}^{t+1} = \frac{1}{n_a n_b} \sum_{(ij)\in\mathcal{E}} \langle \delta_{t_i,a}\delta_{t_j,b}\rangle_t, \qquad n_a^{t+1} = \frac{1}{N}\sum_i \langle \delta_{t_i,a}\rangle_t, \qquad (22.24)$$

where $\langle\cdot\rangle_t$ means an average taken using the parameters at iteration t.

Learning the parameters of the models: *In the context of the RBM, it is also possible using the Bayes theorem to define a learning algorithm to estimate the graph's parameters if unknown.*

22.3.2. *Phase diagram and the detectability transition*

The inference performance in the SBM has received particular attention in the symmetric case, where the intra-community and inter-community connectivity is the same for all groups: $c_{aa} = c_{\mathrm{in}}$, $c_{ab} = c_{\mathrm{out}}$. Tuning the difference between these values allows to interpolate between graphs where no communities are present (by imposing that an edge is present between two nodes independently of the node's group) and thus inference is impossible, to a regime where the graph is made of disconnected clusters and inference is trivial. It was shown in [80] that along this interpolation, the model exhibits a second order phase transition between a paramagnetic phase, where no information can be retrieved on the communities (in the large size limit) to a condensed phase where the equilibrium properties of the Boltzmann distribution are dominated by a state with a strong overlap with the planted community: this is the *detectability transition* which has revived the research on COMDEC. It was later on rigorously validated [81–83] (including in more general settings, see [5]).

Detectability threshold in the two-groups symmetric SBM: *For a graph drawn from the SBM, non-trivial inference of the communities is possible in the large size limit if and only if $(c_{\mathrm{in}} - c_{\mathrm{out}})^2 > 2(c_{\mathrm{in}} + c_{\mathrm{out}})$. If this condition is not met, it is impossible to distinguish a graph from the SBM from a purely random one.*

In both the sparse and dense regimes when the inference occurs on the "Nishimori line" of the Hamiltonian [84], i.e. is done in the Bayesian optimal regime where the SBM parameters are known, it implies that no spin glass phase can be present as strong concentration-of-measure effects take place; this is true more generically for optimal Bayesian inference problems [85]. Therefore the replica symmetric solution for the free energy is exact [86–89].

The phase diagram of the model can be obtained by investigating the local stability of the Belief Propagation (BP) equations close to the paramagnetic fixed point. The BP equations for the SBM are given by

$$\psi^{i \to j}(t_i) \propto n_{t_i} \prod_{k \neq j, i} \sum_{t_k} p_{t_i t_k}^{A_{ik}} \left(1 - p_{t_i t_k}\right)^{1 - A_{ik}} \psi^{k \to i}(t_k) \tag{22.25}$$

where $\psi^{i \to j}$ is the marginal of node i when the link (ij) has been removed. We note again the interesting property of the SBM that "non-edges" yield a contribution in the BP equation. In the symmetric case discussed in the previous paragraph, we can therefore easily identify the paramagnetic fixed point as the one where all the BP messages are uniform $\psi^{i \to j}(t_i) = 1/q$. The perturbation near this solution can be used to find the parameters at which the condensed phase starts, i.e. when the paramagnetic fixed point becomes unstable. It is to be noted that this is the analog to the de Almeida–Thouless line for spin glasses [90].

This description is not always correctly describing the physics of the problem. In fact, the presence of a first order phase transition can complicate the phase diagram.

It is possible to verify if it is the case by analyzing the metastable states nearby the planted community structure. In [7], it is shown that when dealing with some graph's parameters (higher connectivity and number of communities), the SBM can have this type of dynamical transitions preventing efficient algorithms to infer the groups, yielding even richer phase diagrams with, standing in between the detectability transition and the dynamical one, the presence of an algorithmically "hard phase" (also called statistical-to-computational gap). In this phase, the communities do have a statistical reality, yet the inference process is plagued by the "paramagnetic" solution to which the BP algorithm converges in absence of good initial condition provided by an oracle. To distinguish clearly which of the two states (possible recovery or not) dominates the equilibrium distribution and hence to understand if the planted solution is statistically distinguishable from the paramagnetic one, it is enough to compare the free energy of both states. We end up with a picture where the physics of phase-coexistence explains here the different phases of the inference process in the SBM. This past decade it has been understood that the same type of phase diagram and phenomenology holds more generically in a broad class of high-dimensional Bayesian inference and learning problems such as, e.g. in the generalized linear model [91]; see Chapter 22.

Statistical-to-computational gap: *For certain parameters of the SBM with more than two communities, a dynamical transition may prevent efficient algorithms to saturate the detectability transition: an algorithmically hard phase emerges. This phenomenon occurs in many other high-dimensional inference problems.*

The learning equations (22.24) can also be analyzed in some restricted cases [92]. Interestingly, for a given type of graphs parametrized by the degree structure and number of communities, it is possible to understand whether the EM equations can learn the true graph's parameters. Again, the typical phase diagram is made of distinct regions. First, an uninformative region, where basically the learning dynamics is stuck. This region encompasses both the regime where the created graph has no statistically relevant community structure and also a regime where the communities are present but the dynamics is not able to drive the parameters toward their correct values. Finally, in the last region, the EM equations might bring the meta-parameters to their correct values.

22.3.3. *Approach 2: Modularity optimization*

While in the previous section COMDEC was settled by using first a generative model and second an inference algorithm to recover the graph's structure conditionally on this model, other approaches have studied settings where the model mismatched the dataset, which is particularly relevant when dealing with real data for which the generative process is unknown. One of these approaches [93, 94] is based on the maximization of the *modularity* of the graph. Given a graph and the degree k_i of each nodes, the modularity for partitioning two clusters is given by

$$Q(s \mid G, \mathbf{k}) = \frac{1}{4M} \sum_{i<j} \left(A_{ij} - \frac{k_i k_j}{2M} \right) s_i s_j, \tag{22.26}$$

M being the total number of edge and the variables s_i represents the group assignment (here ± 1) of a given node. The modularity tends to optimize the number of edges within a community with respect to the expected number of edges resulting from a random graph. In the first approaches, the modularity was optimized in order to find the best possible partition of the nodes. Yet, since the problem is hard, it is probably impossible to design a polynomial algorithm that finds in general the optimal value of Q. This problem was then addressed in two successive works [8, 95] where a temperature is introduced in order to define the Gibbs–Boltzmann distribution associated to the modularity:

$$P(\boldsymbol{s} \mid G, \mathbf{k}) = \frac{\exp\left(-M\beta Q(\boldsymbol{s} \mid G, \mathbf{k})\right)}{\mathcal{Z}(G, \mathbf{k})}. \tag{22.27}$$

The effect of the temperature is to help avoiding possible overfitting of the modularity, since the marginals obtained by this mean have now to take into account the entropy of the inferred clusters. With this approach it is now possible to study the phase diagram of the model in temperature and as a function of the true graph parameters when dealing with networks generated by the SBM for instance. Interestingly, a spin glass phase is often found at low enough temperature, implying that the optimization problem becomes very hard. At the same time, it emerges a retrieval phase where the communities can be retrieved easily, and which underlines the importance of correctly selecting the temperature.

22.3.4. *Approach 3: Spectral clustering*

A particularly fruitful approach to COMDEC is spectral clustering. Spectral algorithms are very practical, given that they use only basic linear algebra (eigen-decomposition and singular value decomposition) to partition the graph. All the point is therefore to design smartly the matrices to analyze. Variations of the adjacency matrix $\mathbf{A}$ of the graph or of its graph Laplacian $\mathbf{L} = \mathbf{D} - \mathbf{A}$ ($\mathbf{D}$ being the diagonal matrix of nodes degrees) are natural choices [96], but all suffer from the curse of eigenvector localization: their eigenvectors tend to encode local graph structures (like atypical nodes of high connectivity) rather than global ones such as potential communities. But much better choices exist.

A breakthrough in COMDEC came from the discovery that by analyzing the so-called *non-backtracking matrix* $\mathbf{B}$ introduced in the theory of zeta functions [97], one could recover the communities in the SBM down to the detectability threshold whenever no hard phase is present, or down to the best known algorithmic threshold (set by BP), see [98]. This matrix indexed by the directed edges $i \to j \in \mathcal{E}_d$ of the graph ($\mathcal{E}_d$ being of size twice the one of the edge set $\mathcal{E}$) is defined as

$$B_{i \to j, k \to \ell} = \delta_{jk}(1 - \delta_{i\ell}) \tag{22.28}$$

and therefore encodes all possible non-backtracking paths of length two of the graph. As such it is also called "edge adjacency operator". When the graph is sparse, its dimension is of the same order as the number of nodes. Considering again the two-groups symmetric SBM, let the average degree be $c = (c_{\text{in}} + c_{\text{out}})/2$. The key properties of this non-symmetric matrix $\mathbf{B}$ are: (i) it is much less sensitive to the eigenvector localization problem (i.e. to atypical high-degree nodes) than standard operators; (ii) its complex eigenvalues are (asymptotically) confined in a the complex disk of radius $\sqrt{c}$ except for two real eigenvalues $\lambda_1 \approx c$ and $\lambda_2 \approx (c_{\mathrm{in}} - c_{\mathrm{out}})/2$; (iii) the eigenvector $\boldsymbol{v}$ associated with λ_2 is strongly correlated to the hidden communities. More precisely, letting $\hat{t}_i = \mathrm{sign} \sum_{j:j\to i\in\mathcal{E}_d} v_{j\to i}$, then $\{\hat{t}_i\}_{i\leq N}$ correlates with the hidden community structure almost as well as the BP estimate, itself conjectured optimal among polynomial algorithms and information-theoretically optimal when there is no statistical-computational gap (like in the two-groups symmetric SBM).

Why does the spectral algorithm associated to the non-backtracking matrix behave so similarly to BP? Simply because they are closely related. We mentioned already in the Sec. 22.3.2 that the phase diagram of the inference in the SBM could be studied through a linearization of the BP equations around the paramagnetic fixed point. But this idea can also be turned into a spectral algorithm as follows. Still considering the symmetric two-groups SBM, let the BP messages close to the paramagnetic solution be $\psi^{i\to j}(\pm 1) = 1/2 \pm \delta^{i\to j}$. Thus, the vector $\boldsymbol{\delta}$ quantifies the first order deviation of the BP messages around the paramagnetic fixed point. Then the linearization of the BP equation can be re-written as

$$\mathbf{B}\,\boldsymbol{\delta} = \left(\frac{c_{\mathrm{in}} + c_{\mathrm{out}}}{c_{\mathrm{in}} - c_{\mathrm{out}}} \right) \boldsymbol{\delta}. \tag{22.29}$$

Therefore the "BP message deviation" $\boldsymbol{\delta}$ is an eigenvector of the non-backtracking operator $\mathbf{B}$. It thus makes sense that this spectral approach matches closely BP, at least close to its paramagnetic transition. That its performance remains so good far from it is a surprising fact.

Belief Propagation inspired spectral algorithms: *By defining a matrix related to the linearization of the BP equations around its paramagnetic non-informative fixed point, it is possible to saturate the BP performance using its spectral analysis, even without knowing the parameters of the model.*

These desirable properties extend when considering more than two communities: the estimator extracted from $\mathbf{B}$ remains competitive with the BP one until the BP algorithmic transition. Interestingly, the number of real eigenvalues escaping the disk in the complex plane even indicates the number of hidden communities while BP needs that prior information. So it seems that this spectral approach solves all problems at once: it is simply based on linear algebra, robust to localization and competitive with BP. But there are two catches. Firstly, even if the average degree of the graph is bounded the size of this (directed) edges-indexed matrix $\mathbf{B}$ can quickly become unpractical when it comes to diagonalize it. Moreover it is non-symmetric while numerical routines for linear algebra tend to be much more optimized for symmetric matrices. Secondly, despite being robust to localization, it turns out to be hyper sensitive to other type of "noises", i.e. to deviations from the ideal setting where the graph is locally tree-like as in the sparse SBM. One example noticed, e.g. in [99–101] is the appearance of very few small cliques (fully connected sub-graphs) in the graph G which completely breaks apart the approach of [98] based on $\mathbf{B}$. See also [102, 103] for robustness issues.

The first issue on the computational cost has been solved by introducing another linear operator $\mathbf{H}$ sharing the same desirable properties of the non-backtracking operator while being symmetric and of smaller size $N \times N$: it is the *Bethe Hessian* [104] (recall k_i are the nodes degrees)

$$H_{ij}(r) = (r^2 - 1 + k_i)\delta_{ij} - rA_{ij}. \tag{22.30}$$

It can be shown that any r such that $\mathbf{H}$ possesses a vanishing eigenvalue corresponds to a real eigenvalue of the non-backtracking operator, thus its similar properties. Moreover, the minimum of its non-informative bulk of eigenvalues reaches 0 when $r \approx \sqrt{c}$, so that the informative isolated eigenvalues whose associated eigenvectors correlate with the community structure are on the negative axis, a quite convenient property. The name of this matrix comes from the fact that it is proportional to the Hessian of the Bethe free energy (the matrix of second derivatives with respect to the spin magnetizations) of an Ising model living on the edges of the graph G, evaluated at the paramagnetic solution. The approach has also been extended to a close relative of the COMDEC problem, namely tensor principal components analysis. The authors of [105] defined the *Kikuchi Hessian* which, as the name suggests, is related to the Hessian of the Kikuchi free energy, a hierarchical free energy approximation whose first order is the tree approximation (i.e. Bethe free energy) and that takes more and more local structures (such as loops) into account at the next levels of the hierarchy [106]. But despite its many advantages, like the non-backtracking operator, the Bethe Hessian fails whenever the graph is not "locally tree-like enough", see the previous references.

An elegant proposal to cure this latter issue of lack of robustness of spectral approaches is the *X-Laplacian* $\mathbf{L}_X = \mathbf{A} + \mathbf{X}$ [101]. In this rather generic method to solve the eigenvector localization problem and improve noise robustness, a problem-dependent fine tuned Laplacian matrix is iteratively computed by regularizing the adjacency matrix $\mathbf{A}$ with a diagonal $\mathbf{X}$ strongly penalizing eigenvectors which are localized (roughly meaning that their norm is dominated by a few/sub-linear fraction of the components). Along the iterations of the learning procedure the most localized eigenvectors of $\mathbf{L}_X$ among those paired with the top eigenvalues living towards the end of the bulk, and which hide the informative eigenvalues/eigenvectors, are pushed back inside the bulk by the learned regularization $\mathbf{X}$. This has for effect to "uncover" the informative eigenvalues, left untouched by the procedure as their associated eigenvectors were delocalized in the first place.

22.3.5. *Approach 4: Convex relaxation*

Another success story is an algorithm rooted in computer science: convex relaxation and semi-definite programming [107]. In [99] it is proposed to recover the communities in the symmetric two-groups SBM as follows. First, notice that an SBM instance can be mapped onto the $\mathbb{Z}_2$-*synchronization problem* [86]: infer $\mathbf{x} \in \{-1, 1\}^N$ given the gaussian corrupted observations

$$Y_{ij} \sim \mathcal{N}(m = \gamma N^{-1/2} x_i x_j, \sigma^2 = 1), \quad 1 \leq i < j \leq N. \tag{22.31}$$

An heuristic argument to see the connection with the SBM goes as follows: edges being present or not are, conditionally on the planted partition, independent Bernoulli random variables $A_{ij} \sim \text{Ber}(c/N + x_i x_j (c_{\text{in}} - c_{\text{out}})/(2N))$. Their variance is, whenever c_{in} and c_{out} are close, approximately equal to c/N. Matching its first two moments with Gaussian variables yields $\tilde{Y}_{ij} \sim \mathcal{N}(c/N + x_i x_j (c_{\text{in}} - c_{\text{out}})/(2N), c/N)$ which are equivalent in terms of information content to Y_{ij} when setting the signal-to-noise ratio $\gamma = (c_{\text{in}} - c_{\text{out}})/(2\sqrt{c})$ in (22.31). This fruitful connection between the SBM and $\mathbb{Z}_2$-synchronization can be made rigorous and has been exploited to carry precise information-theoretic analyses [86, 108–110].

With this mapping in mind [99] considers the following convex relaxation of $\mathbb{Z}_2$-synchronization: given $\mathbf{Y}$,

$$\text{maximize } \text{Tr}(\mathbf{X}\mathbf{Y}^{\mathsf{T}}) \text{ s.t. } \mathbf{X} \succcurlyeq \mathbf{0} \text{ and } X_{ii} = 1 \text{ for } i = 1, \dots, N. \tag{22.32}$$

Its $N \times N$ matrix solution is easily obtainable with a convex solver. The final estimator is then $\hat{\mathbf{x}}(\mathbf{Y}) = \sqrt{N}T(\gamma)\boldsymbol{\nu}_1$ where $T(\gamma)$ is an appropriate scaling and $\boldsymbol{\nu}_1$ is the eigenvector of the non-negative definite solution of (22.32) with highest eigenvalue. Surprisingly, this estimator is *almost* as good as BP; it does not quite saturate the detectability transition in the two-groups case (while BP does) but its algorithmic transition is extremely close to it. Moreover, by studying a certain vectorial spin model thanks to the replica and cavity methods, it is possible to precisely predict the asymptotic performance of this powerful procedure.

$\mathbb{Z}_2$-**synchronization/SBM equivalence**: *The information-theoretic analysis of the stochastic block model is closely related to the analysis of the $\mathbb{Z}_2$-synchronization (or rank-one matrix factorization) problem. This mapping also serves as inspiration to design new inference algorithms.*

22.4. Dynamic Cavity Method

In the previous sections the graphs represented static interactions. But what about inference from graphs encoding causality and/or time dependencies? In this section we present an approach exploiting message passing techniques. In the literature it is known as Dynamic Cavity. The natural way in which messages and cavity-like equations can be used to solve dynamical problems suggests a more general view of inference outside the realm of Gibbs–Boltzmann distributions which has been our focus this far.

22.4.1. *Definition, specificity and main problem*

The standard cavity method is a means to compute marginals of a Gibbs–Boltzmann distribution by exchanging messages [111]. We consider a dynamics specified by an interaction graph of the same locally tree-like type as where the cavity method has found its main applications. Let the history of variable i up to time t be X_i^t, and let the value of variable i at time t be $\sigma_i(t)$. For an Ising variable we formally define $X_i^t = (\sigma_i(t_0), t_1, t_2, \dots)$ where $\sigma_i(t_0)$ is the initial value of the spin and $t_1, t_2, \dots$ are the set of spin flip times. For a categorical variable history one would additionally have to keep track of between which states the jumps happen. The joint probability of all the variables is supposed to satisfy a high-dimensional differential equation (master equation) of the type

$$\frac{d}{dt}P\left(\sigma_1,\ldots,\sigma_N,t\right) = \sum_{\sigma_1',\ldots,\sigma_N'} \Gamma_{\sigma,\sigma'} P\left(\sigma_1',\ldots,\sigma_N',t\right). \tag{22.33}$$

The locally tree-like interaction graph describes the transition matrices $\Gamma_{\sigma,\sigma'}$ which satisfy $\sum_\sigma \Gamma_{\sigma,\sigma'} = 1$ for every value of σ'. The joint probability over the histories of all the variables can then, up to technicalities, be written

$$P^t(X_1^t,\ldots,X_N^t) = \Gamma_{\sigma(t),\sigma(t-\epsilon)} \cdots \Gamma_{\sigma(t_0+\epsilon),\sigma(t_0)} \cdot P^0(\sigma_1,\ldots,\sigma_N,t_0). \tag{22.34}$$

We either assume that the initial probability distribution P^0 is so far in the past that it does not matter, or that it only has the same dependencies as in Γ. For instance, it can be factorized. We now additionally assume that the probabilities of different variables to flip in a time interval $\Delta t = \epsilon$ are independent. This is natural in the continuous-time limit where these probabilities are given by $\Delta t \cdot r_i$ where r_i is the instantaneous flip rate of spin i. For the Ising ferromagnet with Glauber dynamics, which we show as a numerical example in Fig. 22.1, the rates are

$$r_i(\sigma_i,\sigma_{\partial i}) = \alpha \frac{e^{-\frac{J}{k_B T}\sum_{j\in\partial i}\sigma_i\sigma_j}}{\sum_s e^{-\frac{J}{k_B T}\sum_{j\in\partial i}s\sigma_j}}, \tag{22.35}$$

where α is a constant of dimension inverse time and J is the pairwise interaction energy. In this example the dependencies in the joint probability distribution (22.34) includes effects of the type that if k and j are both in the neighborhood of i as given by the energy function, they are also related by the denominator in the expression for the rate r_i. The total statistical dependencies in (22.34) therefore include many local loops. A systematic approach to resolve these loops is by graph expansion [112, 113]. This approach associates a pair of variables (X_i^t, X_j^t) to each link (ij) in the original dependency graph and imposes hard constraints C_i that all variables of the type X_i^t in all links (ij) take the same value. The probability distribution (22.34) can then equivalently be written

$$P^t\left(\{X_i^{t,(ij)}, X_j^{t,(ij)}\}\right) = \prod_i \Phi_i\left(X_i^t, \{X_j^{t,(ij)}\}_{j\in\partial i}\right) \prod_i C_i \tag{22.36}$$

where the local loops have been resolved. The first argument X_i^t on the right hand of above can be any of the $X_i^{t,(ij)}$ as by the constraint C_i they are all the same. Using the theory of Random Point Processes [114] the local weight functionals can be written

$$\Phi_i\left(X_i^t, X_{\partial i}^t\right) = \prod_{s=1}^{n} r_i\left(\sigma_i(t_s), \sigma_{\partial i}(t_s)\right) \cdot e^{-\int_{t_0}^{t_1} r_i(\sigma_i(\tau),\sigma_{\partial i}(\tau))\,d\tau}$$

$$\cdot \prod_{s=1}^{n} e^{-\int_{t_s}^{t_{s+1}} r_i(\sigma_i(\tau),\sigma_{\partial i}(\tau))\,d\tau} \tag{22.37}$$

where we recall that X_i^t is defined by n, the number of jumps of spin i in a time interval $[t_0, t_f]$, the initial spin state, and the jump times. For given n the last time (t_{n+1}) in above is t_f.

After applying the graph expansion the right-hand side of (22.36) is like a Boltzmann weight with hard constraints in the standard cavity method. In the original formulation (22.34) the marginal probability over one history is defined as

$$P_i^t(X_i^t) = \sum_{\mathbf{X}_{\backslash i}} P^t(X_1^t, \ldots, X_N^t) \tag{22.38}$$

and in the expanded graph we can first marginalize to the joint probability of the set $\{X_i^{t,(ij)}, X_j^{t,(ij)}\}_{j \in \partial i}$, where all the $X_i^{t,(ij)}$ are the same due to the constraint C_i, and then marginalize separately over the $X_j^{t,(ij)}$. The cavity (or belief propagation) output equation is then

$$P_i^t(X_i^t) = \sum_{X_{\partial i}^t} \Phi_i\left(X_i^t, X_{\partial i}^t\right) \prod_{j \in \partial i} \mu_{j \to (ji)}^t(X_j^t, X_i^t). \tag{22.39}$$

In above $\mu_{j \to (ji)}^t(X_j^t, X_i^t)$ (a message with two arguments) follows from the graph expansion, and the egress node notation (ji) indicates that these messages are actually passed around in the expanded graph. The cavity (or BP) update equation is on the same level of abstraction

$$\mu_{j \to (ji)}^t(X_j^t, X_i^t)$$
$$= \sum_{X_{\partial j \backslash i}^t} \Phi_j\left(X_j^t, X_{\partial j}^t\right) \prod_{k \in \partial j \backslash i} \mu_{k \to (kj)}(X_k^t, X_j^t). \tag{22.40}$$

The problem of using (22.39) and (22.40) is that the the argument is very high-dimensional. Various approximations have been introduced in the literature to nevertheless make the dynamic cavity an efficient and accurate modelling approach. As in this chapter we consider statistical inference we will not discuss the use of dynamic cavity to retrodict the origin of epidemics and similar processes, for this see [115] and [116]. To stay inside the sphere of physical problems we will also not consider the recent use of dynamic cavity to model and predict the evolution of an epidemic [117, 118].

22.4.2. *Dealing with the histories*

After deriving (22.40), the next step is to find a convenient parametrization for the histories. In a discrete time setting, a simple parametrization is to consider the values of the spins at different times. Each X_i^t is then approximated by the values of the spins at different times, $X_i^t \approx (\sigma^t, \sigma^{t-\epsilon}, \ldots, \sigma^0)$. To arrive at finite-dimensional messages one can then consider a closure on the last n times, which means to take into account a memory of length $n\delta t$. This was the approach (for $n = 2$) followed in [113, 119] when studying of the kinetic Ising model under synchronous update dynamics. A more advanced approach based on the matrix product expansion from quantum condensed matter theory was investigated in [120].

Continuous-time dynamics is problematic using both the above approaches. In a series of papers reviewed in [121] a continuous-time closure was introduced leading to a cavity master equation. Apart from the kinetic Ising model (pair-wise interactions) this versatile approach has also been applied with good results to the ferromagnetic

p-spin model under Glauber dynamics [122], and to the dynamics of a focused search algorithm to solve the random 3-SAT problem in a random graph [123]. The method has also been generalized to provide master equations for the probability densities of any group of connected variables [118].

Here we will exemplify by a recent development closer in spirit to the form of the dynamic cavity embodied by (22.39) and (22.40). The fundamental object of the cavity update equations are then the final-time marginalizations

$$p_{i\to(ji)}(\sigma_i,\sigma_j) = \sum_{X_i^t:\sigma_i(t)=\sigma_i}\sum_{X_j^t:\sigma_j(t)=\sigma_j} \mu_{i\to(ji)}\left(X_i^t,X_j^t\right) \tag{22.41}$$

and the closure of the cavity update equations as master-equation-like differential equations reads [124]

$$\begin{aligned}
\frac{d}{dt}p_{i\to(ij)}(\sigma_i,\sigma_j) = \sum_{\sigma_{\partial i\backslash j}} &\left[r_i(\sigma_i,\sigma_{\partial i}) \prod_{k\in\partial i\backslash j} p_{k\to(ki)}(\sigma_k\mid\sigma_i)p_{i\to(ij)}(\sigma_i,\sigma_j) \right. \\
&\left. - r_i(-\sigma_i,\sigma_{\partial i}) \prod_{k\in\partial i\backslash j} p_{k\to(ki)}(\sigma_k\mid-\sigma_i)p_{i\to(ij)}(-\sigma_i,\sigma_j) \right] \\
&- r_j(\sigma_j,\sigma_i)p_{i\to(ij)}(\sigma_i,\sigma_j) + r_j(-\sigma_j,\sigma_j)p_{i\to(ij)}(\sigma_i,-\sigma_j).
\end{aligned} \tag{22.42}$$

In the above the conditional probabilities in the cavity are defined as

$$p_{i\to(ij)}(\sigma_i\mid\sigma_j) = \frac{p_{i\to(ij)}(\sigma_i,\sigma_j)}{\sum_s p_{i\to(ij)}(s,\sigma_j)}. \tag{22.43}$$

Further, $r_i(\sigma_i,\sigma_{\partial i})$ and $r_j(\sigma_j,\sigma_i)$ are the defined jump rates of spins i and j in the cavity graph obtained by eliminating all neighbours of j except i. The rate r_i hence depends on all neighbours of i in the original graph, including j, while the rate r_j only depends on i and j.

The fundamental object of the cavity output equations are analogously the final-time marginalizations

$$P_i(\sigma_i) = \sum_{X_i^t:\sigma_i(t)=\sigma_i} P_i^t(X_i^t) \tag{22.44}$$

and the differential equations substituting for (22.39) are

$$\begin{aligned}
\frac{d}{dt}P_i(\sigma_i) = \sum_{\sigma_{\partial i}} &\left[r_i(\sigma_i,\sigma_{\partial i}) \prod_{k\in\partial i\backslash j} p_{k\to(ki)}(\sigma_k|\sigma_i)P_i(\sigma_i) \right. \\
&\left. - r_i(-\sigma_i,\sigma_{\partial i}) \prod_{k\in\partial i\backslash j} p_{k\to(ki)}(\sigma_k|-\sigma_i)P_i(-\sigma_i) \right].
\end{aligned} \tag{22.45}$$

In Fig. 22.1 we show numerical results on the kinetic Ising model obtained using (22.42) and (22.45); it can be checked that they improve on the earlier version of the continuous-time closure [121].

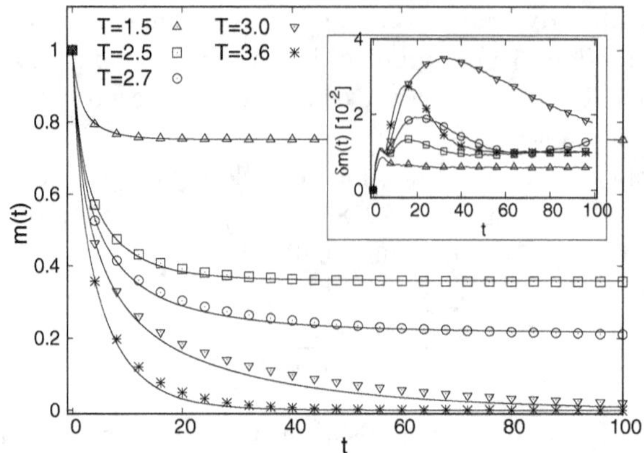

Fig. 22.1.   Continuous-time dynamics of the Ising ferromagnet in a single instance of an Erdős–Rényi graph of size $N = 5000$ and average connectivity $c = 3$. Temperature from $T = 1.5$ to $T = 3.6$ in standard parameterization ($J = k_B = 1$) as indicated. The main panel shows the time evolution of the system magnetization. Points are the averages of $s = 10{,}000$ kinetic Monte Carlo simulations of the dynamics, lines are the results from simulating (22.42) and (22.45). In all calculations, an initially fully magnetized system evolves in time in contact with a heat bath at a given temperature. The inset shows the mean square error $\delta m(t) = (N^{-1} \sum_{i=1}^{N} (m_i^{DCAV}(t) - m_i^{MC}(t))^2)^{1/2}$ on scale of order 10^{-2}. Figure contributed by David Machado Perez.

22.4.3. *Problems and challenges*

We end by listing a set of open problems of a general nature.

Representation of history in dynamic cavity   Almost all uses of dynamic cavity, including the recent one outlined above, have relied on some kind of Markov assumption. As shown in Fig. 22.1 the results can be quite accurate, but are not exact. By analogy to other problems in physical kinetics the Markov assumption ought to be a restrictive assumption when spatial and temporal correlations may dominate the dynamics of the system. At the moment it is a clear challenge to

Develop efficient and general methods to handle the properties of trajectories in a compact way beyond Markov assumptions.

Average dynamics in dynamic cavity   A great success of the cavity method as a physical theory is that it can deal with disorder considering self-consistency equations of distributions over messages. In most cases this has been considered on the level of *Replica Symmetry* where the self-consistency equations take the form average or representative equations. This is the framework exploited by the Dynamic Cavity Method, and then extended to the Cavity Master Equation for continuous time. One approach has been developed for the average case [125], but does not work in many cases. The problem may be on the level of the closure, and not on a more fundamental level (for this, see below). Nevertheless, this remains a challenge which we formulate as

To develop a scheme on the Replica Symmetry level to describe the typical properties of dynamic cavity.

Replica symmetry breaking   An even wider success of the cavity method has of course been its extension beyond replica symmetry, first for the Bethe spin glass [126], and later for many famous constraint satisfaction and combinatorial optimization problems [7, 127–129]. How to extend this theory to dynamics is not clear. On the technical level, iterations in 1-step replica symmetry breaking (survey propagation) are weighted by a free energy shift. As non-equilibrium dynamics includes cyclic motion, in general it is not associated to a globally defined free energy function. We state this challenge as

Can replica symmetry be broken in dynamics? And can one construct a survey-propagation-like scheme to describe a putative 1-step replica symmetry breaking phase of dynamics?

References

[1] Wikipedia. Inference, (2021). https://en.wikipedia.org/wiki/Inference.

[2] M. J. Wainwright and M. I. Jordan, *Found. Trends Mach. Learn.* **1**(1–2), 1–305, (2008).

[3] H. C. Nguyen, R. Zecchina, and J. Berg, *Adv. Phys.* **66**(3), 197–261, (2017).

[4] M. Weigt, R. A. White, H. Szurmant, J. A. Hoch, and T. Hwa, *Proc. Natl. Acad. Sci. U.S.A.* **106**(1), 67–72, (2009).

[5] E. Abbe, *J. Mach. Learn. Res.* **18**(1), 6446–6531, (2017).

[6] C. Moore, *arXiv preprint arXiv:1702.00467.* (2017).

[7] A. Decelle, F. Krzakala, C. Moore, and L. Zdeborová, *Phys. Rev. E.* **84**(6), 066106, (2011).

[8] P. Zhang and C. Moore, *Proc. Natl. Acad. Sci. U.S.A.* **111**(51), 18144–18149, (2014).

[9] B. Derrida, *J. Stat. Mech.: Theory Exp.* **2007**(07), P07023–P07023 (2007).

[10] G. Bresler, D. Gamarnik, and D. Shah, *IEEE Trans. Inf. Theory.* **64**(6), 4072–4080, (2018).

[11] A. Dutt, A. Lokhov, M. D. Vuffray, and S. Misra. In eds. M. Meila and T. Zhang, *38th ICML*, vol. 139, pp. 2914–2925. PMLR (18–24 July, 2021).

[12] Y. Roudi and J. Hertz, *Phys. Rev. Lett.* **106**(4), 048702, (2011).

[13] H.-L. Zeng, M. Alava, E. Aurell, J. Hertz, and Y. Roudi, *Phys. Rev. Lett.* **110**, 210601 (2013).

[14] V. A. Marchenko and L. A. Pastur, *Mat. Sb.* **114**(4), 507–536, (1967).

[15] J. Berg, *J. Stat. Mech: Theory Exp.* **2017**(8), 083402, (2017).

[16] L. Bachschmid-Romano and M. Opper, *J. Stat. Mech.: Theory Exp.* **2017**(6), 063406 (2017).

[17] A. Abbara, Y. Kabashima, T. Obuchi, and Y. Xu, *J. Stat. Mech.: Theory Exp.* **2020** (7), 073402 (2020).

[18] Y. Xu, S. Puranen, J. Corander, and Y. Kabashima, *Phys. Rev. E.* **97**, 062112 (2018).

[19] M. Andreatta, S. Laplagne, S. C. Li, and S. Smale, *arXiv:1311.1301.* (2014).

[20] C.-Y. Gao, H.-J. Zhou, and E. Aurell, *Phys. Rev. E.* **98**, 032407 (2018).

[21] V. Sessak and R. Monasson, *J. Phys. A: Math. Theor.* **42**(5), 055001, (2009).

[22] E. T. Jaynes, *Probability Theory: The Logic of Science.* (Cambridge University Press, 2003).

[23] E. T. Jaynes, *Phys. Rev.* **106**(4), 620, (1957).

[24] R. D. Rosenkrantz, *ET Jaynes: Papers on probability, statistics and statistical physics.* vol. 158, (Springer Science & Business Media, 2012).

[25] S.-i. Amari, *Differential-geometrical methods in statistics.* vol. 28, (Springer Science & Business Media, 2012).

[26] S.-i. Amari, *Japanese J. Math.* **16**, 1–48, (2021).

[27] E. Aurell, *PLoS Comput. Biol.* **12**(5), e1004777, (2016).

[28] G. Auletta, L. Rondoni, and A. Vulpiani, *Eur. Phys. J.: Spec. Top.* **226**(10), 2327–2343, (2017).

[29] D. T. Jones, D. W. A. Buchan, D. Cozzetto, and M. Pontil, *Bioinformatics.* **28**(2), 184–190, (2012).

[30] F. Morcos, A. Pagnani, B. Lunt, A. Bertolino, D. S. Marks, C. Sander, R. Zecchina, J. N. Onuchic, T. Hwa, and M. Weigt, *Proc. Natl. Acad. Sci.* **108**(49), E1293–E1301, (2011).

[31] H. J. Kappen and F. B. Rodríguez, *Neural Comput.* **10**(5), 1137–1156, (1998).

[32] J. Besag, *The Statistician.* **24**(3), 179–195, (1975).

[33] P. Ravikumar, M. J. Wainwright, and J. D. Lafferty, *Ann. Stat.* **38**(3), 1287–1319 (2010).

[34] M. Ekeberg, C. Lövkvist, Y. Lan, M. Weigt, and E. Aurell, *Phys. Rev. E.* **87**, 012707 (2013).

[35] M. Ekeberg, T. Hartonen, and E. Aurell, *J. Comput. Phys.* **276**, 341–356, (2014).

[36] D. J. Thouless, P. W. Anderson, and R. G. Palmer, *Philos. Mag.* **35**(3), 593–601, (1977).

[37] T. Tanaka, *Neural Computation.* **12**(8), 1951–1968 (2000).

[38] S. ichi Amari, S. Ikeda, and H. Shimokawa. Information Geometry of α-Projection in Mean Field Approximation, (2000).

[39] M. Mézard and T. Mora, *J. Physiol. Paris.* **103**(1), 107–113, (2009).

[40] H. C. Nguyen and J. Berg, *J. Stat. Mech.: Theory Exp.* **2012**(03), P03004 (2012).

[41] F. Ricci-Tersenghi, *J. Stat. Mech.: Theory Exp.* **2012**(08), P08015 (2012).

[42] H. C. Nguyen and J. Berg, *Phys. Rev. Lett.* **109**(5), 050602, (2012).

[43] A. Decelle and F. Ricci-Tersenghi, *Phys. Rev. E.* **94**(1), 012112, (2016).

[44] M. Vuffray, S. Misra, A. Lokhov, and M. Chertkov. In eds. D. D. Lee, M. Sugiyama, U. V. Luxburg, I. Guyon, and R. Garnett, *Adv. Neural. Inf. Process. Syst.*, vol. 29, pp. 2595–2603. Curran Associates, Inc., (2016).

[45] A. Y. Lokhov, M. Vuffray, S. Misra, and M. Chertkov, *Sci. Adv.* **4**(3), e1700791 (2018).

[46] G. Bresler. In *47th Proc. Annu. ACM Symp. Theory Comput.*, STOC '15, pp. 771–782 (2015).

[47] E. Schneidman, M. J. Berry, R. Segev, and W. Bialek, *Nature.* **440**(7087), 1007–1012 (2006).

[48] A. Lapedes, B. Giraud, and C. Jarzynski. Using sequence alignments to predict protein structure and stability with high accuracy. arXiv:1207.2484, (2012).

[49] C. Gao, F. Cecconi, A. Vulpiani, H. Zhou, and E. Aurell, *Physical Biology.* **16**(2), 026002 (2019).

[50] H. Zeng and E. Aurell, *Chin. Phys. B.* (2020).

[51] L. Burger and E. van Nimwegen, *PLoS Comput. Biol.* **6**(1), e1000633 (2010).

[52] T. A. Hopf, L. J. Colwell, R. Sheridan, B. Rost, C. Sander, and D. S. Marks, *Cell.* **149**(7), 1607–1621, (2012).

[53] C. Feinauer, M. J. Skwark, A. Pagnani, and E. Aurell, *PLoS Comput. Biol.* **10**(10), e1003847 (2014).

[54] S. Cocco, C. Feinauer, M. Figliuzzi, R. Monasson, and M. Weigt, *Rep. Prog. Phys.* **81**(3), 032601, (2018).

[55] D. T. Jones, T. Singh, T. Kosciolek, and S. Tetchner, *Bioinformatics.* **31**(7), 999–1006 (2015).

[56] V. Golkov, M. J. Skwark, A. Golkov, A. Dosovitskiy, T. Brox, J. Meiler, and D. Cremers. In eds. D. D. Lee, M. Sugiyama, U. V. Luxburg, I. Guyon, and R. Garnett, *Adv. Neural. Inf. Process. Syst.*, vol. 29, pp. 4222–4230. Curran Associates, Inc., (2016).

[57] T. A. Hopf, J. B. Ingraham, F. J. Poelwijk, C. P. I. Scharfe, M. Springer, C. Sander, and D. S. Marks, *Nat. Biotechnol.* **35**(2), 128–135 (2017).

[58] S. Ovchinnikov, H. Park, N. Varghese, P.-S. Huang, G. A. Pavlopoulos, D. E. Kim, H. Kamisetty, N. C. Kyrpides, and D. Baker, *Science.* **355**(6322), 294–298, (2017).

[59] A. W. Senior, R. Evans, J. Jumper, J. Kirkpatrick, L. Sifre, T. Green, C. Qin, A. Žídek, A. W. R. Nelson, A. Bridgland, H. Penedones, S. Petersen, K. Simonyan, S. Crossan, P. Kohli, D. T. Jones, D. Silver, K. Kavukcuoglu, and D. Hassabis, *Nature.* **557**(7792), 706–710, (2020).

[60] N. Hiranuma, H. Park, M. Baek, I. Anishchenko, J. Dauparas, and D. Baker, *Nat. Comm.* **12**, 1340, (2021).

[61] C. Baldassi, M. Zamparo, C. Feinauer, A. Procaccini, R. Zecchina, M. Weigt, and A. Pagnani, *PLoS One.* **9**(3), e92721 (2014).

[62] M. Figliuzzi, H. Jacquier, A. Schug, O. Tenaillon, and M. Weigt, *Mol. Biol. Evol.* **33**(1), 268, (2016).

[63] G. Uguzzoni, S. John Lovis, F. Oteri, A. Schug, H. Szurmant, and M. Weigt, *Proc. Natl. Acad. Sci.* **114**(13), E2662–E2671, (2017).

[64] E. De Leonardis, B. Lutz, S. Ratz, C. Simona, R. Monasson, M. Weigt, and A. Schug, *Biophys. J.* **110**(3, Supplement 1), 364a (2016).

[65] M. J. Skwark, N. J. Croucher, S. Puranen, C. Chewapreecha, M. Pesonen, Y. Y. Xu, P. Turner, S. R. Harris, S. B. Beres, J. M. Musser, J. Parkhill, S. D. Bentley, E. Aurell, and J. Corander, *PLos Genet.* **13**(2), e1006508 (2017).

[66] B. Schubert, R. Maddamsetti, J. Nyman, M. R. Farhat, and D. S. Marks, *bioRxiv.* (2018).

[67] H.-L. Zeng, V. Dichio, E. R. Horta, K. Thorell, and E. Aurell, *Proc. Natl. Acad. Sci. U.S.A.* **117**(49), 31519–31526, (2020).

[68] E. K. Speliotes et al., *Nat. Genet.* **42**, 937–948 (2010).

[69] J. P. Bradfield et al., *Nat. Genet.* **44**, 526–531 (2012).

[70] A. E. Locke et al., *Nature.* **518**, 197–206 (2015).

[71] G. Valiant, *J. ACM.* **62**(2) (2015).

[72] P. Smolensky. Information processing in dynamical systems: Foundations of harmony theory. Technical report, Colorado Univ at Boulder Dept of Computer Science, (1986).

[73] G. E. Hinton, *Neural computation.* **14**(8), 1771–1800, (2002).

[74] K. Shimagaki and M. Weigt, *Phys. Rev. E.* **100**(3), 032128, (2019).

[75] B. Bravi, J. Tubiana, S. Cocco, R. Monasson, T. Mora, and A. M. Walczak, *Cell systems.* **12**(2), 195–202, (2021).

[76] J. Tubiana, S. Cocco, and R. Monasson, *Elife.* **8**, e39397, (2019).

[77] P. W. Holland, K. B. Laskey, and S. Leinhardt, *Social Networks.* **5**(2), 109–137, (1983).

[78] S. Fortunato, *Phys. Rep.* **486**(3-5), 75–174, (2010).

[79] E. Abbe, A. S. Bandeira, and G. Hall, *IEEE Trans. Inf. Theory.* **62**(1), 471–487, (2015).

[80] A. Decelle, F. Krzakala, C. Moore, and L. Zdeborová, *Phys. Rev. Lett.* **107**(6), 065701, (2011).

[81] L. Massoulié. In *46th Proc. Annu. ACM Symp. Theory Comput.*, pp. 694–703, (2014).

[82] E. Mossel, J. Neeman, and A. Sly, *Probability Theory and Related Fields.* **162**(3), 431–461, (2015).

[83] E. Mossel, J. Neeman, and A. Sly, *Combinatorica.* **38**(3), 665–708, (2018).

[84] H. Nishimori, *Statistical physics of spin glasses and information processing: an introduction.* Number 111, (Clarendon Press, 2001).

[85] J. Barbier and D. Panchenko, *Communications in mathematical physics.* (2022).

[86] Y. Deshpande, E. Abbe, and A. Montanari, *Information and Inference: A Journal of the IMA.* **6**(2), 125–170 (2016).

[87] A. Coja-Oghlan, F. Krzakala, W. Perkins, and L. Zdeborová, *Adv. Math.* **333**, 694–795, (2018).

[88] J. Barbier, C. L. Chan, and N. Macris. In *2019 IEEE Int. Symp. Inf. Theory - Proc.*, pp. 405–409. IEEE, (2019).

[89] E. Abbe, E. Cornacchia, Y. Gu, and Y. Polyanskiy. In *Conference on Learning Theory*, pp. 1–25. PMLR, (2021).

[90] J. R. L. de Almeida and D. J. Thouless, *J. Phys. A.* **11**(5), 983–990 (1978).

[91] J. Barbier, F. Krzakala, N. Macris, L. Miolane, and L. Zdeborová, *Proc. Natl. Acad. Sci. U.S.A.* **116**(12), 5451–5460, (2019).

[92] T. Kawamoto, *Phys. Rev. E.* **97**(3), 032301, (2018).

[93] M. E. J. Newman, *Phys. Rev. E.* **67**, 026126 (2003).

[94] M. E. Newman, *Proc. Natl. Acad. Sci. U.S.A.* **103**(23), 8577–8582, (2006).

[95] C. Schülke and F. Ricci-Tersenghi, *Phys. Rev. E.* **92**(4), 042804, (2015).

[96] U. Von Luxburg, *Stat. Comput.* **17**(4), 395–416, (2007).

[97] K.-i. Hashimoto. In *Automorphic forms and geometry of arithmetic varieties*, pp. 211–280. Elsevier, (1989).

[98] F. Krzakala, C. Moore, E. Mossel, J. Neeman, A. Sly, L. Zdeborová, and P. Zhang, *Proc. Natl. Acad. Sci. U.S.A.* **110**(52), 20935–20940, (2013).

[99] A. Javanmard, A. Montanari, and F. Ricci-Tersenghi, *Proc. Natl. Acad. Sci. U.S.A.* **113**(16), E2218–E2223, (2016).

[100] F. Ricci-Tersenghi, A. Javanmard, and A. Montanari. In *Journal of Physics: Conference Series*, vol. 699, p. 012015. IOP Publishing, (2016).

[101] P. Zhang, *Adv. Neural. Inf. Process. Syst.* **29**, (2016).

[102] A. Moitra, W. Perry, and A. S. Wein. In *48th Proc. Annu. ACM Symp. Theory Comput.*, pp. 828–841, (2016).

[103] U. Feige and J. Kilian, *J. Comput. Syst. Sci.* **63**(4), 639–671, (2001).

[104] A. Saade, F. Krzakala, and L. Zdeborová, *Adv. Neural. Inf. Process. Syst.* **27**, (2014).

[105] A. S. Wein, A. El Alaoui, and C. Moore. In *2019 IEEE 60th FOCS*, pp. 1446–1468. IEEE, (2019).

[106] J. S. Yedidia, W. T. Freeman, Y. Weiss, et al., *Exploring artificial intelligence in the new millennium.* **8**(236–239), 0018–9448, (2003).

[107] S. Boyd, S. P. Boyd, and L. Vandenberghe, *Convex optimization.* (Cambridge University Press, 2004).

[108] S. B. Korada and N. Macris, *J. Stat. Phys.* **136**(2), 205–230, (2009).

[109] M. Dia, N. Macris, F. Krzakala, T. Lesieur, L. Zdeborová, et al., *Adv. Neural. Inf. Process. Syst.* **29**, (2016).

[110] M. Lelarge and L. Miolane, *Probability Theory and Related Fields.* **173**(3), 859–929, (2019).

[111] M. Mézard and A. Montanari, *Information, physics, and computation.* (Oxford University Press, 2009).

[112] F. Altarelli, A. Braunstein, L. Dall'Asta, and R. Zecchina, *J. Stat. Mech.: Theory Exp.* **2013**(09), P09011 (2013).

[113] G. Del Ferraro and E. Aurell, *Phys. Rev. E.* **92**, 010102(R), (2015).

[114] N. van Kampen, *Stochastic Processes in Physics and Chemistry.* (Elsevier B.V., 2007).

[115] F. Altarelli, A. Braunstein, L. Dall'Asta, A. Ingrosso, and R. Zecchina, *J. Stat. Mech.: Theory Exp.* **2014**(10), P10016 (2014).

[116] A. Y. Lokhov, M. Mézard, H. Ohta, and L. Zdeborová, *Phys. Rev. E.* **90**, 012801 (2014).

[117] E. Ortega, D. Machado, and A. Lage-Castellanos, *Phys. Rev. E.* **105**, 024308 (2022).

[118] D. Machado and R. Mulet, *Phys. Rev. E.* **104**, 054303, (2021).

[119] I. Neri and D. Bollé, *J. Stat. Mech.: Theory Exp.* **209**, P08009, (2009).

[120] T. Barthel, C. De Bacco, and S. Franz, *Phys. Rev. E.* **97**, 010104 (2018).

[121] E. Domínguez, D. Machado, and R. Mulet, *J. Stat. Mech.: Theory Exp.* **2020**(7), 073304 (2020).

[122] E. Aurell, E. Dominguez, D. Machado, and R. Mulet, *Phys. Rev. E.* **97**, 050103(R), (2018).

[123] E. Aurell, E. Dominguez, D. Machado, and R. Mulet, *Phys. Rev. Lett.* **123**, 230602, (2019).

[124] D. Machado, E. Aurell, and R. Mulet. Instantaneous cavity master equation, (2022). in preparation.

[125] E. Dominguez, D. Machado, and R. Mulet, *J. Stat. Mech.: Theory Exp.* **2020**, 073304, (2021).

[126] M. Mézard and G. Parisi, *Eur. Phys. J. B.* **20**(2), 217–233 (2001).

[127] M. Mézard, G. Parisi, and R. Zecchina, *Science.* **297**(5582), 812–815, (2002).

[128] R. Mulet, A. Pagnani, M. Weigt, and R. Zecchina, *Phys. Rev. Lett.* **89**(26), 268701, (2002).

[129] F. Krzakała, A. Montanari, F. Ricci-Tersenghi, G. Semerjian, and L. Zdeborová, *Proc. Natl. Acad. Sci. U.S.A.* **104**(25), 10318–10323, (2007).

Chapter 23

Disordered Systems Insights on Computational Hardness

David Gamarnik[*], Cris Moore[†] and Lenka Zdeborová[‡]

MIT Sloan School of Management, Cambridge, USA
gamarnik@mit.edu
†*Santa Fe Institute, Santa Fe, USA*
moore@santafe.edu
‡*SPOC laboratory, EPFL, Lausanne, Switzerland*
lenka.zdeborova@epfl.ch

In this chapter, **David Gamarnik**, **Cris Moore** and **Lenka Zdeborová** describe the deep connections between the physics of disordered systems, phase transitions in inference problems, and computational hardness. They discuss several of the emerging ideas to relate computational hardness to the landscape properties studied in statistical physics. This includes a presentation of the overlap gap property, a particular mathematization of clustering or dynamical symmetry breaking, which can be used to show that many algorithms that are local or robust to changes in their input fail. This chapter also presents the sum-of-squares hierarchy, which places bounds on proofs or algorithms that use low-degree polynomials such as standard spectral methods and semidefinite relaxations.

23.1. Introduction

Computational complexity theory aims to answer the question of what are the tasks that can be solved by computers. It is a sub-field of theoretical computer science that aims to classify computational problems according to the amount of resources (usually memory and time) needed to solve the task. Computationally hard problems are those that can be solved in principle but require prohibitively large amount of resources, typically time exponentially large in the size of the problem. The most iconic result of computational complexity theory is the existence of the so-called NP-complete problems [1] that are conjectured to be computationally hard. Resolving this conjecture is considered as the most important problem of theoretical computer science. The possibility of computationally hard problems has fascinating consequences in many areas. Examples include cryptography where we would be unable to transfer information in a secure way without the existence of computationally hard problems. Consequences spread into seemingly unrelated areas such as Darwin's theory of evolution by natural selection where organisms are constrained to evolve only into variants that are in a sense computationally tractable.

453

Seeking connections between the physics of disordered systems and computational complexity comes very naturally since finding a ground state of some of the canonical models of disordered systems is well know to be NP-hard (i.e. at least as hard as the NP-complete problems). Unavoidably, the physical dynamics aiming to seek such a ground state is restricted by the computational difficulty that would be faced by any other algorithm. Connections between computational hardness and phase transitions of various types date back to rather early works, see e.g. [2–4].

In this chapter we review some main current areas of research on the connections between theory of disordered systems and computational hardness. We will discuss two types of computational problems – *optimization problems* where one aims to minimize an objective over a set of variables, and *signal recovery or inference problems* where a signal is observed in an indirect and noisy manner and the task is to reconstruct it back from the observations. In Sec. 23.2 we define canonical examples of both optimization and inference problems, stressing their relationship to the disordered systems studied in physics as well as a broad range of applicability in modelling various computational tasks. In Sec. 23.3 we then expose results on computational hardness of optimization problems based on the overlap gap property. Section 23.4 switches to signal recovery/inference problems and presents a rather generic picture that emerges from the study of phase transition in those problems. Section 23.5 then exposes the sum of squares hierarchy that is currently one of the main tools to prove computational lower bounds in this type of problems.

23.2. The Spiked Tensor Model and Spin Glasses

One of the models we will consider here from the statistics and computational perspective is a very natural variant of the spin glass model with a "planted signal" to be learned. It is called the *spiked tensor model* or *tensor PCA*, and is defined as follows:

$$Y = \lambda_N u^{\otimes p} + J.$$

Here $\lambda_N \in \mathbb{R}$ is the scalar parameter controlling signal strength, $u \in \mathbb{R}^N$ is a vector to be learned and $u^{\otimes p}$ is its p-fold tensor outer product, and $J \in \mathbb{R}^{N \otimes p}$ is an $N \otimes p$ tensor corresponding to the noise. We will assume that the entries of $J = (J_{i_1,\dots,i_p}, 1 \leq i_1 < i_2 < \cdots < i_p \leq N)$ are i.i.d. following some common distribution with mean zero and variance σ_N^2 which will generally depend on N. Other entries of J are fixed by symmetry. The learning goal is to infer the vector u by observing the tensor Y.

Variants of this problem will be considered where different types of restrictions will be placed on u, such as $u \in S_N$, where S_N is an N-dimensional sphere with radius $\sqrt{N}$, $u \in B_N$, where $B_N = \{\pm 1\}^N$ and $u \in B_{N,\rho}$ where $B_{N,\rho} = \{u \in \{\pm 1, 0\}^N : \|u\|_1 = N\rho\}$ (non-integer values of $N\rho$ being ignored). In Bayesian treatment of the signal recovery we consider a uniform measure over these sets as priors on u. The $p = 2$ case is the spiked matrix model also known as spiked covariance model, or low-rank matrix/tensor estimation [5, 6].

The general questions to be addressed are (a) can we learn the planted signal u from observing Y, and (b) can this learning be done by fast (polynomial in N time) algorithms. Here we assume p is a constant, so the polynomiality in N and N^p is identical. Also learning u is considered in the loose sense of producing an algorithmic functional $\hat{u}(Y)$ which correlates non-trivially with the planted unknown signal u.

Question (a) can be answered using the theory of Bayesian inference asserting that the best correlation with the signal can be obtained if one computes the marginals of the posterior probability distribution

$$P(z|Y) = \frac{1}{\mathcal{Z}} P(z) P(Y|z) \quad \text{where} \tag{23.1}$$

$$P(Y|z) = \prod_{1 \leq i_1 < i_2 < \cdots < i_p \leq N} \mathcal{N}(Y_{i_1,\dots,i_p} - \lambda_N z_{i_1} z_{i_2} \cdots z_{i_p}, \sigma_N^2), \tag{23.2}$$

where for concreteness we considered the elements of the noise J to be Gaussian (note that due to universality properties e.g. [6] this is not very restrictive for what follows). The partition function $\mathcal{Z}$ depends explicitly on the matrix Y, and also on parameters of the prior $P(z)$ and of the likelihood $P(Y|z)$ which in our case are λ_N and σ_N. In our notation we drop this explicit dependence. Question (b) boils down to the algorithmic difficulty of computing or approximating the marginals of the posterior.

Another approach for solving the above learning problem is the maximum likelihood estimation (MLE) corresponding to $\max_z \langle Y, z^{\otimes p} \rangle$ where

$$\langle Y, z^{\otimes p} \rangle = \sum_{1 \leq i_1 < i_2 < \cdots < i_p \leq N} Y_{i_1,\dots,i_p} z_{i_1} z_{i_2} \cdots z_{i_p}, \tag{23.3}$$

where z varies in the associated space such as S_N, B_N, etc. It has to be noted that while maximum likelihood and similar extremization-based approaches are very popular, they are in general sub-optimal in high-dimensional settings since the goal is to recover a correlation with the signal u not the extremization of the corresponding loss function *per-se*.

When $\lambda_N = 0$ the MLE corresponds to the optimization problem of p-spin glass with cost function

$$E_{N,p} = -\sum_{1 \leq i_1 < i_2 < \cdots < i_p \leq N} J_{i_1,\dots,i_p} z_{i_1} z_{i_2} \cdots z_{i_p} \tag{23.4}$$

Studying the optimization landscape of this problem is not meaningful as a learning problem, but very relevant to the algorithmic understanding of spin glass systems and thus is very natural. It also serves as a good starting point for understanding the learning problem (23.3) itself. This is the problem we address in Sec. 23.3. For $z \in S_N$ this problem corresponds to spherical p-spin glass model. For $p = 2$ and $z \in B_N$ it corresponds to the Sherrington–Kirkpatrick model [7].

Literature considers variants of the spiked tensor model where the signal is of higher rank, the noise J is more generic including binary or sparse, the tensor product is among p different signal vectors or where observations of different kinds, e.g. several different values of p are combined. All these variants have their interest and applications, see examples in e.g. [6, 8]. In what follows we will be referring several times to sparse version of the spiked matrix model, notably the stochastic block model, also discussed in Chapter 22.

23.3. Hardness of Optimizing p-Spin Models: The Overlap Gap Property and Implications

In this section we discuss the algorithmic hardness of the problem (23.4) of finding near ground states of p-spin models using the overlap gap property (OGP). The OGP is a property of solution space geometry which roughly speaking says that near optimal solutions should be either close or far from each other. It is intimately related to the replica symmetry breaking (RSB) property and the clustering (also sometimes called shattering) property exhibited by some constraint satisfaction problems. In fact it emerged directly as a way to establish the presence of the shattering property in constraint satisfaction problems [9], [10]. There are important distinctions, however, between RSB, clustering and OGP, which we will discuss as well at the end of this section. A survey of OGP-based methods is in [11]. Our main focus is to illustrate how OGP presents a barrier to a certain class of algorithms as potential contenders for finding near ground states. Loosely speaking, it is the class of algorithms exhibiting input stability (noise insensitivity) [12]. Many important algorithms are special cases of this class, including approximate message passing (AMP) [13], Low-Degree-Polynomials [14], [15], Langevin Dynamics [14], and low-depth Boolean circuits [16]. OGP was also established to be a barrier for certain type of quantum algorithms [17], [18], [19], [20]. We will therefore conclude that the values produced by these algorithms are bounded away from optimality. It is entirely possible that models in the OGP regime do not admit any polynomial time algorithms, which at this stage is evidenced by just the lack of those. Proving this say modulo $P \neq NP$ assumption does not yet appear to be within the reach of the known techniques.

23.3.1. *p-spin model, ground states and algorithms*

We recall that our focus is the optimization problem (23.4). The optimization is over choice of z in some space Θ_N which for the purposes of this section is either S_N or B_N. The former is referred to as spherical p-spin model and the latter is called the Ising p-spin model. We assume that the variance σ_N^2 of the i.i.d. entries of the tensor J is $N^{-(p+1)}$. A series of groundbreaking works by Parisi [21], [22], followed by Guerra–Toninelli [23], Talagrand [24], Panchenko [25], [26], Crisanti and Sommers [27] led to proof of the existence and a method for computing a deterministic limit of (23.4) in probability as $N \to \infty$. We denote this limit by $\eta_{\mathrm{p,OPT}}$ in either case, where the choice of Θ_N will be clear from the context. The value of this limit arises as a solution of certain variational problem over the space of one-dimensional probability measures as discussed in Chapter 29. The measure which provides the solution to this variational problem is called the Parisi measure which we denote by μ.

The algorithmic goal under consideration is the goal of constructing a solution $z \in \Theta_N$ which achieves near optimality, namely the value close to $\eta_{\mathrm{p,OPT}}$ when the tensor J is given as an input. Ideally, we want an algorithm $\mathcal{A}$ which for every constant $\epsilon > 0$ produces a solution $\hat{z} \triangleq \mathcal{A}(J)$ satisfying $\langle J, \hat{z}^{\otimes p} \rangle \geq (1 - \epsilon)\eta_{\mathrm{OPT}}$ in polynomial (in N)) time. As discussed in Chapter 29, this was achieved in a series of important recent developments [28], [29], [30], when the associated Parisi measure μ is strictly increasing. This monotonicity property is related to the OGP as we will discuss below.

23.3.2. *OGP and its variants*

The following result states the presence of the OGP for the p-spin models.

Theorem 1. *For every even $p \geq 4$, $\Theta_N = B_N$ and $\Theta_N = S_N$, there exists $\eta_{\mathrm{p,OGP}} < \eta_{\mathrm{p,OPT}}$, $0 < \nu_1 < \nu_2 < 1$ and $c > 0$ such that with probability at least $1 - \exp(-cN)$ for large enough N the following holds. For every $z_1, z_2 \in \Theta_N$ satisfying $\langle J, z_j^{\otimes p} \rangle \geq \eta_{\mathrm{p,OGP}}, j = 1, 2$*

$$\frac{1}{N} |\langle z_1, z_2 \rangle| \notin (\nu_1, \nu_2).$$

Here $\langle x, y \rangle$ denotes the inner product $\sum_{1 \leq i \leq N} x_i y_i$. Namely, modulo exponentially in N unlikely event, the normalized angle (overlap) between any two solutions with value at least $\eta_{\mathrm{p,OGP}}$ cannot fall into the interval (ν_1, ν_2). The model exhibits an overlap gap.

The values $\eta_{\mathrm{p,OGP}}$ and ν_j (and in fact the optimal values $\eta_{\mathrm{p,OPT}}$ themselves) are in general different for Ising and spherical models and their precise values are of no algorithmic significance. While the result is only known to hold for even $p \geq 4$, it is expected to hold for all $p \geq 3$. It is conjectured not to hold when $p = 2$ [22] for the Ising case and the AMP algorithm achieving the near ground state value in this case is effective modulo this conjecture [29]. It does not hold when $p = 2$ for the spherical case for a trivial reason as in this case the problem corresponds to optimizing a quadratic form over sphere S_N. The proof of this Theorem 1 for the Ising case can be found in [31], and is obtained by a detailed analysis of the variational problem associated with pairs of solutions z_1, z_2 within a certain proximity to optimality. The proof for the spherical case can be found in [32].

In order to use this result as an algorithmic barrier, we need to extend this theorem to the following *ensemble* variant of the OGP which we dub e-OGP. For this purpose it will be convenient to assume that the distribution of the entries of J is Gaussian. Consider an independent pair of tensors $J, \tilde{J} \in \mathbb{R}^{N \otimes p}$ with Gaussian entries. Introduce the following natural interpolation between the two: $J(t) = \sqrt{1-t} J + \sqrt{t} \tilde{J}, t \in [0, 1]$. The distribution of $J(t)$ is then identical to one of J and $\tilde{J}$ for every t.

Theorem 2. *For every even $p \geq 4$, $\Theta_N = B_N$ and $\Theta_N = S_N$, for the same choice of parameters $\eta_{\mathrm{p,OGP}}, \nu_1, \nu_2$ as in Theorem 1 the following holds with probability at least $1 - \exp(-cN)$ for some c and large enough N. For every $t_1, t_2 \in [0, 1]$ and every $z_1, z_2 \in \Theta_N$ satisfying $\langle J(t_j), z_j^{\otimes p} \rangle \geq \eta_{\mathrm{p,OGP}}, j = 1, 2$ we have $\langle z_1, z_2 \rangle|/N \notin (\nu_1, \nu_2)$. Furthermore, when $t_1 = 0, t_2 = 1$, it holds $\frac{1}{N} |\langle z_1, z_2 \rangle| \in [0, \nu_1]$.*

The probability event above is with respect to the joint randomness of J and $\tilde{J}$. Theorem 2 says that the OGP holds for pairs of solutions with values above $\eta_{\mathrm{p,OGP}}$ *across the entire* interpolated sequence of instances $J(t)$. Furthermore, at the extremes, that is for the pair of instances J and $\tilde{J}$, these solutions must have overlap at most ν_1. We note that the overlap value 1 is trivially achievable when $t_1 = t_2$ by taking two identical solutions $z_1 = z_2$ with value at least $\eta_{\mathrm{p,OGP}}$. The proof for the Ising case can be found in [13], and for the spherical case in [14], and it is a rather straightforward extension of Theorem 1 by appealing to the chaos property exhibited by many glassy models [33], [34].

23.3.3. *e-OGP as an algorithmic barrier to stable algorithms*

We now discuss how the presence of the e-OGP presents an algorithmic barrier to a class of algorithm we loosely define as stable (noise-insensitive) algorithms. This part will be discussed rather informally, as each concrete instantiation of the arguments is model and algorithm dependent. We think of algorithms as mappings of the form $\mathcal{A}(J) \to \Theta_N$ which map instances (tensors) J into a solution $z = \mathcal{A}(J)$ in the solution space Θ_N. In some cases the algorithms can take advantage of an additional randomization with functions now taking the form $\mathcal{A}(J, \omega)$, where ω is a sample corresponding to the randomization seed. For simplicity, we stick with non-randomized versions $\mathcal{A} : \mathbb{R}^{N \otimes p} \to \Theta_N$. Informally, we say that the algorithm $\mathcal{A}$ is stable (noise-insensitive), if a small change in J results in a small change in the output. Namely, $\|\mathcal{A}(J_1) - \mathcal{A}(J_2)\|$ is likely to be small with respect to the natural metric on Θ_N when $\|J_1 - J_2\|_2$ is small. The choice of metric on Θ_N is driven by the space itself and can be Hamming distance when $\Theta_N = B_N$ or $\mathbb{L}_2$ norm when it is S_N. The "likely" is in reference to the randomness of the tensor J. The following theorem stated informally shows why the presence of the e-OGP presents a barrier to stable algorithms.

Theorem 3 (Informal). *For every stable algorithm $\mathcal{A}$ and every $\epsilon > 0$, $\langle J, (\mathcal{A}(J))^{\otimes p} \rangle \le \eta_{\mathrm{p,OGP}} + \epsilon$ w.h.p. as $N \to \infty$.*

Namely, this theorem states that stable algorithm cannot overcome the OGP barrier.

Proof sketch: We provide an outline of a simple proof of this theorem. The stability of the algorithm can sometimes be used to establish the concentration of its value around expectation, namely that $\langle J, (\mathcal{A}(J))^{\otimes p} \rangle \approx \mathbb{E}\langle J, (\mathcal{A}(J))^{\otimes p} \rangle$ as $N \to \infty$. This is not the case universally, but for simplicity let's assume this for now. Then it suffices to establish the claim $\mathbb{E}\langle J, (\mathcal{A}(J))^{\otimes p} \rangle \le \eta_{\mathrm{p,OGP}} + \epsilon$. Suppose not. Then we have $\mathbb{E}\langle J, (\mathcal{A}(J))^{\otimes p} \rangle \ge \eta_{\mathrm{p,OGP}} + \epsilon$ implying $\mathbb{E}\langle J(t), \mathcal{A}(J(t)) \rangle \ge \eta_{\mathrm{p,OGP}} + \epsilon$ for every t. We will obtain a contradiction.

By the second part of Theorem 2 we then must have w.h.p. and in expectation $\frac{1}{N}|\langle \mathcal{A}(J(0)), \mathcal{A}(J(1)) \rangle| \le \nu_1$, namely $\frac{1}{N}\|\mathcal{A}(J(0)) - \mathcal{A}(J(1))\|_2 \ge \sqrt{2 - 2\nu_1}$. Here we assume that we use $\mathbb{L}_2$ for Θ_N and the norm of every solution produced by the algorithm is $\sqrt{N}$ (which is the case when say $\Theta_N = B_N$). On the other hand trivially $\frac{1}{N}|\langle \mathcal{A}(J(0)), \mathcal{A}(J(0)) \rangle| = 1 > \nu_2$, implying $\frac{1}{N}\|\mathcal{A}(J(0)) - \mathcal{A}(J(1))\|_2 = 0 \le \sqrt{2 - 2\nu_2}$. Stability of the algorithm $\mathcal{A}$ implies then the existence of time τ such that $\frac{1}{N}|\langle \mathcal{A}(J(0)), \mathcal{A}(J(\tau)) \rangle| \in (\nu_1, \nu_2)$, which is a contradiction to the first part of Theorem 2. $\qquad \square$

The proof above is just an outline of the ideas with different implementations. The earliest application of this idea was in [35], in a different context of finding large independent sets in sparse random graphs. In the context of spin glasses, it was shown in [13] that the AMP algorithm is stable and thus cannot overcome $\eta_{\mathrm{p,OGP}}$ barrier.

By leveraging the multi-e-OGP method, which involves studying overlap patterns of more than two solutions, the barrier $\eta_{\mathrm{p,OGP}}$ and its analogues for other models can be pushed to the value achievable by the state of the art algorithms. These algorithms

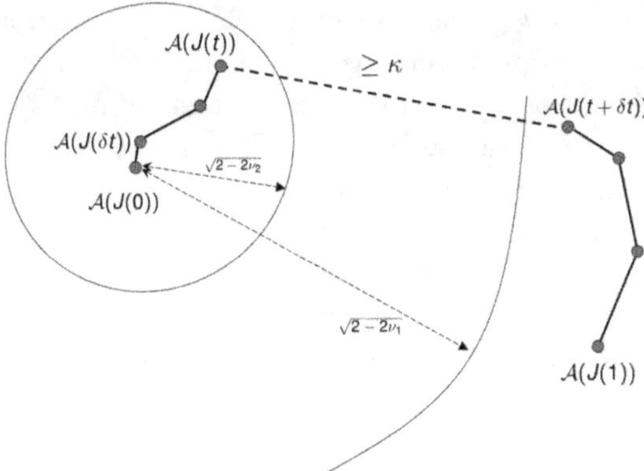

Fig. 23.1. The smaller circle represents $\eta_{\mathrm{p,OGP}}$-optimal solutions at distance $\leq \sqrt{2-2\nu_2}$ from $\mathcal{A}(J(0))$. The complement to the larger circle represents $\eta_{\mathrm{p,OGP}}$-optimal solutions at distance $\geq \sqrt{2-2\nu_2}$ from $\mathcal{A}(J(0))$. As distance between the circle boundaries is $\sqrt{2-2\nu_1} - \sqrt{2-2\nu_2} \triangleq \kappa$, at some instance t the distance between "successive" solutions $\mathcal{A}(J(t))$ and $\mathcal{A}(J(t+\delta t))$ has to be at least κ, contradicting stability.

are AMP in the p-spin Ising case [30] and the spherical p-spin model case [28], simple greedy algorithms for the case of random K-SAT problem and the case of independent sets in sparse random graphs. The implementation of the multi-e-OGP for spin glass models was done by Huang and Sellke [36], who have implemented a very ingenious version of the multi-OGP, called branching-OGP. This version was motivated by the ultrametric structure of the solution space of p-spin models, widely conjectured to hold, see Chapter 29. Arguably the strongest implication of the OGP as an algorithmic barrier is its usage for establishing the state-of-the-art lower bounds on depth of polynomial size Boolean circuits [16].

Broadly speaking a big outstanding challenge is the applicability of OGP or similar methods for models with planted signal, which we discuss in the following sections. While a version of OGP takes place in many such models, its algorithmic implication is far narrower than in the settings discussed above, such as p-spin models and random constraint satisfaction problems. This presents and interesting and rather non-trivial challenge for future.

23.3.4. *Connections with replica symmetry, symmetry breaking and the clustering (shattering) property*

We discuss these connections rather informally now, leaving the technical aspects to other sources which we reference here.

The OGP arose in connection with studying the replica symmetry, replica symmetry breaking and related properties of spin glasses and their variants. Specifically it arose as a method of proving that the set of satisfying solutions of a random constraint satisfaction problem is clustered (sometimes called shattered), meaning that it can be partitioned into "connected" components with order $\Theta(N)$ distance between them. How can one establish the existence of such a clustering picture? If the model exhibits the

OGP say with parameters $\nu_1 < \nu_2$, then clustering follows immediately, provided that solutions at distances $\sqrt{2 - 2\nu_1}$ or larger exist, as in this case one defines clusters as the set of solutions which can be reached from each other by paths in the underlying Hamming cube. The fact that distances between $\sqrt{2 - 2\nu_2}$ and $\sqrt{2 - 2\nu_1}$ do not exist between the pairs of solutions imply that at least two (but in fact many) clusters exist.

There are several caveats associated with this connection between the OGP and the clustering property. First this connection is one directional, in the sense that the presence of clustering does not necessarily imply the OGP, for a very simple reason: the diameter of the cluster can in principle be larger than the distances between the cluster. In this case, while the clustering property takes place, the set of all normalized pairwise distances could potentially span the entire interval $[0, 1]$ without any gaps. In this case the path towards establishing algorithmic lower bounds is not entirely clear.

Second, as it turns out in some models and in some regimes, the clustering picture has been established for the "majority" of the solution space, and not for the entire solution space. We will call it the weak clustering property, to contrast with the strong clustering property, which refers to clustering property without exceptions. For example, for the random K-SAT problem the onset of the clustering property is known to take place close to the threshold $(2^K/K)\log K$ for the clause to variable densities, when K is large, but only in the weak clustering sense discussed above: most but not necessarily all of the solutions can be split into clusters [37].

As it turns out, these exceptions are not just a minor nuisance, and can have profound algorithmic implications. The so-called symmetric perceptron model is a good demonstration of it [38], [39], [40], [41], [42]. For this model, the weak clustering property is known to take place at all constraints to variables densities, yet polynomial time algorithms exist at some strictly positive density values [40]. The multi-OGP analysis conducted in [41] reveals that the gaps in the overlaps occur at densities *higher* than the known algorithmic thresholds and thus the thresholds for the weak clustering property and the OGP do not coincide and, furthermore, the weak clustering property is apparently not a signiture of an algorithmic hardness. Whether the strong clustering property can be used as a "direct" evidence of algorithmic hardness remains to be seen. For the further discussion of the connection between the OGP, the weak and strong clustering properties, and the algorithmic ramifications, we refer the reader to [11].

Next we discuss the connection between the OGP, replica symmetry, symmetry breaking and the Parisi measure μ. The Parisi measure μ arises in studying the Gibbs measure associated with Hamiltonian H. (Very) roughly speaking, it describes an overlap structure of two nearly optimal solutions σ and τ chosen uniformly at random. This can be formalized by introducing a small positive temperature parameter in the Gibbs distribution, but we skip this formalism. The idea is that $(1/N)|\langle \sigma, \tau \rangle|$ has the Cumulative Distribution Function described by μ in the large N limit. The support of μ is naturally some subset of $[0, 1]$. Loosely speaking the model is defined to be in the replica symmetric regime (RS) if μ is just a δ mass at zero, namely, typical pairs of solutions are nearly orthogonal to each other.

Replica symmetry breaking (RSB) then refers to μ being distinct from this singleton structure. Now if the model exhibits OGP, then a part of μ is flat: CDF of the overlaps is constant on (ν_1, ν_2). Namely, the CDF *is not* strictly increasing. The absence of this flat part of μ is exactly what was used in constructions of near optimal solutions in [28], [29], [30] (and the presence of the OGP is an algorithmic obstruction as we have discussed). So presumably, we could have used the flatness of the Parisi measure as a "certificate" of hardness. However, there are challenges associated with this alternative. The reason being that the connection between OGP and the flatness of μ is one directional. The flatness of μ in some intervals (ν_1, ν_2) means only that the density of the overlaps falling into this interval is asymptotically zero after taking N to infinity. It does not imply the absence of such overlaps. This is similar to the distinction between the weak and strong clustering property: most of the overlaps are outside of the flat parts, but the exceptions might exist. The presence of such exceptions is a bad news for the efforts of establishing algorithmic lower bounds. Not only the argument for proving the algorithmic lower bounds appears to break down, but also the presence of exceptions, namely a small number of overlaps falling into this interval, might be potentially a game changer, as we saw in the case of the symmetric perceptron model.

23.4. Statistical and Computational Trade-Offs in Inference

In this section we move from optimization problems to statistical inference, in other words from the non-planted problems to the planted ones. In order to describe the conjectured results on the algorithmic hardness of the planted problems we will first discuss the Bayes-optimal inference of the planted configuration from observations. We will then show how to analyze the performance of the Bayes-optimal inference in the large size limit $N \to \infty$ and under the stated randomness of the generative model. We will then show that phase transitions in the capability of the Bayes-optimal estimator to reconstruct the signal have an intriguing algorithmic role as a suitable type of message passing algorithms are able to reach optimal performance for all parameters except in the metastable region of first order phase transitions. This metastable region is then conjectured algorithmically hard — the hard phase. Section 23.5 will then present the currently strongest known method for showing evidence of such hardness in some cases.

23.4.1. *The minimum mean-squared error*

In the spiked tensor model as defined in Sec. 23.2 the optimal inference of the planted signal u can be achieved by computing the marginals of the posterior probability distribution

$$P(z|Y) = \frac{1}{\mathcal{Z}} P(z) P(Y|z). \tag{23.5}$$

Concretely, when aiming to find an estimator $\hat{z}$ that would minimize the mean-squared error to the signal u

$$\text{MSE}(\hat{z}) = \frac{1}{N} \sum_{i=1}^{N} (u_i - \hat{z}_i)^2 \tag{23.6}$$

we conclude that from all the possible estimators we should take $\hat{z}$ to be the marginal of the posterior

$$\hat{z}_i = \mathbb{E}_{P(z|Y)}(z_i). \tag{23.7}$$

We will call the MSE achieved by this estimator the minimum MSE, abbreviated MMSE. We are interested in the large size limit $N \to \infty$ and computing marginals over a $P(z|Y)$ with $z \in \mathbb{R}^N$ is in general exponentially costly in N and thus potentially computationally hard even in the specific probabilistic setting of Sec. 23.2. Here is where tools from the theory of spin glasses come to the rescue and allow us to analyze the value of the MMSE in the larger size limit as well as design message passing algorithms with properties closely related to the approach to obtain the MMSE. Let us start by describing the form in which we obtain the asymptotic value of the MMSE. Replica theory allows us to derive an explicit formula for a function $\Phi_{RS}(m)$, $m \in \mathbb{R}$, called the replica symmetric free entropy such that

$$\lim_{N \to \infty} \mathbb{E}_{u,J} \log \mathcal{Z} = \max_m \Phi_{RS}(m). \tag{23.8}$$

The function $\Phi_{RS}(m)$ explicitly depends on the parameters of the prior, the likelihood and the ratio $\alpha = N/P$, but in our notation we omit this dependence. We then call

$$m^* = \operatorname{argmax} \Phi_{RS}(m) \tag{23.9}$$

and state a generic result for the MMSE that is given by the global maximizer of the replica symmetric free entropy

$$\lim_{N \to \infty} \mathrm{MMSE} = \rho - m^* \tag{23.10}$$

where the constant $\rho = \mathbb{E}(u_i^2)$ is simply the second moment of the signal components.

The derivations of these result and the explicit formulas for $\Phi_{RS}(m)$ were given in the spin glass literature for many special cases and mostly without a rigorous justification. In the general form considered in this chapter and including rigorous proofs they were given for the spiked tensor model in [43].

An important comment needs to be made here about the very generic validity of the replica symmetric result for the free entropy in the Bayes-optimal setting, i.e. when the prior and likelihood match the corresponding distributions in the model that generated the data. By the very nature of the Bayes' formula the signal u has properties interchangeable with properties of a random sample from the posterior $P(z|Y)$. This is true even at finite size N and even for models where J is not random and where the likelihood and the prior are not separable. A consequence of the interchangibility is that under the averages over the posterior measure and the signal u we can replace the signal u for a random sample from the posterior and vice versa. This is called the Nishimori condition in the statistical physics literature [44, 45]. A direct consequence of the Nishimori conditions is that the magnetization and the overlap have to be equal, which in return means that the overlap distribution needs to be concentrated on a delta function and thus no replica symmetry breaking is possible in the Bayes-optimal setting. The Nishimori conditions also play a key role in the proof techniques used to establish the above results rigorously in [43, 46].

It it also important to note that what we discuss in this section is limited to the large size limit $N \to \infty$ with parameters scaling in such a way with N for the MMSE to go from ρ to 0 as the signal-to-noise ratio α increases from 0 to larger $O(1)$ values. This imposes scaling on the λ_N for the spiked tensor model that is $O(N^{(1-p)/2})$. This will be in particular important for our claims about the optimality of the AMP algorithm that will be restricted to this regime.

23.4.2. *AMP and its state evolution*

In the previous section we analyzed the MMSE as would be achieved by the exact computation of the posterior average. This is, however, in general computationally demanding and thus a next natural question is whether we can reach this MMSE computationally efficiently. Chapter 20 in this book is devoted to the message passing algorithms that provide an algorithmic counter-part of the replica method. In particular, the approximate message passing algorithm (AMP) that is an extension of the TAP equations [47] to the general setting of the spiked tensor model is of interest to us in this chapter. AMP is an iterative algorithm that aims to compute the Bayes-optimal estimator $\hat{z}$. Schematically the update of AMP at time step t for the AMP's estimate $z_{\mathrm{AMP}}^t \in \mathbb{R}^N$ can be written for both the considered models as

$$z_{\mathrm{AMP}}^{t+1} = \mathcal{F}(z_{\mathrm{AMP}}^t) \tag{23.11}$$

for an update function $\mathcal{F}(.)$ that depends on Y, and parameters of the prior and the likelihood. The particular form of this function is discussed in Chapter 20.

The key property that makes AMP so theoretically attractive is that in the large size limit the accuracy of the AMP estimator can be tracked via a low-dimensional set of equations called state evolution. To state this we introduce the correlation between the AMP estimate and the signal at iteration t

$$m_N^t = \frac{1}{N} \sum_{i=1}^{N} u \, z_{\mathrm{AMP}}^t \tag{23.12}$$

The state evolution implies that this quantity in the large size limit $m^t = \lim_{N \to \infty} m_N^t$ behaves as

$$m^{t+1} = f_{\mathrm{SE}}(m^t), \tag{23.13}$$

for a function f_{SE} that depends on the parameters of the models, but not any longer of any high-dimensional quantity. The state evolution of AMP is a crucial contribution that came from mathematical developments of the theory [48, 49] and was not known in its current form in the statistical physics literature before that. The proofs of state evolution have been extended to a broader setting [50–52].

What makes the state evolution particularly appealing in the statistical physics context it its connection to the computation of the MMSE. The fixed points of the expression (23.13) can be expressed at the stationary points of the replica symmetric free entropy

$$m = f_{\mathrm{SE}}(m) \quad \Leftrightarrow \quad \frac{\partial \Phi_{\mathrm{RS}}(m)}{\partial m} = 0 \tag{23.14}$$

where $\Phi_{\mathrm{RS}}(m)$ is indeed the same free entropy as in Eq. (23.8).

Since the signal u is unknown the corresponding initialization is $m^{t=0} = 0$ (for prior distribution with zero mean) and thus the performance of AMP is given by the stationary point of the free entropy that is reached by iterating (23.13) initialized at $m^{t=0} = 0$. The performance of AMP at convergence thus corresponds to the local maximum m_{AMP} of the free entropy $\Phi_{\mathrm{RS}}(m)$ that has the largest error. The corresponding MSE is then

$$\mathrm{MSE}_{\mathrm{AMP}} = \rho - m_{\mathrm{AMP}}. \tag{23.15}$$

23.4.3. *The phase diagrams and the hard phase*

We will now consider all the extremizers of $\Phi_{RS}(m)$ and discuss how they depend on the of signal to noise ratio, which is just $\alpha = \lambda$ in the spiked matrix model. Depending on the model and its parameters we can observe a number of scenarios, we will discuss several of them below and refer to examples where they appear. In Fig. 23.2 all the colored curves are extremizers of $\Phi_{RS}(m)$. Those in blue are the global maximizers of the free entropy corresponding to the MMSE. No algorithmic procedure can achieve an error lower than the MMSE. When the AMP algorithm does not achieve the MMSE, the MSE it reaches at its fixed point corresponds to a maximizer of the free entropy of a higher error $\mathrm{MSE}_{\mathrm{AMP}}$ depicted in green. In red we depict the other extremizers of the free entropy, in dashed red the minimizers, and in full red the other maximizers.

The region of error between the green and the blue curve are values of MSE that are information-theoretically reachable, but the AMP algorithm does not reach them. We call this region the **hard phase**, and its boundaries on the signal-to-noise ratio axes: α_{IT} for the information theoretic threshold where the values of the two maximizers of $\Phi_{\mathrm{RS}}(m)$ switch order, and α_{alg} above which AMP reaches the MMSE. The hard phase exists in between for $\alpha_{\mathrm{IT}} < \alpha < \alpha_{\mathrm{alg}}$. A third threshold α_s marks the spinodal point at which the lower-error maximizer of the free entropy ceases to exist, this point does not have significant algorithmic consequences for finding the signal. In other cases there may be no phase transition at all or a second order (continuous) phase transition marked by α_c.

The physical interpretation of the cases where the hard phase exists is the one of first order phase transition in a high-dimensional (mean-field) system. The α_{IT} corresponds to the thermodynamic phase transition while α_s and α_{alg} are the spinodals, i.e. the boundaries of the metastable regions. In the hard phase the thermodynamic equilibrium correspond to the higher free entropy branch depicted in blue, and the green fixed point corresponds to the metastable state. In the region $\alpha_s < \alpha < \alpha_{\mathrm{IT}}$ the AMP algorithm finds thermodynamic equilibrium, but this state is split into exponentially many separated states, each corresponding to the metastable branch (full red). In the language of replica-symmetry breaking this phase corresponds to the dynamical-1RSB phase (d-1RSB). In the d-1RSB phase the AMP algorithm reached optimal performance in terms of finding the signal, however, sampling the posterior measure in the d-1RSB region is conjectured computationally hard.

Fig. 23.2 depicts a possible structure of extremizers of the free entropy $\Phi_{\mathrm{RS}}(m)$ for models where neither $m = 0$ nor $m = \rho$ are fixed points for $\alpha > 0$. On the left hand side of Fig. 23.2 we depict a case without a phase transition. This arises

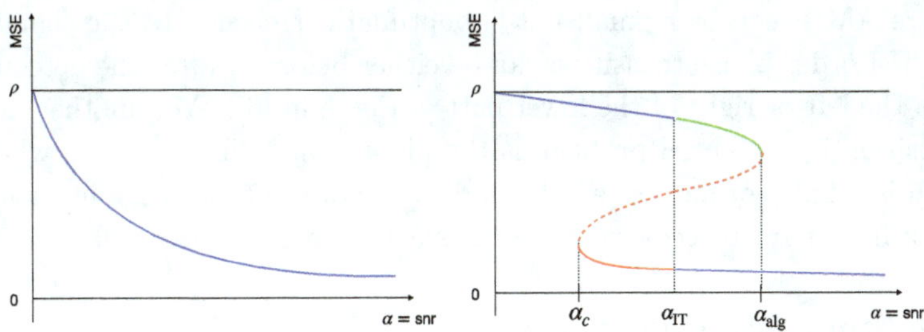

Fig. 23.2.   Extremizers of the replica symmetric free entropy when neither $m = 0$ nor $m = \rho$ are stationary points. Colors explained in the text. (Left) A case without a phase transition. (Right) A case with a first order phase transition.

for instance in generalized linear models with Gaussian prior and a sign activation function, corresponding to the spherical teacher-student perceptron, see e.g. center of Fig. 2 in [46]. On the right-hand side of Fig. 23.2 we depict a case with a first order phase transitions as arises for instance in the spiked matrix model where the prior is sparse with non-zero mean, see e.g. rhs of Fig. 4 in [6].

In some problems $m = 0$ is a fixed point. Such a case with a second order phase transition is for instance the symmetric stochastic block model with two groups, see e.g. Fig. 1 in [53]. A first order phase transition appears in the symmetric stochastic block model with more than 4 groups groups, see e.g. Fig. 3 in [53]. In the case $m = 0$ is a fixed point, the threshold at which it ceases to be a maximum and start to be a minimum is known as the Kesten–Stigum threshold [54]. When $m = 0$ and MMSE $= \rho$ is the thermodynamic equilibrium no correlation with the signal can be obtained and the phase $\alpha < \alpha_{\mathrm{IT}}$ is in this case referred to as the undetectable region, see also Chapter 22. In this phase the planted model is contiguous to the non-planted model in the sense that all high-probability properties in the planted model are the same in the non-planted one other [55]. This is the setting that is most often explored in the sum-of-squares approach of Sec. 23.5.

In other problems $m = \rho$ is a fixed point and thus exact recovery of the signal with MMSE $= 0$ is possible for sufficiently large signal-to-noise ratios. Such a case with a 1st order phase transition is e.g. the teacher-student binary perceptron, see left hand side of Fig. 2 in [46]. A case with a 2nd order phase transition arises e.g. in the generalized linear model with Laplace prior and no noise, corresponding to the minimization of the ℓ_1 regularization, see e.g. Fig. 3 in [56].

We can also have both $m = 0$ and $m = \rho$ to be fixed as in the planted locked constraint satisfaction problems where an all-to-nothing first order phase transition happens between these two fixed points [57]. Both $m = 0$ and $m = \rho$ fixed point also exist for instance in the generalized linear model with Gaussian prior and absolute value activation corresponding to the phase retrieval problem. In that case there is a second order phase transition from the undetectable phase to a detectable one and later on a first order phase transition to exact recovery, see e.g. left hand side of Fig. 5 in [46]. Another generic case is depicted e.g. in Fig. 6 of [6] for the spiked matrix model with symmetric Rademacher–Bernoulli prior. In this case the undetectable phase ($m = 0$ fixed point) is followed by a phase where a correlation with the signal is detectable but small, and where AMP reaches a small but suboptimal correlation to the signal. The position of the first order phase transition can be either before or after the detectability threshold (as in the left or right of the lower part of Fig. 6 in [6]). Yet another example of a phase transition in a planted problem is the planted matching problem where the phase transition is infinite order, i.e. all the derivatives of the order parameter m exist at the transition from partial recovery phase to exact recovery phase [58].

23.4.4. *Is the hard phase really hard?*

An important evidence towards the hardness is summarized in [59] where it is shown that a very broad range of algorithms related structurally to the approximate message passing cannot improve over the AMP that uses the Bayes-optimal parameters. Efforts to prove lower bounds are considerable, as discussed in Sec. 23.5.

It is important to note that there are problems with the phenomenology leading to the hard phase for which polynomial algorithms to find the signal exist nevertheless. One of them is that planted XOR-SAT problem [57, 60], see Sec. 23.5.4. A more surprising and recent example is given by the noise-less phase retrieval problem where the so-called LLL algorithm works in polynomial time down to the information-theoretic threshold [61, 62]. The phase retrieval problem is NP-hard, unlike the planted XOR-SAT. Again the LLL is based on linear algebra and thus in some sense related to Gaussian eliminations, it is not robust to noise, or runs in time that is polynomial with exponent considerably larger than one.

23.4.5. *Hard phase is glassy and further algorithmic hurdles*

We stress that the state evolution that rigorously tracks the performance of the AMP algorithm corresponds to the replica symmetric branch of the free entropy while replica symmetry breaking is needed to describe the physical properties of the metastable state [63].

Physically, and following the success of survey propagation [64] in solving the random K-SAT problem, one may have hoped that including the glassiness in the form of the algorithm, as done in [65], would improve the performance. This is, however, not happening and is rigorously precluded by the proof of [66]. It is interesting to note that early work in statistical physics indeed dismissed the replica symmetric spinodal as non-physical, see [67], and presumed that algorithms will be stopped by the glassiness of the metastable phase. Indeed, if we consider now physical dynamics such and Monte Carlo Markov chains (MCMC) or algorithms updating the signal estimate based on possibly noisy gradient descent they actually perform considerably worse than AMP when the hard phase is present. A very clear-cut examples of gradient-based Langevin algorithms performing worse than AMP are given for the mixed spiked matrix-tensor model in [68] and for the phase retrieval in [69].

23.5. Algebraic Evidence for Hardness

In the absence of a proof that $P \neq NP$, we have no hope of proving that problems in a certain parameter range truly require exponential time. There may in fact be no hard regimes. But we can try to gather the efficient algorithms we know of into large families, each characterized by a particular strategy or kind of reasoning, and show that no algorithm in these families can succeed. In the previous section, we discussed how the overlap gap property can be used to defeat algorithms that are stable to noise or small perturbations in their input.

Here we discuss classes of algorithms that have an algebraic flavor, focusing on the sum-of-squares hierarchy. Many of the best algorithms we know of are captured by this hierarchy, including powerful generalizations of spectral algorithms and classic approximation algorithms. Indeed, for a wide variety of noisy problems, algorithms associated with sum-of-squares are conjectured to be optimal [70]. Thus if we can show that they fail to solve certain problems, or more precisely that they require polynomial "proofs" of high degree, this constitutes additional evidence that these problems are hard.

23.5.1. *Proofs and refutations: The SoS hierarchy*

At its heart, the sum-of-squares (SoS) hierarchy is a way of constructing *refutations* of constraint satisfaction or optimization problems: proofs that a solution does not exist, or that no solution achieves a certain value of the objective function. It comes with a dual problem, of evading refutation by finding a *pseudoexpectation*: a fictional distribution of solutions that looks reasonable as long as we only ask about polynomials up to a certain degree. If a pseudoexpectation can be constructed that "fools" polynomials up to degree d, then any refutation must have degree greater than d.

Let's look at an example. Consider three variables $x, y, z \in \{\pm 1\}$. Is it possible for them to sum to zero? This problem may seem trivial, but bear with us. Algebraically, we are asking whether the following system of polynomials has a solution,

$$\begin{aligned}
x^2 - 1 &= 0 \\
y^2 - 1 &= 0 \\
z^2 - 1 &= 0 \\
x + y + z &= 0.
\end{aligned} \tag{23.16}$$

Here is a proof, that the motivated reader can verify, that no solution exists:

$$\begin{aligned}
\frac{1}{8} &\Big[\left(x^2 + 3(y^2 + z^2) + 4(xy + xz + 3yz) - 3 \right) (x^2 - 1) \\
&+ \left(y^2 + 3(x^2 + z^2) + 4(yz + xy + 3xz) - 3 \right) (y^2 - 1) \\
&+ \left(z^2 + 3(x^2 + y^2) + 4(xz + yz + 3xy) - 3 \right) (z^2 - 1) \Big] \\
&+ (x + y + z)^2 \\
&\qquad\qquad = \frac{1}{8} \left((x + y + z)^2 - 1 \right)^2 + 1. \tag{23.17}
\end{aligned}$$

If the constraints (23.16) hold, then the left-hand side of (23.17) is identically zero. On the other hand, the right-hand side is the square of a polynomial plus 1, giving the contradiction $0 \geq 1$. We will reveal below how we constructed this proof.

More generally, suppose we have a set of polynomials $f_1(\mathbf{x}), \ldots, f_k(\mathbf{x})$ over n variables $x_1, \ldots, x_n$. We wish to prove that there is no $\mathbf{x} \in \mathbb{R}^n$ such that $f_i(\mathbf{x}) = 0$ for all i.

A sum-of-squares proof consists of additional polynomials $g_1, \ldots, g_k$ and $h_1, \ldots, h_t$ such that

$$\sum_{i=1}^{k} g_i(\mathbf{x}) f_i(\mathbf{x}) = \sum_{j=1}^{t} h_j(\mathbf{x})^2 + 1, \qquad (23.18)$$

where 1 on the right-hand side can be replaced by any positive constant. In other words, we find a linear combination of the f_i that is strictly positive everywhere, so they can never be zero simultaneously. Any unsatisfiable system of polynomial equations $\{f_i(\mathbf{x}) = 0\}$ has a refutation of this form [71, 72]. A logician would say that the SoS proof system is *complete*.

Now, we say a SoS proof is of degree d if the polynomials $g_i f_i$ and h_j^2 on the left and right sides of (23.18) have maximum degree d. Thus our example (23.17) is a proof of degree $d = 4$. (By convention d is always even: the h_j have degree at most $d/2 = 2$.) As we increase d, we obtain a hierarchy of increasingly powerful proof systems.

In some cases the lowest possible degree of an SoS proof is much larger than the degree of the original constraints f_i, since we may need high-degree coefficients g_i to create the right cancellations so that the sum can be written as a sum of squares. As we will see below, if the necessary degree grows with the size of the problem, we can interpret this as evidence that the problem is computationally hard.

23.5.2. *From proofs to algorithms: Semidefinite programming*

Of course, the existence of an SoS proof doesn't necessarily make it easy to find. Algorithmically, how would we search for these polynomials? If we choose some ordering for the monomials up to some degree, writing a symbolic vector $\mathbf{m} = (1, x, y, z, x^2, xy, xz, y^2, \ldots)$, then we can represent a polynomial q as a vector $\mathbf{q}$ of its coefficients and write $q(\mathbf{x})$ as an inner product $\langle \mathbf{q} \,|\, \mathbf{m} \rangle$. Multiplying two polynomials is a bilinear operation, and the sum on the right-hand side of (23.18) can be written

$$\sum_{j=1}^{t} h_j(\mathbf{x})^2 = \sum_{j=1}^{t} \langle \mathbf{m} \,|\, \mathbf{h}_j \rangle \, \langle \mathbf{h}_j \,|\, \mathbf{m} \rangle = \langle \mathbf{m} |\, \mathbf{H} \,|\mathbf{m} \rangle$$

$$\text{where} \quad \mathbf{H} = \sum_{j=1}^{t} |\mathbf{h}_j\rangle \, \langle \mathbf{h}_j| \,. \qquad (23.19)$$

This bilinear form $\mathbf{H}$ is positive semidefinite, which we denote $\mathbf{H} \succeq 0$.

With this abstraction, the problem of finding SoS proofs asks for a positive semidefinite matrix that matches the left-hand side of (23.18). To nail this down, for a polynomial q let q_u denote the coefficient of each monomial u. Then summing over all the cross-terms in the product of two polynomials p, q gives

$$(pq)_u = \sum_{v,w:\, vw=u} p_v q_w.$$

Since for any two monomials s, t the entry $H_{s,t} = \langle s |\, \mathbf{H} \,| t \rangle$ must equal the coefficient of $u = st$ on the left-hand side of (23.18), for any s, t such that $st \neq 1$ we have

$$\sum_{i} \sum_{v,w:\, vw=st} (g_i)_s (f_i)_t = H_{s,t},$$

and for $s = t = 1$ we have

$$\sum_i (g_i)_1 (f_i)_1 = 1 + H_{1,1}.$$

For a given set $\{f_i\}$, these constraints are linear in the coefficients of the $\{g_i\}$. Adding the semidefiniteness constraint $\mathbf{H} \succeq 0$ to this linear system of equations makes this a case of *semidefinite programming* or SDP [73–76].

SDP can be solved up to arbitrarily small error in polynomial time whenever the number of constraints and the dimension of the matrices are polynomial. (There is an important caveat, namely that the coefficients of the SoS proof need to be polynomially bounded [77, 78].) Since the number of monomials over n variables of degree d is $\binom{n+d-1}{d} = O(n^d)$, this means that SoS proofs are easy to find whenever the degree d is constant.

On the other hand, if we can somehow prove that the lowest degree of any SoS proof grows with n, this rules out a large class of polynomial-time algorithms. When we can prove them, these SoS lower bounds are thus evidence of computational hardness.

23.5.3. *Sum-of-squares lower bounds: Enter the Charlatan*

To see how we might prove such a lower bound, let's return to our earlier problem. A Charlatan[a] comes along and claims that the system (23.16) has not just one solution, but many. That is, they claim to know a joint probability distribution over reals x, y, z such that $x^2 = y^2 = z^2 = 1$ and $x + y + z = 0$. To convince you, they offer to tell you the expectation $\mathbb{E}[q]$ of any polynomial $q(x, y, z)$ you desire — but only for q of degree d or less, where in this case $d = 2$.

Let's call the Charlatan's claimed value for $\mathbb{E}[q]$ the *pseudoexpectation*, and denote it $\widetilde{\mathbb{E}}[q]$. How might you catch them in a lie? You are no fool; you know that the expectation of a sum is the sum of the expectations. Since the constraints $f_i(\mathbf{x}) = 0$ must hold identically, you also know that any q that has f_i as a factor must have zero expectation. Finally, you are well aware that the square of any polynomial is everywhere nonnegative, and thus has nonnegative expectation.

Putting this together, the pseudoexpectation must be a linear operator from the space of polynomials of degree d to $\mathbb{R}$ with the following properties:

(1) $\widetilde{\mathbb{E}}[1] = 1$
(2) $\widetilde{\mathbb{E}}[f_i q] = 0$ for any polynomial $q(x)$ of degree $d - \deg(f_i)$ or less
(3) $\widetilde{\mathbb{E}}[q^2] \geq 0$ for any polynomial $q(x)$ of degree $d/2$ or less.

Let's think of $\widetilde{\mathbb{E}}$ as a bilinear form that takes two polynomials p, q of degree up to $d/2$ and returns $\widetilde{\mathbb{E}}[pq] = \langle p| \widetilde{\mathbb{E}} |q \rangle$. Then condition (3) corresponds to $\widetilde{\mathbb{E}}$ being positive semidefinite, just as for $\mathbf{H}$ above. Since conditions (1) and (2) are linear, finding a pseudoexpectation is another case of semidefinite programming.

---

[a]Many concepts in theoretical computer science have become personified over the years: the Adversary, the Oracle, Arthur and Merlin, Alice, Bob, and Eve, and so on. We propose that the Charlatan be added to this cast of characters.

In our example, the Charlatan can claim that x, y, z each have expectation $\widetilde{\mathbb{E}}[x] = \langle 1 | \widetilde{\mathbb{E}} | x \rangle = 0$; they each have variance $\widetilde{\mathbb{E}}[x^2] = \langle x | \widetilde{\mathbb{E}} | x \rangle = 1$; and each distinct pair is negatively correlated, with $\widetilde{\mathbb{E}}[xy] = \langle x | \widetilde{\mathbb{E}} | y \rangle = -1/2$. As a result, $\widetilde{\mathbb{E}}[x + y + z] = 0$, and $\widetilde{\mathbb{E}}[(x + y + z)p] = 0$ for any linear function p, satisfying condition (2) above.

This matrix of pseudomoments is positive semidefinite: it is the Gram matrix of three unit vectors that are $120°$ apart. This is impossible for three real-valued variables in $\{\pm 1\}$, but as far as quadratic polynomials of x, y, z are concerned, there is no contradiction.

For each degree d, there is an SoS proof if and only if there is no pseudoexpectation. These problems are dual SDPs; a solution to either is a certificate that the other has no solution. Thus any degree at which the Charlatan can succeed is a lower bound on the degree we need to prove that no solution exists. Here we have shown that degree 4 is necessary and sufficient to prove that no three variables in $\{\pm 1\}$ can sum to zero.

23.5.4. *What does sum-of-squares understand?*

The reader is probably wondering how the SoS framework performs on larger versions of our example. Suppose we have n variables $x_1, \ldots, x_n$. If n is odd, clearly it is impossible to satisfy the system

$$x_i^2 - 1 = 0 \quad \text{for all } i = 1, \ldots, n$$
$$\sum_{i=1}^{n} x_i = 0. \tag{23.20}$$

To put it differently, if you take an odd number of steps in a random walk on the integers, moving one unit to the left or right on each step, there is no way to return to the origin.

It turns out [79–81] that any SoS proof of this fact requires degree $n+1$. That is, the Charlatan can construct a pseudoexpectation for polynomials of degree d up to $n - 1$. This includes the case $n = 3$ we studied above.

The "hardness" of this example may make SoS look like a very weak proof system. But parity is a very delicate thing. If n Boolean variables are represented as $\{0, 1\}$, then their parity is merely their sum mod 2; but if we represent them as spins ± 1, the parity is their product, which is of degree n. When n is large, we would be amazed to find such a term in the Hamiltonian of a physical system. No observable quantity depends on whether the number of atoms in a block of iron is odd or even.

The situation seems similar to XORSAT, whose clauses are linear equations mod 2. Its energy landscape has many of the hallmarks of algorithmic hardness, with clusters, frozen variables, and large barriers between solutions [82]. See also the discussion in Subsec. 23.3.4. In the noise-free case it can be solved in polynomial time using Gaussian elimination over $\mathbb{Z}_2$. But if we add any noise, for instance only requiring that 99% of the XORSAT clauses be satisfied, its algebraic structure falls apart and this algorithmic shortcut disappears. So while parity and XORSAT are good cautionary tales, we shouldn't think of them as representative of more generic problems. As we will see next, for many problems with noise, including those involving random matrices and tensors with planted structure, the SoS framework is associated with many algorithms that are conjectured to be optimal.

23.5.5. *Optimal algorithms and closing the gap with physics: The curious case of tensor PCA*

In many cases, SoS algorithms seem to succeed or fail at the same place where physics suggests a hard/easy transition. Even when these thresholds don't coincide exactly, they often have the same scaling and thus differ by a constant. For example, degree-2 SoS — also known as the Lovász ϑ function — can refute graph colorings in random regular graphs within a factor of 4 of the Kesten–Stigum transition [83], and it's possible that higher-degree SoS do better.

While refuting the existence of a planted solution lets SoS solve the detection problem — distinguishing the null from a planted model — a refinement of this idea often yields algorithms for reconstruction as well. Roughly speaking, if we can refute the existence of a solution when it doesn't exist, we can often find it when it does [84].

To see how this works, consider a planted model, and let x^* denote the ground truth. Let $\phi(x)$ be some polynomial for which $\phi(x^*) \leq \phi^*$: for instance, in PCA, $\phi(x)$ could be the ℓ_2 distance between the signal matrix $|x\rangle \langle x|$ and the observed matrix Y. Now suppose there is a degree-d refutation of the claim that there are any good solutions far from the ground truth: that is, a proof that if $\phi(x) \leq \phi^*$ then $|x - x^*|^2 \leq \varepsilon$. Then any degree-$d$ pseudoexpectation must claim that $|\widetilde{\mathbb{E}}[x] - x^*|^2 \leq \varepsilon$, and $\widetilde{\mathbb{E}}[x]$ is a good estimate of x^*. This approach yields efficient algorithms for many problems [85, 86], including tensor PCA [87].

But for tensor PCA in particular, a curious gap appeared between algorithms and physics. Recall from Sec. 23.2 that tensor PCA, a.k.a. the spiked tensor model, is a model of p-index tensors defined by

$$ Y = \lambda u^{\otimes p} + J. $$

Here λ is the signal-to-noise ratio, the planted vector u is normalized so that $|u|^2 = n$, and the noise tensor J is permutation-symmetric with Gaussian entries $\mathcal{N}(0,1)$. The information-theoretic transition occurs at $\lambda = \lambda_c n^{-(p-1)/2}$ for a constant λ_c depending on p and u's prior [43, 88].

The best known polynomial-time algorithms, on the other hand, require a considerably larger signal-to-noise ratio, $\lambda \gtrsim n^{-p/4}$. One such algorithm, called "tensor unfolding," reinterprets Y as a matrix and iteratively applies PCA to it. For $p = 4$, for instance, we treat Y as an $n^2 \times n^2$ matrix $Y_{ij,k\ell}$ and find its leading eigenvector v. Since $v \approx u \otimes u$, we then treat v as an $n \times n$ matrix and estimate u as its leading eigenvector. At each stage we unfold the tensor into a matrix which is as square as possible.

Other algorithms that succeed for $\lambda \gtrsim n^{-p/4}$ can be derived from sum-of-squares as described above [89]. Conversely, SoS lower bounds suggest that there is no polynomial-time algorithm if $\lambda \lesssim n^{-p/4}$, making this the apparent algorithmic threshold [90].

On the other hand, physics-based algorithms such as belief propagation and its asymptotic cousin approximate message passing (AMP), as well as Langevin dynamics, all fail unless $\lambda \gtrsim n^{-1/2}$, making these algorithms suboptimal whenever $p \geq 3$ [88, 91]. Does sum-of-squares know something that physics doesn't?

This conundrum has a satisfying answer [92]: we were using the wrong physics. Belief propagation keeps track of pairwise correlations. When we compute the Bethe free energy, we pretend that the Gibbs distribution, i.e., the posterior distribution $P(x\,|\,Y)$, has the form

$$P(x) = \prod_i \mu_i(x_i) \times \prod_{(i,j)} \frac{\mu_{ij}(x_i, x_j)}{\mu_i(x_i)\,\mu_j(x_j)}$$

where μ_i and μ_{ij} are one- and two-point marginals. Minimizing the resulting free energy is equivalent to finding fixed points of belief propagation [93].

But when $p \geq 3$, it becomes vital to consider correlations between clusters of p variables. This gives rise to a hierarchy of free energies due to [94]. For $p = 3$, for instance, we assume that the Gibbs distribution has the form

$$P(x) = \prod_i \mu_i \times \prod_{(i,j)} \frac{\mu_{ij}}{\mu_i\,\mu_j} \times \prod_{(i,j,k)} \frac{\mu_{ijk}\,\mu_i\,\mu_j\,\mu_k}{\mu_{ij}\,\mu_{jk}\,\mu_{ik}}$$

(where for readability we suppress (x_i), (x_i, x_j), and so on). At each level of this approximation, we correct for overcounting smaller clusters. Taking the logarithm of this expression and averaging over x gives an inclusion-exclusion-like formula for the entropy.

There are several ways one might turn this into a spectral algorithm. One is to write an iterative algorithm to minimize the free energy. This gives rise to a generalization of belief propagation in which each variable sends messages to clusters of up to $p - 1$ variables with which it interacts [95, 96]. One could then linearize this message-passing algorithm around a trivial fixed point, producing a operator analogous to the non-backtracking operator for belief propagation [97, 98].

An alternate approach is to compute the Hessian of the free energy at a trivial fixed point, generalizing the use of the Bethe Hessian for spectral clustering in graphs [99]. This gives rise to the following operator. For a set $U = \{s_1, \ldots, s_p\}$ with $|U| = p$, let Y_U denote $Y_{s_1, \ldots, s_p}$. Fix $\ell \geq p/2$. Then define the following $\binom{n}{\ell}$-dimensional operator, whose rows and columns are indexed by sets S, T with $|S| = |T| = \ell$:

$$M_{S,T} = \begin{cases} Y_{S \triangle T} & \text{if } |S \triangle T| = p \\ 0 & \text{otherwise,} \end{cases}$$

where $\triangle$ again denotes the symmetric difference.

The spectral norm of M can be used as a test statistic to distinguish the planted model from the null model where $\lambda = 0$. In addition, the leading eigenvector of M points approximately to the minimum of the free energy, and a voting procedure yields a good estimate of the signal u. This yields polynomial-time algorithms for detection and reconstruction whenever $\lambda \gtrsim n^{-p/4}$, matching the SoS threshold. Thus the marriage of algorithms and statistical physics is redeemed [92].

23.5.6. *Conclusion*

What does the future hold? As our understanding of algorithms deepens, we hope to understand the universal characteristics that make problems easy or hard, unifying larger and larger classes of polynomial-time algorithms and connecting them rigorously with physical properties of the energy landscape. Very recently, [100] connected the low-degree likelihood ratio with the Franz–Parisi potential, adding to the evidence that free energy barriers imply computational hardness. We will know much more in a few years than we know now.

Acknowledgments

We are deeply grateful to Tim Kunisky, Tselil Schramm, and Alex Wein for helpful comments on draft versions of Sec. 23.5. C.M. is supported by NSF grant BIGDATA-1838251, D.G. acknowledged the funding from grant DMS-2015517.

References

[1] S. A. Cook. In *Proceedings of the 3rd Annual Symposium on Theory of computing*, pp. 151–158, (1971).

[2] Y. Fu and P. W. Anderson, *J. Phys. A.* **19**(9), 1605, (1986).

[3] P. C. Cheeseman, B. Kanefsky, W. M. Taylor, et al. In *Ijcai*, vol. 91, pp. 331–337, (1991).

[4] R. Monasson, R. Zecchina, S. Kirkpatrick, B. Selman, and L. Troyansky, *Nature.* **400**(6740), 133–137, (1999).

[5] D. L. Donoho, M. Gavish, and I. M. Johnstone, *Annals of statistics.* **46**(4), 1742, (2018).

[6] T. Lesieur, F. Krzakala, and L. Zdeborová, *J. Stat. Mech.: Theory Exp.* **2017**(7), 073403, (2017).

[7] D. Sherrington and S. Kirkpatrick, *Phys. Rev. Lett.* **35**(26), 1792, (1975).

[8] S. D. Babacan, M. Luessi, R. Molina, and A. K. Katsaggelos, *IEEE Trans. Signal Process.* **60**(8), 3964–3977, (2012).

[9] D. Achlioptas and F. Ricci-Tersenghi. In *Proc. 38th Annu. Symp. Theory Comput.*, pp. 130–139, (2006).

[10] M. Mézard, T. Mora, and R. Zecchina, *Phys. Rev. Lett.* **94**(19), 197205, (2005).

[11] D. Gamarnik, *Proc. Natl. Acad. Sci. U.S.A.* **118**(41), (2021).

[12] R. O'Donnell, *Analysis of Boolean functions.* (Cambridge University Press, 2014).

[13] D. Gamarnik and A. Jagannath, *Ann. Probab.* **49**(1), 180–205, (2021).

[14] D. Gamarnik, A. Jagannath, and A. S. Wein. In *61st Ann. IEEE Symp. Found. Comput. Sci.*, (2020).

[15] A. S. Wein, *Mathematical Statistics and Learning. To appear.* (2020).

[16] D. Gamarnik, A. Jagannath, and A. S. Wein, *To appear in Markov Process. Relat. Fields.* (2020).

[17] E. Farhi, D. Gamarnik, and S. Gutmann, *arXiv:2004.09002.* (2020).

[18] C.-N. Chou, P. J. Love, J. S. Sandhu, and J. Shi, *49th International Colloquium on Automata, Languages, and Programming (ICALP 2022).* (2021).

[19] J. Basso, D. Gamarnik, S. Mei, and L. Zhou, *2022 IEEE 63rd Annual Symposium on Foundations of Computer Science (FOCS).* (2022).

[20] A. Anshu and T. Metger, *arXiv:2209.02715.* (2022).

[21] G. Parisi, *J. Phys. A.* **13**(4), L115, (1980).

[22] M. Mézard, G. Parisi, and M. A. Virasoro, *Spin-Glass Theory and Beyond,* Vol. 9 of *Lecture Notes in Physics.* (World Scientific, 1987).

[23] F. Guerra and F. L. Toninelli, *Commun. Math. Phys.* **230**, 71–79, (2002).

[24] M. Talagrand, *Ann. Math.* **163**, 221–263, (2006).

[25] D. Panchenko, *Ann. Math.* **177**, 383–393, (2013).

[26] D. Panchenko, *The Sherrington-Kirkpatrick model.* (Springer Science & Business Media, 2013).

[27] A. Crisanti and H.-J. Sommers, *Z. Phys. B.* **87**(3), 341–354, (1992).

[28] E. Subag, *Commun. Pure Appl. Math.* **74**(5), 1021–1044, (2021).

[29] A. Montanari, *SIAM J. Comput.* (0), FOCS19–1, (2021).

[30] A. El Alaoui, A. Montanari, and M. Sellke, *Ann. Probab.* **49**(6), 2922–2960, (2021).

[31] W.-K. Chen, D. Gamarnik, D. Panchenko, and M. Rahman, *Ann. Probab.* **47**(3), 1587–1618, (2019).

[32] A. Auffinger and W.-K. Chen, *Adv. Math.* **330**, 553–588, (2018).

[33] S. Chatterjee, *arXiv:0907.3381.* (2009).

[34] W.-K. Chen, D. Panchenko, et al., *Ann. Appl. Probab.* **28**(3), 1356–1378, (2018).

[35] D. Gamarnik and M. Sudan, *Ann. Probab.* **45**, 2353–2376, (2017).

[36] B. Huang and M. Sellke, *arXiv:2110.07847.* (2021).

[37] D. Achlioptas, A. Coja-Oghlan, and F. Ricci-Tersenghi, *Random Structures and Algorithms.* **38**, 251–268, (2011).

[38] B. Aubin, W. Perkins, and L. Zdeborová, *J. Phys. A.* **52**(29), 294003, (2019).

[39] E. Abbe, S. Li, and A. Sly, *arXiv:2102.13069.* (2021).

[40] E. Abbe, S. Li, and A. Sly, *arXiv:2111.03084.* (2021).

[41] D. Gamarnik, E. Kizildag, W. Perkins, and C. Xu, *2022 IEEE 63rd Annual Symposium on Foundations of Computer Science (FOCS).* (2021).

[42] W. Perkins and C. Xu. In *53rd Proc. Annu. ACM SIGACT Symp. Theory Comput.*, pp. 1579–1588, (2021).

[43] T. Lesieur, L. Miolane, M. Lelarge, F. Krzakala, and L. Zdeborová. In *2017 IEEE Int. Symp. Inf. Theory - Proc.*, pp. 511–515. IEEE, (2017).

[44] H. Nishimori, *Statistical physics of spin glasses and information processing: an introduction.* Number 111, (Clarendon Press, 2001).

[45] L. Zdeborová and F. Krzakala, *Adv. Phys.* **65**(5), 453–552, (2016).

[46] J. Barbier, F. Krzakala, N. Macris, L. Miolane, and L. Zdeborová, *Proc. Natl. Acad. Sci. U.S.A.* **116**(12), 5451–5460, (2019).

[47] D. J. Thouless, P. W. Anderson, and R. G. Palmer, *Philos. Mag.* **35**(3), 593–601, (1977).

[48] E. Bolthausen, *Commun. Math. Phys.* **325**(1), 333–366, (2014).

[49] M. Bayati and A. Montanari, *IEEE Trans. Inf. Theory.* **57**(2), 764–785, (2011).

[50] A. Javanmard and A. Montanari, *Inf. Inference.* **2**(2), 115–144, (2013).

[51] M. Bayati, M. Lelarge, and A. Montanari, *Ann. Appl. Probab.* **25**(2), 753–822, (2015).

[52] C. Gerbelot and R. Berthier, *arXiv:2109.11905.* (2021).

[53] A. Decelle, F. Krzakala, C. Moore, and L. Zdeborová, *Phys. Rev. E.* **84**(6), 066106, (2011).

[54] H. Kesten and B. P. Stigum, *Ann. Math. Stat.* **37**(5), 1211–1223, (1966).

[55] E. Mossel, J. Neeman, and A. Sly, *Combinatorica* **38**(3), 665–708, (2018).

[56] F. Krzakala, M. Mézard, F. Sausset, Y. Sun, and L. Zdeborová, *J. Stat. Mech.: Theory Exp.* **2012**(08), P08009, (2012).

[57] L. Zdeborová and F. Krzakala, *SIAM J. Discrete Math.* **25**(2), 750–770, (2011).

[58] G. Semerjian, G. Sicuro, and L. Zdeborová, *Phys. Rev. E.* **102**(2), 022304, (2020).

[59] M. Celentano, A. Montanari, and Y. Wu. In *Proc. COLT*, pp. 1078–1141. PMLR, (2020).

[60] S. Franz, M. Mézard, F. Ricci-Tersenghi, M. Weigt, and R. Zecchina, *Europhys. Lett.* **55**(4), 465, (2001).

[61] D. Gamarnik, E. C. Kızıldağ, and I. Zadik, *IEEE Trans. Inf. Theory.* **67**(12), 8109–8139, (2021).

[62] M. J. Song, I. Zadik, and J. Bruna, *Adv. Neural Inf. Process. Syst.* **34**, 29602–29615, (2021).

[63] F. Antenucci, S. Franz, P. Urbani, and L. Zdeborová, *Phys. Rev. X.* **9**(1), 011020, (2019).

[64] A. Braunstein, M. Mézard, and R. Zecchina, *Random Struct. Algor.* **27**(2), 201–226, (2005).

[65] F. Antenucci, F. Krzakala, P. Urbani, and L. Zdeborová, *J. Stat. Mech.: Theory Exp.* **2019**(2), 023401, (2019).

[66] M. Celentano and A. Montanari, *arXiv:1903.10603.* (2019).

[67] H. Sompolinsky, N. Tishby, and H. S. Seung, *Phys. Rev. Lett.* **65**(13), 1683, (1990).

[68] S. S. Mannelli, G. Biroli, C. Cammarota, F. Krzakala, P. Urbani, and L. Zdeborová, *Phys. Rev. X.* **10**(1), 011057, (2020).

[69] S. Sarao Mannelli, G. Biroli, C. Cammarota, F. Krzakala, P. Urbani, and L. Zdeborová, *Adv. Neural Inf. Process. Syst.* **33**, 3265–3274, (2020).

[70] B. Barak and D. Steurer. In *Proc. International Congress of Mathematicians*, (2014).

[71] J.-L. Krivine, *J. Anal. Math.* **12**, 307–326, (1964).

[72] G. Stengle, *Math. Ann.* **207**(2), 87–97, (1974).

[73] N. Z. Shor, *Cybernetics.* **23**(5), 695–700, (1987).

[74] Y. Nesterov. In *High performance optimization*, pp. 405–440. Springer, (2000).

[75] P. A. Parrilo. (2000). Ph.D. Thesis, California Institute of Technology.

[76] J. B. Lasserre, *SIAM J. Optimization.* **11**(3), 796–817, (2001).

[77] R. O'Donnell. In *8th ITCS 2017*, (2017).

[78] P. Raghavendra and B. Weitz. In *44th ICALP*, vol. 80, pp. 80:1–80:13, (2017).

[79] D. Grigoriev, *Comput. Complex.* **10**(2), 139–154, (2001).

[80] D. Grigoriev, *Theor. Comput. Sci.* **259**(1), 613–622, (2001).

[81] M. Laurent, *Math. Oper. Res.* **28**(4), 871–883, (2003).

[82] S. Cocco, O. Dubois, J. Mandler, and R. Monasson, *Phys. Rev. Lett.* **90**, 047205, (2003).

[83] J. Banks, R. Kleinberg, and C. Moore, *SIAM J. Comput.* **48**(3), 1098–1119, (2019).

[84] P. Raghavendra, T. Schramm, and D. Steurer. In *Proc. International Congress of Mathematicians*, pp. 3389–3423, (2018).

[85] B. Barak, J. A. Kelner, and D. Steurer. In *46th Proc. Annu. ACM Symp. Theory Comput.*, STOC '14, p. 31–40, (2014).

[86] B. Barak and A. Moitra. In *Proc. COLT*, pp. 417–445, (2016).

[87] S. B. Hopkins, J. Shi, and D. Steurer. In *Proc. COLT*, pp. 956–1006, (2015).

[88] E. Richard and A. Montanari. In *Adv. Neural Inf. Process. Syst.*, pp. 2897–2905, (2014).

[89] S. B. Hopkins, T. Schramm, J. Shi, and D. Steurer. In *Proceedings of the Forty-Eighth Annual ACM Symposium on Theory of Computing*, p. 178–191, (2016).

[90] S. B. Hopkins, P. K. Kothari, A. Potechin, P. Raghavendra, T. Schramm, and D. Steurer. In *58th Ann. IEEE Symp. Found. Comput. Sci.*, pp. 720–731. IEEE, (2017).

[91] A. Anandkumar, R. Ge, and M. Janzamin, *J. Machine Learning Research.* **18**(1), 752–791, (2017).

[92] A. S. Wein, A. E. K. Alaoui, and C. Moore, *60th Ann. IEEE Symp. Found. Comput. Sci.* pp. 1446–1468, (2019).

[93] J. Yedidia, W. Freeman, and Y. Weiss, *Mitsubishi Elect. Res. Lab.* (TR-2001-22), (2001).

[94] R. Kikuchi, *Phys. Rev.* **81**, 988–1003, (1951).

[95] J. S. Yedidia, W. Freeman, and Y. Weiss. In *Adv. Neural Inf. Process. Syst.*, (2000).

[96] J. Yedidia, W. Freeman, and Y. Weiss, *Mitsubishi Elect. Res. Lab.* (TR-2001-16), (2001).

[97] F. Krzakala, C. Moore, E. Mossel, J. Neeman, A. Sly, L. Zdeborová, and P. Zhang, *Proc. Natl. Acad. Sci. U.S.A.* **110**(52), 20935–20940, (2013).

[98] C. Bordenave, M. Lelarge, and L. Massoulie. In *56th Ann. IEEE Symp. Found. Comput. Sci.*, pp. 1347–1357, (2015).

[99] A. Saade, F. Krzakala, and L. Zdeborová. In *Adv. Neural Inf. Process. Syst.*, pp. 406–414, (2014).

[100] A. S. Bandeira, A. El Alaoui, S. B. Hopkins, T. Schramm, A. S. Wein, and I. Zadik, *arXiv:2205.09727.* (2022).

Chapter 24

Neural Networks: From the Perceptron to Deep Nets

Marylou Gabrié*, Surya Ganguli[†], Carlo Lucibello[‡] and Riccardo Zecchina[§]

*École Polytechnique, Paris, France
[†]Department of Applied Physics, Stanford University, USA
[‡,§]Artificial Intelligence Lab, Bocconi University, Milan, Italy

Artificial networks have been studied through the prism of statistical mechanics as disordered systems since the 1980s, starting from the simple models of Hopfield's associative memory and the single-neuron perceptron classifier. Assuming a data is generated by a teacher model, asymptotic generalisation predictions were originally derived using the replica method and the online learning dynamics has been described in the large system limit. In this chapter, we review the key original ideas of this literature along with their heritage in the ongoing quest to understand the efficiency of modern deep learning algorithms. One goal of current and future research is to characterize the bias of the learning algorithms toward well generalising minima in a complex overparametrized loss landscapes with many solutions perfectly interpolating the training data. Works on perceptrons, two-layer committee machines and kernel-like learning machines shed light on the benefits of overparametrizations. Another goal is to understand the advantage of depth while models now commonly feature tens or hundreds of layers. If replica computations apparently fall short in describing general deep neural networks learning, studies of simplified linear or untrained models, as well as the derivation of scaling laws provide first elements of answers.

24.1. Statistical Physics Approaches to Learning Problems

The replica method of spin glass theory has been successfully applied since the 1980s to characterize the computational capacity of simple neural network models, starting with Hopfield's associative memory model and the simplest of neural classifiers, the perceptron. From the perspective of spin glass physics, the quenched disorder is given by the data, the patterns to be stored or classified. In the theoretical analysis of supervised learning scenarios, the data are often produced by a generative process, the teacher, of which the learning system, the student, may have prior statistical information. These studies concerned mainly the generalization error, that is, the expected error produced by a trained network when a previously unseen data item is presented. The results are derived in the asymptotic regime, in which the number of data points, the dimension of

---

*marylou.gabrie@polytechnique.edu
[†]sganguli@stanford.edu
[‡]carlo.lucibello@unibocconi.it
[§]riccardo.zecchina@unibocconi.it

477

the input and the number of parameters are sent to infinity while maintaining a sensible scaling relationship between them. The statistical mechanics studies of the 80s and 90s have led to important advances, providing results on the storage and generalization capacity of nontrivial systems that were out of reach for mathematically rigorous techniques.

As far as the dynamics of learning processes is concerned, the contribution were mainly limited to the so-called online setting, where the patterns are presented only once and the learning dynamics can be described in the continuous time limit by a set of differential equations. When multiple passes over the dataset are involved instead, gradient descent and stochastic gradient descent on the perceptron model have been analyzed using the much more complicated set of equations given by dynamical mean field theory.

In the conceptual framework of the 1980s–1990s, the role of replica symmetry breaking was key. It allowed to establish the limit of the learning capacity of non-convex classifiers and shed light on the geometrical structure of the loss landscape.

On the algorithmic side, the cavity method has led to the design of an efficient message-passing algorithm that can be used to obtain Bayesian or maximum likelihood predictions in simple neural architectures for which the method is exact (perceptrons, tree-like networks). The fixed points of the algorithm are related to the stationary points of the replica free energy, and the dynamics can be tracked statistically with a simple set of scalar equations called state evolution. More complicated, and of much greater generality and relevance, is the analysis of algorithms such as gradient descent and stochastic gradient descent in non-convex landscapes and their link with good generalization. This is a complex challenge which requires understanding the interplay between complex algorithmic dynamics and the geometry of the learning landscape. The out-of-equilibrium dynamics of algorithms that implement learning processes represents an open conceptual challenge that is only minimally understood and that appears to be essential for a thorough understanding of contemporary neural systems. Effective algorithms do not uniformly sample the solution space but seem to be biased toward configurations that generalized well.

24.1.1. *The storage problem*

The modern application of statistical physics to artificial neural networks had its origins in 1982, with the seminal introduction of the Hopfield model (HM) [1]. The HM was created as a toy biological model of an associative memory, whose goal is to store P binary configurations, called *memories* or *patterns*, that represent the firing or non-firing state of N neurons. The prescribed memories $\xi^\mu \in \{-1, +1\}^N$, for $\mu = 1, \ldots, P$, are by definition successfully stored if the neural network dynamics has a fixed point very close to each pattern. In particular, Hopfield modeled the neural network dynamics as the zero temperature, greedy MCMC dynamics of an Ising spin system: $\sigma_i^{t+1} = \text{sign}(\sum_{j \neq i} J_{ij} \sigma_j^t)$. The synaptic connectivity matrix J is chosen to store the memories via the Hebb rule [2]: $J_{ij} = \sum_{\mu=1}^P \xi_i^\mu \xi_j^\mu$. With a simple signal-to-noise argument, in Ref. [1] it is argued that network can store up to $P \approx 0.15N$ random patterns, yielding an extensive memory capacity proportional to the number of neurons.

Note that the Hopfield dynamics corresponds to minimizing the energy function $E(\sigma) = -\frac{1}{N}\sum_{i<j}\sum_{\mu=1}^{P}\xi_i^\mu\xi_i^\mu\sigma_i\sigma_j$. Amit, Gutfreund and Sompolinsky [3] then precisely characterized the phase diagram of the statistical mechanics system associated with this energy function using replica theory, within a replica symmetric (RS) ansatz. In the temperature T vs memory load $\alpha = P/N$ plane, they found at low α and low T a ferromagnetic region where the memories correspond to stable states that dominate the equilibrium Gibbs state. These states were called retrieval states. At higher α and low T, the retrieval states still exist as metastable states, but the equilibrium is dominated by mixtures of a finite number of patterns. Finally, for high α and low T there is a pure spin glass phase, while at high T there is a paramagnetic phase. In both these last two cases the retrieval states are no longer present. Further analysis showing the existence of a replica symmetry breaking (RSB) instability and the application of the 1RSB formalism, only slightly refines the RS estimates [4].

Hebb's rule, while neurobiologically motivated, is however only one of many possible ways to store the P memories. This raises the natural question of what might be the highest possible storage capacity over all possible choices of connectivity J. The answer to this question, under the statistical assumption of random and independently generated memory patterns, was given by the seminal calculations of Gardner and Derrida for continuous synaptic strengths [5, 6] and Mézard and Krauth for discrete ones [7]. The foundational idea was to consider the space of all possible connectivity matrices J that are consistent with the memory storage fixed point conditions $\xi_i^\mu = \text{sign}(\sum_{j\neq i}J_{ij}\xi_j^\mu)$ for every memory μ. Each memory therefore imposes a constraint on J. Moreover, these constraints decouple, or are independent, across every row of J. Now a single row of J corresponds to the incoming synaptic weights onto a single neuron. Thus the problem of calculating the storage capacity of an associative memory with pairwise interactions reduces to that of a single neuron (perceptron).

Let $\mathbf{w}$ denote vector of synaptic weights onto any one neuron, corresponding to some row of J. The approach pioneered by Gardner was to compute the volume of allowed synaptic weight configurations consistent with the storage of a dataset of P examples, $\mathcal{D} = \{\mathbf{x}^\mu, y^\mu\}_{\mu=1}^{P}$. This volume can be computed via the partition function

$$Z_\mathcal{D} = \int \mathrm{d}P(\mathbf{w}) \prod_{\mu=1}^{P} \Theta\left(\frac{1}{\sqrt{N}}y^\mu \sum_{i=1}^{N} w_i x_i^\mu\right). \tag{24.1}$$

Here $\Theta(x)$ is the Heaviside function, $\Theta(x) = 1$ if $x > 0$ and 0 otherwise and $P(\mathbf{w})$ is the uniform measure on the set of allowed perceptron weights (for continuous weights this is the hypersphere $\sum_i w_i^2 = N$, while for discrete weights this is the hypercube $\{-1,+1\}^N$). We are interested in the *typical* volume in the high dimensional-limit $P, N \to \infty$ with finite $\alpha = P/N$. Therefore we consider the average *entropy*

$$S(\alpha) = \lim_{N\to\infty} \frac{1}{N}\mathbb{E}_\mathcal{D} \log Z_\mathcal{D}. \tag{24.2}$$

The expectation is over i.i.d. standard Gaussian inputs x_i^μ and over uniform i.i.d. $y^\mu \in \{-1,+1\}$ that are also independent of the inputs. As one requires storage of more patterns by increasing α, the entropy and typical volume both decrease. Importantly, at a critical capacity α_c, the volume of the solution space shrinks to zero, indicating more patterns cannot be typically stored for *any* choice of perceptron weights. For continuous spherical weights, a RS calculation gives $\alpha_c = 2$ and $\lim_{\alpha \to 2^-} S(\alpha) = -\infty$. For binary weights instead $\alpha_c \approx 0.83$, as can be obtained from the condition $S(\alpha_c) = 0$. See [8] for an extensive discussion of the storage problem.

Some generalizations of the Hopfield model achieve super-extensive capacity: they are able to store a number of patterns polynomial [9–11] or even exponential [12] in the size N of the system. That is also true when continuous variables and memories are involved, as in the case of the modern Hopfield network of Ref. [13], a model linked to the wildly popular transformer architecture for deep learning [14]).

24.1.2. *Teacher-student scenarios*

From the theoretical analysis of the storage limits of neural networks, we move to learning problems, where the main interest is characterizing the behavior of the generalization error. The theoretical analysis requires the statistical definition of: 1) the data generating process; 2) the model whose parameters have to be learned from the data. This framework is referred as the *teacher-student model* in the literature. In the simplest scenario, both the teacher and the student are perceptrons, characterized by weight vectors $\mathbf{w}^*$ and $\mathbf{w}$ respectively. In an ideal Bayesian framework, the learner has access to the probability distribution from which the teacher weights $\mathbf{w}^*$ are generated and to the likelihood of producing a certain label y given $\mathbf{w}^*$ and an input $\mathbf{x}$. The data generating process is the following:

$$\mathbf{w}^* \sim P_W, \tag{24.3}$$

$$\mathbf{x}^\mu \sim P_X, \tag{24.4}$$

$$y^\mu \sim P\left(y \,\bigg|\, \frac{1}{\sqrt{N}} \sum_i w_i^* x_i^\mu \right) \qquad \mu = 1, \ldots, P. \tag{24.5}$$

In this Bayesian setting, the associated free energy is the log-normalization factor of the posterior distribution of the weights:

$$\phi = \lim_{N \to \infty} \frac{1}{N} \mathbb{E}_{\mathcal{D}} \log \int d\mathbf{w} \; P(\mathbf{w}) P(\mathcal{D} \,|\, \mathbf{w}). \tag{24.6}$$

This can be computed using the replica method. The calculation involves the introduction of a $n \times n$ overlap matrix q_{ab} for the student and of a student-teacher overlap vector r_a:

$$q_{ab} = \frac{1}{N} \sum_i w_i^a w_i^b; \qquad r_a = \frac{1}{N} \sum_i w_i^a w_i^*. \tag{24.7}$$

One then proceeds with a replica symmetry ansatz for these order parameters and sends the number of replicas n to 0 as usual. In this optimal Bayesian setting, where the student is statistically matched to the teacher, the Replica Symmetric ansatz is the correct one, thanks to the Nishimori condition [15–17]. The free energy is simply expressed in terms of a few scalar integrals and obtained through saddle point evaluation of the order parameters.

The expected generalization error is defined as the expectation (over the realizations of the dataset, the test example $(\mathbf{x}, y)$, and the prediction $\hat{y}(\mathbf{x})$ from the model) of a cost function $c(\hat{y}, y)$ comparing the true target and the prediction:

$$\mathcal{E}_{gen} = \mathbb{E}_{\mathcal{D}} \, \mathbb{E}_{\mathbf{x},y} \, \mathbb{E}_{\hat{y} \,|\, \mathbf{x},\mathcal{D}} \; c(\hat{y}, y) \tag{24.8}$$

In classification tasks, the cost function is typically the 0-1 valued error-counting function, while in regression instead it is the mean square error. Crucially, the expected generalization error for the Bayesian prediction $P(\hat{y}|\mathbf{x}, \mathcal{D}) = \int \mathrm{d}\mathbf{w} \, P(\hat{y}|\mathbf{w}) P(\mathbf{w}|\mathcal{D})$ can be simply expressed in terms of the saddle point order parameters. The whole RS replica picture for the Bayesian-optimal perceptron model has been rigorously established in Ref. [18].

In Sec. 24.2 we discuss the generalization of this approach to some simple multi-layer models [19, 20]. Reaching out to more complex teacher and student architectures, e.g. deeper and with proportional widths for all layers, is a major challenge for the statistical physics analysis of neural networks.

24.1.3. *Message passing algorithms*

24.1.3.1. *Belief propagation equations*

The belief propagation (BP) algorithm [21, 22] is a message passing algorithm for computing marginal and free energies in sparse graphical models. Prominent applications are in coding [23] and combinatorial optimization [24] among others. BP has been used to efficiently solve the problem of training a perceptron with binary weights [25] where the iterations of the node-to-factor and factor-to-node messages take the form:

$$m_{i\to\mu}^{(t+1)} = \tanh\left(\sum_{\nu\backslash\mu} \xi_i^\nu \, \hat{m}_{\nu\to i}^{(t)}\right) \tag{24.9}$$

$$\hat{m}_{\mu\to i}^{(t+1)} = f\left(\sum_{j\backslash i} \xi_j^\mu \, m_{j\to\mu}^{(t+1)}, \sum_j \left(m_{j\to\mu}^{(t+1)}\right)^2\right) \tag{24.10}$$

with f a simple function. With respect to the standard BP prescription, the equations here have been simplified exploiting the central limit theorem since the factor graph is dense. This approximation goes under the name of relaxed Belief Propagation [26]. Fixed points of the algorithm give the estimated marginals and can be used to make a Bayesian prediction for a given input. In order to produce a single binary configuration instead, one has to apply a decimation or reinforcement heuristic [25] on top of BP.

24.1.3.2. *Approximate Message Passing and State Evolution*

It turns out that on dense graphical models such as the perceptron and under certain statistical assumptions on the disorder, the BP equations can be further simplified in what is known as the Approximate Message Passing algorithm (AMP). AMP was first proposed in a seminal paper by Donoho and Montanari [27] building on the rigorous analysis of Bolthausen of the TAP equations for the SK model [28]. Compared to BP,

AMP has lower memory complexity since it involves the computation of only node-related quantities instead of edge ones. Moreover, in the high-dimensional limit, the statistics of AMP messages can be rigorously tracked by a dynamical system involving only a few scalar quantities, known as state evolution (SE). Remarkably, SE involves the same quantities appearing in the RS replica calculation, and its fixed points correspond to the stationary points of the RS replica free energy [18]. Due to this connection, AMP has also been used as a proof technique for replica results in convex models [29]. See also [30, 31] for both replica and AMP perspectives on deriving optimal loss functions and regularizers for high dimensional regression.

While Ref. [32] analyzed linear models, AMP was later extended to generalized linear models (where it is called GAMP) [33], and committee machines with few hidden nodes (see Sec. 24.2).

In inference settings, AMP has been applied to multi-layer architectures with an extensive number of hidden nodes but fixed weights [34, 35]. The deep learning setting is much more challenging though, and there have been only limited attempts so far [36]. Being able to scale message passing to deep learning scenarios would allow to perform approximate Bayesian estimation, train discrete weights for computational efficiency and energy saving, have analytically trackable algorithms, and perform cheap hyperparameter selection.

24.1.4. *The geometry of the solution space*

Learning in Neural Networks (NNs) is in principle a difficult computational task: a non-convex optimization problem on a huge number of parameters. However, the problem seems to be relatively easy to solve, as even simple gradient-based algorithms converge to solutions with good generalization capabilities. NNs models are evolving rapidly through a collective effort shared across many labs. It is thus difficult to define a unifying theoretical framework, and current NNs are in a sense similar to complex, highly evolved natural systems.

A major question in deep learning concerns understanding the nonconvex geometry of the error landscape as a function of the parameters, and how this geometry might facilitate gradient based learning. Motivated by the geometry of random Gaussian landscapes [37, 38] (derived via replica theoretic methods), Ref. [39] numerically explored the statistics of extrema of the error landscape of deep and recurrent networks, finding that higher error extrema were typically higher index saddle points, not local minima. Thus high error local minima need not confound deep learning, though low index saddle points might, and [39] developed an algorithm to rapidly escape these saddle points. The authors [40] undertook a careful comparison of the dynamics of stochastic gradient descent on neural networks versus the p-spin spherical spin glass energy function, finding interesting ageing phenomena indicative of the prevalence of more flat directions as once descends the training error. Ref. [41] found an interesting analogy between jamming and the error landscape of deep networks with a hinge loss, building on a prior analogy for the perceptron [42]. As the network size transitions from overparameterized (with many weight configurations at zero error) to underparameterized (with many isolated minima), the error landscape undergoes a jamming transition. Finally Ref. [43]

provided another interesting exploration by extending the Kac–Rice method to count critical points in generalized linear models.

A complementary view comes from some recent works that focus on the role played by rare attractive minima. At least for non-convex shallow neural networks classifying random patterns, it is possible to derive a theoretical description of the geometry of the zero training error configurations (so-called "solutions"). The most immediate result is that the solutions that dominate the zero-temperature Gibbs measure of the error loss (i.e., the most numerous) do not match those found by the efficient learning algorithms. Numerical evidence suggests that in fact the solutions found by the algorithms belong to particularly entropic regions, i.e., with a high density of other nearby solutions [44, 45]. These types of solutions are often referred to as flat minima in the machine learning literature.

In deep learning settings, numerical results consistently show that flatness of a minimizer positively correlates with generalization ability (see e.g. [46]). Different algorithms explicitly targeting flat minima have been proposed [47–49].

The analytical study of flat minima and their generalization properties can be done by resorting to a large deviation technique introduced in Ref. [44] and based on the Franz–Parisi potential [50]. In order to introduce this framework, named local entropy (LE), it is useful to consider the simplest model displaying a rich geometry of the solution space, i.e. the binary perceptron. The LE framework can be applied to more complex architectures and continuous variables as well. The local entropy function is defined as the (normalized) logarithm of the number of solutions $\mathbf{w}'$ at some intensive distance d from a reference solution $\mathbf{w}$:

$$S_{LE}(d, \mathbf{w}) = \frac{1}{N} \ln \sum_{\mathbf{w}'} \mathbb{X}(\mathbf{w}') \, \delta\big(d_H(\mathbf{w}', \mathbf{w}) - dN\big) \tag{24.11}$$

where d_H is the Hamming distance and $\mathbb{X}$ is the data-dependent indicator function for the solutions. The analysis of $S(d, \mathbf{w})$ for uniformly sampled solutions to the training set reveals that *typical solutions are isolated* [51], meaning that no near solutions exist at small d. This is the analogous of sharp minima in continuous networks. It turns out that by sampling solutions according to the LE itself, that is from

$$P_{\mathrm{LE}}(d, \mathbf{w}) \propto e^{yNS_{LE}(d, \mathbf{w})}, \tag{24.12}$$

it is possible to uncover the existence of *rare* (according to the flat measure) regions containing an exponential number of solutions (a large volume in the case of continuous variables). By analogy, these are the flat minima found in continuous and deep architectures. In the last equation y has the role of an inverse temperature conjugated to the local entropy. For large values of y the probability focuses on the $\mathbf{w}$ which are surrounded by an exponential number of solutions at distance d, therefore suppressing isolated solutions when d is small enough. Figure 24.1 displays the coexistence of isolated and dense solutions up to a certain value of α when the dense region (in blue) disappears. In Ref. [44] it is analytically shown that dense solutions generalize better than isolated ones. It must be also noted that isolated solutions cannot be algorithmically accessed by polynomial algorithms. Rigorous results on the geometry of the symmetric variant of the binary perceptron have been obtained in Ref. [52].

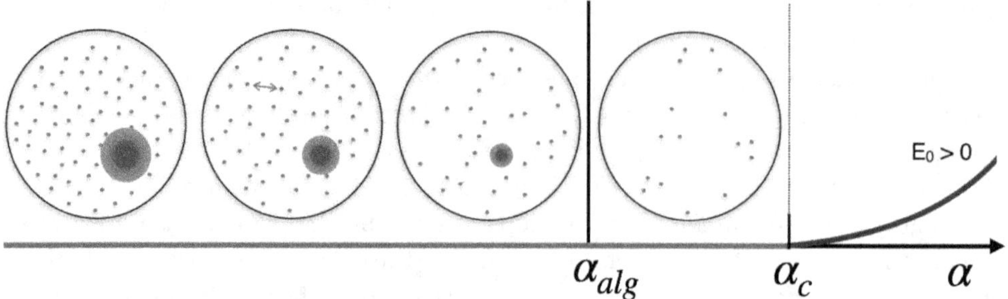

Fig. 24.1.   Geometrical transitions in the solution space for the storage problem of the binary percep-tron at increasing load $\alpha = P/N$. Finding a solution in the connected cluster is easy, while finding a solution after the cluster disappears at $\alpha = \alpha_{alg}$ becomes computationally hard since all of them are isolated. Above $\alpha = \alpha_c$ no zero energy configurations exist.

Adapting the LE definition to generic architectures and continuous weights, one can try direct optimization of S_{LE} instead of the original loss. Estimation and optimization can be done within a double-loop algorithm known as entropy-SGD [47, 48]. Second order approximation of S_{LE} leads to the sharpness aware minimization algorithm of Ref. [49].

Other algorithmic approaches for the generic deep learning setting are obtained as follows [45]. Starting from Eq. (24.12), relax the constraint on the distance with a Lagrange multiplier γ, replace the indicator function in Eq. (24.11) with a Boltzmann weight involving a loss $\mathcal{L}(\mathbf{w}')$, *take integer y*, and unfold the exponential in Eq. (24.12) by introducing y replicas of the original system. We end up with a replicated system with an effective energy

$$\mathcal{L}_{\mathrm{R}}\left(\mathbf{w}, \{\mathbf{w}'^{a}\}_a\right) = \sum_{a=1}^{y} \mathcal{L}\left(\mathbf{w}'^{a}\right) + \gamma \sum_{a=1}^{y} d\left(\mathbf{w}, \mathbf{w}'^{a}\right). \tag{24.13}$$

We thus have a central replica interacting with y peripheral ones that also resent from the data-dependent loss function. As discussed in ref. [45, 53, 54], several algorith-mic schemes can be derived in a straightforward way by optimizing the replicated loss function $\mathcal{L}_{\mathrm{R}}$, for example with gradient-based algorithms, or by sampling the space of solutions with a Markovian process or with Belief Propagation equations. One of these, the flat-minima-seeking algorithm known as rSGD, has been applied to deep neural architectures in Ref. [48].

24.1.5. *Learning dynamics*

With neural network models, the dynamics of gradient descent takes place in a high-dimensional non-convex landscape, therefore its theoretical description is highly non-trivial. For the perceptron and in the continuous time limit, dynamical mean-field theory has been used to provided such description in terms of low-dimensional integro-differential equations involving two-times correlations functions and responses [55]. Such description has been extended to stochastic gradient descent as well [56]. Numerical solution of the equations is particularly challenging, and the framework has not been extended to deeper architectures so far.

In the simpler online setting, where only a single pass over the data points is allowed, a much simpler set of ODE can be derived. For the committee machine architecture detailed in Sec. 24.2 the quantities to be evolved are the student-student and teacher-student overlaps among the hidden perceptrons, $Q_{k,k'}$ and $R_{k,k*}$ respectively [57–60]. In terms of these overlaps, the evolution of the generalization error can be described at each time step. In the same setting, but assuming infinitely wide networks with finite input size, the authors of [61] obtained a mean-field description in terms of a PDE characterizing a diffusion process for the perceptrons' weights.

24.2. Studying Over-Parametrized Models

The repeated breakthroughs of deep learning starting from the 2010s propelled neural networks to the forefront of machine learning [62]. Moreover these neural networks increased rapidly in size; one of the first convolutional networks for document recognition, LeNet-5, had around 61,000 trainable parameters [63], while today's GPT-3 has around 175 billion [64]. This proliferation of trainable parameters leads to highly flexible models, which begs the question of why they don't overfit to their training data and why they can still generalize well to new input examples. Explaining their success in this so-called *over-parametrized* regime constitutes a key theoretical question in machine learning, as it seemingly violates the classical picture of the bias-variance trade-off [65, 66]. In this section, we describe how over-parametrization has been tackled by the statistical mechanics approach.

24.2.1. *Committee machines*

Gardner's program for the perceptron, described above, was soon extended to multi-layer networks. The first analyzed model consisted of summing the outputs of multiple perceptrons with non-overlapping inputs [67]. This tree-like architecture was called *committee machine*. Soon after, this analysis was extended to full connectivity to the input [20, 68]. These architectures are cases of a generic one-hidden layer neural-net,

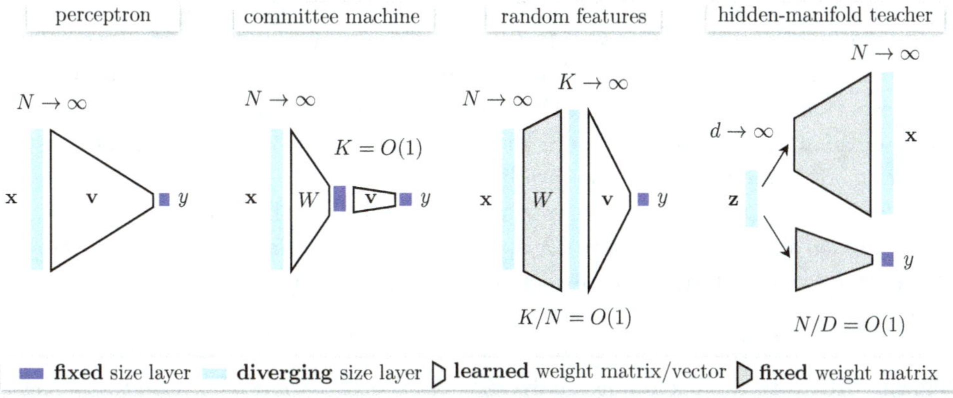

Fig. 24.2.   Scaling comparison of models' dimensions in the thermodynamic limit.

which passes a linear combination of the outputs of K perceptrons, each with non-linearity $\sigma(\cdot)$, through an output activation function $f(\cdot)$, yielding a final output y given by

$$y = f\left(\sum_{k=1}^{K} v_k\, \sigma\left(\sum_{i=1}^{N} W_{ki}\, x_i\right)\right). \tag{24.14}$$

The input to hidden layers weights are parameterized by a matrix $W \in \mathbb{R}^{K \times N}$ and the hidden to output weights are parameterized by a vector $\mathbf{v} \in \mathbb{R}^K$. K denotes the number of *hidden* neurons.

Remarkably, any smooth function on $\mathbb{R}^N$ can be arbitrarily well approximated by (24.14) with a finite, but possibly large, K [69]. This universal approximation theorem motivates the one-hidden layer neural network as a simple yet far-reaching learning model to be studied. Also, these one hidden layer networks allow the study of over-parametrization by considering large student networks with K hidden units learning from data generated by small teacher networks with $M < K$ hidden units.

Scaling and specialization transition — The statistical mechanics analysis of committee machines in the teacher-student scenario mirrors that of the perceptron. Given a dataset $\mathcal{D} = \{\mathbf{x}_\mu, y_\mu\}_{\mu=1}^P$ generated by a teacher committee machine with M hidden units of the form

$$y^\mu = f^*\left(\sum_{k=1}^{M} v_k^*\, \sigma\left(\sum_{i=1}^{N} W_{ki}^*\, x_i^\mu\right)\right), \tag{24.15}$$

one can derive learning curves in the usual high dimensional limit $P, N \to \infty$ with $\alpha = P/N$ held to be $O(1)$. Also the number of hidden units in the teacher (M) and student (K) are both kept $O(1)$ (see Fig. 24.2). The order parameters are the teacher-student and student-student overlaps, as for the perceptron, except now they become matrices for the input layer:

$$R = \frac{WW^{*,\top}}{N} \in \mathbb{R}^{K \times M}, \qquad Q = \frac{WW^\top}{N} \in \mathbb{R}^{K \times K}. \tag{24.16}$$

For simplicity we assume the teacher output $\mathbf{v}^* \in \mathbb{R}^K$ to be the all 1 vector.

A remarkable phenomenology was identified using annealed and quenched replica computations [20, 68] as well as an online learning analysis [57, 58, 70]. Considering matched teacher and students ($M = K$) with fixed student output weights $\mathbf{v} = \mathbf{v}^*$, the Bayes optimal student weights were shown to specialize to the teacher weights only if a critical amount of data was available (i.e. $\alpha > \alpha_c$, see Fig. 24.3). This specialization transition was derived rigorously recently in [71], through AMP and SE. Non-linear hidden units are necessary for specialization to set in, and in scarce data regimes ($\alpha < \alpha_c$) committee machines act no differently than linear models such as perceptrons.

Denoising solution — The online analysis of the specialization transition was also made rigorous recently by [60]. In this work, Goldt and co-authors further extended the analysis to include learnable student output weights $\mathbf{v}$ and uncovered one mechanism of

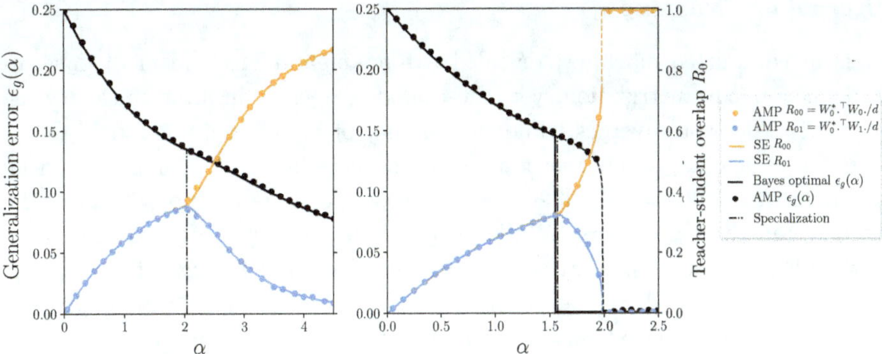

Fig. 24.3. Adapted from [71]. Overlap parameters and generalization for matched teacher-student committee machines with $M = K = 2$ hidden units as a function of the ratio $\alpha = P/N$ between sample size and input dimension, with first layer weights either Gaussian (left) or binary (right). As α grows beyond a critical value, the overlaps account for the specialization of the student hidden units to the teacher's.

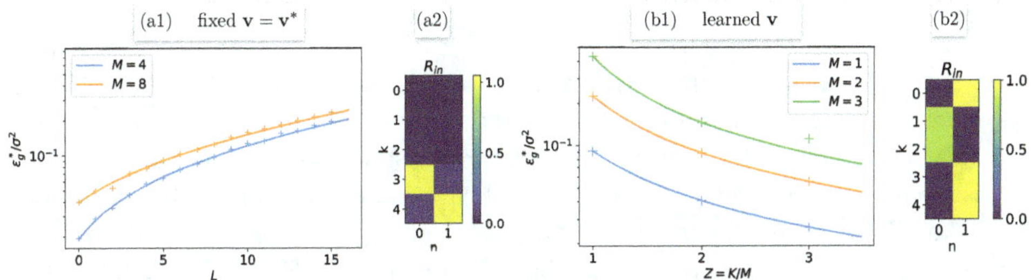

Fig. 24.4. Adapted from [60]. (a1) and (b1) Generalization error as a function of the over-parametrization for sigmoidal committee machines with K hidden units learning from data generated with teachers with M hidden units ($L = K - M$). Generalization deteriorates with over-parametrization when the output weight vector $\mathbf{v}$ is fixed (a1) and improves when $\mathbf{v}$ is learned (b1). This behavior is traced back to the specialization of multiple hidden units for each of the teacher's hidden unit in this second case only as testified by the reported teacher-student overlap matrices (a2) and (b2) for $M = 2$ and $K = 5$.

improved generalization by over-parametrization. Focusing on committee machines with sigmoidal non-linearities, they showed that the generalization error increases (decreases) with overparameterization $L = K - M$ if the output layer weight $\mathbf{v}$ is fixed (learned) (see Fig. 24.4). The natural order parameters, or overlap matrices R and Q, once again, elucidate the mechanism behind this phenomenology. With learnable output weights, several of the K hidden units of the student can (potentially weakly) specialize to one of the M teacher hidden units, and the student output weights can learn to combine, or denoise, the student hidden-unit outputs to mimic the overall teacher output. This *denoising* solution allows the student with more hidden units to build a larger ensemble of regressors of each of the teacher's hidden units, thereby improving its accuracy with over-parameterization. Conversely, when the student output weight $\mathbf{v}$ is fixed, only M among the K student hidden units can effectively participate in the student committee, each specializing to one of the teacher's units. The remaining $L = K - M$ units only contribute noise, so over-parameterization hurts generalization.

24.2.2. *Kernel-like learning*

The analysis of committee machines revealed a fundamental mechanism of generalization through over-parametrization, yet, these models operate in an atypical regime where the input dimension diverges while the number of hidden units is fixed. Operating in a different scaling, kernel methods form another class of models that can be analyzed in depth (see Chapter 16 [72]). Kernel-based learners are non-linear in the inputs but linear in the parameters. While deep neural networks are in essence more expressive than kernel methods,[a] they sometimes behave not much differently from kernels, in particular in cases where they have infinitely wide hidden layers [73] (though see [74] for empirical differences between kernel learners and deep networks at more natural widths). Moreover kernel models already exhibit key features to be understood in deep learning. Notably, the generalization performance of kernel learners undergoes a *double descent* [65, 66, 75]: after an overfitting peak predicted by the classical bias-variance compromise, the generalization improves continuously as the number of parameters increases. Therefore, kernel methods also enjoy good generalization with over-parametrization.

Random features and Gaussian equivalence   — The random feature model [76], is a simple kernel-like model that is closely related to the one-hidden layer model defined above in (24.14). It only differs by fixing first-layer weights W to random values from a given distribution, such as a Gaussian or select Fourier modes at random frequencies. The only learnable parameters are in the output weight $\mathbf{v} \in \mathbb{R}^K$, and the flexibility of the model can be controlled by the number of hidden units K (see Fig. 24.2). In the scaling limit where K and the sample size P scale linearly with the dimension of input N, the generalization error can be characterized asymptotically through different methods. With the additional assumption that the input data is Gaussian distributed and the teacher input-output rule is a perceptron: $y^\mu = f^*\left(\mathbf{v}^{*\top}\mathbf{x}^\mu\right)$, learning curves were derived using random matrix theory [77], replica computations [78, 79] and Gaussian convex inequalities [80]. An important insight common to these analyses is the equivalence of the non-linear features with a Gaussian model with matching moments. That is the generalization error averaged over the teacher data distribution

$$E_g = \mathbb{E}_{\mathbf{x},y}\left[\left(f\left(\mathbf{v}^\top \sigma\left(W\mathbf{x}\right)\right) - f^*\left(\mathbf{v}^{*\top}\mathbf{x}^\mu\right)\right)^2\right], \tag{24.17}$$

concentrates in the thermodynamic limit around a function of the ratios $\alpha = P/N$ and $\gamma = K/N$ given by

$$\mathcal{E}_g(\alpha, \gamma) = \lim_{N \to \infty} E_g = \int_{\mathbb{R}^2} (f(\lambda) - f^*(\nu))^2\, \mathcal{N}(\lambda, \gamma\,;\, 0, \Sigma_{\alpha,\gamma})d\lambda d\nu, \tag{24.18}$$

where the covariance of the jointly Gaussian scalars λ and ν are themselves function of the overlap order parameters of the problem and constants accounting for the choice of non-linearity σ and input distribution. This so-called *Gaussian equivalence principle* [81]

---

[a]Kernel models are not universal approximators.

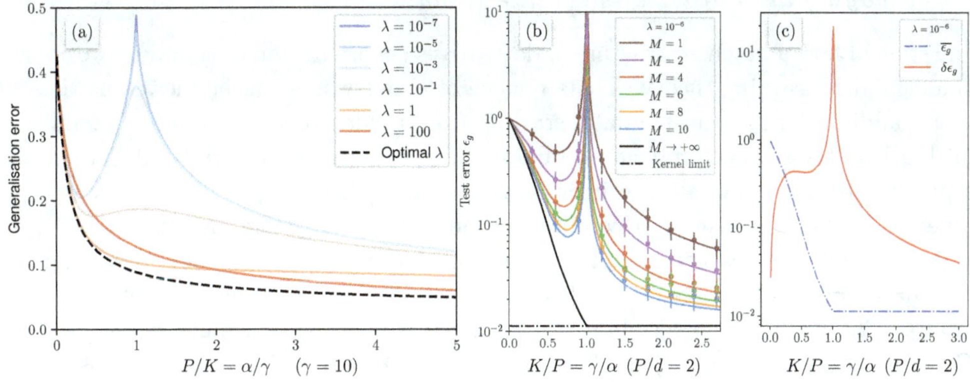

Fig. 24.5. The double descent analyzed in random-feature models through replica computation of the generalization error. (a) As an ℓ_2 regularization of strength λ is adjusted, the overfitting peak at $P/K = 1$ vanishes. (b) Similarly, averaging the prediction over an ensemble of M models mitigates the double descent pointing to the origin of the overfitting in exploding variance, as the computed decomposition shows in (c). Adapted from [78] (a) and [29] (b) and (c).

was first described for square losses using rigorous random matrix theories [77, 82] and later extended to generic convex losses [83, 84]. This formulation finally allows to predict theoretically the origin of the overfitting peak in the double descent. At the interpolation threshold, where the learning model has just enough parameters to perfectly fit the training data, the variance of the learned predictor explodes [29, 77, 85]. Beyond the interpolation threshold, over-parametrized models feature many minimizers of the training loss, yet implicit or explicit regularization of the training typically selects a minimizer with good generalization (see Fig. 24.5).

Universality — Beyond random features in a teacher-student scenario, kernel-learning has been analyzed in great generality using statistical mechanics tools. Loureiro and collaborators first replaced shallow random maps with learned deep feature maps [86], and then formulated a universal theory for any generalized linear model trained through the empirical risk minimization of a convex loss [29]. Interestingly, the latter result is mathematically rigorously proven through a novel proof technique relying on AMP [87].

Focusing instead on a generic formulation of kernel regression, Canatar and collaborators developed a widely applicable theory of learning encompassing arbitrary training data [88]. A replica computation yields the generalization error as a function of the kernel spectral decomposition, the training data distribution and the sample size. This analysis highlights the impact of the data distribution through the eigenmodes of the kernel and through the so-called *alignment* between the data and the task to be learned. Along these lines, one can show in simple linear settings that learning curves with respect to the amount of data can exhibit an arbitrary number of multiple descent peaks equal to the number of scales in the data [89]. This further highlights the importance of understanding how non-random structure in data impacts learning properties of neural networks.

24.2.3. *Studying the impact of structure in data*

The question of how and when structure in data drives generalization in neural networks is fundamental in learning theory. The sequence of above works can be viewed as the successive addition of structure in data, starting from random uncorrelated inputs and output labels in the storage problem, to random i.i.d inputs that are correlated to their corresponding outputs through the introduction of a teacher. More recent work has examined the important generalization of going beyond i.i.d. random inputs.

A first notable step is the introduction of the *hidden manifold* model assuming that the data and labels are generated from a low-dimensional representation [81] (see Fig. 24.2). The analytical description of learning in committee machines, relying on the Gaussian equivalence principle, shows that generalization is tied to the dimension of the underlying manifold. These results are consistent with the analyses of random-feature models trained on anisotropic Gaussian data combining a high-variance *strong* subspace and a low-variance *weak* subspace [79, 90]. The concept of data-task alignment is here again identified as a determinant of generalisation: it ensures that the effective dimension of the problem is small and allows for good generalisation at small sample size.

Another model of structure in data, especially relevant for classification problems, is the Gaussian mixture model of inputs. Limits of separability and generalization behavior can be derived for classification of Gaussian clusters with generalized linear models [91] and committee machines [92]. In particular, the latter work demonstrates that some configurations of clusters unlearnable with random features (an instance of a generalized linear model) can be separated by committee machines. The 2-layer neural network learns appropriate features to allow for a proper task-data representation alignment, whereas generalized linear models are limited by their fixed feature-maps, which may not be appropriate for the task.

24.2.4. *Non-convex overparametrized neural networks*

Finally, in Ref. [93] the computational consequences of overparameterization in non-convex neural network models are analyzed. In the simple case of discrete binary weights, a non-convex classifier is connected to a random features projection. The analysis shows that as the number of connection weights increases multiple phase transitions happen in the zero error landscape. A first transition happens at the so-called interpolation point, when solutions begin to exist (perfect fitting becomes possible). A second transition occurs with the discontinuous appearance of a different kind of "atypical" structures corresponding to high local entropy regions with good generalization properties.

24.3. Going Deeper

Much of the remarkable progress in artificial intelligence over the last decade has been driven by our ability to train very deep networks with many successive nonlinear layers. Formally, the simplest version of a feedforward neural network with D layers is the multi-layer perceptron, defined through

$$\mathbf{x}^l = \phi(\mathbf{h}^l) \qquad \mathbf{h}^l = W^l \mathbf{x}^{l-1} + \mathbf{b}^l \quad \text{for } l = 1, \ldots, D. \tag{24.19}$$

Here, $\mathbf{x}^0 \in \mathbb{R}^{N_0}$ is the input, which propagates through the network to generate a sequence of activity vectors $\mathbf{x}^l \in \mathbb{R}^{N_l}$ in layer l with N_l neurons. W^l is an $N_l \times N_{l-1}$ weight matrix connecting neurons in layer $l-1$ to layer l, $\mathbf{b}^l$ is a vector of biases to neurons in layer l, $\mathbf{h}^l$ is the pattern of inputs to neurons at layer l, and ϕ is a single neuron scalar nonlinearity that acts component-wise to transform inputs $\mathbf{h}^l$ to activities $\mathbf{x}^l$. The final output of the network is $\mathbf{y} = \mathbf{x}^D(\mathbf{x}^0, \mathbf{w})$ where $\mathbf{w}$ collectively denotes all D neural network parameters $\{W^l, \mathbf{b}^l\}_{l=1}^D$.

The theoretical analysis of such deep networks in full generality raises several difficult challenges which remain open to this day [94–96]. For example, how can we describe their learning dynamics? What can deep networks express that their shallow counterparts cannot? How should we initialize the weights to optimize their learning dynamics? What does their training error landscape look like? How can we use them for generative modeling? How does their performance scale with network size? In the following we review some recent progress on these questions that involves ideas from both equilibrium and non-equilibrium statistical mechanics, nonlinear dynamical systems, random matrix theory, and free probability.

24.3.1. *Exact learning dynamics for deep linear networks*

A gold standard of understanding deep learning would be an exact solution to the learning dynamics of both training and generalization error as a function of training time, for arbitrarily deep networks and for arbitrarily structured data. While this is challenging for networks of the form in (24.19), remarkably it is possible in the case of linear networks with $\phi(x) = x$ and squared loss [97, 98]. Despite the linearity of the network, the learning dynamics is highly nonlinear. Exact solutions to these dynamics reveal that deep linear networks learn by successively approximating the singular value decomposition (SVD) of the input-output correlation matrix of the training data mode by mode. Each mode is learned on a time scale inversely related to its singular value.

Intriguingly, while deep nonlinear networks have long been used in psychology to model the developmental dynamics of semantic cognition infants [99], a recent analysis [100] showed that much of this developmental learning dynamics could be qualitatively captured by deep linear networks, thereby accounting for a diversity of phenomena, including progressive differentiation of semantics, semantic illusions, item typicality, category coherence, dynamic patterns of inductive projection, and the conservation of semantic similarity across species.

Additionally, recent advances in self-supervised learning [101, 102] yield new types of learning dynamics that can also be well modelled by deep linear networks [103, 104], even in settings where the learning dynamics does not correspond to gradient descent on any function [102]. Moreover, these simpler learning models have prescriptive value: analytically derivable hyperparameter choices that work well for training deep linear models also work well for their highly nonlinear counterparts [104], thereby opening the door to the use of mathematical analysis to drive practical design decisions.

24.3.2. *Expressivity and signal propagation in random nets*

Even before one trains a network, one has to choose the initial weights and biases, for example $\{W^l, \mathbf{b}^l\}_{l=1}^D$ in (24.19), and the choice of such an initialization can have a dramatic practical impact on subsequent learning dynamics. A common choice is a zero mean i.i.d. Gaussian initialization with variance σ_w^2/N_{l-1} for weights W_{ij}^l and variance σ_b^2 for biases b_i^l. This relative scaling ensures weights and biases exert similar control over a neuron in layer l as any previous layer width N_{l-1} becomes large.

In the limit of large N_l, [105] analyzed the propagation of signals through (24.19) via dynamical mean field theory and found an order to chaos phase transition in the σ_w^2 by σ_b^2 plane for sigmoidal nonlinearities ϕ. In the ordered regime with small σ_w^2 relative to σ_b^2, the network contracts nearby inputs as they propagate forward through the network and backpropagated error gradients vanish exponentially in depth. In the chaotic phase with σ_w^2 large relative to σ_b^2, forward propagation chaotically amplifies and then folds small differences in inputs, leading to highly flexible and expressive input-output maps, while backpropagated error gradients explode exponentially in depth. Initializing networks near the edge of chaos in the σ_w^2 by σ_b^2 plane yields good, well-conditioned initializations. Indeed [106] found that the closer one initializes to the edge of chaos, the deeper a network one can train.

Subsequent work [107, 108] showed that one can go beyond i.i.d. Gaussian initializations to speed up learning especially in very deep or recurrent networks. They considered the Jacobian

$$J = \frac{\partial \mathbf{x}^D}{\partial \mathbf{x}^0} = \prod_{l=1}^{D} D^l W^l. \tag{24.20}$$

Here D^l is a diagonal matrix with entries $D_{ij}^l = \phi'(h_i^l)\,\delta_{ij}$ and $\mathbf{h}^l$ is defined in (24.19). J measures the susceptibility of the network's output to small changes in the input. Related susceptibilities play a fundamental role in the backpropagation of error that guides gradient based learning. Initializing at the edge of chaos controls the mean squared singular value of J to be 1. But for very deep networks, J could still become ill conditioned with the maximal singular value growing at a rate that is linear in the depth, even at the edge of chaos. [107, 108] controlled this growth by analytically computing the *entire* singular value spectrum of J using free probability, exploiting the fact that J is a product of random matrices, and then determined how and when we can ensure *dynamically isometric* initializations in which the *entire* singular value distribution can be tightly concentrated around 1. In particular, orthogonal weight matrices with sigmoidal nonlinearities achieve such dynamical isometry, which was shown to speed up training.

Building on these works [109] extended dynamically isometric initializations to convolutional neural networks, and showed how to train 10,000 layer models without any of the complex normalization tricks used in deep learning. Thus overall, studies of signal propagation and initialization in random deep networks provide an example of how statistical mechanics type analyses can guide engineering design decisions.

24.3.3. *Generative models via non-equilibrium dynamics*

A recent major advance in deep learning is the ability to generate remarkable, novel photorealistic images from text descriptions (see e.g. [110–112]). Intriguingly one component of models that can do this well was inspired by ideas in non-equilibrium statistical mechanics [113, 114]. In particular, being able to generate images requires modeling the probability distribution over natural images. Equilibrium methods for modelling complex distributions involve creating a Markov chain that obeys detailed balance with respect to the distribution. However if the distribution has multiple modes, such Markov chains can take very long to mix.

[113] instead suggested training a finite time nonequilibrium stochastic process to generate images starting from noise. The method of training involved taking natural images and allowing them to diffuse in a high-dimensional pixel space, thereby destroying their structure and converting them to noise. Then a neural network was trained to reverse the flow of time in this otherwise irreversible structure destroying diffusion process. The result is then a trained neural network that can sample images by converting any white noise image into a particular naturalistic image through an approximate reversal of the diffusion process. Thus this provides another example of how ideas in statistical mechanics can eventually lead to state of the art systems in artificial intelligence.

24.3.4. *Neural scaling laws governing deep learning*

Another major shift in deep learning over the last few years has been the immense scaling up of both dataset and model sizes. This has partially been motivated by empirically observed neural scaling laws [115–121] in many domains of machine learning, including vision, language, and speech, which demonstrate that test error often falls off as a power law with either the amount of training data, model size, or compute. Such power law scaling has motivated significant societal investments in data collection, compute, and associated energy consumption. However, obtaining a theoretical understanding of the origins of these scaling laws, and the dependence of their exponents on structure in data, model architecture, learning hyperparameters, etc... constitutes a major research question [122].

Also interesting is whether power law neural scaling can be beaten. Recent work [123] explored scaling with respect to dataset size to analyze wether intelligent data pruning methods [124] that involve careful subselection of training data, could lead to more efficient scaling of error w.r.t. pruned dataset sizes. Returning to the perceptron, [123] developed a replica calculation to compute the test error for non-Gaussian pruned data, and showed it is possible to beat power law scaling, and even approach exponential scaling, provided one has access to a good data pruning metric. Then going beyond the perceptron [123] showed how to beat power law scaling in modern architectures like ResNets trained on modern datasets, including ImageNet.

Overall, a deeper understanding of the origin of neural scaling laws, and the emergent capabilities that arise [125], constitutes a major open question, which may benefit from the analysis of appropriate statistical mechanics models capturing the essence of these phenomena.

References

[1] J. J. Hopfield, *Proc. Natl. Acad. Sci. U.S.A.* **79**(8), 2554–2558, (1982).

[2] D. O. Hebb, *The organization of behavior.* (Wiley, 1949).

[3] D. J. Amit, H. Gutfreund, and H. Sompolinsky, *Ann. Phys.* **173**(1), 30–67, (1987).

[4] A. Crisanti, D. J. Amit, and H. Gutfreund, *Europhys. Lett.* **2**(4), 337–341 (1986).

[5] E. Gardner and B. Derrida, *J. Phys. A.* **21**(1), 271–284 (1988).

[6] E. Gardner, *J. Phys. A.* **21**(1), 257–270 (1988).

[7] M. Mezard, *J. Phys. A.* **22**(12), 2181–2190 (1989).

[8] A. Engel and C. Van den Broeck, *Statistical Mechanics of Learning.* (Cambridge University Press, 2001). ISBN 9781139164542.

[9] E. Gardner, *J. Phys. A.* **20**(11), 3453–3464 (1987).

[10] D. Krotov and J. J. Hopfield, *Adv. Neural Inf. Process. Syst.* pp. 1180–1188 (2016).

[11] L. Albanese, F. Alemanno, A. Alessandrelli, and A. Barra, *J. Stat. Phys.* **189**(2), 24 (2022).

[12] M. Demircigil, J. Heusel, M. Löwe, S. Upgang, and F. Vermet, *J. Stat. Phys.* **168**(2), 288–299 (2017).

[13] H. Ramsauer, B. Schäfl, J. Lehner, P. Seidl, M. Widrich, T. Adler, L. Gruber, M. Holzleitner, M. Pavlović, G. K. Sandve, V. Greiff, D. Kreil, M. Kopp, G. Klambauer, J. Brandstetter, and S. Hochreiter, *arXiv: 2008.02217* (2020).

[14] A. Vaswani, N. Shazeer, N. Parmar, J. Uszkoreit, L. Jones, A. N. Gomez, L. Kaiser, and I. Polosukhin. In *Adv. Neural Inf. Process. Syst.*, pp. 5998–6008, (2017).

[15] H. Nishimori, *J. Phys. C.* **13**(21), 4071–4076 (1980).

[16] Y. Iba, *J. Phys. A.* **32**(21), 3875–3888 (1999).

[17] L. Zdeborová and F. Krzakala, *Adv. Phys.* **65**(5), 453–552 (2016).

[18] J. Barbier, F. Krzakala, N. Macris, L. Miolane, and L. Zdeborová, *Proc. 31st COLT.* **PMLR 75**, 728–731 (2018).

[19] R. Monasson and R. Zecchina, *Phys. Rev. Lett.* **75**(12), 2432–2435, (1995).

[20] H. Schwarze and J. Hertz, *Europhys. Lett.* **21**(7), 785–790, (1993).

[21] J. S. Yedidia, W. T. Freeman, and Y. Weiss, *Intelligence.* **8**, 236–239, (2002).

[22] M. Mézard and A. Montanari, *Information, Physics, and Computation.* (Oxford University Press, 2009).

[23] Y. Kabashima and D. Saad, *Europhys. Lett.* **44**(5), 668 (1998).

[24] F. Krzakala, A. Montanari, F. Ricci-Tersenghi, G. Semerjian, and L. Zdeborová, *Proc. Natl. Acad. Sci. U.S.A.* **104**(25), 10318–23 (2007).

[25] A. Braunstein and R. Zecchina, *Phys. Rev. Lett.* **96**(3), 030201 (2006).

[26] M. Mézard, *Phys. Rev. E.* **95**(2), 022117 (2017).

[27] D. L. Donoho, A. Maleki, and A. Montanari, *Proc. Natl. Acad. Sci. U.S.A.* **106**(45), 18914–18919 (2009).

[28] E. Bolthausen, *Commun. Math. Phys.* **325**(1), 333–366, (2014).

[29] B. Loureiro, C. Gerbelot, M. Refinetti, G. Sicuro, and F. Krzakala. Fluctuations, *Proc. 39th ICML*, 14283–14314, PMLR, (2022).

[30] M. Advani and S. Ganguli, *Phys. Rev. X.* **6**, 031034 (2016).

[31] M. Advani and S. Ganguli, *Adv. Neural Inf. Process. Syst.* **29**, (2016).

[32] D. L. Donoho, *IEEE Transactions on Information Theory.* **52**(4), 1289–1306 (2006).

[33] S. Rangan. In *2011 IEEE International Symposium on Information Theory Proceedings*, pp. 2168–2172. IEEE (2011).

[34] A. Manoel, F. Krzakala, M. Mézard, and L. Zdeborová. In *2017 IEEE International Symposium on Information Theory (ISIT)*, pp. 2098–2102. IEEE (2017).

[35] A. K. Fletcher, S. Rangan, and P. Schniter, *2018 IEEE International Symposium on Information Theory (ISIT).* **1**(8), 1884–1888 (2018).

[36] C. Lucibello, F. Pittorino, G. Perugini, and R. Zecchina, *Mach. learn.: sci. technol.* **3**(3), 035005 (2022).

[37] A. J. Bray and D. S. Dean, *Phys. Rev. Lett.* **98**(15), 150201, (2007).

[38] Y. V. Fyodorov and I. Williams, *J. Stat. Phys.* **129**(5-6), 1081–1116, (2007).

[39] Y. N. Dauphin, R. Pascanu, C. Gulcehre, K. Cho, S. Ganguli, and Y. Bengio. In *Adv. Neural Inf. Process. Syst.*, pp. 2933–2941, (2014).

[40] M. Baity-Jesi, L. Sagun, M. Geiger, S. Spigler, G. B. Arous, C. Cammarota, Y. LeCun, M. Wyart, and G. Biroli, *Proc. 35th ICML.* (2018).

[41] M. Geiger, S. Spigler, S. d'Ascoli, L. Sagun, M. Baity-Jesi, G. Biroli, and M. Wyart, *Phys. Rev. E.* **100**, 012115 (2019).

[42] S. Franz and G. Parisi, *J. Phys. A.* **49**(14), 145001 (2016).

[43] A. Maillard, G. Ben Arous, and G. Biroli. In eds. J. Lu and R. Ward, *Proc. MSML*, vol. 107, *Proceedings of Machine Learning Research*, pp. 287–327. PMLR, (2020).

[44] C. Baldassi, A. Ingrosso, C. Lucibello, L. Saglietti, and R. Zecchina, *Phys. Rev. Lett.* **115**(12), 128101, (2015).

[45] C. Baldassi, C. Borgs, J. T. Chayes, A. Ingrosso, C. Lucibello, L. Saglietti, and R. Zecchina, *Proc. Natl. Acad. Sci. U.S.A.* **113**(48), E7655–E7662, (2016).

[46] Y. Jiang, B. Neyshabur, H. Mobahi, D. Krishnan, and S. Bengio (2020).

[47] P. Chaudhari, A. Choromanska, S. Soatto, Y. LeCun, C. Baldassi, C. Borgs, J. Chayes, L. Sagun, and R. Zecchina, In *Proc. 5th ICLR*, (2017).

[48] F. Pittorino, C. Lucibello, C. Feinauer, G. Perugini, C. Baldassi, E. Demyanenko, and R. Zecchina, *J. Stat. Mech.: Theory Exp.* **2021**(12), 124015 (2021).

[49] P. Foret, A. Kleiner, H. Mobahi, and B. Neyshabur (2022).

[50] S. Franz and G. Parisi, *J. Physique.* **5**(11), 1401–1415 (1995).

[51] H. Huang, K. Y. M. Wong, and Y. Kabashima, *J. Phys. A.* **46**(37), 375002 (2013).

[52] E. Abbe, S. Li, and A. Sly. In *Proceedings of the 54th Annual ACM SIGACT Symposium on Theory of Computing*, pp. 860–873, (2022).

[53] C. Baldassi, A. Ingrosso, C. Lucibello, L. Saglietti, and R. Zecchina, *J. Stat. Mech.: Theory Exp.* **2016**(2), 023301, (2016).

[54] C. Baldassi, F. Pittorino, and R. Zecchina, *Proc. Natl. Acad. Sci. U.S.A.* **117**(1), 161–170, (2020).

[55] E. Agoritsas, G. Biroli, P. Urbani, and F. Zamponi, *J. Phys. A.* **51**(8), 085002 (2018).

[56] F. Mignacco, F. Krzakala, P. Urbani, and L. Zdeborová. In *Adv. Neural Inf. Process. Syst.*, vol. 33, pp. 9540–9550. Curran Associates, Inc., (2020).

[57] D. Saad and S. A. Solla, *Phys. Rev. Lett.* **74**(21), 4337–4340, (1995).

[58] D. Saad and S. A. Solla, *Phys. Rev. E.* **52**(4), 4225–4243, (1995).

[59] D. Saad, *On-Line Learning in Neural Networks.* (Cambridge University Press, 1999).

[60] S. Goldt, M. S. Advani, A. M. Saxe, F. Krzakala, and L. Zdeborová. In *Adv. Neural Inf. Process. Syst.*, vol. 1906.08632, (2019).

[61] S. Mei, A. Montanari, and P.-M. Nguyen, *Proc. Natl. Acad. Sci. U.S.A.* **115**(33), E7665–E7671 (2018).

[62] Y. LeCun, Y. Bengio, and G. E. Hinton, *Nature.* **521**(7553), 436–444, (2015).

[63] Y. LeCun, L. Bottou, Y. Bengio, and P. Haffner, *Proc. IEEE.* **86**(11), 2278–2323, (1998).

[64] T. B. Brown, G. Krueger, B. Mann, A. Askell, A. Herbert-voss, C. Winter, D. M. Ziegler, A. Radford, and S. Mccandlish. In *Adv. Neural Inf. Process. Syst.*, (2020).

[65] S. Spigler, M. Geiger, S. D'Ascoli, L. Sagun, G. Biroli, and M. Wyart, *J. Phys. A.* **52**(47), 474001 (2019).

[66] M. Belkin, D. Hsu, S. Ma, and S. Mandal, *Proc. Natl. Acad. Sci. U.S.A.* **116**(32), 15849–15854 (2019).

[67] G. Mato and N. Parga, *J. Phys. A.* **25**(19), 5047–5054, (1992).

[68] H. Schwarze, *J. Phys. A.* **26**(21), 5781–5794, (1993).

[69] K. Hornik, *Neural Networks.* **4**(1989), 251–257, (1991).

[70] M. Biehl and H. Schwarze, *J. Phys. A. Math. Gen.* **28**(3), 643–656, (1995).

[71] B. Aubin, A. Maillard, J. Barbier, F. Krzakala, N. Macris, and L. Zdeborová. In *Adv. Neural Inf. Process. Syst.*, pp. 1–44, (2018).

[72] S. Shalev-Shwartz and S. Ben-David, *Understanding Machine Learning: From Theory to Algorithms.* (Cambridge University Press, 2014).

[73] A. Jacot, F. Gabriel, and C. Hongler. In *Adv. Neural Inf. Process. Syst.*, (2018).

[74] S. Fort, G. K. Dziugaite, M. Paul, S. Kharaghani, D. M. Roy, and S. Ganguli. In *Adv. Neural Inf. Process. Syst.*, (2020).

[75] M. S. Advani, A. M. Saxe, and H. Sompolinsky, *Neural Networks.* **132**, 1–32, (2020).

[76] A. Rahimi and B. Recht. In *Adv. Neural Inf. Process. Syst.*, (2017).

[77] S. Mei and A. Montanari, *Commun. Pure Appl. Math.* **75**(4), 667–766 (2021).

[78] F. Gerace, B. Loureiro, F. Krzakala, M. Mézard, and L. Zdeborová. In *Proc. 37th ICML*, vol. 119, pp. 3452–3462. PMLR, (2020).

[79] S. D'Ascoli, M. Gabrié, L. Sagun, and G. Biroli. In *Adv. Neural Inf. Process. Syst.*, (2021).

[80] O. Dhifallah and Y. M. Lu, *arXiv:2008.11904.* (3), (2020).

[81] S. Goldt, M. Mézard, F. Krzakala, and L. Zdeborová, *Phys. Rev. X.* **10**(4), 041044 (2020).

[82] J. Pennington and P. Worah. In *Adv. Neural Inf. Process. Syst.*, number 31, pp. 2634–2643, (2017).

[83] S. Goldt, B. Loureiro, G. Reeves, M. Mézard, F. Krzakala, L. Zdeborová, B. Loureiro, G. Reeves, F. Krzakala, M. Mézard, and L. Zdeborová, *Proc. MSML.* **145**, 1–37, (2021).

[84] H. Hu and Y. M. Lu, *arXiv:2009.07669.* (2020).

[85] S. D'Ascoli, M. Refinetti, G. Biroli, and F. Krzakala. In *Proc. 37th ICML*, (2020).

[86] B. Loureiro, C. Gerbelot, H. Cui, S. Goldt, F. Krzakala, M. Mézard, and L. Zdeborová, *Adv. Neural Inf. Process. Syst.* **22**, 18137–18151, (2021).

[87] C. Gerbelot and R. Berthier, *arXiv:2109.11905.* (2021).

[88] A. Canatar, B. Bordelon, and C. Pehlevan, *Nat. Comm.* **12**(1), 2914 (2021).

[89] G. Mel and S. Ganguli. In eds. M. Meila and T. Zhang, *Proc. 38th ICML*, vol. 139, pp. 7578–7587. PMLR, (2021).

[90] B. Ghorbani, S. Mei, T. Misiakiewicz, and A. Montanari. In *Adv. Neural Inf. Process. Syst.*, (2020).

[91] B. Loureiro, G. Sicuro, C. Gerbelot, A. Pacco, F. Krzakala, and L. Zdeborová. In *Adv. Neural Inf. Process. Syst. 35*, (2021).

[92] M. Refinetti, S. Goldt, F. Krzakala, and L. Zdeborova, *Proc. 38th ICML, 8936–8947, PMLR* (2021).

[93] C. Baldassi, C. Lauditi, E. M. Malatesta, R. Pacelli, G. Perugini, and R. Zecchina, *Phys. Rev. E.* **106**(1), 014116, (2022).

[94] Y. Bahri, J. Kadmon, J. Pennington, S. S. Schoenholz, J. Sohl-Dickstein, and S. Ganguli, *Annu. Rev. Condens. Matter Phys.* **11**(1), 501–528, (2020).

[95] M. Gabrié, *J. Phys. A.* **53**(22), 223002 (2020).

[96] A. Maillard, F. Krzakala, M. Mézard, and L. Zdeborová, *J. Stat. Mech.: Theory Exp.* **2022**(8), 083301 (2022).

[97] A. M. Saxe, J. L. McClelland, and S. Ganguli, *Adv. Neural Inf. Process. Syst.* (2013).

[98] A. K. Lampinen and S. Ganguli. In *Proc. 6th ICLR*, (2018).

[99] T. T. Rogers and J. L. McClelland, *Semantic cognition: A parallel distributed processing approach.* (The MIT Press, 2004).

[100] A. M. Saxe, J. L. McClelland, and S. Ganguli, *Proc. Natl. Acad. Sci. U. S. A.* (2019).

[101] T. Chen, S. Kornblith, M. Norouzi, and G. Hinton. In eds. H. D. Iii and A. Singh, *Proc. 37th ICML*, vol. 119, pp. 1597–1607. PMLR, (2020).

[102] Grill, Strub, Altché, Tallec, and others, *Adv. Neural Inf. Process. Syst.* (2020).

[103] Y. Tian, L. Yu, X. Chen, and S. Ganguli, *arXiv:2010.00578* (2020).

[104] Y. Tian, X. Chen, and S. Ganguli. In eds. M. Meila and T. Zhang, *Proc. 38th ICML*, vol. 139, pp. 10268–10278. PMLR, (2021).

[105] B. Poole, S. Lahiri, M. Raghu, J. Sohl-Dickstein, and S. Ganguli, *Adv. Neural Inf. Process. Syst.* (2016).

[106] S. S. Schoenholz, G. Brain, J. Gilmer, G. Brain, S. Ganguli, J. Sohl-Dickstein, and G. Brain. In *International Conference on Learning Representations 2017*, pp. 1–18, (2017).

[107] J. Pennington, S. Schoenholz, and S. Ganguli. In *Adv. Neural Inf. Process. Syst.* (2017).

[108] J. Pennington, S. S. Schoenholz, and S. Ganguli. In *AISTATS*, (2018).

[109] L. Xiao, Y. Bahri, J. Sohl-Dickstein, S. Schoenholz, and J. Pennington. In *Proc. 35th ICML*, pp. 5393–5402, (2018).

[110] R. Rombach, A. Blattmann, D. Lorenz, P. Esser, and B. Ommer, *Proc. IEEE/CVF CVPR.* pp. 10684–10695 (2022).

[111] C. Saharia, W. Chan, S. Saxena, L. Li, J. Whang, E. Denton, S. K. S. Ghasemipour, B. K. Ayan, S. Sara Mahdavi, R. G. Lopes, T. Salimans, J. Ho, D. J. Fleet, and M. Norouzi, *arXiv:2205.11487* (2022).

[112] A. Ramesh, P. Dhariwal, A. Nichol, C. Chu, and M. Chen, *arXiv:2204.06125* (2022).

[113] J. Sohl-Dickstein, E. A. Weiss, N. Maheswaranathan, and S. Ganguli, *Proc. 32nd ICML.* (2015).

[114] J. Ho, A. Jain, and P. Abbeel, *Adv. Neural Inf. Process. Syst.* **33**, 6840–6851, (2020).

[115] J. Hestness, S. Narang, N. Ardalani, G. Diamos, H. Jun, H. Kianinejad, M. Patwary, M. Ali, Y. Yang, and Y. Zhou, *arXiv:1712.00409.* (2017).

[116] J. Kaplan, S. McCandlish, T. Henighan, T. B. Brown, B. Chess, R. Child, S. Gray, A. Radford, J. Wu, and D. Amodei, *arXiv:2001.08361.* (2020).

[117] T. Henighan, J. Kaplan, M. Katz, M. Chen, C. Hesse, J. Jackson, H. Jun, T. B. Brown, P. Dhariwal, S. Gray, et al., *arXiv:2010.14701.* (2020).

[118] M. A. Gordon, K. Duh, and J. Kaplan. In *Proc. 2021 Conference on Empirical Methods in Natural Language Processing*, pp. 5915–5922. ACL (2021).

[119] D. Hernandez, J. Kaplan, T. Henighan, and S. McCandlish, *arXiv:2102.01293.* (2021).

[120] X. Zhai, A. Kolesnikov, N. Houlsby, and L. Beyer, *arXiv:2106.04560.* (2021).

[121] J. Hoffmann, S. Borgeaud, A. Mensch, E. Buchatskaya, T. Cai, E. Rutherford, D. d. L. Casas, L. A. Hendricks, J. Welbl, A. Clark, et al., *arXiv:2203.15556.* (2022).

[122] Y. Bahri, E. Dyer, J. Kaplan, J. Lee, and U. Sharma, *arXiv:2102.06701* (2021).

[123] B. Sorscher, R. Geirhos, S. Shekhar, S. Ganguli, and A. S. Morcos, *arXiv:2206.14486* (2022).

[124] M. Paul, S. Ganguli, and G. K. Dziugaite, *Adv. Neural Inf. Process. Syst.* **34** (2021).

[125] J. Wei, Y. Tay, R. Bommasani, C. Raffel, B. Zoph, S. Borgeaud, D. Yogatama, M. Bosma, D. Zhou, D. Metzler, E. H. Chi, T. Hashimoto, O. Vinyals, P. Liang, J. Dean, and W. Fedus, *arXiv:2206.07682* (2022).

Chapter 25

From the Statistical Physics of Disordered Systems to Neuroscience

This chapter studies the bridges and differences between the statistical physics of disordered systems, as developed notably in the context of spin glass theory, and problems in neuroscience. In a first contribution (Sec. 25.1), **Nicolas Brunel, Rémi Monasson** and **Haim Sompolinsky** first recall the main lines of the statistical physics approach to neural networks models as developed in the 1980s and 1990s. They then survey more recent developments at the interface between statistical physics and neuroscience, including the inference of synaptic plasticity rules and the statistics of synaptic connectivity. Finally they present the Tempotron model for learning temporal patterns. In a second contribution (Sec. 25.2), **Leo van Hemmen** discusses the difference between real spin glasses, neuronal networks (of real biological neurons) and neural networks (of artificial neurons); with illustrations ranging from site-disorder models of spin glasses to temporal coding in neuronal networks and unlearning.

25.1. Statistical Physics and Neuroscience

Nicolas Brunel[*], Rémi Monasson[†] and Haim Sompolinsky[‡]

Department of Neurobiology and Department of Physics, Duke University
nicolas.brunel@duke.edu
†*Department of Physics, Ecole Normale Supérieure, PSL University*
remi.monasson@ens.fr
‡*Hebrew University of Jerusalem, Jerusalem, Israel,*
and Harvard University, Cambridge, USA
haim@fiz.huji.ac.il

25.1.1. *Introduction*

From McCullough and Pitts to Hopfield

The field of neural network modeling was born in 1943 with the pioneering work of Warren McCulloch and Walter Pitts [1], who introduced networks of binary neurons (sometimes called McCullough–Pitts (MCP) neurons), and showed that with appropriate connectivity, such networks could perform arbitrary Boolean computations, with suitably chosen synaptic weights. The next major step forward was by Franck Rosenblatt, who studied simple feedforward networks of MCP neurons termed *perceptrons*, and how such network could learn (i.e. adjust their synaptic weights) to perform simple computations such as classification of input patterns [2]. In the simplest such network

499

(with just two layers, an input and an output layer), he showed that a very simple learning algorithm (the so-called perceptron learning algorithm) is guaranteed to converge to a solution, provided it exists. The realization that computational abilities of perceptrons are rather limited held the field back for some time [3], but in the 1980s, work on multi-layer perceptrons accelerated with the introduction of simple but effective learning rules (e.g. backpropagation), paving the way for the more recent deep learning revolution, which is discussed in Chapter 24.

Hopfield

In parallel, physicists also started to get interested in models of networks of neurons and proposed fruitful analogies with systems of interacting spins [5, 6], with neurons being analogs of spins, and synaptic connections the analogs of couplings between spins. A major step forward occurred in 1982 when John Hopfield published his seminal paper 'Neural networks and physical systems with emergent collective computational abilities' [7]. While content-addressable memory models had been introduced and studied previously (e.g. [8]), Hopfield's paper had a tremendous impact on the field, attracting many physicists to the study of neural networks. He considered a fully connected network of N binary neurons, whose states $S_i(t)$ could take values ± 1. 'Memories' stored in the network were defined as random i.i.d. 'patterns' of network activity. To store these patterns in memory, Hopfield used a simple 'learning rule', that modified synaptic connectivity as the product of the states of the two neurons connected by the synapse (pre and post-synaptic neurons). This plasticity rule is 'Hebbian' in the sense that it implements in particular a principle proposed in the 1940s by Donald Hebb: That a synapse should potentiate when two neurons connected by this synapse are repeatedly active together [9]. Starting from a 'tabula rasa' matrix, after learning p random patterns $\xi_i^\mu = \pm 1$ ($i = 1, \ldots, N$, $\mu = 1, \ldots, p$), the resulting connectivity matrix can be written

$$J_{ij} = \frac{1}{N} \sum_\mu \xi_i^\mu \xi_j^\mu$$

Using numerical simulations, Hopfield showed that this connectivity matrix endowed network dynamics with fixed point attractors close to the stored memories, provided the number of stored patterns was not large, $p < p_{max} \sim 0.14N$. Furthermore, he showed that this model had pattern completion properties - when initialized with a noisy version of the stored patterns, the network dynamics converges to the stored pattern itself, or a network state very close to it (see Fig. 25.1(A) for a schematic depiction of the state space of the Hopfield model).

    A few years later, the model was solved analytically by Daniel Amit, Hanoch Gutfreund and one of us (HS) using the replica method [10]. This calculation allowed them to derive the phase diagram of the model in the $T - \alpha$ plane, where T is the temperature and $\alpha \equiv p/N$ is the number of stored memories per neuron. This phase diagram is depicted in Fig. 25.1(B).

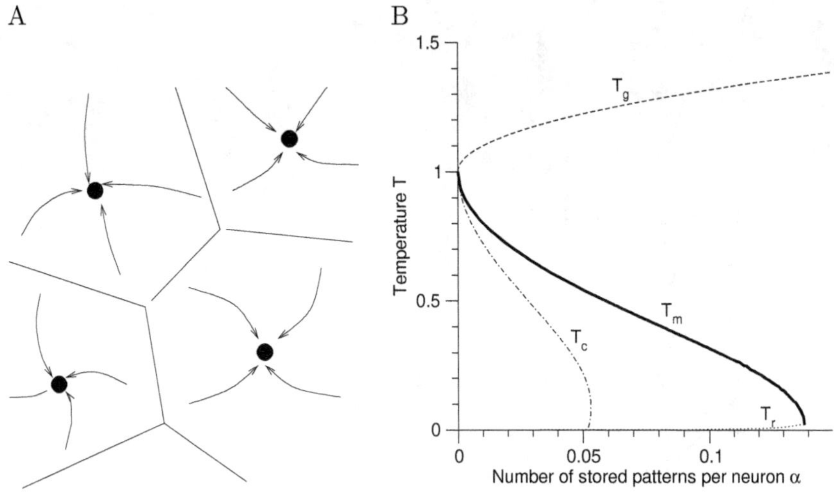

Fig. 25.1.   A: Attractor landscape. Each of the circles represent one stored memory. These stored memories have large basins of attraction around them, leading to pattern completion (or error correction) properties. B: Phase diagram of the Hopfield model [4]. The retrieval phase (where stored memories can be retrieved) lies below the T_m line. Retrieval states become states of lowest energy below the T_c line. Finally, RSB occurs below the T_r line at very low temperatures.

Gardner

A completely different approach was introduced by Elizabeth Gardner in landmark 1988 papers [12, 13]. Instead of focusing on a specific learning rules as Hopfield had done, she considered the space of all possible connectivity matrices that allow a network to embed a given set of fixed point attractors, with a given robustness level, and a constraint on the norm of synaptic weight vectors (see Fig. 25.2(A) for a schematic depiction of the space of solutions).

She then realized it was possible to compute the typical volume of the subspace of solutions to this storage problem, again using the replica method. Thus, rather than doing statistical mechanics in the space of neuronal variables with a fixed connectivity matrix, as Amit, Gutfreund and one of us (HS) had done for the Hopfield model, she performed statistical mechanics calculations in the space of synaptic variables, with a fixed set of patterns to be memorized.

Using this approach, she could obtain the storage capacity in the limit when the volume of solution weights goes to zero. The result for the capacity, in the absence of robustness constraints, coincided with an old calculation by Cover [14] that had used a completely different method. However, the power of this new method was that, unlike with Cover's method, it became possible to generalize these calculations to include robustness constraints, biased patterns, various constraints on weights, etc.. Fig. 25.2(B) shows in particular the trade-off between capacity and robustness, and it also shows the capacity increases when patterns are biased. Note that the RS solution is stable in the whole region below maximal capacity, but that RSB occurs beyond the critical line $\alpha_c(K)$. The power of this method is also that it provides an upper bound on the storage capacity of any learning rule, and it can thus tell us about how efficient a given learning

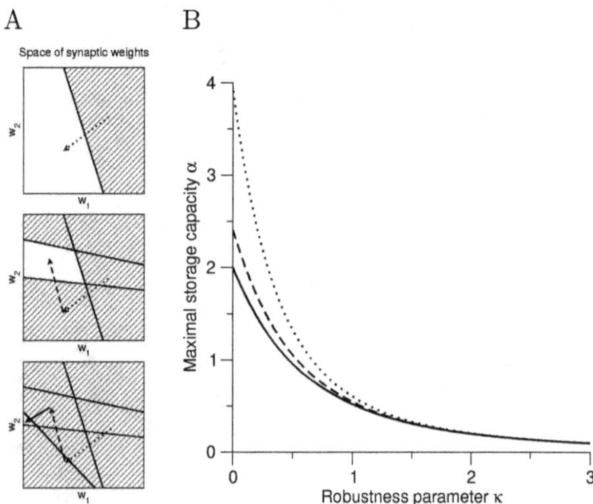

Fig. 25.2.   A: Schematic depiction of space of solutions with varying number of stored patterns. From [11].   B: Storage capacity α_c vs robustness level κ, for several values of the bias of memories - the sparser memories are, the higher maximal capacity [12].

rule is at storing patterns, by comparing its capacity with Gardner's upper bound. For instance, it shows that the learning rule used by Hopfield is not very efficient, since the capacity of the Hopfield model is only $\alpha_c \sim 0.14$, compared to an upper bound of $\alpha_{c,max} = 2$.

Evidence for attractor dynamics

One of the crucial properties of the Hopfield model is that, due to the fact that retrieval states are attractors of the dynamics, once the network is in a state correlated with one of the stored memories, this state can persist for a long time — typically, until an external input drives the network to another state. Thus, the network can maintain information about a transient input in short term memory. This model thus predicts that in tasks with short-term memory components, there should exist populations of neurons with persistent elevated activity while a stimulus is maintained in short-term (or working) memory. The phenomenon of persistent activity in tasks with a working memory component (delayed response tasks) has been documented in multiple cortical areas, consistent with attractor dynamics in primates [15–21] and humans [22]. More recently, persistent activity has also been observed in mice [23] and flies [24]. In both mice and flies, optogenetic tools [25] have allowed experimentalists to perturb the activity of the relevant circuits during maintenance of information in short-term memory. The results of such experiments are entirely consistent with attractor dynamics: With weak perturbations, the network returns to unperturbed state, and the animal can perform the task correctly; With stronger perturbations, the network goes to a different state, leading to an error [23, 24].

First steps towards neurobiology

The Hopfield model is a highly simplified model and as such has been criticized by neurobiologists for being very far from the reality of neurobiological networks. In response to these criticisms, theorists worked in the following years on generalizations that make the model more realistic.

- Neurobiological networks are far from being fully connected. Several authors thus considered a diluted version of the Hopfield model,

$$J_{ij} = \frac{c_{ij}}{cN} \sum_{\mu} \xi_i^{\mu} \xi_j^{\mu}$$

  where $c_{ij} = 1, 0$ with probability $c, 1 - c$ and the capacity is redefined as $\alpha_c = p_{max}/(cN)$. It was shown that diluting the connectivity matrix in a symmetric fashion does not affect the qualitative properties of the network [26]. In a model with highly diluted asymmetric connectivity [27], the capacity was shown to be $\alpha_c = 2/\pi \sim 0.637$ in the sparse connectivity limit. Thus, randomly diluting the connectivity matrix in an asymmetric fashion leads to a more efficient storage of information.

- Activity in the brain is typically sparse, with far less than half of the neurons being activated by a particular stimulus. Motivated by this observation, [28] (see also [29, 30]) studied models with 0,1 neurons and sparsely encoded memories $\xi_i^{\mu} = 0, 1$ with probability $1 - f, f$, where the connectivity matrix was defined as

$$J_{ij} = \frac{1}{f(1 - f)N} \sum_{\mu} (\xi_i^{\mu} - f)(\xi_j^{\mu} - f). \tag{25.1}$$

  They showed that $\alpha_c \sim 1/(2f \log(1/f))$ in the sparse ($f \to 0$) coding limit, and thus the capacity diverges in that limit. Information stored per synapse increases with decreasing f up to $1/(2 \log 2) \sim 0.721$ bits per synapse when $f \to 0$. Interestingly, Gardner's calculation for the capacity upper bound has the same scaling in the sparse coding limit, indicating that in that limit the simple learning rule of Eq. (25.1) becomes optimal.

- Neurobiological synapses are either excitatory or inhibitory, and are thus sign-constrained. Using Gardner's approach, [31] showed that imposing such sign constraint exactly halves the capacity upper bound, i.e. $\alpha = 1$ in the specific case of unbiased patterns and no robustness constraints.

- Networks with discrete weights have also been studied extensively, using either a 'clipped' Hebbian rule [26], or Gardner's approach [32, 33]. Here RSB does play an important role in determining the storage capacity [32, 33] (see also [34] for a detailed exploration of the space of solutions).

- Applying the Hebbian learning rule of the Hopfield model leads to the so-called 'memory blackout' or 'catastrophic forgetting' if too many patterns are learned - beyond storage capacity, all information is lost. Various authors have proposed simple solutions to this problem that preserve the essential properties of the model, using either synaptic decay [35] or bounds [36].

- Neurons are far more complex than simple binary devices. This has motivated in particular implementations of networks of spiking neurons with separate excitatory and inhibitory populations. These models can in particular reproduce states of network activity where neurons fire irregularly at low firing rates, as seen in electrophysiological recordings (see e.g. [37, 38])

More recent developments

After this brief introduction on work by statistical physicists on neural network models in the 1980s and 1990s, we now turn to more recent developments at the interface between statistical physics and neuroscience.

- Attractor network models use simplified Hebbian synaptic plasticity rules, but it is unclear whether synapses in cortex *in vivo* obey these rules. Can we infer plasticity rules from data? Can networks with plasticity rules inferred from data generate attractor dynamics? These questions are examined in Sec. 25.1.2.
- The Gardner approach can be used to compute various statistics of network connectivity when the network is on the critical line shown in Fig. 25.2(B), as discussed in Sec. 25.1.3.
- Models studied initially by physicists ignored the temporal structure in neuronal activity. Tempotrons, i.e. generalizations of perceptrons to temporally structured input patterns, are discussed in Sec. 25.1.4.

25.1.2. *Inferring synaptic plasticity rules from data*

A long-standing question in theoretical neuroscience is to understand the mechanisms of synaptic plasticity, and to derive synaptic plasticity rules that capture experimental data quantitatively. Most of what we know about synaptic plasticity comes from *in vitro* data [40–42], and this data has been used by theorists to build synaptic plasticity rules in which synaptic efficacy variables are driven by spikes of pre- and post-synaptic neurons [43–46]. The most recent versions of these rules are able to reproduce the experimentally observed dependence of synaptic plasticity both on spike timing and on firing rate. In particular, these rules lead to potentiation when both pre and post-synaptic neurons are firing at high rates, consistent at least superficially with Hebbian rules. It has been shown by various authors that spiking network implementations with such synaptic plasticity rules can lead to the emergence of attractor dynamics in a purely unsupervised way, provided additional homeostastic plasticity mechanisms are added [47–49].

It is however unclear to which degree synaptic plasticity rules built from *in vitro* data describe synaptic plasticity *in vivo*. This is because synaptic plasticity depends sensitively on multiple variables (such as extra-cellular concentrations of calcium and various neuromodulators, etc.) that can differ quite significantly between *in vitro* and *in vivo* conditions [50]. Ideally, one would like to study synaptic plasticity *in vivo*. However, the methods that are used to study synaptic plasticity *in vitro*, through direct measurements of synaptic efficacy using paired intracellular recordings, can still not be applied *in vivo*. Thus, more indirect methods are needed.

One such method was introduced a few years ago by Lim *et al.* [39]. The idea of the method is to compare the statistics of neuronal responses to novel and familiar stimuli. The hypothesis is that: (i) When novel stimuli are experienced, they lead to specific patterns of neuronal activity in relevant sensory circuits; (ii) These patterns of neuronal activity elicit synaptic plasticity in these circuits; (iii) These changes in synaptic efficacy in turn lead to changes in how neurons respond to a particular stimulus, as it becomes familiar. A natural question is then whether we can reverse engineer a synaptic plasticity rule from changes in statistics of neuronal responses with familiarity.

For this method to be feasible, statistics of responses to familiar stimuli should be different from responses to novel stimuli. Such differences have been documented by multiple studies, in particular in inferior temporal (IT) cortex, the last stage of purely visual processing in the visual system [51, 52]. These experiments show that average neuronal responses decrease with familiarity [51, 52], but also that in response to familiar visual stimuli, the firing rates of the most active neurons are higher than in response to novel stimuli (see Fig. 25.3(A)).

To understand which plasticity rules are consistent with this data, Lim *et al.* [39] considered a firing rate model [53], i.e. a network of N neurons described by their firing rates $r_i(t)$ $(i = 1, \ldots, N)$, whose dynamics obey

$$\frac{dr_i}{dt} = -r_i(t) + \phi \left[\sum_{i \neq j}^{N} J_{ij} r_j(t) + I_i \right],$$

where ϕ is the single neuron input/output transfer function (f-I curve), that can be inferred from data, assuming that the distribution of inputs when novel stimuli are presented is a Gaussian (see Fig. 25.3(B)); J_{ij} is the synaptic connectivity matrix; And I_i are external inputs, describing how external stimuli drive the network.

Lim *et al.* [39] then assumed that the synaptic connectivity matrix obeys an unsupervised Hebbian plasticity rule, $\Delta J_{ij} \sim A f(r_i) g(r_j)$, where f and g describe the dependence of synaptic plasticity on post and presynaptic firing rates, respectively. Note that

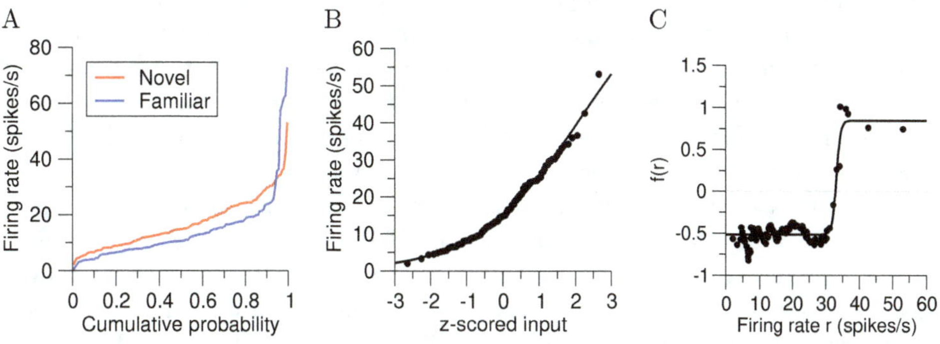

Fig. 25.3.   A. Quantile functions of visual responses to sets of novel (red) and familiar (blue) images of a neuron in primate IT cortex. Note that the distribution of responses to familiar stimuli has a smaller mean, but a fatter tail, that the distributions of responses to novel stimuli. B. Transfer function inferred from data, and sigmoidal fit. C. Dependence of synaptic plasticity rule on post-synaptic firing rate, and sigmoidal fit. Note depression for rates below a threshold $\sim 30/s$, and potentiation above this threshold [39].

this rule is a simple generalization of synaptic plasticity rules used in the Refs. [7, 28]. Lim *et al.* [39] then showed that it is possible to infer the dependence of plasticity on post-synaptic firing rates, from distributions of responses to novel and familiar stimuli. The resulting function f is shown in Fig. 25.3(C). For the particular neuron shown in Fig. 25.3, it is an increasing function of the firing rate, with a sigmoidal shape. The function is negative for rates below a threshold of about 30 spikes/second, and positive above this threshold. Intuitively, the negative part of the function f is responsible for the decrease in rates that happens for the vast majority of shown stimuli, while the positive part of the distribution is responsible for the increase in rates that occur for a small fraction of shown stimuli — the ones that initially drive the neuron above the potentiation threshold. The function g cannot be fully inferred, but can be shown to be positively correlated with the pre-synaptic firing rate. The resulting synaptic plasticity rule bears similarities with the standard covariance rule used in many theoretical studies, but with two crucial differences: The threshold between potentiation and depression is much higher than the average post-synaptic firing rate; And the dependence on rate is highly non-linear.

Using these results, one can build a Hopfield-type network, in which both distributions of stored patterns and synaptic plasticity rule are both inferred from data. It was shown that such a network can exhibit attractor dynamics [54]. The observation of attractor dynamics, and the distributions of firing rates in background, stimulus-driven and memory states, are all consistent with experimental data in primate IT cortex [17, 55]. Ref. [54] also showed that the storage capacity of the network can be maximized by using step functions for f and g, which might provide an explanation for the highly non-linear dependence shown in Fig. 25.3(C). Interestingly, in this limit the plasticity rule first binarizes firing rates prior to storage in the connectivity matrix.

25.1.3. *Statistics of synaptic connectivity in optimal networks*

Gardner's approach has been used to compute the storage capacity of networks with various architectures, statistics of stored patterns, and/or constraints on synaptic weights (see Introduction for a brief review). Another promising direction has been to use Gardner's approach to characterize the statistics of synaptic connectivity that optimizes information storage. If one makes the hypothesis that brain areas have been optimized to stored information about the external world, these calculations lead to predictions about these statistics in networks involved in memory storage.

The first such calculation was to compute the distribution of synaptic weights in a simple perceptron [56]. Motivated by an analogy of Purkinje cells, the only output cells of cerebellar cortex, an area involved in motor learning, with perceptrons, they computed distributions of synaptic weights in perceptrons in which synaptic weights are constrained to be positive. This constraint is due to the fact that in Purkinje cells, learning is thought to occur through modifications of excitatory synapses from presynaptic granule cells. On the critical line $\alpha_c(\kappa)$ on which the volume of solutions vanishes, the distribution becomes the sum of a delta function (zero weight, i.e. 'silent' synapses) and a truncated Gaussian (see Fig. 25.4(A)). The fraction of zero-weight synapses, or equivalently the effective connection probability, was shown to depend

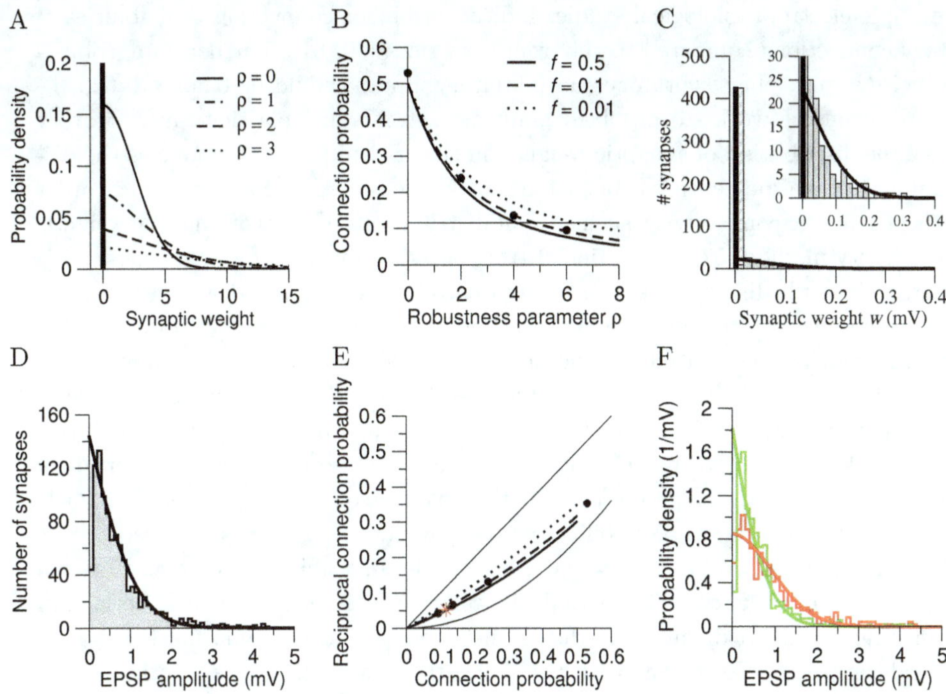

Fig. 25.4. A. Distribution of synaptic weights in networks at maximal capacity, for several values of the robustness parameter. The distribution is composed of a delta function in zero ('silent', or 'potential' synapses), and a truncated Gaussian. B. Connection probability, i.e. fraction of synapses with non-zero weights as a function of robustness parameter, for several values of the 'coding level' or sparseness f. C. Fit of granule cell to Purkinje cell synaptic weight histogram by distribution of weights in an optimal perceptron. D. Histograms of synaptic weights in synaptic connections between cortical pyramidal cells vs theoretical distribution. E. Reciprocal connection probability vs connection probability in optimal networks for several values of the coding level (indicated in panel B). F. Experimental and theoretical distributions of synaptic weights of neurons that are bidirectionnally connected (red), or unidirectionnally connected (green) [56, 57].

strongly on the robustness parameter: In the absence of robustness constraints, exactly half synapses are silent, but the fraction of silent synapses increases with the degree of robustness of learning, and connection probability goes to zero in the strong robustness limit (Fig. 25.4(B)). The distribution provides a good fit of the experimentally observed distribution of granule cell to Purkinje cell synaptic weigths, and in particular it provides an explanation for the surprising result that approximately 80% are silent (i.e. with no detectable synaptic current when the presynaptic cell is stimulated). This result shows that distributions of synaptic weights of Purkinje cells are consistent with these cells either maximizing their storage capacity for a given robustness constraint, or instead maximizing the degree of robustness of learning for a given amount of stored information.

These calculations have been also extended to the case in which neurons have plastic excitatory and inhibitory synapses [58, 59]. Interestingly, these calculations predict that while excitatory connection probability should be smaller than 50%, inhibitory connection probability should instead be larger than 50% [58]. This is in broad agreement with multiple electrophysiological studies indicating higher connection probabilities of inhibitory connections compared to the excitatory ones [60, 61]. Furthermore, robustness to noise implies that excitatory and inhibitory inputs should be balanced [62].

In a recurrent network storing fixed point attractors using plasticity in excitatory synapses, the distribution of synaptic weights on the critical line is the same as the distribution for optimal perceptrons. In such networks, one can also compute higher order statistics of synaptic connectivity, such as joint distributions of pairs of synaptic weights, using the cavity method [57]. In particular, the joint distribution of weights connecting two neurons in both directions is a truncated correlated Gaussian distribution. Such networks have an intermediate degree of symmetry — there is an overrepresentation of bidirectionnally connected pairs of neurons compared to a random asymmetric network, but the network is not fully symmetric (see Fig. 25.4(E)). A non-zero degree of symmetry is necessary for the network to exhibit attractor dynamics, but a fully symmetric network turns out to be sub-optimal for memory storage. These properties of synaptic connectivity are fully consistent with synaptic connectivity in recurrent networks in cortex: Connection probability between pyramidal cells at short distances is typically on the order of 10% [41, 42, 60, 63], while anatomical studies have shown that such local networks could potentially be fully connected [64]. Thus, the lack of full connectivity at short distances might be due to optimization of information storage by cortical networks. Consistent with this idea, the distribution of synaptic weights for pairs of cortical neurons is well fitted by data (see Fig. 25.4(D), data from [65]). In addition, there is a strong overrepresentation of bidirectionnally connected pairs of neurons, both in cortex [41, 65, 66], with the notable exception of barrel cortex [67], and in hippocampus [68] (Fig. 25.4(E)). Finally, distributions of weights for bidirectionnally and unidirectionnally connected pairs of neurons are also in striking agreement with data (Fig. 25.4(F)).

25.1.4. *Learning temporal patterns: Tempotron*

25.1.4.1. *Definition of the model*

Many models for supervised learning with neural networks assume static spatial patterns of intensities, such as the celebrated perceptron. Yet activities in a neural population are intrinsically time dependent, and it is natural to wonder to what extent computational tasks, such as classification, could exploit this temporal structure. We report here results on the classification properties of the tempotron, introduced by Gütig and one of us (HS) [69], a model of neuron able to decode information embedded in spatio-temporal spike patterns. In the continuous time formulation the tempotron neuron integrates the spikes coming from N input neurons $i = 1...N$, by updating its membrane potential with time:

$$U(t) = \sum_{i=1}^{N} J_i \sum_{\ell:t_{i,\ell}<t} u(t - t_{i,\ell}), \tag{25.2}$$

where J_i is the synaptic efficacy of the connection between neuron i and the tempotron, and $t_{j,\ell}$ is the time of emission of the lth spike of neuron j; the model is therefore

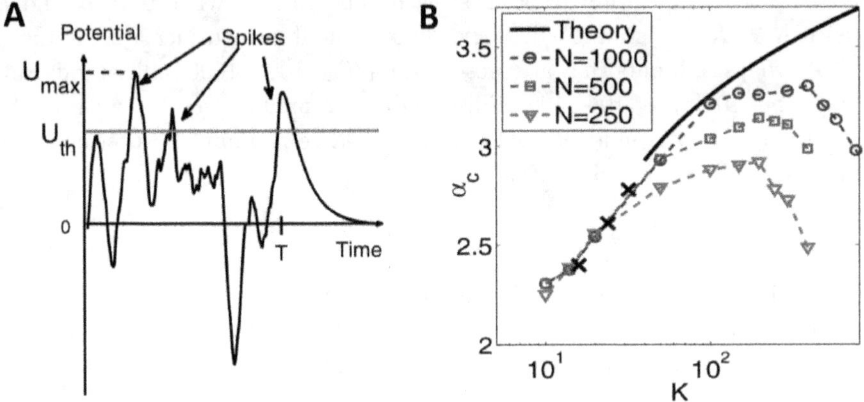

Fig. 25.5.　**The tempotron, a spike-timing-based classifier. A.** Typical time course of the (membrane) potential of the tempotron neuron. Each time an input neuron i emits a spike the potential transiently increases (if the synaptic coefficient $J_i > 0$) or decreases (if $J_i < 0$). Each time the potential exceeds the threshold value U_{th} the tempotron neuron becomes active (here, 3 spikes are emitted), otherwise it remains silent. **B.** Capacity α_c of the tempotron vs. K. Lines with symbols show results from the learning algorithm of [69], which, for each pattern μ, strenghtens (for $y^\mu = +1$) or discounts ($y^\mu = -1$) the synaptic coefficient J_i proportionally to the contribution of neuron i to the maximum of the potential, U_{max}. The solid line shows the large-K theory in Eq. 25.4, with an additive constant fitted to the predictions of the replica method for the discrete tempotron for $K_{discrete} =1$, 2, 3, and 4 (symbols, no line), see [70] for details. To compare the theory of the discrete tempotron with the simulation results of the continuous time tempotron, we used $K_{discrete} = K/8$. From [70].

equivalent to a linear integrate-and-fire neuron. The kernel is $u(\tau) = e^{-\tau/\tau_m} - e^{-\tau/\tau_s}$, where τ_m, τ_s correspond to, respectively, the membrane and synaptic time constants. Each spike received by the tempotron neuron therefore results in a transient increase or decrease (depending on the sign of the synaptic connection) of the potential U. If U exceeds the threshold value U_{th} at some time t the tempotron emits an output spike; Otherwise, if $U(t) < U_{th}$ at all times it remains silent, see Fig. 25.5(A).

We focus on the standard task of classifying a set of $p = \alpha N$ random patterns, where α denotes the load. For each pattern $\mu = 1, ..., p$, the timings of the input spikes from each input neuron i are randomly chosen from independent Poisson processes with a rate $1/T$, where T is the duration of the input patterns (Fig. 25.5(A)), and the desired output, $y^\mu = \pm 1$, is randomly and independently chosen with equal probabilities. A solution to the classification problem is a set of synaptic weights J_i that yields a correct classification of all p patterns. We are interested in the maximal load that can be accomodated by the tempotron, referred to as critical capacity and denoted by α_c, as well as in the nature of the set of solutions in the N-dimensional weight space $\{J_i\}$ when $\alpha < \alpha_c$. The presentation below reproduces the one of [70].

25.1.4.2. *The critical capacity*

The theoretical analysis of the problem defined above shows that a fundamental parameter is the duration of the input pattern, T, relative to the neural time scales,

$$K = \frac{T}{\sqrt{\tau_s \tau_m}}. \tag{25.3}$$

The properties of the tempotron can be most easily understood, when both N and K are large, with $N \gg K$. This limit is biologically sensible if we consider a neuron with $N \sim 10^3 - 10^4$ synapses, inputs that are presented for $T \sim 100 - 1000$ milliseconds, and constants $\tau_s \sim 1 - 10$, $\tau_m \sim 10 - 100$ milliseconds. We predict (see below) that, for any fixed K, the capacity is independent of N in the large-N limit. Furthermore, the capacity asymptotically grows with K as

$$\alpha_c = \frac{\ln \ln K}{2 \ln 2}. \qquad (25.4)$$

Equation (25.4) implies that the capacity of the tempotron is not bounded as K increases, and may exceed the capacity of the perceptron model, whose architecture is similar to the tempotron. Note that for a fixed N and increasing K, the few input spikes that arrive within a single decision time window, T/K, do not carry sufficient information to classify the patterns. We therefore expect that, for any fixed N, α_c is a non-monotonic function of K while the value of K that maximizes the capacity increases with N, as implied by Eq. (25.4). This prediction is corroborated by numerical simulations in Fig. 25.5(B). Interestingly, according to Eq. (25.3), the performance is sensitive also to the time behavior of the kernel u. In particular, the rise time τ_s of u determines how fast the membrane potential U significantly changes. The shorter the rise time is, the easier it is to distinguish between inputs that arrive within a short interval of time, and the larger the capacity α_c is according to Eq. (25.4).

25.1.4.3. *The structure of the solution space*

As shown in Fig. 25.2(A), in the perceptron model, the solution space for a given classification problem is a convex volume, which shrinks in size and ultimately vanishes as α approaches the capacity, α_c. The overlap between two typical solutions, q_0, defined by the inner product between their normalized weight vectors, approaches 1 at the critical capacity. In contrast the solution space of the tempotron is of a strikingly different nature (Fig. 25.6(A)). First, the overlap between two tempotron weight vectors that solve the random classification problem, q_0, approaches zero in the $K \gg 1$ limit, for every $\alpha < \alpha_c$. Secondly, the solution space is connected for small α only. For larger values of α still far below capacity, the solution space breaks into a large number of small clusters, spread across the entire weight space. The overlap between solutions within the same cluster, q_1, is close to 1, while two randomly chosen solutions are likely to lie in different clusters and have overlap $q_0 \to 0$. Simulations making use of the learning algorithm of [69] support this picture (results not shown): the overlap between two solutions obtained by the learning algorithm from two different initial choises of weight vectors vanishes for all values of α, while the auto-correlation function of a random walk starting from a randomly chosen solution hardly decays (unless α is very small) as expected for a clustered solution space.

25.1.4.4. *Internal representations and explicit Replica Symmetry Breaking*

From a spin-glass point of view, the picture of the solution space as stated above is reminiscent of (spontaneous) Replica Symmetry Breaking (RSB), with the emergence of

A

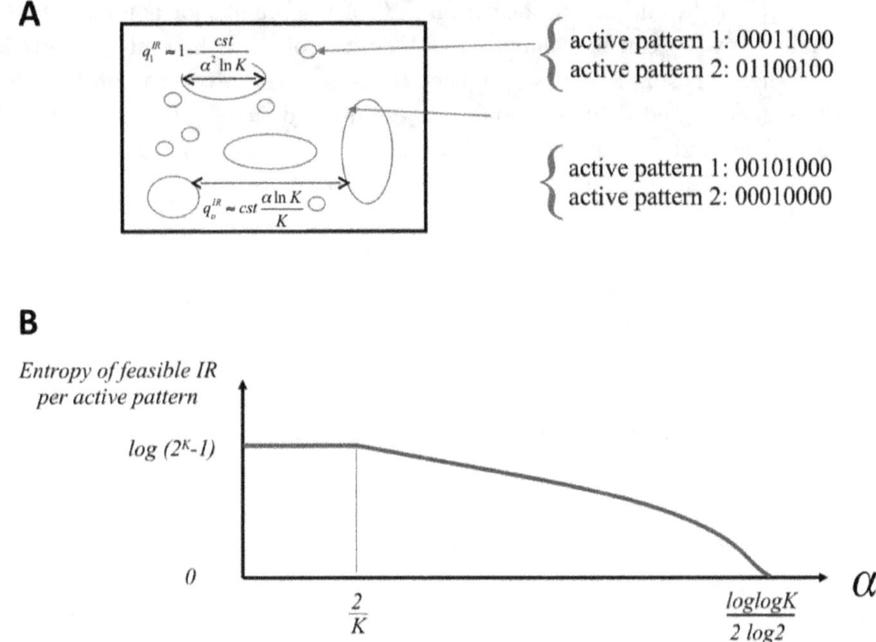

B

Fig. 25.6. **Representations of temporal patterns by the tempotron. A.** Sketch of the weight space. Solution weight vectors define connected domains of solutions, labelled by a representation of the training patterns. The intra- and inter-domain overlaps correspond to, respectively, q_1^{IR} and q_0^{IR}. **B.** Qualitative behaviour of the entropy of admissible representations (associated to non-empty domains and normalized by the number of $y = +1$-patterns) vs. load α. The entropy is maximal up to $\alpha = \frac{2}{K}$, and vanishes at the critical capacity α_c.

a complex structure of the overlap distribution. In practice, this picture was obtained through an explicit RSB scheme, based on the internal-representation (IR) domain approach developed by O'Kane and one of us (RM) [71], see [72] for a survey of the approach and of applications. Briefly speaking, internal representations keep track of all possible ways to correctly classify the patterns. A $y = -1$ pattern can be classified in a single way: the tempotron should fire no spike, or, equivalently, have 0 activity in all K effective decision time windows at its disposal; thus the IR of a $y = -1$-pattern can be written as a string of K zeros: 000...000. Conversely, patterns associated to $y = +1$ are correctly classified if the tempotron emits at least one spike. Admissible IR are thus K-strings with at least one 1, e.g. 010..011 or 111...000. There are at most $2^K - 1$ such representations per $y = +1$ patterns, and thus $(2^K - 1)^{P/2}$ possible IR for the whole set of patterns to be classified. A key observation is that finding the set of weight vectors associated with one of these IR is equivalent to solving a perceptron-like classification problem [71]. The (possibly empty) set of solution weight vectors is therefore a convex domain, which can be described with a single overlap q_1^{IR} as in Gardner's framework, see Fig. 25.6(A). At least one additional overlap, q_0^{IR}, is needed to account for the typical overlap between solutions belonging to different domains. Hence, characterizing IR domains is required to explicitly break the symmetry between replicas (of weight vectors).

The values of q_1^{IR}, q_0^{IR}, and of the logarithm S^{IR} of the number of non-empty IR domains (normalized by N) can be calculated as functions of α, with results reported in Fig. 25.6(B). When α is very small ($< \frac{2}{K}$), each IR-associated perceptron problem is below its critical capacity and defines a non-empty solution domain. Hence all IR are feasible in this regime, and S^{IR} is maximal and equal to $\frac{\alpha}{2} \ln\left(2^K - 1\right)$. For larger α some IR cannot be realized any longer. For even larger loads α, we have

$$S^{IR} \simeq \frac{1}{2} \ln \ln K - \alpha \ln 2. \tag{25.5}$$

The value of α at which S^{IR} vanishes allows us to locate the critical capacity α_c, and gives Eq. (25.4). The similarity between quantities defined in terms of connected clusters of solutions, and those defined in terms of IR domains is a consequence of the 'all-or-nothing' nature of the large K limit: overlaps can take almost 0 or almost 1 values only, which allow different definitions to capture the same structure of the solution space.

25.1.5. *Conclusion*

As we have briefly reviewed in this section, statistical physics methods have allowed theorists to characterize in depth learning and memory properties of various neural network models. The pioneering work of physicists in the 1980s have provided solid foundations on which many later studies have been built. While initially restricted to highly simplified models, later studies have characterized more realistic models, as shown in this section. As a result these methods now belong to the standard toolbox of theoretical neuroscientists.

In parallel with this theoretical work, progress in experimental methods make it now possible to test model predictions. While the phenomenon of selective persistent activity, consistent with attractor dynamics, has been documented for decades in non-human primates, more recent data indicate persistent activity is also present in flies, mice and humans. Furthermore, recently introduced optogenetic techniques allow experimentalists to perturb selectively circuits that are known to be required for persistent activity maintenance. In both flies and mice, the results of these experiments have been consistent with attractor models. Further progress towards bridging theoretical models to data includes the observation that synaptic plasticity rules inferred from data seem well suited to store a large number of memories as fixed point attractor states, and that the statistics of network connectivity obtained from in vitro experiments are also consistent with systems that are close to optimizing information storage.

Far from being confined to purely feedforward networks or recurrent networks with symmetric connectivity, methods from statistical physics can also be used to characterize the dynamics of networks with asymmetric connectivity, and thus to understand potential mechanisms of phenomena such as oscillations, generation of sequential activity, and chaotic dynamics. In particular, dynamical mean-field theory (discussed in more detail in Chapter 28) has provided a powerful tool to understand the dynamics of networks with random asymmetric connectivity (see e.g. [73–77]). Methods from statistical physics can also be applied to networks that store continuous attractors [78–82], potentially shedding light on the dynamics of hippocampal networks storing spatial representations.

Many formidable challenges still await theorists working on neural systems. The advent of connectomics (e.g. [83, 84]) will lead to far more detailed information about synaptic connectivity that has been available so far. One important challenge will be to infer from this vast amount of data information about memories stored in reconstructed circuits [85]. Progress in high-throughput transcriptional profiling reveal far more cell types than models typically incorporate (e.g. [86, 87]), leading to challenges in understanding the functional roles of these different cell types. Increasingly larger scale neuronal recordings, both at the single area level [88], but also in simultaneous recordings from multiple areas [89] or even the whole brain [90], provide additional challenges for theorists. Overcoming these challenges will require synergistic interactions between experimentalists and theorists, and should lead to breakthroughs in our understanding of how neural systems work.

25.2. Neuronal Networks and Spin Glasses: A Non-Existing Relationship

J. Leo van Hemmen

Physik Department T35, Technische Universität München, Germany
lvh@tum.de

25.2.1. *Introduction*

Replica symmetry breaking (RSB) is a notion introduced by Giorgio Parisi in a sequence of papers devoted to solving the Sherrington–Kirkpatrick (SK) model of a spin glass (SG). In this very first sentence we already meet the three notions that are the key to the present book: RSB, SK, and SG. They often require long deliberations that we will not delve into. For RSB there is an early and nice reference, the book by Mézard, Parisi, and Virasoro [91], also including reprints of many original papers. An early and still one of the best characterizations of a spin glass that (practically) everyone agrees on is due to Gérard Toulouse [92]: Both randomness *and* frustration are core concepts giving rise to the spin-glass phase in many three-dimensional "spin glasses" once the temperature is low enough. For an early (1983) and thorough discussion of SG problems, one may consult the proceedings of the *Heidelberg Colloquium on Spin Glasses* [93].

What we will do here is not unfolding RSB, SK, and SG but analyzing what will turn out to be a non-existing but nevertheless highly fascinating, though virtual, relationship between SG physics and learning in neuronal networks. We will then hit upon the "real" stuff, fascinating science in its own right, viz., how a neuronal network as a biological entity of interacting neurons in an animal's brain "learns" spatio-temporal patterns that are imposed upon or evolve in the network.

25.2.2. *Neural versus Neuronal Networks*

A neuronal network is a configuration of biological neurons, of course in some brain, whereas a neural network is a computer-science notion that originated from backpropagation — viz., steepest descent of some error function — as learning mechanism and is meanwhile used (e.g., through "deep" learning) on a huge scale. The latter is nevertheless a nice starting point for the present considerations. In 1982 John Hopfield [7] introduced an abstract model that was meant to perform the storage of static patterns in a neural network consisting of elements that we call S_i. Each element has only two states, which we describe by Ising spins $S_i = \pm 1$.

Why only two states? The idea goes back to the well-known paper [1] due to McCulloch and Pitts published in 1943. McCulloch was a famous neurobiologist and Pitts was a formally working logician who wrote the paper, often quoted but inaccessible to nearly everyone. Here a biological neuron was reduced to its "essence", being active $(+1)$ or inactive (0 or, equivalently, -1). Hence, discrete Ising spins.

As network states that need to be stored, Hopfield [7] took patterns $\boldsymbol{\xi}^\mu = \{\xi_i^\mu; 1 \leq i \leq N\}$ labeled by $1 \leq \mu \leq q$ and living in a finite network of $1 \leq i \leq N$ Ising spins where the $\xi_i^\mu = \pm 1$ are independent, identically distributed (i.i.d.) random variables labeled by both i and $1 \leq \mu \leq q$ and assuming the values ± 1 with equal probability. They are picked and then remain fixed. As an ansatz that successfully functioned for storage, he took interactions J_{ij} and a Hamilton function H_N of the form

$$J_{ij} = N^{-1} \sum_{1 \leq \mu \leq q} \xi_i^\mu \xi_j^\mu = J_{ji} \quad \Rightarrow \quad H_N = -\frac{1}{2} \sum_{i \neq j} J_{ij} S_i S_j. \tag{25.6}$$

A little bit of algebra tells us that, when substituting $S_i = \xi_i^{\mu_\circ}$ into (25.6), we obtain from the above expression an energy per spin (up to an irrelevant constant),

$$\frac{1}{N} H_N = -\sum_{\mu=1}^q \left(\frac{1}{N} \sum_{i=1}^N \xi_i^\mu S_i\right)^2 \Rightarrow -\sum_\mu \left(\frac{1}{N} \sum_{i=1}^N \xi_i^\mu \xi_i^{\mu_\circ}\right)^2 = -1 + \mathcal{O}((q-1)/N)$$

$$\tag{25.7}$$

The term in the middle gives $= -1$ for $\mu = \mu_\circ$ and for the other $(q-1)$ terms with $\mu \neq \mu_\circ$ we find $\mathcal{O}(1/N)$ for N large as a consequence of the central limit theorem [94] because for each $\mu \neq \mu_\circ$ we face a sum of independent random variables $\{\xi_i^\mu \xi_i^{\mu_\circ}, 1 \leq i \leq N\}$ with mean $= 0$.

On the other hand, for an arbitrary spin configuration, i.e., drawn randomly from the 2^N spin configurations, we get an irrelevant response at most of order $\mathcal{O}(q/N)$ since each of the q groups consists of independent random variables with mean $= 0$. For $q = \alpha N$, a more detailed analysis is required, and extensively available. In other words, we can imagine at least q valleys in the energy landscape generated by the Hamilton function H_N of (25.7). Only when a system starts in a (generously proportioned) neighborhood of a minimum given by an unperturbed pattern such as $\{\xi_i^{\mu_\circ}, 1 \leq i \leq N\}$, does it converge to this minimum. The lower the temperature, the larger the domain of attraction.

As the above model (25.6) has no dynamics by itself it is given one by means of a Monte Carlo algorithm [95], which by its very definition contains a temperature. Hence we are back in the realm of equilibrium statistical mechanics, where the partition function $Z_N = \text{Tr} \exp(-\beta H_N)$ is the key element, the trace Tr being a sum over all 2^N spin configurations. We then need to evaluate the free energy $f(\beta)$ belonging to the Hamiltonian H_N of (25.6) as a function of the inverse temperature β,

$$-\beta f(\beta) = \lim_{N \to \infty} \frac{1}{N} \ln \text{Tr} \exp(-\beta H_N). \tag{25.8}$$

The ansatz (25.6) functioned wonderfully well in that for finitely many patterns a $\boldsymbol{\xi}^{\mu}$ with not too noisily spoiled input will be retrieved flawlessly when $T = 0$ and with some errors for $T > 0$ whereas for $q = \alpha N$ with $\alpha > 0$ but small enough a finite fraction of errors occurs at $T = 0$ while for $\alpha > \alpha_c = 0.14$ retrieval breaks down completely.

The number $\alpha_c = 0.14$ arose from numerical simulations and got a theoretical foundation through a statistical-mechanical study [10] of the free energy of the Hamiltonian (25.6) with $q = \alpha N$ in the limit $N \to \infty$ as specified by (25.8). One then finds a critical temperature $T_c > 0$, below which the patterns to be stored (and quite a few more) live as "condensed" states. In other words, the noise represented by $\mathcal{O}((q-1)/N)$ in (25.8) at $T = 0$ takes over as soon as the fraction $\alpha = q/N > 0$ exceeds a critical α_c. For more information on the Hopfield model and its solution in the limit of (25.8), one may profit from extensive reviews presented elsewhere; e.g., in this book.

25.2.3. *Hopfield model in spin-glass context*

The interaction that characterizes the Hopfield model is of the random-site type. That is, the coupling $\xi_i^{\mu}\xi_j^{\mu}$ depends on ξ_i^{μ} and ξ_j^{μ} bilinearly so that its probability distribution is a product distribution of that belonging to i and j and each of them is drawn independently of the other from some, usually the same, distribution, for each μ anew. In a random-bond model the J_{ij} are drawn for each pair (i, j) from some distribution independently of the other pairs. The Sherrington–Kirkpatrick model with i.i.d. J_{ij} is random-bond and ought to describe a spin glass, the Hopfield model [7] is random-site and has been built for storing stationary patterns, $1 \leq \mu \leq q$. They are different models meant to describe different physics.

Now a key question that science has been facing for at least half a century since its very discovery [96] is: What characterizes a spin glass? The first SG experiments of Canella and Mydosh [96] were on alloys such as Au*Fe* or Cu*Mn* where the magnetic moments of *Fe* or *Mn* have assumed random positions but at a low percentage in a non-magnetic metallic matrix, an alloy. The moments are interacting through a long-range and oscillating (as a function of the distance) RKKY interaction [97, p. 343], the disorder is correspondingly a random-site instead of random-bond one as the SK model. As a function of the distance, the RKKY interaction oscillates around zero, which is also called Friedel oscillation, and the random positioning of the moments induces the frustration.

The van Hemmen model [98] of a spin glass therefore started with a random-site disorder that is represented by interactions containing both randomness and frustration [92, 99] of the form

$$J_{ij} = \frac{J}{2N}(\xi_i \eta_j + \xi_j \eta_i), \tag{25.9}$$

and giving rise to the classical Hamiltonian

$$H_N = -\frac{J_o}{2N} \sum_{i \neq j} S_i S_j - \frac{1}{2N} \sum_{i \neq j} J_{ij} S_i S_j - h \sum_i S_i \tag{25.10}$$

where the first term (J_o) is a globally acting magnetic interaction while a probing magnetic field represented by h has been included (for free) as well. As explained in the literature [98–101], the model can be solved exactly and truly represents a spin glass but, as a "mean-field" model, only describes the thermodynamic and not the dynamic properties of a spin glass at low temperatures, below T_c. In addition, various random-site models of the van Hemmen type have been studied [102, 103], also as extension to non-mean-field situations, and have been applied [104, 105] to problems with disorder but of a nature completely different from spin glasses.

In conclusion, we have seen that random-site models can also represent completely different kinds of physics from spin glasses, do include lots of randomness and, if desired, frustration but do not necessarily need RSB to get solved.

25.2.4. *Neuronal learning vs. spin-glass-type coding*

Physiological learning is a dominating topic in neuroscience. Here we will only treat the bare essentials so as to see the huge difference between neuronal and spin-glass type learning. As we will focus on the "real" stuff, a decent introduction providing more details regarding the core concept of spike-timing-dependent plasticity (STDP) may be helpful [106–108]. Though clumsy, the full name does precisely what it says, though its abbreviation STDP is far more user-friendly.

Neurons spike. That is, they send axon potentials or spikes, i.e., electric pulses of approximately 1 ms duration and of a biologically huge amplitude of about 0.1 Volt, through axons to other neurons. The axons are active conductors that allow a propagation speed of up to meters per second. Particularly, myelinated axons are fast as they are covered by a sheet of insulating myelin.

When a spike emitted by neuron A arrives at another neuron B, its impulse is transmitted through a synapse somewhere on the surface of neuron B. The 'synaptic strength' determines the strength of the input signal to B. Neuronal learning happens at the synapses, through the waxing and waning of their synaptic strength. During their travel from neuron A to neuron B spikes experience by the very nature of the axonal transport an intrinsic delay, which is essential to the brain's facility of storing spatio-*temporal* patterns that evolve in space *and* time. So to speak, only by knowing the past can the system pick the "right" future.

The mechanism of time-resolved, spatio-temporal synaptic learning was proposed as late as 1996 [111]. To see how it works, let us focus on a synapse, which we will call i, its synaptic strength being J_i. The firing times of the postsynaptic neuron the synapse i is on are denoted by t^n, it being understood that n is a label like f. Given the firing times, the change $\Delta J_i(t) := J_i(t) - J_i(t - T_l)$ of the efficacy of synapse i (synaptic strength) during a learning session of duration T_l and ending at time t is governed by several factors, mathematically described by

$$\Delta J_i(t) = \eta \left[\sum_{t-T_l \leq t_i^f < t} w^{\text{in}} + \sum_{t-T_l \leq t^n < t} w^{\text{out}} + \sum_{t-T_l \leq t_i^f, t^n < t} W(t_i^f - t^n) \right]. \qquad (25.11)$$

Here the firing times t^n of the post-synaptic neuron may, and in general will, depend on J_i. We now focus on the individual terms. The prefactor $0 < \eta \ll 1$ reminds us explicitly of learning being slow on a neuronal time scale — at least, mostly.

Each incoming spike and each action potential of the postsynaptic neuron change the synaptic efficacy by ηw^{in} and ηw^{out}, respectively. The last, and key, term in (25.11) represents the *learning window* $W(s)$, which indicates the synaptic change in dependence upon the time difference $s = t_i^f - t^n$ between an incoming spike t_i^f and an outgoing spike t^n. When the former precedes the latter, we have $s < 0 \Leftrightarrow t_i^f < t^n$, and the result is $W(s) > 0$, implying potentiation: see Fig. 25.7.

The learning rule (25.11) with leaning window W has been experimentally [112] verified, was named STDP a bit later [106], and is by now a standard in neuroscience. The fundamental idea is simple. We focus on an excitatory synapse (there are also inhibitory ones, providing negatively charged input to the post-synaptic neuron). If a spike arrives slightly before the neuron fires, the synapse will be strengthened. So to speak, the synapse has done its job correctly and should be "rewarded." If, on the other hand, it comes too late, i.e., after the neuron has fired, it should be "punished," as it did not do the job it should do as excitatory synapse, viz., firing the neuron in time. Accordingly, it should be weakened.

That is, the time of a spike's arrival at the synapse with respect to the firing time of the postsynaptic neuron determines the amount of waxing and waning of the synapse, mathematically described by the learning window W, shown in Fig. 25.7. W is a core concept in neurobiology that allows quantifying timing at a synapse. Each spike arrival changes the synaptic strength by a small amount. Map formation [111] is a synergy of many neurons of which the synaptic development is steered by STDP. Given the neuroanatomy, it is a collective, self-organizing, process. The system needs weeks — two weeks for the barn owl — or even much longer, as in the human brain [113].

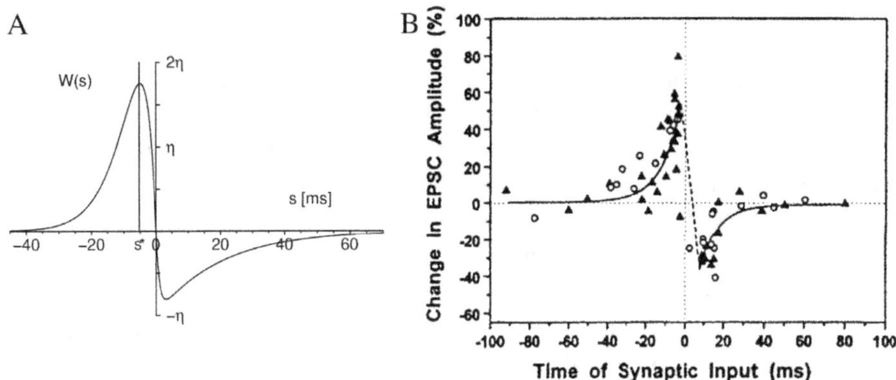

Fig. 25.7.   **A.** STDP's learning window W as function of the delay $s = t_i^f - t^n$ between presynaptic spike arrival at synapse i at time t_i^f and postsynaptic firing at time t^n. If $W(s)$ is positive (negative) for some s the synaptic efficacy J_i is increased (decreased). The increase of the excitatory J_i is most efficient, if a presynaptic spike arrives a few milliseconds *before* the postsynaptic neuron starts firing (vertical line at $s = s^*$). For $|s| \to \infty$ we have $W(s) \to 0$. Taken from [109]. **B.** Experimentally obtained learning window of a cell in rat hippocampus; reprinted by permission [110]. The similarity with the left figure is evident. It is important to realize that the width of the learning window is to be in agreement with other neuronal time constants. In the auditory system, for instance, these are nearly two orders of magnitude smaller than e.g. in hippocampus so that the learning window's width scales accordingly.

In short, whereas in a spin glass the *spatial* arrangement of the spins in conjunction with a random positioning or a random choice of the interaction strengths is the key to understanding their dynamics, in neuronal synaptic plasticity it is the *relative timing* of spike arrival and neuronal response of the receiving neuron that determines the coding locally and only then globally, which may lead to a correlation catastrophe.

25.2.4.1. *Unlearning*

Spatio-temporal patterns in nature are in general highly correlated, both in space and in time. Once learned by means of STDP, their retrieval seems to become catastrophic as their many correlations ought to drown out the patterns into a big uniform "marsh of correlations" so that retrieval as separate entities is illusory. Indeed it is. So what could nature do? There is an algorithm of which a first implementation goes back to Hopfield *et al.* [116] while the wonderful key idea is due to Crick and Mitchison [114]; full details can be found elsewhere [115].

Their idea is really cute. REM sleep is one (#4) of the four stages of sleep, lasting for about 3-4 hours. In contrast to what the word "sleep" suggests, the brain is highly active. The short, frightening, "dreams" that are often a mix of different events of the past day are a dominating aspect of what people, such as you, can remember. Crick and Mitchison proposed a mechanism that is repeated again and again and that consists of three steps: (i) random excitement in the brain that then (ii) relaxes during a short period of time at the end of which (iii) the final state is unlearned, i.e., through the very same learning STDP learning rule (25.11) but with a small dimensionless prefactor $\epsilon \ll 1$ accompanied by a *negative* sign signifying *un*learning. The latter is the key to the success of unlearning, which is impressive [115]. What REM sleep does is "decorrelating correlated data" [115] and in this way is accompanying learning. Young children REM sleep most ;-)

Hopfield *et al.* [116] have implemented the above idea through an algorithm for Ising spins and a few stationary random patterns and showed its success for very small systems. It has meanwhile [115] been verified for large systems and extended to biased and spatio-temporal patterns. It always works, is robust, and increases the performance of the network by an order of magnitude. Only for true instead of formal 0/1 or ± 1 neurons a full verification of its power is still a challenging problem.

Conclusion Neural networks are meanwhile highly potent computer-science constructs that are able to solve complicated technical problems and handle huge amounts of data. Neuronal networks are "intelligent" dynamical systems that are an integral part of animal brains, operate in space and time, and need to handle inputs that are also correlated in space and time. For both types of network, learning is essential. Nevertheless, the *modus operandi* of the two are practically disjoint, spin glasses constituting a virtual bridge that was quite helpful to science in the past. A decisive difference is in the *spatial* arrangement of the spins and the *relative timing* of spike arrival and neuronal response. A conjunction of the two worlds of neurons and spins is hard to imagine.

References

[1] W. S. McCulloch and W. A. Pitts, *Bull. Math. Biophys.* **5**, 115–133, (1943).
[2] F. Rosenblatt, *Principles of Neurodynamics.* (Spartan Books, 1962).
[3] M. Minsky and S. Papert, *Perceptrons: An Introduction to Computational Geometry.* (MIT Press, 1969).
[4] D. Amit, H. Gutfreund, and H. Sompolinsky, *Phys. Rev. A.* **35**, 2293–2303, (1987).
[5] B. G. Cragg and H. N. V. Temperley, *Electroencephalogr. Clin. Neurophysiol.* **6**, 85–92, (1954).
[6] W. A. Little, *Math. Biosci.* **19**, 101–119, (1974).
[7] J. J. Hopfield, *Proc. Natl. Acad. Sci. U.S.A.* **79**, 2554–2558, (1982).
[8] S.-I. Amari, *IEEE Trans. Comput. C.* **21**, 1197–1206, (1972).
[9] D. O. Hebb, *Organization of behavior.* (Wiley, 1949).
[10] D. J. Amit, H. Gutfreund, and H. Sompolinsky, *Phys. Rev. Lett.* **55**, 1530–1531, (1985).
[11] B. Barbour, N. Brunel, V. Hakim, and J. Nadal, *Trends Neurosci.* **30**, 622–629, (2007).
[12] E. J. Gardner, *J. Phys. A.* **21**, 257–270, (1988).
[13] E. J. Gardner and B. Derrida, *J. Phys. A.* **21**, 271, (1988).
[14] T. M. Cover, *IEEE Trans.* **EC-14**, 326, (1965).
[15] J. M. Fuster and G. Alexander, *Science.* **173**, 652–654, (1971).
[16] J. M. Fuster and J. P. Jervey, *Science.* **212**, 952–955, (1981).
[17] Y. Miyashita, *Nature.* **335**, 817–820, (1988).
[18] Y. Miyashita and H. S. Chang, *Nature.* **331**, 68–70, (1988).
[19] S. Funahashi, C. J. Bruce, and P. S. Goldman-Rakic, *J. Neurophysiol.* **61**, 331–349, (1989).
[20] P. S. Goldman-Rakic, *Neuron.* **14**, 477–485, (1995).
[21] J. M. Fuster, *Memory in the cerebral cortex.* (MIT Press, 1995).
[22] S. Kornblith, R. Quian Quiroga, C. Koch, I. Fried, and F. Mormann, *Curr Biol.* **27**, 1026–1032, (2017).
[23] H. K. Inagaki, L. Fontolan, S. Romani, and K. Svoboda, *Nature.* **566**, 212–217, (2019).
[24] S. S. Kim, H. Rouault, S. Druckmann, and V. Jayaraman, *Science.* **356**, 849–853, (2017).
[25] C. K. Kim, A. Adhikari, and K. Deisseroth, *Nat Rev Neurosci.* **18**, 222–235, (2017).
[26] H. Sompolinsky, *Phys. Rev. A.* **34**, 2571–2574, (1986).
[27] B. Derrida, E. Gardner, and A. Zippelius, *Europhys. Lett.* **4**, 167–173, (1987).
[28] M. Tsodyks and M. V. Feigel'man, *Europhys. Lett.* **6**, 101–105, (1988).
[29] M. Tsodyks, *Europhys. Lett.* **7**, 203–208, (1988).
[30] J. Buhmann, R. Divko, and K. Schulten, *Phys. Rev. A.* **39**, 2689–2692, (1989).
[31] D. Amit, K. Wong, and C. Campbell, *J. Phys. A Math. Gen.* **22**, 2039–2045, (1989).
[32] W. Krauth and M. Mézard, *J. Phys. (France).* **50**, 3057, (1989).
[33] H. Gutfreund and Y. Stein, *J. Phys. A.* **23**, 2613–2630, (1990).
[34] C. Baldassi, A. Ingrosso, C. Lucibello, L. Saglietti, and R. Zecchina, *Phys. Rev. Lett.* **115**, 128101, (2015).
[35] M. Mézard, J.-P. Nadal, and G. Toulouse, *J. Physique.* **47**, 1457–1462, (1986).
[36] G. Parisi, *J. Phys. A.* **19**, L617, (1986).
[37] D. J. Amit and N. Brunel, *Cerebral Cortex.* **7**, 237–252, (1997).
[38] X.-J. Wang, *Trends Neurosci.* **24**, 455–463, (2001).
[39] S. Lim, J. L. McKee, L. Woloszyn, Y. Amit, D. J. Freedman, D. L. Sheinberg, and N. Brunel, *Nat. Neurosci.* **18**, 1804–1810, (2015).
[40] S. M. Dudek and M. F. Bear, *J Neurosci.* **13**, 2910–2918, (1993).
[41] H. Markram, J. Lübke, M. Frotscher, A. Roth, and B. Sakmann, *J. Physiol. (London).* **500**, 409–440, (1997).

[42] P. J. Sjöström, G. G. Turrigiano, and S. Nelson, *Neuron.* **32**, 1149–1164, (2001).

[43] S. Song, K. D. Miller, and L. F. Abbott, *Nat. Neurosci.* **3**, 919–926, (2000).

[44] J. Pfister and W. Gerstner, *J. Neurosci.* **26**, 9673–9682, (2006).

[45] C. Clopath, L. Busing, E. Vasilaki, and W. Gerstner, *Nat. Neurosci.* **13**, 344–352, (2010).

[46] M. Graupner and N. Brunel, *Proc. Natl. Acad. Sci. U.S.A.* **109**, 3991–3996, (2012).

[47] G. Mongillo, E. Curti, S. Romani, and D. Amit, *Eur J Neurosci.* **21**, 3143–3160, (2005).

[48] A. Litwin-Kumar and B. Doiron, *Nat. Commun.* **5**, 5319, (2014).

[49] F. Zenke, E. J. Agnes, and W. Gerstner, *Nat. Commun.* **6**, 6922, (2015).

[50] Y. Inglebert, J. Aljadeff, N. Brunel, and D. Debanne, *Proc. Natl. Acad. Sci. U.S.A.* **117**, 33639–33648, (2020).

[51] L. Li, E. K. Miller, and R. Desimone, *J. Neurophysiol.* **69**, 1918–1929, (1993).

[52] L. Woloszyn and D. L. Sheinberg, *Neuron.* **74**, 193–205, (2012).

[53] J. J. Hopfield, *Proc. Natl. Acad. Sci. U.S.A.* **81**, 3088–3092, (1984).

[54] U. Pereira and N. Brunel, *Neuron.* **99**, 227–238, (2018).

[55] K. Nakamura and K. Kubota, *J. Neurophysiol.* **74**, 162–178, (1995).

[56] N. Brunel, V. Hakim, P. Isope, J. P. Nadal, and B. Barbour, *Neuron.* **43**, 745–57, (2004).

[57] N. Brunel, *Nat. Neurosci.* **19**, 749–755, (2016).

[58] J. Chapeton, T. Fares, D. LaSota, and A. Stepanyants, *Proc. Natl. Acad. Sci. U.S.A.* **109**, E3614–3622, (2012).

[59] D. B. Rubin, S. D. Van Hooser, and K. D. Miller, *Neuron.* **85**, 402–417, (2015).

[60] C. Holmgren, T. Harkany, B. Svennenfors, and Y. Zilberter, *J. Physiol.* **551**, 139–153, (2003).

[61] E. Fino and R. Yuste, *Neuron.* **69**, 1188–1203, (2011).

[62] R. Rubin, L. F. Abbott, and H. Sompolinsky, *Proc. Natl. Acad. Sci. U.S.A.* **114**, E9366–E9375, (2017).

[63] A. Mason, A. Nicoll, and K. Stratford, *J. Neurosci.* **11**, 72–84, (1991).

[64] N. Kalisman, G. Silberberg, and H. Markram, *Proc. Natl. Acad. Sci. U.S.A.* **102**, 880–885, (2005).

[65] S. Song, P. J. Sjostrom, M. Reigl, S. Nelson, and D. B. Chklovskii, *PLoS Biol.* **3**, e68, (2005).

[66] Y. Wang, H. Markram, P. H. Goodman, T. K. Berger, J. Ma, and P. S. Goldman-Rakic, *Nat Neurosci.* **9**, 534–542, (2006).

[67] S. Lefort, C. Tomm, J. C. Floyd Sarria, and C. C. Petersen, *Neuron.* **61**, 301–316, (2009).

[68] S. J. Guzman, A. Schlogl, M. Frotscher, and P. Jonas, *Science.* **353**, 1117–1123, (2016).

[69] R. Gütig and H. Sompolinsky, *Nat. Neuro.* **9**(3), 420–428, (2006).

[70] R. Rubin, R. Monasson, and H. Sompolinsky, *Phys. Rev. Lett.* **105**, 218102, (2010).

[71] R. Monasson and D. O'Kane, *Europhys. Lett.* **27**(21), 85–90, (1994).

[72] A. Engel and C. Van den Broeck, *Statistical mechanics of learning.* (Cambridge University Press, 2001).

[73] H. Sompolinsky, A. Crisanti, and H. J. Sommers, *Phys. Rev. Lett.* **61**, 259–262, (1988).

[74] M. Tsodyks, *Mod. Phys. Lett. B.* **4**, 713–716, (1990).

[75] J. Kadmon and H. Sompolinsky, *Phys. Rev. X.* **5**, 041030, (2015).

[76] O. Harish and D. Hansel, *Plos. Comput. Biol.* **11**, e1004266, (2015).

[77] U. Pereira, J. Aljadeff, and N. Brunel, *arxiv:2112.00119.* (2021).

[78] F. P. Battaglia and A. Treves, *Phys. Rev. E.* **58**, 7738–7753, (1998).

[79] R. Monasson and S. Rosay, *Phys Rev E Stat Nonlin Soft Matter Phys.* **87**, 062813, (2013).

[80] R. Monasson and S. Rosay, *Phys Rev E Stat Nonlin Soft Matter Phys.* **89**, 032803, (2014).

[81] R. Monasson and S. Rosay, *Phys Rev Lett.* **115**, 098101, (2015).

[82] A. Battista and R. Monasson, *Phys. Rev. Lett.* **124**, 048302, (2020).

[83] K. L. Briggman, M. Helmstaedter, and W. Denk, *Nature.* **471**, 183–188, (2011).

[84] A. Bae et al., *bioRxiv:2021.07.28.454025.* (2021).

[85] S. Goldt, F. Krzakala, L. Zdeborová, and N. Brunel, *arXiv:2105.07416.* (2021).

[86] K. S. Matho, D. Huilgol, W. Galbavy, M. He, G. Kim, X. An, J. Lu, P. Wu, D. J. Di Bella, A. S. Shetty, R. Palaniswamy, J. Hatfield, R. Raudales, A. Narasimhan, E. Gamache, J. M. Levine, J. Tucciarone, E. Szelenyi, J. A. Harris, P. P. Mitra, P. Osten, P. Arlotta, and Z. J. Huang, *Nature.* **598**, 182–187, (2021).

[87] V. Kozareva, C. Martin, T. Osorno, S. Rudolph, C. Guo, C. Vanderburg, N. Nadaf, A. Regev, W. G. Regehr, and E. Macosko, *Nature.* **598**, 214–219, (2021).

[88] C. Stringer, M. Michaelos, D. Tsyboulski, S. E. Lindo, and M. Pachitariu, *Cell.* **184**(10), 2767–2778 (2021).

[89] N. A. Steinmetz, P. Zatka-Haas, M. Carandini, and K. D. Harris, *Nature.* **576**, 266–273, (2019).

[90] E. A. Naumann, J. E. Fitzgerald, T. W. Dunn, J. Rihel, H. Sompolinsky, and F. Engert, *Cell.* **167**, 947–960, (2016).

[91] M. Mézard, G. Parisi, and M. A. Virasoro, *Spin Glass Theory and Beyond.* (World Scientific, 1987).

[92] G. Toulouse, *Commun. on Phys.* **2**, 115–119, (1977).

[93] J. L. van Hemmen and L. Morgenstern, Eds., *Heidelberg Colloquium on Spin Glasses*, Lecture Notes in Physics **192**. (Springer, 1983).

[94] J. L. Lamperti, *Probability.* There are two editions but the first one captivates the reader by both clarity and succinctness. (Benjamin, 1966).

[95] K. Binder and D. W. Heermann, *Monte Carlo Simulation in Statistical Physics*, 6th ed. (Springer, 2019).

[96] V. Cannella and J. A. Mydosh, *Phys. Rev. B.* **6**, 4220–4237, (1972).

[97] N. W. Ashcroft and D. Mermin, *Solid State Physics.* (Saunders, 1976).

[98] J. L. van Hemmen, *Phys. Rev. Lett.* **49**, 409–413, (1982).

[99] J. L. van Hemmen, *J. Phys. C.* **19**, L379–L382, (1986).

[100] T. C. Choy and D. Sherrington, *J. Phys. C: Solid State Phys.* **17**, 739–745, (1984).

[101] J. L. van Hemmen, A. C. D. van Enter, and J. Canisius, *Z. Phys. B.* **50**, 331–336, (1983).

[102] D. M. de Morais, M. Godoy, A. S. de Arruda, J. N. da Silva, and J. R. de Sousa, *J. Magn. Magn. Mat.* **398**, 253–258, (2016).

[103] J. R. Viana, Y. Nogueira, and J. R. de Sousa, *Phys. Rev. B.* **66**, 113307, (2002).

[104] I. M. Kloumann, I. M. Lizarraga, and S. H. Strogatz, *Phys. Rev. E.* **89**, 012940, (2014).

[105] S. G. Magalhaes, F. M. Zimmer, and B. Coqblin, *Phys. Rev. B.* **81**, 094424, (2010).

[106] G.-Q. Bi and M.-M. Poo, *J. Neurosci.* **18**, 10464–10472, (1998).

[107] J. L. van Hemmen. In eds. F. Moss and S. Gielen, *Handbook of Biological Physics, Vol. 4: Neuro-Informatics, Neural Modelling.* Elsevier, (2001).

[108] J. L. van Hemmen, *Biol. Cybern.* **115**, 655–664, (2021).

[109] R. Kempter, W. Gerstner, and J. L. van Hemmen, *Phys. Rev. E.* **59**, 4498, (1999).

[110] L. I. Zhang, H. W. Tao, C. E. Holt, W. A. Harris, and M.-M. Poo, *Nature.* **395**, 37–44, (1998).

[111] W. Gerstner, J. L. van Hemmen, and J. Cowan, *Neural Comput.* **8**, 1653–1676, (1996).

[112] H. Markram, J. Lübke, M. Frotscher, and B. Sakmann, *Science.* **275**, 213–215, (1997).

[113] O.G. Wenisch, J. Noll, J. L. van Hemmen, *Biol. Cybern.* **93**, 239–247, (2005).

[114] F. Crick and G. Mitchison, *Nature.* **304**, 111–114, (1983).

[115] J. L. van Hemmen, *Network: Comput. Neural Syst.* **8**, V1–V17, (1997).

[116] J. J. Hopfield, D. I. Feinstein, and R. G. Palmer, *Nature.* **304**, 158–159, (1983).

Chapter 26

Statistical Physics of Biological Molecules

This chapter reviews the use of statistical mechanics techniques, and in particular those inspired by disordered systems and spin glasses, for the study of biological molecules.

In a first contribution (Sec. 26.1), **Cocco**, **De Martino**, **Pagnani**, and **Weigt** review how statistical mechanics methods can give insight into the properties of RNA molecules at many different scales. They first discuss models and algorithms for the prediction of the secondary structure, how a random RNA sequence freezes into a disorder structure via a glass-like transition, and how the free energy landscape of folding into such structures can be inferred from data (a topic that is covered in more depth in the second contribution by Ritort, Sec. 26.2). Next, they describe how pairwise disordered Potts models can be used to obtain insight into the secondary and tertiary structure of RNA, via the so-called direct coupling analysis, and to generate artificial RNA with similar properties to natural ones. Finally, they discuss how distinct RNAs interact in the cell, giving rise to a complex regulatory network.

In a second contribution (Sec. 26.2), **Ritort** reviews experimental techniques for the study of single biological molecules, in particular with the goal of measuring the free energy landscape for folding and unfolding. A complex landscape full of local minima emerges, and the analogies and differences with similar rough landscapes characteristic of spin glasses are discussed.

26.1. Statistical-Physics Approaches to RNA Molecules, Families and Networks

Simona Cocco[*], Andrea De Martino[†,‡], Andrea Pagnani[†,†,§] and Martin Weigt[¶]

*Laboratoire de Physique de l'Ecole Normale Supérieure,
PSL and CNRS, Paris, France;*
†*Politecnico di Torino, Corso Duca degli Abruzzi, 24, I-10129, Torino, Italy;*
‡*Italian Institute for Genomic Medicine, IRCCS Candiolo, SP-142, Candiolo, Italy;*
§*INFN, Sezione di Torino, Torino, Via Pietro Giuria, 1 10125 Torino Italy;*
¶*Sorbonne Université, CNRS, Institut de Biologie Paris Seine,
Computational and Quantitative Biology – LCQB,
75005 Paris, France*

26.1.1. *Introduction*

Our contribution focuses on the fascinating RNA molecule, its sequence-dependent folding driven by base-pairing interactions, the interplay between these interactions and natural evolution, and its multiple regulatory roles. The four of us have dug into these topics using the tools and the spirit of the statistical physics of disordered systems, and in particular the concept of a disordered (energy/fitness) landscape. After an introduction to RNA molecules and the perspectives they open not only in evolutionary and synthetic biology but also in medicine, we will introduce the important notions of energy and fitness landscapes for these molecules. In Sec. 26.1.2 we will review some models and algorithms for RNA sequence-to-secondary-structure mapping. Section 26.1.3 discusses how the secondary-structure energy landscape can be derived from unzipping data. Section 26.1.4 deals with the inference of RNA structure from evolutionary sequence data sampled in different organisms. This will shift the focus from the 'sequence-to-structure' mapping described in Sec. 26.1.2 to a 'sequence-to-function' landscape that can be inferred from laboratory evolutionary data on DNA aptamers. Finally, in Sec. 26.1.5, we discuss the rich theoretical picture linking networks of interacting RNA molecules to the organization of robust, systemic regulatory programs. Along this path, we will therefore explore phenomena across multiple scales in space, number of molecules and time, showing how the biological complexity of the RNA world can be captured by the unifying concepts of statistical physics.

26.1.1.1. *The diverse roles of RNA molecules*

Classical genetics in the middle of the 20th century consisted of a mere description of the passage of traits through generations, the biological underlying nature of "Mendelian Genes" being still unknown at the time. In 1944 O. Avery proved that the "transforming principle" in aqueous cell-free extracts of pneumococci was desoxy-ribonucleic acid (DNA) [1]. From this seminal discovery, the central role of the different nucleic acids became increasingly clear, along with their compartmentalization in the cell. While the eukaryotic nucleus hosted DNA molecules, proteins were synthesized in the cytoplasm and RNA molecules proved to be pivotal in this process [2]. James Watson sketched the "central dogma" as early as 1952 (as anecdotically reported in [3] and more precisely in [4]) proposing the now standard scenario of a protein-coding RNA (messenger RNA, mRNA) that is passed from the DNA to the protein synthetic machinery in the cytoplasm.

A second class of functional RNA was proposed in 1958 by Francis Crick in his "adaptor" hypothesis [4], positing the existence of a molecule that translates the triplets of the genetic code into corresponding amino acids. Interestingly, Crick suggested that not only such an adaptor would be an RNA, but also that RNA would be a better evolutionary fit over proteins as the material for his adaptors, because specific base-paring made it the ideal RNA-recognition molecule. His intuition finally found an experimental proof in the discovery of transfer RNAs (tRNA) by Mahlon Hoagland and co-workers [5].

RNA, originally considered in the "central dogma" as a mere information carrying molecule, in the following decades has been found to have a multitude of distinct functions. For instance, in protein synthesis, besides the already discovered mRNAs and tRNAs, the structural and enzymatic role of ribosomal RNA (rRNA) was identified. In the last two decades, many other forms of RNA have been discovered, including micro-RNAs (miRNA), small interfering RNAs (siRNA), small nuclear RNAs (snRNA), small nucleolar RNAs (sncsRNA), circular RNAs (circRNA), and long non-coding RNAs (lncRNA). Notably, mRNA remains the only protein-coding RNA species discovered to date. Actually, the overwhelming majority of cellular RNA (by weight) in mammals is formed by non-coding molecules. This plethora of different non-coding RNAs performs diverse and sophisticated regulatory functions, some of them still poorly or not completely understood: from helping to turn genes on and off to slicing other RNA/DNA or transporting and ligating amino-acids.

This versatility is nowadays in the spotlight of at least three different fields: synthetic biology, evolutionary biology and medicine. In the field of synthetic biology, RNA-DNA based computing systems have been recently developed using DNA/RNA as a material capable of self-construction and communication and demonstrating its ability to perform adaptable logic gates [6, 7].

In evolutionary biology, its versatility makes RNA an ideal candidate for playing the role of pre-Darwinian self-replicating molecules, which predate the proper Darwinian DNA- and protein-based evolution as we know it today. The so-called *RNA world* hypothesis [8], posits a stage of life on Earth, in which self-replicating RNA molecules proliferate. Virtually all biologists nowadays agree that bacterial cells cannot form from nonliving chemicals in one step. If life arose from nonliving chemicals, there must have been intermediate forms — *precellular life* — populating our pre-Darwinian Earth around 4 billion years ago. Since RNA may act both as a gene (i.e. as a template genetic information storage) and as an enzyme, it bypasses the "chicken-and-egg" problem: genes require enzymes; and enzymes require genes. As a last asset of the RNA world hypothesis, it is worth recalling that RNA can be (retro-)transcribed into DNA, in reverse of the normal process of transcription.

Finally the diverse RNA roles have inspired ideas on how to use RNA in medicine to develop RNA-based therapies, both using them as vaccines against cancers and pathogens in form of mRNA templates for the synthesis of the prescribed proteins, and as drugs to target and regulate nucleic acids (RNA and DNA) and proteins [9]. In particular several drugs have been developed based on oligonucleotides, small stretches of single-strand DNA, made up of about 10-30 nucleotides, which are used to prevent RNA from being translated into proteins by several mechanisms including blocking the start of translation, altering RNA splicing or tagging mRNA degradation. Small RNA or DNA molecules that target proteins, called aptamers, have been also designed to bind a specific site of a specific protein to modulate its function [10].

26.1.1.2. *From fitness to energy landscapes*

The notion of landscape was introduced in biology in the late 1930s by Sewall Wright [11], in order to describe evolution as an adaptive walk in a fitness landscape. Nowadays landscapes appear in so different fields as physics of spin glasses, computer science of combinatorial complexity, evolution, neural networks, gene regulatory networks, maturation of immune response, and biophysics of macro-molecules. A geographical landscape can be described by a height function defined on the two-dimensional Cartesian plane. Here, more generally the notion of landscape relates to a function $F(\mathbf{x})$, which assigns a real number to all points $\mathbf{x} = (x_1, x_2, \ldots, x_n)$ of a n-dimensional space, also called configuration space. In geographical landscapes, the configuration space is continuous, and the most natural metric is often the Euclidean one. In the case of RNA and other sequence-based biological molecules, we frequently consider fitness landscapes defined on a discrete support. We can more formally define a landscape as a triple (X, d, F), where the configuration space X is a (possibly finite) set, $d : X \times X \to \mathbb{R}^+$ is a metric, and $F : X \to \mathbb{R}$ the landscape function. In the following we will assume that F is a bounded-from-below energy/cost function, or bounded-from-above fitness function. Here the field-specific definitions disagree: biologists follow Wright's original definition of maximum fitness, while physicists prefer to think in terms of (free)-energy minimization. A simple minus sign relates the two.

It is instructive to think about biological landscapes in the context of optimization theory, i.e. in terms of a minimization problem of a given cost function (sometimes internal energy or free energy, sometimes negative fitness). Ever since Darwin, evolution has been considered as the result of the competition between mutation and selection: mutation acts on the genotype (ultimately encoded in the DNA of the organism), while selection on the phenotype. Their competition rules the complex dynamics of evolution. It is evident that this point of view can hardly be predictive without a suitable notion of energy or fitness function – a daunting task, which needs to take into account the distinct scales at which mutation and selection act, from the "microscopic" genetic scale up to all the complexity involved for instance in organismal selection.

However, when we concentrate on bio-molecules, the situation becomes somewhat simpler. In particular RNA makes a landscape-based modeling of sequence and structure particularly promising: RNA is indeed a genetically active molecule whose genotype (sequence) directly undergoes and inherits mutations. Proteins, for instance, do not possess this feature. Moreover, RNA secondary structure, thanks to its simplicity, facilitates the task of defining a reliable cost function useful for structural prediction from sequence — i.e. of a biophysically motivated landscape function.

26.1.2. *RNA folding models*

RNA can be described via a hierarchy of structures. The primary structure is the linear sequence composed by the four-letter RNA alphabet formed by the bases (or nucleotides) Adenine (A), Uracil (U), Cytosine (C), and Guanine (G). As compared to DNA, the Thymine (T) in DNA is substituted by Uracil (U) in RNA. However, much like DNA, RNA can form stable double helices of complementary strands. Since RNA usually occurs single stranded, formation of double helical regions is accomplished by the molecule folding back onto itself to form Watson–Crick (WC) base pairs (G≡C and A=U), or the slightly less stable G–U wobble pair (note that here the $\equiv, =, -$ symbols are used just to give a rank of the interaction energies). One of the most appealing features of RNA secondary structure is that the obtained graph — formed by the primary structure and the base pairs — is planar as shown in Fig. 26.1. Empirically, it turns out that this planarity condition is often violated in particular in long structural RNAs: so-called pseudo-knots (i.e. structural contacts violating the planarity condition), are known to occur, although most of the RNA secondary structure elements are planar. As is explained in the following, the planarity condition allows for polynomial-time (in sequence length) algorithms to compute the partition function of a given RNA sequence. When, in particular as statistical physicists, we try to describe a complex object such as an RNA molecule, some kind of coarse-graining is necessary. As usual, there are different languages for the different levels of phenomenological descriptions. The secondary-structure one is particularly interesting for the following reasons: (i) conventional base pairing and base pair stacking (viz. the stabilizing effect of sequences of "consecutive" base pairs $\{(p-k, q+k), (p-k+1, q+k-1), ..., (p,q)\}$) provide the major part of the free energy of folding; (ii) secondary structure has been used successfully by biologists in the interpretation of RNA function and activity; (iii) secondary structure is conserved from an evolutionary standpoint. Physicists, computer scientists and bioinformaticians have always been interested in RNA secondary structures due to their discrete nature. RNA secondary structures are easy to compare and to visualize. Lastly, and perhaps most importantly here, the planarity condition allows for the implementation of polynomial-time algorithms for the computation of the native structure [12–16]. These algorithms use dynamic programming, i.e. a recursive strategy starting from small solvable sub-problems and iterating towards larger and larger sub-problems, a technique resembling transfer matrices in statistical physics, or message passing/belief propagation in computer science.

26.1.2.1. *A mathematical model for the secondary structure description of RNAs*

The secondary structure of RNA is defined via a set of base pairs occurring in its three-dimensional structure. Let us define a sequence as $\mathcal{R} := \{r_1, r_2, ..., r_n\}$, with $r_i \in \{A, C, G, U\}$ being the i-th base. A secondary structure on $\mathcal{R}$ is a set $\mathcal{S}$ of base pairs (i, j), with the convention $1 \leq i \leq j \leq n$, fulfilling the following constraints:

(1) r_i and r_j form an allowed Watson–Crick or wobble pair;
(2) $j - i \geq 4$: this restriction permits RNA to loop back onto itself and to form antiparallel double-stranded stem helices;
(3) two distinct base pairs $(i, j), (i', j') \in \mathcal{S}$ are not nested: when assuming $i < i'$ without loss of generality, they fulfill one of the following conditions

    (a) $i < j < i' < j'$: the pair (i, j) precedes (i', j'), or
    (b) $i < i' < j' < j$: the pair (i, j) includes (i', j').

The last condition defines a planar graph (i.e. the graph structure can be drawn on a plane without link crossings) as shown in Fig. 26.1. Although in nature there

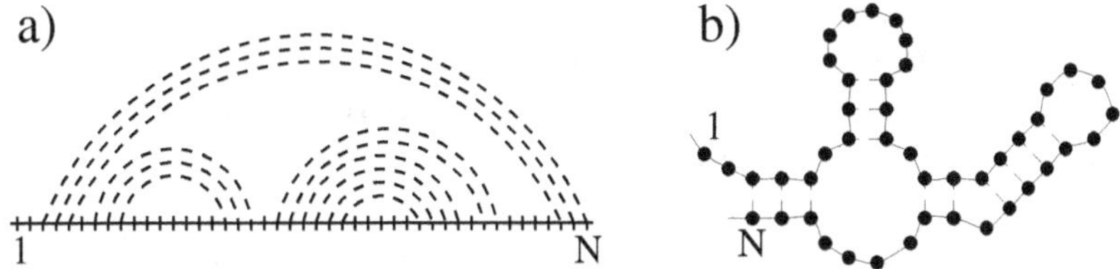

Fig. 26.1. Isomorphic representations of secondary structures in RNA: a) rainbow representation; b) cactus representation.

are examples of RNA structures which are knotted, we relate the existence of knotted structures to the formation of tertiary structure (pseudo-knots).

26.1.2.2. *Statistical mechanics of the secondary structure of random RNA sequences*

Knowing the fold of biomolecules like RNA and proteins is crucial for understanding their biological functionality. Despite decades of active research to solve the so-called sequence-structure relationship, the computational prediction of biomolecular structure still remains a challenging problem. While there has been a major breakthrough in 2021 in the case of proteins [17], the problem remains widely open for RNA for what concerns in particular the prediction of tertiary (i.e. the overall three dimensional arrangement of an RNA molecule) and quaternary structures (i.e. the structure of an RNA molecule in complex with other biomolecules).

Real RNA sequences are not uniformly random; they show a remarkable sequence variability with subtle correlations that become visible when homologous RNA sequences (i.e. sequences deriving from a common ancestral sequence) are compared using multi-species multiple-sequence alignments (MSA) [18]. The interest in studying the limiting and somehow not biologically motivated case of really random sequences arises from the need of answering the following question: is the folding transition, that forces real biomolecules into their functional shapes, characteristic of sequences selected by the evolution? Or is it also present in random sequences? This issue is particularly relevant in a prebiotic/pre-Darwinian era when, according to the RNA-world hypothesis, sequences [8] started populating the environment, and, arguably, the self-replicating selective pressure was acting on a pool of initially random RNA sequences.

In our model, we introduce a drastic approximation. The energy of a structure is simply defined as

$$H[\mathcal{S}] = \sum_{(i,j)\in\mathcal{S}} e(r_i, r_j). \tag{26.1}$$

Simple but reasonable values for $e(r_i, r_j)$ are $-3, -2, -1$ kcal/mole for G$\equiv$C, A$=$U, G–U base pairs respectively. More precise values of these parameters, taking into account the specific stacking energies of two consecutive base pairs, which depend on the base pair and the following one, loop-conformational entropies, salt and temperature dependence [13], have to be considered to effectively describe the whole complexity of the energy landscape, e.g. when fitting single molecule experiments, see Secs. 26.1.3.1 and 26.1.3.2. One of the advantages of this model is that we clearly separate the role of disorder (encoded in the sequence $\mathcal{R}$) from that of frustration (induced by the planarity condition on the structure $\mathcal{S}$). Thanks to the planarity condition, it is possible to use a simple dynamic-programming algorithm to compute the partition function $Z_{i,j}$, which corresponds to the sum over all possible pairings between sites $i < j$:

$$Z_{i,j} = Z_{i+1,j} + \sum_{k=i+1}^{j} Z_{i+1,k-1} e^{-\beta e(r_i, r_k)} Z_{k+1,j}, \tag{26.2}$$

as illustrated in Fig. 26.2, with $Z_{i,i} = Z_{i,i-1} = 1$ for all $i \in 1,\dots,L$.

Fig. 26.2. Graphical representation of Eq. (26.2). We display as filled grey bubbles the partition function between the two extremes of the bubble, and a term proportional to $e^{-\beta e(r_i, r_j)}$ as a dotted semi-circular link.

This recursion relation is particularly efficient since the time needed for the computation of $Z_{1,L}$, i.e. of the total partition function, scales as $\mathcal{O}(L^3)$. From the recursion, we can compute explicitly many interesting quantities, such as the probability that sites i and j are linked [15], integer moments of the internal energy $U = \langle H^k[\mathcal{S}] \rangle$, and the entropy.

26.1.2.3. *A glassy transition for disordered RNA models*

The model introduced in the previous subsection is a one-dimensional model with long-range interactions. Numerically, it is indeed shown that the probability of base pairing decays with the base pair distance with an exponent $3/2$ at high-temperatures and somehow slower, with an exponent near the value $4/3$, at low temperatures [19].

A numerical study of the specific heat [16] shows clear signs of a freezing phase transition to a low-temperature glassy regime. From the sequence-to-sequence critical temperature fluctuations, a specific heat critical exponent $\alpha \sim -1.9(1)$ is inferred; and the second derivative of the specific heat with respect to the temperature should thus display a very mild divergence or a finite jump. Near criticality, the entropy of the model has a crossing point [16], which signals a rapid shrinking of the available phase space. Moreover, the model has a finite zero-temperature entropy. A simple generalization of the dynamic-programming equation, allows for an efficient exact enumeration of all the ground-state structures (GSS) for any given sequence. Since the model turns out to be highly degenerate in the low-temperature phase, the natural question is how these GSS are organized. It is quite obvious that a very different physical behavior may appear in a model whose GSS are all very similar (like an ordered or "ferromagnetic" behavior) compared to a model whose GSS are dispersed over the whole configuration space. A more quantitative analysis can be achieved introducing the notion of distance between structures and a classification based on these distances. In order to quantify the relative distance between two structures, the overlap of secondary structures is defined as

$$q_{\mathcal{S},\mathcal{S}'} = \frac{1}{L} \sum_{i,j} l_{i,j}^{(\mathcal{S})} l_{i,j}^{(\mathcal{S}')}, \tag{26.3}$$

where the Boolean variable $l_{i,j}^{(\mathcal{S})}$ is 1 if i is connected to j in the structure $\mathcal{S}$, and zero otherwise. By definition, the overlap takes values in the interval $[0,1]$. For any given disorder realization (i.e. sequence) $\mathcal{R}$, we define the zero-temperature probability distribution function (pdf) of the overlaps:

$$P_{\mathcal{R}}(q) = \sum_{\mathcal{S},\mathcal{S}' \in \Gamma_{\mathcal{R}}} \delta(q - q_{\mathcal{S},\mathcal{S}'}), \tag{26.4}$$

with $\Gamma_{\mathcal{R}}$ being the GSS set. This definition can be easily generalized to any temperature by summing over all the structures and weighting each term with its Gibbs–Boltzmann factor. The usual classification of disordered systems is based upon the average pdf of the overlaps, the so-called $P(q) := \overline{P_{\mathcal{R}}(q)}$, where the overline indicates a disorder average taken over RNA sequences. In the high-temperature phase, the system is characterized by a simple paramagnetic $P(q)$ whose limiting behavior for large L is a delta function (the width of the distribution goes to zero as $1/\sqrt{L}$). However, in the low-temperature phase, the great majority of the sequences shows a very broad $P_{\mathcal{R}}(q)$, signaling a strong heterogeneity in the GSS. Moreover, the shape of the pdf becomes strongly sequence-dependent (viz. non self-averaging). Nevertheless, some common features can be easily recognized: while single-peaked $P_{\mathcal{R}}(q)$ functions are mostly associated with low-entropy sequences, highly structured $P_{\mathcal{R}}(q)$ functions do not seem to be correlated to the sequence's entropy, and they give rise to the broadness of the average $P(q)$.

The structural heterogeneity signalled by the broadness of the $P(q)$ for random sequences — those that most likely dominated the early stage of prebiotic life – has some interesting, albeit speculative, consequences for the RNA-world hypothesis. In principle two competing scenarios could have been possible:

- A *ferromagnetic* scenario where all thermodynamically relevant structures look pretty much the same independently from the realization of the sequence.
- A (possibly effective) *replica-symmetry breaking* scenario, where structures are strongly dependent on the sequence realization.

From the results summarized above, the second scenario seems to be more likely. Of course, we have no hints on whether the structural richness displayed by this simple random RNA model is enough to maintain a prebiotic RNA world, the question being currently completely out of any experimental control. Still, the RSB scenario is a stimulating starting point.

26.1.2.4. *Secondary-structure prediction*

The zero-temperature limit of Eq. (26.2) relates closely to one of the most prominent classical algorithms in RNA bioinformatics, the Nussinov algorithm [12] predicting the secondary structure for a given RNA sequence. The algorithm aims at finding the planary secondary structure which maximizes the number of realized Watson–Crick or wobble base pairs, i.e. it corresponds to a simplified energy $e(r_i, r_j) = -1$ if r_i and r_j are complementary in the before-mentioned sense, and to $e(r_i, r_j) = 0$ else.

The algorithm uses dynamic programming, and calculates iteratively the score $S(i, j)$ counting the maximum number of base pairs in the sub-sequence $r_i, ..., r_j$. As an initialization, it starts from all sub-sequences of length zero and one, which naturally cannot have base pairs,

$$\forall i : S(i, i - 1) = S(i, i) = 0. \tag{26.5}$$

In case of a constraint on the minimal loop length due to RNA stiffness, the initialization can be generalized easily.

As a next step, the zero-temperature limit of Eq. (26.2) is iterated. The sum over Boltzmann weights becomes a maximization:

$$S(i,j) = \max \begin{cases} S(i+1,j) & \text{if } i \text{ unpaired} \\ S(i+1,j-1) - e(r_i, r_j) & \text{if } i \text{ and } j \text{ paired} \\ \max_{k \mid i<k<j} S(i,k) + S(k+1,j) & \text{if } i \text{ paired with internal } k. \end{cases} \tag{26.6}$$

The final score $S(1,L)$ gives the maximum number of possible base pairs formed by the sequence $\{r_1, ..., r_L\}$ within a secondary structure. To get this secondary structure, we have to trace back the algorithm to extract the path, which realized the final maximum score.

While this algorithm is pretty efficient – it predicts the secondary structure in time $\mathcal{O}(L^3)$ — the accuracy of the prediction is very limited. This can be improved along a number of lines, in all cases maintaining the basic algorithmic structure of the Nussinov algorithm. First, instead of counting base pairs, we can minimize their free energy, also taking into account the different binding energies of the different base pairs, the stacking of base pairs in stems, and the conformational entropy of loops; this is implemented in particular in the Vienna package [20]. Second, we can determine the consensus secondary structure of a MSA of homologous RNAs. This will be discussed in more detail below.

26.1.3. *RNA unzipping: From experiments to theory*

In all regulatory processes mentioned in Sec. 26.1.1.1, the RNA complementary pairing plays a key role. For example, in therapeutic aptamers designed as anticoagulants that bind the thrombin protein thus avoiding its auto-aggregation, a simple hairpin structure is present. The sequence in the loop structure is designed to bind thrombin [22]. In other cases, such as the specific recognition and binding in the CRISPR-Cas9 gene editing system [23], RNA-DNA pairing is at the basis of the direct interaction with the DNA to be cut. Finally, both direct pairing and loop binding mechanisms are present in the regulatory RNAs called riboswitches, which upon binding to metabolites, control gene expression [24]. Riboswitches are aptamers characterized by structures made by few helix-loop units (see Fig. 26.1 and Sec. 26.1.4). The interaction with the metabolite happens on an unpaired nucleotide and brings to an alternative secondary structure, in which the riboswitch directly pairs to the expression platform of the ribosome binding site of the nearby gene and turns it on and off.

In the natural regulatory RNA described in the examples above, the pairing has to be strong enough to make the regulatory process happen, but it also has to be transitory, to allow to stop the regulatory interaction and to enable a different operation to be carried out on the gene. We are just starting to understand the importance and complexity of such dynamical pairing/unpairing processes and how to engineer DNA/RNA oligonucleotides able to have desired secondary structure and dynamical properties, such as multi-stable desired structures. Achieving such control could open the field to the bio-engineering of RNA/DNA regulation processes and DNA bio-computing [7].

Since the 1990s, single molecule manipulations [25] have made possible the direct investigation of the DNA pairing/unpairing dynamics. Thanks to optical and magnetic traps, single RNA and DNA molecules can be stretched or unzipped, by separating the complementary strands and breaking the base pairing between them; interactions with other nucleic acid or proteins can also be investigated [26–30]. A more detailed description of single-molecule experiments by optical traps is given in Sec. 26.2 by F. Ritort.

In the following, we describe how the statistical physics of random walks in a disordered energy landscape — with the disorder again introduced by the RNA sequence — has contributed to the interpretation of single molecule experiments and the general understanding of pairing/unpairing processes in RNA [30–32]. We describe some works we have carried out to reproduce the unzipping dynamics of simple RNA hairpins [21] and the displacement interactions between oligo-nucleotides bound on a DNA strand and the DNA closing hairpin [33]. The inverse problem of inferring the RNA and DNA sequence for unzipping experiments [34] will be also mentioned.

26.1.3.1. *Unzipping and RNA secondary structure*

The free energy to unzip the first n out of N base pairs in a RNA hairpin at constant force f (cf. Fig. 26.3(a)) reads

$$H[\mathcal{R}, f, n] = -\sum_{a=1}^{n} \left\{ e(r_{i(a)}, r_{i(a+1)}, r_{j(a)}, r_{j(a+1)}) - 2ng_s(f, a) \right\}, \qquad (26.7)$$

where the pairing free energy parameters $e_a = e(r_{i(a)}, r_{j(a)}, r_{j(a)}, r_{j(a+1)})$ depend on the identity of the ath base pair $\{i(a), j(a)\}$, $1 \le a \le N$, and on its stacking with the

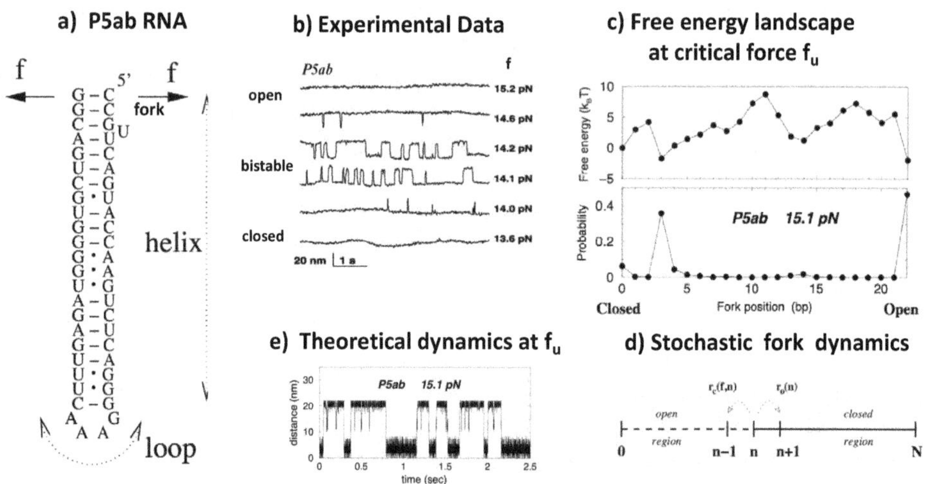

Fig. 26.3. a) Sketch of the unzipping by a constant force of the P5ab hairpin. b) Experimental unzipping signal given by the distance between the two extremities of the RNA as a function of the time for different forces. For $f < f_u$ the molecule stays closed, at $f = f_u$ a bistable signal is observed, at $f > f_u$ the molecule stays open. c) The sequence dependent unzipping free energy landscape at force f_u shows three minima in 0, 3 and 21 opened base pairs, on which the configurational probability is peaked. d+e) A stochastic dynamics for the opening force in the unzipping landscape reproduces the unzipping signal. The figure is adapted from Ref. [21].

$(a+1)$st base pair (if adjacent), since both base pairing and stacking need to be broken by the applied force. They are determined by thermodynamic measurements. The parameters taken from, e.g., RNAfold [20] were obtained by thermodynamic calibration. The negative $2g_s(f,a)$ is the stretching energy gained when opening the ath base pair [21]. Polymer physics models have been used to describe such elastic response and the parameters have been calibrated by single molecule experiments [26, 32]. An unzipping force of about $15pN$ compensates the loss in pairing energy (of the order of $-2.5k_BT$) with the gain in stretching free energy of the opened base pair. This value gives the typical critical unzipping forces at which the molecule starts to open.

The unzipping free energy landscape of a homopolymer is flat at the critical unzipping force: every configuration of n open base pairs is equally probable and the opening fork makes a diffusive motion between a closed and an open molecule. However for a heteropolymer like RNA, a free energy landscape with barriers and minima determines a characteristic opening-closing time for the molecule, much longer than the diffusive time. As is shown in Fig. 26.3(c) for the simple P5ab RNA hairpin, and more generally valid for all hairpins with stem-loop structures, large barriers are still present at the critical unzipping force. This is due to the fact that when opening a single unpaired base (mismatch) or a region of them (loop) there is no cost in pairing energy, the contribution of this region to the opening free energy is therefore negative, and a peak and a barrier form in the free energy landscape.

The P5ab free-energy landscape [21] is characterized by three minima, in which the opening fork has the largest probabilities to be located. The telegraphic signal experimentally observed [35], see Fig. 26.3(b), corresponds to the persistence in these states and jumps between them. This signal can be precisely described by a stochastic dynamics of the opening fork in the above free energy landscape with opening $R_o(n)$ and closing $R_c(f,n)$ rates,

$$R_o(a) = R\, e^{e_a/k_BT}, \qquad R_c(f,a) = R\, e^{2g_s(f,a)/k_BT}, \qquad (26.8)$$

where R is the microscopic fluctuation rate for a base pair; it was estimated to be $R \approx 5 \times 10^6 s^{-1}$ by computing the inverse self-diffusion time for a few-nanometer diameter object [36].

The rates in Eq. (26.8) lead to a master equation for the probability $\rho_a(t)$ for the opening fork to be at site a at time t,

$$\rho_a(t + \delta t) = \rho_a(t) + \delta t \left[-\rho_a(t)\left(R_o(a) + R_c(f,a)\right) \right.$$
$$\left. + \rho_{a-1}(t)R_o(a-1) + \rho_{a+1}(t)R_c(f,a+1) \right] \qquad (26.9)$$

or, equivalently, in the time continuum limit,

$$\frac{d\,\rho_a(t)}{d\,t} = -\sum_{b=0}^{N} T_{a,b}\, \rho_b(t). \qquad (26.10)$$

This $(N+1) \times (N+1)$ matrix $T_{a,b}$ is tridiagonal, corresponding to opening one base pair at the time, with nonzero entries $T_{a-1,a} = -R_c(f,a)$, $T_{a+1,a} = -R_o(a)$, and $T_{a,a} = R_c(f,a) + R_o(a)$. The characteristic switching time can be computed through the smallest non-zero eigenvalue of the transition matrix, $t_{switch} = 1/(\lambda_1 R)$ with

$\lambda_1 = 2 \times 10^{-6}$ for P5ab, which is well separated from the others. By fitting the value of $R = 3.6 \times 10^6 \; s^{-1}$ one finds back the observed switching time $t = 0.14s$.

It is possible to reverse engineer the problem to design hairpin structures displaying bistable dynamics on a desired time scale. For a uniform sequence this can be easily achieved just by acting on the loop and hairpin lengths. Consider a constant pairing free energy e_0 for each base pair. The free energy barrier G^* at criticality for a N-base-pair RNA stem (i.e. double helix) followed by a L-base loop (closing free energy $g_{loop}(L)$ at zero force) (Fig. 26.3) can be easily estimated. The critical force f_u is given by the condition that the free energy of the open molecule equals the free energy of the closed molecule: $G(0, f_u) = G(N, f_u)$, that is, $0 = -N\,e_0 + (2N + L)\,g_{ss}(f_u) + g_{loop}(L)$. The barrier height $G^*(N, L) \equiv G(N - 1, f_u)$ then reads

$$G^*(N, L) = (N - 1)(-e_0 + 2\,g_{ss}(f_u)) = \frac{(N - 1)\,(-e_0\,L - 2\,g_{loop}(L))}{L + 2N}. \qquad (26.11)$$

As sketched in the introduction, the possibility of bio-engineering switching times is important in the field of DNA/RNA-computing to create dynamical programming with this elementary processes [7, 37]. Another interesting application of DNA/RNA unzipping is in sequencing technologies, by reconstructing the amino-acid sequence from the unzipping energy landscape and its heterogeneities due to the sequence [25, 34, 38, 39]. Sequencing through unzipping could be advantageous with respect to existing sequencing technologies by avoiding short reads which make difficult, e.g., the correct sequencing of repeated sequences. Fluctuations of the open single strand have so far made it difficult to practically use this idea to sequence long molecules. The problem of reconstructing the sequence from the opening signal is, however, a very interesting theoretical problem, corresponding to the inverse problem of the Sinai model with a drift describing random walks in a disordered free energy landscape tilted by a force [40, 41]. Applications of the inverse problem have been realized in nanopore sequencing, in which the sequence is unzipped by passing through a nanopore channel: from the detected electrical signal, the unzipped base pair is reconstructed [42].

26.1.3.2. *Oligonucleotides displacement models*

In the following, we will illustrate how single molecule experiments and the RNA/DNA opening free energy landscape can be used to predict for how long and where a probe made by a complementary segment of DNA can be bound to a DNA strand, before dissociating naturally or being displaced by another DNA. More precisely, in the experiment described below (Fig. 26.4), the closure of a double-stranded DNA can be blocked by the hybridization of the complementary probe, and the position and the blocking time can be monitored and theoretically predicted. This technique can be used in single-molecule sequencing [43] to find a particular sequence on a DNA molecule. Moreover, monitoring the blocking time allows one to detect the presence of a mutation or a mismatch between the probe and the DNA sequence, typically giving shorter blocking times. The unzipping free-energy landscape Eq. (26.1), at room temperature and zero unzipping force, quantifies the cost to spontaneously dissociate a DNA or RNA molecule from a DNA substrate. For each base pair to break, the increase of free energy

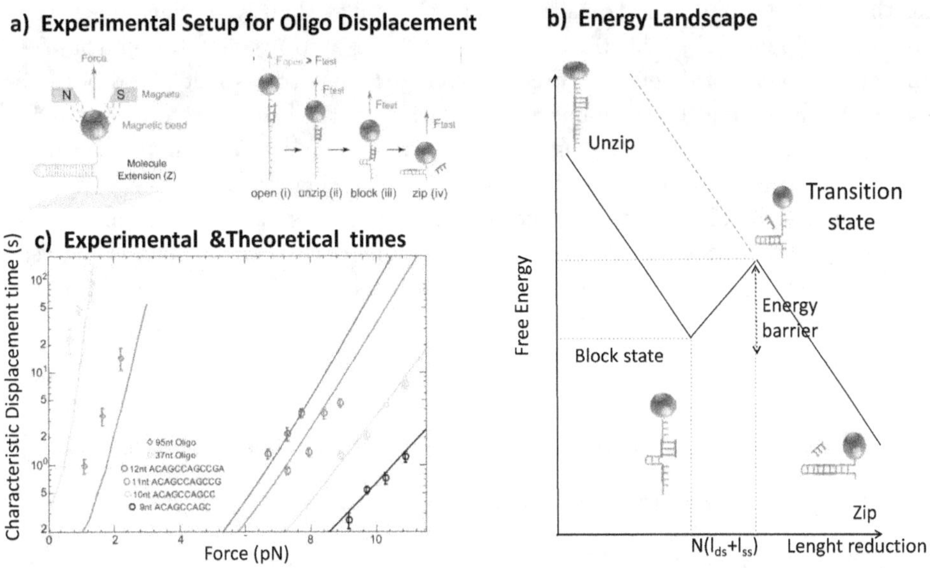

Fig. 26.4.   a) Experimental Setup for the single-molecule oligonucleotide displacement process. The complementary DNA strand is first unzipped at large unzipping force ($f > 15pN$) and an oligonucleotide is let to hybridize on its complementary segment. The force is then lowered to the test force $f_{test} < 15pN$, and the DNA strand starts to close at such force until the closing strand hits the oligonucleotide, which has to be displaced before continuing the closing process. This obstacle generates a barrier in the energy landscape (b). c) Measured and theoretical characteristic displacement times as a function of the test force for oligonucleotides of sizes between 9 and 95 nucleotides. The figure is re-adapted from Ref. [33].

of about $2.5k_BT$ multiplies the opening time by a factor 10. It is therefore impossible to observe the spontaneous dissociation of a DNA/RNA probe of more than a dozen base pairs from its complementary DNA/RNA strand. This can be a serious limitation not only *in vitro* to monitor the blocking time, but mainly *in vivo* for the regulatory processes RNA has to carry out on DNA genomes, cf. the introduction, as well as for the bio-engineered imitations of such processes. One way out is to exploit the base-by-base displacement process. It has been shown by single molecule experiments that this is a very efficient and powerful mechanism to dissociate molecules, not only for DNA/RNA oligonocleotides but also for proteins [33, 44, 45], which are otherwise very stably bound to the complementary DNA. The replacement process happens thanks to thermal fluctuation by replacing one component of the bound molecule at the time [46] and can dissociate, in few minutes, DNA oligonucleotides as long as 95 bases, as observed by the single molecule experiments [33] described in Fig. 26.4. Similarly to unzipping, a model describing the random motion of the opening fork on the displacement landscape (cf. Fig. 26.4(b)) can be introduced to mathematically describe the replacement process at any unzipping force f (even very small). The predicted displacement times as a function of the length of the complementary oligonucleotide and its sequence are in good agreement with experiments, as is shown in Fig. 26.4(c). Differently from Eq. (26.7), the energy barrier for the progression of the displacement fork does not include any pairing energy, as the same pairing energy lost for the bound oligonucleotide is gained by closing the DNA-hairpin. The transition matrix becomes slightly more complex than the one for unzipping, Eq. (26.10), as it needs to take into account the hairpin fork and the two oligonucleotide ends. Moreover, configurations corresponding to both the closing DNA hairpin and the oligonucleotide pairing on the same base does not exist. Still it is possible to numerically diagonalize this matrix and to obtain very accurate estimates of the replacement times, cf. Fig. 26.4. Interestingly the displacement times are not strongly affected by changing the pairing parameters, as they only marginally depend on pairing energies. On the contrary, as soon as there is an asymmetry between the bound molecule and the invader, e.g. for hybrid RNA-DNA molecules and for mismatches, the displacement times become very sensitive to the sequence and mismatch position.

26.1.4. *RNA evolution, coevolution, and statistical sequence models*

26.1.4.1. *RNA families and (co)evolutionary constraints*

As all biological molecules, RNAs are subject to natural evolution. Nucleotide mutations introduce random changes into the RNA sequence. But not all changes lead to functional variants, and natural selection tends to suppress deleterious mutations. In the case of functional RNA, two selective constraints are of particular importance: (i) some functionally important motifs contain combinations of positions in the sequence, which cannot be changed, they are highly conserved, (ii) functional RNA tend to conserve their secondary structure, realized via the complementarity of the concerned base pairs. If, e.g., the first nucleotide in the base pair C-G is mutated into an A, the pairing is disrupted, and the corresponding secondary structure weakened. However, if also the second position is changed into a U, we find an alternative base pair A-U. The two positions thus cannot evolve independently, they *coevolve* [47, 48].

Databases like Rfam [49] collect families of homologous RNA sequences, i.e. of sequences having common ancestry in evolution, having typically very similar secondary structure and biological function, but potentially distantly diverged sequences. These families are provided in the form of *multiple-sequence alignments* (MSA), i.e. in the form of rectangular matrices, where each row corresponds to an individual RNA sequence, and each column to a nucleotide position resulting from shared evolutionary ancestry, cf. the schematic representation in Fig. 26.5. The problem of aligning multiple RNA sequences is non-trivial: first, sequences may change their length via nucleotide insertions or deletions, therefore MSA do not only contain the four nucleotides A, C, G and U, but also the alignment *gap* "–" accounting for missing nucleotides. A gap may indicate a deletion in the sequence, or an insertion into another sequence. Second, in the case of base pairs, the individual nucleotides may be highly variable, but their complementarity needs to be conserved. In difference to standard MSA techniques developed for DNA or protein sequences [50], algorithms for RNA sequence alignment need to take this coevolutionary information into account [18].

But how much does the conservation of the secondary structure restrict the viable RNA sequence space? Advanced MCMC sampling techniques are used [51] in combination with secondary structure prediction tools [52] to estimate the size of the

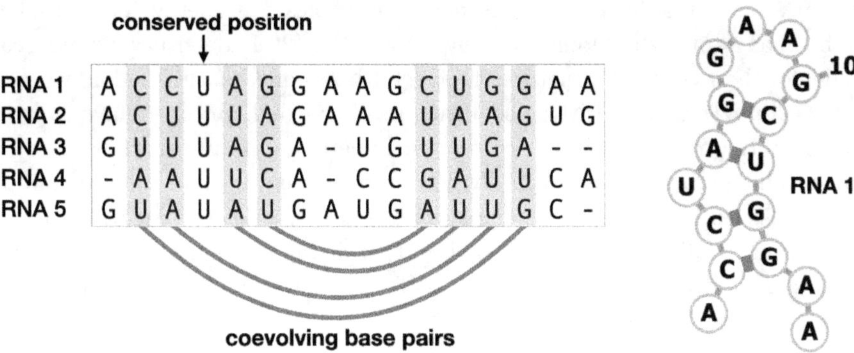

Fig. 26.5.   Coevolution of base pairs in RNA secondary structure, as represented in a small MSA of RNA sequences. The evidenced pairs of columns are coevolving. While the individual nucleotides change from sequence to sequence, the pairs of same color are compatible with base pairing (Watson–Crick or wobble pairs). All sequences are compatible with the secondary structure depicted on the right (nucleotides labeled according to the first sequence, coevolving secondary-structure pairs connected by bold lines).

so-called *neutral network* [53] in RNA sequence space, defined as the collection of all nucleotide sequences, which would fold into the same secondary structure. These studies found an impressive reduction in viable sequence numbers: to give an example, for RNA sequences of 200 nucleotides, the sequence space is reduced from a total of $4^{200} \simeq 2.6 \times 10^{120}$ sequences to "only" about 7×10^{86} sequences being predicted to have the correct secondary structure. While this corresponds to a reduction of over 30 orders of magnitude, the resulting neutral network is still astronomically large (for comparison, there are about 10^{80} atoms in the entire universe).

So, it becomes clear that evolutionary constraints — conservation and coevolution — play a crucial role on RNA evolution and should leave important statistical traces in MSA of homologous sequences. However, even the largest families sample only a tiny fraction of the viable sequence space. The tRNA family has currently 1.4 million sequence entries in Rfam, being by far the largest RNA family. All other families have (in most cases much) less than 200,000 sequences. Statistical analysis or modeling of RNA sequences therefore works in the regime of extreme undersampling — despite what is called the "data revolution" or "sequencing revolution" in modern biology.

26.1.4.2. *Profile and covariance models*

Assume an MSA $\mathcal{M} = (r_i^\mu)_{i=1,\ldots,L}^{\mu=1,\ldots,M}$ of M homologous RNA sequences of aligned length L to be given. The aim of statistical sequence models is to represent the statistical properties of these RNA sequences via a statistical model $P(r_1,\ldots,r_L)$ assigning a probability to each possible nucleotide sequence over the extended alphabet $\{A,C,G,U,-\}$ containing the four possible nucleotides and the alignment gap. In analogy to statistical mechanics, we will represent these statistical models as Boltzmann distributions $P(r_1,\ldots,r_L) \sim \exp\{-H(r_1,\ldots,r_L)\}$ introducing the *statistical energy* $H(r_1,\ldots,r_L)$. This function has to be learnt from the MSA $\mathcal{M}$.

Two remarks are in order: first, the model resembles the energy introduced in Eq. (26.1), but has a totally different meaning. While Eq. (26.1) describes a statistical-physics model for the secondary structure of a *given* RNA sequence, the random variable in $P(r_1, ..., r_L)$ (or $H(r_1, ..., r_L)$) is the sequence itself. Second, since we have to learn our statistical energy from data in the case of extreme undersampling, we need to assume some suitable parameterization of H. We need to keep in mind that too simple parameterizations will not be able to represent the statistics of the MSA, while too complex models may suffer from overfitting, i.e. from fitting the noise contained in the specific finite sample given by the MSA. In the bioinformatics of RNA sequences, two classes of statistical models are intensively used [54].

The simplest non-trivial class of models are *profile models* [54]. In their simplest form, their statistical energy takes the form

$$H(r_1, ..., r_L) = -\sum_{i=1}^{L} h_i(r_i) \tag{26.12}$$

of a sum of position-dependent local "fields" (or biases), i.e. the model $P(r_1, ..., r_L)$ describes L statistically independent positions. A simple maximum-likelihood approach allows to relate the fields to the statistics of single MSA columns. Let us consider $f_i(r) = \frac{1}{M} \sum_\mu \delta_{r,r_i^\mu}$ the fraction of sequences in $\mathcal{M}$ having nucleotide (or gap) r in position (or MSA column) i. The local fields are then directly given by the empirical log-frequencies,

$$h_i(r) = \ln f_i(r). \tag{26.13}$$

Note that profile models can capture patterns of nucleotide conservation due to the position-specific fields: a nucleotide frequently observed in a position will have a more favorable local field than a rare nucleotide. However, due to their factorized form, profile models cannot capture coevolution. Nevertheless they belong to the most successful statistical models in sequence bioinformatics, in particular for DNA and protein sequences, and are at the basis of most approaches to sequence alignment, homology detection or phylogeny reconstruction [54].

We motivated coevolution by the need to conserve secondary structure in RNA evolution. In a base pair, connecting two columns i and j in our MSA, we will therefore find more Watson–Crick or wobble pairs A-U, U-A, G-C, C-G, G-U and U-G than any other nucleotide pair. This means that the joint nucleotide frequency $f_{i,j}(r, r') = \frac{1}{M} \sum_\mu \delta_{r,r_i^\mu} \delta_{r',r_j^\mu}$ of nucleotide pairs (r, r') in positions i and j deviates strongly from the factorized expression $f_i(r)f_j(r')$. This fact is taken into account in *covariance models* for RNA sequence ensembles at given secondary structure $\mathcal{S}$ [55]. Their statistical energy reads

$$H(r_1, ..., r_L | \mathcal{S}) = -\sum_{i=1}^{L} h_i(r_i) - \sum_{(ij) \in \mathcal{S}} J_{ij}(r_i, r_j), \tag{26.14}$$

i.e. covariance models introduce explicit pair couplings for all base pairs in $\mathcal{S}$. Also here the simple graphical structure of $\mathcal{S}$ allows us to analytically find the maximum-likelihood parameters for fields and couplings: sites are at most included in one base pair, and Eq. (26.14) describes a collection of individual sites and paired dimers, which are statistically independent between each other. While the fields are still given by Eq. (26.13), the couplings read

$$J_{ij}(r, r') = \ln \frac{f_{i,j}(r, r')}{f_i(r) f_j(r')} \tag{26.15}$$

for all $(ij) \in \mathcal{S}$: they are given as the log-ratio between the joint empirical frequency and the factorized expression. Covariance models, while still being easily treatable, greatly enhance the accuracy of RNA-sequence alignment and homology detection [18].

26.1.4.3. *Coevolution-based secondary structure prediction*

Using a covariance model given by a secondary RNA structure $\mathcal{S}$ and the maximum-likelihood parameters in Eqs. (26.13) and (26.15), and assuming that the sequences in the MSA $\mathcal{M}$ are independently drawn from each other (an assumption typically violated by sequence data characterized by phylogenetic correlations), we can calculate the log-probability of the MSA:

$$\ln P(\mathcal{M}|\mathcal{S}) = \frac{1}{M} \sum_{\mu=1}^{M} \ln P(r_1^\mu, ..., r_L^\mu | \mathcal{S})$$

$$= -\sum_{i=1}^{L} s_i + \sum_{(ij) \in \mathcal{S}} MI_{ij}, \tag{26.16}$$

where we have introduced the empirical single-site entropies

$$s_i = -\sum_r f_i(r) \ln f_i(r) \tag{26.17}$$

characterizing the variation (or conservation) of individual positions, and the mutual information

$$MI_{ij} = \sum_{r,r'} f_{ij}(r, r') \ln \frac{f_{i,j}(r, r')}{f_i(r) f_j(r')} \tag{26.18}$$

measuring the covariation (or coevolution) of pairs of positions. Following standards in inference, we can use this expression as the log-likelihood of the secondary structure $\mathcal{S}$ given the data $\mathcal{M}$, which up to $\mathcal{S}$-independent terms reads

$$\mathcal{L}(\mathcal{S}|\mathcal{M}) = \sum_{(ij) \in \mathcal{S}} MI_{ij} + \text{const}, \tag{26.19}$$

and find the best possible secondary structure by maximum likelihood. Note that again this has a very striking similarity to the single-sequence energy in Eq. (26.1), but with the physical interactions between nucleotides replaced by the mutual information between nucleotide positions (or MSA columns). It is now pretty straightforward to generalize the Nussinov algorithm for single-sequence secondary-structure prediction to the prediction of a *consensus secondary structure* of the MSA, by replacing the number of base pairs with their cumulative mutual information. This maximizes the likelihood of $\mathcal{S}$ for a given MSA over all non-nested planar secondary structures.

In RNA bioinformatics, it is well known that single-sequence secondary-structure prediction is imprecise. Therefore many current secondary-structure prediction tools use MSA and pairwise mutual information in their core algorithms [20].

26.1.4.4. *Direct-coupling analysis for RNA families*

Proceeding in this way, we need to first calculate the mutual information MI_{ij} for all pairs (ij) of positions, i.e. for all $1 \leq i < j \leq L$. Out of these $\binom{L}{2}$ pairs, less than $L/2$ can be part of the base pairs of the secondary structure. Analyses of MI values in biological MSA show that not only these base pairs coevolve, but there are further pairs showing considerable correlation in nucleotide usage. Some of them correspond to neighboring positions along the sequence (primary structure), some to the before mentioned pseudo-knots or other three-dimensional contacts between nucleotides, others lack a simple interpretation.

It seems therefore wise to take into account in the statistical modeling of an RNA family also the coevolution between nucleotide pairs not paired in the secondary structure. In the absence of a clear selection criterion for important pairs, we follow the idea of the *Direct-Coupling Analysis* (DCA) [56, 57] also explained more theoretically and for proteins in the chapter by Aurell et al. We construct a *Potts model* (aka Markov Random Field or Boltzmann machine) given by the statistical energy

$$H(r_1, ..., r_L) = - \sum_{1 \leq i \leq L} h_i(r_i) - \sum_{1 \leq i < j < L} J_{ij}(r_i, r_j), \qquad (26.20)$$

which is characterized by a fully connected network of — *a priori* fully disordered — pairwise couplings. In practice, these couplings are disordered but (up to some gauge or reparameterization invariance) determined by the conditions

$$\sum_{r_1, ..., r_L} P(r_1, ..., r_L) \delta_{r, r_i} = f_i(r),$$

$$\sum_{r_1, ..., r_L} P(r_1, ..., r_L) \delta_{r, r_i} \delta_{r', r_j} = f_{ij}(r, r'), \qquad (26.21)$$

i.e. all one- and two-site marginals of P have to coincide with the corresponding empirical nucleotide frequencies. Obviously, the determination of the model parameters – fields and couplings – now becomes a computationally hard task, since the exact calculation of the marginals of a given models requires the sum over 5^L possible aligned nucleotide sequences.

The computationally simplest but rather time-demanding way is to estimate the left-hand site of Eqs. (26.21) using MCMC simulations, and to iteratively update the model parameters to reach equality with the empirical frequencies. While this procedure, known as Boltzmann-machine learning [58], leads to very precise models, in many tasks much faster but less accurate approximations can be used. The chapter by Aurell et al. describes in particular the widely used mean-field [56] and pseudo-likelihood maximization [59, 60] approaches, in particular the first one being motivated by prior work on high-temperature expansions in spin-glass systems [61, 62].

Once model parameters are inferred, we can use them to extract biologically important information [63, 64]:

(1) *Secondary-structure prediction:* Instead of using mutual information for secondary-structure prediction as discussed in the last subsection, we can use the statistical couplings J_{ij}. This was found to slightly improve the predicted secondary structure.

(2) *Tertiary-structure prediction:* More importantly, the couplings may contain information going beyond secondary structure, they may describe also tertiary-structure contacts. While it was found that this signal is rather weak compared to the strong base-pair coevolution, it is still able to help tertiary structure prediction.

(3) *Evolution-guided sequence design:* Accurately inferred DCA models (using Boltzmann-machine learning) were found to be generative [65]. This means that sequences sampled from the model using MCMC are statistically hardly distinguishable from natural RNA sequences. This observation opens for the possibility to generate non-natural functional RNA molecules. The idea has been explored recently in the case of proteins [66], its validation is forthcoming for RNA.

Note that the applications to structure prediction are completely unsupervised: we use the parameters of a statistical model of an RNA family, but no direct structural data coming, e.g., from experimentally determined structures available in the Protein Data Bank [67]. The quality of RNA structure prediction can be increased using supervised learning [68, 69], even if successes similar to proteins [17] are still missing.

26.1.4.5. *Direct-Coupling Analysis and Restricted Boltzmann Machines for Aptamer Design*

Statistical modeling from sequence data was recently used by some of us to reconstruct the binding fitness landscape of DNA aptamers [70]. DNA aptamers are small molecules with an hairpin structure (stem and loop), and even if they are DNA rather than RNA, the statistical modeling techniques are equivalent. Laboratory selection experiments called SELEX [71, 72] have been recently shown to be very powerful tools to design molecules with desired properties, such as clinical aptamers, mentioned in introduction, which avoid blood coagulation by strong binding to thrombin. SELEX starts from an initial library of 10^{12} random initial sequences for the two loops, each of 20 nucleotides, of a 2-loop aptamer. Sequences are passed through 8 rounds of selection and amplification to extract very strongly bivalent binders to thrombin. During the experiment 10^5 sequences have been collected starting from round 5 [22]. Such data have been used to infer the parameters of two generative models in machine learning, DCA as described above in Eq. (26.20) and Restricted Boltzmann Machines (RBM) described by the energy function

$$H(r_1, ..., r_L, y_1, ..., y_P) = -\sum_{1 \leq i \leq L} h_i(r_i) - \sum_{i,\mu} w_{i\mu}(r_i) y_i^\mu + \sum_{1 \leq \mu \leq P} \mathcal{U}_\mu(y_i). \qquad (26.22)$$

RBM are two-layer networks described by two sets of variables: (i) the variables $r_1, ..., r_L$ in the visible layer, which stand for the RNA sequence, and (ii) the variables $y_1, ..., y_P$ which act as feature detectors in the hidden layer. This simple bipartite network can directly implement the dualism between data and their representations: extract features from data and generate data with desired features. RBM are also appealing in statistical mechanics because they are an extension of Hopfield models with P stored patterns [73], for non binary patterns (Potts spins rather than Ising spins) and non quadratic hidden units. Using an appropriate regularisation, which implements sparsity conditions, the weights $w_{i\mu}$ have been shown to reflect key sequence motifs [74, 75]: here the so-called G-quadruplex motif is important to bind thrombin. The RBM and DCA models, learnt from the sequence data at round 6, are able to predict the most selected sequences at the next rounds: the log-likelihood of a sequence, corresponding to minus the RBM/DCA energy Eqs. (26.22) and (26.20), can be used as a sequence score and is linearly correlated to the fitness as measured by the sequence enrichment ratio (logarithm of the number of molecules selected at round $t+1$ divided the ones selected at the round t, i.e. presented at round $t+1$). Moreover RBM can be used to design new binders which have not been found through the sequencing procedure, and to predict deleterious mutations which can interrupt binding [70].

26.1.5. *RNA networks and the coordination of systemic regulatory programs*

26.1.5.1. *MicroRNAs and the ceRNA hypothesis*

As mentioned at the beginning of this chapter, it has long been known that not all RNA molecules are protein-coding [76]. For example, transfer RNAs (tRNAs), the best known among all non-coding RNAs (ncRNAs), play a key role in protein synthesis by carrying aminoacids to the elongation sites in ribosomes bound to protein-coding RNAs (messenger RNA, mRNA). In this process, the interaction between tRNA and mRNA is effectively catalyzed by another type of ncRNA, namely ribosomal RNA (rRNA). rRNA is especially remarkable because, besides being a key structural component of ribosomes, it constitutes over 80% of the total RNA of animal cells [77]. So most of our RNA is non-coding. In many organisms, then, stalled protein synthesis is rescued by another class of ncRNA known as transfer-messenger RNA (tmRNA), whose powers include the ability to degrade aberrant mRNA and to recycle the ribosome. We could continue with many more examples of ncRNAs from all domains of life acting in a myriad of biological processes. The list of known ncRNAs and their associated functions has indeed been growing steadily since the early 1980s, and with a particularly fast pace since the advent of high-throughput sequencing. But a whole new level of regulatory organisation managed by ncRNAs was uncovered when the mechanism known as RNA interference (RNAi) was first brought to light in 1998 [78].

In short, RNAi occurs when ncRNA molecules repress the expression of a gene by protein-mediated binding to specific sequence motifs on the mRNA. The most famous and possibly most important class of ncRNAs capable of performing RNAi in regulatory networks is formed by microRNAs (miRNAs [79]), small (ca. 22 nt typically), highly conserved and highly stable eukaryotic RNA molecules whose life cycle can be summarized as follows [80]: after being transcribed (from introns of protein-coding genes or miRNA-specific genes), they undergo a series of enzyme-catalyzed maturation steps before being incorporated into large protein complexes called RISCs (RNA-Induced Silencing Complexes); miRNA-RISCs expose specific nucleotide sequences through which they can bind short segments on their target RNAs called miRNA response elements (MREs); MREs are usually just 6 to 9 nt long, implying relatively low binding affinities and therefore a potentially significant interference from other short sequences to which they can bind in purely electrostatic manner; miRNAs can target both coding and non-coding RNAs; if the target is a mRNA, the bulky RISC bound to the mRNA impedes translation by blocking the ribosome; finally, miRNA-target complex degradation is elicited and can occur through two distinct pathways: a so-called 'catalytic' pathway leading to the re-cycling of the miRNA; and a 'stoichiometric' pathway leading to the degradation of both miRNA and target [81].

If one focuses on sequence-specific interactions, different types of miRNAs have different binding sites and hence repress different genes, often acting within clearly identifiable regulatory motifs whose functions have been subject of much work [82]. On a broader scale, however, the global interaction network linking miRNAs to their targets (both coding and non-coding) spans across the entire transcriptome and is strongly heterogeneous, as each miRNA can repress many distinct RNA targets and, vice-versa, each RNA species can be the target of many miRNA species [83]. Cells therefore invest serious molecular and energy resources (e.g. via specialized maturation enzymes, RISC proteins, biosynthetic machinery, etc.) into maintaining and conserving across generations functional batteries of miRNAs together with their interaction networks, despite the fact that the individual miRNA-target coupling, while evolutionarily preserved, can be rather weak. Given that gene expression can be repressed in many ways, the obvious question is what makes miRNAs so convenient for cells.

Two answers have so far attracted the largest attention. In the first scenario, miRNAs provide an essential contribution to the fine tuning of gene expression levels [84]. It is well known that protein levels are tightly regulated in higher organisms. This requires molecular mechanisms that are capable of processing the inherent stochasticity of regulatory processes (e.g. due to transcription factors diffusing to their binding sites, bursty transcription events, etc). Experimental and theoretical work has indeed shown that gene expression noise is reduced in presence of miRNAs, albeit not always by spectacular amounts compared to the unregulated case or to alternative regulatory means [85–87]. Besides their ability to repress gene expression, this noise-reducing capability is without doubt an added value of miRNAs.

The second scenario adds a totally different ingredient, as it postulates that miRNAs can establish weak but extended crosstalk interaction networks between their targets, which effectively allow for a degree of systemic cross-modulation of expression levels [88]. In other words, miRNAs orchestrate a large-scale regulatory network that can (weakly) coordinate the translation levels of *all* RNAs in the transcriptome. The key to unlock this scenario is competition: if a miRNA species interacts with two different targets (say A and B), an increase in the availability of A will draw more miRNAs towards it and therefore lift repression, at least partially, from B. In other words, upon increasing the expression level of one miRNA target, the expression level of the other increases as well (Fig. 26.6). It is easy to see how such a mechanism can effectively link the entire transcriptome via chains of miRNA-target interactions [89]. Unfortunately, quantifying

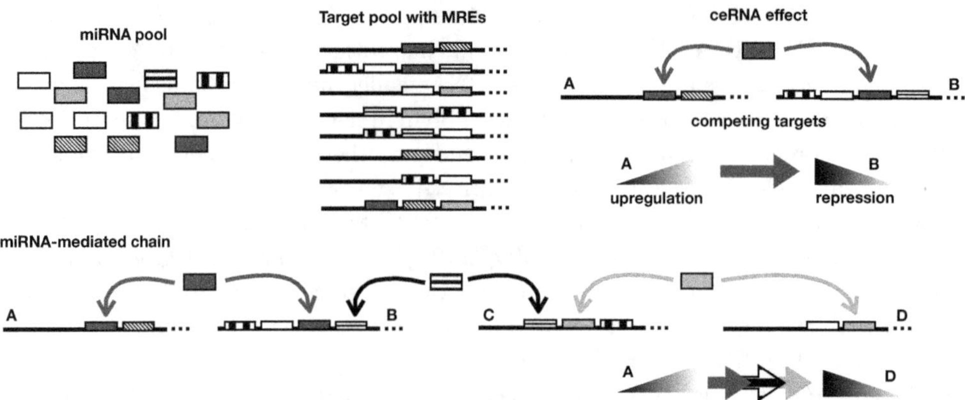

Fig. 26.6.   A diverse pool of miRNAs coexists in cells with a diverse pool of targets. Targets sharing at least one miRNA species as regulator compete to bind it. If the level of target A is increased while keeping all else fixed, the likelihood of the miRNA binding target A increases. In turn, repression is increasingly lifted off target B, which could then become more likely available for e.g., translation. This effect can propagate between targets that do not share any common miRNA regulators, such as A and D above, through chains of miRNA-mediated couplings induced by the same competition mechanism.

its relevance in a physiological context is hard due to the weakness of the individual miRNA-target interactions [90, 91], although traces of its action can be found in indirect effects [92]. The main questions are the following: under which circumstances can the myriad of weak miRNA-target couplings encoded in the RNA sequences build up to generate coherent target-target interactions spanning across the whole transcriptome? Can these interactions affect system-level outcomes? Are these properties embedded in the specific topology of the miRNA-target network? How strongly do they depend on the interaction parameters (e.g. the binding affinities)?

In view of the experimental limitations, some understanding can only be achieved through a theoretical approach. Luckily, all of these questions echo classical problems in statistical mechanics and complexity theory. Methods developed in these fields (and, as we shall see, for disordered systems specifically) are therefore ideally suited for this task.

26.1.5.2. *A statistical theory of competition in RNA networks*

A (simplified) theory of RNA networks starts from the dynamics of molecular levels. Denoting respectively by μ_a $(a = 1, \dots, M)$ and m_i $(i = 1, \dots, N)$ the levels of miRNA species a and target species i, and using the shorthand $\dot{x} \equiv \frac{dx}{dt}$, the deterministic mass action kinetics of a miRNA-target network is described by (see e.g. [93–95])

$$\dot{\mu}_a = \beta_a - \delta_a \mu_a - \sum_i k_{ia}^+ m_i \mu_a + \sum_i (k_{ia}^- + \kappa_{ia}) c_{ia}, \qquad (26.23)$$

$$\dot{m}_i = b_i - d_i m_i - \sum_a k_{ia}^+ m_i \mu_a + \sum_a k_{ia}^- c_{ia}, \qquad (26.24)$$

$$\dot{c}_{ia} = k_{ia}^+ m_i \mu_a - (\sigma_{ia} + \kappa_{ia} + k_{ia}^-) c_{ia}, \qquad (26.25)$$

where c_{ia} stands for the level of miRNA-target complexes while synthesis rates (b_i, β_a), degradation rates (d_i, δ_a), association and dissociation rates $(k_{ia}^{\pm})$ and complex processing rates $(\sigma_{ia}, \kappa_{ia})$ represent kinetic parameters whose values are mostly unknown (and likely unknowable). To get some intuition of what this system looks like if seen through a statistical-physics lens, one can first observe that, if $\sigma_{ia} + \kappa_{ia} + k_{ia}^{-}$ is much larger than both d_i and δ_a, Eq. (26.25) equilibrates much faster than the other two. In this limit, and under reasonable assumptions for kinetic rates, the steady state values of m_i and μ_a can be found by minimizing the (Lyapunov) function [96]

$$L(\{m_i\}, \{\mu_a\}) = \sum_{i,a} k_{ia}^{+} m_i \mu_a - \sum_{i} (b_i \log m_i - d_i m_i) - \sum_{a} (\beta_a \log \mu_a - \delta_a \mu_a). \quad (26.26)$$

It is easy to see that, for any physically consistent choice of the kinetic parameters, L has a unique non-trivial minimum (i.e. with non-zero concentration vectors). To a first approximation, then, stochastic effects that were neglected in writing Eqs. (26.23)–(26.25) can be captured by assuming that fluctuations around the minimum of L correspond to sampling molecular levels from a Boltzmann–Gibbs distribution

$$P(\{m_i\}, \{\mu_a\}) = \frac{e^{-L/T}}{Z(T)}, \qquad Z(T) = \sum_{\{m_i\}, \{\mu_a\}} e^{-L/T}. \quad (26.27)$$

where $T > 0$ is a (fictitious) "temperature" parameter that is expected to correlate with the strength of the molecular noise to be added to Eqs. (26.23)-(26.25) for a full stochastic description. The above considerations suggest a theoretical approach based on the following points:

(i) The *intensity* of miRNA-mediated crosstalk between targets i and j at equilibrium (i.e. at stationarity) can be quantified via the susceptibility [93]

$$\chi_{ij} = \frac{\partial \langle m_i \rangle}{\partial b_j}, \quad (26.28)$$

where $\langle \cdots \rangle$ denotes equilibrium values. χ_{ij} can be computed either from the steady states of the dynamics or within a purely statistical mechanics framework in which $\langle \cdots \rangle = \sum_{\{m_i\}, \{\mu_a\}} \cdots P(\{m_i\}, \{\mu_a\})$ (see Eq. (26.27)). Importantly, because $\langle m_i \rangle = -T \frac{\partial}{\partial d_i} \log Z(T)$, one can immediately see that $\chi_{ij} \neq \chi_{ji}$: miRNA-mediated crosstalk interactions are non-symmetric.

(ii) The cross-regulatory equilibrium *effectiveness* of miRNA-mediated interactions versus the standard regulatory control exerted on a target (say j) by its transcription factor (TF) can be quantified by comparing the mutual informations $I(m_j, f_j)$ and $I(m_j, f_i)$, where f_j (resp. f_i) denotes the level of the transcription factor controlling j (resp. one of j's competitors to bind miRNAs), while as usual

$$I(m_j, f) = \int df \, P(f) \int dm_j \, P(m_j | f) \log_2 \frac{P(m_j | f)}{P(m_j)}. \quad (26.29)$$

One would specifically like to identify the conditions under which miRNA-mediated control and TF-mediated control are equally effective. Such an analysis only requires a slight generalization of Eqs. (26.23)–(26.25) to include transcription factors. In the above formula, $P(m_j)$ and $P(m_j|f)$ represent, respectively, the equilibrium distributions of the level of target j and of the level of target j given the level of TF f, whereas $P(f)$ stands for the probability density of transcription factor levels. The latter quantity is treated as an exogenous variable. In fact, I depends on the choice of $P(f)$. To establish a benchmark, it is therefore useful to compare the optimal values of $I(m_j, f_j)$ and $I(m_j, f_i)$ obtained by maximizing the two quantities with respect to $P(f_j)$ and $P(f_i)$, respectively. [97, 98]

(iii) As the exact values of kinetic parameters are impossible to quantify in practice even for small systems, the *typical (or context-independent) large-scale properties* of the emerging cross-talk network at stationarity can be found by analysing, for large N and M, averages of physical observables like expression levels or susceptibilities over ensembles of kinetic parameter values [99]. In such a scenario, kinetic parameters are treated as *quenched disorder*, so that the function L in Eq. (26.26) effectively becomes a *disordered cost function* whose minima depend on the specific realization of the disorder. The *stability* of expression profiles and their *robustness* against changes in kinetic parameters would immediately follow from this analysis. Notice that typical properties are physiologically relevant, as they are expected to hold (for a large network) independently of the specific values of the parameters.

(iv) *Out-of-equilibrium properties*, describing e.g. the approach to equilibrium or the transient response of the network to perturbations, can instead be derived by studying the linearized version of Eqs. (26.23)–(26.25) in the limit of small perturbations. [100]

The above program has been carried out starting in 2013 over a series of papers by various authors, covering aspects ranging from the off-equilibrium dynamics of small miRNA-mediated circuits to the typical system-level properties of crosstalk in the human transcriptome (see Ref. [101] for a thorough review). For sakes of clarity, we focus here on two sets of results with high biological significance, concerning the roles of (a) transcriptional heterogeneities and (b) topological heterogeneities in shaping the emergent network-scale expression profiles in the human miRNA interactome mapped via the CLASH protocol (Crosslinking, Ligation And Sequencing of Hybrids), accounting for $\mathcal{O}(10^7)$ potential miRNA-mediated cross-regulatory interactions, each quantifiable by the value of χ_{ij}.

Transcriptional heterogeneities — Estimated transcription rates vary drastically from one transcript to another, as some genes are naturally much more expressed than others. An important question is how crosstalk patterns, i.e. the statistics of $\chi = \{\chi_{ij}\}$ that is generated between miRNA targets in an extended network of miRNA-target interactions, are affected by such variability. Results based on averaging over ensembles of transcription rates have shown that [99]:

- The average intensity of crosstalk interactions, namely $\overline{\langle \chi \rangle}$ (with the inner average over pairs of targets and the outer average over disorder) is weakly dependent on the strength of transcriptional heterogeneities: the typical susceptibility of the network is robust to baseline gene expression variability.

- On the other hand, the maximum achievable value of χ_{ij} increases as transcription rates become more heterogeneous: in other words, heterogeneous kinetic parameters favour the establishment of stronger crosstalk links. Importantly, the stability of expression profiles is maximal (i.e. sample-to-sample fluctuations are smaller) when the strongest crosstalk is achieved.
- In view of this, crosstalk gets more *selective* as heterogeneity increases, i.e., in each condition, only a sub-network of cross-regulatory couplings is effectively active.
- Perhaps most remarkably, heterogeneities enhance crosstalk non-locality, as crosstalk patterns become less and less correlated with local interaction parameters (e.g. association rates) as transcriptional variability increases. In practice, extended chains of strong miRNA-mediated crosstalk interactions become more and more frequent as heterogeneity increases. In this respect, one can say that the highly promiscuous miRNAs exploit the large-scale 'disorder' of kinetic parameters to implement a system-level regulatory layer that coordinates and stabilizes expression levels.

Topological heterogeneities — Evolution in the miRNA interactome effectively acts on the structure of miRNA-target interactions. To what degree are crosstalk patterns controlled by the specific wiring of the miRNA-target network? To answer this question, one can re-analyze the emergent crosstalk patterns after properly randomizing the empirical interactome. The surprising result [99] is that all properties discussed above survive as long as the randomization protocol preserves the degrees of the nodes (i.e. the number of in-coming and out-going links). By contrast, any randomization that alters the degree sequence (for instance by making the network more homogeneous through the re-wiring of the most connected species) generates weaker and more local crosstalk interactions, while the stability of expression profiles is higher in absence of crosstalk. This strongly suggests that certain features of miRNA-mediated RNA crosstalk patterns (selectivity, maximal intensity, stability etc.) are encoded in the detailed structure of the miRNA-target interaction network by natural selection.

System-level regulatory mechanisms are likely ubiquitous (especially if driven by competition for limited molecular resources) and have just begun to be understood. There is little doubt in our view that the concepts and tools developed for spin glasses and complex physical systems will play a major role in the analysis of these phenomena (and of their physiological relevance) in the coming years.

26.2. Molecular Replica Symmetry Breaking

Felix Ritort

Small Biosystems Lab
Department de Física de la Matèria Condensada
Facultat de Física, Universitat de Barcelona
Carrer de Martí i Franqués 1, 08028 Barcelona (Spain)
ritort@ub.edu, fritort@gmail.com

A brief overview of mechanical unzipping experiments of single nucleic acids and proteins shows the power of single-molecule techniques to unravel molecular energy landscapes with kcal/mol (kilocalories per mole) accuracy. I argue that pulling experiments offer an ideal playground to explore rugged free-energy landscapes and replica symmetry breaking at the single-molecule level.

26.2.1. *Biomolecules and spin glasses*

Nucleic acids (NA) are found in double-stranded and single-stranded forms [102]. The DNA double helix comprises two covalently linked sugar-phosphate strands of nucleotides stabilized by base pairing and stacking interactions. RNA is mostly found in single-stranded form and participates in many regulatory processes in the cell (see Sec. 26.1 by Cocco et al.). Chemically, RNA differs from DNA in that the nucleotide U-uracyl replaces T-thymine, and the sugar (ribose) in the phosphate chain contains a polarizable OH group that coordinates metal ions such as magnesium and calcium [103–105]. In contrast, proteins are chains of covalently linked amino acids that fold into specific three-dimensional shapes [106] with multiple structural, signaling, and enzymatic functions. Proteins catalyze a myriad of reactions essential for life.

NA and proteins are intrinsically disordered and heterogeneous, their extraordinary organizing power is due to the strong sensitivity of the monomer interactions to changes in sequence and environment. This sensitivity originates from the acute energy balance of molecular interactions in water. Multiple forces such as hydrogen bonding, Van der Waals, and the hydrophobic effect concur to fold biomolecules into the specific native structure, a free energy minimum in the space of conformations [107]. In thermodynamics, Gibbs free energy $G = H - TS$ results from the balance between enthalpy H (the equivalent of the potential energy in mechanics) and entropy S, a statistical measure of the disorder, with T the temperature. Minimizing G requires H minimum and S maximum, which for molecular driving forces often leads to conflicting results. An example of the competition between H and S is the hydrophobic effect of non-polar molecules that repel water. In truth, it is the opposite effect; non-polar molecules tend to form stable hydrogen bonds with water (~ 7 kcal/mol per bond), yet this comes at the price of a large entropic cost of hydrogen-bonding alignment, so the overall free energy change is positive. Enthalpy-entropy compensation in molecular folding results in very low folding ΔG (positive) values compared to ΔH and $T\Delta S$, $\Delta G \ll \Delta H, T\Delta S$ with ΔH comparable to $T\Delta S$. For example, at room temperature $T = 25°C$, the 110 amino acids ribonuclease protein barnase has a folding free energy value of $\Delta G = 10$ kcal/mol with $\Delta H \sim 115$ kcal/mol, $T\Delta S = 105$ kcal/mol. Hydrogen bonds and Van der Waals forces are critical for folding. While hydrogen bonding mostly drives the formation of the transition state that precedes native folding, Van der Waals forces are responsible for closely packing nucleotides in NA and side chains in proteins. The large $1/r^6$ energy dependence of the latter contributes to the large energy collapse between the transition and the native state.

Structural rearrangements in NA and proteins lead to conflicting energy interactions and rugged free energy landscapes, a typical feature of spin glasses containing disorder and frustration. Two are the main differences though. While biomolecules are nanometer-sized, spin and structural glass samples are meso- and macroscopic. Moreover, evolutionary forces have built biomolecules into polymer chains that have a specific purpose or function, a feature absent in ordinary matter such as spin glasses (diluted random alloys) and structural glasses. Many structural glasses are homogeneous liquids that crystallize if cooled slowly enough. Otherwise, they enter the supercooled liquid region and a glassy phase [108]. Although covalent bonds determine the high viscous phase of glass-forming liquids such as pure silica (SiO_2), which crystallizes at 1475K, weak interactions also form glassy phases in organic substances and water [109].

Spin glasses, structural glasses, and disordered matter are characterized by rough free energy landscapes with many states, mathematically described by the replica symmetry breaking transition (RSB) in spin glass theory [110]. Can the remarkable thermodynamic and kinetic phenomena of replica symmetry breaking be observed at the molecular level in NAs and proteins? A primary tool to answer this question is single-molecule force spectroscopy, where an individual molecule can be mechanically pulled from its ends to monitor the folding reaction in real-time [111, 112]. Pulling experiments permit us to derive free energy differences by mechanical work measurements, mostly with laser optical tweezers and magnetic tweezers, atomic force cantilevers, acoustic sound waves, and others [113, 114] (see also Secs. 26.1.2 and 26.1.3 by Cocco et al.).

26.2.2. *Molecular free energy landscapes*

In pulling experiments, the end-to-end distance x is a reaction coordinate that quantifies the progress of the hybridization reaction in a DNA duplex and the folding of an RNA or protein. In single-trap optical tweezers [115, 116], the molecule under study is inserted between flanking handles. The molecular construct is tethered between a surface and an optically trapped bead using specific linkages (Fig. 26.7(A)). The trap-position distance λ comprises the extension of the handles and the molecule under study x and the micron-sized bead displacement $\lambda = x_b + x$. In this experimental setup, λ is the control parameter and does not fluctuate, whereas x and the force applied to the system, $f = k_b x_b$, fluctuate due to Brownian noise. Typically, the bead stiffness $k_b \sim 0.01-1$ pN/nm permits force measurements in the range $0.1-100$ pN. By repeatedly moving the optical trap back and forth, we measure the force-distance curve (FDC), where the force f is plotted versus the distance λ. In unzipping experiments a DNA hairpin is tethered between the two extremities and the two strands pulled apart by mechanical forces [117, 118]. Figure 26.7(B) shows the FDC of unzipping a 6.8kbp DNA molecule at

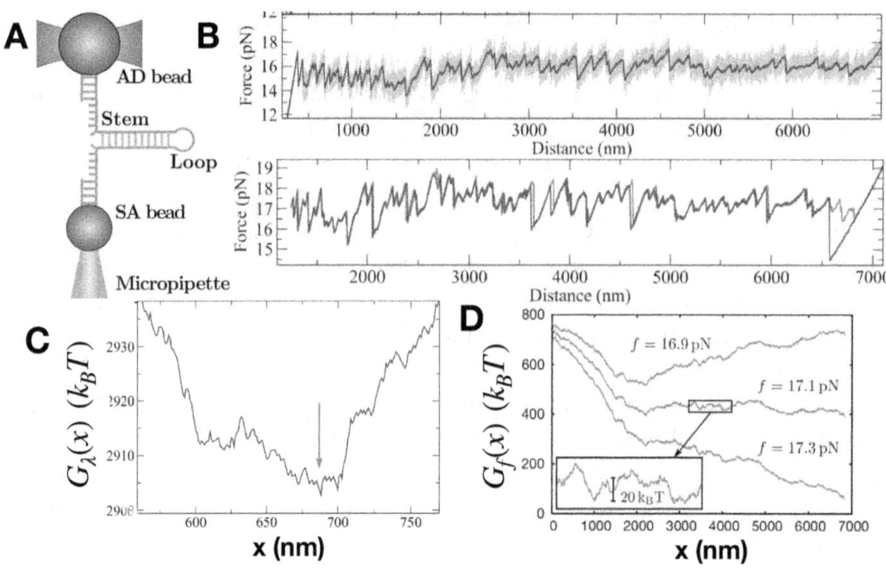

Fig. 26.7. Unzipping free energy landscapes. A) Experimental setup. B) Unzipping FDC of a 6.8kbp DNA hairpin. (Top) Filtered data at 1Hz (continuous black line) and raw data at 1kHz (grey band). (Bottom) Unzipping (grey) and rezipping (black) FDCs are near reversible, except for the effect of the refolding loop at the end. Data from Ref. [119]. C,D) Free energy landscapes in the trap-position ensemble $G_\lambda(x)$ for a given trap position λ and in the force ensemble $G_f(x)$.

standard conditions ($T = 298$K, 1M NaCl). In the upper panel, we show the average FDC (black line) and the raw data (grey band) showing Brownian force fluctuations. In the bottom panel, the unzipping (grey) and rezipping (black) curves superimpose, showing that the unzipping-rezipping reaction is quasi-reversible [119].

For fixed λ, experimental measurements of the fluctuating extension x, permit us to extract the molecular free energy landscape, $G_\lambda(x)$, using the Boltzmann formula,

$$P_\lambda(x) = \frac{\exp(-\beta G_\lambda(x))}{Z_\lambda}, \qquad G_\lambda(x) = -k_BT \log P_\lambda(x) - k_BT \log Z_\lambda, \qquad (26.30)$$

with Z_λ the equilibrium partition function. The constant $G_\lambda = -k_BT \log Z_\lambda$ is the equilibrium free energy of the molecule at λ, an overall shift to the free energy landscape. A typical unzipping free energy landscape $G_\lambda(x)$ for a given trap position λ is shown in Fig. 26.7(C). The profile has been calculated using the nearest neighbor (NN) model for DNA [120]. In the NN model, the free energy of the duplex is the sum of the stacking and hydrogen bond interactions between all adjacent base pairs. The free energy is rough with many local minima, a feature of disordered and frustrated systems. From $G_\lambda(x)$ one can also calculate the free energy landscape in the force ensemble where force is fixed, $G_f(x)$. This ensemble is implemented in magnetic tweezers where a pair of magnets produce a constant magnetic field gradient force. $G_f(x)$ for the 6.8kbp DNA is shown in Fig. 26.7(D) for three force values, 16.9, 17.1, 17.3 pN. Again, $G_f(x)$ is rough with many minima (inset) and energy barriers of roughly $20k_BT$.

The unzipping free energy landscape is an experimental realization of the 1D Sinai's model commonly used to illustrate spin-glass free energy landscapes. Unzipping measurements permit us to measure free energy differences by applying the thermodynamic identity, $\Delta G_\lambda = W$ with W the mechanical work exerted by the optical tweezers instrument on the molecule. By comparing the measured FDC with the theoretical prediction based on the NN model, the ten nearest-neighbor energy parameters have been derived over several decades of salt concentration in sodium and magnesium with 0.1 kcal/mol accuracy [121, 122].

26.2.3. *Barrier energy landscapes*

Disorder and frustration also affect the folding kinetics of biomolecules [123]. RNAs form secondary structures made of single-stranded unpaired regions and stem loops stabilized by hydrogen bonds and stacking [124]. The promiscuity of base pairing in RNA is facilitated by non-Watson–Crick or wobble base pairs (such as GU) that enlarge the diversity of tertiary structures. The ribose C3'-endo conformation also makes RNA adopt the more compact A-form with a stronger base stacking than for DNA. Upon folding, RNA can be kinetically trapped into structures other than the native (misfolding), a typical feature of glassy matter. In Fig. 26.8(A), we show unzipping curves at room temperature (T=298 K) and 10 mM $MgCl_2$ for a 2kbp RNA hairpin [125]. Compared to DNA (Fig. 26.7(B), bottom), hysteresis between the unzipping (grey) and rezipping (black) FDCs is apparent. Such irreversibility has been

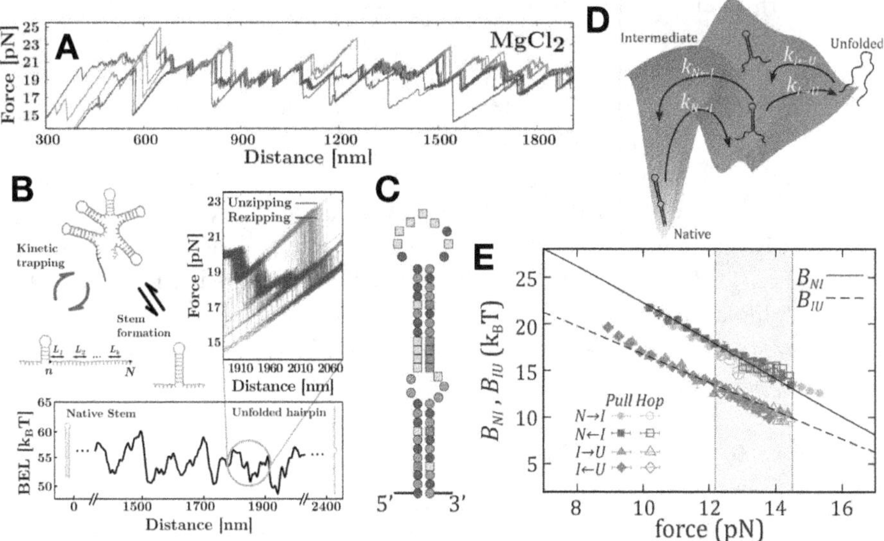

Fig. 26.8. Barrier energy landscapes. A) Unzipping (grey) and rezipping (black) FDCs of 2kbp RNA hairpin at 10 mM $MgCl_2$ showing hysteresis. Data from Ref. [125]. B) The barrier energy landscape (BEL, bottom) is determined by stem-loops formed along the unpaired strands. C) A hairpin sequence with an internal loop produces a folding intermediate. D) Energy landscape showing different states and kinetic rates. E) Force-dependent kinetic barriers between different states (N, native; I, intermediate; U, unfolded) obtained from kinetic rates measured in nonequilibrium pulling (Pull) and equilibrium hopping (Hop) compared to the Kramers formula Eq. (26.31) (continuous and dashed lines). Data in C,D,E from Ref. [127].

interpreted as due to competing off-pathway structures formed along the unpaired strands during the unzipping-rezipping reaction, Fig. 26.8(B) [125, 126]. Segments of various lengths $L_1, L_2, ..., L_k$ can be transiently stabilized at forces as high as 17pN. Barrier energy landscape (BEL) minima are correlated with high hysteresis regions (e.g., Fig.26.8(B), zoom).

The notion of the BEL finds its most natural example in Kramers theory of 1D systems. For a NA hairpin of N bases pulled at a force f, the kinetic rate of unfolding k_U is given by [128, 129]

$$k_U(f) = k_0 \exp\left[-\frac{B_U(f)}{k_B T}\right],$$
$$\frac{B_U(f)}{k_B T} = \log\left[\sum_{m=0}^{N}\sum_{m'=0}^{m} \exp(\frac{G_m(f) - G_{m'}(f)}{k_B T})\right],$$

(26.31)

with k_0 an attempt rate, $B_U(f)$ the kinetic barrier, and $G_m(f)$ ($m = 0, 1, ..., N$) the free energy landscape at force f. For landscapes with a maximum at a force-dependent position $m = m^*(f)$, the sum over m in $B_U(f)$ is dominated by $m^*(f)$ giving the Arrhenius formula, $k_U(f) = k_0 \exp(-\frac{\Delta G_{m^*(f)}}{k_B T})$ and $\Delta G_{m^*(f)} = G_{m^*(f)} - G_0$. In general, m^* depends on f leading to brittle (m^* small) or fragile (m^* large) behavior [130]. Equation (26.31) has been used to derive k_0 and the folding free energy of NA hairpins (Fig. 26.8(C)) in free energy landscapes with intermediates (Fig. 26.8(D)). The barrier to unfold $B_U(f)$, and the equivalent one to fold $B_F(f)$ (obtained by transforming $m \to N - m$ in Eq. (26.31)), fulfill detailed balance, $\Delta G_N(f) = B_U(f) - B_F(f)$. Experimental measurement of $k_U(f), k_F(f)$ permit us to calculate $B_U(f), B_F(f)$ (Eq. (26.31), lhs) and derive $\Delta G_N(f)$ by matching the profiles of $B_U(f)$ and $B_U(f) + \Delta G_N(f)$. The so-called Continuous Effective Barrier Approach (CEBA) works well for deriving free energy differences of NA hairpins with multiple intermediates and pathways [127].

The mathematical expression for $B_U(f)$ in Eq. (26.31) reminds of a partition function or potential of mean force. For disordered landscapes, $B_U(f)$ is sensitive to small changes in the energies explaining the strong dependence of folding kinetics with NA sequence. However, Eq. (26.31) cannot explain the irreversibility observed in Fig. 26.8(A), particularly upon comparing with the DNA case (Fig. 26.7(A)). Off-pathway structures are then needed to estimate barrier energy landscapes, a difficult problem without reliable tertiary RNA prediction tools.

26.2.4. *From NAs to protein folding*

Randomized ssDNA folds into heterogeneous structures. To investigate ssDNA folding, the blocking oligo method has been used [131, 132] in which a specifically designed 20-30b oligo hybridizes with the loop region preventing hairpin reannealing below 15 pN (Fig. 26.9(A)). A helix-coil model [133] of compact and free alternating regions describes the pulling curves at different salt conditions (Fig. 26.9(B)). The model contains two parameters: the energy gain per base in a compact domain, ϵ, and the cooperativity parameter γ for the interfacial energy of a domain wall separating compact and free regions. The compact regions formed by the ssDNA are heterogeneous blobs containing

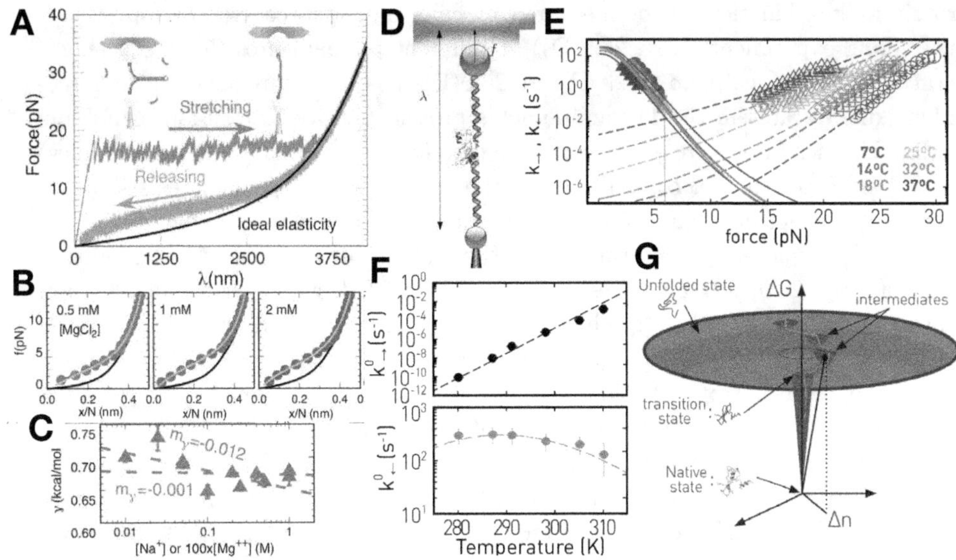

Fig. 26.9. ssDNA and protein folding. A) ssDNA unzipping and the blocking oligo method. Deviations of the releasing FDC from the ideal elastic response are due to non-specific secondary structure formation. B) A helix coil model fit (continuous light color lines) to the experimental force versus extension/base data in magnesium (dots). The back line is the ideal elastic response obtained by measurements in glyoxal. C) Cooperative parameter γ fitted to $\gamma = \gamma_0 + m_\gamma \log(c)$ with c the salt concentration in molar units (dashed lines). The value of the salt correction parameter $m_\gamma \ll \gamma_0 (= \gamma(c=1))$ (both in kcal/mol) shows weak salt dependence. D) Pulling a protein using dsDNA handles. E) Calorimetric force spectroscopy measurements of unfolding (empty symbols) and folding (filled symbols) kinetic rates at various temperatures fitted to the Bell-Evans model (dashed lines). F) Extrapolated rates at zero force. G) Funnel free energy landscape representation where the z-axis stands for the free energy and the x-y plane for the change in the number of degrees of freedom n upon folding. The latter is related to the measured heat capacity change, $\Delta C_p = k_B \Delta n/2$. A-C data from Ref. [133]. D-G data from Ref. [134]

10-30 bases on average. More important, the cooperativity parameter $\gamma \sim 0.7$ kcal/mol is salt independent (Fig. 26.9(C)), and larger than the energy per base in compact regions, $\epsilon \sim 0 - 0.2$ kcal/mol. Parameters γ, ϵ are equivalent to the magnetic field h and exchange coupling J in the 1D Ising model, showing that cooperativity drives non-specific secondary structure formation in ssDNA.

Cooperativity is also key in protein folding. In the *foldon* hypothesis (FH), amino acids chains fold by forming compact units (foldons) sequentially and cooperatively [135, 136]. In the energy landscape hypothesis (ELH), there are multiple folding pathways connecting the unfolded (U) chain and the native (N) state in a funnel-like or golf-course energy landscape [137, 138]. The hole in that landscape represents the transition state (TS) that precedes folding to N. The nature of TS has been long debated. In the molten globule hypothesis (MGH) the TS is a native-like expanded structure with the backbone formed, but with side chains loosely packed [139, 140]. Related to the ELH is the downhill hypothesis (DH) where folding is barrierless even in two-state proteins [141].

Protein folding kinetics can be measured by calorimetric force spectroscopy carrying out pulling experiments (Fig. 26.9(D)) at different temperatures (5-40°C) using a temperature jump optical trap [142]. Figure 26.9(E) shows measurements of the force-dependent kinetic rates in the 110 amino acids protein barnase [134, 143]. Unfolding and folding kinetics rates were extrapolated to zero force (continuous and dashed lines) using the Bell–Evans model combined with the temperature-dependent elastic properties of the polypeptide chain. While the unfolding kinetic rate $k_\rightarrow$ changes by ten decades over the explored temperature range, the folding rate $k_\leftarrow$ is nearly temperature independent (Fig. 26.9(F)). These results support the ELH, where the unfolded chain folds into a molten globule first (the hole of the funnel), followed by the collapse of the molten globule into N (Fig. 26.9(G)). It was found in Ref. [134] that 80% of the free energy, enthalpy and entropy of folding of barnase occurs in the collapse between TS and N, whereas 90% of the total folding heat capacity change, $\Delta C_p \sim 1000$ cal/(mol K), occurs between U and TS. These results highlight a TS of high energy and low configurational entropy that is structurally similar to N. Barnase is an example of a protein where the FH, ELH, MGH and DH are compatible. We emphasize the close connection between protein folding and the first-order RSB transition in structural glasses [144]. The loss of the configurational entropy (also denoted as complexity) between U and TS defines a transition between a disordered paramagnetic phase (the unfolded chain) and a spin-glass phase (molten globule) where side chains are rightly positioned in space but loosely packed. The transition between the molten globule and N is a *solidification* transition driven by enthalpy and entropy collapse.

The folding kinetics of biomolecules and spin glasses share much in common. Endowed with single-molecule tools, scientists can now monitor folding events one molecule at a time and test the most elusive predictions of RSB. In 1969, Levinthal noticed that a polypeptide chain could not fold into the native state by random search in configurational space [145]. The configurational space of biomolecules is large enough to abide by the tenets of spin glass theory [146]. Single-molecule research offers a terrific playground for a future test of its most notable predictions.

Acknowledgments

We are deeply indebted to Giorgio Parisi for many years — past and future — of inspiring discussions and collaborations. We are likewise grateful to the many colleagues and friends with whom some of the ideas presented in this chapter have been developed. ADM, AP, and MW wish to acknowledge partial financial support from the EC funded Marie Skłodowska-Curie program under grant agreement no. 734439 (InferNet).

I (Felix Ritort) am indebted to my mentor and friend, Giorgio Parisi, for his guidance and wisdom during my beautiful years in Rome (1989–1994) and after. Financial support from project PID2019-111148GB-I00 (Spanish Research Council) and Icrea Academia Prize 2018 (Catalan Government) is acknowledged.

References

[1] O. T. Avery, C. M. MacLeod, and M. McCarty, *J. Exp. Med.* **79**(2), 137–158 (1944).

[2] J. Brachet and H. Chantrenne. In *Cold Spring Harbor Symposia on Quantitative Biology*, vol. 21, pp. 329–337. Cold Spring Harbor Laboratory Press, (1956).

[3] A. Kornberg, *The golden helix: inside biotech ventures.* (University Science Books, 2002).

[4] F. H. Crick. In *Symp Soc Exp Biol*, p. 8, (1958).

[5] M. B. Hoagland, M. L. Stephenson, J. F. Scott, L. I. Hecht, and P. C. Zamecnik, *J. Biol. Chem.* **231**(1), 241–257, (1958).

[6] L. Kari, G. Păun, G. Rozenberg, A. Salomaa, and S. Yu, *Acta Inform.* **35**(5), 401–420, (1998).

[7] B. Yurke, A. J. Turberfield, A. P. Mills, F. C. Simmel, and J. L. Neumann, *Nature.* **406** (6796), 605–608, (2000).

[8] F. Gesteland Raymond, C. Thomas, and F. Atkins John, *The RNA world: the nature of modern RNA suggests a prebiotic RNA.* (Cold Spring Harbor Laboratory Press, 1993).

[9] S. DeWeerdt, *Nature.* **574**(7778), S2–S2, (2019).

[10] T. R. Damase, R. Sukhovershin, C. Boada, F. Taraballi, R. I. Pettigrew, and J. P. Cooke, *Front. bioeng. biotechnol.* **9**, (2021).

[11] S. Wright, *Genetics.* **16**(2), 97–159 (1931).

[12] R. Nussinov and A. B. Jacobson, *Proc. Natl. Acad. Sci. U.S.A.* **77**(11), 6309–6313, (1980).

[13] M. Zuker and D. Sankoff, *Bulletin of Mathematical Biology.* **46**(4), 591–621, (1984).

[14] W. Fontana, D. A. Konings, P. F. Stadler, and P. Schuster, *Biopolymers.* **33**(9), 1389–1404, (1993).

[15] P. G. Higgs, *Phys. Rev. Lett.* **76**, 704–707 (1996).

[16] A. Pagnani, G. Parisi, and F. Ricci-Tersenghi, *Phys. Rev. Lett.* **84**, 2026–2029 (2000).

[17] J. Jumper, R. Evans, A. Pritzel, T. Green, M. Figurnov, O. Ronneberger, K. Tunyasu-vunakool, R. Bates, A. Žídek, A. Potapenko, et al., *Nature.* **596**(7873), 583–589, (2021).

[18] E. P. Nawrocki and S. R. Eddy, *Bioinformatics.* **29**(22), 2933–2935 (2013).

[19] W. D. Baez, K. J. Wiese, and R. Bundschuh, *Phys. Rev. E.* **99**(2), 022415, (2019).

[20] R. Lorenz, S. H. Bernhart, C. Höner zu Siederdissen, H. Tafer, C. Flamm, P. F. Stadler, and I. L. Hofacker, *Algorithms for Molecular Biology.* **6**(1), 1–14, (2011).

[21] S. Cocco, J. F. Marko, and R. Monasson, *The European Physical Journal E.* **10**(2), 153–161, (2003).

[22] Y. Zhou, X. Qi, Y. Liu, F. Zhang, and H. Yan, *ChemBioChem.* **20**(19), 2494–2503, (2019).

[23] M. Jinek, K. Chylinski, I. Fonfara, M. Hauer, J. A. Doudna, and E. Charpentier, *Science.* **337**(6096), 816–821, (2012).

[24] A. G. Vitreschak, D. A. Rodionov, A. A. Mironov, and M. S. Gelfand, *Trends in Genetics.* **20**(1), 44–50, (2004).

[25] U. Bockelmann, B. Essevaz-Roulet, and F. Heslot, *Phys. Rev. Lett.* **79**(22), 4489, (1997).

[26] J. F. Marko and S. Cocco, *Physics World.* **16**(3), 37, (2003).

[27] C. Bustamante, J. F. Marko, E. D. Siggia, and S. Smith, *Science.* **265**(5178), 1599–1600, (1994).

[28] P. Cluzel, A. Lebrun, C. Heller, R. Lavery, J.-L. Viovy, D. Chatenay, and F. Caron, *Science.* **271**(5250), 792–794, (1996).

[29] J. F. Allemand, D. Bensimon, R. Lavery, and V. Croquette, *Proc. Natl. Acad. Sci. U.S.A.* **95**(24), 14152–14157, (1998).

[30] I. Tinoco, P. T. Li, and C. Bustamante, *Quarterly Reviews of Biophysics.* **39**(4), 325–360, (2006).

[31] D. K. Lubensky and D. R. Nelson, *Phys. Rev. Lett.* **85**(7), 1572, (2000).

[32] S. Cocco, J. F. Marko, and R. Monasson, *C. R. Phys.* **3**(5), 569–584, (2002).

[33] F. Ding, S. Cocco, S. Raj, M. Manosas, T. T. T. Nguyen, M. M. Spiering, D. Bensimon, J-F. Allemand, V. Croquette. *Nucleic Acids Res.* **50**(21), 12082, (2022).

[34] V. Baldazzi, S. Cocco, E. Marinari, and R. Monasson, *Phys. Rev. Lett.* **96**(12), 128102, (2006).

[35] J. Liphardt, B. Onoa, S. B. Smith, I. Tinoco Jr, and C. Bustamante, *Science.* **292**(5517), 733–737, (2001).

[36] M. Doi, S. F. Edwards, and S. F. Edwards, *The theory of polymer dynamics.* vol. 73, (Oxford University Press, 1988).

[37] F. Wang, H. Lv, Q. Li, J. Li, X. Zhang, J. Shi, L. Wang, and C. Fan, *Nat. Commun.* **11**(1), 1–8, (2020).

[38] V. Baldazzi, S. Bradde, S. Cocco, E. Marinari, and R. Monasson, *Phys. Rev. E.* **75**(1), 011904, (2007).

[39] C. Barbieri, S. Cocco, T. Jorg, and R. Monasson, *Biophys. J.* **106**(2), 430–439, (2014).

[40] S. Cocco and R. Monasson, *EPL.* **81**(2), 20002, (2007).

[41] S. Cocco and R. Monasson. In *J. Phys. Conf.*, vol. 197, p. 012005, (2009).

[42] J. Mathé, H. Visram, V. Viasnoff, Y. Rabin, and A. Meller, *Biophys. J.* **87**(5), 3205–3212, (2004).

[43] Z. Wang, J. Maluenda, L. Giraut, T. Vieille, A. Lefevre, D. Salthouse, G. Radou, R. Moulinas, S. Astete, P. D'Avezac, et al., *Commun. Biol.* **4**(1), 1–14, (2021).

[44] J. S. Graham, R. C. Johnson, and J. F. Marko, *Nucleic Acids Res.* **39**(6), 2249–2259, (2011).

[45] W. Tang, W. Zhong, Y. Tan, G. A. Wang, F. Li, and Y. Liu, *DNA Nanotechnology.* pp. 377–406, (2020).

[46] S. Cocco, J. F. Marko, and R. Monasson, *Phys. Rev. Lett.* **112**(23), 238101, (2014).

[47] M. Levitt, *Nature.* **224**(5221), 759–763, (1969).

[48] G. E. Fox and C. R. Woese, *Nature.* **256**(5517), 505–507, (1975).

[49] I. Kalvari, E. P. Nawrocki, N. Ontiveros-Palacios, J. Argasinska, K. Lamkiewicz, M. Marz, S. Griffiths-Jones, C. Toffano-Nioche, D. Gautheret, Z. Weinberg, et al., *Nucleic Acids Res.* **49**(D1), D192–D200, (2021).

[50] S. R. Eddy, *PLoS Comput. Biol.* **7**(10), e1002195, (2011).

[51] T. Jörg, O. C. Martin, and A. Wagner, *BMC Bioinform.* **9**(1), 1–12, (2008).

[52] A. R. Gruber, R. Lorenz, S. H. Bernhart, R. Neuböck, and I. L. Hofacker, *Nucleic Acids Res.* **36**(suppl_2), W70–W74, (2008).

[53] P. Schuster, W. Fontana, P. F. Stadler, and I. L. Hofacker, *Proc. Royal Soc. B.* **255**(1344), 279–284, (1994).

[54] R. Durbin, S. R. Eddy, A. Krogh, and G. Mitchison, *Biological sequence analysis: probabilistic models of proteins and nucleic acids.* (Cambridge University Press, 1998).

[55] S. R. Eddy and R. Durbin, *Nucleic Acids Res.* **22**(11), 2079–2088, (1994).

[56] F. Morcos, A. Pagnani, B. Lunt, A. Bertolino, D. S. Marks, C. Sander, R. Zecchina, J. N. Onuchic, T. Hwa, and M. Weigt, *Proc. Natl. Acad. Sci. U.S.A.* **108**(49), E1293–E1301, (2011).

[57] S. Cocco, C. Feinauer, M. Figliuzzi, R. Monasson, and M. Weigt, *Rep. Prog. Phys.* **81**(3), 032601, (2018).

[58] D. H. Ackley, G. E. Hinton, and T. J. Sejnowski, *Cogn. Sci.* **9**(1), 147–169, (1985).

[59] S. Balakrishnan, H. Kamisetty, J. G. Carbonell, S.-I. Lee, and C. J. Langmead, *Proteins.* **79**(4), 1061–1078, (2011).

[60] M. Ekeberg, C. Lövkvist, Y. Lan, M. Weigt, and E. Aurell, *Phys. Rev. E.* **87**(1), 012707, (2013).

[61] T. Plefka, *J. Phys. A.* **15**(6), 1971, (1982).

[62] A. Georges and J. S. Yedidia, *J. Phys. A.* **24**(9), 2173, (1991).

[63] E. De Leonardis, B. Lutz, S. Ratz, S. Cocco, R. Monasson, A. Schug, and M. Weigt, *Nucleic Acids Res.* **43**(21), 10444–10455, (2015).

[64] C. Weinreb, A. J. Riesselman, J. B. Ingraham, T. Gross, C. Sander, and D. S. Marks, *Cell.* **165**(4), 963–975, (2016).

[65] F. Cuturello, G. Tiana, and G. Bussi, *RNA.* **26**(5), 637–647, (2020).

[66] W. P. Russ, M. Figliuzzi, C. Stocker, P. Barrat-Charlaix, M. Socolich, P. Kast, D. Hilvert, R. Monasson, S. Cocco, M. Weigt, et al., *Science.* **369**(6502), 440–445, (2020).

[67] "wwPDB consortium", *Nucleic Acids Res.* **47**(D1), D520–D528, (2019).

[68] R. J. Townshend, S. Eismann, A. M. Watkins, R. Rangan, M. Karelina, R. Das, and R. O. Dror, *Science.* **373**(6558), 1047–1051, (2021).

[69] M. B. Zerihun, F. Pucci, and A. Schug, *Nucleic Acids Res.* **49**(22), 12661–12672, (2021).

[70] A. Di Gioacchino, J. Procyk, M. Molari, J. S. Schreck, Y. Zhou, Y. Liu, R. Monasson, S. Cocco, and P. Šulc, *bioRxiv.* (2022).

[71] C. Tuerk and L. Gold, *Science.* **249**(4968), 505–510, (1990).

[72] A. D. Ellington and J. W. Szostak, *Nature.* **346**(6287), 818–822, (1990).

[73] A. Barra, A. Bernacchia, E. Santucci, and P. Contucci, *Neural Networks.* **34**, 1–9, (2012).

[74] J. Tubiana, S. Cocco, and R. Monasson, *eLife.* **8**, e39397, (2019).

[75] K. Shimagaki and M. Weigt, *Phys. Rev. E.* **100**(3), 032128, (2019).

[76] T. R. Cech and J. A. Steitz, *Cell.* **157**(1), 77–94, (2014).

[77] S. Zhao, Y. Zhang, R. Gamini, B. Zhang, and D. Von Schack, *Sci. Rep.* **8**(1), 1–12, (2018).

[78] A. Fire, S. Xu, M. K. Montgomery, S. A. Kostas, S. E. Driver, and C. C. Mello, *Nature.* **391**(6669), 806–811, (1998).

[79] A. M. Gurtan and P. A. Sharp, *J. Mol. Biol.* **425**(19), 3582–3600, (2013).

[80] S. Jonas and E. Izaurralde, *Nat. Rev. Genet.* **16**(7), 421–433, (2015).

[81] A. Baccarini, H. Chauhan, T. J. Gardner, A. D. Jayaprakash, R. Sachidanandam, and B. D. Brown, *Curr. Biol.* **21**(5), 369–376, (2011).

[82] A. Re, M. Caselle, F. Bussolino, et al., *Phys. Biol.* **14**(4), 045001, (2017).

[83] A. Franks, E. Airoldi, and N. Slavov, *PLoS Comput. Biol.* **13**(5), e1005535, (2017).

[84] D. Baek, J. Villén, C. Shin, F. D. Camargo, S. P. Gygi, and D. P. Bartel, *Nature.* **455**(7209), 64–71, (2008).

[85] V. Siciliano, I. Garzilli, C. Fracassi, S. Criscuolo, S. Ventre, and D. Di Bernardo, *Nat. Commun.* **4**(1), 1–7, (2013).

[86] J. M. Schmiedel, S. L. Klemm, Y. Zheng, A. Sahay, N. Blüthgen, D. S. Marks, and A. van Oudenaarden, *Science.* **348**(6230), 128–132, (2015).

[87] A. Riba, C. Bosia, M. El Baroudi, L. Ollino, and M. Caselle, *PLoS Comput. Biol.* **10**(2), e1003490, (2014).

[88] L. Salmena, L. Poliseno, Y. Tay, L. Kats, and P. P. Pandolfi, *Cell.* **146**(3), 353–358, (2011).

[89] M. Nitzan, A. Steiman-Shimony, Y. Altuvia, O. Biham, and H. Margalit, *Biophys. J.* **106**(10), 2254–2266, (2014).

[90] R. Denzler, V. Agarwal, J. Stefano, D. P. Bartel, and M. Stoffel, *Mol. Cell.* **54**(5), 766–776, (2014).

[91] A. D. Bosson, J. R. Zamudio, and P. A. Sharp, *Mol. Cell.* **56**(3), 347–359, (2014).

[92] A. Martirosyan, A. De Martino, A. Pagnani, and E. Marinari, *Sci. Rep.* **7**(1), 1–11, (2017).

[93] M. Figliuzzi, E. Marinari, and A. De Martino, *Biophys. J.* **104**(5), 1203–1213, (2013).

[94] C. Bosia, A. Pagnani, and R. Zecchina, *PLoS ONE.* **8**(6), e66609, (2013).

[95] J. Noorbakhsh, A. H. Lang, and P. Mehta, *PLoS ONE.* **8**(8), e72676, (2013).

[96] A. Martirosyan, M. Marsili, and A. De Martino, *Biophys. J.* **113**(1), 206–213, (2017).

[97] G. Tkačik, C. G. Callan Jr, and W. Bialek, *Phys. Rev. E.* **78**(1), 011910, (2008).

[98] A. Martirosyan, M. Figliuzzi, E. Marinari, and A. De Martino, *PLoS Comput. Biol.* **12**(1), e1004715, (2016).

[99] M. Miotto, E. Marinari, and A. De Martino, *PLoS Comput. Biol.* **15**(11), e1007474, (2019).

[100] M. Figliuzzi, A. De Martino, and E. Marinari, *Biophys. J.* **107**(4), 1011–1022, (2014).

[101] A. Martirosyan, M. Del Giudice, C. Enrico Bena, A. Pagnani, C. Bosia, and A. De Martino, *Computational Biology of Non-Coding RNA*. pp. 367–409, (2019).

[102] C. R. Calladine and H. Drew, *Understanding DNA: the molecule and how it works*. (Academic press, 1997).

[103] A. Pyle, *J. Biol. Inorg. Chem.* **7**(7), 679–690, (2002).

[104] P. Auffinger, N. Grover, and E. Westhof, *Met. Ions Life Sci.* **9**(1), 9781849732512–00001, (2011).

[105] J. Lipfert, S. Doniach, R. Das, and D. Herschlag, *Annu. Rev. Biochem.* **83**, 813, (2014).

[106] K. A. Dill and J. L. MacCallum, *Science.* **338**(6110), 1042–1046, (2012).

[107] K. A. Dill, S. Bromberg, and D. Stigter, *Molecular driving forces: statistical thermodynamics in biology, chemistry, physics, and nanoscience.* (Garland Science, 2010).

[108] A. Cavagna, *Phys. Rep.* **476**(4-6), 51–124, (2009).

[109] P. G. Debenedetti, *J. Phys. Condens. Matter.* **15**(45), R1669, (2003).

[110] M. Mezard and A. Montanari, *Information, physics, and computation.* (Oxford University Press, 2009).

[111] F. Ritort, *J. Phys. Condens. Matter.* **18**(32), R531, (2006).

[112] C. J. Bustamante, Y. R. Chemla, S. Liu, and M. D. Wang, *Nat. Rev. Methods Primers.* **1**(1), 1–29, (2021).

[113] K. C. Neuman, T. Lionnet, and J.-F. Allemand, *Annu. Rev. Mater. Res.* **37**(1), 33–67, (2007).

[114] H. Miller, Z. Zhou, J. Shepherd, A. J. Wollman, and M. C. Leake, *Rep. Prog. Phys.* **81**(2), 024601, (2017).

[115] J. R. Moffitt, Y. R. Chemla, S. B. Smith, and C. Bustamante, *Annu. Rev. Biochem.* **77**, 205–228, (2008).

[116] J. Gieseler, J. R. Gomez-Solano, A. Magazzù, I. P. Castillo, L. P. García, M. Gironella-Torrent, X. Viader-Godoy, F. Ritort, G. Pesce, A. V. Arzola, et al., *Adv. Opt. Photonics.* **13**(1), 74–241, (2021).

[117] B. Essevaz-Roulet, U. Bockelmann, and F. Heslot, *Proc. Natl. Acad. Sci. U.S.A.* **94**(22), 11935–11940, (1997).

[118] M. Rief, H. Clausen-Schaumann, and H. E. Gaub, *Nat. Struct. Biol.* **6**(4), 346–349, (1999).

[119] J. M. Huguet, N. Forns, and F. Ritort, *Phys. Rev. Lett.* **103**(24), 248106, (2009).

[120] J. SantaLucia Jr, *Proc. Natl. Acad. Sci. U.S.A.* **95**(4), 1460–1465, (1998).

[121] J. M. Huguet, C. V. Bizarro, N. Forns, S. B. Smith, C. Bustamante, and F. Ritort, *Proc. Natl. Acad. Sci. U.S.A.* **107**(35), 15431–15436, (2010).

[122] J. M. Huguet, M. Ribezzi-Crivellari, C. V. Bizarro, and F. Ritort, *Nucleic Acids Res.* **45**(22), 12921–12931, (2017).

[123] D. Thirumalai and S. Woodson, *Acc. Chem. Res.* **29**(9), 433–439, (1996).

[124] N. B. Leontis, A. Lescoute, and E. Westhof, *Curr. Opin. Struct. Biol.* **16**(3), 279–287, (2006).

[125] P. Rissone, C. V. Bizarro, and F. Ritort, *Proc. Natl. Acad. Sci. U.S.A.* **119**(3), (2022).

[126] P. Rissone and F. Ritort, *Life.* **12**(7), 1089, (2022).

[127] M. Rico-Pasto, A. Alemany, and F. Ritort, *J. Phys. Chem. Lett.* **13**(4), 1025–1032, (2022).

[128] R. Zwanzig, *Nonequilibrium statistical mechanics.* (Oxford University Press, 2001).

[129] M. Manosas, D. Collin, and F. Ritort, *Phys. Rev. Lett.* **96**(21), 218301, (2006).

[130] A. Alemany and F. Ritort, *J. Phys. Chem. Lett.* **8**(5), 895–900, (2017).

[131] M. Manosas, X. G. Xi, D. Bensimon, and V. Croquette, *Nucleic Acids Res.* **38**(16), 5518–5526, (2010).

[132] A. Bosco, J. Camunas-Soler, and F. Ritort, *Nucleic Acids Res.* **42**(3), 2064–2074, (2014).

[133] X. Viader-Godoy, C. Pulido, B. Ibarra, M. Manosas, and F. Ritort, *Phys. Rev. X.* **11**(3), 031037, (2021).

[134] M. Rico-Pasto, A. Zaltron, S. J. Davis, S. Frutos, and F. Ritort, *Proc. Natl. Acad. Sci. U.S.A.* **119**(11), e2112382119, (2022).

[135] R. L. Baldwin, *J. Biomol. NMR.* **5**(2), 103–109, (1995).

[136] H. Maity, M. Maity, M. M. Krishna, L. Mayne, and S. W. Englander, *Proc. Natl. Acad. Sci. U.S.A.* **102**(13), 4741–4746, (2005).

[137] H. Frauenfelder, S. G. Sligar, and P. G. Wolynes, *Science.* **254**(5038), 1598–1603, (1991).

[138] J. D. Bryngelson, J. N. Onuchic, N. D. Socci, and P. G. Wolynes, *Proteins.* **21**(3), 167–195, (1995).

[139] O. Ptitsyn, *Adv. Protein Chem.* **47**, 83–229, (1995).

[140] R. L. Baldwin and G. D. Rose, *Curr. Opin. Struct. Biol.* **23**(1), 4–10, (2013).

[141] W. A. Eaton, *Proc. Natl. Acad. Sci. U.S.A.* **96**(11), 5897–5899, (1999).

[142] S. De Lorenzo, M. Ribezzi-Crivellari, J. R. Arias-Gonzalez, S. B. Smith, and F. Ritort, *Biophys. J.* **108**(12), 2854–2864, (2015).

[143] A. Alemany, B. Rey-Serra, S. Frutos, C. Cecconi, and F. Ritort, *Biophys. J.* **110**(1), 63–74, (2016).

[144] T. Kirkpatrick and D. Thirumalai, *Rev. Mod. Phys.* **87**(1), 183, (2015).

[145] C. Levinthal, *J. Chim. Phys.* **65**, 44–45, (1968).

[146] M. Mézard, G. Parisi, and M. A. Virasoro, *Spin glass theory and beyond: An Introduction to the Replica Method and Its Applications.* vol. 9, (World Scientific Publishing Company, 1987).

Chapter 27

Application of Spin Glass Ideas
in Social Sciences, Economics and Finance

Jean-Philippe Bouchaud[*,†,‡], Matteo Marsili[§] and Jean-Pierre Nadal[¶,‖]

[*] *Chair of Econophysics and Complex Systems, École polytechnique,*
91128 Palaiseau Cedex, France
[†] *Capital Fund Management, 23 Rue de l'Université, 75007 Paris, France*
[‡] *Académie des Sciences, 23 Quai de Conti, 75006 Paris, France*
[§] *The Abdus Salam International Centre for Theoretical Physics,*
34151 Trieste, Italy
[¶] *Laboratoire de Physique de l'Ecole Normale Supérieure, ENS, Université PSL,*
CNRS, Sorbonne Université, Université Paris Cité, F-75005 Paris, France
[‖] *Centre d'analyse et de mathématique sociales (CAMS), EHESS-CNRS,*
54 bd Raspail, F-75006 Paris

Classical economics has developed an arsenal of methods, based on the idea of representative agents, to come up with precise numbers for next year's GDP, inflation and exchange rates, among (many) other things. Few, however, will disagree with the fact that the economy is a complex system, with a large number of strongly heterogeneous, interacting units of different types (firms, banks, households, public institutions) and different sizes.

Now, the main issue in economics is precisely the emergent organization, cooperation and coordination of such a motley crowd of micro-units. Treating them as a unique "representative" firm or household clearly risks throwing the baby with the bathwater. As we have learnt from statistical physics, understanding and characterizing such emergent properties can be difficult. Because of feedback loops of different signs, heterogeneities and non-linearities, the macro-properties are often hard to anticipate. In particular, these situations generically lead to a very large number of possible equilibria, or even the lack thereof.

Spin glasses and other disordered systems give a concrete example of such difficulties. In order to tackle these complex situations, new theoretical and numerical tools have been invented in the last 50 years, including of course the replica method and replica symmetry breaking, and the cavity method, both static and dynamic. In this chapter we review the application of such ideas and methods in economics and social sciences. Of particular interest are the proliferation (and fragility) of equilibria, the analogue of satisfiability phase transitions in games and random economies, and condensation (or concentration) effects in opinion, wealth, etc.

27.1. Game Theory

Can we expect cooperation in a population of selfish interacting individuals? Will a particular technology be adopted? How will firms behave when competing in the same sector? What is the optimal way of choosing a route to destination for a taxi driver in a crowded city? All these questions involve phenomena whose outcomes depend on how humans interact with each other.

Game theory is a general, idealized framework that addresses these questions under the assumption that each individual behaves rationally in order to maximize his/her utility. Because such an assumption is quite unreasonable, the predictions of game theory — the so-called Nash equilibria — are often incorrect when compared to real life outcomes. Yet, they provide a useful benchmark for understanding the richness that may result from human interaction. This is particularly true in "large games", when statistical behavior with its regularities is expected to set in.

There are two dimensions with respect to which a game can be "large": one is when the number of available strategies[a] for each individual player becomes large, the other is when the number of players itself becomes large. The generic outcome in "large games" is that the number of possible Nash equilibria may become very large, i.e. exponential in the number of players or strategies, much like the number of equilibrium states in spin glasses [1].

Take for example a simple game: N individuals have to decide whether to take one of two routes of the same length, to go from A to B. If their travel takes a time that decreases with the number of people who took their same choice, it is intuitive that the optimal outcome is one where the population will split exactly in two equal parts over the two choices. There are $\binom{N}{N/2} \sim e^{N \log 2}$ arrangements of this type.

When heterogeneity is taken into account, either because strategies are different or because the agents are different, the analysis of large games reveals a rich phenomenology with multiple equilibria, phase transitions and complex behavior, that calls for methods of statistical physics of disordered systems.

Two-player games, each with many different strategies were considered in Refs. [2–4], within an evolutionary setting,[b] and then by Berg and Engel [5, 6], who analyzed games of two players, each of which has N possible strategies. These are called bi-matrix games, because the payoffs to the players depending on the strategy choices of players can be encoded in two $N \times N$ matrices. When these matrices are random, Berg and Engel [5, 6] show that the number of Nash equilibria $\mathcal{N} \sim e^{NS}$ is exponentially large in N and that the entropy S can be computed using the replica method. Given such degeneracy, the game's outcome can hardly be predicted. Yet, typical Nash equilibria share characteristic properties that provide statistical predictions on the outcomes that we may expect in these settings.[c]

The replica and cavity method has also allowed one to shed light on the typical properties of games of heterogeneous interacting agents, in the limit where the number N of agents diverge. The Minority Game (MG) [7] is probably the prototypical model in this class. It describes the competition of many agents with different strategies on a set of resources. It was introduced as a simplification of the El Farol bar problem, originally

---

[a]A strategy is a possible course of action in the game.

[b]The equilibria of a game can be thought of as the equilibria of an ecosystem of species each of which plays one of the strategies, against randomly chosen opponents in a well mixed population.

[c]For example, it is possible to estimate the number of strategies that will be actually played by the two players, among the N possible ones.

proposed by Brian W. Arthur [8] as a critique of the deductive rationality approach assumed in game theory. The MG will be discussed in more detail in Sec. 27.5. In brief, it extends the example of choosing the least congested route discussed above to the case where the origin and destination of each agent differ and the available routes for each of them intersects in complex ways with the one of others. In these situations, the MG assumes that each agent adapts to his/her "environment", neglecting the fact that they also contribute to it (i.e. to traffic congestion). Hence the MG is not really a game, because agents do not behave strategically. As we shall see in Sec. 27.5, this makes the equilibrium of the game unique, i.e. replica symmetric [7]. When instead agents behave strategically (as in game theory) taking into account their systemic impact, replica symmetry is broken, and the game features an exponential number of Nash equilibria [9].

Players' heterogeneity may also result from the fact that each of them interacts with a different sub-set of players. In these *network games* [10], each player sits on the nodes of a network and interacts only with his/her neighbors.[d] The ensemble of games where the network is chosen at random can be studied with cavity methods borrowed from the theory of disordered systems. Consider, for example, a "local public good" setting where each player can exploit a resource either by buying it, at some cost, or by free riding on the resources bought by their neighbors. Given a network, who should invest in buying the resource? Dall'Asta *et al.* [11] show that finding all Nash equilibria of this game is equivalent to finding all maximal independent sets of the network, which is an NP-hard problem. Still, the number of Nash equilibria and their typical properties in the limit of infinite networks can be computed using belief propagation approaches. Dall'Asta *et al.* [12] use similar methods in order to understand under what conditions players in a social network can sustain cooperation, in a repeated prisoners' dilemma game.

27.2. Choice under Social Influence and "Bandwagon" Goods

As mentioned above, the success of the replica and cavity methods in dealing with complex physical systems has triggered a general interest in the physics community for the study of many complex systems outside the traditional domain of physics, like socio-economic systems (whether or not these require to rely on such advanced statistical physics techniques). On the methodological side, the use of well controlled agent-based simulations, further discussed in Sec. 27.4 below, is one example of physicists contributions, as such simulations often reveal collective, emergent phenomena typically encountered in statistical mechanics.

At the conceptual level, the importance of multiple equilibria and the difference between quenched and annealed disorder can be quite subtle (see e.g. [1, 13]) and not always fully understood in the economics literature. One reason comes from the standard view point in theoretical economy based on game theory, introduced in the previous section. At each instant of time, the 'true' underlying dynamics is supposed to be known to the players who compute the Nash equilibria, and then simultaneously play Nash,

---

[d]Network games also include problems where the network itself — i.e. whom to interact with — can be chosen strategically by the players [10].

anticipating that all the other agents will do the same. Even with rational agents, such anticipations are not possible whenever there are multiple equilibria. Although, as reviewed above, many games turn out to have a large number of equilibria, the classical view in economics is either that models should be defined such that there will be a single equilibrium, or that some postulated dynamics *justifies* the selection of one of the equilibria — but such dynamics usually does not correspond to any actual agents' dynamics!

'Heterodox' approaches in economics are more in line with the physicist approach, modeling the dynamics of agents with limited rationality [14] and plausible learning rules [7, 15]. The analysis of any such dynamics requires to specify the time scale over which the interactions or other parameters change with time.

One example of interest is the general problem of the collective behavior of agents making a binary choice under social influence, such as buying or not buying a fashion good, sorting or not sorting the waste, joining or not a riot, etc. Each agent i has their idiosyncratic willingness to adopt (or to buy), h_i. This willingness is increased if others do the same (a case of "positive externalities"), so that if the price (or cost) of the active decision is P, agent i wants to make the decision iff

$$h_i - P + J\eta > 0,$$

where $J > 0$ is the strength of the social influence and η the current fraction of adopters.

When the idiosyncratic willingness h_i are random but time independent, this specification is equivalent to the mean-field random field Ising model (RFIM). Such model is a particular instance of the *random utility model* [16] in theoretical economy and is also equivalent to the 'dying seminar' model of the social scientist T. C. Schelling [17]. With an approach more similar to the one of physicists than that of economists, Schelling correctly inferred the generic existence of multiple equilibria and hysteresis, leading to the notion of critical mass (or tipping point). Ising (or "Markov Random Fields" in the mathematical terminology) and RFIM type models have been used to model socio-economic systems by mathematicians [18], economists [19–21], physicists [22–25], to mention but a few: see e.g [26] for a review and further references, in particular in the context of multiple choices [27].

The statistical physics approach leads to the detailed study of the phase diagram in the parameter space (mean willingness to adopt $\langle h \rangle$ and strength of social influence J) [25]. Considering the vicinity of the critical point, one can predict a scaling law in the case of continuous change of (collective) behavior [28]: the height of the variation peak should scale with the width w as $\sim w^{-2/3}$. This prediction appears to be in good agreement with empirical data on cell phones adoption and birth rates evolution. This is a strong support to the relevance of this type of modeling, since it is hard to think of an alternative argument that would lead to such anomalous scaling.

In an economic context, considering that the seller is a profit-maximizer leads to the appearance of systemic risk. Indeed, the price of the good that would maximize the seller's profit is generically very close to the value at which the demand, corresponding to a large number of buyers, disappears abruptly. At this critical price value, one indeed crosses the line separating a regime with two Nash equilibria (the 'fashion good' equilibrium with a high demand and the low-demand equilibrium) and a regime with a single Nash equilibrium, for which only the rare agents with a very high idiosyncratic willingness to pay buy the good [29]. Hence, for prices slightly higher than the optimal price, demand falls precipitously!

This can be called a "cliff-edge" maximization situation: optimization can be tantamount to fragility. As discussed in Sec. 27.4, this situation is common in complex systems, which tend to spontaneously stabilize close to a point where the system becomes unstable (on this topic, see also [30]).

27.3. Opinion Dynamics

There is a large literature on the modeling of opinion dynamics. The boundaries of this research domain are ill-defined: many models of social behavior may be interpreted as models of opinion dynamics, including the binary choice RFIM discussed in Sec. 27.2. Another example is given by models of language change resulting from interactions between locutors, which can be seen as describing a dynamics of opinions on the meaning of words [31].

In this section, we restrict to models more specifically related to opinion dynamics. The main opinion dynamics models (with their variants) are the Voter model (see [31] and references therein), the Hegselmann and Krause model [32], the Deffuant bounded-interaction model [33], the Sznajd model [34], and the Galam consensus model [23] based on the RFIM (see Sec. 27.2). All these models explore the hypothesis that opinion may change due to interactions with others, with an imitation behavior — a search for consensus. For general reviews of opinion dynamics model inspired by statistical mechanics, see [31, 35]. Although not fully developed, the use of the cavity method to understand how opinions or rumors spread on a network like epidemics (see e.g. [36–41]) is surely an interesting path. Here we add a note on the less often mentioned Seceder model [42] exploring a different hypothesis, the case where every agent wants to imitate those who are not like everyone else.

Dittrich *et al.* [42] have introduced a model of agents trying to adopt opinions/behaviors different from the ones of others. In the context of genetic evolution (genes being analogous to opinions), the model explores the outcome of giving an advantage to individuals sufficiently different from the others (see also [43]). The authors show that clusters can emerge from a dynamics with such rule. Soulier and Halpin-Healy [44] have considered a simple variant with such dynamics "pitting conformity against dissent". Opinions are described by vectors of continuous variables in d dimension. At each time step, one randomly selects an agent (the voter). Then one picks at random a set of m individuals, the polling group. The individual with opinions most distant from the mean opinion of the polling group is selected. Then the voter adopts, with small variations in opinion values, the opinions of this group-dissident agent.

The model behavior changes abruptly with the group size at small values of m. A surprise is that the mean field behavior is reached at $m = 4$. In opinion dimension $d = 1$, for $m \geq 4$, the population clusters into two groups. The authors consider a variant with discrete opinions, in which the randomly chosen agent adopts exactly the opinions of the distant outlier of the group. They can then write deterministic equations of the replicator type. The analysis of the model leads to a quite remarkable result. If d is equal or larger than 3, and $m \geq 4$, the dynamics always leads to a condensation of opinions in a space of two dimensions, with the emergence of three clusters in the space of opinions.

Most of the opinion dynamics model have been introduced on the basis of theoretical motivations. As pointed in [45], from the study of many variants one observes non-robust results when rules are changed. Although it is useful to explore the space of possibilities, and interesting to discover a rich variety of model behaviors, this calls for restricting such studies to more empirically based models.

One should note that most models do not really make the difference between 'having an opinion' and 'making a decision' — except for the fact that a decision may be the noisy outcome of the opinion. When considering voting behavior, models do not address issues of strategic behaviors.

Only few works try to test models on data or define data-specific models (see e.g. [46]). However, models with rules inspired by the social psychology literature are being considered [35]. This allows one to study the outcome of behavioral rules motivated by experimental findings. Much work remains to be done along such lines. The increasing possibility to access data and to perform online experiments should trigger studies more directly linked to empirical behavior.

27.4. Firm Networks, Ecologies and Portfolios

There is a renewed interest in models of networks of interacting firms as a possible framework that accounts for excess fluctuations in economic systems, arising from "contagion" or default cascades that propagate along the supply chains (see [47] for a recent review). Similar ideas also exist in the context of bank networks [48, 49] or overlapping portfolios [50] to account for banking crises and deleveraging spirals in financial markets.

The economic behavior of firm networks depends on the *production function* that models how input goods and labor are transformed into a certain product. A classic production function that expresses *non-substitutability* of inputs is the Leontief model, that reads:

$$\pi_i = z_i \min_j \left\{ \frac{Q_{ij}}{J_{ij}} \right\}, \tag{27.1}$$

where π_i is the amount of goods firm i produces, z_i is the so-called productivity of firm i, Q_{ij} is the amount of goods j available to i and J_{ij} are similar to "stoichiometric coefficients" in chemistry, measuring how many units of j are needed to build i (when $z_i = 1$). Conventionally, labor corresponds to good $j = 0$.

Once the production function is specified, the equilibrium state of the economy is obtained by imposing (a) that firms attempt to maximize their profit and (b) that markets clear, i.e. that everything that is produced is consumed. These two conditions translate into enough equations to determine equilibrium prices p_i and productions π_i. For example, for a Leontief production function the equations for the vector of prices $\vec{p}$

(given in units of the cost of labor) read [51]

$$\mathbb{M}\,\vec{p} = \vec{V}, \qquad \mathbb{M}_{ij} = z_i\delta_{ij} - J_{ij}, \tag{27.2}$$

where $V_i = J_{i0}$.

The problem with such a set of equations is that the solution $\vec{p}$ is not necessarily a positive vector [52]. In other words, some constraints must be fulfilled by the z_i's and the J_{ij}'s for the economy to be viable.[e] If such constraints are not satisfied, some firms (the least productive ones) must necessarily be removed for the economy to become viable. So, much as counting the number of equilibrium states in spin glasses, one can ask the following question: for given productivities z_i and interaction matrix J_{ij}, how many viable economic equilibrium states are possible as a function of the number of firms N? And for a generic equilibrium, what is the eigenvalue spectrum of $\mathbb{M}$, which determines the dynamical stability of such an equilibrium?

Interestingly, the very same questions arise in the context of the Lotka–Volterra description of complex ecological networks. Denoting now as p_i the population size of specie i, the equilibrium states of the Lotka–Volterra equation are such that

$$p_i\left(V_i - z_i p_i + \sum_{j\neq i} J_{ij}p_j\right) = 0, \tag{27.3}$$

where now V_i describes the fitness of specie i, z_i is a saturation (self-interaction) term, and J_{ij} models the interactions between species: $J_{ij} > 0$ means that the presence of species j favors the growth of specie i, whereas $J_{ij} < 0$ means that the presence of specie j hampers the growth of specie i. Ecological equilibria are thus such that either $p_i = 0$ (i.e. specie i is extinct) or, for all remaining species, Eq. (27.2) leads to a positive solution. When J_{ij} is a symmetric matrix, the Lotka–Volterra model can be mapped onto a spin-glass problem [53, 54].

For independent random symmetric J_{ij}, there exists a replica symmetry broken phase, corresponding to a proliferation of possible ecological equilibria. These equilibria are furthermore found to be *marginally stable*, in the sense that the eigenvalue spectrum of $\mathbb{M}$ touches zero, meaning that such equilibria are extremely fragile to perturbations, for example small changes in the interaction matrix J_{ij} [53]. In this phase, evolution naturally leads to a self-organized critical state, where the stability criterion proposed by R. May in his famous paper is exactly saturated [55] (see also [56, 57] for further developments). One can speculate that economies, too, spontaneously evolve towards a marginally stable state, for which small external shocks may lead to anomalously high volatility [51].

Yet another, completely different setting where the very same mathematical discussion arises is portfolio construction with constraints. Markowitz' celebrated optimal portfolio (also known as mean variance optimization) states that the weight p_i of asset i should be chosen as the solution of Eq. (27.2), where now $\mathbb{M}$ is the covariance matrix,

---

[e]When all J_{ij} are positive, the matrix $\mathbb{M}$ is an "M-matrix" and the constraints boil down to imposing that all eigenvalues of $\mathbb{M}$ have a positive real part.

measuring how the returns of asset i and asset j are correlated, and $\vec{V}$ is the vector of predicted gains for each asset. Positive weights correspond to long positions, whereas negative weights indicate that the asset manager should go short on the corresponding asset.

But more often than not, asset managers cannot take short positions. In other words, their portfolios must satisfy a positivity constraint, $p_i \geq 0$, $\forall i$, much like prices in the firm network model and population sizes in the Lotka–Volterra model. So we are again back to the same "spin-glass" type problem [58–63]: what is the number of positive solutions of Eq. (27.2) as a function of the number of assets and the parameters of the problem? A fully soluble case is when there is a unique risk factor that correlates the returns of different assets [60]. This corresponds to $\mathbb{M}_{ij} = z_i \delta_{ij} + \beta_i \beta_j (1 - \delta_{ij})$, where β_i is the exposure of asset i to the common risk factor. One finds that for such a problem, optimal portfolios are typically sparse, and the total number of solutions grows sub-exponentially with the number of assets — whereas spin-glass problems typically have an exponentially large number of local optimums. But, in common with spin-glass problems, one can find very different, quasi-degenerate optimal portfolios in the presence of non-negative constraints, or other types of non-linear constraints (see also [61, 63]).

In fact, many problems in economics and finance are constrained optimization problems, or constraint satisfaction problems (see e.g. [64, 65] for a recent example). It is expected that many of these problems share with spin-glasses two important properties, typical of replica symmetry broken systems: a) the existence of a large number of quasi-degenerate solutions, that are nearly equally good in terms of their performance but very far from one another in phase space (e.g. surviving firms, surviving species, assets with non-zero weights in the above examples); b) parameter "chaos", i.e. the sensitivity of these solutions to the precise specification of the parameters of the problem [66–68]. In other words, the optimal solution for one choice of parameters can become suboptimal, or even disappear, when these parameters are only slightly changed (in the limit of a large number of degrees of freedom N: number of firms, number of species, number of assets).

Explosion of the number of optimal solutions and parameter chaos raise many difficulties in the modelling of complex systems. The classical approach in terms of probabilities is doomed by non-ergodicity, and the need to think in terms of probabilities of probabilities, like in spin-glasses [69]. Such difficulties, that one could coin as "radical complexity" [70] with a nod to Keynes' "radical uncertainty", should lead to significant rekindling of the way complex socio-economic problems are addressed. Two particularly interesting directions are (a) minority games and complex game theory and their relation with spin-glasses, see [4, 6, 7] and Sec. 27.1; (b) agent based modelling and scenario identification [70–72].

27.5. Replica Method for Financial Markets and Large Random Economies

The mutual attraction between finance and physics has diverse roots. One is to be found in the financial industry's thirst for analysts with a quantitative training. On the other side, the increasing availability of financial data has attracted the curiosity of physicists interested in understanding the non-trivial statistical features of market prices, which suggest analogies with fluid turbulence, avalanches, earthquakes and other phenomena in natural sciences.

On the theoretical side, the prevailing neo-classical paradigm relies on the pillars of the no-arbitrage hypothesis and the efficient market hypothesis (EMH) [73, 74] — according to which price behavior cannot be predicted and hence no excess gain can be extracted from speculative trading. This provides a theoretical foundation for asset pricing, but it was soon realized that these assumptions lead to conceptual inconsistencies [75] and that observed market behavior is incompatible with the neo-classical assumption of traders with rational expectations. (There is an enormous literature on this last point, for a physicist viewpoint and many references, see [76, Chapter 20].)

On the other hand, early simulations of agent based models [77] have shown that simple models with way less sophisticated traders could reproduce the main stylized facts observed in real financial markets. This spawned a line of research (see [78] for an early review, and [79] for a more recent one) aimed at understanding financial markets within simple models of interacting adaptive agents, that could explain the observed stylized facts and be amenable to theoretical analysis (see e.g. [80–82] for some early examples).

27.5.1. *The Minority Game*

The Minority Game [7] was introduced [83] as one such attempts. It depicts the interaction between financial traders as follows: in order to out-compete other traders, a trader needs to anticipate when most of them will buy, so that the trader can sell at a high price (or vice-versa). Each trader then aims at being in the minority group of either sellers or buyers. Note that this interaction promotes the diversification of strategies across traders. A strategy prescribes whether to buy or to sell, depending on the pattern of the m most recent signs of the price fluctuations. Therefore each strategy is a table of $P = 2^m$ numbers, and each trader is assigned few (say two) randomly drawn strategies. Each trader evaluates the performance of his/her strategies in the course of time and then plays the best one — i.e. the one that would have placed him/her most often in the minority — at each time step.

The stationary state of the MG can be fully analyzed with techniques coming from the statistical mechanics of disordered systems [84, 85]. The main insight that the MG provides on the behavior of financial markets is that, as the number of traders N increases, the market becomes less and less predictable and, at a critical value n_c of the ratio $n = N/P$, it becomes completely unpredictable, meaning that the expected value of future returns is independent of the past history. The point n_c marks a second order phase transition between a symmetric (information efficient) phase for $n \geq n_c$ and an asymmetric (inefficient) phase. In other words, the MG provides a stylized description of how a market becomes informationally efficient as more and more (diverse) traders join it. The phase transition is also accompanied by critical fluctuations similar to those observed in the statistics of real returns [86], which suggests that the observed anomalous fluctuations in financial markets are the other side of the coin of market's information efficiency. The relation between market efficiency and criticality emerges also in other modelling approaches to financial markets, see e.g. [76, 87].

The MG has proven to be a wellspring of further interesting results. Cavagna *et al.* [88] introduced a thermal version of the MG whereby agents chose the strategy they play stochastically. Detailed analysis of the dynamics [89] reveals that the "temperature" introduced at the microscopic scale in this way turns out to play the role of the inverse of a "temperature" at the collective level. The symmetric phase exhibits a peculiar type of broken ergodicity where the stationary state "remembers" the initial conditions, e.g. the prior beliefs of agents. The replica theory of MG provided a playground for addressing several issues, such as the effect of a Tobin tax [90] or a prediction of the market impact of meta-orders [92].[f]

The mechanism underlying the phase transition in the MG is rather generic. It also describes information aggregation in an asset market with traders with heterogeneous information [93], leading to conclusions similar to those discussed above.

27.5.2. *Large random economies*

Indeed, the nature of such a phase transition is similar to that occurring in large random systems of linear equations with non-negative constraints (see e.g. [61, 62]), that can describe ecologies, firm networks and economies, see Sec. 27.4. The financial industry as a whole can be considered as a large random economy and therefore the statistical mechanics analysis, thanks to the replica method, can shed light on the consequences of the expansion of the repertoire of financial instruments, such as the one we have witnessed since the nineties. The neo-classical lore maintains that the more financial instruments consumers have at their disposal, the better they can hedge their risks. The ideal situation is that of *complete markets*, when the repertoire of financial instruments is so large that risk can be eliminated altogether, as in Black–Scholes theory of option pricing [94].

The replica method [95] however reveals that the quest for market completeness can lead to financial instability [95]. The volumes of interbank trading necessary to hedge all financial instruments, as well as the susceptibility of the equilibrium to exogenous shocks, diverge as the financial sector approaches the ideal limit of complete markets even in an ideal model. Similar conclusions were derived within a different modelling approach [96], suggesting that the same may apply to real markets. As already mentioned above, "efficiency" and "optimality" can lead complex systems to the brink of instability.

The effects of technological innovation in a large random production economy can be analyzed in a similar way. In this economy, firms produce final goods for household consumption from either primary goods or inputs produced by other firms, through a linear transformation. Each firm's technology is then a random vector in the space of

---

[f]Meta-orders are long sequences of orders in the same direction, i.e. either buy or sell, by the same investor. A key issue is whether meta-order have a permanent effect on prices or not [76, 91]. In the MG the permanent impact can be computed analytically and it is non-zero only in the asymmetric phase, whereas it vanishes when the market is unpredictable.

commodities. In this standard set-up [98], firms maximize profit, consumers buy and consume final goods maximizing their utility and market prices are fixed by market clearing. Bardoscia *et al.* [97] show that a statistical mechanics analysis of the way the equilibrium of such a large random economy changes (as more and more technologies are "invented") has suggestive similarities with the industrial development we have witnessed so far. As long as the number of technologies does not exceed a given threshold[g] consumers can rely only on those final goods that are also primary goods, because no firm can operate. When the number of technologies exceeds this threshold, an "industrial revolution" takes place as a sharp phase transition. Beyond this point, the introduction of new successful[h] technologies increases the scale of production of already existing technologies. This suggests that firms have incentives to incorporate all the technologies needed to produce final goods, as well as to carry out in-house research and development. This is reminiscent of the early stages of industrialization, which was characterized by vertically integrated firms [99], where all intermediate production processes were managed within the firm. As technological innovation proceeds, the economy crosses over to a regime characterized by a saturated technological repertoire. Beyond this second transition, that occurs close to the maximum in Fig. 27.1, the introduction of further technologies is disruptive: most of the technological innovations are not viable and the few that are successful displace other technologies when they are introduced, reducing their scales of production. In this regime, the growth of the

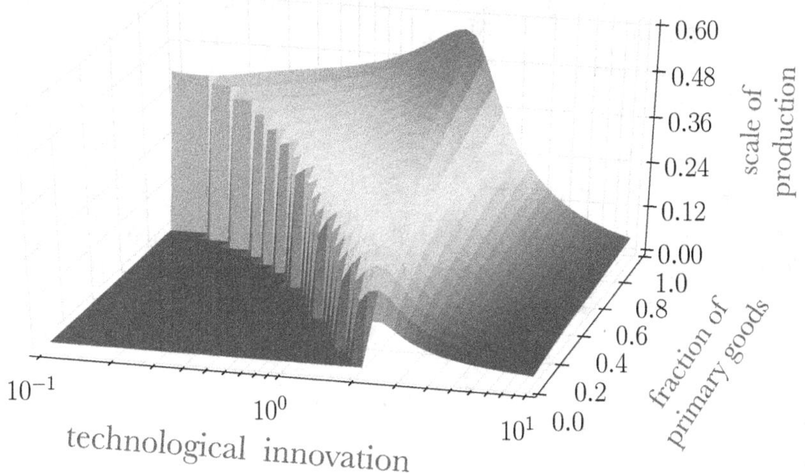

Fig. 27.1.   Phase diagram of the general equilibrium of a large random economy, from [97]. The technological innovation axis is the ratio between the number of technologies and the number of goods. The introduction of new technologies amounts to a shift on the right along this axis. The introduction of new goods reduces both this coordinate and the fraction of primary goods, so it corresponds to shifts towards the origin.

---

[g]Which is proportional to the number of goods. In the statistical mechanics analysis both the number of goods and the number of technologies diverge, with a fixed ratio.
[h]A new (random) technology is adopted only if it generated profits at the current prices. It is not adopted if the profit is negative.

economy is not driven by the introduction of new technologies but by the introduction of new goods. This is evocative of the expansion of markets for intermediate goods, those who are neither primary nor final goods (e.g. parts of a final good, like electronic components) and a parallel outsourcing of segments of the processes involved in the production of complex goods. These are both processes that advanced capitalist countries have experienced [99].

The prediction of the stylized picture provided by this model is on the one hand that, pursuing economic growth, advanced economies are expected to converge to the critical point separating the two regimes, on the other that the expansion of intermediate goods markets and outsourcing may lead the economy to a collapse, crossing the "industrial revolution" phase transition point.

27.6. Intermittency and Condensation Phenomena

27.6.1. *Sums of exponentials and RSB*

In many cases of interest in physics, but also in finance, social sciences and economics, one has to deal with sums of exponentials of random variables. In statistical physics, the *partition function* is defined as the sum over all configurations of the Boltzmann–Gibbs weight, which is itself the exponential of (minus) the energy of that configuration divided by temperature. When these energies are random variables, one is confronted to a sum of exponentials of random variables – this is Derrida's Random Energy Model (REM), which is well-known to be characterised by a 1-RSB glassy phase at low temperatures [100–102]. Population growth or survival [13], city growth [103] or wealth growth [104] are other examples where such sums of exponentials naturally appear.

So let us consider, generically,

$$Z_N = \sum_{i=1}^{N} z_i, \qquad z_i := e^{t\xi_i}, \tag{27.4}$$

where t is a positive parameter and ξ_i are *i.i.d.* random variables, that we can always choose to be of zero mean and unit standard deviation. We also assume that the right tail of the distribution of ξ's decays as

$$\rho(\xi) \sim_{\xi \to \infty} C e^{-A\xi^b}, \tag{27.5}$$

where A, C are positive parameters and $b > 1$ (corresponding to super-exponential decay). When $b = 1$ the distribution of z's has a power-law tail for large z, $z^{-1-\mu}$, with a tail exponent $\mu = A/t$, such that n-th moments with $n \geq \mu$ are divergent. When $b > 1$, on the other hand, all moments $\mathbb{E}[e^{nt\xi}]$ exist and are finite when $t \geq 0$. Hence, formally, the Central Limit Theorem (CLT) applies and, for large N, Z_N should converge to a Gaussian distribution. In particular, the Law of Large Numbers suggests that for large N

$$Z_N \approx N\mathbb{E}[e^{t\xi}]. \tag{27.6}$$

However, consider the case where N is large but finite and take t to infinity first. Then, the whole sum Z_N will be concentrated in its largest term:

$$Z_N \approx_{t \to \infty} e^{t\xi^*}, \tag{27.7}$$

where $\xi^\star = \max_{i=1,\dots,N} \xi_i$. We thus see that depending on whether N is taken to infinity at fixed t, or t is taken to infinity at fixed N, the result is markedly different.

More generally, one finds that for a given large value of N, the relevant tail of the distribution of z is again a power law, but with an N-dependent tail exponent:

$$\mu = \frac{bA^{1/b}}{t}\,(\log N)^{1-\frac{1}{b}}.\tag{27.8}$$

We are now in position to state the following result, which generalizes the 1-RSB transition of the REM. Suppose that both N and t go to infinity, with μ (as given by Eq. (27.8)) fixed. Then, depending on the value of μ, the sum of exponentials of random variables, $Z_N = \sum_i \exp(t\xi_i)$, obeys either the standard CLT or the generalized (Lévy) CLT [13, 105, 106]:

- $\mu > 2$: Z_N converges towards a Gaussian random variable of mean $N\mathbb{E}[e^{t\xi}]$ and variance $N(\mathbb{E}[e^{2t\xi}] - \mathbb{E}[e^{t\xi}]^2)$.
- $1 < \mu < 2$: $(Z_N - N\mathbb{E}[e^{t\xi}])/N^{1/\mu} = u$ converges towards a Lévy-stable random variable, with $P(u) = L_{\mu,\beta=1}(u)$, the totally asymmetric Lévy distribution of index μ.
- $\mu < 1$: $Z_N/N^{1/\mu} = u$ converges towards a Lévy-stable random variable, with, again, $P(u) = L_{\mu,\beta=1}(u)$, the totally asymmetric Lévy distribution of index μ.

Hence, for $\mu > 2$, the LLN result holds (see Eq. (27.6)), but completely falls apart when $\mu < 1$.

Take for simplicity $\rho(\xi) = \exp(-\xi^2/2\sigma^2)/\sqrt{2\pi\sigma^2}$. In this case, $A = 1/(2\sigma^2)$ and $b = 2$, so that $\mu = \sqrt{2\log N}/(\sigma t)$. What we learn from the previous discussion is that for small enough t, Z_N is Gaussian and the inverse participation ratio (called the Herfindahl index in social sciences), defined as:[i]

$$\mathcal{H} = \frac{\sum_{i=1}^{N} z_i^2}{Z_N^2},\tag{27.9}$$

is of order N^{-1}, i.e. the whole sum is spread out over all elements. As t increases, the Herfindahl index increases and Z_N becomes more and more concentrated in a few terms. When $t > t_{\rm c} = \sqrt{2\log N}/\sigma$, the Herfindahl index becomes of order unity, even as $N \to \infty$. This corresponds to a genuine "condensation" or "localization" transition, with many relevant applications, in particular in the context of the glass transition [107].

As a vivid illustration, imagine a portfolio composed of many different assets, each with a different rate of return r_i. At time zero, the total capital K_0 is invested uniformly across all these N assets. After time t, the capital has accrued and is given by

$$K(t) = \frac{K_0}{N} \sum_{i=1}^{N} e^{tr_i}.\tag{27.10}$$

The above analysis tells us that there exists a critical time $t_{\rm c}$ beyond which the initially diversified capital becomes concentrated among a small subset of assets. Furthermore, at large t, the growth rate of $K(t)$ is given by $r^\star = \max\{r_i\}$. A way to avoid such a

---

[i]This quantity is often noted Y_2 in the spin-glass literature, see e.g. [105].

condensation phenomenon is to periodically rebalance the portfolio, redistributing the profit and losses of the portfolio among all assets. But if the redistribution graph is sparse, or low dimensional, condensation still takes place if the redistribution rate is small enough [104]. One can similarly consider a multiplicative growth model for firms, wealth, cities, biological species, etc. The model can also be used in the context of the famous "exploration-exploitation" tradeoff [108].

Note that these random growth with redistribution problems map onto the directed polymer problem — a "baby spin-glass" problem where disorder and interactions compete. The case of directed polymers on a tree-like graph, introduced by Derrida and Spohn [109], can in fact be solved using either replicas, or propagating front methods (see also [108, 110]). The "condensed" phase corresponds to the pinned, glassy phase of the directed polymer. The Derrida–Spohn model has also strong connections with the multifractal model of financial price series, as discussed below.

27.6.2. *Multiscaling, intermittency and RSB*

The scaling behavior of the different moments of a random variable brings us to the topic of *multiscaling*, which is an important feature of intermittent systems, like turbulent flows where it was first discovered (for a review, see [111]). Consider a fluctuating time series $x(t)$, for example the velocity in a turbulent flow, the (log-)price of a stock, or the output level of an economy, etc.

A natural question to ask is: how much does $x(t)$ varies between two instant of times? One usually first "detrends" the time series by removing a (generalized) drift, defined as:

$$m_1(\tau) := \langle x(t+\tau) - x(t) \rangle_T, \tag{27.11}$$

where $\langle \ldots \rangle_T$ denotes an empirical sliding average over a total interval of size T.

Assuming stationarity in time, the *fluctuation* around the trend is often characterized by the variance of the de-trended increments of $x(t)$, i.e.

$$\sigma^2(\tau) := \langle (x(t+\tau) - x(t) - m_1(\tau))^2 \rangle_T. \tag{27.12}$$

The simplest example of a random time series is the Brownian motion. Once detrended, the increments $\Delta = x(t+\tau) - x(t)$ are Gaussian random variables with zero mean and variance $\sigma^2(\tau) = \Sigma^2 \tau$. Hence all higher moments can be computed and expressed in terms of $\sigma(\tau)$, as $m_q(\tau) = C_q \sigma^q(\tau)$, where C_q are the moments of the standard normal distribution. In other words, the moment of order q simply scales as the q-th power of the standard deviation. All moments thus give the same characterization of the time evolution of the fluctuations of $x(t)$. One speaks of "monoscaling" in such a case.

This is however not the only possibility. An example coming from the Burgers equation, and again deeply related to 1-RSB and pinning problems, is the following [102, 112]. Consider a time series made of upward "ramps" of constant slope S, separated by downward "shocks", i.e. discontinuities of amplitude $-\Delta_0$ appearing at a Poisson rate λ. We choose the parameters S, Δ_0 and λ in such a way that our time series has no long term bias. The computation of the different moments $m_q(\tau)$ is easy in the limit where $\lambda\tau \ll 1$, i.e. when the probability $p(\tau) \approx \lambda\tau$ for a shock to exist between t and

$t + \tau$ is very small. The scaling behaviour of $m_q(\tau)$ for $\lambda\tau \ll 1$ is found to be very different depending on whether q is ≤ 1 or ≥ 1 [113]:

$$\begin{cases} m_q(\tau) \sim (\lambda\tau)^q \sim \sigma^{2q}(\tau), & \forall q \leq 1, \\ m_q(\tau) \sim \lambda\tau \sim \sigma^2(\tau), & \forall q \geq 1. \end{cases} \tag{27.13}$$

Note, interestingly, that $m_2(\tau)$ grows like τ both for the standard Brownian motion and for the "ramps and shocks" model, although the underlying processes are clearly very different. This shows that the second moment is totally blind to intermittency effects.

In order to characterize these intermittency effects, one defines an exponent $\zeta(q)$ from the scaling of the q-th moment, as:

$$m_q(\tau) \sim [\sigma(\tau)]^{\zeta(q)}. \tag{27.14}$$

Any concave deviation away from the monoscaling behavior $\zeta(q) = q$ is a signature of "intermittency", i.e. the concentration of activity (here the variations of $x(t)$) in some particular regions of space and/or time.

A well studied model of intermittency is the "multifractal Brownian motion" (MBM) [114, 115]. The (detrended) MBM $x(t)$ can be constructed as follows:

$$dx(t) = \Sigma\, e^{\omega(t)}\, dW(t), \tag{27.15}$$

where $W(t)$ is a standard Wiener process (or Brownian motion) and $\omega(t)$ is itself a Gaussian random variable with logarithmic correlations, i.e. a very long memory process:[j]

$$\mathbb{E}\left[\omega(t)\omega(t+\tau)\right] = \kappa \max(\log(\tau/T), 0), \qquad 0 \leq \kappa < \frac{1}{2}, \tag{27.16}$$

where κ is the so-called intermittency parameter, and T is a large time scale cut-off, beyond which volatility is uncorrelated. When $\kappa = 0$, the process recovers the standard Brownian motion with a constant volatility. In financial parlance, ω is the local log-volatility of the price $x(t)$. One can show that within this model,

$$\sigma^2(\tau) = \Sigma^2\tau, \tag{27.17}$$

independently of κ. In other words, the second moment of $x(t + \tau) - x(t)$ is the same for the standard Brownian motion and for the MBM. For other moments, however, differences appear. In particular, one finds that the multi-scaling exponent $\zeta(q)$ is given by [114]:

$$\zeta(q) = q - \kappa q(q - 2), \qquad (q\kappa < 1), \tag{27.18}$$

i.e. a linear function for $\kappa = 0$ (no intermittency) and a concave function for $\kappa > 0$ when volatility is fluctuating. (When $q\kappa \geq 1$, the corresponding moment is infinite: the MBM develops power-law tail increments, with a tail index $\mu = 1/\kappa$ [114].)

The deep relation with the REM is the following. The MBM is a Brownian motion subordinated to a "fractal time" s defined as:

$$s^2 := \int_0^t dt'\, e^{2\omega(t')}, \tag{27.19}$$

---

[j]Here there is a subtlety that we carelessly sweep under the rug: in order to be well defined, the log function must be regularized for small τ, see e.g. [116].

which can be seen as the partition function Z_t of a particle in a logarithmically correlated one-dimensional random potential $\omega(\cdot)$ at inverse temperature $\beta = 2$. It turns out that this problem has been thoroughly studied [110, 117], in particular in connection with the Derrida-Spohn directed polymer problem and other specific models of glasses, with the Gaussian free field in two dimensions and "multiplicative chaos" [116] and with random matrix theory problems [118]. Physically, we recover the same phenomenology as the Derrida-Spohn model: there is a 1-RSB low temperature phase (corresponding to $\kappa > 1$), although the distribution of low-lying energy states has a tail that is slightly different from that of the Gumbel distribution, which characterizes the pure REM [110, 117].

Note finally that one can generalize such a logarithmically correlated random potential, which corresponds to a 1-RSB REM, to the full replica symmetry broken case, providing an explicit construction of hierarchical Parisi landscapes in finite dimensions [119].

References

[1] M. Mézard, G. Parisi, and M. A. Virasoro, *Spin glass theory and beyond: An Introduction to the Replica Method and Its Applications.* vol. 9, (World Scientific Publishing Company, 1987).

[2] H. Rieger, *J. Phys. A.* **22**(17), 3447, (1989).

[3] M. Opper and S. Diederich, *Phys. Rev. Lett.* **69**(10), 1616, (1992).

[4] T. Galla and J. D. Farmer, *Proc. Natl. Acad. Sci. U.S.A.* **110**(4), 1232–1236, (2013).

[5] J. Berg and A. Engel, *Phys. Rev. Lett.* **81**(22), 4999, (1998).

[6] J. Berg, *Phys. Rev. E.* **61**(3), 2327, (2000).

[7] D. Challet, M. Marsili, and Y.-C. Zhang, *Minority games: interacting agents in financial markets.* (Oxford University Press, 2004).

[8] W. B. Arthur, *Am. Econ. Rev.* **84**(2), 406–411, (1994).

[9] A. De Martino and M. Marsili, *J. Phys. A.* **34**(12), 2525, (2001).

[10] M. O. Jackson and Y. Zenou. In *Handbook of game theory with economic applications*, vol. 4, pp. 95–163. Elsevier, (2015).

[11] L. Dall'Asta, P. Pin, and A. Ramezanpour, *J. Public Econ. Theory.* **13**(6), 885–901, (2011).

[12] L. Dall'Asta, M. Marsili, and P. Pin, *Proc. Natl. Acad. Sci. U.S.A.* **109**(12), 4395–4400, (2012).

[13] G. Ben Arous, L. V. Bogachev, and S. A. Molchanov, *Probab. Theory Relat. Fields.* **132**(4), 579–612, (2005).

[14] A. Kirman, *Complex economics: individual and collective rationality.* (Routledge, 2010).

[15] Y. Sato and J. P. Crutchfield, *Phys. Rev. E.* **67**(1), 015206, (2003).

[16] C. F. Manski, *Theory Decis.* **8**, 229–254, (1977).

[17] T. S. Schelling, *Micromotives and Macrobehavior.* (W.W. Norton and Co, N. Y., 1978).

[18] H. Föllmer, *J. Math. Econ.* **1**, 51–62, (1974).

[19] W. A. Brock and S. N. Durlauf, *Rev. Econ. Stud.* **68**, 235–260, (2001).

[20] L. E. Blume, *Games Econ. Behav.* **11**, 111–145, (1995).

[21] E. Glaeser and J. A. Scheinkman. In eds. M. Dewatripont, L. Hansen, and S. Turnovsky, *Advances in Economics and Econometrics: Theory and Applications, Eight World Congress*, pp. 339–369. Cambridge University Press, (2003).

[22] W. Weidlich, *Collective Phenomena.* **1**, 51–59, (1971).

[23] S. Galam, Y. Gefen, and Y. Shapir, *J. Math. Sociol.* **9**, 1–13, (1982).

[24] G. Weisbuch and D. Stauffer, *Physica A.* **323**, 651–662, (2003).

[25] J.-P. Nadal, D. Phan, M. B. Gordon, and J. Vannimenus, *Quant. Finance.* **5**, 557–568, (2006).

[26] J.-P. Bouchaud, *J. Stat. Phys.* **151**(3), 567–606, (2013).

[27] C. Borghesi and J.-P. Bouchaud, *Qual. Quant.* **41**(4), 557–568, (2007).

[28] Q. Michard and J.-P. Bouchaud, *Eur. Phys. J. B.* **47**, 151, (2005).

[29] M. B. Gordon, J.-P. Nadal, D. Phan, and V. Semeshenko, *J. Stat. Phys.* **151**, 494–522, (2013).

[30] M. Müller and M. Wyart, *Annu. Rev. Condens. Matter Phys.* **6**(1), 177–200, (2015).

[31] C. Castellano, S. Fortunato, and V. Loreto, *Rev. Mod. Phys.* **81**, 591–646 (2009).

[32] R. Hegselmann and U. Krause, *J. Artif. Soc. Soc. Simul.* **5**, 2, (2002).

[33] G. Deffuant, D. Neau, F. Amblard, and G. Weisbuch, *Adv. Complex Syst.* **3**, 87–98, (2000).

[34] K. Sznajd-Weron and J. Sznajd, *Int. J. Mod. Phys. C.* **11**, 1157–1165, (2000).

[35] A. Jedrzejewski and K. Sznajd-Weron, *C. R. Acad. Sci. Physique.* **20**(4), 244–261, (2019).

[36] Y. Moreno, M. Nekovee, and A. F. Pacheco, *Phys. Rev. E.* **69**(6), 066130, (2004).

[37] M. E. J. Newman, *Phys. Rev. E.* **66**, 016128 (2002).

[38] K. Anand, A. Kirman, and M. Marsili, *Eur. J. Finance.* **19**(5), 438–447, (2013).

[39] K. Anand and R. Kühn, *Phys. Rev. E.* **75**, 016111 (2007).

[40] F. Altarelli, A. Braunstein, L. Dall'Asta, A. Lage-Castellanos, and R. Zecchina, *Phys. Rev. Lett.* **112**, 118701 (2014).

[41] A. Baker, I. Biazzo, A. Braunstein, G. Catania, L. Dall'Asta, A. Ingrosso, F. Krzakala, F. Mazza, M. Mézard, A. P. Muntoni, et al., *Proc. Natl. Acad. Sci. U.S.A.* **118**(32), e2106548118, (2021).

[42] P. Dittrich, F. Liljeros, A. Soulier, and W. Banzhaf, *Phys. Rev. Lett.* **84**, 3205–3208 (2000).

[43] B. de Courson, L. Fitouchi, J.-P. Bouchaud, and M. Benzaquen, *Sci. Rep.* **11**(1), 1–15, (2021).

[44] A. Soulier and T. Halpin-Healy, *Phys. Rev. Lett.* **90**, 258103 (2003).

[45] S. Redner, *Comptes rendus de l'Académie des Sciences – Physique.* **20**, 275–292, (2019).

[46] M. Galesic and D. L. Stein, *arXiv:1706.02287.* (2017).

[47] V. M. Carvalho and A. Tahbaz-Salehi, *Annu. Rev. Econom.* **11**, 635–663, (2019).

[48] A. G. Haldane and R. M. May, *Nature.* **469**(7330), 351–355, (2011).

[49] P. Gai, A. Haldane, and S. Kapadia, *J. Monet. Econ.* **58**(5), 453–470, (2011).

[50] F. Caccioli, M. Shrestha, C. Moore, and J. D. Farmer, *J. Bank. Financ.* **46**, 233–245, (2014).

[51] J. Moran and J.-P. Bouchaud, *Phys. Rev. E.* **100**(3), 032307, (2019).

[52] D. Hawkins and H. A. Simon, *Econometrica.* pp. 245–248, (1949).

[53] G. Biroli, G. Bunin, and C. Cammarota, *New J. Phys.* **20**(8), 083051, (2018).

[54] A. Altieri, F. Roy, C. Cammarota, and G. Biroli, *Phys. Rev. Lett.* **126**(25), 258301, (2021).

[55] R. M. May, *Nature.* **238**(5364), 413–414, (1972).

[56] Y. V. Fyodorov and B. A. Khoruzhenko, *Proc. Natl. Acad. Sci. U.S.A.* **113**(25), 6827–6832, (2016).

[57] G. B. Arous, Y. V. Fyodorov, and B. A. Khoruzhenko, *Proc. Natl. Acad. Sci. U.S.A.* **118**(34), (2021).

[58] S. Galluccio, J.-P. Bouchaud, and M. Potters, *Physica A.* **259**(3-4), 449–456, (1998).

[59] S. Ciliberti, I. Kondor, and M. Mézard, *Quant. Finance.* **7**(4), 389–396, (2007).

[60] J. Garnier-Brun, M. Benzaquen, S. Ciliberti, and J.-P. Bouchaud, *J. Stat. Mech. Theory Exp.* **2021**(9), 093408, (2021).

[61] S. Landmann and A. Engel, *Physica A.* **552**, 122544, (2020).

[62] S. Landmann and A. Engel, *Phys. Rev. E.* **101**, 062119 (2020).

[63] A. Prüser, I. Kondor, and A. Engel, *Entropy.* **23**(7), 805, (2021).

[64] D. Sharma, J.-P. Bouchaud, M. Tarzia, and F. Zamponi, *J. Stat. Mech. Theory Exp.* **2019**(12), 123301, (2019).

[65] D. Sharma, J.-P. Bouchaud, M. Tarzia, and F. Zamponi, *J. Stat. Mech. Theory Exp.* **2021**(6), 063403, (2021).

[66] D. S. Fisher and D. A. Huse, *Phys. Rev. B.* **43**(13), 10728, (1991).

[67] A. J. Bray and M. A. Moore, *Phys. Rev. Lett.* **58**(1), 57, (1987).

[68] T. Rizzo and A. Crisanti, *Phys. Rev. Lett.* **90**(13), 137201, (2003).

[69] G. Parisi, *Adv. Complex Syst.* **10**(supp02), 223–232, (2007).

[70] J.-P. Bouchaud, *Entropy.* **23**(12), 1676, (2021).

[71] S. Gualdi, M. Tarzia, F. Zamponi, and J.-P. Bouchaud, *J. Econ. Dyn. Control.* **50**, 29–61, (2015).

[72] D. Sharma, J.-P. Bouchaud, S. Gualdi, M. Tarzia, and F. Zamponi, *PloS one.* **16**(3), e0247823, (2021).

[73] P. A. Samuelson, *Manag. Rev.* **6**(2), (1965).

[74] E. F. Fama, *J. Finance.* **25**(2), 383–417, (1970).

[75] S. J. Grossman and J. E. Stiglitz, *Am. Econ. Rev.* **70**(3), 393–408, (1980).

[76] J.-P. Bouchaud, J. Bonart, J. Donier, and M. Gould, *Trades, quotes and prices: financial markets under the microscope.* (Cambridge University Press, 2018).

[77] R. G. Palmer, W. B. Arthur, J. H. Holland, B. LeBaron, and P. Tayler, *Physica D.* **75**(1-3), 264–274, (1994).

[78] J. D. Farmer, *Int. J. Theor. Appl. Finance.* **3**(03), 311–333, (2000).

[79] M. Cristelli, L. Pietronero, and A. Zaccaria, *arXiv:1101.1847.* (2011).

[80] P. Bak, M. Paczuski, and M. Shubik, *Physica A.* **246**(3-4), 430–453, (1997).

[81] W. A. Brock and C. H. Hommes, *J. Econ. Dyn. Control.* **22**(8-9), 1235–1274, (1998).

[82] R. Cont and J.-P. Bouchaud, *Macroecon. Dyn.* **4**(2), 170–196, (2000).

[83] D. Challet and Y.-C. Zhang, *Physica A.* **246**(3-4), 407–418, (1997).

[84] D. Challet, M. Marsili, and R. Zecchina, *Phys. Rev. Lett.* **84**(8), 1824, (2000).

[85] A. C. Coolen, *The mathematical theory of minority games: statistical mechanics of interacting agents.* (Oxford University Press, 2005).

[86] D. Challet and M. Marsili, *Phys. Rev. E.* **68**(3), 036132, (2003).

[87] J.-P. Bouchaud, Y. Gefen, M. Potters, and M. Wyart, *Quant. Finance.* **4**(2), 176, (2003).

[88] A. Cavagna, J. P. Garrahan, I. Giardina, and D. Sherrington, *Phys. Rev. Lett.* **83**(21), 4429, (1999).

[89] M. Marsili and D. Challet, *Phys. Rev. E.* **64**(5), 056138, (2001).

[90] G. Bianconi, T. Galla, M. Marsili, and P. Pin, *J. Econ. Behav. Organ.* **70**(1-2), 231–240, (2009).

[91] B. Tóth, Y. Lemperiere, C. Deremble, J. De Lataillade, J. Kockelkoren, and J.-P. Bouchaud, *Phys. Rev. X.* **1**(2), 021006, (2011).

[92] A. C. Barato, I. Mastromatteo, M. Bardoscia, and M. Marsili, *Quant. Finance.* **13**(9), 1343–1352, (2013).

[93] J. Berg, M. Marsili, A. Rustichini, and R. Zecchina, *Quant. Finance.* **1**(2), 203–211, (2001).

[94] J. Hull, *Options, futures, & other derivatives. Solutions manual.* (Prentice Hall International, 2006).

[95] M. Marsili, *Quant. Finance.* **14**(9), 1663–1675, (2014).

[96] W. A. Brock, C. H. Hommes, and F. O. Wagener, *J. Econ. Dyn. Control.* **33**(11), 1912–1928, (2009).

[97] M. Bardoscia, G. Livan, and M. Marsili, *J. Stat. Mech. Theory Exp.* **2017**(4), 043401, (2017).

[98] K. Lancaster, *Mathematical economics.* (Courier Corporation, 2012).

[99] R. N. Langlois, *Ind. Corp. Chang.* **12**(2), 351–385, (2003).

[100] B. Derrida, *Phys. Rev. B.* **24**(5), 2613, (1981).

[101] D. J. Gross and M. Mézard, *Nucl. Phys. B.* **240**(4), 431–452, (1984).

[102] J.-P. Bouchaud and M. Mézard, *J. Phys. A.* **30**(23), 7997, (1997).

[103] X. Gabaix, *Q. J. Econ.* **114**(3), 739–767, (1999).

[104] J.-P. Bouchaud and M. Mézard, *Physica A.* **282**(3-4), 536–545, (2000).

[105] B. Derrida. In *On Three Levels*, pp. 125–137. Springer, (1994).

[106] A. Bovier, I. Kurkova, and M. Löwe, *Ann. Probab.* **30**(2), 605–651, (2002).

[107] G. Biroli and J.-P. Bouchaud, *Structural Glasses and Supercooled Liquids: Theory, Experiment, and Applications.* pp. 31–113, (2012).

[108] T. Gueudré, A. Dobrinevski, and J.-P. Bouchaud, *Phys. Rev. Lett.* **112**(5), 050602, (2014).

[109] B. Derrida and H. Spohn, *J. Stat. Phys.* **51**(5), 817–840, (1988).

[110] D. Carpentier and P. Le Doussal, *Phys. Rev. E.* **63**(2), 026110, (2001).

[111] U. Frisch, *Turbulence: the legacy of AN Kolmogorov.* (Cambridge University Press, 1995).

[112] J.-P. Bouchaud, M. Mézard, and G. Parisi, *Phys. Rev. E.* **52**(4), 3656, (1995).

[113] J. Bec and K. Khanin, *Phys. Rep.* **447**(1-2), 1–66, (2007).

[114] J.-F. Muzy and E. Bacry, *Phys. Rev. E.* **66**(5), 056121, (2002).

[115] J.-F. Muzy, E. Bacry, and A. Kozhemyak, *Phys. Rev. E.* **73**(6), 066114, (2006).

[116] R. Rhodes and V. Vargas, *Probab. Surv.* **11**, 315–392, (2014).

[117] Y. V. Fyodorov and J.-P. Bouchaud, *J. Phys. A.* **41**(37), 372001, (2008).

[118] Y. Fyodorov, B. Khoruzhenko, and N. Simm, *Ann. Probab.* **44**(4), 2980–3031, (2016).

[119] Y. V. Fyodorov and J.-P. Bouchaud, *J. Phys. A.* **41**(32), 324009, (2008).

Chapter 28

Complex Dynamics in Ecological Systems
and Animal Behavior

This chapter is based on three contributions that illustrate recent progresses focusing mainly on the physics of active matter, on collective behavior of flocks of birds and on models in theoretical ecology. First, **M. C. Marchetti** discusses how key concepts developed to quantify the behavior of disordered condensed matter systems, from window glass to spin glasses, are impacting the physics of active matter. Second, **I. Giardina** reviews some of the main experimental findings that have been obtained along the years on natural flocks of birds, and we describe how, starting from experimental data, theoretical descriptions of their collective behavior have been developed. Finally, **A. Altieri** reviews some of the most used models in theoretical ecology along with appealing reformulations and recent results in terms of diversity, stability and functioning of large well-mixed ecological communities.

28.1. Active Glasses and "Flying" Spin Glasses

M. Cristina Marchetti

Department of Physics, University of California Santa Barbara,
Santa Barbara, USA
cmarchetti@ucsb.edu

28.1.1. *Introduction*

The key property of an active particle is its ability to consume energy to generate autonomous directed motion and forces. Through interactions, collectives of active particles organize in emergent structures on scales much larger than that of the individuals. There are many examples of this spontaneous organization in the living world: motor proteins orchestrate the organization of genetic material inside cells, swarming bacteria self-organize into biofilms, epithelial cells migrate collectively to fill in wounds, fish school and birds flock to confuse predators or forage for food. In active systems energy is injected at the small scale and transmitted through interactions to sustain coordinated motion at large scale [1]. For instance, proteins like myosins inside living cells transform chemical energy into mechanical forces to control how everybody moves and functions. A variety of synthetic microswimmers often referred to as active colloids have also been engineered. The simplest realization are spherical micron-size particles fueled by chemical reactions that generate tangential flows at the particle's surface, which turn the colloid into a swimmer [2].

To the physicist, a collection of interacting active particles provides a vast playground for realizing new complex states of matter out of equilibrium. These include active gases that accumulate at the walls of a container instead of spreading uniformly through the bulk [3], active fluids that flow without externally applied forces featuring novel rheology [4], and active solids where crowding suppresses motility, allowing the system to remain cohesive in spite of the continuous energy input at the microscale [5]. Much progress has been made in the last two decades towards formulating a quantitative description of active phases and active phase transitions, but many open challenges remain.

The hallmark of the field of active matter has been the understanding of the emergence of directed collective motions or flocking [6]. In recent years there has also been a lot of interest in understanding how collective motion can be suppressed by crowding or disrupted by extrinsic disorder. Both are highly relevant to biological systems. For instance, epithelial tissues where the cells are densely packed with no intervening gaps have been shown to behave like active systems capable of tuning themselves between fluid states where cells are motile and frequently exchange neighbors and solid states exhibiting the very slow relaxation of glassy materials [7]. This ability to self-tune the material's rheological state underlies many biological processes, from wound healing to cancer invasion and development, where cells need to flow coherently like a flocking fluid to respond to physiological changes or perturbations, but must be able to sustain shear stresses once they have reached the desired configuration. Similarly many active agents operate in highly disordered environments that can disrupt the collective behavior found in clean settings. For instance, bacteria often move through porous gels that can qualitatively affect both their individual and collective dynamics [8]. These observations have motivated much ongoing work on the behavior of active glassy states of matter.

Disordered and amorphous solids are ubiquitous in the materials world, where glassy dynamics can arise from both intrinsic sources resulting in geometric constraints, as in jammed granular matter, and kinetic arrest, as in window glasses, or from extrinsic quenched disorder, as in spin glasses — topics to which Giorgio Parisi has made key contributions. In both cases the amorphous nature of the material is accompanied by breaking of ergodicity and lack of self-averaging. These problems have a very long history, but are also still the subject of intense studies. The goal of this short report is to highlight how some of the ideas developed in the context of glasses and spin glasses are having new impact in active matter physics.

28.1.2. *Active Brownian Particles*

The key property of an active particle is the directed self-sustained nature of its dynamics. A minimal implementation of this is an active Brownian particle (ABP): a spherical bead endowed with a propulsive speed v_0 along an axis $\hat{n}$ whose direction varies randomly in time [9]. The dynamics of a single ABP is governed by

$$\partial_t \mathbf{r} = v_0 \hat{n} + \mu \mathbf{F} + \sqrt{2D_t}\, \boldsymbol{\xi}(t), \tag{28.1}$$

$$\partial_t \hat{n} = \sqrt{2D_r}\, \boldsymbol{\xi}_r(t) \times \hat{n}, \tag{28.2}$$

where $\mathbf{F}$ represents the force due for instance to interactions with other particles, $\mu = D_t/k_B T$ is the mobility and the components of $\boldsymbol{\xi}(t)$ and $\boldsymbol{\xi}_r(t)$ describe Gaussian white noise with zero mean and unit variance. It is important to emphasize that, in contrast to particles driven by an external field, the direction of motion of an ABP is set independently for each particle by an orientation that varies in time. A free ABP ($\mathbf{F} = 0$) performs a persistent random walk with persistence time $\tau = 1/D_r$ and persistence length $\ell_p = v_0\tau$.

ABPs break detailed balance in a minimal way because the stochastic propulsive force provides a time-correlated noise that is not matched by similar memory in the particle mobility. This becomes evident when rewriting the stochastic dynamics given in Eq. (28.2) as a single equation [3]

$$\partial_t \mathbf{r} = \boldsymbol{\xi}^{sp}(t) + \mu\mathbf{F} + \sqrt{2D_t}\,\boldsymbol{\xi}(t), \tag{28.3}$$

where $\boldsymbol{\xi}^{sp}(t) = v_0\hat{\mathbf{n}}(t)$ is a non-Markovian noise with zero mean and correlations

$$\langle \xi_i^{sp}(t)\xi_j^{sp}(t')\rangle = \delta_{ij}\frac{v_0^2}{2}e^{-|t-t'|/\tau} \equiv \delta_{ij}\,\mu k_B T_a\frac{e^{-|t-t'|/\tau}}{\tau}, \tag{28.4}$$

and $k_B T_a = \frac{v_0^2\tau}{2\mu}$ has been interpreted as an effective temperature, although, as we see below, the fluctuation-dissipation theorem (FDT) is violated. The meansquare displacement of a free ABP can be calculated exactly and is given by

$$\langle [\mathbf{r}(t) - \mathbf{r}(t)]^2 \rangle = 4dD_t t + 2v_0^2\tau\left[t - \tau\left(1 - e^{-t/\tau}\right)\right], \tag{28.5}$$

with d the dimensionality. In other words, the dynamics is simply diffusive for $t \gg \tau$ with an effective diffusivity $D = D_t + D_a$ and $D_a = \mu k_B T_a \gg D_t$. The local breaking of detailed balance embodied by the persistence of the single particle dynamics yields, however, unexpected and surprising behavior in the presence of interparticle interactions or interactions with walls when τ is comparable to or larger than other characteristic times scales.

The form of the dynamics as given in Eqs. (28.3) and (28.4) highlights the importance of the precise way in which the limits of large and small persistence are considered. If we take the limit $\tau \to 0$ keeping T_a fixed in Eq. (28.4) and use that $\lim_{\tau\to 0} e^{-|t|/\tau}/\tau = \delta(t)$, we find that the stochastic force $\boldsymbol{\xi}^{sp}$ reduces to thermal-like noise with an active temperature T_a. In this regime of rapidly fluctuating active forcing, an ABP behaves like a thermal Brownian particle, albeit typically with an effective temperature much higher than the thermal one. This limit is equivalent to the choice of a stochastic propulsive force described by a Ornstein–Uhlenbeck process, i.e., $\tau\partial_t\boldsymbol{\xi} = -\boldsymbol{\xi} + \sqrt{2k_B T_a}\boldsymbol{\eta}(t)$, with $\boldsymbol{\eta}(t)$ a Gaussian random force with unit variance. The corresponding model is usually referred to as active Ornstein–Uhlenbeck particles [10]. On the other hand, in the limit of $\tau \to 0$ for fixed v_0 (or propulsive force $f_0 = \mu v_0$) the noise amplitude simply vanishes. It is then evident that when examining the role of τ on the emergent organization of interacting ABPs one must carefully distinguish whether one is considering constant effective temperature or constant propulsive force. Finally, in the limit $\tau \to \infty$ the noise becomes essentially quenched. We will see below that in the presence of interactions such infinitely persistent ABPs exhibit some of the behavior of athermal sheared granular matter.

28.1.3. *Active glasses*

At high density interactions and persistent motility conspire in driving new behaviors. The most striking phenomenon is motility induced phase separation (MIPS), where at packing fractions just above 40% purely repulsive active particles spontaneously phase separate into a dense liquid surrounded by an active gas [10–12]. Equilibrium phase separation of immiscible liquids, such as oil and vinegar, requires attractive interactions to overcome the entropy of mixing. In active matter phase separation is driven by the persistent nature of the single-particle dynamics that generically results in the tendency of motile entities to accumulate where they move slower. Interactions with other particles described by a pair potential $V(r)$ and leading to a force $\mathbf{F} = -\boldsymbol{\nabla}_{\mathbf{r}} \sum_{\mathbf{r}_j \neq \mathbf{r}} V(|\mathbf{r}-\mathbf{r}_j|)$ renormalize the particle's motility, with $v_0 \to v_0 + \langle \mathbf{n} \cdot \mathbf{F} \rangle \equiv v(\rho)$. For repulsive interactions collisions suppress the motility and $v(\rho) < v_0$. The breaking of detailed balance of the single particle dynamics then allows partcices to accumulate where $v(\rho)$ is small. This further increases the local density, which then suppresses motility in a feedback loop that engenders a spinodal instability. A simple estimate of the onset of MIPS can be obtained by equating the persistence time to mean free time between collisions $\tau_f \sim (2\sigma\rho v_0)^{-1}$. When $\tau > \tau_f$ the particles cannot turn their nose away after colliding with neighbors and become trapped by other particles, eventually resulting in phase separation.

MIPS, first noted for run-and-tumble particles such as *E. coli* [11, 13], has now been the subject of extensive analytical and numerical work. It has been established in both two and three dimensions for various types of repulsive interactions, for both particles that are monodisperse and polydisperse in size. It has also been shown that for moderate persistence times, many aspects of the dynamics of motile active particles with repulsive interactions can be mapped onto that of attractive passive colloids. One can therefore formulate a mean-field description of MIPS by essentially mapping it onto gas-liquid phase separation. There are, however, subtle deviations from this mapping that reveal the nonequilibrium dynamics of active particles and lead for instance to the arrest of phase separation and the formation of steady states of finite size clusters and bubbles.

At higher packing fraction, polydispersed active particles exhibit dynamical arrest and typical features of glassy dynamics, including slow density relaxation and dynamical heterogeneities, but also important differences, such as "long-range" velocity correlations [5, 14]. Active glassy dynamics has now been observed ubiquitously in active systems, from active colloids to the cell cytoplasm to epithelia. In inert matter there are different paths to the emergence of rigidity in amorphous materials. Dense liquids can become glasses upon decreasing temperature when they are kinetically trapped in metastable disordered states and the relaxation of density fluctuations becomes extremely slow. The corresponding glass transition is a dynamical phenomenon driven by the suppression of thermally-induced fluctuations. Alternatively, dense particulate packings may jam at zero temperature upon increasing density or pressure. In this case jamming is driven by the geometric constraints arising from crowding and associated with the onset of finite energy barriers to particle motion. Geometric incompatibility in underconstrained systems, such as metamaterials, random spring networks and vertex models [15] of dense biological tissue, can also also provide a route to the onset of zero-temperature rigidity. This occurs when the local constraints on the structure of the elastic network are incompatible for instance with the shape or size of the system [16, 17]. The onset of rigidity is then associated with a gapped ground state and the spontaneous appearance of a finite self stress. The fluid state additionally strain stiffens when subject to finite externally applied shear deformations [18].

All these different routes to rigidity have been identified in active systems. In fact, the persistence time of particulate active glasses provides a new handle that offers the opportunity to qualitatively tune the single-particle dynamics and explore in a single system the crossover from the behavior of thermal-like glasses to the physics of athermal jamming. A dense collection of ABPs undergoes a glass transition with increasing density when crowding suppresses directed motility [20, 21]. For moderate values of the persistence time the active glass shares much of the behavior of a thermal glass of attractive colloids at a temperature T_a as motility plays a role similar to that of thermal noise, although T_a is generally orders of magnitudes larger that the actual temperature. As in thermal colloidal glasses, the onset of rigidity or glass transition is signaled by the divergence of the alpha-relaxation time τ_α that describes the time scale for local structural rearrangements [14]. In the glassy state particles are caged by their neighbors and the mean square displacement saturates to a constant value at long times. Upon approaching the glassy state one observes ubiquitously spatio-temporally correlated patterns of particle displacement known as dynamical heterogeneities that can be captured via a normal mode analysis of correlated fluctuations around local minima. As in thermal colloidal glasses, τ_α decreases with increasing effective temperature, as shown in Fig. 28.1(Right), suggesting that increasing persistence promotes rigidity. Apparently contradictory results concerning the shift of the glass transition with increasing persistence time have been reported in the literature. Figure 28.1(Right) shows that τ_α increases with increasing persistence time, which is indeed the case when τ is increased at fixed T_a. On the other hand, increasing τ at fixed motility v_0 shifts the glass transition to higher packing fractions [20, 22]. This can be understood by noting that the persistent dynamics opens up new relaxation pathways that allow particles to escape their local cages, hence fluidizing the system. Nonmonotonic behavior where the active fluid relaxes faster than its passive counterpart at small persistence, but increasing persistence beyond a certain value promotes glassiness has also been reported.

The behavior is, however, qualitatively different in the limit of very large persistence times, where the analogy with colloidal glasses and the notion of effective temperature fail to capture the behavior of dense collections of active agents. For very large τ, the system can become momentarily arrested in a local minimum where propulsive forces and repulsive interactions are mechanically balanced, and then rearrange irreversibly and essentially instantaneously through plastic deformations when changes in the direction of the propulsive force disrupt the force balance [23, 24]. The resulting intermittent dynamics resemble that of of sheared athermal granular materials [25], which is also controlled by the interplay of stress build-up and stress relaxation via plastic events. A difference is that in granular matter sheared quasistatically at zero temperature the externally imposed deformation is uniformly prescribed across the system,

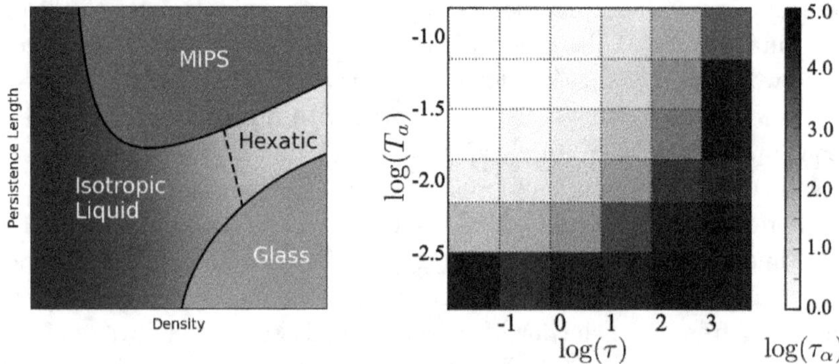

Fig. 28.1. Left: Schematic phase diagram of $2D$ ABPs in terms of areal density and persistence length $\ell_p = v_0\tau$, showing liquid, glass and phase separated (MIPS) states. Simulations have revealed hexatic orientational order in the liquid region intervening between glass and MIPS [19]. Right: Structural relaxation time τ_α as a function of T_a and persistence time τ from ABP simulations, showing that the effective temperature serves as a good predictor of the glass transition and that the system becomes more glassy with increasing τ at constant T_a. Courtesy of Silke Henkes, see also Ref. [14].

while in persistent active glasses the perturbations that drive plastic events are local and stochastic. This has been shown to lead to subtle differences in the aging dynamics.

Finally, epithelial tissue has come forward as a remarkable example of realizations of active systems that sit near a liquid-glass transition [7]. In this case the transition can be tuned not only by the interplay of crowding and persistent motility, but can also occur at constant packing fraction through the tuning of cell-cell interactions and the stiffening of cell edge tensions that control cell shape and the geometry of the cellular network. It is tempting to speculate that biological tissue may take advantage of geometry-driven rigidity to tune their fluidity locally while maintaining a constant cell density, and tissue integrity, as indeed seen for instance in embryo development [26].

28.1.4. *"Flying" spin glasses*

Spatial quenched disorder has been studied extensively in passive systems, from spin glasses to disordered superconductors, where it has been shown to qualitatively alter states, phase transitions and transport properties. The same type of disorder is important and ubiquitous in active matter because active agents, from bacteria to epithelial cells to wilder beasts, often move through porous media or on rough substrates, or encounter randomly placed obstacles that disrupt their motion. It is only relatively recently, however, that the role of quenched disorder in active matter has begun to be explored [27–31]. Many open questions remain and, while the topic is far from ripe for review, recent work has begun to employ ideas first introduced in the context of spin glasses, highlighting how these concepts can be used to understand problems in a truly vast range of fields. It seems therefore fitting to briefly describe here emerging work on what we could call "flying spin glasses".

As described in the section by Irene Giardina, the field of active matter can trace its origin to 1995 when Tamas Vicsek proposed a model of bird flocking inspired by the physics of magnetism [32]. In the Vicsek model, birds or active agents are described as velocity vectors of fixed length that tend to align their direction with that of their neighbors according to noisy rules. A collection of such flying spins exhibits a transition from a disordered state with zero mean velocity to an ordered state with finite mean velocity — a flock. Remarkably the ordered state exhibits long range order in both two and three dimensions. In the same year John Toner and Yuhai Tu developed a continuum model by merging the relaxational dynamics of magnets with flow advection as captured by the Navier–Stokes equation [33]. The flocking transition exhibited by the Vicsek model, and now understood as a phase separation into a disordered gas and an ordered liquid [34] has become the paradigm of collective motion. Experiments demonstrating the flocking of colloidal Quincke rotors — rolling particles that turn rotational motion induced by an electric field into translational self-propulsion through the interaction with a substrate — have provided a beautiful realization of the transition in a controlled setting, where the continuum model could be derived from known microscopic interactions and quantitatively tested [35].

The continuum theory of Toner and Tu provides a convenient starting point for describing the effect of quenched disorder on the flocking transition. Here the system is described by density and velocity fields ρ and $\mathbf{v}$. In a minimal form of the model the equations are

$$\partial_t \rho = -\boldsymbol{\nabla} \cdot (\rho \mathbf{v}) = 0, \tag{28.6}$$

$$\partial_t \mathbf{v} + \lambda \mathbf{v} \cdot \boldsymbol{\nabla} \mathbf{v} = (1 - |\mathbf{v}|^2)\mathbf{v} + K\nabla^2 \mathbf{v} - \chi\boldsymbol{\nabla}\rho + \mathbf{f}, \tag{28.7}$$

where we have chosen parameters to place ourselves well within the ordered liquid phase where the mean velocity is $|\mathbf{v}| = 1$. Here λ controls self-advection, K penalizes flow distortions and χ is a compressibility controlled by interactions among the active agents. Finally, $\mathbf{f}$ embodies the effect of disorder.

As in passive system, one can expect different behavior in systems disordered by quenched random force or by quenched random potential. A random force (or random field) describes the situation where the orientation of each active agent is rotated by a fixed angle drawn from a distribution defined at each spatial location. Quenched random potential disorder is realized for instance by a random distribution of repulsive obstacles. In the model described by Eq. (28.7), a quenched random force corresponds to a static force $\mathbf{f}$ with zero mean and short-ranged spatial correlations $\langle f_i(\mathbf{r}) f_j(\mathbf{r}') \rangle = \Delta \delta_{ij} \delta(\mathbf{r}-\mathbf{r}')$. This type of quenched disorder has been studied in both continuum and agent-based models and was found not to qualitatively alter the phase diagram of the clean system, although it turns the long-range-order (LRO) of the $2d$ active polar liquid to quasi-LRO [27, 29, 31, 36]. In other words, random forces have a rather weak effect on the flocking state which is much more robust than in equilibrium where even arbitrarily weak random fields destroy LRO ferromagnetic order for $d \leq 4$.

The situation is markedly different for random potential disorder. In this case the force $\mathbf{f}$ in Eq. (28.7) can be written as the gradient of a random potential, $\mathbf{f} = -\beta\boldsymbol{\nabla}\Phi$, with $\Phi(\mathbf{r})$ the obstacle density field, with mean set by the mean obstacle area fraction Φ_o

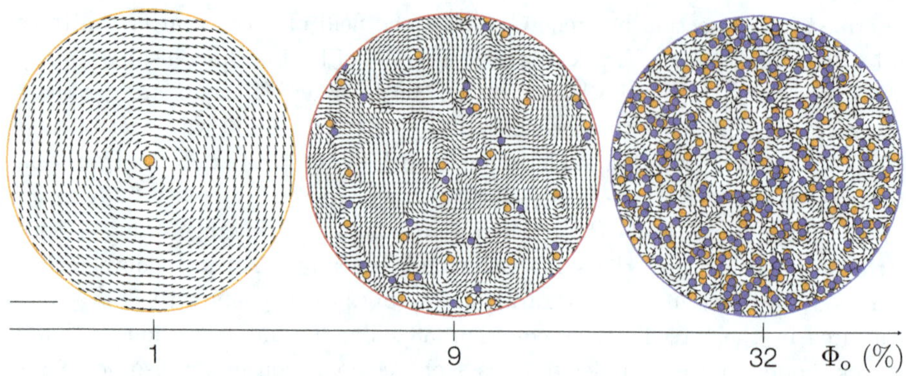

Fig. 28.2. Dynamical states of colloidal rollers in a disk upon increasing the packing fraction Φ_0 of obstacles. The black lines represent the polarization field and the dots are topological defects: +1 (orange), -1 (blue). Right: a uniformly flocking fluid, which in the circular geometry corresponds to a single single giant vortex. Center: a frozen pattern of meandering flow with a finite concentration of topological defects. Right: a disordered gas. Scale bar $0.5mm$. Courtesy of Amélie Chardac and Denis Bartolo, see also Ref. [30].

and short-range correlations $\langle (\Phi(\mathbf{r}) - \Phi_o)(\Phi(\mathbf{r}') - \Phi_o) \rangle = \Phi_o \delta(\mathbf{r} - \mathbf{r}')$. Essentially $-\beta \boldsymbol{\nabla} \Phi$ acts as a quenched random pressure gradient, repelling the fluid away from regions of high obstacle density. This type of quenched disorder has been implemented experimentally in suspensions of Quincke colloids [28, 30]. Denis Bartolo and his students have examined the effect of a random distribution of flocking obstacles on the flocking state of these colloidal rollers. It was found that while the flocking state survives at very small densities of obstacles, collective motion is disrupted above a critical obstacle packing fraction, with associated loss of orientational order [28]. As disorder is increased the flock morphology evolves into a network of river-like flow structures that becomes increasingly sparse with increasing disorder [30]. This dynamics bears a striking similarity to the river-like structures found in the plastic depinning of vortices in type-II superconductors. But most remarkable is the behavior at somewhat higher concentrations of both rollers and obstacles, where a new phase intermediate between the polar flock and the disordered gas is observed. In this phase, global polar order and associated coherent flows are lost, but the system self-organizes into a frozen pattern of meandering flows with a finite frozen density of topological defects. The time persistence or "memory" of the flow patterns is revealed by the finite value of an Edwards–Anderson-type order parameter $q_{EA} = \lim_{T \to \infty} \langle \hat{\mathbf{v}}(t + T) \cdot \hat{\mathbf{v}}(t) \rangle$ that measures correlations in the direction $\hat{\mathbf{v}}(t)$ of the flow velocity. The overlap of the flow patterns observed in replicas of the experiments with identical disorder realizations reveals a clear bias of both structure and direction of the meandering flows determined by the obstacle distribution. This state represents a dynamical realization of a vortex glass, akin to that established many years ago in disordered superconductors [37]. The relevance of this mechanism to a broader class of disordered active matter is yet to be established [31], but it is clear that the ideas introduced by Giorgio Parisi in the context of spin glasses are likely to have profound impact on active matter physics.

28.2. Collective Behavior in Natural Flocks: From Data to Models

Irene Giardina

Department of Physics, Sapienza University of Rome,
Institute for Complex Systems,
Consiglio Nazionale delle Ricerche and INFN Roma1
P.le A. Moro 2, 00185, Rome, Italy

28.2.1. *Introduction*

Flocks of birds are widely considered as an archetype of self-organized collective behavior, where a collection of individuals displays emergent patterns on the large scale. There are many examples of this kind in the biological world, ranging from the microscale of cells, amoebae and bacteria, to the macroscopic one of animal groups (insects, birds, mammals) [1, 38]. From the perspective of statistical physics, flocks represent a paradigmatic instance of interacting active matter [1, 39]: individuals endowed with self-propulsion, i.e. an autonomous mechanism converting energy into motion, interact with each other giving rise to non-trivial large scale behavior.

Powerful and elegant theoretical frameworks have been developed in the last twenty years to describe these systems and predict their properties [1, 6, 40]. When it comes to natural flocks, an important question to be addressed is whether, and to what extent, they are in fact amenable of such descriptions. The underlying assumption behind a statistical physics approach is that the system's details do not matter when looking at the large scale: only a few relevant ingredients must be incorporated in the theory and simple models can be formulated that appropriately capture collective behavior. While these premises have been amply justified in condensed matter, they cannot be given for granted in living groups, where the units partaking in the system are themselves complex animals and interactions are not just of mechanical or chemical origin, but are due to non-trivial cognitive processes. It is therefore important, in this case more than others, to gather experimental data, verify the robustness of statistical laws and build models based on empirical findings.

In this short report, I (Irene Giardina) will review some of the main experimental results that we obtained on natural flocks over the years, how they helped us to assess the validity of existing theoretical frameworks and how we used experimental data to extract information on the relevant ingredients necessary for simple models to explain the observed phenomenology. More detailed accounts can be found in [41, 42].

28.2.2. *Self-propelled models of collective motion*

Models of collective motion have been formulated since the late eighties from biologists [43–45], computer scientists [46], control theorists [47, 48] and physicists [6]. All these models share the same crucial ingredient: mutual alignment. The underlying idea is that the prominent behavioral trait in gregarious groups of animals is imitation: each bird (or insect, fish, mammal) updates its own flight direction in order to follow neighbors. Even though additional 'rules' can certainly be considered (such as attraction-repulsion forces between individuals), an effective directional coupling remains fundamental to produce long range polar order. The model that incorporates alignment in the simplest setting is the Vicsek model [32]. Vicsek and collaborators considered a system of self-propelled particles moving at fixed speed v_0 interacting with each other only via short-range alignment. The equation of motion for the particles are easily expressed in terms of the individual positions $\vec{r}_i$ and velocities $\vec{v}_i$

$$\vec{v}_i(t + \Delta t) = v_0 \, \mathcal{R}_\eta \left(\frac{\vec{v}_i(t) + \Delta t \, \vec{F}_i^{al}(t)}{\left| \vec{v}_i(t) + \Delta t \, \vec{F}_i^{al}(t) \right|} \right) \tag{28.8}$$

$$\vec{r}_i(t + 1) = \vec{r}_i(t) + \vec{v}_i(t + 1), \tag{28.9}$$

where

$$\vec{F}_i^{al}(t) = J \sum_j n_{ij}(t)\vec{v}_j(t) \tag{28.10}$$

is the *alignment* force pulling the flight direction of particle i towards the mean one of neighbors, n_{ij} is the *connectivity* matrix specifying who are the interacting neighbors, and $\mathcal{R}_\eta(\vec{X})$ is a noise operator that perturbs the vector $\vec{X}$ by a random angle within a cone of amplitude η. There are several possible ways to write down Vicsek-like equations for self-propelled particles, but some general features of this class of models can be immediately grasped from Eqs. (28.8) and (28.9). First of all, as already mentioned, the alignment nature of mutual interactions. Second, the presence of activity, i.e. of a motor controlling the individual speeds, here in the form of a sharp constraint $|\vec{v}_i| = v_0$. Finally, the non-equilibrium nature of the dynamics, encoded in the time dependence of the connectivity matrix n_{ij}: since particles move and exchange positions, interacting neighbors at a given time are not necessarily so at later ones. Equation (28.8) represents a Markovian dissipative dynamics for fixed norm directional degrees of freedom interacting via alignment. If particles were not allowed to move, i.e. if we considered pointers rather than flockers, Eq. (28.8) would be analogous to the dynamics of an Heisenberg model on a fixed network specified by n_{ij}. In that case the stationary state would be described by an equilibrium canonical measure. What marks the departure from equilibrium is therefore the rearrangement in time of the interaction network, and we expect a stronger non-equilibrium behavior the faster is the network dynamics is compared to the relaxational dynamics of velocities.

In the original Vicsek model [32], which is formulated in $d = 2$, the connectivity matrix n_{ij} is chosen according to a *metric* rule, being equal to 1 for neighbors j within distance r_0 from individual i, and 0 otherwise. In this case, the relevant effective parameters controlling the behavior of the system are the strength of the noise, and the average density (fixing the typical number of interacting neighbors). In [32] the authors numerically showed that at low enough noise (and/or large enough density) this model exhibits a kinetic ordering transition into a flocking polar phase, where the global degree of alignment (the so-called polarization) is different from zero. Surprisingly, long range order is thermodynamically stable in two dimensions, contrary to the passive counterpart of the model (the XY ferromagnet). The particles' activity provides an additional mechanism to transmit information through the system, depleting fluctuations and stabilizing order. These results have been consolidated and generalized in a number of subsequent works, using both numerical simulations [49, 49, 50] and coarse-grained field theories [39, 40, 51] [see e.g. the contribution of Cristina Marchetti to this chapter]. For flocking systems with metric interactions the ordering transition turns out to be first order, with presence of a strong coupling between local density and local order, the occurrence of heterogeneous aggregated structures in the critical region, and large density fluctuations in the ordered one. Predictions of relevant exponents can be obtained via field theory, and have been observed in various experimental settings.

Are natural flocks of birds appropriately described within this theoretical framework? Does the Vicsek model account for the behavior of real groups? If not, what ingredients should be modified or added to the theoretical description?

28.2.3. *Results from experiments*

The first large-scale experiments on natural flocks were performed within the Starflag project in 2005–2007. Experiments were realized using stereoscopic photography and advanced computer vision techniques for 3D tracking [52–54] that allowed reconstructing the three-dimensional positions and velocities of flocks of up to a few thousands birds. Statistical analysis of such variables revealed a few unexpected findings.

28.2.3.1. *Topological interactions*

When considering how individuals are distributed in space, a specific kind of anisotropy emerges in a statistically robust way: each individual is more likely to have its first neighbors on the sides rather than along the direction of motion. Such an anisotropy is necessarily the consequence of mutual interactions, and its degree can then be used as a proxy for the interaction strength. In Fig. 28.3 the degree of anisotropy is plotted as a function of the order n of the neighbor considered: as n increases the anisotropy decreases indicating that interactions decay with distance, as one would expect. An interaction range n_c, i.e. the number of interacting neighbors, can be established as the value of n for which the anisotropy disappears. Likewise, a metric interaction distance r_c can be defined as the distance from the focal bird of its n_c^{th} neighbor. When plotting these two ranges, the *topological* one n_c and the *metric* one r_c, for different flocks as a function of the group's density, one discovers that n_c does not depend on density and fluctuates around a mean value of order $n_c \sim 7$; by contrast, r_c decreases with density (i.e. increases with sparseness). These findings are consistent with a scenario where interactions are topological, rather than metric [52]: each bird interacts with its first $n_c \sim 7$ neighbors, independently of their distance. Topological interactions are connected with the cognitive nature of mutual adaptation [52], and provide a nice example where living systems display features that would not be present in standard physical ones. In terms of collective behavior, being independent of density, they enhance global cohesion, as temporary dilations of mutual distances — caused by external disturbances or endogenous noise — do not affect how individuals are connected to the rest of the group, decreasing the occurrence of stragglers and fragmentation [52, 55]. In the context of self-propelled particles models, this result indicates that to describe natural flocks the original prescription proposed by Vicsek and co-workers must be modified: the interaction network should be defined using a topological rather than a metric rule. Several analysis have since been performed on topological Vicsek-like models [52, 55–57]. Such models display large scale properties in part different from metric ones. There is

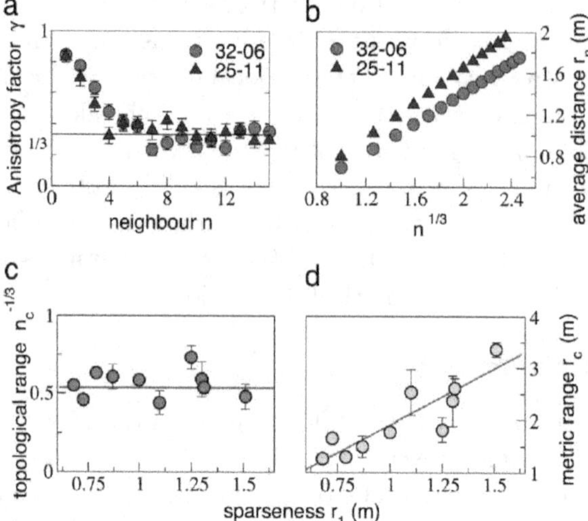

Fig. 28.3. Natural flocks exhibit topological rather than metric interactions. a) Degree of anisotropy γ as a function of the order of the neighbor considered for two flocking events. γ is computed by taking the scalar product between the direction of minimal crowding of the nth neighbor and the mean group velocity (see [52] for details). For an isotropic distribution γ would be $1/3$, therefore the point where the curve reaches this value can be identified as the decay range of the anisotropy, and it provides an estimate of the interaction range. b) Relationship between order of the neighbor n and its distance r_n from the focal bird. c) and d) Topological and metric interaction range as a function of the group's density for several flocks. Figure from [52].

less or no coupling between local density and local order, heterogeneous structures are not present, and the transition — at least for balanced and Voronoi rules — seems to be second order.

28.2.3.2. *Scale free velocity correlations*

The most visible expression of collective motion is certainly the global degree of alignment in the system, i.e. the polarization $\Phi = 1/N \sum_i \vec{v}_i/|\vec{v}_i|$. In natural flocks, the polarization is very large, of order ~ 0.9, indicating very coherent groups. A more significant characterization of collective behavior, however, is provided by correlation functions, which quantify how strongly individuals are able to influence each other across the group. Connected velocity correlations as a function of distance have been measured in natural flocks of birds in [58], both for the full velocity vectors (Fig. 28.4(A)) and for the individual speeds (Fig. 28.4(B)). The decay length of such functions, the correlation length, is a measure of the extension of correlated domains, where changes in flight direction and speed of pairs of individuals are not independent. Remarkably, when the correlation length is plotted against the group's size, it displays a neat linear dependence indicating scale-free behavior both for orientations and speeds. No intrinsic scale therefore exists for the decay of correlations, the only present scale being the system size itself. Scale free correlations describe systems where information is shared and transmitted over the whole group and are a signature of the system's ability to globally change its state in response to external perturbations.

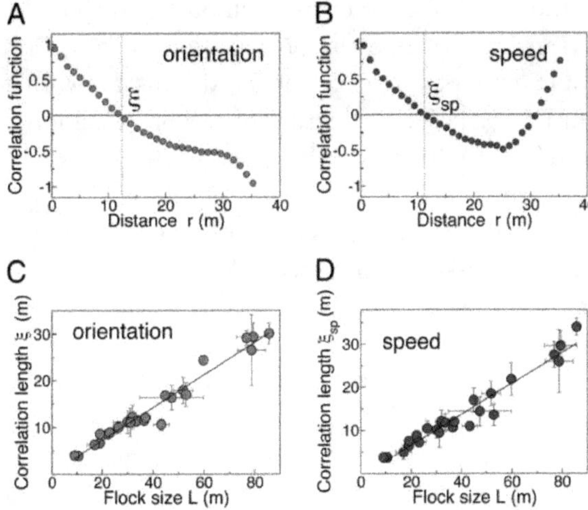

Fig. 28.4. Connected correlations are scale-free. a) Connected correlation function for the velocity vectors, as a function of distance. The correlation is defined as $C(r) = <\delta\vec{v}_i \cdot \delta\vec{v}_j>_{r_{ij}=r}$, where $\delta\vec{v}_i = \vec{v}_i - 1/N\sum_k \vec{v}_k$ is the fluctuation from the mean group velocity, and the average is taken over all pairs of birds at mutual distance r. b) Connected correlation for the speeds: the definition is analogous to the orientational correlation but fluctuations of the individual speeds are considered instead of full velocity vectors, i.e. $\delta v_i = v_i - 1/N\sum_k v_k$, where $v_i = |\vec{v}_i|$. Figure from [58].

From a theoretical perspective the scale free nature of correlations has a different interpretation in the case of orientations and speeds. Being a system ruled by alignment interactions, we expect flocks to exhibit scale free orientational correlations merely due to symmetry reasons. When a system with a continuous symmetry (the rotational symmetry of the velocities in this case) is in the ordered phase — where the symmetry is spontaneously broken — soft (Goldstone) modes appear in the subspace orthogonal to the global order parameter [59, 60]. These modes are an heritage of the original symmetry and correspond to easy fluctuations with scale free decay. This is what happens for ferromagnetic systems at equilibrium and to Vicsek-like models in the stationary dynamics [40].

For speeds, however, the argument does not hold. Speeds are not endowed with any continuous symmetry, whose breaking can generate soft modes. On the contrary, in models driven by alignment forces the opposite usually happens. In the ordered phase, perpendicular fluctuations (the soft modes described above) are scale-free, but the modulus of the degrees of freedom (the speed in our case) is a hard mode with short range correlations [58, 61]. In the Vicsek model, where speeds are fixed by a hard constraint, the phenomenology is absent by construction. Variants with soft constraints on the speed [62, 63] do not generically produce scale-free speed correlations, nor do standard flocking field theories [40]. Some other non-trivial mechanism must therefore be at play.

28.2.3.3. *Speed control*

Usually, one possible cause of scale-free correlations is proximity to a critical point. Since flocks are in the deeply ordered phase in terms of directional variables, this putative transition should refer to the speed degrees of freedom only and should not be confused with the polar ordering transition (where the polarization is zero). In the context of flocking models, one should first of all relax the hard constraint on the speed, and assume a control potential $V(\{|\vec{v}_i|\})$ for its fluctuations. The social force acting on each individual would then read $\vec{F}_i = -\partial H/\partial \vec{v}_i$, where the (pseudo) Hamiltonian contains both an alignment/imitation term and the speed control, i.e. $H = J\sum_{i,j} n_{ij}(\vec{v}_i - \vec{v}_j)^2 + V(\{v_i\})$ (where we assume that individuals adapt both their directions and speeds to neighbors). The question to be asked is then what kind of speed potential is able to produce a critical point for the speeds, what is the nature of such point and what is the control parameter regulating the proximity to it.

A first attempt to address this issue was done in [64], where a harmonic potential for the speed $V(\{|\vec{v}_i|\}) = g\sum_i(|\vec{v}_i| - v_0)^2$ was considered (i.e. a linear control force). It was shown that for a soft enough potential - when g is small enough - the model is able to reproduce the large scale speed correlations observed in the data (see Fig. 28.5(a)). In this case, g plays the role of the control parameter regulating the speed correlation length $\xi_{sp} \sim \sqrt{J/g}$, and proximity to the speed critical point $g = 0$. The intuitive idea behind the theory is that if individuals have a large flexibility in tuning their individual speed they can swiftly adapt to neighbors producing correlations on the large scale. Unfortunately, linear speed control has a major drawback: when individual speeds are allowed to fluctuate more (low g) so does the mean group speed, leading to unrealistic values at low-to-moderate group sizes. This problem became evident recently, when new experiments produced a larger dataset comprising groups with a wider size range. Data show that natural flocks exhibit scale-free speed correlations and well confined group speeds across all sizes. Linear speed control is not able to reproduce this behavior: a small value of g is needed to reproduce scale-free correlations up to the largest groups, but this value would lead to very large mean speeds at small sizes, which are not observed (Fig. 28.5(b)). A different kind of speed control mechanism is therefore required. To solve this conundrum we recently proposed a *marginal* speed control [65, 66] $V(\{|\vec{v}_i|\}) = \lambda\sum_i(|\vec{v}_i|^2 - v_0^2)^4$, where the potential is locally flat around the 'cruising' speed v_0, but has sharp walls for larger speed values. Small speed fluctuations are therefore extremely easy (they are soft modes), while larger ones are strongly suppressed. The overall effect on the velocities of the control potential and the imitation term is regulated by the noise strength η. At finite noise the local shape of the speed potential is not relevant and the behavior is similar to other Vicsek-like models, i.e. there is a purely directional transition at a finite value $\eta = \eta_c$ to a state of collective motion with finite polarization. When the noise is further decreased, however, entropic effects are suppressed and the presence of soft modes in the speed becomes relevant. A second transition is present for $\eta = 0$, where ξ_s diverges and speed correlations become scale free, while the mean group speed remains bounded due to the rapid increase of the control. The marginal model at small noise is therefore able to reproduce all the phenomenological facts observed in the data: a very large polarization, a well confined group speed, scale free directional correlations, and scale-free speed correlations (Figs. 28.5(c,d)). Comparison between simulations and data have demonstrated the predictive power of the model [66].

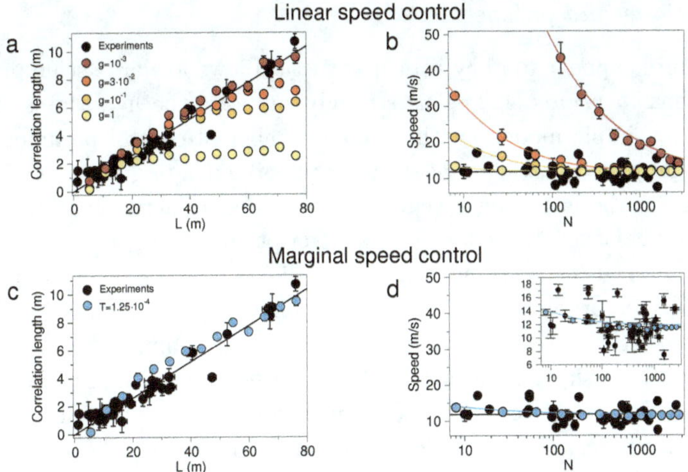

Fig. 28.5. Marginal vs linear speed control. a) and c) Speed correlation length vs group size. Black points correspond to experimental data, colored points to numerical simulations with a linear speed control (panel a), and marginal speed control at low noise (panel c). b) and d) Mean group speed versus group size. Points as in panel a,b; curves represent the theoretical prediction in the mean-field limit (see [66]). Linear control cannot reproduce at the same time scale-free correlations and confined mean speed. Marginal speed control, by contrast, correctly reproduces the behavior of both correlations and mean speed. Figure from [66].

28.2.4. *From data to models*

As discussed in previous sections, statistical analysis of experimental data provides an indispensable guide towards modeling. Once the general theoretical framework is defined, important additional information can be gathered using techniques from statistical inference. The maximum entropy approach is a method that derives 'minimal' models (i.e. using minimal information) based on some experimental input [67]. Using this method one can show that alignment-based models are the minimal effective models consistent with the observed velocity correlations [64, 68, 69]. Inference of the interaction range also shows that such effective alignment interactions are topological rather than metric [68, 70], confirming the results obtained in [52]. This finding is by far non trivial since the analysis in [52] relied on purely structural information (i.e. the anisotropy of the distribution of neighbors in space), while inference in [68, 70] exploits information from the velocity correlation functions. Further generalization of the method [69, 71] allows to retrieve the typical timescale of the local relaxational dynamics. Interestingly, it turns out that this timescale is *smaller* than the rearrangement time of the connectivity matrix: on the time it takes for a bird to change its interacting neighbors, the velocity correlations between them have already relaxed. This defines a situation of *local equilibrium* and suggests that coupling between local order and local density is in fact not strong in these systems. This finding can be rationalized from a theoretical perspective: it has been shown in [57] that departure from equilibrium in models of polar collective motion peaks around the ordering transition, while it tends to zero in the deeply ordered phase — i.e. precisely in the phase of natural flocks.

28.2.5. *Conclusions and perspectives*

Natural flocks of birds appear to obey robust statistical laws for large scale properties, correlation functions *in primis* [42]. This strongly supports the hypothesis that they can be described by simple models, with a small number of control parameters. The class of polar self-propelled particle models and the corresponding coarse-grained field theories, developed in the last twenty years in the context of active matter, represent the primary theoretical framework for such a description. However, investigation of experimental data indicates that some crucial ingredients must be incorporated in this framework in order to reproduce the observed phenomenology. Alignment interactions between individuals are topological rather than metric, determining much less dependence on density and density fluctuations. Then, a speed control mechanism must be assumed that allows for scale-free speed fluctuations in the highly ordered region. More recent experimental findings [72] on collective turns furthermore indicate that second order terms (i.e. rotational inertia) in the dynamical update equations for the individual velocities must be taken into account to explain how information propagates through the groups [73]. The emergent picture points to minimal models of self-propelled particles with inertial dynamics, topological alignment and marginal speed control. A full systematic investigation of such models is an open program for the future. At the field theory level, incorporating all the ingredients mentioned above can be demanding but some steps have already been taken in this direction [74–78].

Finally, an important aspect of natural flocks is that they are finite groups with well defined boundaries. The finite size implies that there might be different regimes where the system behaves differently, and dynamical crossovers acquire a new relevance in the description of the observed phenomenology (see e.g. [73, 75]). Up to certain sizes, flocks behave as quasi-equilibrium systems regulated by second order dynamics and able to perform coherent changes of group direction perfectly retaining their shape, as observed in groups of up to a few thousand individuals. For larger sizes, dissipative effects and coupling with density might originate a different kind of excitations. More analysis, both experimental and theoretical, is needed to elucidate this issue.

28.3. Glassy Features and Complex Dynamics in Ecological Systems

Ada Altieri

*Laboratoire Matière et Systèmes Complexes (MSC), Université Paris Cité
CNRS, 75013 Paris, France*
ada.altieri@u-paris.fr

28.3.1. *Introduction*

Emergent properties of many-species ecological communities have a variety of applications: for example, the activity of the gut microbiota is believed to be crucial for human health; sustaining natural diversity is essential for services such as food supply, pollination and climate regulation. There is growing awareness that human activity is causing irreversible species extinction and ecosystem simplifications, generally considered a *global biodiversity crisis.* The Earth Microbiome Project[a] and the Human Microbiome Project[b] are aiming to identify and characterize all diverse microorganisms and their relationship to ecological stability and disease development.

The incredible biodiversity that characterizes natural ecosystems has attracted ecologists for a long time but has more recently started gathering interest also among theoretical physicists. From a theoretical perspective, modeling the interactions between many different components — from bacteria in a microbial community to plant-pollinator impact in a forest to starling murmurations — can become extremely complicated. A single, well-established theory allowing one to bridge the gap between empirical data made available from an enormous number of controlled experiments and more sophisticated techniques is nevertheless still missing. In addition to the need for a general criterion that would enable to discriminate between *niche theory* — for which each niche is occupied by a single species according to the competitive exclusion principle [79] — and *neutral models* — in which differences are only attributed to stochasticity — other crucial questions come to the stage and play an ever-increasing key role: i) relaxation either to a single fixed point or a multiple fixed point regime; ii) definition of ecosystem diversity, i.e. the number of surviving species; iii) typical behavior of fluctuations and functional responses to external perturbations; iv) investigation of the interplay between stochastic and deterministic processes and how community diversity and variability are related to them; v) emergence of possible chaotic dynamics and limiting cycles to be experimentally measured.

In this section, I present different statistical physics frameworks that rely on advanced spin-glass techniques, for which Giorgio Parisi has been a pioneer as well as a beacon outlining the right direction in a multitude of complex scenarios.

28.3.1.1. *More is different*

Theory has long predicted that large complex systems are intrinsically unstable [80, 81], which is a long-standing puzzle given the complexity observed in Nature. In the last years, there is nevertheless a growing interest in systems composed of an enormous number of species interacting in myriad ways in very complex environments. Such systems can thus be rephrased through the prism of statistical physics using sophisticated concepts and powerful methods in this direction [82–90]. In a bottom-up approach, the detailed structure of individual interactions and how such coefficients scale with system size is unknown since they are particularly difficult to infer in diversity-rich ecosystems. Hence, to tackle the staggering complexity of large ecological communities, one can follow a long tradition rooted in Robert May's seminal works [80, 81] and assume the interaction matrix to be random. May considered the Jacobian (or *community*) matrix H of size $S \times S$, S being the total number of species in the pool and H_{ij} standing for the effect of species j on i around a feasible fixed point. In this picture, the self-regulation term corresponding to diagonal elements is fixed to -1, whereas off-diagonal elements are drawn from a random distribution with zero mean and variance σ^2 — sometimes

---

[a]https://earthmicrobiome.org/
[b]https://www.hmpdacc.org/

referred to as heterogeneity parameter – with associated probability C. According to May's conjecture, if $\sigma\sqrt{SC} > 1$ the system is inevitably unstable under infinitesimally small perturbations and cannot persist. Hence, as a system becomes more diverse (controlled by the number of species S in the pool), more connected (in terms of the connectivity C), and strongly interacting (tuned by σ), a transition to instability occurs with a probability of persisting close to zero. In the large S limit, random matrix theory comes into play claiming that the eigenvalues of the community or Jacobian matrix must be contained inside a circle of radius $\sigma\sqrt{SC}$ in the complex plane. Therefore, the system's stability is conditional on the fact that the resulting circle is located in the left half-plane with all eigenvalues having negative real parts.

To provide general criteria that could encompass all diversified cases, one can then play with the interaction matrix by changing the strength and mutual sign. A suitable reshuffling of local interactions clearly raises a number of questions on how different combinations affect the stability of the overall community and what would be a good trade-off (weak/strong, mutualistic/competitive) to avoid, for instance, destabilization of a prey-predator chain if weak interactions are preponderant [91].

28.3.2. *High-dimensional MacArthur model at the edge of stability*

In the following, we shall focus on mathematical models that offer a suitable platform to understand the behavior of large ecosystems: giving some input information, predictions on species survival, responses to external perturbations, and the emergence of patterns can be extracted as an output. We will start with a very influential one, the MacArthur resource-consumer model, originally designed to shape competition among S different species for N non-interacting resources [92]. Notably, if the dynamics describing resource evolution is much faster than the populations' one, the former can be integrated out leading to the generalized Lotka–Volterra equations [93, 94]. The random Lotka–Volterra model will thus represent the second core of this chapter, through which we will figure out how to overcome certain inherent limitations of such a resource-consumer model.

By taking advantage of the definition of self-averaging quantities, MacArthur's model has been recently reformulated as a problem of statistical physics of disordered systems and then solved analytically in the limit of an infinite number of species and resources [95]. We will especially use it to probe several underlying connections between the phenomenology of jamming [96] and criticality in large ecosystems.

The dynamics of the model is defined by linear differential equations for n_μ individuals, where the index $\mu = 1, \ldots, S$ denotes the different species:

$$\frac{dn_\mu}{dt} \propto n_\mu \Delta_\mu, \tag{28.11}$$

and Δ_μ is the *resource surplus*. As long as one is concerned with equilibrium, the proportionality factor in the dynamical equation above can safely be neglected. The equilibrium condition from Eq. (28.11) leads to two possibilities: i) $n_\mu > 0$ & $\Delta_\mu = 0$ (survival); ii) $n_\mu = 0$ & $\Delta_\mu < 0$ (extinction).[c] The variables Δ_μ depend then on the availabilities of resources h_i (with $i = 1, ..., N$) and the *metabolic strategies*, $\sigma_{\mu i}$'s, by

---

[c]The case $\Delta_\mu > 0$ is actually forbidden by the model definition.

which species demand and possibly meet their requirement χ_μ:

$$\Delta_\mu = \sum_{i=1}^{N} \sigma_{\mu i} h_i - \chi_\mu. \qquad (28.12)$$

For each species μ, the metabolic strategy represents a random binary vector whose components $\sigma_{\mu i}$ are extracted from a distribution that takes values 1 and 0 with probabilities p and $1-p$ respectively. The parameter p determines whether the species in the ecosystem are either specialists ($p \ll 1$), each requiring a small number of well-defined metabolites necessary for their survival, or generalists ($p \sim 1$), meaning that many different metabolites can be appropriate for their needs. In turn, individuals n_μ depend on the availability of resources, h_i, according to a feedback loop mechanism, which is essentially modulated by the efficiencies through which species exploit resources. By defining a total demand, $T_i = \sum_\mu n_\mu \sigma_{\mu i}$, the availabilities h_i can simply be expressed as a decreasing function of it. For instance, one can consider $h_i = \frac{R_i}{\sum_\mu n_\mu \sigma_{\mu i}}$ where R_i is the resource surplus whose average is constant whereas its variance, δR^2, can fluctuate and be used to reproduce the resulting phase diagram.

Over the years several mechanisms have been put forward to explain the fact that complex — and in particular living — systems tend to be poised at the edge of stability: edge of chaos [97], self-organized criticality [98], self-organized instability, scale-free behavior, etc. Here we propose an example that leverages an alternative principle [86]. It is based on recasting the MacArthur model in terms of a constraint satisfaction problem (CSP). Hence, in analogy with a standard CSP, above the hyperplane $\vec{h} \cdot \vec{\sigma}_\mu$ species are able to survive and multiply; conversely, if $\vec{h} \cdot \vec{\sigma}_\mu < \chi_\mu$, the sustainability of the species' pool is no longer guaranteed. All $\vec{h}$ such that $\vec{h} \cdot \vec{\sigma}_\mu < \chi_\mu$ define the so-called *unsustainable region*, for each species μ. One can now re-express the requirement χ_μ via a random variable *i.e.* $\chi_\mu = \sum_i \sigma_{\mu i} + \epsilon x_\mu$ [95], where the parameter ϵ plays the role of an infinitesimal cost scatter and x_μ is a zero-mean and unit-variance Gaussian variable. It has been shown that, in the $\epsilon \to 0$ limit, the model undergoes a phase transition between two qualitatively different regimes: i) a *shielded phase*; ii) a *vulnerable phase* [95]. In the shielded phase, $\mathcal{S}$, a collective behavior emerges with no influence of external conditions. If the availabilities are set to one in such a way that neither specialists nor generalists are favored, and a sufficiently small perturbation is applied to the system, a feedback mechanism between h_i and n_μ contributes to adjusting mutual species' abundance and to keeping the availabilities almost unchanged, $\forall i$. The situation is quite different in the *vulnerable phase*, $\mathcal{V}$, where species cannot self-sustain and turn out to be strongly affected by changes and improvements in the immediate environment.

To characterize the stability of a general competing system against perturbations in a more rigorous way, one can introduce a Lyapunov function and compute the density of fluctuations in the two phases. The positive or vanishing behavior of such a function, together with its time derivative, provide information on whether the equilibrium is unstable, locally asymptotically stable, or globally asymptotically stable. In this specific case, the Lyapunov function reads

$$F(\{n_\mu\}) = \sum_i R_i \log\left(\sum_\mu n_\mu \sigma_{\mu i}\right) - \sum_\mu n_\mu \chi_\mu, \qquad (28.13)$$

which is bounded from above, hence guaranteeing that an equilibrium always exists. By differentiating Eq. (28.13) to the second order, one eventually obtain

$$\frac{d^2 F}{dn_\mu dn_\nu} = -\sum_i \sigma_{\mu i}\sigma_{\nu i}\frac{R_i}{(\sum_\rho n_\rho \sigma_{\rho i})^2} = -\sum_i \sigma_{\mu i}\sigma_{\nu i}\left(\frac{h_i^2}{R_i}\right). \tag{28.14}$$

In the $\mathcal{S}$ phase, *i.e.* for $h_i \simeq 1$, this expression leads to a modified Wishart matrix whose eigenvalue distribution is defined by a Marchenko–Pastur law [99] in the limit of a large number of species and resources. Accordingly, the resulting spectral density reads:

$$\rho(\lambda) = \frac{1}{2\pi}\frac{\sqrt{(\lambda - \lambda_-)(\lambda_+ - \lambda)}}{\lambda}, \tag{28.15}$$

where the upper and lower edges of the spectrum are $\lambda_\pm = (\sqrt{[1]} \pm 1)^2$. The quantity [1] denotes the fraction of active species at criticality or, borrowing the CSP jargon, the fraction of *satisfied constraints* for which $\Delta_\mu = 0$. In analogy with the so-called SAT/UNSAT transition, we can associate the $\mathcal{V}$ phase to a *hypostatic regime*, with a smaller number of satisfied constraints than the total number of variables [100, 101]: this case corresponds to a gapped spectral density without any signature of an emerging criticality. Conversely, the $\mathcal{S}$ phase would correspond to an *isostatic regime* – where the number of satisfied constraints equals the overall space dimension, and a gapless spectrum for the distribution of eigenvalues appears. Because the lower edge of the spectrum $\lambda_- \to 0$ tends to zero upon approaching the $\mathcal{V}/\mathcal{S}$ transition line, the eigenvalue density contribution in the $\mathcal{S}$ phase becomes:

$$\rho(\lambda) \sim \sqrt{(4 - \lambda)/\lambda}. \tag{28.16}$$

A vanishing lower edge is in turn related to the appearance of a zero mode in the Hessian matrix of the replicated free energy (so-called *replicon eigenvalue*): this translates into a diverging spin-glass susceptibility [102, 103] as further evidence of being close to a critical point. A large response function can be interpreted as the fact that — rather than being governed by a single leader — the system tends to self-organize and respond collectively to external perturbations [104].

It is worth noticing that since the Lyapunov function in Eq. (28.13) is convex everywhere, a replica-symmetry-broken regime cannot occur. The most likely scenario taking place here is akin to the phenomenology of a *random linear programming* problem [101]. Even though replica symmetry continues to hold, a marginally stable regime takes place for some specific values of the control parameters.

The advantage of introducing a high-dimensional version of the MacArthur model is that it provides an appealing and easily-defined reference model albeit, in its current form, lends itself to describing only competitive interactions. To suitably address a wider spectrum of ecological scenarios, the random version of the Lotka–Volterra model will be presented in the following accounting either for the competitive or cooperative case.

28.3.3. *The generalized random Lotka–Volterra model*

A wide range of phenomena in population dynamics, including predation, mutualism, and resource-consumer interactions, can be reasonably well captured by a much simpler reference model: the disordered Lotka–Volterra model whose typical features are highlighted by tuning a few control (universal) parameters. Moreover, it not only reproduces phenomenologically multiple facets of well-mixed ecosystems [105] but also turns out to be of great interest in interdisciplinary domains such as genetics, epidemiology [106], and evolutionary game theory [107, 108] up to the modelization of complex financial markets [109, 110]. The Lotka–Volterra equations describe the evolution of S species subject to random interactions α_{ij} [84, 85]:

$$\frac{dN_i}{dt} = N_i \left[1 - N_i - \sum_{j,(j\neq i)} \alpha_{ij} N_j \right] + \sqrt{N_i}\,\eta_i(t) + \lambda_i, \qquad (28.17)$$

where $N_i(t)$ is the relative abundance of species i (with $i = 1, ..., S$) at time t meaning that the population is normalized with respect to the total number of individuals N_{ind} that would be present in the absence of interaction. The elements of the random matrix α_{ij} are independent and identically distributed with mean $\langle \alpha_{ij} \rangle = \mu/S$, variance $\langle \alpha_{ij}^2 \rangle_c = \sigma^2/S$ and $\langle \alpha_{ij}\alpha_{ji} \rangle_c = \gamma \langle \alpha_{ij}^2 \rangle_c$, where the subscript c stands for the connected part of the correlation. The parameter γ ranges from -1 (completely antisymmetric case to which prey-predator interactions belong) to 1 (fully symmetric, for which a Lyapunov function exists).

The demographic noise contribution, accounting for deaths, births, and other unpredictable events, is modelled by $\eta_i(t)$, a Gaussian variable with zero mean and variance $\langle \eta_i(t)\eta_j(t') \rangle = 2T\delta_{ij}\delta(t - t')$, whose amplitude T is inversely proportional to the total number of individuals N_{ind}. Such a multiplicative noise term allows us to investigate the effect of demographic stochasticity in a continuous setting [111–113]: the larger the global population, the smaller the strength T of the demographic noise. Then, to guarantee that probability distribution is integrable at small abundances, we need to introduce a small but finite immigration rate, which will be assumed to be constant over species, *i.e.* $\lambda_i = \lambda$. This is a smart way to avoid an absorbing boundary in $N_i = 0$: in other words, demographic fluctuations would inevitably push a finite fraction of species to zero.[d]

In the case of random symmetric interactions, the stochastic process induced by Eq. (28.17) admits an equilibrium-like stationary distribution [115, 116] with associated Hamiltonian:

$$H = -\sum_i \left(N_i - \frac{N_i^2}{2} \right) + \sum_{i<j} \alpha_{ij} N_i N_j + \sum_i [T \ln N_i - \ln \theta(N_i - \lambda)]. \qquad (28.18)$$

The penultimate term is due to the demographic noise[e] whereas the counterbalancing role of the immigration is formally modelled by the Heaviside function $\theta(x)$, which corresponds to imposing a reflecting wall at $N_i = \lambda$.

---

[d]With no demographic noise and no immigration, a similar model was proposed in the nineties by Biscari and Parisi [114] and analyzed by studying the stability of the replica symmetric solution (single fixed point regime).

[e]The parameter T plays the role of the temperature in a statistical mechanics setting. The mapping can be easily established by writing the corresponding Fokker–Planck equation with a white Gaussian noise.

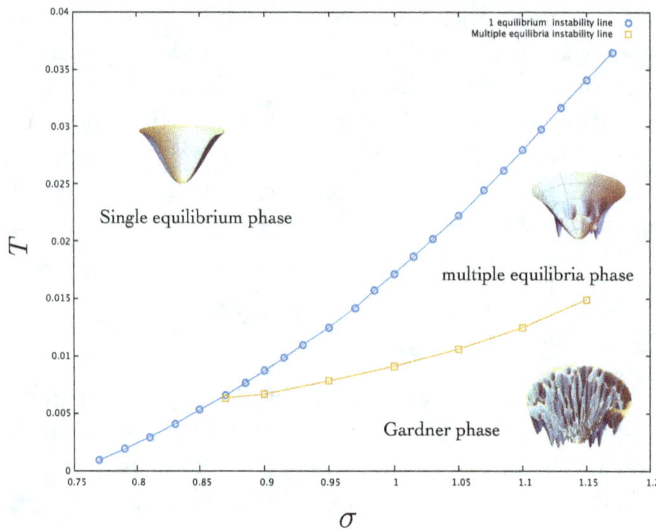

Fig. 28.6.   Phase diagram showing how the variation of the demographic noise strength, T, and the heterogeneity of interactions, σ, can lead to three different phases. In particular: i) a single equilibrium phase where the configurational landscape is purely convex; ii) a multiple equilibria regime, which is characterized by a 1RSB stable solution and an exponential number of locally stable equilibria; iii) a *Gardner phase*, which turns out to be associated with a hierarchical organization of the equilibria in the free energy landscape. Figure taken from [116].

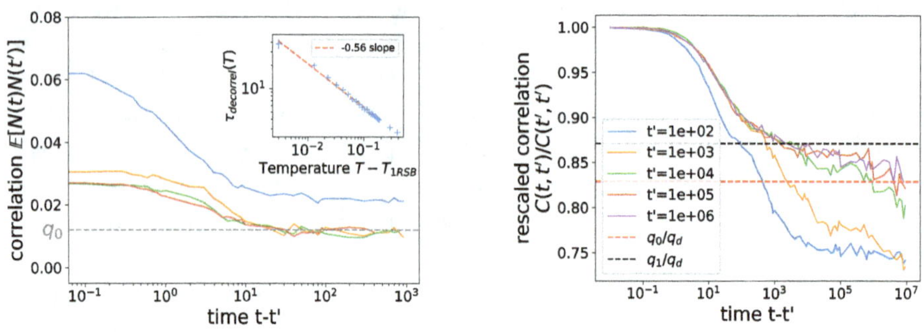

Fig. 28.7.   Numerical simulations based on DMFT. Two-time correlator $C(t, t')$ in the single-equilibrium phase (RS, on the left) compared with the same correlator in the multiple equilibria phase (1RSB, on the right) plotted for different t' and $S = 500$. The dashed lines correspond to the values of the overlap parameters, which are obtained by the replica method. The inset in the left plot highlights a divergence in the decorrelation time as $T \to T_{1\mathrm{RSB}}$, the critical temperature associated with an instability of the RS solution. Figures taken from [116].

28.3.3.1.   *Glassy phases and out-of-equilibrium dynamics*

Adding a finite demographic noise not only allows us to get a more general picture but also to properly characterize the resulting phase diagram — see Fig. 28.6 — connecting peculiar properties of each regime to the ones of equilibria.

Then one may wonder how all these outcomes are expected to change when asymmetric interactions are also taken into account and which strategy proves to be the most appropriate in this case. Non-symmetric interactions strongly complicate the analysis since they correspond to plugging non-conservative forces in the dynamics thus violating the fluctuation-dissipation theorem (FDT) and bringing the system out of equilibrium. Since it is no longer possible to define a Hamiltonian to be minimized and analyzed in terms of harmonic fluctuations around each of the minima, the cavity [102, 117] and Dynamical Mean-Field Theory [118, 119] formalisms come into play. The last method, in particular, allows us to map a multi-variable problem into a single-body stochastic formalism, which eventually involves time-delayed friction and colored noise whose features have to be determined self-consistently. In other words, the two-time correlation $C(t, t')$ and response $R(t, t')$ functions are fixed in a self-consistent way given the probability distribution associated with the stochastic process and the distribution of random interactions.

A similar analysis, as illustrated for the symmetric case in Fig. 28.6, can be performed. Without demographic fluctuations, increasing the variability of the interactions σ would destabilize the single-fixed-point regime and eventually result in chaotic phases as for neural networks and spin-glass models in the presence of asymmetric couplings. The introduction of a positive immigration rate would lead to the stabilization of chaotic dynamics — with an indefinitely long lifetime — corresponding to what we have referred to as *multiple equilibria regime* in the purely symmetric case. However, as soon as the immigration rate is set to zero, the chaotic regime is no longer stable [89, 120], replaced by slower and slower dynamics (*aging*).

28.3.3.2. *Non-logistic growth functions and pseudo-gap distributions*

The Lotka–Volterra equations analyzed in the large-S limit thus far allow for analytical advances in a very broad class of problems. In particular, by slightly modifying the dynamical Eq. (28.17) through the introduction of a higher-order one-species potential, one can also investigate the so-called *Allee effect* [121], which describes a positive correlation between mean individual fitness (or per-capita growth rate) and population density over some finite interval [122, 123]. This positive feedback loop mechanism, which inherited the name from the famous zoologist Warder Clyde Allee, essentially relies on the observation that in many species under-crowding, and not only competition, contributes to limiting population growth. The Allee effect is called *strong* if there exists an initial population threshold in the sense that the species pool needs a sufficiently large initial population to avoid extinction, whereas it is denoted as *weak* if no threshold exists. Even in this second case, intra-specific cooperation leads to an initial increase in the growth rate as population increases (see Fig. 28.8).

In the same spirit as before, one can take advantage of thermodynamic analysis and shed light on the resulting phase diagram by tuning the strength of random interactions and the demographic noise. Remarkable differences emerge with respect to the Lotka–Volterra logistic-growth case [124]. First, the number of states below the critical transition line is no longer exponential in the system size nor separated by extensive barriers, exactly as it would happen in equilibrium states of mean-field spin glasses (*i.e.* the Sherrington-Kirkpatrick model [102]). Furthermore, as soon as one considers a non-linear functional response of the species abundances, a pseudo-gap

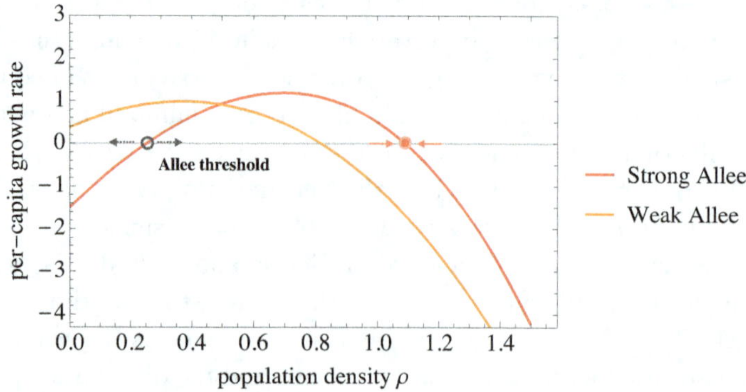

Fig. 28.8.   Sketch of the strong Allee effect (in red) compared to a weak Allee effect (in orange). In the former, the finite threshold corresponds to an unstable fixed point (empty black circle); in the latter, no threshold in the population exists.

distribution in the local curvatures of the single-species effective potential appears,[f] $P(V''_{\text{eff}}(N^*)) \sim |V''_{\text{eff}}(N^*)|^\alpha$, as a clear signature of a marginal low-demographic noise (low-temperature) phase [124]. This outcome nicely generalizes the pseudo-gap distribution that was found for instantaneous local fields in mean-field spin glasses — and was obtained before only in the case of discrete degrees of freedom [125] – to a complex ecological model.

28.3.4. *Conclusions and perspectives*

Along the different sections of this short report, I has mostly discussed analytical outcomes made possible by the use of mean-field limits. These pages are therefore intended as a tribute to Giorgio Parisi, a way to thank him for the innovative and insightful techniques that have been successfully applied to such diverse and interdisciplinary contexts.

As for future research, an interesting direction would be the investigation of spatially extended models either in a completely-connected topology where multiple patches (locations in space) are coupled by diffusion or in a sparse network with finite connectivity on each site. On the one hand, this metapopulation scenario, as originally proposed by Levins [126–128], would allow us for a more tangible comparison with real data, starting for instance with populations of small mammals and insects [129]; on the other hand, new appealing phenomena — such as pattern formation, traveling waves and activity fronts [130, 131] — are expected to appear. A rigorous theoretical analysis with an increasingly large number of species and, possibly, not only pairwise interactions is still missing.

A parallel line of research would concern an in-depth analysis of the role of different kinds of fluctuations — demographic and environmental ones that might violate detailed balance — and their interplay with the deterministic dynamics. Such a classification will drive a better comparison with observational data, in particular for reproducing species

---

[f]With the exponent $\alpha \geq 1$.

abundance distributions (SAD) of large ecological communities as well as for achieving a deeper understanding of the formal expression of functional responses given by local perturbations. This information would be extremely useful in the attempt to recover power-law and log-normal distributions for the species abundances that have not yet been identified in models accounting only for demographic fluctuations and symmetric interactions [132].

Acknowledgments

M. C. Marchetti thank Denis Bartolo for a critical reading of the manuscript and Amélie Chardac, Silke Henkes and Austin Hopkins for providing figures. This work is supported by the US National Science Foundation through grant DMR-2041459.

I. Giardina's work was supported by the Italian Ministry of Foreign Affairs and International Cooperation through the Adinmat project, and MIUR PRIN2020 grant n. 2020PFCXPE.

A. Altieri thank Matthieu Barbier, Giacomo Gradenigo and Frédéric van Wijland for a critical reading of the draft manuscript.

References

[1] M. Marchetti, J. Joanny, S. Ramaswamy, T. Liverpool, J. Prost, M. Rao, and R. A. Simha, *Rev. Mod. Phys.* **85**(3), 1143, (2013).

[2] C. Bechinger, R. Di Leonardo, H. Löwen, C. Reichhardt, G. Volpe, and G. Volpe, *Rev. Mod. Phys.* **88**(4), 045006, (2016).

[3] M. C. Marchetti, Y. Fily, S. Henkes, A. Patch, and D. Yllanes, *Curr. Opin. Colloid Interface Sci.* **21**, 34–43, (2016).

[4] T. Sanchez, D. T. Chen, S. J. DeCamp, M. Heymann, and Z. Dogic, *Nature.* **491**(7424), 431–434, (2012).

[5] L. M. Janssen, *J. Phys. Condens. Matter.* **31**(50), 503002, (2019).

[6] T. Vicsek and A. Zafeiris, *Phys. Rep.* **517**(3), 71–140, (2012).

[7] E. Lawson-Keister and M. L. Manning, *Curr. Opin. Cell Biol.* **72**, 146–155, (2021).

[8] T. Bhattacharjee and S. S. Datta, *Soft Matter.* **15**(48), 9920–9930, (2019).

[9] J. R. Howse, R. A. Jones, A. J. Ryan, T. Gough, R. Vafabakhsh, and R. Golestanian, *Phys. Rev. Lett.* **99**(4), 048102, (2007).

[10] M. E. Cates and J. Tailleur, *Annu. Rev. Condens. Matter Phys.* **6**(1), 219–244, (2015).

[11] J. Tailleur and M. Cates, *Phys. Rev. Lett.* **100**(21), 218103, (2008).

[12] Y. Fily and M. C. Marchetti, *Phys. Rev. Lett.* **108**(23), 235702, (2012).

[13] M. J. Schnitzer, *Phys. Rev. E.* **48**(4), 2553, (1993).

[14] S. Henkes, K. Kostanjevec, J. M. Collinson, R. Sknepnek, and E. Bertin, *Nat. Comm.* **11**(1), 1–9, (2020).

[15] R. Farhadifar, J.-C. Röper, B. Aigouy, S. Eaton, and F. Jülicher, *Current Biology.* **17**(24), 2095–2104, (2007).

[16] M. Moshe, M. J. Bowick, and M. C. Marchetti, *Phys. Rev. Lett.* **120**(26), 268105, (2018).

[17] M. Merkel, K. Baumgarten, B. P. Tighe, and M. L. Manning, *Proc. Natl. Acad. Sci. U.S.A.* **116**(14), 6560–6568, (2019).

[18] J. Huang, J. O. Cochran, S. M. Fielding, M. C. Marchetti, and D. Bi, *Phys. Rev. Lett.* **128**(17), 178001, (2022).

[19] P. Digregorio, D. Levis, A. Suma, L. F. Cugliandolo, G. Gonnella, and I. Pagonabarraga, *Phys. Rev. Lett.* **121**(9), 098003, (2018).

[20] Y. Fily, S. Henkes, and M. C. Marchetti, *Soft matter.* **10**(13), 2132–2140, (2014).

[21] L. Berthier, *Phys. Rev. Lett.* **112**(22), 220602, (2014).

[22] D. Bi, X. Yang, M. C. Marchetti, and M. L. Manning, *Phys. Rev. X.* **6**(2), 021011, (2016).

[23] R. Mandal, P. J. Bhuyan, P. Chaudhuri, C. Dasgupta, and M. Rao, *Nat. Comm.* **11**(1), 1–8, (2020).

[24] R. Mandal and P. Sollich, *J. Phys. Condens. Matter.* **33**(18), 184001, (2021).

[25] C. Maloney and A. Lemaitre, *Phys. Rev. Lett.* **93**(1), 016001, (2004).

[26] S. J. Streichan, M. F. Lefebvre, N. Noll, E. F. Wieschaus, and B. I. Shraiman, *Elife.* **7**, e27454, (2018).

[27] O. Chepizhko, E. G. Altmann, and F. Peruani, *Phys. Rev. Lett.* **110**(23), 238101, (2013).

[28] A. Morin, N. Desreumaux, J.-B. Caussin, and D. Bartolo, *Nat. Phys.* **13**(1), 63–67, (2017).

[29] J. Toner, N. Guttenberg, and Y. Tu, *Phys. Rev. Lett.* **121**(24), 248002, (2018).

[30] A. Chardac, S. Shankar, M. C. Marchetti, and D. Bartolo, *Proc. Natl. Acad. Sci. U.S.A.* **118**(10), (2021).

[31] Y. Duan, B. Mahault, Y.-q. Ma, X.-q. Shi, and H. Chaté, *Phys. Rev. Lett.* **126**(17), 178001, (2021).

[32] T. Vicsek, A. Czirók, E. Ben-Jacob, I. Cohen, and O. Shochet, *Phys Rev Lett.* **75**(6), 1226–1229 (1995).

[33] J. Toner and Y. Tu, *Phys. Rev. Lett.* **75**(23), 4326, (1995).

[34] H. Chaté, *Annu. Rev. Condens. Matter Phys.* **11**, 189–212, (2020).

[35] A. Bricard, J.-B. Caussin, N. Desreumaux, O. Dauchot, and D. Bartolo, *Nature.* **503**(7474), 95–98, (2013).

[36] R. Das, M. Kumar, and S. Mishra, *Phys. Rev. E.* **98**(6), 060602, (2018).

[37] T. Nattermann and S. Scheidl, *Adv. Phys.* **49**(5), 607–704, (2000).

[38] J. Krause and G. D. Ruxton, *Living in groups.* (Oxford University Press, 2002).

[39] S. Ramaswamy, *Annu. Rev. Condens. Matter Phys.* **1**, 323, (2010).

[40] J. Toner, Y. Tu, and S. Ramaswamy, *Annals of Physics.* **318**(1), 170–244, (2005).

[41] A. Cavagna and I. Giardina, *Annu. Rev. Condens. Matter Phys.* **5**(1), 183–207, (2014).

[42] A. Cavagna, I. Giardina, and T. S. Grigera, *Phys. Rep.* **728**, 1–62, (2018).

[43] A. Huth and C. Wissel, *J. Theor. Biol.* **156**(3), 365–385, (1992).

[44] I. D. Couzin, J. C. Krause, N. R. Franks, and S. A. Levin, *Nature.* **433**(7025), 513–6 (2005).

[45] C. K. Hemelrijk and H. Hildenbrandt, *PloS one.* **6**(8), e22479, (2011).

[46] C. W. Reynolds. In *Proc. 14th SIGGRAPH*, pp. 25–34, (1987).

[47] F. Cucker and S. Smale, *IEEE Trans. Automat. Contr.* **52**(5), 852–862, (2007).

[48] A. Jadbabaie, J. Lin, and A. S. Morse, *IEEE Trans. Automat. Contr.* **48**(6), 988–1001, (2003).

[49] H. Chaté, F. Ginelli, G. Grégoire, F. Peruani, and F. Raynaud, *Eur. Phys. J. B.* **64**(3-4), 451–456, (2008).

[50] F. Ginelli, *Eur. Phys. J. Special Topics.* **225**(11-12), 2099–2117, (2016).

[51] J. Toner and Y. Tu, *Phys. Rev. E.* **58**(4), 4828, (1998).

[52] M. Ballerini, N. Cabibbo, R. Candelier, A. Cavagna, E. Cisbani, I. Giardina, V. Lecomte, A. Orlandi, G. Parisi, A. Procaccini, et al., *Proc. Natl. Acad. Sci. U.S.A.* **105**(4), 1232–1237, (2008).

[53] A. Cavagna, I. Giardina, A. Orlandi, G. Parisi, A. Procaccini, M. Viale, and V. Zdravkovic, *Anim. Behav.* **76**, 217–236 (2008).

[54] A. Cavagna, I. Giardina, A. Orlandi, G. Parisi, and A. Procaccini, *Anim. Behav.* **76**, 237–248 (2008).

[55] M. Camperi, A. Cavagna, I. Giardina, G. Parisi, and E. Silvestri, *Interface Focus.* **2**(6), 715–725, (2012).

[56] F. Ginelli and H. Chaté, *Phys Rev Lett.* **105**(16), 168103 (2010).

[57] F. Ferretti, S. Grosse-Holz, C. Holmes, J. L. Shivers, I. Giardina, T. Mora, and A. Walczak, *arXiv:2205.14505*. (2022).

[58] A. Cavagna, A. Cimarelli, I. Giardina, G. Parisi, R. Santagati, F. Stefanini, and M. Viale, *Proc. Natl. Acad. Sci. U.S.A.* **107**(26), 11865–70 (2010).

[59] G. Parisi, *Statistical field theory*. Frontiers in Physics, (Addison-Wesley, Redwood City, CA, 1988).

[60] J. Goldstone, *Il Nuovo Cimento (1955-1965)*. **19**(1), 154–164, (1961).

[61] A. Z. Patashinskii and V. L. Pokrovskii, *Fluctuation Theory of Phase Transitions*. (Pergamon Press, 1979).

[62] C. K. Hemelrijk and H. Hildenbrandt, *Ethology*. **114**(3), 245–254, (2008).

[63] M. R. D'Orsogna, Y.-L. Chuang, A. L. Bertozzi, and L. S. Chayes, *Phys. Rev. Lett.* **96**(10), 104302, (2006).

[64] W. Bialek, A. Cavagna, I. Giardina, T. Mora, O. Pohl, E. Silvestri, M. Viale, and A. M. Walczak, *Proc. Natl. Acad. Sci. U.S.A.* **111**(20), 7212–7217, (2014).

[65] A. Cavagna, A. Culla, L. Di Carlo, I. Giardina, and T. S. Grigera, *C. R. Acad. Sci. Physique*. **20**, 319–328 (2019).

[66] A. Cavagna, A. Culla, X. Feng, I. Giardina, T. S. Grigera, W. Kion-Crosby, S. Melillo, G. Pisegna, L. Postiglione, and P. Villegas, *Nat. Comm.* **13**(1), 1–11, (2022).

[67] D. J. MacKay, *Information theory, inference and learning algorithms*. (Cambridge University Press, 2003).

[68] W. Bialek, A. Cavagna, I. Giardina, T. Mora, E. Silvestri, M. Viale, and A. M. Walczak, *Proc. Natl. Acad. Sci. U.S.A.* **109**(13), 4786–91 (2012).

[69] T. Mora, A. M. Walczak, L. Del Castello, F. Ginelli, S. Melillo, L. Parisi, M. Viale, A. Cavagna, and I. Giardina, *Nat. Phys.* **12**(12), 1153–1157, (2016).

[70] A. Cavagna, L. Del Castello, S. Dey, I. Giardina, S. Melillo, L. Parisi, and M. Viale, *Phys. Rev. E.* **92**(1), 012705, (2015).

[71] A. Cavagna, I. Giardina, F. Ginelli, T. Mora, D. Piovani, R. Tavarone, and A. M. Walczak, *Phys. Rev. E.* **89**(4), 042707, (2014).

[72] A. Attanasi, A. Cavagna, L. Del Castello, I. Giardina, T. S. Grigera, A. Jelić, S. Melillo, L. Parisi, O. Pohl, E. Shen, et al., *Nat. Phys.* **10**(9), 691–696, (2014).

[73] A. Cavagna, L. Del Castello, I. Giardina, T. Grigera, A. Jelic, S. Melillo, T. Mora, L. Parisi, E. Silvestri, M. Viale, et al., *J. Stat. Phys.* **158**(3), 601–627, (2015).

[74] A. Peshkov, S. Ngo, E. Bertin, H. Chaté, and F. Ginelli, *Phys. Rev. Lett.* **109**(9), 098101, (2012).

[75] A. Cavagna, I. Giardina, T. S. Grigera, A. Jelic, D. Levine, S. Ramaswamy, and M. Viale, *Phys. Rev. Lett.* **114**(21), 218101, (2015).

[76] X. Yang and M. C. Marchetti, *Phys. Rev. Lett.* **115**(25), 258101, (2015).

[77] A. Cavagna, L. Di Carlo, I. Giardina, T. S. Grigera, S. Melillo, L. Parisi, G. Pisegna, and M. Scandolo, *arXiv:2107.04432*. (2021).

[78] A. Cavagna, A. Culla, and T. S. Grigera, *arXiv:2202.04605*. (2022).

[79] G. Hardin, *Science*. **131**(3409), 1292–1297, (1960).

[80] R. M. May, *Nature*. **238**(5364), 413–414, (1972).

[81] R. M. May and P. Allen, *IEEE Trans. Syst. Man Cybern. Syst.* (12), 887–887, (1976).

[82] K. Faust and J. Raes, *Nat. Rev. Microbiol.* **10**(8), 538–550, (2012).

[83] D. Fisher, M. Lässig, and B. Shraiman, *J. Stat. Mech.: Theory Exp.* **2013**(01), N01001, (2013).

[84] D. A. Kessler and N. M. Shnerb, *Phys. Rev. E.* **91**(4), 042705, (2015).

[85] G. Bunin, *Phys. Rev. E.* **95**(4), 042414, (2017).

[86] A. Altieri and S. Franz, *Phys. Rev. E.* **99**(1), 010401 (R), (2019).

[87] C. A. Serván, J. A. Capitán, J. Grilli, K. E. Morrison, and S. Allesina, *Nat. Ecol. Evol.* **2**(8), 1237–1242, (2018).

[88] R. Marsland, W. Cui, and P. Mehta, *Sci. Rep.* **10**(1), 1–17, (2020).

[89] M. T. Pearce, A. Agarwala, and D. S. Fisher, *Proc. Natl. Acad. Sci. U.S.A.* (2020).

[90] J. Wu, P. Mehta, and D. Schwab, *arXiv:2103.02081*. (2021).

[91] S. Allesina and S. Tang, *Nature.* **483**(7388), 205–208, (2012).

[92] R. MacArthur, *Theor. Popul. Biol.* **1**(1), 1–11, (1970).

[93] A. J. Lotka, *Proc. Natl. Acad. Sci. U.S.A.* **6**(7), 410–415, (1920).

[94] V. Volterra, *Variazioni e fluttuazioni del numero d'individui in specie animali conviventi.* (C. Ferrari, 1927).

[95] M. Tikhonov and R. Monasson, *Phys. Rev. Lett.* **118**(4), 048103, (2017).

[96] A. Altieri. In *Jamming and Glass Transitions*, pp. 133–152. Springer, (2019).

[97] S. A. Kauffman and S. Johnsen, *J. Theor. Biol.* **149**(4), 467–505, (1991).

[98] P. Bak, *How nature works: the science of self-organized criticality.* (Springer Science & Business Media, 2013).

[99] V. A. Marčenko and L. A. Pastur, *Mat. Sb.* **1**(4), 457, (1967).

[100] M. Wyart, *arXiv:0512155*. (2005).

[101] S. Franz and G. Parisi, *J. Phys. A.* **49**(14), 145001, (2016).

[102] M. Mézard, G. Parisi, and M. Virasoro, *Spin glass theory and beyond: An Introduction to the Replica Method and Its Applications.* vol. 9, (World Scientific Publishing Company, 1987).

[103] C. De Dominicis and I. Giardina, *Random fields and spin glasses: a field theory approach.* (Cambridge University Press, 2006).

[104] T. Mora and W. Bialek, *J. Stat. Phys.* **144**(2), 268–302, (2011).

[105] M. Barbier, J.-F. Arnoldi, G. Bunin, and M. Loreau, *Proc. Natl. Acad. Sci. U.S.A.* **115**(9), 2156–2161, (2018).

[106] R. D. Holt and J. Pickering, *Am. Nat.* **126**(2), 196–211, (1985).

[107] T. Galla and J. D. Farmer, *Proc. Natl. Acad. Sci. U.S.A.* **110**(4), 1232–1236, (2013).

[108] J. B. Sanders, J. D. Farmer, and T. Galla, *Sci. Rep.* **8**(1), 1–13, (2018).

[109] J. Sprott, *Phys. Lett. A.* **325**(5-6), 329–333, (2004).

[110] J. Moran and J.-P. Bouchaud, *Phys. Rev. E.* **100**(3), 032307, (2019).

[111] G. Domokos and I. Scheuring, *J. Theor. Biol.* **227**(4), 535–545, (2004).

[112] T. Rogers, A. J. McKane, and A. G. Rossberg, *EPL.* **97**(4), 40008, (2012).

[113] H. Weissmann, N. M. Shnerb, and D. A. Kessler, *Phys. Rev. E.* **98**(2), 022131, (2018).

[114] P. Biscari and G. Parisi, *J. Phys. A.* **28**(17), 4697, (1995).

[115] G. Biroli, G. Bunin, and C. Cammarota, *New J. Phys.* **20**(8), 083051, (2018).

[116] A. Altieri, F. Roy, C. Cammarota, and G. Biroli, *Phys. Rev. Lett.* **126**(25), 258301, (2021).

[117] M. Mezard and A. Montanari, *Information, physics, and computation.* (Oxford University Press, 2009).

[118] F. Roy, G. Biroli, G. Bunin, and C. Cammarota, *J. Phys. A.* **52**(48), 484001, (2019).

[119] A. Altieri, G. Biroli, and C. Cammarota, *J. Phys. A.* **53**, 375006, (2020).

[120] F. Roy, M. Barbier, G. Biroli, G. Bunin, et al., *PLOS Comput. Biol.* **16**(5), 1–14, (2020).

[121] W. C. Allee, *J. Exp. Zool.* **45**(1), 255–277, (1926).

[122] J. Gascoigne and R. N. Lipcius, *Mar. Ecol. Prog. Ser.* **269**, 49–59, (2004).

[123] A. M. Kramer, L. Berec, and J. M. Drake. Editorial: Allee effects in ecology and evolution, (2018).

[124] A. Altieri and G. Biroli, *SciPost Phys.* **12**(1), 013, (2022).

[125] R. Palmer and C. Pond, *J. Phys. F.* **9**(7), 1451, (1979).

[126] I. Hanski, *Nature.* **396**(6706), 41–49, (1998).

[127] I. Hanski and O. Ovaskainen, *Nature.* **404**(6779), 755–758, (2000).

[128] R. S. Etienne, *Comments Theor. Biol.* **7**(4), 257–281, (2002).

[129] B. Elmhagen and A. Angerbjörn, *Oikos.* **94**(1), 89–100, (2001).

[130] A. Curatolo, N. Zhou, Y. Zhao, C. Liu, A. Daerr, J. Tailleur, and J. Huang, *Nat. Phys.* **16**(11), 1152–1157, (2020).

[131] K. Manna, V. Volpert, and M. Banerjee, *Bull. Math. Biol.* **83**(5), 1–35, (2021).

[132] G. G. Lorenzana and A. Altieri, *Phys. Rev. E.* **105**(2), 024307, (2022).

Chapter 29

Optimization of Random High-Dimensional Functions: Structure and Algorithms

Antonio Auffinger[*], Andrea Montanari[†] and Eliran Subag[‡]

*Department of Mathematics, Northwestern University, USA
auffing@math.northwestern.edu

†Department of Electrical Engineering and Department of Statistics,
Stanford University, USA
montanari@stanford.edu

‡Department of Mathematics, Weizmann Institute, Israel
eliran.subag@gmail.com

Replica symmetry breaking postulates that near optima of spin glass Hamiltonians have an ultrametric structure. Namely, near optima can be associated with leaves of a tree, and the Euclidean distance between them corresponds to the distance along this tree. We survey recent progress toward a rigorous proof of this picture in the context of mixed p-spin spin glass models. We focus in particular on the following topics: (i) The structure of critical points of the Hamiltonian; (ii) The realization of the ultrametric tree as near optima of a suitable TAP free energy; (iii) The construction of an efficient optimization algorithm that exploits this picture.

29.1. Introduction

Mean field spin glasses are high-dimensional random functions $H_N : \Sigma_N \to \mathbb{R}$, $\Sigma_N \subseteq \mathbb{R}^N$ with special symmetry properties. In the most studied cases, for any k points (spin configurations) $\sigma_1, \ldots, \sigma_k \in \Sigma_N$, the joint distribution of $H_N(\sigma_1), \ldots H_N(\sigma_k)$ only depends on the configurations through their joint empirical distribution $N^{-1} \sum_{i=1}^{N} \delta_{\sigma_{1,i}, \ldots, \sigma_{k,i}}$.

These models were originally motivated by the study of disordered magnetic materials. However, it soon became clear that a large number of random optimization problems of interest in computer science and statistics fit this framework [1]. In this chapter we survey recent rigorous work aimed at describing the structure of near optima of spin glasses, with a focus on questions that are relevant for optimization.

We will consider the most classical mean-field spin glass model, namely the mixed p-spin spin glass, with either $\Sigma_N = \{+1, -1\}^N$ (Ising model) or $\Sigma_N = \mathbb{S}^{N-1}(\sqrt{N})$ (spherical model). The Hamiltonian is defined by

$$H_N(\boldsymbol{\sigma}) := \sum_{k \geq 2} \frac{c_k}{N^{\frac{k-1}{2}}} \langle \boldsymbol{G}^{(k)}, \boldsymbol{\sigma}^{\otimes k} \rangle = \sum_{k \geq 2} \frac{c_k}{N^{\frac{k-1}{2}}} \sum_{i_1, \ldots, i_k = 1}^{N} G^{(k)}_{i_1 \ldots i_k} \sigma_{i_1} \cdots \sigma_{i_k}, \qquad (29.1)$$

where $\boldsymbol{G}^{(k)} = (G^{(k)}_{i_1\ldots i_k})_{i_1,\ldots,i_k \leq n}$ is a tensor with i.i.d. Gaussian components $G^{(k)}_{i_1\ldots i_k} \sim$ N(0,1).

It is immediate to see that $\{H_N(\boldsymbol{\sigma})\}_{\boldsymbol{\sigma} \in \Sigma_N}$ is a centered Gaussian process on Σ_N, with covariance

$$\mathbb{E}\big[H_N(\boldsymbol{\sigma})H_N(\boldsymbol{\sigma}')\big] = N\xi(\langle \boldsymbol{\sigma}, \boldsymbol{\sigma}' \rangle / N), \qquad (29.2)$$

where $\xi(x) := \sum_{k \geq 2} c_k^2 x^k$. A term linear in $\boldsymbol{\sigma}$ (a 'magnetic field' in physics language) could be added but we omit it here because this simplifies some of the statements and discussions below. We will assume throughout that the non-random coefficients c_k decay fast enough that $\sum_{k \geq 2} c_k^2 k^C < \infty$ for any $C > 0$.

Understanding the structure of optima and near optima of spin glass Hamiltonians is a central concern of the theory. The most basic quantity is of course the optimum value

$$\mathsf{OPT}_N := \frac{1}{N}\mathbb{E}\max_{\boldsymbol{\sigma} \in \Sigma_N} H_N(\boldsymbol{\sigma}), \quad \mathsf{OPT} := \lim_{N \to \infty} \mathsf{OPT}_N. \qquad (29.3)$$

(The standard physics convention is to study the minimum of $-H_N(\boldsymbol{\sigma})$, but of course the two formulations are equivalent.) We occasionally use $\mathsf{OPT}_N(H_N) := \max_{\boldsymbol{\sigma} \in \Sigma_N} H_N(\boldsymbol{\sigma})/N$ for the maximum of the random Hamiltonian H_N. The $N \to \infty$ limit above was proven to exist and to be given by a 'zero-temperature' version of Parisi's formula, which is a variational principle over the following space of functions:

$$\mathscr{U} := \left\{ \gamma \colon [0,1) \to \mathbb{R}_{\geq 0} \colon \gamma \text{ non-decreasing}, \int_0^1 \gamma(t)\mathrm{d}t < \infty \right\}. \qquad (29.4)$$

For $\gamma \in \mathscr{U}$, let $\Phi_\gamma \colon [0,1] \times \mathbb{R} \to \mathbb{R}$ be the solution of the following PDE, known as *the Parisi PDE*

$$\partial_t \Phi_\gamma(t,x) + \frac{1}{2}\xi''(t)\left(\partial_x^2 \Phi_\gamma(t,x) + \gamma(t)(\partial_x \Phi_\gamma(t,x))^2\right) = 0, \qquad (29.5)$$

with terminal condition at $t = 1$:

$$\Phi_\gamma(1,x) = \begin{cases} x^2/2 & \text{if } \Sigma_N = \mathbb{S}^{N-1}(\sqrt{N}), \\ |x| & \text{if } \Sigma_N = \{+1,-1\}^N. \end{cases} \qquad (29.6)$$

The Parisi functional $\mathsf{P} \colon \mathscr{U} \to \mathbb{R}$ is then defined by

$$\mathsf{P}(\gamma) \equiv \Phi_\gamma(0,0) - \frac{1}{2}\int_0^1 t\xi''(t)\gamma(t)\,\mathrm{d}t. \qquad (29.7)$$

The zero-temperature variational principle is stated below: its proof builds on earlier results at positive temperature proved by Talagrand [2] and Panchenko [3, 4].

Theorem 1 ([5–7]). *The limit* $\mathsf{OPT} := \lim_{N \to \infty} \mathsf{OPT}_N$ *exists and is given by*

$$\mathsf{OPT} = \inf_{\gamma \in \mathscr{U}} \mathsf{P}(\gamma). \qquad (29.8)$$

We also recall that classical Gaussian concentration results imply that $\max_{\boldsymbol{\sigma} \in \Sigma_N} H_N(\boldsymbol{\sigma})/N$ is exponentially concentrated around OPT_N and therefore the asymptotic value OPT is representative of the typical optimal value for large N.

Of course, characterizing the typical value of the optimum is only a first step towards understanding the landscape structure. A more detailed picture is obtained by considering the random superlevel sets

$$\mathsf{L}_N(\eta) := \{\boldsymbol{\sigma} \in \Sigma_N : H_N(\boldsymbol{\sigma}) \geq N\eta\}, \tag{29.9}$$

where η is a fixed real number. It is clear that for $\eta_1 \leq \eta_2$, $\mathsf{L}_N(\eta_2) \subseteq \mathsf{L}_N(\eta_1)$. Of course, the maximum of H_N can be written as

$$\mathsf{OPT}_N(H_N) := \frac{1}{N} \max_{\boldsymbol{\sigma} \in \Sigma_N} H_N(\boldsymbol{\sigma}) = \sup \{\eta \in \mathbb{R} : \mathsf{L}_N(\eta) \neq \emptyset\}. \tag{29.10}$$

An interesting approach to study the geometry of the random set $\mathsf{L}_N(\eta)$ is to consider the uniform measure over this set $U_{N,\eta}(\mathrm{d}\boldsymbol{\sigma}) \propto \mathbf{1}_{\mathsf{L}_N(\eta)}(\boldsymbol{\sigma})\mathrm{d}\boldsymbol{\sigma}$. This turns out to be closely approximated by the following Gibbs measure (for a suitable choice of $\beta = \beta_*(\eta)$)

$$G_{N,\beta}(\mathrm{d}\boldsymbol{\sigma}) = \frac{1}{Z_{N,\beta}} e^{\beta H(\boldsymbol{\sigma})} \, \mathrm{d}\boldsymbol{\sigma}. \tag{29.11}$$

Here $\mathrm{d}\boldsymbol{\sigma}$ is the uniform measure over the sphere $\Sigma_N = \mathbb{S}^{N-1}(\sqrt{N})$ or the counting measure over the hypercube $\Sigma_N = \{+1, -1\}^N$ (in the latter case we keep writing integrals instead of sums).

The free energy density is defined as the exponential growth rate of the partition function $Z_{N,\beta}$:

$$F_{N,\beta} := \frac{1}{N} \log Z_{N,\beta} = \frac{1}{N} \log \int_{\Sigma_N} e^{\beta H_N(\boldsymbol{\sigma})} \, \mathrm{d}\boldsymbol{\sigma}. \tag{29.12}$$

Roughly speaking (and if $\beta = \beta_*(\eta)$ is chosen as mentioned above), we have $F_{N,\beta} \approx \beta\eta + N^{-1} \log \mathrm{Vol}(\mathsf{L}_N(\eta))$.

The rest of this article is organized as follows:

- We begin by discussing some fundamental geometric and topological properties of the optimization landscape in Sec. 29.2. In particular, the number of local maxima of $H_N(\boldsymbol{\sigma})$ in the superlevel set $\mathsf{L}_N(\eta)$ is often exponentially large in the dimension N. Further, nearly orthogonal vectors can be found in $\mathsf{L}_N(\eta)$, for η close to OPT.
- While the previous section indicates that the spin glass landscape is not only non-convex but in fact extremely rough, Sec. 29.3 outlines the hidden tree structure behind this seemingly unstructured landscape. We switch from the level sets $\mathsf{L}_N(\eta)$ to the Gibbs measure $G_{N,\beta}(\mathrm{d}\boldsymbol{\sigma})$. The space Σ_N can be partitioned hierarchically into sets ('ancestor states') of decreasing normalized radius (from 1 to $(1 - q_{\mathrm{EA}})^{1/2}$), and to each of these sets α can be associated its barycenter[a] $\boldsymbol{m}^{(\alpha)} \in \overline{\Sigma}_N := \mathrm{conv}(\Sigma_N)$. The vectors $\boldsymbol{m}^{(\alpha)}$ are organized according to an ultrametric tree.
- Can we use the ultrametric tree to explore the structure of optima or near optima of $H_N(\boldsymbol{\sigma})$? Section 29.4 shows that this is indeed the case by constructing two efficient algorithms that output configurations $\boldsymbol{\sigma}^{\mathrm{alg}} \in \Sigma_N$ by constructing random paths in $\overline{\Sigma}_N$. The asymptotic value achieved by these algorithms

---

[a]Here and below $\mathrm{conv}(S)$ denotes the convex hull of a set $S \in \mathbb{R}^d$.

$\mathsf{ALG} := \lim_{N \to \infty} H_N(\boldsymbol{\sigma}^{\mathrm{alg}})/N$ turns out to be given by a modified Parisi formula. In particular, when the optimizer of Eq. (29.8) is strictly monotone ('no overlap gap'), we have $\mathsf{ALG} = \mathsf{OPT}$.

29.2. Critical Points and the Landscape Structure

In this section, we focus on two fundamental questions:

(a) Computing the number of critical points (local maxima, saddles) of H_N at different values of the energy. In particular, we describe the exponential growth rate of this number, known in physics as the complexity function.
(b) Studying the geometry of the superlevel set $\mathsf{L}_N(\eta)$ when η is close to the maximum OPT. In particular, we will discuss the connection between Parisi's replica symmetry breaking formula and the range of values of $\langle \boldsymbol{\sigma}^1, \boldsymbol{\sigma}^2 \rangle / N$ when $\boldsymbol{\sigma}^1, \boldsymbol{\sigma}^2 \in \mathsf{L}_N(\eta)$.

Throughout this section we will refer to ξ as a mixture and use the shorthands:

$$\xi := \xi(1) > 0, \qquad \xi' := \xi'(1) > 0, \qquad \xi'' := \xi''(1) > 0.$$

We say that the model is pure (of degree p) if $\xi(x) = c_p^2 x^p$, which amounts to say that the Hamiltonian is a homogeneous polynomial of degree p. Note that $\xi'' \geq \xi'$ with equality only in the pure case with $p = 2$.

29.2.1. *Complexity of critical points*

Consider the case where $\Sigma_N = \mathbb{S}^{N-1}(\sqrt{N})$ and the subsets (29.9) are smooth submanifolds of $\mathbb{S}^{N-1}(\sqrt{N})$. We introduce the complexity of spherical spin glasses as follows. For any $\eta \in \mathbb{R}$ and integer $0 \leq k < N$, we consider the (random) number $\mathrm{Crt}_{N,k}(\eta)$ of critical points of the Hamiltonian H_N in the set $\mathsf{L}_N(\eta)$ with index equal to $N - 1 - k$,

$$\mathrm{Crt}_{N,k}(\eta) = \sum_{\boldsymbol{\sigma}: \, \nabla H_N(\boldsymbol{\sigma})=0} \mathbf{1}\{\boldsymbol{\sigma} \in \mathsf{L}_N(\eta)\} \, \mathbf{1}\{i(\nabla^2 H_N(\boldsymbol{\sigma})) = N - 1 - k\}. \tag{29.13}$$

Here $i(\nabla^2 H_N(\boldsymbol{\sigma}))$ is the index of $\nabla^2 H_N$ at $\boldsymbol{\sigma}$, that is, the number of negative eigenvalues of the Hessian $\nabla^2 H_N(\boldsymbol{\sigma})$. As an illustration, $\mathrm{Crt}_{N,0}(\eta)$ counts the number of local maxima with energy value larger than $N\eta$, while $\mathrm{Crt}_{N,1}(\eta)$ counts the number of saddles in $\mathsf{L}_N(\eta)$ with "one positive direction," and so on. Here ∇, ∇^2 are the Riemannian gradient and Riemannian Hessian which act on the tangent space of $\mathbb{S}^{N-1}(\sqrt{N})$.

We will also consider the (random) total number $\mathrm{Crt}_N(\eta)$ of critical values of the Hamiltonian H_N in the set $\mathsf{L}_N(\eta)$ (whatever their index)

$$\mathrm{Crt}_N(\eta) = \sum_{\boldsymbol{\sigma}: \, \nabla H_N(\boldsymbol{\sigma})=0} \mathbf{1}\{\boldsymbol{\sigma} \in L_N(\eta)\}. \tag{29.14}$$

Note that $\mathrm{Crt}_{N,k}(\eta) \leq \mathrm{Crt}_N(\eta)$ for all $k \geq 0$.

For general mixtures, the asymptotics of the mean of $\mathrm{Crt}_{N,k}(\eta)$ was first derived in [8].

Theorem 2 (Theorem 1 in [8]). *For any $\eta \in \mathbb{R}$, and any fixed $k \geq 0$, there exist $\Sigma_k(\eta), \Sigma(\eta) \in \mathbb{R}$ such that*

$$\lim_{N \to \infty} \frac{1}{N} \log \mathbb{E}\, \mathrm{Crt}_{N,k}(\eta) = \Sigma_k(\eta),$$

and

$$\lim_{N \to \infty} \frac{1}{N} \log \mathbb{E}\, \mathrm{Crt}_N(\eta) = \Sigma(\eta).$$

The exact expression for $\Sigma(\eta), \Sigma_k(\eta)$ can be found in [8, Equations (2.13)]. These functions depend on the model ξ (we avoid explicitly writing this dependence in our notation) and are called the (averaged or annealed) complexity of critical points and (averaged or annealed) complexity of critical points of index $N - 1 - k$.

The complexity functions Σ_k, Σ have a number of interesting properties, which we next summarize. Set

$$\mathsf{THR}' = \frac{2\xi'\sqrt{\xi''}}{(\xi' + \xi'')\xi}, \qquad \mathsf{THR} = \frac{(\xi'' - \xi')\xi + \xi'^2}{\xi'\sqrt{\xi\xi''}}. \tag{29.15}$$

Then we have the following:

(*i*) $\mathsf{THR}' \leq \mathsf{THR}$ with equality if and only the model is pure.

(*ii*) The functions $\eta \to \Sigma_k(\eta)$ and $\eta \to \Sigma(\eta)$ are continuous and non-increasing. (Note that monotonicity follows by definition.)

(*iii*) For each k, $\Sigma_k(\eta)$ is strictly decreasing on (THR', ∞), with

$$\lim_{\eta \to \infty} \Sigma_k(\eta) = -\infty.$$

Further, on $(-\infty, \mathsf{THR}')$, Σ_k is constant (and taking its maximum value) with

$$\eta \in (-\infty, \mathsf{THR}') \quad \Rightarrow \quad \Sigma_k(\eta) = \frac{1}{2}\log \frac{\xi''}{\xi'} - \frac{\xi'' - \xi'}{\xi'' + \xi'} > 0.$$

(*iv*) For any $k, k' \in \mathbb{N}$ with $k < k'$, $\Sigma_k(\eta) > \Sigma_{k'}(\eta)$ for all $\eta \in (\mathsf{THR}, \infty)$.

(*v*) For $\eta \in (\mathsf{THR}', \infty)$, $\Sigma_0(\eta) = \Sigma(\eta)$.

What do these properties and Theorem 2 above tell us about the landscape? First, define $\mathsf{E}_k \in \mathbb{R}$ to be the unique energy value such that

$$\Sigma_k(\mathsf{E}_k) = 0. \tag{29.16}$$

These quantities are well-defined due to properties (*ii*) and (*iii*). A simple application of Markov's inequality yields

$$\mathbb{P}\left(\mathrm{OPT}_N(H_N) \geq \eta\right) = \mathbb{P}(\mathsf{L}_N(\eta) \neq \emptyset) = \mathbb{P}(\mathrm{Crt}_0(\eta) \geq 1) \leq \mathbb{E}\,\mathrm{Crt}_0(\eta).$$

Combined with Theorem 2 this leads to the bound

$$\mathsf{OPT} \leq \mathsf{E}_0. \tag{29.17}$$

Note that, in general, we cannot argue in the opposite direction. Even if $\Sigma_0(\eta) > 0$, we cannot conclude that with high probability there exist local maxima in $\mathsf{L}_N(\eta)$. However, as discussed below, in some cases this conclusion holds.

In fact, Markov's inequality also implies that, for any $\varepsilon > 0$, the event that there is a critical value of the Hamiltonian H_N above level $N(\mathsf{E}_k + \varepsilon)$ and with index $N - 1 - k$ (or larger) has an exponentially small probability. Loosely speaking, as N diverges, there are no saddles with k positive directions above E_k. This is a good moment to remind the reader that the scaling of $\mathsf{L}_N(\eta)$ contains a factor N: namely, $\mathsf{L}_N(\eta)$ is the set of spin configurations $\boldsymbol{\sigma}$ satisfying $H_N(\boldsymbol{\sigma}) \geq N\eta$. If $\eta > \mathsf{E}_1$, $\mathsf{L}_N(\eta)$ contains no saddles, with high probability (by argument given above). If $\mathsf{L}_N(\eta)$ is non-empty and contains multiple local maxima, it must be the case that $\mathsf{L}_N(\eta)$ is formed by disconnected components. Each component contains one local maximum and they can only be connected if we decrease the energy by an amount $\Theta(N)$. In other words, in such setting, energy barriers are of order N. As we will see shortly, this scenario indeed holds for the spherical pure p-spin.

First of all, the formulas for the complexity functions $\Sigma_k(\eta), \Sigma(\eta)$ have a simpler form for the spherical pure p-spin. If this is the case, we can assume, without loss of generality, $\xi(t) = t^p$. It was shown in [9] that

$$\Sigma(\eta) = \begin{cases} \frac{1}{2}\log(p-1) & \text{if } \eta \leq 0, \\ \frac{1}{2}\log(p-1) - \frac{p-2}{4(p-1)}\eta^2 & \text{if } 0 \leq \eta \leq \mathsf{THR}, \\ \frac{1}{2}\log(p-1) - \frac{p-2}{4(p-1)}\eta^2 - J(\eta) & \text{if } \mathsf{THR} \leq \eta, \end{cases} \tag{29.18}$$

where $\mathsf{THR} = \mathsf{THR}(p) = 2\sqrt{\frac{p-1}{p}}$ and for $\eta \geq \mathsf{THR}$,

$$J(\eta) = \frac{\eta}{\mathsf{THR}^2}\sqrt{\eta^2 - \mathsf{THR}^2} - \log\left(\eta + \sqrt{\eta^2 - \mathsf{THR}^2}\right) + \log \mathsf{THR}.$$

Further, in this case, $\mathsf{THR} = \mathsf{THR}'$. A straightforward consequence of these formulas (and of the strict monotonicity of $\Sigma_k(\eta)$ in k for $\eta > \mathsf{THR}$ by property (*iv*) above) is that in the spherical pure p-spin,

$$\mathsf{E}_k > \mathsf{E}_{k+1} > \mathsf{THR} = \mathsf{THR}' = 2\sqrt{\frac{p-1}{p}} \quad \text{for all } k \geq 0. \tag{29.19}$$

Second, and more importantly, in the spherical pure p-spin the exponential growth rate of the typical number (as opposed to the average number) of critical points can be rigorously computed. This is referred to in physics as the *quenched* complexity, and turns out to coincide with the annealed complexity given above. This was established in [10, 11].

Theorem 3 (Theorem 1 in [10]). *For any $p \geq 3$ and $\eta \in (\mathsf{THR}, \mathsf{E}_0)$,*

$$\lim_{N \to \infty} \frac{\mathbb{E}\left[(\mathrm{Crt}_N(\eta))^2\right]}{\left(\mathbb{E}\left[\mathrm{Crt}_N(\eta)\right]\right)^2} = 1. \tag{29.20}$$

Consequently, in L^2 and in probability,

$$\frac{\mathrm{Crt}_N(\eta)}{\mathbb{E}\,\mathrm{Crt}_N(\eta)} \xrightarrow{N \to \infty} 1. \tag{29.21}$$

The same result was also proved for $\eta \in (-\infty, \mathsf{THR})$ in [11] but only for $p \geq 32$. It is expected to be true for any $p \geq 3$. For models ξ that are close to a pure p-spin, the logarithm of the ratio in (29.20) was shown to be $o(N)$ for energies η close to E_0, see [12]. Let us now explain in words some important consequences of Theorem 3 above. First, one obtains that for any $\eta < \mathsf{E}_0$, we have $\mathrm{Crt}_N(\eta) = \exp\{N\Sigma(\eta) + o(N)\} \geq 1$ with high probability. This implies the inequality that complements (29.17), namely

$$\mathsf{OPT} \geq \mathsf{E}_0,$$

establishing, without the need to use the Parisi formula, the value of the ground state energy.

Further, the scenario described above of minima separated by barriers of order N holds in this case by Theorem 3 and Eq. (29.19). Namely, for values of $\eta \in (\mathsf{E}_1, \mathsf{E}_0)$, $\mathsf{L}_N(\eta)$ can be written as

$$\mathsf{L}_N(\eta) = \bigcup_{\alpha=1}^{M} C_\alpha$$

where the sets C_α are connected, disjoint sets, each one homeomorphic to a point and $M = \exp(N\Sigma(\eta) + o(N))$.

A further consequence of Theorem 2 — always in the pure p-spin spherical model — is the role played by the energy threshold THR. This is the unique value of energy such that the complexities of critical points of fixed index k coincide, namely,

$$\Sigma_k(\mathsf{THR}) = \Sigma_{k'}(\mathsf{THR}) \text{ for all } k, k' \geq 0,$$

and such that for any $\varepsilon > 0$ the probability that there exists a critical point of index $N - 1 - k$ in $H_N(\boldsymbol{\sigma}) \leq N(\mathsf{THR} - \varepsilon)$ decays exponentially for large N, see [9, Theorem 2.14]. In other words, with high probability, for any fixed $k \geq 0$, a critical point of index $N - k - 1$ can only exist at energy density values in the interval $[\mathsf{THR}, \mathsf{E}_k]$. By symmetry, critical points of index k can only exist at energy density values in the interval $[-\mathsf{E}_k, -\mathsf{THR}]$.

Remark 29.2.1 (A short comment on methods). The main tool to study the moments of the random variables $\mathrm{Crt}_N(\eta)$ and establish the results above is the Kac-Rice formula (see [13] and Chapter 6). This formula relates the ℓ-th moment of $\mathrm{Crt}_N(\eta)$ to ℓ-fold integrals of certain functions of ℓ determinants of $\nabla^2 H_N(\boldsymbol{\sigma})$. The collection $\{\nabla^2 H_N(\boldsymbol{\sigma})\}_{\boldsymbol{\sigma} \in \Sigma_N}$ is a family of correlated random matrices whose entry distributions can be explicitly evaluated. It turns out that these Hessians can be analyzed as coupled Gaussian orthogonal ensembles plus a random shift and tools from random matrix theory (in particular, large deviation principles) become available [9].

Remark 29.2.2 (Other directions). Here we focused on the spherical mixed p-spin model. The complexity of the pure p-spin model was first computed using non-rigorous tools from statistical physics in [14]. The rigorous landscape-complexity program — counting critical points of high-dimensional random functions to understand their geometry — initiated with a breakthrough insight by Y. Fyodorov in [15, 16], who studied isotropic Gaussian fields followed by the work [9]. More recently, this line of work led to the analysis of other disordered models including the bipartite spin glass [17, 18], the spiked-tensor model [19, 20], models with less invariance [21], and Gaussian fields with isotropic increments [22].

29.2.2. *The landscape near* OPT

As we saw above, in the pure p-spin spherical model, the value of OPT can be computed from the annealed complexity of critical points $\Sigma(\eta)$ and it is equal to the unique point E_0 such that $\Sigma(\mathsf{E}_0) = 0$. In this section we also consider the Ising case where $\Sigma_n = \{+1, -1\}^N$.

In the general case, the value of OPT is characterized by the zero-temperature Parisi formula, cf. Theorem 1. The minimizer $\gamma_\star$ of (29.8) is known to be unique, and is referred to as the Parisi measure at zero temperature. We write $\mathrm{supp}(\gamma_\star)$ for its support, that is

$$\mathrm{supp}(\gamma_\star) = \big\{ q \in [0, 1] : \gamma_\star \text{ is not constant in any neighborhood of } q \big\}.$$

The structure of $\gamma_\star$ and in particular its support contains information about the structure of the superlevel set $\mathsf{L}_N(\eta)$ when η is close to OPT, as will be discussed below.

Physicists have put forward several predictions about the structure of $\gamma_\star$ for different models, on the basis of heuristic arguments and numerical solutions of the variational principle. Unfortunately verifying rigorously these predictions is very challenging, especially for the Ising model $\Sigma_N = \{+1, -1\}^N$, since in this case there is no closed form expression for $\gamma_\star$.

In particular, in the case $\Sigma_N = \{+1, -1\}^N$, it is expected that there exists $0 \leq a < 1$ such that $[a, 1] \subseteq \mathrm{supp}\,\gamma_\star$. This is known as full replica symmetry breaking (FRSB) prediction at zero temperature. For the special case of the Sherrington–Kirkpatrick model, i.e., $\xi(t) = t^2$ and $\Sigma_N = \{+1, -1\}^N$, it is believed that $\mathrm{supp}(\gamma_\star) = [0, 1]$. In this direction, the current state of the art is given by the result of Auffinger–Chen–Zeng [23] that establishes that $\mathrm{supp}(\gamma_\star)$ contains infinitely many points for any mixture ξ. In contrast to the FRSB prediction, in the spherical case, there exist models ξ such that $\#\{\mathrm{supp}(\gamma_\star)\} = k$, for $k = 1, 2$ [24]. (Here we continue to assume no magnetic field, i.e., no linear field in the Hamiltonian H_N.)

Roughly speaking, the connection between $\gamma_\star$ and the geometry of near optima is in the fact that the support of $\gamma_\star$ consists of all the values taken by the 'overlap' $\langle \boldsymbol{\sigma}^1, \boldsymbol{\sigma}^2 \rangle / N$, when $\boldsymbol{\sigma}^1, \boldsymbol{\sigma}^2 \in \mathsf{L}_N(\eta)$ and η is close to OPT.

In order to formalize this statement, for fixed $\eta > 0$ and Borel measurable set $A \subset [-1, 1]$, set

$$\mathrm{P}_N(\eta, A) := \mathbb{P}\big(\exists\, \boldsymbol{\sigma}^1, \boldsymbol{\sigma}^2 \in \mathsf{L}_N(\eta) \text{ with } \langle \boldsymbol{\sigma}^1, \boldsymbol{\sigma}^2 \rangle / N \in A \big). \tag{29.22}$$

In other words, $\mathrm{P}_N(\eta, A)$ is the probability that there exist two spin configurations with energy values above $N\eta$ and whose overlap lies in A.

Theorem 4 ([5, 25]). *Consider* $\Sigma_N = \{+1, -1\}^N$ *or* $\Sigma_N = \mathbb{S}^{N-1}(\sqrt{N})$, *and the Hamiltonian* H_N, *with no magnetic field. Assume* ξ *to be even. Let* $u \in [-1, 1]$ *with* $|u| \in \mathrm{supp}(\gamma_\star)$. *Then, for any* $\varepsilon > 0, \eta < $ OPT, *there exists* $K > 0$ *such that for all* $N \geq 1$,

$$\mathrm{P}_N\big(\eta, (u - \varepsilon, u + \varepsilon)\big) \geq 1 - K e^{-\frac{N}{K}}. \tag{29.23}$$

One should expect that for values of u outside the support of $\gamma_\star$ the opposite holds. Namely, for η sufficiently large but smaller than OPT, the probability of finding two configurations $\boldsymbol{\sigma}^1, \boldsymbol{\sigma}^2 \in \mathsf{L}_N(\eta)$ with overlap u such that $|u| \notin \mathrm{supp}(\gamma_\star)$ should approach zero as $N \to \infty$. This is only known in the case of either positive external field or in the spherical model under the extra assumption that the 1-RSB occurs at zero temperature[b] [25]. The last condition is known to hold (in the spherical model) for instance if the model satisfies $\xi'(1) > \xi''(0)(1+z)$ and $s/\xi'(s)$ is convex on $(0,1)$, where z is the unique solution of

$$\frac{1}{\xi'(1)} = \frac{1+z}{z^2} \log(1+z) - \frac{1}{z}. \tag{29.24}$$

We conclude this section by mentioning that both in the spherical and in the Ising model, it is known that there exist exponentially many nearly orthogonal configurations near the ground state energy [5, 25]. More precisely, for $\epsilon, \eta, K > 0$ and $q \in [0,1]$, denote by $\overline{\mathrm{P}}_N(\varepsilon, \eta, q, K)$ the probability that there exists a subset $O_N \subseteq \Sigma_N$ such that

 (i) $O_N \subset \mathsf{L}_N(\eta)$.
 (ii) O_N contains at least $Ke^{N/K}$ many elements.
 (iii) $|\langle \boldsymbol{\sigma}, \boldsymbol{\sigma}' \rangle| \leq N\varepsilon$ for all distinct $\boldsymbol{\sigma}, \boldsymbol{\sigma}' \in O_N$.

Then is its known that for any $\varepsilon, \eta > 0$, there exists $K > 0$ such that for any $N \geq 1$,

$$\overline{\mathrm{P}}_N(\varepsilon, \eta, q_0, K) \geq 1 - Ke^{-N/K}.$$

This phenomenon is connected to chaos in disorder and was explored by many authors [25–27].

29.3. The TAP Approach and Free Energy

Can we approximate the superlevel sets $\mathsf{L}_N(\eta)$ by simpler subsets of Σ_N? One way to make this question more precise is to consider an explicit family of subsets of Σ_N. It turns out that a convenient such family is provided by thin 'bands' of the form

$$\mathrm{Band}(\boldsymbol{m}, \delta) := \{\boldsymbol{\sigma} \in \Sigma_N : |\langle \boldsymbol{\sigma} - \boldsymbol{m}, \boldsymbol{m} \rangle| < N\delta\},$$

around points $\boldsymbol{m} \in \overline{\Sigma}_N := \mathrm{conv}(\Sigma_N)$ with small $\delta > 0$. We then can ask how can we choose $\boldsymbol{m} \in \overline{\Sigma}_N$ so that the volume of $\mathrm{Band}(\boldsymbol{m}, \delta) \cap \mathsf{L}_N(\eta)$ is approximately the same as the volume of $\mathsf{L}_N(\eta)$. Since the volumes of $\mathrm{Band}(\boldsymbol{m}, \delta)$ and $\mathsf{L}_N(\eta)$ are exponentially smaller than the volume of Σ_N, it makes sense to require that the approximation holds on the logarithmic scale:

$$\log \mathrm{Vol}(\mathrm{Band}(\boldsymbol{m}, \delta) \cap \mathsf{L}_N(\eta)) = \log \mathrm{Vol}(\mathsf{L}_N(\eta)) + o(N). \tag{29.25}$$

Note that, if we could answer this question for all $\eta < \mathsf{OPT}$, we would also be able to identify near optima of H_N.

Equation (29.25) requires that $\mathrm{Band}(\boldsymbol{m}, \delta)$ has measure not exponentially small under the uniform measure on $\mathsf{L}_N(\eta)$. An essentially equivalent way to formulate the same

---

[b]Namely, $\gamma_\star(t) = c_0 + c_1 \mathbf{1}(t \geq t_0)$ for some constants c_0, c_1, t_0.

condition is to consider the Gibbs measure of Eq. (29.11) and ask that

$$\log G_{N,\beta}(\mathrm{Band}(\boldsymbol{m},\delta)) = o(N). \tag{29.26}$$

This can be restated in terms of the free energy of Eq. (29.12). The question is then for which points $\boldsymbol{m} \in \overline{\Sigma}_N$, we have

$$F_{N,\beta} = F_{N,\beta}(\boldsymbol{m},\delta) + o_N(1), \tag{29.27}$$

$$F_{N,\beta}(\boldsymbol{m},\delta) := \frac{1}{N} \log \left\{ \int_{\mathrm{Band}(\boldsymbol{m},\delta)} e^{\beta H_N(\boldsymbol{\sigma})} \mathrm{d}\boldsymbol{\sigma} \right\}.$$

After giving it some thought, one realizes that the set of such points $\boldsymbol{m}$ can be very large, and it might be a good idea to look for a subset of 'special' such points. The basic problem is that if there is a small region of Σ_N containing a large portion of the Gibbs measure $G_{N,\beta}$, there are many possible ways to choose $\boldsymbol{m}$ such that the band $\mathrm{Band}(\boldsymbol{m},\delta)$ will contain most of this region. As an extreme example, consider the case in which $G_{N,\beta}$ concentrates at a single configuration $\boldsymbol{\sigma}_0$. Then, all vectors $\boldsymbol{m} \in \overline{\Sigma}_N$ such that $\|\boldsymbol{m} - \boldsymbol{\sigma}_0/2\|_2^2 \approx \|\boldsymbol{\sigma}_0/2\|_2^2$ would be selected.

In light of this example, we could require that the Gibbs measure on the band $\mathrm{Band}(\boldsymbol{m},\delta)$ does not concentrate in any specific direction within the band. Namely, that for any non-random $\boldsymbol{\sigma}' \in \mathrm{Band}(\boldsymbol{m},\delta)$ and small $\varepsilon > 0$,

$$G_{N,\beta}\left(\left|\langle \boldsymbol{\sigma},\boldsymbol{\sigma}'\rangle - \langle \boldsymbol{m},\boldsymbol{m}\rangle\right| < \varepsilon N \,\Big|\, \boldsymbol{\sigma} \in \mathrm{Band}(\boldsymbol{m},\delta)\right) = 1 - o_N(1).$$

For reasons that will become clearer below, we will work with a weaker condition. We require that given two constants $\varepsilon > 0$ (small) and k (large),

$$\frac{1}{N}\log G_{N,\beta}^{\otimes k}\left(\forall i\neq j\colon \left|\langle \boldsymbol{\sigma}^i,\boldsymbol{\sigma}^j\rangle - \langle \boldsymbol{m},\boldsymbol{m}\rangle\right| < \varepsilon N \,\Big|\, \boldsymbol{\sigma}^i \in \mathrm{Band}(\boldsymbol{m},\delta)\forall i\right) = o_N(1). \tag{29.28}$$

Defining $\tilde{\boldsymbol{\sigma}} := \boldsymbol{\sigma} - \boldsymbol{m}$, for small δ and ε the above means that the probability to sample many replicas from $\mathrm{Band}(\boldsymbol{m},\delta)$ such that $\langle \tilde{\boldsymbol{\sigma}}^i, \tilde{\boldsymbol{\sigma}}^j\rangle/N = o(1)$ for all $i \neq j$ is not exponentially small.

With this extra constraint, can we identify the heavy bands which satisfy both Eq. (29.27) and Eq. (29.28)? It turns out that the answer is positive, and that they are characterized asymptotically by the simple approximate equality

$$\frac{\beta}{N}H_N(\boldsymbol{m}) + \mathrm{TAP}_\beta(\mu_{\boldsymbol{m}}) = F_{N,\beta} + o_N(1), \tag{29.29}$$

where $\mathrm{TAP}_\beta(\mu_{\boldsymbol{m}})$ is a deterministic functional of the empirical measure $\mu_{\boldsymbol{m}} := N^{-1}\sum_i \delta_{m_i}$.

Recall that we started this section by asking whether we can approximate the level sets $\mathsf{L}_N(\eta)$ (or the Gibbs measure $G_{N,\beta}$) by simpler subsets of Σ_N: thin bands $\mathrm{Band}(\boldsymbol{m},\delta)$. At first sight, this question seems significantly harder than the one of finding near maxima of $H_N(\boldsymbol{\sigma})$. However, Eq. (29.29) suggests that we can reduce the problem of finding the optimal band centers $\boldsymbol{m}$ to the one of maximizing the free energy functional $\beta H_N(\boldsymbol{m}) + N\mathrm{TAP}_\beta(\mu_{\boldsymbol{m}})$.

As implied by the notation, the functional $\mathrm{TAP}_\beta(\mu_{\boldsymbol{m}})$, which was introduced in [28, 29], is a generalization of the TAP free energy invented by Thouless, Anderson and

Palmer [30]. We will define it and explain how it is computed in the Sec. 29.3.1. By maximizing over $\boldsymbol{m}$, the characterization (29.29) above also leads to a generalized TAP representation for the free energy which we will state in Sec. 29.3.2. Finally, in Sec. 29.3.3 we will describe how one can obtain from the classical pure states decomposition a tree all of whose vertices satisfy (29.29), which will motivate some of the algorithms in Sec. 29.4.

29.3.1. *Generalized TAP correction*

Define the set of k-tuples from the band $\mathrm{Band}(\boldsymbol{m},\delta)$:

$$\mathrm{Band}_k(\boldsymbol{m},\delta,\varepsilon) := \left\{ (\boldsymbol{\sigma}^1,...,\boldsymbol{\sigma}^k) \in \mathrm{Band}(\boldsymbol{m},\delta)^k : \forall i \neq j, |\langle \boldsymbol{\sigma}^i, \boldsymbol{\sigma}^j \rangle - \langle \boldsymbol{m},\boldsymbol{m} \rangle| < N\varepsilon \right\}$$

and the replicated free energy

$$\mathrm{TAP}_{N,\beta,k}(\boldsymbol{m},\delta,\varepsilon) := \frac{1}{kN} \log \left\{ \int_{\mathrm{Band}_k(\boldsymbol{m},\delta,\varepsilon)} e^{\beta \sum_{i \leq k}[H_N(\boldsymbol{\sigma}^i) - H_N(\boldsymbol{m})]} \mathrm{d}\boldsymbol{\sigma}^1 \cdots \mathrm{d}\boldsymbol{\sigma}^k \right\}. \qquad (29.30)$$

Observe that

$$F_{N,\beta}(\boldsymbol{m},\delta) = \frac{\beta}{N} H_N(\boldsymbol{m}) + \mathrm{TAP}_{N,\beta,1}(\boldsymbol{m},\delta,\varepsilon) \geq \frac{\beta}{N} H_N(\boldsymbol{m}) + \mathrm{TAP}_{N,\beta,k}(\boldsymbol{m},\delta,\varepsilon), \qquad (29.31)$$

where the difference of the two sides of the inequality is exactly the left-hand side of (29.28) divided by k.

Define the limit

$$\mathrm{TAP}_\beta(\mu) := \inf_{\delta,\varepsilon,k} \lim_{N \to \infty} \mathbb{E}\,\mathrm{TAP}_{N,\beta,k}(\boldsymbol{m}_N,\delta,\varepsilon), \qquad (29.32)$$

where $\boldsymbol{m}_N$ is an arbitrary sequence such that $\mu_{\boldsymbol{m}_N} \Rightarrow \mu$. The fact that the limit in Eq. (29.32) exists is of course highly non-trivial and is established in [29, Theorem 1] for Ising models and in [28, Propostion 1] for spherical models.[c] Below we will give more explicit expressions for $\mathrm{TAP}_\beta(\mu)$ and sketch how it is computed. Before that, we discuss one of its key properties: the fact that it concentrates uniformly in $\boldsymbol{m}$.

For a single point $\boldsymbol{m}$ and any δ, ε and k, the deviation of $\mathrm{TAP}_{N,\beta,k}(\boldsymbol{m},\delta,\varepsilon)$ from its mean is small with high probability, as for the usual free energy. More precisely, standard concentration-of-measure arguments imply that, for any $\boldsymbol{m} \in \overline{\Sigma}_N$ and any $k,\varepsilon,\delta,t > 0$ there exists $c > 0$ such that, for all N large enough

$$\mathbb{P}\left(\left| \mathrm{TAP}_{N,\beta,k}(\boldsymbol{m},\delta,\varepsilon) - \mathbb{E}\mathrm{TAP}_{N,\beta,k}(\boldsymbol{m},\delta,\varepsilon) \right| < t \right) > 1 - e^{-cN}. \qquad (29.33)$$

The maximal deviation over all $\boldsymbol{m}$, however, is typically of order $O(1)$.

However, the concentration of $\mathrm{TAP}_{N,\beta,k}(\boldsymbol{m},\delta,\varepsilon)$ improves as k gets larger and ε,δ get smaller. Indeed, the strength of the concentration is dictated by the maximal variance of the process $\sum_{i \leq k}[H_N(\boldsymbol{\sigma}^i) - H_N(\boldsymbol{m})]$ over $\mathrm{Band}_k(\boldsymbol{m},\delta,\varepsilon)$ divided by k^2, (coming from the division by k before the log) which is of the order of $N(1/k + \delta + \varepsilon)$. As we let $\delta,\varepsilon \to 0$ and $k \to \infty$ we have the following uniform concentration result.

---

[c]To be precise, what is proved is that with the limit in N replaced either by lim sup or lim inf the above converges to the same quantity. Technically, in the definition above we should use either of them.

Theorem 5 (Generalized TAP correction [29, Theorem 1], [28, Proposition 1]). *For any $c, t > 0$, if $\delta, \varepsilon > 0$ are small enough and $k \geq 1$ is large enough, then for large N,*

$$\mathbb{P}\left(\forall m \in \overline{\Sigma}_N : \left| \mathrm{TAP}_{N,\beta,k}(m, \delta, \varepsilon) - \mathrm{TAP}_\beta(\mu_m) \right| < t \right) > 1 - e^{-cN}.$$

Next we discuss the computation of $\mathrm{TAP}_\beta(\mu)$. Recall the notation $\tilde{\sigma} = \sigma - m$. If $\sigma \in \mathrm{Band}(m, \delta)$, for small δ,

$$H_N(\sigma) - H_N(m) = H_N^m(\tilde{\sigma}) + \nabla H_N(m) \cdot \tilde{\sigma} + NO(\delta). \tag{29.34}$$

We can think of $H_N^m(\tilde{\sigma})$ as the residual of the first order Taylor expansion of $H_N(\sigma)$ around m. This turns out to be a Gaussian spin glass Hamiltonian, with covariance

$$\mathbb{E} H_N^m(\tilde{\sigma}^1) H_N^m(\tilde{\sigma}^2) = N \tilde{\xi}_q(\langle \tilde{\sigma}^1, \tilde{\sigma}^2 \rangle / N). \tag{29.35}$$

Here $\tilde{\xi}_q(x) := \xi(x + q) - \xi(q) - \xi'(q)x$. Note that $\tilde{\xi}_q(0) = \tilde{\xi}_q'(0) = 0$ corresponding to the fact that the Hamiltonian $H_N^m(\tilde{\sigma})$ which does not contain linear terms in $\tilde{\sigma}$ (a 'random field' or '1-spin interaction' in physics language).

Denote by $\mathrm{TAP}^0_{N,\beta,k}(m, \delta, \varepsilon)$ the free energy defined as in Eq. (29.30), but with $H_N(\sigma^i) - H_N(m)$ replaced by $H_N^m(\tilde{\sigma}^i)$, for each $i \leq k$. Note that if $|\langle \tilde{\sigma}^i, \tilde{\sigma}^j \rangle| < N\varepsilon$ for any $i < j \leq k$, then

$$\left| \frac{1}{k} \sum_{i \leq k} \nabla H_N(m) \cdot \tilde{\sigma}^i \right| \leq \left\| \frac{1}{k} \sum_{i \leq k} \tilde{\sigma}^i \right\| \cdot \left\| \nabla H_N(m) \right\|$$

$$\leq \sqrt{N(1/k + \varepsilon)} \left\| \nabla H_N(m) \right\| = \sqrt{1/k + \varepsilon} \cdot O(N). \tag{29.36}$$

Hence,

$$\mathbb{E} \, \mathrm{TAP}_{N,\beta,k}(m, \delta, \varepsilon) = \mathbb{E} \, \mathrm{TAP}^0_{N,\beta,k}(m, \delta, \varepsilon) + o_{\delta,\varepsilon,k}(1), \tag{29.37}$$

where $o_{\delta,\varepsilon,k}(1)$ denotes an error bounded uniformly in N by a quantity that vanishes if we let $\delta, \varepsilon \to 0$ and $k \to \infty$.

At this point, the treatment is slightly different in the spherical and Ising cases.

In the spherical case $\Sigma_N = \mathbb{S}^{N-1}(\sqrt{N})$, it can be shown that for small δ and any ε and k,

$$\mathbb{E} \, \mathrm{TAP}^0_{N,\beta,k}(m, \delta, \varepsilon) = \mathbb{E} \, \mathrm{TAP}^0_{N,\beta,1}(m, \delta) + o_\delta(1), \tag{29.38}$$

where $o_\delta(1)$ denotes an error bounded uniformly in N by a quantity independent of k, ε, that vanishes if we let $\delta \to 0$. Note that $\mathrm{TAP}^0_{N,\beta,1}(m, \delta) := \mathrm{TAP}^0_{N,\beta,1}(m, \delta, \varepsilon)$ does not depend on ε, as it is computed with one replica. That is, once we remove the external field in (29.34), computing the free energy with many replicas instead of one has no cost asymptotically.

By combining the above one obtains that the TAP correction only depends on μ via its second moment $q = \int x^2 \mu(dx)$ and, for an arbitrary sequence $m = m_N$ such that $\langle m_N, m_N \rangle / N \to q$, is given by

$$\mathrm{TAP}_\beta(\mu) = \inf_\delta \lim_{N \to \infty} \mathbb{E}\mathrm{TAP}^0_{N,\beta,1}(m, \delta) = \frac{1}{2} \log(1 - q) + F_\beta(q). \tag{29.39}$$

The logarithmic term, which accounts for a change of volume, is equal to the asymptotic entropy

$$\inf_{\delta} \lim_{N \to \infty} \frac{1}{N} \log \mathrm{Vol}(\mathrm{Band}(\boldsymbol{m}_N, \delta)) = \frac{1}{2} \log(1 - q). \tag{29.40}$$

The term $F_\beta(q)$ is more interesting and is defined as the free energy of the spherical spin glass model with mixture $\xi_q(x) := \tilde{\xi}_q((1-q)x)$. The expression of Eq. (29.39) simplifies when $q = q_{\mathrm{EA}}$ is the Edwards–Anderson parameter, i.e., the rightmost point in the support of the Parisi measure. In this case, the model for $\tilde{\boldsymbol{\sigma}}$ is in its paramagnetic phase, which means that its partition function is well approximated by its expectation: in particular, this submodel is replica symmetric. Hence, we get the simple expression $F_\beta(q_{\mathrm{EA}}) = \frac{1}{2}\beta^2 \xi_{q_{\mathrm{EA}}}(1)$, see [28, Corollaries 5,11], which is known as the Onsager correction term and appears in the original TAP formulation.

In the Ising case $\Sigma_N = \{+1, -1\}^N$, computing $\mathbb{E} \, \mathrm{TAP}^0_{N,\beta,k}(\boldsymbol{m}, \delta, \varepsilon)$ is more challenging, as Eq. (29.38) does not hold anymore. In other words, removing the 'magnetic field' term is not enough to make the replicas roughly independent.

In this case, for a function $h \colon [-1, 1] \to \mathbb{R}$, denote by $\mathrm{TAP}^h_{N,\beta,k}(\boldsymbol{m}, \delta, \varepsilon)$ the free energy computed as in Eq. (29.30), but with $H_N(\boldsymbol{\sigma}^i) - H_N(\boldsymbol{m})$ now replaced by $H_N^m(\tilde{\boldsymbol{\sigma}}^i) + \sum_{j \leq N} h(m_j)\tilde{\boldsymbol{\sigma}}^i_j$. By a bound similar to (29.36), the approximation as in (29.37) also holds for such general h instead of $h \equiv 0$. Using Eq. (29.31), we therefore have that for large k,

$$\begin{aligned}
\mathbb{E} \, \mathrm{TAP}_{N,\beta,k}(\boldsymbol{m}, \delta, \varepsilon) &= \mathbb{E} \, \mathrm{TAP}^h_{N,\beta,k}(m, \delta, \varepsilon) + o_{\delta,\varepsilon,k}(1) \\
&\leq \mathbb{E} \, \mathrm{TAP}^h_{N,\beta,1}(\boldsymbol{m}, \delta) + o_{\delta,\varepsilon,k}(1).
\end{aligned} \tag{29.41}$$

It is possible to show that there exists a specific choice of an external field h such that the last inequality asymptotically holds as an equality, and therefore

$$\mathrm{TAP}_\beta(\mu) = \inf_{h,\delta} \lim_{N \to \infty} \mathbb{E} \, \mathrm{TAP}^h_{N,\beta,1}(\boldsymbol{m}_N, \delta),$$

where $\boldsymbol{m}_N \in [-1, 1]$ is an arbitrary sequence such that $\mu_{\boldsymbol{m}_N} \Rightarrow \mu$.

The last result was proved in [29], which also prove that the TAP correction admits the following Parisi type formula,

$$\mathrm{TAP}_\beta(\mu) = \inf_{\zeta \in \mathscr{P}([0,1])} \left(\int \Lambda_\zeta(q, a)\, \mu(\mathrm{d}a) - \frac{1}{2}\beta^2 \int_q^1 s\xi''(s)\zeta(s)\, \mathrm{d}s \right),$$

where $q = \int x^2\, \mu(\mathrm{d}x)$, $\mathscr{P}([0,1])$ is the space of probability measures on $[0,1]$, $\Lambda_\zeta(q, a) := \inf_{x \in \mathbb{R}} \left(\Phi_\zeta(q, x) - ax \right)$ and $\Phi_\zeta(q, x)$ is the solution of the Parisi PDE

$$\partial_t \Phi_\zeta = -\frac{1}{2}\beta^2 \xi''(t) \left(\partial_{xx} \Phi_\zeta + \zeta([0,t])(\partial_x \Phi_\zeta)^2 \right)$$

on $[0, 1] \times \mathbb{R}$ with boundary condition $\Phi_\zeta(1, x) = \log 2 \cosh x$. This is the non-zero temperature version of the Parisi PDE of Eq. (29.5).

Again, the expression for $\mathrm{TAP}_\beta(\mu)$ simplifies when $q = q_{\mathrm{EA}}$, in certain cases. Namely, under a certain optimality condition which implies Plefka's condition [31], which holds at least for some points $\boldsymbol{m}$ with $\|\boldsymbol{m}\|^2/N = q = q_{\mathrm{EA}}$, it was proved in [29] that the correction coincides with the classical Onsager correction

$$\mathrm{TAP}_\beta(\mu) = -\int_{\mathbb{R}} I(x)\,\mu(\mathrm{d}x) + \frac{1}{2}\beta^2 \xi_q(1).$$

Here $I(x) = \frac{1+x}{2}\log\frac{1+x}{2} + \frac{1-x}{2}\log\frac{1-x}{2}$ and the first term above corresponds to the entropy of the band as before.

29.3.2. *Generalized TAP representation*

For q in the support of the Parisi measure, there exists a (random) sequence $\boldsymbol{m}_\star = \boldsymbol{m}_{\star,N}$ with $\langle \boldsymbol{m}_\star, \boldsymbol{m}_\star \rangle / N = q$ such that for any ε, δ and k, with high probability both (29.27) and (29.28) hold, or equivalently,

$$F_{N,\beta} = F_{N,\beta}(\boldsymbol{m}_\star, \delta) + o_N(1) = \frac{\beta}{N}H_N(\boldsymbol{m}_\star) + \mathrm{TAP}_{N,\beta,k}(\boldsymbol{m}_\star, \delta, \varepsilon) + o_N(1)$$

$$= \frac{\beta}{N}H_N(\boldsymbol{m}_\star) + \mathrm{TAP}_\beta(\mu_{\boldsymbol{m}_\star}) + o_N(1), \tag{29.42}$$

where the last approximation follows from the concentration of Theorem 5. By (29.31), for any m,

$$F_{N,\beta} \geq \frac{\beta}{N}H_N(\boldsymbol{m}) + \mathrm{TAP}_\beta(\mu_{\boldsymbol{m}}) + o_N(1).$$

The following theorem follows.

Theorem 6 (Generalized TAP representation [29, Theorem 2], [28, Theorem 4]). *For any q in the support of the Parisi measure, in probability,*

$$\lim_{N\to\infty}\left|F_{N,\beta} - \max_{\|\boldsymbol{m}\|_2^2 = Nq}\left(\frac{\beta}{N}H_N(\boldsymbol{m}) + \mathrm{TAP}_\beta(\mu_{\boldsymbol{m}})\right)\right| = 0. \tag{29.43}$$

An explicit expression using the Parisi measure for the value of $\frac{1}{N}H_N(\boldsymbol{m})$ at any approximate maximizer of the above can also be derived, see [28, Proposition 10] and [32, Theorem 5].

In the spherical case, $\mathrm{TAP}_\beta(\mu_{\boldsymbol{m}})$ is constant on the sphere and only the Hamiltonian is maximized in (29.43). For the pure spherical models, this can be used to compute the free energy at any temperature [33], also for multi-species models [34, 35]. For earlier results on the TAP representation with the classical Onsager correction see [12, 14, 36–40, 51].

Remark 29.3.1. It is useful to comment on the implication of Theorem 6 for optimization. In this case we are interested in maximizing $H_N(\boldsymbol{m})$ subject to $\boldsymbol{m} \in \overline{\Sigma}_N$ and $\langle \boldsymbol{m}, \boldsymbol{m} \rangle / N = 1$ (the last two constraints are equivalent to $\boldsymbol{m} \in \Sigma_N$).

Since we are only interested in achieving any value $\eta < \mathsf{OPT}$, it is reasonable to perturb this problem in two ways. First, we will accept $\langle \boldsymbol{m}, \boldsymbol{m} \rangle / N \geq q_\star$ for some $q_\star$ close to 1. Second, we perturb the cost function $H_N(\boldsymbol{m})$ by considering $H_N(\boldsymbol{m}) + (N/\beta)\mathrm{TAP}_\beta(\mu_{\boldsymbol{m}})$.

Theorem 6 states a remarkable property of this modified objective function. Namely, for any q in the support of Parisi's measure (and therefore, possibly, for any $q \in [0, q_\star]$)

this objective function has an optimizer on the sphere of radius $\sqrt{Nq}$, with value close to the optimum on the sphere $\sqrt{Nq_\star}$. This naturally suggests to find the latter by gradually increasing this radius. This is indeed what we will do in Sec. 29.4, although not explicitly using the free energy $H_N(\boldsymbol{m}) + (N/\beta)\mathrm{TAP}_\beta(\mu_{\boldsymbol{m}})$.

29.3.3. *The tree of pure states*

Recall the pure state decomposition of the Gibbs measure [1, 41, 42]. Namely, at low temperatures there exists (as proven in [41, 42] for 'generic' mixtures ξ) a partition $\Sigma_N = \cup_{\alpha \in \mathcal{S}} B_\alpha \cup D$, so that $G_{N,\beta}(D) = o_N(1)$ (D is negligible) and therefore

$$G_{N,\beta}(\cdot) \approx \sum_{\alpha \in \mathcal{S}} w_\alpha G^{(\alpha)}(\cdot), \quad w_\alpha := G_{N,\beta}(B_\alpha), \quad G^{(\alpha)}_{N,\beta}(\cdot) := G_{N,\beta}(\cdot | B_\alpha). \tag{29.44}$$

Further, each 'pure state' $G^{(\alpha)}_{N,\beta}$ can be characterized by its barycenter (magnetization)

$$\boldsymbol{m}^{(\alpha)} := \int \boldsymbol{x}\, G^{(\alpha)}_{N,\beta}(\mathrm{d}\boldsymbol{x}).$$

Namely, uniformly in $\alpha, \alpha' \in \mathcal{S}$, for any $\varepsilon > 0$,

$$G^{(\alpha)}_{N,\beta} \otimes G^{(\alpha')}_{N,\beta}\big(|\langle \boldsymbol{\sigma}^1, \boldsymbol{\sigma}^2 \rangle - \langle \boldsymbol{m}^{(\alpha)}, \boldsymbol{m}^{(\alpha')} \rangle| \geq N\varepsilon\big) = o_N(1). \tag{29.45}$$

If the Parisi distribution has an atom at q_{EA} then the weights w_α are of order $O(1)$, otherwise they decay to zero sub-exponentially as $N \to \infty$. In both cases, their asymptotic distribution can be described by Ruelle probability cascades or a limit of such.

The pure states are arranged ultrametrically [3, 43, 44]: namely for any three pure states $\alpha_1, \alpha_2, \alpha_3 \in \mathcal{S}$, letting $R_{ij} = N^{-1}|\langle \boldsymbol{m}^{(\alpha_i)}, \boldsymbol{m}^{(\alpha_j)} \rangle|$, we have $R_{12} = \max(R_{13}, R_{23}) + o_N(1)$, where the term $o_N(1)$ is uniform in $\alpha_1, \alpha_2, \alpha_3$. As a consequence, we can cluster hierarchically the pure states, and associate to each cluster C the average $\boldsymbol{m}^{(C)} := \frac{1}{|C|} \sum_{\alpha \in C} \boldsymbol{m}^{(\alpha)}$.

This hierarchical structure can be represented by a rooted tree $\mathcal{T}_{N,\beta}$. Leaves of the tree are indexed by $\alpha \in \mathcal{S}$ and associated to pure states centers $\boldsymbol{m}^{(\alpha)}$. Each other vertex of the tree corresponds to a cluster. Clusters will be indexed by $\alpha \in \mathcal{V} \setminus \mathcal{S}$, and are associated to the cluster center $\boldsymbol{m}^{(\alpha)} \in \overline{\Sigma}_N$. The theorem below summarizes a few properties of this structure. We denote by $\alpha_1 \wedge \alpha_2$ the least common ancestor of α_1 and α_2, by $|\alpha|$ the depth of α (the depth of the root being 0, and write $\alpha_1 \preceq \alpha_2$ if α_2 is a descendant of α_1 (including $\alpha_1 = \alpha_2$).

Theorem 7 (Ultrametric tree [28, Corollary 13]). *If $\xi(t) = \sum_{k \geq 2} c_k^2 t^k$ is generic[d] and β is in the RSB phase,[e] then there exist a decomposition of the Gibbs measure of the form (29.44) and an associated rooted tree $\mathcal{T}_{N,\beta}$ with vertex set $\mathcal{V} = \mathcal{V}_{N,\beta} \in \overline{\Sigma}_N$, and associated vectors $\{\boldsymbol{m}^{(\alpha)}\}_{\alpha \in \mathcal{V}}$ with the following properties:*

(1) The leaves of $\mathcal{T}_{N,\beta}$ are the barycenters $\{\boldsymbol{m}^{(\alpha)} : \alpha \in \mathcal{S}\}$ of the pure states $G^{(\alpha)}_{N,\beta}$.

---

[d]Namely, there are infinitely many values of k even such that $c_k \neq 0$ and infinitely many values of k odd such that $c_k \neq 0$.
[e]Namely, Parisi's measure is not a single point mass.

(2) *The tree is regular and complete (i.e. all leaves have the same depth) and its degree diverges.*

(3) *For any $\alpha \in \mathcal{V}$, the value of $\|\boldsymbol{m}^{(\alpha)}\|_2^2/N$ only depends on the depth $|\alpha|$.*

(4) *In the k-RSB case (that is, if Parisi's measure consists of $k+1$ point masses) the depth of the tree is equal to k. Further $Q := \{\|\boldsymbol{m}^{(\alpha)}\|_2^2/N : \alpha \in \mathcal{V}\}$ is equal to the support of the Parisi measure.*

(5) *In the full-RSB case (that is, if the support of Parisi's measure has infinite cardinality) the depth of the tree diverges and Q converges to the support of Parisi's measure as $N \to \infty$.*

(6) *Finally, the following hold with probability going to 1, for all $\alpha_1, \alpha_2 \in \mathcal{V}$ and $\alpha \in \mathcal{S}$ (for a deterministic $\delta_N = o_N(1)$):*

    (a) $\boldsymbol{m}^{(\alpha_1)} \preceq \boldsymbol{m}^{(\alpha)} \implies B_\alpha \subset \mathrm{Band}(\boldsymbol{m}^{(\alpha_1)}, \delta_N)$.

    (b) $\langle \boldsymbol{m}^{(\alpha_1)}, \boldsymbol{m}^{(\alpha_2)} \rangle/N = \|\boldsymbol{m}^{(\alpha_1 \wedge \alpha_2)}\|_2^2/N + o_N(1)$.

    (c) $\beta N^{-1} H_N(\boldsymbol{m}^{(\alpha_1)}) + \mathrm{TAP}_\beta(\mu_{\boldsymbol{m}^{(\alpha_1)}}) = F_{N,\beta} + o_N(1)$.

Remark 29.3.2. Except for the last part involving the TAP correction, this theorem follows from the decomposition of [42]. For inner vertices, the last point follows since the corresponding band contains many orthogonal pure states.

29.4. Algorithms

29.4.1. *Typical case approximation*

Is there a polynomial-time algorithm that finds near optima of the spin glass Hamiltonian $H_N(\boldsymbol{\sigma})$? From a worst case perspective, the answer is likely to be negative. Consider, to be definite, the pure degree-k Hamiltonian $H_N^{(k)}(\boldsymbol{\sigma}) = N^{-(k-1)/2}\langle \boldsymbol{G}^{(k)}, \boldsymbol{\sigma}^{\otimes k}\rangle$. In theoretical computer science, the problem of maximizing this function over Σ_N is formulated in terms of existence of an 'approximation algorithm.' An approximation algorithm accepts as input $\boldsymbol{G}^{(k)}$ and outputs $\boldsymbol{\sigma}^{\mathrm{alg}} \in \Sigma_N$ such that, for any input $\boldsymbol{G}^{(k)}$, we are guaranteed to have

$$\max_{\boldsymbol{\sigma} \in \Sigma_N} H_N^{(k)}(\boldsymbol{\sigma}) \geq H_N^{(k)}(\boldsymbol{\sigma}^{\mathrm{alg}}) \geq \rho \cdot \max_{\boldsymbol{\sigma} \in \Sigma_N} H_N^{(k)}(\boldsymbol{\sigma}), \tag{29.46}$$

with ρ independent of H_N (but possibly dependent on N). It is immediate to show that this can be achieved for the quadratic Hamiltonian $H_N^{(k=2)}(\boldsymbol{\sigma})$ under the spherical constraint $\Sigma_N = \mathbb{S}^{N-1}(\sqrt{N})$. Indeed in this case the problem can be reduced to an eigenvalue problem that is solved efficiently for any fixed approximation ratio $\rho \in (0,1)$.

However, for all the other cases this objective is all but hopeless for any constant $\rho \in (0,1)$. Indeed, achieving $\rho > 1/(\log N)^c$ (for c a small constant) is NP-hard for $k = 2$ and $\Sigma_N = \{+1, -1\}^N$ [45] (the SK model). For higher-order polynomials, the task is even more difficult. For instance, [46] proves that obtaining $\rho > \exp(-(\log N)^c\}$ is NP-hard already for the spherical case $\Sigma_N = \mathbb{S}^{N-1}(\sqrt{N})$.

These hardness results motivate the search for algorithm that achieve approximation factor ρ *with high probability* with respect to the realization of the Hamiltonian. Insights from spin glass theory can be brought to bear on the optimization question when considering random realizations of the objective.

It is convenient to come back to the general case of a mixed spin glass $H_N(\boldsymbol{\sigma})$, as defined in Eq. (29.1). Formally, we are interested in achieving the following guarantee, in polynomial time:

$$\lim_{N\to\infty} \mathbb{P}\left(H_N(\boldsymbol{\sigma}^{\mathrm{alg}}) \geq \rho \cdot \max_{\boldsymbol{\sigma}\in\Sigma_N} H_N(\boldsymbol{\sigma})\right) = 1. \tag{29.47}$$

The supremum value of ρ such that this is possible will be referred to as the 'typical case' approximation ratio ρ_*. Since $\max_{\boldsymbol{\sigma}\in\Sigma_N} H_N(\boldsymbol{\sigma})/N$ concentrates around its expectation, which has a limit as $N \to \infty$ given by Parisi formula (29.7), determining such an approximation ratio (for a specific algorithm), amounts to determine the asymptotics of $H_N(\boldsymbol{\sigma}^{\mathrm{alg}})/N$.

The structure of the space of near optima described in the previous section suggests a possible approach to construct approximate ground states. Summarizing, near optima are organized according to a tree with vertices associated to 'magnetization' vectors, i.e. vectors $\boldsymbol{m}^{(\alpha)} \in \overline{\Sigma}_N := \mathrm{conv}(\Sigma_N)$. At zero temperature, leaves of the tree are configurations $\boldsymbol{\sigma}^{(\alpha)} \in \Sigma_N$, and near optima are concentrated in the vicinity of such configurations. As in the rest of the chapter, we will assume for simplicity $\xi'(0) = 0$ (no magnetic field). In this case the root of the tree can be taken to be the zero vector $\boldsymbol{0}$.

If the Hamiltonian $H_N(\boldsymbol{\sigma})$ presents replica symmetry breaking at zero temperature with un-normalized Parisi measure γ_*, then there exist internal nodes of this tree at nearly every radius in the support of γ_*. Namely, for any $q \in \mathrm{supp}(\gamma_*)$, there exists a node $\boldsymbol{m}^{(\alpha)}$ of the tree with $\|\boldsymbol{m}^{(\alpha)}\|_2^2 = Nq + o(n)$. (See Theorem 7.)

This picture suggests a possibility for constructing an algorithm that finds near ground states: if $\mathrm{supp}(\gamma_*) = [0, 1]$, we can hope to initialize the algorithm with $\hat{\boldsymbol{m}}^0 = \boldsymbol{0}$, and then follow a branch of the tree by constructing a trajectory $t \mapsto \hat{\boldsymbol{m}}^t \in \overline{\Sigma}_N$, indexed by the 'time' variable $t \in [0, 1]$. Of course time will have to be discretized in the algorithm, and hence we will compute recursively $\hat{\boldsymbol{m}}^{t+\delta}$ as a function of $\hat{\boldsymbol{m}}^{\leq t} := (\hat{\boldsymbol{m}}^s)_{s\leq t}$.

One observation turns out to be crucial in the construction of such an algorithm. If α' is a descendant of α in the tree (See Theorem 7), then $\boldsymbol{m}^{(\alpha')} - \boldsymbol{m}^{(\alpha)}$ is roughly orthogonal to $\boldsymbol{m}^{(\alpha)}$ (namely, $\langle \boldsymbol{m}^{(\alpha')} - \boldsymbol{m}^{(\alpha)}, \boldsymbol{m}^{(\alpha)}\rangle = o(N)$). It is natural to enforce the same property in the algorithm updates by requiring that the update $\hat{\boldsymbol{m}}^{t+\delta} - \hat{\boldsymbol{m}}^t$ is roughly orthogonal $\hat{\boldsymbol{m}}^t$.

In Secs. 29.4.2.1 and 29.4.2.2 we will discuss two implementations of this idea that yield two algorithms, respectively for the spherical case $\Sigma_N = \mathbb{S}^{N-1}(\sqrt{N})$ or the general case $\Sigma_N \in \{\mathbb{S}^{N-1}(\sqrt{N}), \{+1, -1\}^N\}$. Before describing these algorithms, we state a result characterizing the energy $H_N(\boldsymbol{\sigma}^{\mathrm{alg}})$ that they achieve (and hence the corresponding approximation ration ρ). As we will see in Sec. 29.4.3 this is the optimal energy achieved by any algorithm in a broader class, which includes, among others, simulated-annealing type algorithms (when run for physical time independent of N).

In order to state the characterization of $H_N(\boldsymbol{\sigma}^{\mathrm{alg}})$, we introduce the following space of order parameters:

$$\mathcal{L} := \left\{ \gamma\colon [0,1)\to\mathbb{R}_{\geq 0} \ :\ \|\xi''\gamma\|_{\mathrm{TV}[0,t]}<\infty \ \forall t\in[0,1), \int_0^1 \xi''\gamma(t)\mathrm{d}t<\infty \right\}. \tag{29.48}$$

We endow this space with the weighted L^1 metric

$$\|\gamma_1 - \gamma_2\|_{1,\xi''} := \|\xi''(\gamma_1 - \gamma_2)\|_1 = \int_0^1 \xi''(t)|\gamma_1(t) - \gamma_2(t)|\mathrm{d}t, \qquad (29.49)$$

hence implicitly identifying γ_1 and γ_2 if they coincide for almost every $t \in [0,1)$.

The usual space of order parameters $\mathscr{U}$ appearing in Parisi formula is given by non-decreasing right-continuous functions $\gamma \colon [0,1) \to \mathbb{R}_{\geq 0}$. Hence $\mathscr{U} = \mathscr{L} \cap \{\gamma \text{ non-decreasing}\}$. The asymptotics of the energy density $H_N(\boldsymbol{\sigma}^{\mathrm{alg}})/N$ is given by a modified variational principle in which the Parisi functional is minimized over the larger space $\mathscr{U}$.

Theorem 8 ([47, Theorem 3]). *Assume that the infimum $\inf_{\gamma \in \mathscr{L}} \mathsf{P}(\gamma)$ is achieved at a function $\gamma^\star_{\mathscr{L}} \in \mathscr{L}$. Further denote by χ the computational complexity of evaluating $\nabla H_N(\boldsymbol{m})$ at a point $\boldsymbol{m} \in \overline{\Sigma}_N$, and by χ_1 the complexity of evaluating one coordinate of $\nabla H_N(\boldsymbol{m})$ at a point $\boldsymbol{m} \in \overline{\Sigma}_N$.*

Then for every $\varepsilon > 0$ there exists an algorithm with complexity at most $C(\varepsilon) \cdot (\chi + N) + N\chi_1$ which outputs $\boldsymbol{\sigma}^{\mathrm{alg}} \in \Sigma_N$ such that

$$\frac{1}{N} H_N(\boldsymbol{\sigma}^{\mathrm{alg}}) \geq \mathsf{ALG} - \varepsilon, \qquad \mathsf{ALG} := \inf_{\gamma \in \mathscr{L}} \mathsf{P}(\gamma), \qquad (29.50)$$

with probability converging to one as $N \to \infty$.

Remark 29.4.1. For the spherical model $\Sigma_N = \mathbb{S}^{N-1}(\sqrt{N})$, the Parisi PDE can be solved explicitly, yielding the following explicit form of Parisi's functional

$$\mathsf{P}(\gamma) = \inf_{L \geq \int_0^1 \gamma(s)\mathrm{d}s} \frac{1}{2} \int_0^1 \left(\xi''(t)\Gamma(t) + \frac{1}{\Gamma(t)} \right) \mathrm{d}t, \qquad (29.51)$$

$$\Gamma(t) := L - \int_0^t \gamma(s)\mathrm{d}s. \qquad (29.52)$$

This is minimized at $\Gamma(t) = 1/\sqrt{\xi''(t)}$, yielding the following simple formula for the algorithmic threshold:

$$\mathsf{ALG} = \inf\left\{\mathsf{P}(\gamma) : \gamma \in \mathscr{L}\right\} = \int_0^1 \sqrt{\xi''(t)}\,\mathrm{d}t. \qquad (29.53)$$

Still focusing on the spherical case, the order parameter $\gamma^\star_{\mathscr{L}}$ minimizing $\mathsf{P}(\gamma)$ over $\mathscr{L}$ is given by

$$\gamma^\star_{\mathscr{L}}(t) = -\frac{\mathrm{d}}{\mathrm{d}t}\xi''(t)^{-1/2} = \frac{\xi'''(t)}{2\xi''(t)^{3/2}}. \qquad (29.54)$$

If $t \mapsto \xi'''(t)/\xi''(t)^{3/2}$ is non-decreasing, this obviously minimizes $\mathsf{P}(\gamma)$ over $\mathscr{U}$ as well. Therefore, in this case, there exists a polynomial-time algorithm that achieves a $(1-\varepsilon)$-approximation of the ground start for every $\varepsilon > 0$.

For the Ising case $\Sigma_N = \{+1, -1\}^N$, the variational principle does not admit an explicit solution, and we therefore introduce the following condition.

Definition 29.4.1 (No overlap gap at zero temperature). *A mixed p-spin model with mixture ξ is said to satisfy the no-overlap gap property at zero-temperature if there exists $\gamma_\star \in \mathcal{U}$ strictly increasing in $[0,1)$ such that $\mathsf{P}(\gamma_\star) = \inf_{\gamma \in \mathcal{U}} \mathsf{P}(\gamma)$.*

(Equivalently, this condition holds if the unique solution $\gamma_\star$ of Parisi's formula is strictly increasing.)

Corollary 29.4.2. *Assume the no-overlap gap at zero temperature to hold for the mixture ξ. Then for every $\varepsilon > 0$ there exists an algorithm with the same complexity as in Theorem 8 which outputs $\boldsymbol{\sigma}^{\mathrm{alg}} \in \Sigma_N$ such that*

$$\frac{1}{N} H_N(\boldsymbol{\sigma}^{\mathrm{alg}}) \geq \frac{1}{N} \max_{\boldsymbol{\sigma} \in \Sigma_N} H_N(\boldsymbol{\sigma}) - \varepsilon, \tag{29.55}$$

with probability converging to one as $N \to \infty$.

In particular, it is currently believed that the classical SK model (corresponding to $\xi(t) = ct^2$) enjoys the no overlap gap property, and hence a $(1 - \varepsilon)$ approximation algorithm exist for any $\varepsilon > 0$.

29.4.2. *Description of the optimization algorithms*

We will next succinctly review the algorithms that achieve the energy value of Theorem 8, referring to the original papers for further detail.

29.4.2.1. *The Hessian ascent algorithm*

This algorithm was designed [48] for the spherical case $\Sigma_N = \mathbb{S}^{N-1}(\sqrt{N})$, and hence operates on a vector $\boldsymbol{m}^t \in \overline{\Sigma}_N = \mathsf{B}^N(\sqrt{N})$ (the ball of radius $\sqrt{N}$ in N dimensions). This vector is updated at discrete times $t \in \{\delta, 2\delta, \ldots, 1 - \delta, 1\}$ starting from the initialization $\boldsymbol{m}^\delta = \mathrm{Unif}(\mathbb{S}^{N-1}(\sqrt{N\delta}))$. At each $t \in \delta\mathbb{N}$, this vector is updated according to:

$$\mathcal{H}_t^\perp = \boldsymbol{P}_{\boldsymbol{m}^t}^\perp \nabla^2 H_N(\boldsymbol{m}^t) \boldsymbol{P}_{\boldsymbol{m}^t}^\perp, \tag{29.56}$$

$$\boldsymbol{m}^{t+\delta} = \boldsymbol{m}^t + \sqrt{N\delta}\, \boldsymbol{v}_1(\mathcal{H}_t^\perp). \tag{29.57}$$

Here $\nabla^2 H_N$ is the (ordinary, Euclidean) Hessian of $H_N \colon \mathbb{R}^N \to \mathbb{R}$, $\boldsymbol{P}_{\boldsymbol{m}^t}^\perp = \boldsymbol{I}_N - \boldsymbol{m}^t(\boldsymbol{m}^t)^\mathsf{T}/\|\boldsymbol{m}^t\|_2^2$ is the projector orthogonal to the current state $\boldsymbol{m}^t$, and $\boldsymbol{v}_1(\boldsymbol{M})$ denotes the (unit norm) eigenvector of a matrix $\boldsymbol{M}$ corresponding to the largest eigenvalue. The sign ambiguity of $\boldsymbol{v}_1$ can be removed so as to ensure $\langle \boldsymbol{m}^{t+\delta} - \boldsymbol{m}^t, \nabla H_N(\boldsymbol{m}^t) \rangle \geq 0$ (which is convenient for the proof) or also at random. Any other degeneracy is removed at random.

By the Pythagorean theorem, $\|\boldsymbol{m}^{t+\delta}\|_2^2 = \|\boldsymbol{m}^t\|_2^2 + N\delta$, whence $\|\boldsymbol{m}^t\|_2 = \sqrt{Nt}$. The algorithm outputs $\boldsymbol{\sigma}^{\mathrm{alg}} := \boldsymbol{m}^1 \in \mathbb{S}^{N-1}(\sqrt{N})$.

The rationale for the iteration (29.57) is relatively easy to understand. At each iteration, the algorithm tries to improve the current value by exploiting the curvature of the Hessian. However, instead of maximizing the quadratic approximation of the cost at $\boldsymbol{m}^t$ along all directions, we only consider directions that are orthogonal to the current state $\boldsymbol{m}^t$.

The use of orthogonal updates is inspired by the structure of the space of near optima described in the previous sections. Technically, it allows to remove dependencies between gains made at different time steps. Notice indeed that, by rotational invariance, for any $\boldsymbol{m} \in \mathbb{R}^N$, and for any k, we have (recalling that $H_N^{(k)}(\boldsymbol{\sigma}) = N^{-(k-1)/2}\langle \boldsymbol{G}^{(k)}, \boldsymbol{\sigma}^{\otimes k}\rangle$ is the degree-k component of the Hamiltonian)

$$\boldsymbol{P}_{\boldsymbol{m}}^{\perp}\nabla^2 H_N^{(k)}(\boldsymbol{m})\boldsymbol{P}_{\boldsymbol{m}}^{\perp}$$
$$\overset{\mathrm{d}}{=} \left(\frac{\|\boldsymbol{m}\|_2^2}{N}\right)^{(k-2)/2}\sqrt{\frac{k(k-1)}{2N}}((G^{(k)})_{i,j,1,\ldots,1} + (G^{(k)})_{j,i,1,\ldots,1})_{2\leq i,j\leq N}, \quad (29.58)$$

whence,[f] for $\|\boldsymbol{m}\|_2^2 = Nt$, $\boldsymbol{P}_{\boldsymbol{m}}^{\perp}\nabla^2 H_N(\boldsymbol{m})\boldsymbol{P}_{\boldsymbol{m}}^{\perp} \overset{\mathrm{d}}{=} \sqrt{\xi''(t)(1-N^{-1})}\mathsf{GOE}(N-1)$. If $\boldsymbol{m}^t$ was independent of H_N, the energy increment at each step of the algorithm would therefore be

$$H_N(\boldsymbol{m}^{t+\delta}) - H_N(\boldsymbol{m}^t) \geq \frac{1}{2}N\delta\lambda_1(\boldsymbol{P}_{\boldsymbol{m}^t}^{\perp}\nabla^2 H_N(\boldsymbol{m}^t)\boldsymbol{P}_{\boldsymbol{m}^t}^{\perp}) + No(\delta),$$
$$\lambda_1(\boldsymbol{P}_{\boldsymbol{m}^t}^{\perp}\nabla^2 H_N(\boldsymbol{m}^t)\boldsymbol{P}_{\boldsymbol{m}^t}^{\perp}) \geq 2\sqrt{\xi''(t)}\delta - o_N(1). \tag{29.59}$$

(The first inequality holds because the contribution of the first order term in the Taylor expansion is non-negative by our choice of the sign of $\boldsymbol{v}_1$. The second because $\lambda_1(\mathsf{GOE}(N)) = 2 - o_N(1)$.) A concentration argument justifies treating $\boldsymbol{m}^t$ was independent of H_N.

By taking $N \to \infty$ first and $\delta \to 0$ afterwards, we obtain Eq. (29.53).

29.4.2.2. *Incremental Approximate Message Passing*

A different approach [47, 49] leverages the general analysis of approximate message passing (AMP) algorithms developed in [50, 52–54]. We begin by describing the general framework of [49] and then describe how it specializes to optimization in mean field spin glasses.

For $t \in \delta\mathbb{N}$, let $f_t: \mathbb{R}^{(t/\delta)+1} \to \mathbb{R}$ be a real-valued Lipschitz function, and let $f_{-\delta} \equiv 0$. For a sequence of vectors $\boldsymbol{z}^{\leq t} := (\boldsymbol{z}^0, \boldsymbol{z}^\delta, \ldots, \boldsymbol{z}^t)$, $\boldsymbol{z}^s \in \mathbb{R}^N$ we use the notation $f_t(\boldsymbol{z}^{\leq t})$ for the vector $(f_t(z_i^0, \ldots, z_i^t))_{1\leq i\leq N}$. For a symmetric tensor $\boldsymbol{W} \in (\mathbb{R}^N)^{\otimes p}$ and a vector $\boldsymbol{u} \in \mathbb{R}^N$ we denote by $\boldsymbol{W}\{\boldsymbol{u}\}$ the vector with i-th coordinate $\sum_{1\leq i_1,\ldots,i_{p-1}\leq N} W_{i,i_1,\ldots,i_{p-1}}u_{i_1}\cdots u_{i_{p-1}}/(p-1)!$

Let $Z_0 \sim \mathsf{N}(0, Q_{0,0})$. For each $t \in \delta\mathbb{N}$, let $(Z_\delta, Z_{2\delta}, \ldots, Z_t)$ be a centered Gaussian vector independent of Z_0 with covariance $Q_{s,t} = \mathbb{E}[Z_s Z_t]$ defined recursively by

$$Q_{s+\delta,t+\delta} = \xi'\big(\mathbb{E}(M_s M_t)\big) \quad M_s := f_s(Z_{\leq s}), \quad s \geq 0. \tag{29.60}$$

The message passing algorithm starts with $\boldsymbol{z}^0$ with coordinates drawn i.i.d. with distribution $\mathsf{N}(0, Q_{0,0})$ independently of everything else. The general message passing

---

[f] We denote by $\boldsymbol{A} \sim \mathrm{GOE}(m)$ a matrix from the Gaussian orthogonal ensemble, i.e. a symmetric matrix with $(A_{ij})_{i\leq j\leq m}$ independent such that $A_{ii} \sim \mathsf{N}(0, 2/m)$ and $A_{ij} \sim \mathsf{N}(0, 1/m)$ for $i < j$.

iteration takes the form

$$z^{t+\delta} = \sum_{p=2}^{\infty} c_p G^{(p)}\{m^t\} - \sum_{j=0}^{\ell} d_{t,s} m^{s-\delta}, \qquad m^s = f_s(z^{\leq s}),$$

$$d_{t,s} = \xi''(\mathbb{E}[M_t M_{s-\delta}]) \cdot \mathbb{E}\left[\frac{\partial f_t}{\partial z^s}(Z^{\leq t})\right]. \tag{29.61}$$

It can be proven that, for any fixed t, the empirical distribution $N^{-1}\sum_{i=1}^{N} \delta_{(z_i^0,\dots,z_i^t)}$ is asymptotically Gaussian, with the same covariance as $(Z_0,\dots,Z_t)$. This asymptotic normality result, along with the rule (29.60) for evolution of covariances is known as 'state evolution' and was proven (to various degrees of generality) in [50, 52–54] for matrices (the case $p=2$), and generalized in [49] to tensors.

Hiding some technical conditions, state evolution implies the following. Given a discrete time stochastic process $(M_t)_{t\in\delta\mathbb{N}}$, that depends causally on the Gaussian process $(Z_t)_{t\in\delta\mathbb{N}}$ and satisfies Eq. (29.60), the AMP construction provides (efficiently computable) sequences $(z^t)_{t\in\delta\mathbb{N}}$, $(m^t)_{t\in\delta\mathbb{N}}$, that are functions of[g] the disorder H_N and are approximately isometric to the original processes. Namely

$$\frac{1}{N}\langle m^t, m^s\rangle = \mathbb{E}[M_t M_s] + o_N(1), \qquad \frac{1}{N}\langle z^t, z^s\rangle = \mathbb{E}[Z_t Z_s] + o_N(1). \tag{29.62}$$

We are planning to output $\sigma^{\text{alg}} = m^{t_*}$ for a certain (fixed) time t_*, or $\sigma^{\text{alg}} = \text{Round}(m^{t_*})$ for a suitable rounding procedure $\text{Round} : \mathbb{R}^N \to \Sigma_N$. In practice, m^{t_*} will lie close to Σ_N, so the rounding operation does not play an important role in the algorithm.

Motivated by the structure of the space of near optima, and the orthogonality property of the associated tree, we seek an algorithm with roughy orthogonal increments: $\langle m^t - m^s, m^s\rangle/N = o(1)$ for all $t > s$. This translates into $\mathbb{E}[(M_t - M_s)M_s] = 0$. Further, without loss of generality, we can always assume the normalization $\|m^t\|_2^2 = N(t+\delta)$, whence $\mathbb{E}[M_t^2] = t + \delta$. Using Eq. (29.60), this implies that (Z_t) is a Gaussian process with covariance $\mathbb{E}[Z_t Z_s] = \xi'(t \wedge s)$. In other words, Z_t has independent increments, and therefore must be a time change of the Brownian motion. Indeed we can write it as

$$Z_t = \int_0^t \sqrt{\xi''(s)}\, \mathrm{d}B_s, \tag{29.63}$$

with $(B_t)_{t\geq 0}$ a standard Brownian motion. We are then left with the task of constructing a process (M_t) that causally depend on (Z_t) (equivalently, on B_t) and satisfies $\mathbb{E}[M_t M_s] = (t \wedge s)_+\delta$ for $t, s \in \delta\mathbb{N}$. It turns that these constraints nearly[h] fix M_t to be of the form

$$M_t = M_0 + \sum_{s\in\{0,\delta,\dots,t-\delta\}} U_s(Z_{s+\delta} - Z_s), \tag{29.64}$$

where $M_0 \sim \mathsf{N}(0,\delta)$ and the process (U_t) depends causally on (Z_t).

---

[g]In mathematical language, (M_t) is progressively measurable with respect to (Z_t), and (z^t), (m^t) are measurable with respect to H_N.

[h]Indeed, by the martingale representation theorem, the choice is unique when we formally set $\delta \to 0$.

We are therefore left with the task of constructing $U_t = F_u(Z_0, \ldots, Z_t)$. The asymptotic value achieved by the algorithm can be computed in terms of this process yielding[i]

$$\lim_{N \to \infty} \frac{1}{N} H_N(\boldsymbol{m}^t) = \mathbb{E}\left[\int_0^t \xi''(s) U_s \, \mathrm{d}s\right] + o_1(\delta). \tag{29.65}$$

The algorithm design reduces therefore to the following optimization problem with respect to $(U_t)_{t \geq 0}$, whose value we denote by SOC (stochastic optimal control)

$$\text{maximize} \quad \mathbb{E}\left[\int_0^t \xi''(s) U_s \, \mathrm{d}s\right],$$

$$\text{subject to} \quad \mathbb{E}[M_t^2] = t \;\; \forall t \in [0,1], \mathrm{Law}(M_1) \in \mathscr{P}_\Sigma, \tag{29.66}$$

$$M_t = \int_0^t \sqrt{\xi''(s)}\, U_s \, \mathrm{d}B_s.$$

Here it is understood that U_t should depend causally on the Brownian motion $(B_t)_{t \geq 0}$, and $\mathscr{P}_\Sigma$ is a set of probability distributions over $\mathbb{R}$ that reflect the structure of the constraint set Σ_N. Namely

$$\Sigma_N = \mathbb{S}^{N-1}(\sqrt{N}) \; : \;\; \mathscr{P}_\Sigma = \left\{\nu \in \mathscr{P}(\mathbb{R}) : \int x^2 \nu(\mathrm{d}x) = 1\right\}, \tag{29.67}$$

$$\Sigma_N = \{+1, -1\}^N \; : \;\; \mathscr{P}_\Sigma = \left\{\nu \in \mathscr{P}(\mathbb{R}) : \mathrm{supp}(\nu) \in [-1, +1]\right\}. \tag{29.68}$$

Notice that naively one would have imposed the constraint $\mathrm{supp}(\nu) \in \{+1, -1\}$. However the optimal solution to the problem with constraint $M_1 \in [+1, -1]$ turns out to have M_1 indeed concentrated on the extremes, and the interval constraint is more convenient analytically.

The problem (29.66) is a stochastic optimal control problem in one dimension and continuous time: we want to design the control process $(U_t)_{t \geq 0}$ as to satisfy the constraints and maximize the objective. It is not obvious that the sequence of approximations (for large N and small δ) leading to it can indeed be implemented as to yield an actual algorithm of the form (29.61). However this turns out the case, and therefore denoting by SOC the value achieved by problem (29.66), there exists an AMP algorithm such that

$$\lim_{N \to \infty} \frac{1}{N} H_N(\boldsymbol{\sigma}^{\mathrm{alg}}) = \mathsf{SOC}. \tag{29.69}$$

Finally, a duality argument can be used to show that, under technical conditions SOC = ALG.

29.4.3. *Hardness*

When the infimum (29.50) is achieved on $\gamma_{\mathscr{L}}^\star$ non-monotone, we necessarily have OPT > ALG and therefore there is a gap between the maximum energy and the energy achieved by the efficient algorithms described in the previous section. It is natural to ask whether this gap is fundamental, or there exists other polynomial-time algorithms that achieve a better energy than ALG. From a physics perspective, one may wonder

---

[i]The left-hand side converges in probability to a non-random quantity given by the right-hand side.

about the behavior of physical dynamics, such as Langevin dynamics or simulated annealing. These are expected to converge to a threshold energy, which depends on the details of the dynamics (e.g. the annealing schedule) but has proven challenging to compute (with the notable exception of homogeneous, degree p spherical models). What is the relation between ALG and the energy achieved by such annealing algorithms?

It was proven in [55] that ALG is the maximum energy achieved by a broad class of 'Lipschitz' algorithms. This includes Langevin dynamics and simulated annealing as special cases (run for physical time of order one as $N \to \infty$).

In order to state this result formally, we view an algorithm as a function that takes as input a Hamiltonian and returns as output as a configuration:

$$\mathcal{A} : H_N \mapsto \mathcal{A}(H_N) \in \overline{\Sigma}_N. \tag{29.70}$$

Notice that we accept as output magnetization vectors in $\overline{\Sigma}_N = [-1, +1]^N$ (Ising) or $\overline{\Sigma}_N = \mathsf{B}^N(\sqrt{N})$. There is no loss of generality here because magnetization vectors can be rounded to spin vectors without decreasing significantly the energy [56].

For a given Hamiltonian H_N, we denote by $\boldsymbol{G}(H_N) = (\boldsymbol{G}^{(k)})_{k \geq 2}$ the vector obtained by listing all the couplings (notice that these are normalized to be typically of order one). An algorithm $\mathcal{A}$ as Lipschitz constant L if, for any two Hamiltonians H_N, H'_N:

$$\frac{1}{\sqrt{N}} \big\| \mathcal{A}(H_N) - \mathcal{A}(H'_N) \big\|_2 \leq L \big\| \boldsymbol{G}(H_N) - \boldsymbol{G}(H'_N) \big\|_2. \tag{29.71}$$

We can now state the Lipschitz hardness result.[j]

Theorem 9. *Consider a spin glass Hamiltonian (either Ising or spherical), with $c_k = 0$ for k odd (equivalently, ξ an even function). If $\mathcal{A}$ is an L Lipschitz algorithm (for L a constant), then, letting $\boldsymbol{\sigma}^{\mathrm{alg}} = \mathcal{A}(H_N)$, we have*

$$\lim_{N \to \infty} \frac{1}{N} H_N(\boldsymbol{\sigma}^{\mathrm{alg}}) \leq \mathsf{ALG}. \tag{29.72}$$

Remarkably, the proof of this theorem relies on a geometric description of the computational barrier at energy ALG. Roughly speaking, $N \cdot \mathsf{ALG}$ is the largest energy such that for any ultrametric overlap structure, we can find K configurations $\boldsymbol{\sigma}^1, \boldsymbol{\sigma}^2, \ldots, \boldsymbol{\sigma}^K$ with the assigned energy, and whose overlap matrix matches a target overlap matrix associated to the Parisi measure $\gamma^\star_{\mathscr{L}}$.

The reason why this might lead to an algorithmic barrier can be gleaned by noticing that both algorithms described in the previous sections can be modified to produce not one but multiple configurations. For instance, the Hessian ascent algorithm can be randomized by using not the top eigenvector of the Hessian, but one of the eigenvectors with eigenvalues larger than $(1 - \varepsilon)$ of the largest. By the semicircle law and a large deviation bound, there will be (with high probability) at least $c(\varepsilon)N$ such eigenvectors for some constant $c(\varepsilon) > 0$. Randomized Hessian ascent follows a direction in the subspace spanned by them uniformly at random.

---

[j]The statement proven in [55] is stronger than the version given here in two directions. First, the probability $H_N(\boldsymbol{\sigma}^{\mathrm{alg}}) \geq N(\mathsf{ALG} + \varepsilon)$ is shown to be exponentially small in N. Second, the result holds for a somewhat broader class of "overlap concentrated" algorithms.

We can then generate two configurations $\sigma^{1,\mathrm{alg}}$, $\sigma^{2,\mathrm{alg}} \in \mathbb{S}^{N-1}(\sqrt{N})$ with energies $H_N(\sigma^{1,\mathrm{alg}}), H_N(\sigma^{2,\mathrm{alg}}) \approx N\mathsf{ALG}$ as follows. Run two copies of the randomized Hessian ascent algorithm $m^{1,t}, m^{2,t}$ by using the same randomness for $t \le t_*$, and independent randomness (independent choice of the Hessian eigenvector) for $t > t_*$. This results in two spin configurations $\sigma^{1,\mathrm{alg}}, \sigma^{2,\mathrm{alg}}$ with the claimed energy, and $\langle \sigma^{1,\mathrm{alg}}, \sigma^{2,\mathrm{alg}} \rangle / N = t_* + o_N(1)$. Analogous constructions hold for the IAMP algorithm of Sec. 29.4.2.2.

This discussion clarifies why Hessian ascent and IAMP cannot find spin configurations at energies at which we cannot construct K-tuples of spin configurations with arbitrary overlap matrix. However, it does not explain why the same limitation holds for arbitrary Lipschitz algorithms. The key idea is to run the same algorithm $\mathcal{A}$ on two Hamiltonians $H_N^{(1)}$, $H_N^{(2)}$, that are identically distributed, jointly Gaussian *correlated* copies of H_N. As a consequence of the Lipschitz property, the algorithms output $\mathcal{A}(H_N^{(1)})$, $\mathcal{A}(H_N^{(2)})$ have overlap that is a nearly deterministic function of the correlation between the Hamiltonians.

This construction is repeated in a hierarchical fashion to show that $\mathcal{A}$ can find K configurations σ^1, $\sigma^2, \ldots, \sigma^K$, with a certain ultrametric overlap matrix, and a certain energy with respect to the sum of correlated Hamiltonians $H_N^{(1)} + H_N^{(2)} + \cdots + H_N^{(K)}$. Such a constellation is shown not to exist above energy ALG via an interpolation argument.

Acknowledgements

AM was supported by the NSF grant CCF-2006489 and the ONR grant N00014-18-1-2729. AA was supported by the NSF CAREER grant DMS-1653552. ES is the incumbent of the Skirball Chair in New Scientists and was supported by the Israel Science Foundation grant 2055/21.

References

[1] M. Mézard, G. Parisi, and M. A. Virasoro, *Spin glass theory and beyond.* vol. 9, (World Scientific, 1987).

[2] M. Talagrand, *Ann. Math.* pp. 221–263, (2006).

[3] D. Panchenko, *Ann. Math.* pp. 383–393, (2013).

[4] D. Panchenko, *The Sherrington–Kirkpatrick model.* (Springer Science & Business Media, 2013).

[5] W.-K. Chen and A. Sen, *Commun. Math. Phys.* **350**(1), 129–173, (2017).

[6] A. Jagannath and I. Tobasco, *Commun. Math. Phys.* **352**(3), 979–1017, (2017).

[7] A. Auffinger and W.-K. Chen, *Ann. Probab.* **45**(6B), 4617–4631, (2017).

[8] A. Auffinger and G. Ben Arous, *Ann. Probab.* **41**(6), 4214–4247, (2013).

[9] A. Auffinger, G. Ben Arous, and J. Černỳ, *Comm. Pure Appl. Math.* **66**(2), 165–201, (2013).

[10] E. Subag, *Ann. Prob.* **45**(5), 3385–3450, (2017).

[11] E. Subag and O. Zeitouni, *J. Math. Phys.* **62**(12), 123301, (2021).

[12] G. B. Arous, E. Subag, and O. Zeitouni, *Comm. Pure Appl. Math.* **73**(8), 1732–1828, (2020).

[13] R. J. Adler, J. E. Taylor, et al., *Random fields and geometry.* vol. 80, (Springer, 2007).

[14] A. Crisanti and H.-J. Sommers, *J. Phys. I (France).* **5**(7), 805–813, (1995).

[15] Y. V. Fyodorov, *Phys. Rev. Lett.* **92**(24), 240601, (2004).

[16] Y. V. Fyodorov and I. Williams, *J. Stat. Phys.* **129**(5), 1081–1116, (2007).

[17] A. Auffinger and W.-K. Chen, *J. Stat. Phys.* **157**(1), 40–59, (2014).

[18] B. McKenna, *arXiv:2105.05043*. (2021).

[19] G. B. Arous, S. Mei, A. Montanari, and M. Nica, *Comm. Pure Appl. Math.* **72**(11), 2282–2330, (2019).

[20] V. Ros, G. B. Arous, G. Biroli, and C. Cammarota, *Phys. Rev. X.* **9**(1), 011003, (2019).

[21] G. B. Arous, P. Bourgade, and B. McKenna, *arXiv:2105.05051*. (2021).

[22] A. Auffinger and Q. Zeng, *arXiv:2007.07668*. (2020).

[23] A. Auffinger, W.-K. Chen, and Q. Zeng, *arXiv:1703.06872*. (2017).

[24] A. Auffinger and Q. Zeng, *Commun. Math. Phys.* **370**(1), 377–402, (2019).

[25] A. Auffinger and W.-K. Chen, *Adv. Math.* **330**, 553–588, (2018).

[26] S. Chatterjee, *Superconcentration and related topics.* vol. 15, (Springer, 2014).

[27] J. Ding, R. Eldan, and A. Zhai, *Ann. Probab.* **43**(6), 3468–3493, (2015).

[28] E. Subag, *arXiv:1804.10576*. (2018).

[29] W.-K. Chen, D. Panchenko, and E. Subag, *Comm. Pure Appl. Math.* (2018).

[30] D. J. Thouless, P. W. Anderson, and R. G. Palmer, *Philos. Mag.* **35**(3), 593–601, (1977).

[31] T. Plefka, *J. Phys. A.* **15**(6), 1971, (1982).

[32] W.-K. Chen, D. Panchenko, and E. Subag, *Commun. Math. Phys.* **381**(1), 257–291, (2021).

[33] E. Subag, *arXiv:2101.04352*. (2021).

[34] E. Subag, *arXiv:2111.07132*. (2021).

[35] E. Subag, *arXiv:2111.07134*. (2021).

[36] D. Belius and N. Kistler, *Commun. Math. Phys.* **367**(3), 991–1017, (2019).

[37] G. B. Arous and A. Jagannath, *arXiv:2104.08299*. (2021).

[38] W.-K. Chen and D. Panchenko, *Commun. Math. Phys.* **362**(1), 219–252, (2018).

[39] J. Kurchan, G. Parisi, and M. A. Virasoro, *J. Phys. I (France).* **3**(8), 1819–1838, (1993).

[40] E. Subag, *Invent. Math.* **210**(1), 135–209, (2017).

[41] M. Talagrand, *Probab. Theory Relat. Fields.* **148**(3), 601–643, (2010).

[42] A. Jagannath, *Comm. Pure Appl. Math.* **70**(4), 611–664, (2017).

[43] M. Mézard, G. Parisi, N. Sourlas, G. Toulouse, and M. Virasoro, *Phys. Rev. Lett.* **52**(13), 1156, (1984).

[44] M. Mézard, G. Parisi, N. Sourlas, G. Toulouse, and M. Virasoro, *J. Phys. (France).* **45**(5), 843–854, (1984).

[45] S. Arora, E. Berger, H. Elad, G. Kindler, and M. Safra. In *46th Annual IEEE Symposium on Foundations of Computer Science (FOCS'05)*, pp. 206–215. IEEE, (2005).

[46] B. Barak, F. G. Brandao, A. W. Harrow, J. Kelner, D. Steurer, and Y. Zhou. pp. 307–326, (2012).

[47] A. El Alaoui, A. Montanari, and M. Sellke, *Ann. Probab.* **49**(6), 2922–2960, (2021).

[48] E. Subag, *Comm. Pure Appl. Math.* **74**(5), 1021–1044, (2021).

[49] A. Montanari, *SIAM Journal on Computing.* pp. FOCS19–1, (2021).

[50] E. Bolthausen, *Commun. Math. Phys.* **325**(1), 333–366, (2014).

[51] E. Bolthausen. In Statistical Mechanics of Classical and Disordered Systems, pp. 63–93, Springer, (2019).

[52] M. Bayati and A. Montanari, *IEEE Transactions on Information Theory.* **57**(2), 764–785, (2011).

[53] A. Javanmard and A. Montanari, *Inf. Inference.* **2**(2), 115–144, (2013).

[54] R. Berthier, A. Montanari, and P.-M. Nguyen, *Inf. Inference.* **9**(1), 33–79, (2020).

[55] B. Huang and M. Sellke, *arXiv:2110.07847*. (2021).

[56] M. Sellke, *C. R. Math.* **359**(9), 1097–1105, (2021).

Chapter 30

Rigorous Results in the Sherrington–Kirkpatrick Model

Since the proposal of the solution of the SK model by Giorgio Parisi, the mathematical community has investigated the rigorous foundations of the results obtained by means of the replica method: this chapter focuses on some of the outcomes of such investigations. In the first part, **Wei-Kuo Chen** discusses the Parisi formula for the free energy of the SK model, the stability of the replica-symmetric solution, and the most recent results on disorder chaos. In the second part, **Dmitry Panchenko** reviews the central concept of ultrametricity, its relation with the Ghirlanda–Guerra identities in a large class of spin systems, and its implications on their landscape structure. Finally, in the last part, **Francesco Guerra** overviews the interpolating method for the SK model and the REM, and the emergent variational principle associated to these models.

30.1. The Parisi Formula

Wei-Kuo Chen

School of Mathematics, University of Minnesota, USA
wkchen@umn.edu

In this chapter, we will discuss the Sherrington–Kirkpatrick (SK) model introduced in the seminal work [1]. Its Hamiltonian is defined as

$$-H_N(\sigma) = \tfrac{1}{\sqrt{N}} \sum_{1 \leq i < j \leq N} g_{ij}\sigma_i\sigma_j$$

for $\sigma = (\sigma_1,\ldots,\sigma_N) \in \{-1,1\}^N$, where $(g_{ij})_{1 \leq i < j \leq N}$ are i.i.d. standard Gaussian random variables. For a given inverse temperature $\beta > 0$ and external field $h \in \mathbb{R}$, we will denote by

$$G_N(\sigma) = \tfrac{1}{Z_N}\, e^{-\beta H_N(\sigma) - h\sum_{i=1}^{N}\sigma_i} \quad \text{and} \quad F_N = \tfrac{1}{N}\log Z_N$$

the Gibbs measure and free energy corresponding to the parameters (β, h), where the normalizing constant Z_N is called the partition function. In Ref. [1], the authors computed the limit of the free energy by means of the replica method with a replica symmetric ansatz, but, soon after, Jairo de Almeida and David Thouless pointed out that their solution could only be valid up to a transition line now known as the AT line [2]. A complete solution was found by Giorgio Parisi in his celebrated work [3, 4], where he proposed an ultrametric replica symmetry breaking ansatz and arrived at the following variational formula for the free energy.

Denote by $\Pr[0,1]$ the space of probability measures on $[0,1]$ and, for $x \in \Pr[0,1]$, consider the functional

$$\mathcal{P}(x) = \log 2 + \Phi_x(0,h) - \frac{\beta^2}{2} \int_0^1 q x(q) \, \mathrm{d}q,$$

where $x(q) := x([0,q])$ is the c.d.f. of x, and $\Phi_x(q,y)$ is the weak solution [5, 6] to the following PDE,

$$\partial_q \Phi_x(q,y) = -\frac{\beta^2}{2}\left(\partial_{yy}\Phi_x(q,y) + x(q)\left(\partial_y \Phi_x(q,y)\right)^2\right),$$

for $(q,y) \in [0,1) \times \mathbb{R}$, with the boundary condition $\Phi_x(1,y) = \log\cosh(y)$.

Theorem 1 (Parisi formula). *Almost surely,*

$$\lim_{N\to\infty} F_N = \inf_{x\in\Pr[0,1]} \mathcal{P}(x). \tag{30.1}$$

The Parisi formula was first rigorously proved in a remarkable work of Talagrand [7] following a breakthrough discovery in Ref. [5] of the replica symmetry breaking (RSB) interpolation, which yielded the Parisi formula as an upper bound on the free energy. Another approach to proving the lower bound was given in Ref. [8], based on the cavity method combined with the ultrametricity result discussed in Sec. 30.2 below. The cavity method was first introduced in the physics literature in Ref. [9], where it was applied directly within the framework of the Parisi ansatz. In the form that it is known today in the mathematical literature, the cavity method seems to have first appeared in Ref. [10]. However, it is now better known under the name of the Aizenman–Sims–Starr scheme [11], after the authors that popularized it, in addition to introducing other important ideas, such as the proof of Guerra's RSB bound using Ruelle probability cascades [12], and random overlap structures (ROSts) as a way of thinking about the asymptotic Gibbs measures. Over the past decade, the analogues of the Parisi formula (30.1) have also been established in a variety of mean-field spin glass models [13–22].

Properties of the Parisi functional   The Parisi functional $\mathcal{P}(x)$ has several intriguing analytic properties. Its derivative along certain directions was computed via a subtle calculation in Ref. [23] (see also Ref. [24]). A more robust tool for analyzing the Parisi functional appeared in Ref. [25], where the authors introduced a representation of the solution of the Parisi PDE via a Hamilton–Jacobi–Bellman equation induced by a linear diffusion control problem. In the same spirit, a more canonical representation was established in Ref. [26], namely,

$$\Phi_x(0,\beta h) = \max_{u\in\mathcal{D}} \mathbb{E}\left[\log\cosh\left(h + \beta^2 \int_0^1 x(q)u(q)\,\mathrm{d}q + \beta B(1)\right) - \frac{\beta^2}{2}\int_0^1 x(q)u(q)^2\,\mathrm{d}q\right], \tag{30.2}$$

where $\mathcal{D}$ is the space of all progressively measurable processes with respect to a standard Brownian motion $(B(q))_{0\le q\le 1}$. The maximum is achieved by the process $u_x(q) := \partial_q \Phi_y(q, X(q))$, where $(X(q))_{0\le q\le 1}$ is the solution of $\mathrm{d}X(q) = \beta^2 x(q)\partial_y\Phi_x(q,X(q))\,\mathrm{d}q + \beta\,\mathrm{d}B(q)$, $0 \le q \le 1$, with the initial condition $X(0) = 0$. In view of the representation

(30.2), the dependence of the Parisi PDE on the functional order parameter $x \in \mathrm{Pr}[0,1]$ and the external parameters is rather explicit, which makes it possible to analyze some fundamental properties of the Parisi functional.

First, Auffinger and Chen [26] established the strict convexity of the Parisi functional based on (30.2) and, as a result, the minimizer x_P in (30.1) is unique (see also Ref. [6] for a simplified argument). This minimizer x_P is called the Parisi measure. Second, Chen, Jagannath and Tobasco [27, 28] again made use of (30.2) to derive the directional derivative of the Parisi functional, and showed that, for any $x_0, x_1 \in \mathrm{Pr}[0,1]$ and $x_\theta := (1-\theta)x_0 + \theta x_1$ for $0 \le \theta \le 1$, the right derivative of $\theta \mapsto \mathcal{P}(x_\theta)$ equals

$$\frac{\mathrm{d}}{\mathrm{d}\theta^+}\mathcal{P}(x_\theta)\Big|_{\theta=0} = \frac{\beta^2}{2}\int_0^1 (x_1(q) - x_0(q))(\mathbb{E}u_{x_0}(q)^2 - q)\,\mathrm{d}q.$$

This in particular yields a useful fact [27], that x_0 is the Parisi measure x_P if and only if the derivative above is nonnegative for all $x_1 = \delta_q$ for $0 \le q \le 1$, providing a theoretical guarantee for implementing numerical simulations for the Parisi measures. More properties on the Parisi functional and measure can be found in Refs. [24, 27–29].

Phase transition   In Ref. [2], it was argued that the SK model exhibits the replica symmetric solution, i.e., $x_P = \delta_q$ for some $q \in [0,1]$, if and only if (β, h) satisfies

$$\beta^2 \mathbb{E}\frac{1}{\cosh^4(\beta z\sqrt{q} + h)} \le 1, \tag{30.3}$$

where z is standard normal and q is the solution of $\mathbb{E}\tanh^2(\beta z\sqrt{q}+h) = q$.[a] The famous AT line is given by the pairs (β, h) satisfying the equality in (30.3), and it is expected to be the transition line distinguishing between replica symmetric and replica symmetry breaking solutions in the Parisi formula. In one direction, Toninelli [31] showed that the SK model cannot possess a replica symmetric solution above the AT line. On the other hand, Talagrand and Jagannath and Tobasco [28, 30] showed that for a fairly large regime inside the AT line, the SK model does exhibit a replica symmetric solution. In a different approach, Bolthausen and Morita, and Brennecke and Yau [32, 33] established the replica symmetric solution via a large deviation argument. Up to now, the proof of the exactness of the AT line remains incomplete. Nevertheless, it was shown in Ref. [34] that in the SK model with centered Gaussian external field, the corresponding AT line is exact.

Ground state energy and ground state   As a soft approach to obtaining the limiting ground state energy of the SK model, it is desirable to study the Parisi formula in the limit of zero temperature and external field parameters. In Ref. [5], it was pointed out that one can obtain an analogous RSB bound for the ground state energy of the SK model after proper rescaling. The matching lower bound was settled in Ref. [35] using (30.2), which resulted in a Parisi-type variational principal for the limiting ground state energy. Let $\mathcal{M}[0,1)$ be the collection of all positive measures on $[0,1)$ with

---

[a]The solution is unique for $h \neq 0$ by the Latala–Guerra lemma, see Ref. [30, A.14]

$\int_0^1 \gamma(q)\mathrm{d}q < \infty$ for $\gamma(q) := \gamma([0,q])$. As in the Parisi formula, for any $\gamma \in \mathcal{M}[0,1)$, we introduce the following PDE with boundary condition $\Psi_\gamma(1,x) = |x|$,

$$\partial_q \Psi_\gamma(q,y) = -\tfrac{1}{2}\left(\partial_{yy}\Psi_\gamma(q,y) + x(q)\left(\partial_y \Psi_\gamma(q,y)\right)^2\right).$$

The work [35] showed that

$$\lim_{N\to\infty}\min_{\sigma\in\{-1,1\}^N}\left(\frac{H_N(\sigma)}{N}+h\frac{\sum_{i=1}^N \sigma_i}{N}\right) = -\inf_{\gamma\in\mathcal{M}[0,1)}\left(\Psi_\gamma(0,h)-\frac{1}{2}\int_0^1 q\gamma(q)\mathrm{d}q\right). \quad (30.4)$$

Here the functional on the right-hand side is again strictly convex and has a unique minimizer, see Ref. [35, 36]. When the external field is absent, numerical simulations [37–39] have indicated that the minimum here as well as in the original Parisi formula (30.1) in the low temperature are both attained by measures supported on the entire interval $[0,1)$. Lately this observation has been playing a crucial assumption in the construction of polynomial-time algorithms for the near ground state in the SK model [40, 41]. Although a proof for justifying the observation above remains unavailable so far, a partial positive result was obtained in Ref. [42], where it was proved that the minimizer in the Parisi formula for the ground state energy must be supported on infinitely many points.

The Parisi-type formula at zero temperature has also been extended to a number of mean-field spin glass models [14, 22, 43–48].

Disorder chaos and energy landscape   The energy landscape of the SK model was discussed in the physics literature, see, for instance, Ref. [37]. A large subject related to this matter lies on the so-called chaos problem [49, 50], in which one attempts to understand the structure of the Gibbs measure by measuring the cross overlap between two spin configurations sampled from two Gibbs measures, where their external parameters, such as temperature, external field, or disorder correlation, are slightly deviated away from each other. The phenomenon one seeks to obtain is that this overlap is concentrated around a deterministic constant as opposed to the usual overlap between two replicas sampled from the same system, where it exhibits nontrivial distribution in the low temperature regime.

The mathematical study of the chaos problem in the SK model was pioneered by Chatterjee [51, 52]. He studied chaos in disorder in the absence of external field formulated as follows. Consider σ sampled from the SK Gibbs measure G_N and τ sampled from another SK Gibbs measure G_N', whose temperature and external field are the same as G_N, but its disorder matrix is replaced by $\sqrt{t}g_{ij} + \sqrt{1-t}g_{ij}'$ parametrized by a correlation parameter $0 \le t \le 1$ for $(g_{ij}')_{i<j}$ an independent copy of $(g_{ij})_{i<j}$. It was shown that the cross overlap between σ and τ, $R(\sigma,\tau) = \frac{1}{N}\sum_{i=1}^N \sigma_i\tau_i$, is concentrated around the origin as long as the two disorder matrices in G_N and G_N' are decoupled, i.e., $0 \le t < 1$. Later on, by adapting a two-dimensional version of Guerra's RSB bound for the coupled free energy, Chen [53] showed that chaos in disorder remains valid in the SK model in the presence of external field and the exact value of the cross overlap was identified in terms of the Parisi measure and PDE. Over the past decade, many results on chaos problems have also been made available in a number of variants of the SK model and some diluted models [27, 36, 54–61].

The phenomenon of disorder chaos we described above has a close connection to the so-called multiple valley structure in the description of the energy landscape of the model. As argued in Ref. [51], in the SK model without external field, one can utilize the chaotic property of the cross overlap to construct multiple valleys in the sense that, with high probability, there exist logarithmically many near ground states that are nearly orthogonal to each other. The size on the number of valleys was strengthened in Ref. [62] to a polynomial order. By using the zero-temperature Parisi formula (30.4), the work [36] was able to validate chaos in disorder at zero temperature and showed that the size on the number of orthogonal valleys is of exponential order.

Additionally, chaos in disorder has many profound consequences concerning the fluctuation of the free energy and hardness of randomized algorithms in the optimizations of mean field spin glasses. First of all, Chatterjee [52, 63] showed that in the SK model without external field, chaos in disorder is indeed equivalent to superconcentration of the free energy, namely, the variance of the free energy is of smaller order than the one obtained from the Poincaré bound; analogous results have also been shown for the ground state energy in Refs. [36, 45, 59]. In sharp contrast, when the external field is present, it was studied in Refs. [36, 64] that both the free energy and the ground state energy in the SK model have Gaussian fluctuations at any temperature. Finally, we mention that disorder chaos has also been greatly used to construct the overlap gap property for the near ground states in some spin glass models, which has been playing a key role in tracking the hardness of simulating the corresponding near ground states via certain classes of random algorithms [65–67].

30.2. Ultrametricity in Spin Glasses

Dmitry Panchenko

Department of Mathematics, University of Toronto, Canada
panchenk@math.toronto.edu

The celebrated solution of the Sherrington–Kirkpatrick model [1] by Giorgio Parisi in [3, 4] contained several key steps, but it all started with a particular choice of the replica symmetry breaking of the Q-matrix that appeared in the replica calculation. Given integer numbers $n = m_0 > m_1 > \ldots > m_r > m_{r+1} = 1$ such that m_i is divisible by m_{i+1}, and real numbers $0 \leq q_0 \leq q_1 \leq \ldots \leq q_r \leq 1$ ($q_r = q_{\text{EA}}$ is the Edwards-Anderson parameter), the $n \times n$ replica matrix Q was defined by

$$Q_{\ell,\ell'} = q_{i-1} \text{ if } \left\lceil \frac{\ell}{m_i} \right\rceil \neq \left\lceil \frac{\ell'}{m_i} \right\rceil \text{ and } \left\lceil \frac{\ell}{m_{i-1}} \right\rceil = \left\lceil \frac{\ell'}{m_{i-1}} \right\rceil \tag{30.5}$$

for $i = 1, \ldots, r + 1$, and the diagonal $Q_{\ell,\ell} = 1$. In other words, the matrix consisted of nested diagonal blocks with values increasing as the block size is getting smaller.

A couple of years later, Parisi [68] interpreted the original ansatz in terms of a decomposition of the Gibbs measure into a mixture of pure states, and soon after it was understood in Refs. [69, 70] that the structure (30.5) of the Q-matrix corresponds to a special geometric organization of the pure states, called ultrametricity. It can be expressed in terms of the array of overlaps $R_{\ell,\ell'} = \frac{1}{N}\sum_{i=1}^{N}\sigma_i^\ell\sigma_i^{\ell'}$ between replicas $(\sigma^\ell)_{\ell\geq 1}$ from the Gibbs measure by saying that, for any $q \in [0,1]$, the relation $\ell \sim_q \ell'$ on the replica indices defined by

$$\ell \sim_q \ell' \iff R_{\ell,\ell'} \geq q \tag{30.6}$$

is an equivalence relation (that separates replicas into disjoint clusters), in the infinite volume limit. Given the distribution x of $R_{1,2}$, the block size m_i in (30.5) roughly corresponds to $nx([q_i,1])$ – an average block size among n replicas with all overlaps $R_{\ell,\ell'} \geq q_i$. In the $n \downarrow 0$ limit in the replica method Parisi formally replaced a decreasing sequence m_i by an increasing one that ended up being $x([0,q_i))$. This reordering of parameters is another remarkable step in the Parisi ansatz that turned out to be the right one.

In addition to discovering the ultrametric geometry of pure states, the statistical properties of pure states and $\sim_q$ equivalence clusters (30.6), corresponding to the so-called ancestor states, were studied in Refs. [71, 72]. It was shown in Refs. [71, 73, 74] that these statistical properties match those of the random energy model, REM, and the generalized random energy model, GREM, introduced by Derrida [75–78]. When Ruelle [12] gave an explicit description of the Gibbs measure in the GREM in terms of Poisson–Dirichlet processes, this meant that one now had an explicitly defined object (called the Ruelle probability cascades, or RPC) conjecturally describing the Gibbs measure in the SK model. As a result, RPC became an important landmark in further developments.

In the mid-nineties, Francesco Guerra made a fundamental observation [79] that, for a typical temperature, the Hamiltonian of the SK model $H_N(\sigma)/N$ concentrates, which was later extended to the mixed p-spin models by Ghirlanda and Guerra [80]. By testing this concentration against a test function $f = f(R^n)$ of the overlaps $R^n = (R_{\ell,\ell'})_{1\leq\ell,\ell'\leq n}$, one gets identities of the form

$$\mathbb{E}\langle fR_{1,n+1}^p \rangle \approx \frac{1}{n}\mathbb{E}\langle f\rangle\mathbb{E}\langle R_{1,2}^p\rangle + \frac{1}{n}\sum_{\ell=2}^{n}\mathbb{E}\langle fR_{1,\ell}^p\rangle,$$

again, on average over temperature. In the infinite volume limit, these identities can be expressed by saying that the conditional distribution of the overlap $R_{1,n+1}$ given R^n is a mixture

$$\mathcal{L}(R_{1,n+1} \mid R^n) = \frac{1}{n}\mathcal{L}(R_{1,2}) + \frac{1}{n}\sum_{\ell=2}^{n}\delta_{R_{1,\ell}}. \tag{30.7}$$

It was then observed in Ref. [81] that such identities also follow from the replica calculation under the assumption of replica equivalence; it was also noted there that together with ultrametricity, these identities uniquely determine the distribution of the overlap array and, as a result, for a while it was naturally assumed that ultrametricity and the Ghirlanda–Guerra identities are complementary properties.

A pivotal moment came in a work of Arguin and Aizenman [82], where, under a technical assumption that the overlaps take finitely many values, it was shown that ultrametricity arises from the so called Aizenman–Contucci stochastic stability [83], which is closely related to the Ghirlanda–Guerra identities. (The RPC and some of their properties proved in Ref. [84] played a very important role on a technical level.) Shortly after, a similar result based on the Ghirlanda–Guerra identities was proved Ref. [85] (see also [86]) and a few years later all technical assumptions were removed [87].

Theorem 2 (Panchenko [87]). *If the overlap array satisfies the Ghirlanda–Guerra identities (30.7) then it must be ultrametric.*

In other words, the Ghirlanda–Guerra identities is one possible starting point to justify the ultrametric choice of the overlap array in the Parisi ansatz. On the other hand, because these identities are satisfied by the RPC (see e.g. Ref. [88]), in order to recover the full ansatz described by the physicists one has to somehow ensure the validity of the Ghirlanda–Guerra identities anyway. Fortunately, the Ghirlanda–Guerra on average over temperature follow from some mild self-averaging of the free energy and, as a result, one can induce them via perturbations in many different situations, as well as for different definitions of the overlap as we discuss below. Let us also mention that ultrametricity in the thermodynamic limit can be translated into approximate ultrametricity for finite size systems [89–91].

Synchronization mechanism Next, we will describe how the Ghirlanda–Guerra identities for more general overlaps can be used to study various generalizations of the SK model. For illustration purposes, we will use the following two examples.

Example 1 (Nonhomogeneous SK model, [92]). Suppose that spins are divided into two groups, $G_1 = \{1, \ldots, N_1\}$ and $G_2 = \{N_1 + 1, \ldots, N\}$, where $N_1/N \to \lambda \in (0, 1)$, and suppose that the variance of the Gaussian interactions depends on the group membership, $\mathrm{Var}(g_{ij}) = \sigma_{S,S'}^2$, if $i \in S, j \in S'$ for $S, S' \in \{G_1, G_2\}$. Otherwise, the Hamiltonian is the same as in the SK model. In this case, the computation of the free energy involves understanding the joint distribution of two types of overlaps, $R_{\ell,\ell'}^S = \frac{1}{N} \sum_{i \in S} \sigma_i^\ell \sigma_i^{\ell'}$ for $S \in \{G_1, G_2\}$, over the entire array $\ell, \ell' \geq 1$.

Example 2 (Potts SK model). Consider $K \geq 2$, and suppose that spins $\sigma_i \in \{1, \ldots, K\}$. Suppose that $\lim_{N\to\infty} |\{i : \sigma_i = k\}|/N = p_k \in (0, 1)$ for all $k \leq K$, where $\sum_{k \leq K} p_k = 1$. In this case, the Hamiltonian is defined by $H_N(\sigma) = N^{-1/2} \sum_{1 \leq i,j \leq N} g_{ij} \mathrm{I}(\sigma_i = \sigma_j)$, and the computation of the free energy involves understanding the joint distributions over all $\ell, \ell' \geq 1$ of the matrix of overlaps

$$R(\sigma^\ell, \sigma^{\ell'}) = \left(R_{k,k'}(\sigma^\ell, \sigma^{\ell'})\right)_{1 \leq k,k' \leq K}, \tag{30.8}$$

where $R_{k,k'}(\sigma^\ell, \sigma^{\ell'}) = \frac{1}{N} \sum_{i=1}^{N} \mathrm{I}(\sigma_i^\ell = k)\mathrm{I}(\sigma_i^{\ell'} = k')$ is the proportion of spins taking value k in one assignment σ^ℓ and k' in another assignment $\sigma^{\ell'}$.

In order to study joint distributions of more than one type of overlap, a synchronization mechanism was developed in Refs. [18–20], which we will now describe. Let Σ_N be the space of spin configurations, namely, $\Sigma_N = \{-1, 1\}^N$ in the SK model and nonhomogeneous SK model, and $\Sigma_N = \{1, \ldots, K\}^N$ in the Potts model. Let H be a Hilbert space and $\Phi_N : \Sigma_N \to H$ be such that $\|\Phi_N(\sigma)\|_H = \mathrm{const}$, where for simplicity we will assume that this constant in independent of N. We will call the scalar product

$R_{\ell,\ell'} = \Phi_N(\sigma^\ell) \cdot \Phi_N(\sigma^{\ell'})$ a generalized overlap. Since we can define a Gaussian process with the covariance equal to this generalized overlap (and its powers), one can design a small perturbation in a way that forces any such generalized overlap to satisfy the Ghirlanda–Guerra identities and, by way of Theorem 2, satisfy ultrametricity in the limit $N \to \infty$. Moreover, if we consider two generalized overlaps $R_{\ell,\ell'}$ and $Q_{\ell,\ell'}$ then $R_{\ell,\ell'}^n Q_{\ell,\ell'}^m$ will also be a generalized overlap for any integer $n, m \geq 0$, and the perturbative approach allows to simultaneously force all of them to be ultrametric in the limit. This ultrametricity puts strong constraints on how this can happen and, in fact, implies that $R_{\ell,\ell'}$ and $Q_{\ell,\ell'}$ have to be synchronized in the following sense [18]:

$$R_{\ell,\ell'} = f(R_{\ell,\ell'} + Q_{\ell,\ell'}) \text{ and } Q_{\ell,\ell'} = g(R_{\ell,\ell'} + Q_{\ell,\ell'}) \tag{30.9}$$

for some deterministic 1-Lipschitz functions f and g that depend only on the distribution of the array (R, Q). This synchronization is similar to the so-called overlap equivalence [93].

In the case of the nonhomogeneous SK model, this means that overlaps $R_{\ell,\ell'}^S$ for $S \in \{G_1, G_2\}$ are determined by their sum, i.e. the usual overlap $R_{\ell,\ell'}$. When the matrix of variances $\Sigma = (\sigma_{S,S'}^2)_{S,S' \in \{G_1,G_2\}}$ is positive definite, this allows to compute the Parisi type formula for the free energy [18, 94]. When Σ is not positive definite, the upper bound via Guerra's interpolation [5] is missing and the problem is open, but the synchronization mechanism plays a crucial role in another promising approach to this problem developed in a series of papers [95–100].

In the setting of the Potts model in Example 2, a quadratic form $\sum_{k,k' \leq K} R_{k,k'}(\sigma^\ell, \sigma^{\ell'})^m \lambda_k \lambda_{k'}$ is a generalized overlap for any $m \in \mathbb{N}$ and $\lambda \in \mathbb{R}^K$, and, again, one can force all of them to be synchronized in the sense of the equation (30.9). This yields even more surprising constraints on the overlap matrix (30.8) in the limit $N \to \infty$. Namely, in this case, one can show that $R(\sigma^\ell, \sigma^{\ell'}) = \Phi\big(\mathrm{tr}(R(\sigma^\ell, \sigma^{\ell'}))\big)$ for some deterministic function $\Phi: \mathbb{R} \to \mathrm{SPD}$ (where SPD is the set of symmetric nonnegative definite matrices) that depends only on the distribution of the array R. Moreover Φ is Lipschitz element-wise, and nondecreasing in SPD, i.e. $\Phi(a) - \Phi(b) \in$ SPD for any $a \geq b$. The reason such constraints are surprising is that a priori the matrix $R(\sigma^\ell, \sigma^{\ell'})$ in (30.8) is not even symmetric. However, synchronization of the generalized overlaps above enforces such strong symmetries and, in particular, all the overlaps are determined by the trace $\mathrm{tr}\big(R(\sigma^\ell, \sigma^{\ell'})\big)$. This yields a Parisi-type formula for the free energy [19, 20]. In the case of equal group sizes, $p_k = 1/K$, the formula of Gross–Kanter–Sompolinsky [101] corresponds to a linear path Φ in the space SPD, which, perhaps, can be checked numerically, but it is not clear a priori whether such a strong extra symmetry is a reasonable assumption.

Besides the above two examples, some more general results include showing that the upper bounds of Talagrand [30, 102] for multiple systems with overlap constraints are sharp. These results and the synchronization mechanism itself were used in a variety of other applications (see e.g. Refs. [15, 16, 22, 103–106]).

Hierarchical exchangeability of pure states Another application of the Ghirlanda–Guerra identities and ultrametricity is that they imply the so called hierarchical exchangeability of pure states [107], which together with the representation from Ref. [108] allows to recover part of the Mézard–Parisi ansatz [109] in the setting of diluted spin glass models. To state what hierarchical exchangeability means, suppose that the support of the distribution x of the overlap contains at least $r + 1$ points for some $r \geq 1$, that is, it is not replica symmetric and at least r-RSB. Let us cover the support of x by $r + 1$ disjoint intervals $\operatorname{supp}(x) \subseteq \bigcup_{0 \leq p \leq r} I_p$, such that $x(I_p) > 0$ for all $0 \leq p \leq r$. Any interval could also be a single point. For simplicity, suppose that $x(\{q_{\mathrm{EA}}\}) > 0$ and $I_r = \{q_{\mathrm{EA}}\}$.

Because of ultrametricity, if we coarse-grain the overlaps between pure states by the intervals I_p, we will obtain a rooted tree of ancestor states that we can index by $\mathcal{A} = \{\emptyset\} \cup \mathbb{N} \cup \mathbb{N}^2 \cup \ldots \cup \mathbb{N}^r$. In particular, we index the pure states by $\alpha \in \mathbb{N}^r$ and denote by $\alpha \wedge \beta$ the level at which the pure states merge. Let $V = (V_\alpha)_{\alpha \in \mathcal{A}}$ be the Gibbs weights of all ancestor (and pure) states and, for each pure state $\alpha \in \mathbb{N}^r$, let $m_\alpha = (m_{\alpha,i})_{i \geq 1}$ be its magnetization (i.e. the barycentre of the conditional Gibbs measure). The entire construction is in the infinite volume limit, which can be formalized mathematically [107]. Consider the family of permutations $\pi \colon \mathbb{N}^r \to \mathbb{N}^r$ of the pure states

$$\mathcal{H} = \big\{\pi \text{ is a bijection}, \pi(\alpha) \wedge \pi(\beta) = \alpha \wedge \beta \text{ for all } \alpha, \beta \in \mathbb{N}^r\big\}$$

that respect the structure of the tree. Then, it was shown in Ref. [107] that the Ghirlanda–Guerra identities imply that the arrays $(m_\alpha)_{\alpha \in \mathbb{N}^r}$ and $(V_\alpha)_{\alpha \in \mathcal{A}}$ are independent and

$$\big(m_{\pi(\alpha)}\big)_{\alpha \in \mathbb{N}^r} \overset{d}{=} \big(m_\alpha\big)_{\alpha \in \mathbb{N}^r} \text{ for any } \pi \in \mathcal{H}.$$

The last property is called hierarchical exchangeability. By a result in Ref. [108], such array can be generated (denoting by $p(\alpha)$ the path from the root $\emptyset$ to the pure state α) as

$$m_{\alpha,i} = f\big(\omega_\emptyset, (\omega_\beta)_{\beta \in p(\alpha)}, \omega_\emptyset^i, (\omega_\beta^i)_{\beta \in p(\alpha)}\big),$$

for some function $f \colon [0,1]^{2(r+1)} \to [-1,1]$ and i.i.d. $U[0,1]$ random variables $\omega_\alpha, \omega_\alpha^i$ for $\alpha \in \mathcal{A}$ and $i \in \mathbb{N}$. Under the so-called reproducibility hypothesis (that multi-overlaps are continuous functions of the overlaps, which would imply that the dependence on the variables $(\omega_\beta)_{\beta \in p(\alpha)}$ becomes negligible as the coarse-graining of the overlaps becomes refined), this allows to recover the Mézard–Parisi ansatz and formula for the free energy in the diluted spin glass models. The reproducibility hypothesis is a wide open problem mathematically, but quite general special cases were proved in Refs. [110, 111] using the cavity equations for spin distributions. For further discussion in this direction, see Ref. [112].

Chaos in temperature Another application of ultrametricity is to chaos in temperature that was first studied in the physics literature by Fisher and Huse [50] and Bray and Moore [49]. It states that the Gibbs measure is chaotic under small changes of temperature. The ideas in the proof of Theorem 2 turned out to be useful in the study of this problem and, in particular, chaos in temperature was proved in Ref. [60] for generic mixed even p-spin models of the form $H_N = \sum_{p \geq 2} \gamma_p H_{N,p}$, where $H_{N,p}$ is the pure p-spin model, $\gamma_p = 0$ for odd $p \geq 3$, and $\sum_{p \geq 1} p^{-1} I(\gamma_p \neq 0) = \infty$. This last condition means that a linear span of power functions x^p for even $p \geq 2$ such that

$\gamma_p \neq 0$ is dense in $C([0,1], \| \cdot \|_\infty)$ or, in other words, sufficiently many p-spin terms are included in the model. In such models, it was proved in Ref. [60] that, if replicas σ and ρ are sampled from the Gibbs measure with the inverse temperatures $\beta_1 \neq \beta_2$ then their overlap $R(\sigma, \rho)$ goes to zero in probability. (There is also a more general result for models with non-zero externals fields.)

The proof of this result follows the strategy in the proof of Theorem 2 by using the Ghirlanda–Guerra identities for coupled systems to prove a joint clustering (ultrametricity). In addition to ensuring joint clustering, these identities for coupled systems possess a certain built-in asymmetry due to the fact that $\beta_1 \neq \beta_2$, which turns out to be incompatible with the symmetry expressed by the joint clustering, unless the overlaps $R(\sigma, \rho)$ is zero. Of course, there are other technicalities involved, but ultrametricity plays a key role. Various results related to chaos in temperature appeared in Refs. [54, 55, 57, 58].

30.3. The Replica Trick in the Frame of the Interpolation Perspective

Francesco Guerra

Department of Physics, Sapienza University of Rome, Italy
francesco.guerra@roma1.infn.it

As it is very well known, the study of the statistical mechanics of disordered systems is based on the ingenious method called replica trick [3, 4, 37]. Here, firstly the replicated systems are considered for all integer values of the replicas. The annealed free energy is found to be given by simple expressions, which can be evaluated through appropriate variational principles in the infinite volume limit, involving the order parameters. Replica symmetry is found to be enforced for all the integer values of the replicas. Then the physically significant zero-replica limit is found through a daring trip based on analytic continuation in the number of replicas, where physical intuition plays a considerable role. Then there is the surprise that, in the zero-replicas limit, replica symmetry is broken, and an infinite number of equilibrium states show up, which enjoy ultra-metric properties. In the general frame of our research, based on interpolation methods, we have found convenient to avoid analytic continuation to connect systems with different number of replicas, by resorting to a direct interpolation on the number of replicas, so that systems connected to a generic number of replicas, even non integers, have a life in themselves [113, 114]. Therefore it is possible to introduce phase diagrams where the basic parameters are the number of replicas and the thermodynamic variables, such as temperature and external fields. A peculiar variational principle emerges on this phase diagram. Moreover, the phenomenon of replica symmetry breaking appears as a phase transition on this extended phase diagram. We give some peculiar aspects of these structures by considering the cases of the Sherrington–Kirkpatrick model and the Derrida random field model.

Integer number of replicas Let us recall that the Sherrington–Kirkpatrick model [1] is defined by introducing a set of real valued random variables $\sigma \to \mathcal{K}(\sigma)$, associated to the N spin Ising configurations

$$\sigma : (1, 2, \ldots, N) \ni i \to \sigma_i = \pm 1. \tag{30.10}$$

We can assume these 2^N variables to be Gaussian, with zero averages, and covariances given for example by

$$\mathbb{E}(\mathcal{K}(\sigma)\mathcal{K}(\sigma')) = q_{\sigma\sigma'}^2, \tag{30.11}$$

where $q_{..}$ are the configuration overlaps defined by

$$q_{\sigma\sigma'} = \frac{1}{N}\sum_{i=1}^{N}\sigma_i\sigma_i'. \tag{30.12}$$

On the other hand, in the case of the Derrida random energy model [76], we define $q_{\sigma\sigma'} = 1$ if the two configurations are equal and $q_{\sigma\sigma'} = 0$ if they are different, i.e. $q_{\sigma\sigma'} = \delta_{\sigma\sigma'}$.

The partition function is

$$Z_N(\beta) = \sum_{\sigma} e^{\beta\sqrt{\frac{N}{2}}\mathcal{K}(\sigma)}, \tag{30.13}$$

where β is the inverse of the temperature. The (random) free energy $F_N(\beta)$ is defined by

$$-\beta F_N(\beta) = \log Z_N(\beta). \tag{30.14}$$

We are interested in the infinite volume limit of the quenched free energy per site, which but for inessential constants is given by

$$A(\beta) = \lim_{N\to\infty}\frac{1}{N}\mathbb{E}\log Z_N(\beta), \tag{30.15}$$

where $\mathbb{E}$ is the expectation with respect to the noise due to the $\mathcal{K}(\sigma)$'s.

Obviously we could take also the annealed expectation i.e., average before taking the log, so that the external noise does participate to the thermodynamic equilibrium

$$\bar{A}(\beta) = \lim_{N\to\infty}\frac{1}{N}\log\mathbb{E}Z_N(\beta) = \log 2 + \frac{1}{4}\beta^2. \tag{30.16}$$

Due to the concavity of the log we have the bound

$$A(\beta) = \lim_{N\to\infty}\frac{1}{N}\mathbb{E}\log Z_N(\beta) \leq \log 2 + \frac{1}{4}\beta^2. \tag{30.17}$$

We are interested in the explicit expression for $A(\beta)$ in the form of a variational principle.

Basic to the replica trick is the preliminary consideration of the replicated annealed free energy. Therefore for each integer s let us consider

$$\phi_N(s,\beta) = \frac{1}{sN}\log\mathbb{E}Z_N^s(\beta), \quad s = 1,2,..., \tag{30.18}$$

with a deep motivation made explicit in the following. Obviously, if $s = 1$ we have simply the annealed case, considered above.

It is easy to study the thermodynamic limit $N \to \infty$ of $\phi_N(s,\beta)$, with very interesting results. The limit, $\phi(s,\beta)$, does exist for any integer $s = 1,2,...$, and can be explicitly expressed through a variational principle. We only give the general structure. We have to specify the order parameters and the trial function. Let us consider firstly the Sherrington–Kirkpatrick model. Since the s are integer, the annealed averages can be explicitly calculated. At the end of standard procedures involving ferromagnetic systems [113] we find that the appropriate order parameters are given by an array of numerical overlaps $q_{ab} \geq 0$. There are $s(s-1)/2$ order parameters.

The trial function $\tilde{\phi}(s, \beta; q_{..})$ is a function which is replica symmetric in the $q_{..}$, explicitly given by

$$\tilde{\phi}(s, \beta; q_{..}) = \frac{\beta^2}{4} + \frac{1}{s} \log \sum_{\sigma_1, \ldots \sigma_s} \exp\left(\beta \sum_{(ab)} q_{ab} \sigma_a \sigma_b\right) - \frac{\beta^2}{4s} \sum_{(ab)} q_{ab}^2. \tag{30.19}$$

We see that the trial function involves an s-site Ising model, with a disordered two body ferromagnetic interaction given by the trial parameters q_{ab}. If the replicas are permuted its value clearly does not change. The trial function is replica symmetric. The variational principle states

$$\lim_{N \to \infty} \phi_N(s, \beta) = \phi(s, \beta) = \sup_{q_{..}} \tilde{\phi}(s, \beta; q_{..}). \tag{30.20}$$

The variational principle enjoys a remarkable property. In fact, the sup is realized for values of the order parameters, where all $q_{..}$ have the same value $\bar{q} \geq 0$. There is full replica symmetry for the optimal values. This is a central point.

Let us define the value $\tilde{\phi}_{\mathrm{RS}}(s, \beta; \bar{q})$ of the trial function $\tilde{\phi}(s, \beta; q_{..})$ in the case when all $q_{..}$ assume the same value $\bar{q}$ by

$$\tilde{\phi}_{\mathrm{RS}}(s, \beta; \bar{q}) := \tilde{\phi}(s, \beta; q_{..} = \bar{q}). \tag{30.21}$$

(the suffix RS standing for "replica symmetric"). An easy direct calculation shows

$$\tilde{\phi}_{\mathrm{RS}}(s, \beta; \bar{q}) = \log 2 + \frac{1}{s} \log \int (\cosh(\beta\sqrt{\bar{q}}z))^s \, d\mu(z) + \frac{\beta^2}{4}(1 - 2\bar{q} - (s-1)\bar{q}^2), \tag{30.22}$$

where $d\mu(z)$ is the unit Gaussian measure on the real line.

For a simple sketch of the proof we refer to Ref. [113], where we follow a standard method exploited in the statistical mechanics of disordered ferromagnetic systems in order to "tame the disorder", see also the analogous treatment in Ref. [30].

Interpolating on the number of replicas The aim of the replica trick is to show that all properties of the system are in some way derived from the treatment at integer values of s. Here we give a formulation of the replica trick in the frame of replica interpolation. The first step is to extend the definition of the auxiliary function $\phi_N(s, \beta)$, from the integers $s = 1, 2, \ldots$ to any real value of s. For the sake of simplicity we consider only the case $s > 0$.

This extension is easily obtained by noticing that the very definition

$$\phi_N(s, \beta) = \frac{1}{sN} \log \mathbb{E} Z_N^s(\beta), \tag{30.23}$$

originally introduced only for integer values of s, in the replica frame, has a perfect rigorous meaning also for any $s > 0$. For a study of $\phi_N(s, \beta)$, based on large deviation techniques, we refer to Ref. [102]. Of course when s is real but not integer the auxiliary function $\phi_N(s,\beta)$ cannot be explicitly calculated, but in any case we can reach a complete control of the whole system.

For the β derivative, we easily find, through a direct calculation involving also integration by parts on the Gaussian noise,

$$\frac{\partial}{\partial\beta}\phi_N(s,\beta) = \frac{\beta}{2}(1 + (s-1)\langle q^2_{\sigma\sigma'}\rangle),\qquad(30.24)$$

for an appropriately defined average $\langle\,\cdot\,\rangle$, involving two replicas

$$\langle q^2_{\sigma\sigma'}\rangle = \frac{\mathbb{E}(Z^s\Omega(q^2_{\sigma\sigma'}))}{\mathbb{E}(Z^s)}.\qquad(30.25)$$

Here we have introduced the Boltzmann-Gibbs average for two replicas

$$\Omega(F(\sigma,\sigma')) = Z^{-2}\sum_{\sigma\sigma'}F(\sigma,\sigma')\exp\left(\beta\sqrt{\frac{N}{2}}(\mathcal{K}(\sigma)+\mathcal{K}(\sigma'))\right),\qquad(30.26)$$

for any function F depending on the spins of the two replicas.

Notice the presence of the term $(s-1)$. Its sign changes at $s=1$. It is responsible of many notable inversions, as for example superadditivity in N versus subadditivity, and inf versus sup in variational principles.

According to a well established and suggestive tradition, we continue to consider the real number s as the "number of replicas", even when s is not integer.

The hope is that the experience accumulated in the study of $\phi_N(s,\beta)$, and its limit $\phi(s,\beta)$, for integer s, can produce some information in the case of generic values $s > 0$.

The interest in generic values of s is a deep aspect of the "replica trick". As a matter of fact, we find that in the limit $s \to 0$ the auxiliary function ϕ_N reduces to the quenched value

$$\lim_{s\to 0}\phi_N(s,\beta) = \frac{1}{N}\mathbb{E}\log Z_N(\beta),\qquad(30.27)$$

a very important relation which holds also in the thermodynamic limit $N \to \infty$

$$\lim_{s\to 0}\phi(s,\beta) = A(\beta),\qquad(30.28)$$

(with $A(\beta)$ defined as in (30.15)). Therefore, the auxiliary function ϕ, for very small values of s, reduces to the expression of the quenched free energy (corresponding to (30.15)) we are interested in.

By a systematic exploitation of the general interpolation methods it is easy to establish the following important properties of $\phi_N(s,\beta)$, as recalled in Refs. [113, 114].

It turns out that $N\phi_N(s,\beta)$ is subadditive in N for $s \geq 1$ and superadditive for $s \leq 1$. The thermodynamic limit $N \to \infty$ follows in the form

$$\phi(s,\beta) = \lim_{N\to\infty}\phi_N(s,\beta) = \inf_N\phi_N(s,\beta),\qquad(30.29)$$

for $s \geq 1$, and

$$\phi(s,\beta) = \lim_{N\to\infty}\phi_N(s,\beta) = \sup_N\phi_N(s,\beta),\qquad(30.30)$$

for $s \leq 1$.

The functions $\phi_N(s, \beta)$ and $\phi(s, \beta)$ are monotone nondecreasing in the parameter s and convex in $1/s$, for any value of β. These properties easily follow as a consequence of Hölder's inequality.

Moreover, we can also prove that the functions $\phi_N(s, \beta)$ and $\phi(s, \beta)$ are convex, not only in $1/s$, but also in s [114]. The proof is very simple if we exploit the deep stochastic variational representations as introduced by Michelle Boué and Paul Dupuis in [115].

The functions $\phi_N(s, \beta)$ and $\phi(s, \beta)$ are convex in β, for any fixed value of s, as a simple direct calculation shows.

The replica trick in the random energy model and the emergence of the universal order parameter In order to explore the potentialities of the interpolating replica trick, now we shift to the laboratory of the random energy model [76]. Here we can show, by following Refs. [113, 114], that the new interpretation of the trick gives the right order parameter, the right trial function and the right variational principle, for any value of s, starting only from the elementary variational principle at integer values $s = 1, 2, 3, \dots$.

We show that in this case the replica symmetry is minimally broken in a well defined sense. The deep reason for spontaneous replica symmetry breaking arises quite naturally.

We refer to Refs. [113, 114] for all details. Here we report only the main final results.

It turns out that the order parameter can be taken as a real number $m \geq 0$, while the convex trial function $\tilde{\phi}(m, \beta)$ is defined independently of the number s of replicas by

$$0 < m \to \tilde{\phi}(m, \beta) = \frac{1}{m} \log 2 + \frac{\beta^2}{4} m. \tag{30.31}$$

Then it is easy to establish the following

Theorem 3. *For the order parameter $m > 0$, introduce the convex trial function*

$$\tilde{\phi}(m, \beta) = \frac{1}{m} \log 2 + \frac{\beta^2}{4} m. \tag{30.32}$$

Then, we have in the infinite volume limit ($N \to \infty$) for the auxiliary function $\phi(s, \beta)$ for any $s \geq 0$ the following variational principle:

$$\phi(s, \beta) = \sup_{1 \leq m \leq s} \tilde{\phi}(m, \beta), \tag{30.33}$$

for $s \geq 1$, and

$$\phi(s, \beta) = \inf_{s \leq m \leq 1} \tilde{\phi}(m, \beta), \tag{30.34}$$

for $0 \leq s \leq 1$.

The inversion from a sup to an inf, by crossing the $s = 1$ line is completely analogous to the mentioned inversion from subadditivity to superadditivity.

Notice that, while the trial function $\tilde{\phi}(m, \beta)$ does not depend on s, some bounds on m are enforced by the variational procedure.

Since $\tilde{\phi}(m, \beta)$ is convex, the sup for $s \geq 1$ can be reached only at the boundaries $m = 1$ or $m = s$, and the replica symmetry cannot be broken. On the other hand, when $s < 1$, it can happen that the minimum for $\tilde{\phi}(m, \beta)$ is in the interval $s \leq m \leq 1$, and replica symmetry is broken.

Globally the space (s, β), for $s \geq 0$ is split into three regions. For $s \geq 1$ we are always in the replica symmetric case. For $\beta < \beta_c(s)$, with $\beta_c^2(s) = 4 \log 2/s$, we have

$$\phi(s, \beta) = \log 2 + \frac{\beta^2}{4}. \tag{30.35}$$

From

$$\frac{\partial}{\partial \beta} \phi_N(s, \beta) = \frac{\beta}{2}(1 + (s - 1)\langle \delta_{\sigma\sigma'} \rangle), \tag{30.36}$$

we see that here $\langle \delta_{\sigma\sigma'} \rangle = 0$ in the limit. For $\beta > \beta_c(s)$ we have

$$\phi(s, \beta) = \frac{1}{s} \log 2 + \frac{\beta^2}{4} s, \tag{30.37}$$

and here $\langle \delta_{\sigma\sigma'} \rangle = 1$ in the limit.

These results extend the given expression from the case where s is an integer, to any $s \geq 0$. Notice that the line at $\beta_c(s)$ is a first order transition line. The function $\phi(s, \beta)$ is continuous, as it should be, because of the convexity in β. But its derivative in β has a sudden jump.

For $s < 1$ the situation is more complicated. There are two second order transition lines, the first at $\beta_c = 2\sqrt{\log 2}$, the second at $\beta_c'(s) = 2\sqrt{\log 2}/s$. The two merge at $s = 1$, but in general $\beta_c < \beta_c'(s)$ holds.

For $\beta \leq \beta_c$, replica symmetry holds,

$$\phi(s, \beta) = \log 2 + \frac{\beta^2}{4}, \tag{30.38}$$

and $\langle \delta_{\sigma\sigma'} \rangle = 0$.

For $\beta \geq \beta_c'(s)$, replica symmetry is restored in the form

$$\phi(s, \beta) = \frac{1}{s} \log 2 + \frac{\beta^2}{4} s, \tag{30.39}$$

but now $\langle \delta_{\sigma\sigma'} \rangle = 1$.

In the region $\beta_c \leq \beta \leq \beta_c'(s)$ replica symmetry is broken, and we have

$$\phi(s, \beta) = \beta \sqrt{\log 2}, \tag{30.40}$$

independently of s.

Now the formula (30.36) gives

$$\langle \delta_{\sigma\sigma'} \rangle = \frac{1}{1 - s} \left(1 - \frac{2\sqrt{\log 2}}{\beta} \right), \tag{30.41}$$

with a smooth interpolation between the value $\langle \delta_{\sigma\sigma'} \rangle = 0$ at $\beta = \beta_c$, and $\langle \delta_{\sigma\sigma'} \rangle = 1$ at $\beta = \beta_c'(s)$.

We can see that replica symmetry breaking is not connected to a difficulty in the analytic continuation of the replica symmetric solution.

In fact let us take $\beta > \beta_c$ and a large value of s, where

$$\phi(s, \beta) = \frac{1}{s}\log 2 + \frac{\beta^2}{4}s. \tag{30.42}$$

At fixed β, there is no problem in the analytic continuation of this expression to all values of $s > 0$ well inside the region of symmetry breaking, for $s < s_c = 2\sqrt{\log 2}/\beta$. However, for $s < s_c$, the equation (30.42) can no longer be true for a very simple reason.

In fact, at fixed β, the function

$$\frac{1}{s}\log 2 + \frac{\beta^2}{4}s \tag{30.43}$$

is decreasing, with decreasing s, up to the point $s = s_c$, where there is an inversion, and the function starts to increase with decreasing s. Notice that the derivative

$$\frac{\partial}{\partial s}\left(\frac{1}{s}\log 2 + \frac{\beta^2}{4}s\right) = -\frac{1}{s^2}\log 2 + \frac{\beta^2}{4} \tag{30.44}$$

is positive in s for $s > s_c$, zero at $s = s_c$, and negative in s for $s < s_c$. Since $\phi(s, \beta)$ must be increasing in s, we surely have

$$\phi(s, \beta) \le \frac{1}{s_c}\log 2 + \frac{\beta^2}{4}s_c. \tag{30.45}$$

As a matter of fact equality holds here, since for $s = s_c = 2\sqrt{\log 2}/\beta$ we have exactly

$$\frac{1}{s_c}\log 2 + \frac{\beta^2}{4}s_c = \beta\sqrt{\log 2}. \tag{30.46}$$

We say that in this case that "replica symmetry is minimally broken". Replica symmetry holds everywhere, with the exception of the region where this cannot be true, for simple thermodynamic reasons. Then, necessarily

$$\phi(s, \beta) = \phi(s_c(\beta), \beta). \tag{30.47}$$

Notice that $\phi(s, \beta)$, at each fixed value of β, is convex both in s and $1/s$, as it should be.

This ends our discussion of the replica trick for the random energy model. We have seen how to reach the right order parameter, and the right trial function, through a direct inspection of the variational behavior of the trial function for the system at integer values of s.

The emergence of the order parameter and the trial function in the Sherrington–Kirkpatrick model   We will try to show that an appropriate form of the variational principle for integer values of s does immediately suggest the right form of the variational principle for all value of s, in particular at $s = 0$. As in the case of the random energy model, the main ingredients of the emerging structure are provided by two facts. The new order parameter, call it symbolically x, and the trial function $\tilde\phi(\beta, x)$ must be independent of s. Then the order parameter x must belong to a convex space, and the trial function $\tilde\phi$, as a function of x, must be convex in x. The variational principle for $s \ge 1$ should be a $\sup_x$ principle, with some constraints on x

which here we denote symbolically by $1 \leq x \leq s$, while for $0 < s \leq 1$ it should be a $\min_x$ principle with constraints on s of the type $s \leq x \leq 1$.

Obviously the two forms of variational principles holding for integer s in the Sherrington–Kirkpatrick model, which we have found in (30.20), do not satisfy these properties. In the general form (30.20), the qualitative aspects of the order parameters q_{ab} do strongly depend on s, while no kind of convexity is visible. As a matter of fact, it is possible to easily verify that the trial function $\tilde{\phi}(s, \beta; q_{ab})$ in (30.20) is *concave* separately in each of the q_{ab}^2. In a sense, we must transform variational principles where concave trial functions are involved, into equivalent variational principles where *convex* trial functions appear, through an appropriate transformation of the order parameters.

The way out is very simple, but conceptually very deep. We give a synthetic sketch of the general strategy.

Firstly we have to resort to an old result coming from a simple form of interpolation, which was presented for the first time in Ref. [116]. Let us recall that the infinite volume limit $\lim_{N\to\infty} \phi_N(s, \beta) = \phi(s, \beta)$, holding in the form of an inf or a sup, as a consequence of subadditivity or superaddivity in N, for $s \geq 1$, or $s \leq 1$ respectively, can be recast, on a general basis, as a Cesàro limit for marginal quantities in the volume N, according to $\phi(s, \beta) = c\lim_{N\to\infty}((N+1)\phi_{N+1} - N\phi_N)$. For a generic sequence $N \to a_N, N = 1, 2, \ldots$, the Cesàro limit is defined as $c\lim_{N\to\infty} a_N = \lim_N N^{-1} \sum_{K=1}^{N} a_K$. Partial averages are involved, so that the Cesàro limit is equal to the standard limit if this does exist, but it can exist in some cases where the standard limit does not exist. A typical case is the alternating sequence $0, 1, 0, 1, \ldots$ which has $1/2$ as Cesàro limit.

Now we follow the strategy outlined in [116] for the case $s = 0$, but easily extended to any s. We can write

$$(N+1)\phi_{N+1} - N\phi_N = s^{-1} \log \frac{\mathbb{E} Z_{N+1}^s}{\mathbb{E} Z_N^s}$$

$$= \log 2 + s^{-1} \log \mathbb{E}\Omega^s (\exp(\log\cosh(\beta\eta(\sigma))) - B, \qquad (30.48)$$

where we have explicitly performed the sum over σ_{N+1}, which gives rise to the $\log 2$ and the cosh put at the exponent under log for convenience, Ω is a random state depending on the $\sigma_1, \sigma_2, \ldots, \sigma_N$, the "cavity variables", $\eta(\sigma)$ denotes the interaction of the spin associated to the site $N + 1$ with the cavity σ variables, given essentially by

$$\eta(\sigma) = \frac{1}{\sqrt{N}} \sum_{i=1}^{N} J_{iN+1}\sigma_i. \qquad (30.49)$$

The quantity B in (30.48) is an additional important term which is not necessary to specify here. Its form, in terms of the relevant order parameter will be clear later.

The interpolating method proposed here is very simple [116]. Firstly consider a nonrandom state Ω and introduce an interpolating parameter $0 \leq q \leq 1$, and an auxiliary function $f(q, y)$, where y is a real variable, with given final boundary value $f(1, y) = \log\cosh(\beta y)$. We will try to adjust the function f in such a way that the quantity

$$s^{-1} \log \mathbb{E}\Omega^s (\exp f(q, \sqrt{q}\eta(\sigma))) \qquad (30.50)$$

does not depend on q. If this is the case then

$$s^{-1} \log \mathbb{E}\Omega^s \left(\exp \log \cosh(\beta\eta(\sigma))\right) = f(0,0). \tag{30.51}$$

By taking the explicit derivative with respect to q, and integrating by parts on the J_{iN+1} Gaussian random variables [116], with some surprise we immediately have that the quantity in (30.50) really does not depend on q *provided* that the auxiliary function f satisfies the Hamilton–Jacobi–Bellmann equation

$$(\partial_q f)(q,y) + \frac{1}{2}\left(f''(q,y) + x(q)f'^2(q,y)\right) = 0, \tag{30.52}$$

with final condition

$$f(1,y) = \log \cosh(\beta y). \tag{30.53}$$

In (30.52), $f' = \partial_y f$ and $f'' = \partial_y^2 f$, while x is a functional order parameter

$$[0,1] \ni q \to x(q), \tag{30.54}$$

satisfying the bound $1 \leq x(q) \leq s$, for the case $s \geq 1$, and $s \leq x(q) \leq 1$ for the case $s \leq 1$.

By following the methods in Ref. [116] it is possible to show that there are order parameters x such that the representation given in (30.51) holds, even in cases where (30.50) does not hold, because of a compensation of terms for different values of q. Moreover the representation holds also for random Ω's and Cesàro sums.

Notice that the equation (30.52) is nothing but Parisi equation, and the functional order parameter x is the Parisi functional order parameter, extended to any value of s. Here, they are given for free through interpolation starting from the marginal $(N+1)\phi_{N+1} - N\phi_N$.

Recently, through ground breaking work of Antonio Auffinger and Wei-Kuo Chen [26], it has been proven that $f(0,0;x)$ is strictly convex in x. The methods they exploited are partly based on Ref. [115].

Now we can invoke the powerful broken replica bounds introduced in Ref. [5], extended to any value of s, in order to produce the right candidate for the variational trial functional with the correct properties. Let us notice that from (30.48), (30.51) we know that there exists an order parameter x such that

$$\phi_N(s,\beta) = \log 2 + f(0,0;x) - B. \tag{30.55}$$

Of course, we do not know the value of x, nor the expression of B. However we can try to compare $\phi_N(s,\beta)$ with $f(0,0;x)$ through an interpolation argument similar to what was done in Ref. [5] in the case $s = 0$. We end up with the following sum rule holding for any x

$$\phi_N(s,\beta) = \log 2 + f(0,0;x) - \frac{\beta^2}{2}\int q\, x(q)\, \mathrm{d}q + R, \tag{30.56}$$

where the error term R shares the following remarkable properties, uniformly in N: in the case $s \geq 1$ it happens that $R \geq 0$ *provided* $x(q)$ is non-increasing in q and bounded by $s \geq x(q) \geq 1$, and we call this condition $\mathcal{X}_-(s)$, while in the case $0 \leq s \leq 1$ the error term is $R \leq 0$ *provided* $x(q)$ is non-decreasing in q and bounded by $s \leq x(q) \leq 1$, and we call this condition $\mathcal{X}_+(s)$.

Therefore, the whole procedure induces to define

$$\tilde{\phi}(\beta; x) = \log 2 + f(0, 0; x) - \frac{\beta^2}{2} \int q \, x(q) \, \mathrm{d}q \tag{30.57}$$

as the trial functional, independent of s and strictly convex in x, as requested.

The sum rule implies

$$\phi_N(s, \beta) \geq \phi(s, \beta) \geq \tilde{\phi}(\beta; x), \tag{30.58}$$

in the case $s \geq 1$ with $x \in \mathcal{X}_-(s)$, while

$$\phi_N(s, \beta) \leq \phi(s, \beta) \leq \tilde{\phi}(\beta; x), \tag{30.59}$$

in the case $0 \leq s \leq 1$ with $x \in \mathcal{X}_+(s)$.

Notice that both $\mathcal{X}_-(s)$ and $\mathcal{X}_+(s)$ are convex spaces of functions.

For a moment let us go back to the case of where s is an integer. Through a direct calculation, we immediately see that the replica symmetric trial in (30.22) can be expressed also as

$$\tilde{\phi}_{\mathrm{RS}}(s, \beta; \bar{q}) = \tilde{\phi}(\beta; x_{\bar{q}}), \tag{30.60}$$

where $x_{\bar{q}}$ is the order parameter in $\mathcal{X}_-(s)$ defined by $x_{\bar{q}}(q) = s$ for $0 \leq q \leq \bar{q}$, and $x_{\bar{q}}(q) = 1$ for $\bar{q} \leq q \leq 1$. Order parameters of the type $x_{\bar{q}}$ are extremals in the convex space $\mathcal{X}_-(s)$.

Finally we have the Theorem

Theorem 4. *Define the* s *independent trial functional* $\tilde{\phi}(\beta; x) = \log 2 + f(0, 0; x) - \frac{\beta^2}{2} \int q \, x(q)\mathrm{d}q$, *strictly convex in the functional order parameter then the infinite volume limits* $\phi(s, \beta)$ *are given by the constrained variational principles*

$$\phi(s, \beta) = \sup_{x \in \mathcal{X}_-(s)} \tilde{\phi}(\beta; x) \tag{30.61}$$

for $s \geq 1$, *and*

$$\phi(s, \beta) = \inf_{x \in \mathcal{X}_+(s)} \tilde{\phi}(\beta; x) \tag{30.62}$$

for $0 \leq s \leq 1$.

Of course, in order to have the bounds in the opposite direction, we have to rely on the extension of the basic results of Michel Talagrand [7] and Dmitry Panchenko [87, 88].

Acknowledgments

W.-K. Chen was supported by the NSF Career grant DMS-1752184.

References

[1] D. Sherrington and S. Kirkpatrick, *Phys. Rev. Lett.* **35**(26), 1792, (1975).

[2] J. R. de Almeida and D. J. Thouless, *J. Phys. A.* **11**(5), 983, (1978).

[3] G. Parisi, *Phys. Rev. Lett.* **43**(23), 1754, (1979).

[4] G. Parisi, *J. Phys. A.* **13**(4), L115, (1980).

[5] F. Guerra, *Commun. Math. Phys.* **233**(1), 1–12, (2003).

[6] A. Jagannath and I. Tobasco, *Proc. Am. Math. Soc.* **144**(7), 3135–3150, (2016).

[7] M. Talagrand, *Ann. Math.* pp. 221–263, (2006).

[8] D. Panchenko, *Ann. Probab.* **42**(3), 946–958, (2014).

[9] M. Mézard, G. Parisi, and M. Virasoro, *Europhys. Lett.* **1**(2), 77–82, (1986).

[10] F. Guerra. In eds. F. K. S. De Lillo, P. Sodano and G. Semenoff, *Field Theory And Collective Phenomena.* World Scientific, (1995).

[11] M. Aizenman, R. Sims, and S. L. Starr, *Phys. Rev. B.* **68**(21), 214403, (2003).

[12] D. Ruelle, *Commun. Math. Phys.* **108**(2), 225–239, (1987).

[13] W.-K. Chen, *Electron. J. Probab.* **18**, 1–14, (2013).

[14] A. Jagannath and S. Sen, *Annales de l'Institut Henri Poincaré D.* **8**(1), 35–88, (2020).

[15] A. Jagannath, J. Ko, and S. Sen, *Ann. Appl. Probab.* **28**(3), 1536–1572, (2018).

[16] J. Ko, *Electron. J. Probab.* **25**, 1–34, (2020).

[17] D. Panchenko, *Rev. Math. Phys.* **17**(07), 793–857, (2005).

[18] D. Panchenko, *Ann. Probab.* **43**(6), 3494–3513, (2015).

[19] D. Panchenko, *Ann. Probab.* **46**(2), 829–864, (2018).

[20] D. Panchenko, *Ann. Probab.* **46**(2), 865–896, (2018).

[21] M. Talagrand, *Probab. Theory Relat. Fields.* **134**(3), 339–382, (2006).

[22] T. Dominguez, *Electron. J. Probab.* **27**, 1–46, (2022).

[23] M. Talagrand, *J. Funct. Anal.* **231**(2), 269–286, (2006).

[24] A. Auffinger and W.-K. Chen, *Probab. Theory Relat. Fields.* **161**(3-4), 817–850, (2015).

[25] A. Bovier and A. Klimovsky, *Electron. J. Probab.* **14**, 161–241, (2009).

[26] A. Auffinger and W.-K. Chen, *Commun. Math. Phys.* **335**(3), 1429–1444, (2015).

[27] W.-K. Chen, *Ann. Probab.* **45**(6A), 3929–3966, (2017).

[28] A. Jagannath and I. Tobasco, *Probab. Theory Relat. Fields.* **167**(3-4), 615–672, (2017).

[29] A. Auffinger and W.-K. Chen, *Commun. Math. Phys.* **348**(3), 751–770, (2016).

[30] M. Talagrand, *Mean-field models for spin glasses.* vol. 54, 55, (Springer-Verlag, 2011).

[31] F. L. Toninelli, *Europhys. Lett.* **60**(5), 764, (2002).

[32] E. Bolthausen. In *International Conference on Statistical Mechanics of Classical and Disordered Systems*, pp. 63–93. Springer, (2018).

[33] C. Brennecke and H.-T. Yau, *J. Math. Phys.* **63**(7), 073302, (2022).

[34] W.-K. Chen, *arXiv:2103.04802.* (2021).

[35] A. Auffinger and W.-K. Chen, *Ann. Probab.* **45**(6B), 4617–4631, (2017).

[36] W.-K. Chen, M. Handschy, and G. Lerman, *Probab. Theory Relat. Fields.* **171**(1), 53–95, (2018).

[37] M. Mézard, G. Parisi, and M. A. Virasoro, *Spin glass theory and beyond: An Introduction to the Replica Method and Its Applications.* vol. 9, (World Scientific, 1987).

[38] R. Oppermann and D. Sherrington, *Phys. Rev. Lett.* **95**(19), 197203, (2005).

[39] R. Oppermann, M. J. Schmidt, and D. Sherrington, *Phys. Rev. Lett.* **98**(12), 127201, (2007).

[40] A. Montanari. In *2019 IEEE 60th Annual Symposium on Foundations of Computer Science (FOCS)*, pp. 1417–1433. SIAM, (2019).

[41] A. El Alaoui, A. Montanari, and M. Sellke, *Ann. Probab.* **49**(6), 2922–2960, (2021).

[42] A. Auffinger, W.-K. Chen, and Q. Zeng, *Commun. Pure Appl. Math.* **73**(5), (2020).

[43] A. Auffinger and Y. Zhou, *Stoch. Process. Their Appl.* **146**, 382–413, (2022).

[44] W.-K. Chen and D. Panchenko, *Commun. Math. Phys.* **362**(1), 219–252, (2018).

[45] W.-K. Chen and A. Sen, *Commun. Math. Phys.* **350**(1), 129–173, (2017).

[46] W.-K. Chen, D. Panchenko, and E. Subag, *Commun. Math. Phys.* **381**(1), 257–291, (2021).

[47] W.-K. Chen and A. Sen, *International Mathematics Research Notices.* (2020).

[48] A. Jagannath and I. Tobasco, *Commun. Math. Phys.* **352**(3), 979–1017, (2017).

[49] A. J. Bray and M. A. Moore, *Phys. Rev. Lett.* **58**(1), 57, (1987).

[50] D. S. Fisher and D. A. Huse, *Phys. Rev. Lett.* **56**(15), 1601, (1986).

[51] S. Chatterjee, *arXiv:0907.3381.* (2009).

[52] S. Chatterjee, *Superconcentration and related topics.* vol. 15, (Springer, 2014).

[53] W.-K. Chen, *Ann. Probab.* **41**(5), 3345–3391, (2013).

[54] G. Ben Arous, E. Subag, and O. Zeitouni, *Commun. Pure Appl. Math.* **73**(8), 1732–1828, (2020).

[55] W.-K. Chen, *Commun. Math. Phys.* **328**(3), 867–901, (2014).

[56] W.-K. Chen and D. Panchenko, *Probab. Theory Relat. Fields.* **157**(1-2), 389–404, (2013).

[57] W.-K. Chen and D. Panchenko, *J. Stat. Phys.* **166**(5), 1151–1162, (2017).

[58] W.-K. Chen and D. Panchenko, *Ann. Appl. Probab.* **28**(3), 1356–1378, (2018).

[59] R. Eldan, *J. Stat. Phys.* **181**(4), 1266–1276, (2020).

[60] D. Panchenko, *Commun. Math. Phys.* **346**(2), 703–739, (2016).

[61] E. Subag, *Invent. Math.* **210**(1), 135–209, (2017).

[62] J. Ding, R. Eldan, and A. Zhai, *Ann. Probab.* **43**(6), 3468–3493, (2015).

[63] S. Chatterjee, *arXiv:0810.4221.* (2008).

[64] W.-K. Chen, P. Dey, and D. Panchenko, *Probab. Theory Relat. Fields.* **168**(1), 41–53, (2017).

[65] W.-K. Chen, D. Gamarnik, D. Panchenko, and M. Rahman, *Ann. Probab.* **47**(3), 1587–1618, (2019).

[66] D. Gamarnik, A. Jagannath, and A. S. Wein. In *2020 IEEE 61st Annual Symposium on Foundations of Computer Science (FOCS)*, pp. 131–140. IEEE, (2020).

[67] D. Gamarnik and A. Jagannath, *Ann. Probab.* **49**(1), 180–205, (2021).

[68] G. Parisi, *Phys. Rev. Lett.* **50**(24), 1946, (1983).

[69] M. Mézard, G. Parisi, N. Sourlas, G. Toulouse, and M. Virasoro, *Phys. Rev. Lett.* **52**(13), 1156, (1984).

[70] M. Mézard, G. Parisi, N. Sourlas, G. Toulouse, and M. Virasoro, *J. Phys. (France).* **45**(5), 843–854, (1984).

[71] M. Mézard, G. Parisi, and M. Virasoro, *J. Phys. Lett. (France).* **46**(6), 217–222, (1985).

[72] M. Mézard and M. A. Virasoro, *J. Phys. (France).* **46**(8), 1293–1307, (1985).

[73] B. Derrida and G. Toulouse, *J. Phys. Lett. (France).* **46**(6), 223–228, (1985).

[74] C. De Dominicis and H. Hilhorst, *J. Phys. Lett. (France).* **46**(19), 909–914, (1985).

[75] B. Derrida, *Phys. Rev. Lett.* **45**(2), 79, (1980).

[76] B. Derrida, *Phys. Rev. B.* **24**(5), 2613, (1981).

[77] B. Derrida, *J. Phys. (France), Lett.* **46**(9), 401–407, (1985).

[78] B. Derrida and E. Gardner, *J. Phys. C.* **19**(13), 2253, (1986).

[79] F. Guerra, *Int. J. Mod. Phys. B.* **10**(13n14), 1675–1684, (1996).

[80] S. Ghirlanda and F. Guerra, *J. Phys. A.* **31**(46), 9149, (1998).

[81] G. Parisi, *arXiv preprint cond-mat/9801081.* (1998).

[82] L.-P. Arguin and M. Aizenman, *Ann. Probab.* **37**(3), 1080–1113, (2009).

[83] M. Aizenman and P. Contucci, *J. Stat. Phys.* **92**(5), 765–783, (1998).

[84] E. Bolthausen and A.-S. Sznitman, *Commun. Math. Phys.* **197**(2), 247–276, (1998).

[85] D. Panchenko, *Ann. Probab.* **38**(1), 327–347, (2010).

[86] D. Panchenko, *C. R. Acad. Sci.* **349**(13-14), 813–816, (2011).

[87] D. Panchenko, *Ann. Math.* pp. 383–393, (2013).

[88] D. Panchenko, *The Sherrington-Kirkpatrick model.* (Springer Science & Business Media, 2013).

[89] M. Talagrand, *Probab. Theory Relat. Fields.* **148**(3), 601–643, (2010).

[90] A. Jagannath, *Commun. Pure Appl. Math.* **70**(4), 611–664, (2017).

[91] S. Chatterjee and L. Sloman, *Adv. Math.* **376**, 107417, (2021).

[92] S. Franz, G. Parisi, and M. Virasoro, *Europhys. Lett.* **17**(1), 5, (1992).

[93] G. Parisi and F. Ricci-Tersenghi, *J. Phys. A.* **33**(1), 113, (2000).

[94] A. Barra, P. Contucci, E. Mingione, and D. Tantari. In *Ann. Henri Poincaré*, vol. 16, pp. 691–708. Springer, (2015).

[95] A. Barra, A. Di Biasio, and F. Guerra, *J. Stat. Mech.: Theory Exp.* **2010**(09), P09006, (2010).

[96] E. Agliari, A. Barra, R. Burioni, and A. Di Biasio, *J. Math. Phys.* **53**(6), 063304, (2012).

[97] J.-C. Mourrat, *Can. J. Math.* pp. 1–23, (2019).

[98] J.-C. Mourrat and D. Panchenko, *Electron. J. Probab.* **25**, 1–17, (2020).

[99] J.-C. Mourrat, *arXiv:2010.09114.* (2020).

[100] J.-C. Mourrat, *PMP.* **2**(2), 61–119, (2021).

[101] D. J. Gross, I. Kanter, and H. Sompolinsky, *Phys. Rev. Lett.* **55**(3), 304, (1985).

[102] M. Talagrand, *J. Stat. Phys.* **126**, (2007).

[103] P. Contucci and E. Mingione, *Commun. Math. Phys.* **368**(3), 1323–1344, (2019).

[104] G. Ben Arous and A. Jagannath, *Commun. Math. Phys.* **361**(1), 1–52, (2018).

[105] W.-K. Chen, *Ann. Stat.* **47**(5), 2734–2756, (2019).

[106] A. Adhikari and C. Brennecke, *J. Math. Phys.* **61**(8), 083302, (2020).

[107] D. Panchenko, *Probab. Theory Relat. Fields.* **161**(3), 619–650, (2015).

[108] T. Austin and D. Panchenko, *Probab. Theory Relat. Fields.* **159**(3-4), 809–823, (2014).

[109] M. Mézard and G. Parisi, *Eur. Phys. J. B.* **20**(2), 217–233, (2001).

[110] D. Panchenko, *J. Stat. Phys.* **155**(1), 1–22, (2014).

[111] D. Panchenko, *J. Stat. Phys.* **162**(1), 1–42, (2016).

[112] G. Parisi, *J. Stat. Phys.* **167**(3-4), 515–542, (2017).

[113] F. Guerra. In *International Conference on Statistical Mechanics of Classical and Disordered Systems*, pp. 171–191. Springer, (2018).

[114] F. Guerra. In eds. S. Albeverio, E. Mastrogiacomo, E. Rosazza Gianin, and S. Ugolini, *Complexity and Emergence*, pp. 63–86. Springer, (2022).

[115] M. Boué and P. Dupuis, *Ann. Probab.* **26**(4), 1641–1659, (1998).

[116] F. Guerra. In eds. U. C. S. Albeverio and D. Merlini, *Stochastic Processes, Physics and Geometry, II.* World Scientific, (1995).

Chapter 31

Random Energy Models:
Broken Replica Symmetry and Activated Dynamics

The random energy model (REM) and the generalized random energy model (GREM) are simple spin glass models which play an important role in the theory of spin glasses. The connection with more complex spin glass models can be made using the p-spin generalisation of the SK model, which, in the large p limit, gives precisely the REM. The REM and GREM allow us to illustrate and to test in a simple framework several central ideas of the theory both from an equilibrium and from a dynamical point of view. They were also used in several contexts such as the problem of protein folding or error-correcting codes. This chapter presents the basic ideas and some recent developments for two aspects:

(1) The random energy models and replica symmetry breaking, by **B. Derrida** and **P. Mottishaw**.

(2) Aging in the activated dynamics of the REM and the p-spin SK models, by **V. Gayrard**.

31.1. The Random Energy Models and Replica Symmetry Breaking

Bernard Derrida* and Peter Mottishaw[†]

*Collège de France and École Normale Supérieure, Paris, France
bernard.derrida@ens.fr
[†]University of Edinburgh, Edinburgh, United Kingdom
peter.mottishaw@ed.ac.uk

31.1.1. *Introduction*

At the end of the 1970s there were considerable efforts among theoretical physicists to try to solve the Sherrington–Kirkpatrick (SK) model [1]. This led to the invention by Parisi of his replica symmetry breaking (RSB) scheme in 1979 (see [2] and references therein).

Trying to develop possible ways of understanding the SK model, a generalization of the SK model, the p-spin model [3], was introduced in 1980 which reduces to the SK model when $p = 2$ and has two simple limits, the case $p = 1$ where the spins are independent and the case $p = \infty$ which is precisely the random energy model (REM). Initially the goal was to try to approach the SK model through perturbative expansions around these two exactly soluble cases.

The p-spin model describes a system of N Ising spins $\sigma_i = \pm 1$ with infinite-ranged random p-spin interactions. The energy of a configuration $\mathcal{C} = \{\sigma_1 \cdots \sigma_N\}$ can be written as

$$E(\mathcal{C}) = - \sum_{i_1 < i_2 \cdots < i_p} A_{i_1 \cdots i_p} \, \sigma_{i_1} \sigma_{i_2} \cdots \sigma_{i_p} \tag{31.1}$$

where the p-spin interactions $A_{i_1 \cdots i_p}$ are quenched random variables distributed according to

$$\rho(A_{i_1 \cdots i_p}) = \sqrt{\frac{N^{p-1}}{\pi \, J^2 \, p!}} \, \exp\left[-\frac{(A_{i_1 \cdots i_p})^2 \, N^{p-1}}{J^2 \, p!} \right]. \tag{31.2}$$

For the p-spin model (as well as for many other disordered systems) the partition function $Z(\beta)$

$$Z(\beta) = \sum_{\mathcal{C}=1}^{2^N} e^{-\beta E(\mathcal{C})} \tag{31.3}$$

is nothing but a sum of exponentials of correlated Gaussian random variables,

$$P(E(\mathcal{C})) \simeq \frac{1}{\sqrt{N\pi}\, J} \exp\left[-\frac{E(\mathcal{C})^2}{N J^2} \right] \tag{31.4}$$

with known correlations

$$\langle E(\mathcal{C}) E(\mathcal{C}') \rangle = \frac{N J^2}{2} \, q(\mathcal{C}, \mathcal{C}')^p \tag{31.5}$$

where the overlap between the pair of configurations $\mathcal{C}, \mathcal{C}'$ is defined by

$$q(\mathcal{C}, \mathcal{C}') = \frac{1}{N} \sum_{i=1}^{N} \sigma_i \, \sigma_i'. \tag{31.6}$$

Here, and elsewhere in this chapter, $\langle \cdot \rangle$ denotes an average over disorder, i.e. over the energies $E(\mathcal{C})$. Clearly in the large p limit the energies of different configurations become uncorrelated. Therefore in this limit, the p-spin model becomes the random energy model with a partition function $Z(\beta)$ given by (31.3), the energies $E(\mathcal{C})$ being 2^N i.i.d. random variables distributed according to (31.4). That the partition function can be seen as a sum of independent random variables greatly simplifies the analysis of the REM [4–6].

31.1.2. *The phase diagram of the REM*

A simple way of obtaining the phase diagram of the REM is to use the microcanonical ensemble. For a given sample, i.e. for a given realization of the 2^N energies $E(\mathcal{C})$, let $\mathcal{N}(E)$ be the number of configurations with an energy in the interval $(E, E + \delta E)$ (we choose δE to be small compared to N, but not exponentially small in N). Obviously the average of $\mathcal{N}(E)$ over the samples is $\langle \mathcal{N}(E) \rangle = 2^N P(E) \delta E$. Then because the energies are independent, one has that for a typical sample $\mathcal{N}(E) \simeq \langle \mathcal{N}(E) \rangle$ in the range of energies where $\langle \mathcal{N}(E) \rangle \gg 1$ (i.e. when $|E/N| < J\sqrt{\log 2}$) and $\mathcal{N}(E) = 0$ in the range where $\langle \mathcal{N}(E) \rangle \ll 1$. This immediately tells us that the ground state energy is such that $E_{\mathrm{GS}}/N = -J\sqrt{\log 2}$ and that the entropy in the range $|E|/N < J\sqrt{\log 2}$ is given by

$S(E) = N \log 2 - E^2/(NJ^2)$. Outside this range, there is no energy level (for a typical sample) and thus $S(E) = -\infty$. In summary,

$$\frac{S(E)}{N} = \begin{cases} \log 2 - \frac{E^2}{N^2 J^2} & \text{for } \frac{|E|}{NJ} < \sqrt{\log 2} \\ -\infty & \text{otherwise.} \end{cases} \tag{31.7}$$

Then using the fact that $\beta = \frac{\mathrm{d}\, S(E)}{\mathrm{d}\, E}$ one gets the following expression for the free energy of a typical sample:

$$\frac{\log Z(\beta)}{N} = \begin{cases} \log 2 + \frac{\beta^2 J^2}{4} & \text{for } \beta < \beta_c \\ \beta J \sqrt{\log 2} & \text{for } \beta > \beta_c \end{cases} \qquad \text{where} \quad \beta_c = 2\sqrt{\log 2}\, J^{-1}. \tag{31.8}$$

This shows that the REM exhibits a phase transition at $\beta = \beta_c$. In the low temperature phase the energy becomes independent of β which means that the system is frozen in its lowest energy levels (see Sec. 31.1.3).

To investigate the magnetic properties of the REM [3, 7], one can introduce a magnetic field and a magnetization in the REM by considering that among the 2^N configurations, $\binom{N}{\frac{N+M}{2}}$ have a total magnetization M (with $M = -N, -N+2, -N+4 \cdots, N$). By repeating the above reasoning which led to (31.8) for the typical number $\mathcal{N}(E, M)$ of configurations with energy E and magnetization M, one can calculate the entropy and then the free energy as a function of the temperature and of the magnetic field. The outcome is the following expression of the zero field magnetic susceptibility

$$\chi = \begin{cases} \beta & \text{for } \beta < \beta_c \\ \beta_c & \text{for } \beta > \beta_c \end{cases} \tag{31.9}$$

with a cusp at the transition very reminiscent of the susceptibility of spin glasses. Moreover the REM exhibits a phase transition in a non-zero magnetic field [3] as the SK model does along the de Almeida–Thouless line [2].

Many other properties of the REM can be determined like the location of the zeroes in the complex temperature plane [8–10] or the finite size corrections to the average free energy [3, 7]. For example, when $\beta > \beta_c$,

$$\langle \log Z(\beta) \rangle = N \frac{\beta \beta_c J^2}{2} - \frac{\beta}{2\beta_c} \log N + R(\beta) \tag{31.10}$$

with the $O(1)$ correction

$$R(\beta) = \frac{\beta}{\beta_c} \log\left(\frac{\Gamma\left(1 - \frac{\beta_c}{\beta}\right)}{J \beta_c \sqrt{\pi}} \right) + \left(1 - \frac{\beta}{\beta_c}\right) \Gamma'(1) + o(1). \tag{31.11}$$

Expressions like (31.8)–(31.10) or other properties can also be generalized to cases where the energies $E(\mathcal{C})$ are still independent but are no longer Gaussian random variables [4, 11–14].

31.1.3. *The low temperature phase of the REM*

In the low temperature phase ($\beta > \beta_c$), the extensive part of the free energy is frozen and the partition function is dominated by the ground state and the energy levels at a distance of order 1 from this ground state. Close to the ground state energy, (in fact for all energies E such that $|E + NJ\sqrt{\log 2}| \ll \sqrt{N}$) the distribution (31.4) can be approximated by an exponential distribution

$$P\big(E(\mathcal{C})\big) \sim \frac{1}{\sqrt{N\pi}\,J} \frac{1}{2^N} \, \mathrm{e}^{\beta_c\left(E(\mathcal{C})+NJ\sqrt{\log 2}\right)} . \tag{31.12}$$

One can then rewrite the partition function (31.3) as a sum

$$Z(\beta) = Z_0 \sum_{\mathcal{C}=1}^{2^N} x(\mathcal{C}) \quad \text{where} \quad Z_0 = \mathrm{e}^{N\,\beta J\sqrt{\log 2}} \tag{31.13}$$

of 2^N i.i.d. random variables $x(\mathcal{C}) = \mathrm{e}^{-\beta\left(E(\mathcal{C})+NJ\sqrt{\log 2}\right)}$ which, using (31.12), have a distribution $\mathcal{P}(x)$ with a heavy tail in the range of energies close to the ground state energy

$$\mathcal{P}\big(x(\mathcal{C})\big) \simeq \frac{1}{\sqrt{N\pi}\,\beta J} \frac{1}{2^N} \, x(\mathcal{C})^{-1-\frac{\beta_c}{\beta}} \quad \text{in the range } |\log x| \ll \sqrt{N}. \tag{31.14}$$

Thinking of the partition function (31.13) as the sum of 2^N random variables distributed according to a heavy tail distribution like (31.14) allows to determine most of the properties of the low temperature phase in the large N limit [15, 16]. For example, one can recover the low temperature expression (31.10) including the $O(1)$ correction (31.11) of the free energy using the identity

$$\langle \log Z(\beta) \rangle = \int_0^\infty \frac{\mathrm{d}t}{t}\left(1 - \langle \mathrm{e}^{-tZ(\beta)}\rangle\right)$$

and that

$$\left\langle \mathrm{e}^{-tZ(\beta)} \right\rangle = \left[1 + \int_0^\infty \mathrm{d}x\, \mathcal{P}(x)\big(\mathrm{e}^{-Z_0\,t\,x} -1\big)\right]^{2^N} \simeq \exp\left[\frac{\Gamma(-\frac{\beta_c}{\beta})}{\sqrt{N\pi}\,\beta J}\,(Z_0\,t)^{\frac{\beta_c}{\beta}}\right]. \tag{31.15}$$

This also allows to obtain the distribution of the fluctuations of order 1 of the free-energy [17] in particular that [7]

$$\langle (\log Z(\beta))^2 \rangle - \langle \log Z(\beta) \rangle^2 = \frac{\pi^2}{6} \frac{\beta^2 - \beta_c^2}{\beta_c^2}$$

or to predict that the ground state energy has a Gumbel distribution [18].

31.1.4. *The overlaps in the low temperature phase of the REM*

Overlaps (31.6) which measure the distance between configurations play a central role in the theory of spin glasses. One striking outcome of the RSB theory [2] is that, even in the large N limit, the distribution $P(q)$ defined by

$$P(q) = \frac{1}{Z(\beta)^2} \sum_{\mathcal{C}} \sum_{\mathcal{C}'} \mathrm{e}^{-\beta\left(E(\mathcal{C})+E(\mathcal{C}')\right)} \delta\big(q(\mathcal{C},\mathcal{C}') - q\big) \tag{31.16}$$

remains broad and non-self averaging (i.e., it remains sample dependent). As discussed below, this is indeed what also happens for the REM.

In the low temperature phase the configurations $\mathcal{C} = \{\sigma_1 \cdots \sigma_N\}$ which dominate the partition function, i.e. whose energies are close to the ground state, are likely to be very scattered in phase space and have zero overlaps between themselves. Therefore, in the large N limit, $P(q)$ has the form

$$P(q) = (1 - Y_2)\,\delta(q) + Y_2\,\delta(q - 1) \tag{31.17}$$

where Y_2 is the probability of finding at equilibrium two copies of the system in the same configuration

$$Y_2 = \frac{\sum_\mathcal{C} e^{-2\beta E(\mathcal{C})}}{\left(\sum_\mathcal{C} e^{-\beta E(\mathcal{C})}\right)^2} = \frac{\sum_\mathcal{C} x(\mathcal{C})^2}{\left(\sum_\mathcal{C} x(\mathcal{C})\right)^2}.$$

Averaging over the $x(\mathcal{C})$ distributed according to the heavy tail distribution (31.14) one gets [14, 19, 20] in the large N limit

$$\langle Y_2 \rangle = 1 - \frac{\beta_c}{\beta}; \quad \langle Y_2^2 \rangle - \langle Y_2 \rangle^2 = \frac{1}{3}\frac{\beta_c}{\beta}\left(1 - \frac{\beta_c}{\beta}\right). \tag{31.18}$$

This shows that, in the whole low temperature phase, $P(q)$ in (31.17) is a sum of two delta functions whose relative weights fluctuate even in the large N limit. In fact the whole distribution of Y_2, in the large N limit, can be determined [2, 15].

The expressions (31.18) can be generalized to calculate various correlations between the probabilities Y_k of finding k copies of the same system in the same configuration. For example

$$\langle Y_k \rangle = \left\langle \frac{\sum_\mathcal{C} e^{-k\beta E(\mathcal{C})}}{\left(\sum_\mathcal{C} e^{-\beta E(\mathcal{C})}\right)^k} \right\rangle = \frac{\Gamma\left(k - \frac{\beta_c}{\beta}\right)}{\Gamma(k)\,\Gamma\left(1 - \frac{\beta_c}{\beta}\right)}. \tag{31.19}$$

An equivalent but slightly different way of thinking of the statistical properties of the energy levels which contribute in the low temperature phase and to recover all the statistical properties of the overlaps (such as (31.18) or (31.19)) is to say that the energies $E(\mathcal{C})$ are generated by a Poisson point process with a density [20]

$$\rho(E) = 2^N P(E) \sim \frac{1}{\sqrt{N\pi}\, J} \, e^{\beta_c\left(E + NJ\sqrt{\log 2}\right)}. \tag{31.20}$$

As we will see in Sec. 31.1.6 this Poisson point process is at the basis of the Ruelle cascade which allows to calculate the overlaps in the GREM [21, 22].

More recently it has also been possible to calculate the finite size corrections to (31.18), (31.19), the effect of a discrete distribution of energies $P(E(\mathcal{C}))$ or the overlap between two copies of the same system at different temperatures [14, 20, 23, 24].

31.1.5. *The replica approach and the REM*

In the theory of spin glasses the replica approach consists in trying to determine the average free energy $\langle \log Z(\beta) \rangle$ from the knowledge of the moments of the partition function $\langle Z(\beta)^n \rangle$ via

$$\langle \log Z(\beta) \rangle = \lim_{n \to 0} \frac{\log\langle Z(\beta)^n \rangle}{n}. \tag{31.21}$$

The well known difficulty with (31.21) is that it requires the knowledge of non integer moments of the partition function and it is based on the wishful idea that these non integer moments can be determined by some kind of continuation to non-integer n of expressions for the integer moments which are usually easier to obtain. The breakthrough of the RSB theory was to discover the correct solution for the SK model [25].

For the REM, it is in fact possible to calculate directly integer as well as non-integer moments of the partition function [26]. For example from (31.15) (and an identity of the form $\Gamma(-\nu)\, Z^\nu = \int d\,t \exp[-tZ]\, t^{-\nu-1}$ for negative ν) one can show that, in the low temperature phase, for $-\infty < \nu < \frac{\beta_c}{\beta} < 1$

$$\langle Z^\nu \rangle \simeq Z_0^\nu \left(\frac{\Gamma(1 - \frac{\beta_c}{\beta})}{J\beta_c\,\sqrt{\pi N}} \right)^{\nu \frac{\beta}{\beta_c}} \frac{\Gamma(1 - \nu\frac{\beta}{\beta_c})}{\Gamma(1 - \nu)}$$

from which one can recover (31.10,31.11) in the $\nu \to 0$ limit.

If however one tries to follow the standard replica approach, i.e. to obtain the free energy (31.3) from the knowledge of the integer moments the starting point is the following expression of these integer moments [7, 24, 27]

$$\langle Z(\beta)^n \rangle = \sum_{r\geq 1} \frac{n!}{r!} 2^{Nr} \sum_{\mu_1 \geq 1} \cdots \sum_{\mu_r \geq 1} \frac{\exp\left[N\frac{J^2\beta^2}{4}(\mu_1^2 + \cdots \mu_r^2) \right]}{\mu_1! \times \cdots \times \mu_r!}\, \delta_{\mu_1 + \cdots \mu_r - n} \qquad (31.22)$$

which is exact in the case of the Poisson REM [20]. In (31.22) each term in this sum corresponds to a partition of the n replicas into r blocks of $\mu_1, \cdots \mu_r$ replicas. For integer n, the sum in the large N limit is dominated by the largest term. This leads to [7, 26]

$$\langle Z(\beta)^n \rangle \sim \begin{cases} \exp[Nn(\log 2 + \frac{J^2\beta^2}{4})] & \text{for} \quad \beta < \frac{\beta_c}{\sqrt{n}} \\ \exp[N(\log 2 + n^2\frac{J^2\beta^2}{4})] & \text{for} \quad \beta > \frac{\beta_c}{\sqrt{n}}. \end{cases} \qquad (31.23)$$

Although, for small β the replica formula (31.21) leads to (31.8), there is no way to recover the low temperature expression (31.8) from (31.23).

If however, one follows Parisi's original approach [25] by allowing r and the μ_i's to become real numbers, by assuming that for non-integer n, the sum in (31.22) is dominated by a single term where all the μ_i's are equal to μ so that $r = \frac{n}{\mu}$, by reversing the inequality $1 \leq \mu \leq n$ to become $0 \leq \mu \leq 1$ in the $n \to 0$ limit)

$$\langle Z(\beta)^n \rangle \sim \exp\left[Nn \left(\frac{\log 2}{\mu} + \frac{\mu J^2\beta^2}{4} \right) \right] \qquad (31.24)$$

and by looking for a minimum over μ rather than a maximum, one gets

$$\mu = \min\left[\frac{\beta_c}{\beta}, 1 \right]. \qquad (31.25)$$

Doing so one recovers in the $n \to 0$ limit [7] the free energy (31.8) by replacing μ by this value in (31.24).

This is the simplest form of RSB, the one-step RSB: the n replicas have been divided into n/μ blocks of μ replicas each. It is then possible to recover the expressions (31.18),

(31.19) by simply writing that $\langle Y_k \rangle$ is the probability of finding in the same block k replicas among n different replicas.

$$\langle Y_k \rangle = \lim_{n \to 0} \frac{n}{\mu} \times \frac{\mu(\mu-1)\cdots(\mu-k+1)}{n(n-1)\cdots(n-k+1)}.$$

For the p-spin model with Ising spins, it has been shown that for large enough p, the replica approach leads to such a one-step RSB transition [28–31] and to the free energy (31.8) in the large p limit. This transition is followed at a lower temperature by a full RSB transition, the Gardner transition [29]. The p-spin model in its spherical version also exhibits a one-step RSB [32, 33].

Trying to understand the finite size corrections to the free energy (31.10), (31.11) or to the overlaps using the replica approach is not so easy [34]. To do so it seems that one should let the μ_i's fluctuate around (31.25) and even take complex values [20]. Fluctuating block sizes are also present when one looks at two-temperature overlaps of the REM or when the energies $E(\mathcal{C})$ take only discrete energies [14, 24].

31.1.6. *The GREM*

The Generalized Random Energy Model (GREM) was invented as an elementary way of introducing correlations between the energies $E(\mathcal{C})$ of the configurations. In its simplest version [35], the configurations are structured into α_1^N groups $\mathcal{G}$ of α_2^N configurations each and the energy of each configuration $\mathcal{C}$ is by definition the sum of two Gaussian random energies

$$E(\mathcal{C}) = E_1(\mathcal{G}) + E_2(\mathcal{C})$$

of variance $NJ^2 a_1/2$ and $NJ^2 a_2/2$. All the energies $E_1(\mathcal{G})$ and $E_2(\mathcal{C})$ are independent, but configurations $\mathcal{C}$ in the same group $\mathcal{G}$ have all the same $E_1(\mathcal{G})$. Therefore the energies of two configurations $\mathcal{C}, \mathcal{C}'$ are correlated if they are in the same group (we will say that $q(\mathcal{C}, \mathcal{C}') = Q$) and are uncorrelated if they belong to two distinct groups (we will say that their overlap $q(\mathcal{C}, \mathcal{C}') = 0$). The overlap can therefore take three possible values: 1 , Q and 0 (taking by definition $q(\mathcal{C}, \mathcal{C}) = 1$).

For the total number of configurations to be 2^N and for the distribution of individual energies to still be given by (31.4) we impose the following normalization

$$\log \alpha_1 + \log \alpha_2 = \log 2; \quad a_1 + a_2 = 1.$$

The GREM can be solved [35–37] by using the same reasoning as for the REM in Sec. 31.1.2: the typical $\mathcal{N}_1(E_1)$ number of groups with an energy E_1 is equal to its average when this average is much larger than 1 and is 0 when this average is much smaller than 1.

$$\mathcal{N}_1(E_1) \sim \begin{cases} \exp\left[N \log \alpha_1 - \dfrac{E_1^2}{NJ^2 a_1}\right] & \text{for } \dfrac{|E_1|}{N} < J\sqrt{a_1 \log \alpha_1} \\ 0 & \text{otherwise.} \end{cases}$$

Then the average of $\mathcal{N}(E)$ given the function $\mathcal{N}_1(E_1)$ is

$$\langle \mathcal{N}(E) \rangle \sim \max_{E_1}\left\{ \alpha_2^N \exp\left[-\frac{(E-E_1)^2}{NJ^2 a_2}\right] \mathcal{N}_1(E_1) \right\}.$$

As E varies (in the range where $\mathcal{N}(E) \gg 1$), the optimal E_1 either sticks to one of its extremal values $E_1/N = \pm J\sqrt{a_1 \log \alpha_1}$ or varies with E. This leads to distinguish two cases.

(1) <u>First case:</u> if $\frac{\log \alpha_1}{a_1} < \frac{\log \alpha_2}{a_2}$ defining

$$\mathcal{E}_i = NJ\sqrt{a_i \log \alpha_i} \tag{31.26}$$

one gets for the entropy

$$\frac{S(E)}{N} = \begin{cases} \log 2 - \frac{E^2}{N^2 J^2} & \text{for } |E| < \left(1 + \frac{a_2}{a_1}\right)\mathcal{E}_1 \\ \log \alpha_2 - \frac{(E+\mathcal{E}_1)^2}{N^2 J^2 a_2} & \text{for } -\mathcal{E}_1 - \mathcal{E}_2 < E < -\left(1 + \frac{a_2}{a_1}\right)\mathcal{E}_1 \\ -\infty & \text{for } E < -\mathcal{E}_1 - \mathcal{E}_2 \end{cases} \tag{31.27}$$

which leads to the following expression of the free energy:

$$\frac{\langle \log Z(\beta)\rangle}{N} = \begin{cases} \log 2 + \frac{\beta^2 J^2}{4} & \text{for } \beta < \beta_c^{(1)} \\ \beta J\sqrt{a_1 \log \alpha_1} + \log \alpha_2 + \frac{\beta^2 J^2 a_2}{4} & \text{for } \beta_c^{(1)} < \beta < \beta_c^{(2)} \\ \beta J\left(\sqrt{a_1 \log \alpha_1} + (\sqrt{a_2 \log \alpha_2})\right) & \text{for } \beta_c^{(2)} < \beta \end{cases} \tag{31.28}$$

where the inverse transition temperatures $\beta_c^{(i)}$ are defined by

$$\beta_c^{(i)} = \frac{2}{J}\sqrt{\frac{\log \alpha_i}{a_i}}. \tag{31.29}$$

(Note that this first case is precisely the case where $\beta_c^{(1)} < \beta_c^{(2)}$).

So the system undergoes two phase transitions. In the high temperature phase, both the energies $E_1(\mathcal{G})$ and $E_2(\mathcal{C})$ of typical configurations vary with temperature. In the intermediate phase, the energy $E_1(\mathcal{G})$ is frozen at its minimal value $(E_1(\mathcal{G})/N = -J\sqrt{a_1 \log \alpha_1})$ while the energy $E_2(\mathcal{C})$ still varies with temperature. Lastly in the low temperature phase, both energies E_1 and E_2 are frozen at their minimal values.

In each of these phases, one can determine the distribution of overlaps

$$\langle P(q)\rangle = \begin{cases} \delta(q) & \text{for } \beta < \beta_c^{(1)} \\ \frac{\beta_c^{(1)}}{\beta}\delta(q) + \frac{\beta - \beta_c^{(1)}}{\beta}\delta(q - Q) & \beta_c^{(1)} < \beta < \beta_c^{(2)} \\ \frac{\beta_c^{(1)}}{\beta}\delta(q) + \frac{\beta_c^{(2)} - \beta_c^{(1)}}{\beta}\delta(q - Q) + \frac{\beta - \beta_c^{(2)}}{\beta}\delta(q - 1) & \beta_c^{(2)} < \beta. \end{cases} \tag{31.30}$$

This is one of the simplest examples of a 2-step RSB since in the lowest temperature phase the overlap can take two possible non-zero values. In this phase, only the groups with an energy E_1 close to $-NJ\sqrt{a_1 \log \alpha_1}$ and inside these groups, only the configurations with an energy E_2 close to $-NJ\sqrt{a_2 \log \alpha_2}$ contribute. The statistics of the energies $E(\mathcal{C}) = E_1(\mathcal{G}) + E_2(\mathcal{C})$ of these configurations can be accurately described by a decorated Poisson process: the energies $E_1(\mathcal{G})$ of the groups are generated by a Poisson process with an exponential density $\rho_1(E_1) \sim \exp[\beta_c^{(1)}(E_1 + N\sqrt{a_1 \log \alpha_1})]$ and the energies $E_2(\mathcal{C})$ of the configurations in each group are generated by a Poisson process of density $\rho_2(E_2) \sim \exp[\beta_c^{(2)}(E_2 + N\sqrt{a_2 \log \alpha_2})]$. This is an example of a Ruelle cascade where the levels are generated by a succession of nested Poisson processes [21, 22, 38]

(2) <u>Second case:</u> if $\frac{\log \alpha_1}{a_1} > \frac{\log \alpha_2}{a_2}$ i.e. $\beta_c^{(1)} > \beta_c^{(2)}$ one can repeat the above reasoning, and one finds a single phase transition at $\beta = \beta_c$ with a free energy and overlaps given by (31.8) and (31.18), (31.19).

This is an example where the correlations between the energies $E(\mathcal{C})$ are not strong enough to have any effect on the free energy.

The expressions of the free energy in all cases can be recovered from the following expression: [39]

$$\frac{\langle \log Z(\beta) \rangle}{N} = \min_{0 \leq \mu_1 \leq \mu_2 \leq 1} \left[\frac{\log \alpha_1}{\mu_1} + \frac{\beta^2 J^2 a_1 \mu_1}{4} + \frac{\log \alpha_2}{\mu_2} + \frac{\beta^2 J^2 a_2 \mu_2}{4} \right]. \tag{31.31}$$

Depending on β and on the parameters a_i and α_i one finds that the minimum is achieved for $\mu_1 = \mu_2 = 1$ (high temperature phase), $\mu_1 < \mu_2 = 1$ (intermediate phase in the first case), $\mu_1 < \mu_2 < 1$ (low temperature phase in the first case), $\mu_1 = \mu_2 < 1$ (low temperature phase in the second case).

The expression (31.31) can be recovered by a replica calculation [40, 41]: one writes the moments $\langle Z^n \rangle$ as we did in (31.22), (31.24) and then one assumes that the minimum is achieved when there are n/μ_1 groups of μ_1 replicas each and that in each group there are μ_1/μ_2 blocks of μ_2 replicas.

The above two level structure of the GREM can be generalized to hierarchies with an arbitrary number k of levels [42, 43], the configurations being organized in groups inside groups inside groups etc. ...: at each level i a group splits into α_i^N subgroups with a Gaussian contribution to the energy E_i.

The solution leads to distinguish various cases depending on the relative values of the $\beta_c^{(i)}$ but as for the above two level GREM, it can be written in a compact form valid at all temperatures and for arbitrary choices of the parameters a_i and $\log \alpha_i$

$$\frac{\langle \log Z \rangle}{N} = \min_{0 \leq \mu_1 \leq \cdots \leq \mu_k \leq 1} \left[\sum_{1 \leq i \leq k} \left(\frac{\log \alpha_i}{\mu_i} + \frac{\mu_i\, a_i\, \beta^2 J^2}{4} \right) \right]. \tag{31.32}$$

This can also be interpreted as a scheme à la Parisi where at each level i, blocks of μ_{i-1} replicas are divided into μ_{i-1}/μ_i blocks of μ_i replicas each.

As for the REM, one can introduce a magnetic field in the GREM [40] and one finds a cusp in the magnetic susceptibility and a de Alemida–Thouless line.

31.1.7. *The directed polymer on a tree*

For a GREM with an arbitrary number k of levels, if all the α_i and all the a_i are equal, the extensive part of the free energy and the overlaps are still given by (31.8), (31.18), (31.19). The finite size corrections are however different [44–46]. The same is true [47] for the directed polymer on a binary tree, of height N, where on the $2^{N+1} - 2$ edges b there are i.i.d. Gaussian energies ϵ_b (with $P(\epsilon_b) = (\pi J^2)^{-1/2} \exp[-\epsilon_b^2/J^2]$).

The 2^N configurations $\mathcal{C}$ are then all the paths connecting the top to the bottom of the tree, the energy $E(\mathcal{C})$ being the sum of the N edges b visited by the path. One main difference between the REM and the directed polymer on a tree is that the average free energy in (31.10) becomes

$$\langle \log Z(\beta) \rangle = N\beta\beta_c J^2 - \frac{3\beta}{2\beta_c} \log N + R_{\text{tree}}(\beta) \tag{31.33}$$

so that the $1/2$ in (31.10) is replaced by a $3/2$ in the $\log N$ correction. This $3/2$ factor has the same origin as the well known Bramson $3/2$ logarithmic correction in the position of a traveling wave in the Fisher–KPP equation [48, 49] and is also present in other random energy models with logarithmic correlations [50]. On the other hand, in contrast to (31.11), the explicit expression of $R_{\text{tree}}(\beta)$ is not known.

The other difference [51] is that the first large N correction to the 1-step RSB (31.17,31.18) is for any fixed $0 < q < 1$

$$P(q) \simeq \frac{1}{\sqrt{N}} \frac{\beta_c}{\beta} \sqrt{\frac{1}{4\pi \log 2}} \left(q(1-q) \right)^{-\frac{3}{2}} \quad \text{for} \quad \beta > \beta_c \tag{31.34}$$

where the overlap $q(\mathcal{C}, \mathcal{C}')$ is just the fraction of their length that two paths $\mathcal{C}, \mathcal{C}'$ have in common. This shows that the first finite size correction transforms a 1-step RSB into a full RSB.

Also like for the extremal points of the branching Brownian motion and for the GREM, the lowest energy levels can be represented by a decorated Poisson process with an exponential density [52–57].

31.1.8. *Conclusion*

The random energy models (REM and GREM) are simple spin glass models which exhibit a number of features common to many other spin glass models (cusp in the magnetic susceptibily, de Almeida–Thouless line, replica symmetry breaking and non-selfaveraging effects, slow dynamics and aging at low temperature). Compared to other spin glass models they have the advantage of being exactly solvable by elementary mathematical methods.

They can also be solved using the Parisi replica approach. Doing so, one recovers the correct phase diagrams and the extensive part of the free energy. It remains however an open question on how to recover in this way more subtle properties such as finite size effects like (31.34) or expressions of the overlaps between two temperatures or for discrete energies. This seems to require to allow the blocks sizes in the replica approach to fluctuate.

The random energy models have also been equipped by dynamical rules and their dynamics have motivated a large number of studies (see [58–67] and references therein).

Beyond their interest as spin glass models, they have been useful in a number of other contexts ranging from problems of protein folding [11, 68] or evolution [69] in biology to error-correcting codes [70–72].

31.2. The Arcsine Law as a Universal Aging Scheme for Activated Dynamics of Random Energy Models

Véronique Gayrard

Aix Marseille Univ, CNRS, I2M, Marseille, France
veronique.gayrard@math.cnrs.fr

31.2.1. *Introduction*

In glassy dynamics, the concept of *aging* refers to out-of-equilibrium relaxation behaviours that are dominated by ever slower transients and, as such, are history dependent. *Mean-field spin glasses* such as the REM [35] and the p-spin SK models ($p \geq 2$) [1, 3] endowed with a suitable dynamics have been advocated, since the early theoretical work on aging, as fruitful testing grounds for understanding this phenomenon, giving rise to a host of often drastically simplified theoretical approaches, among which *trap models* have, and continue, to play a key role [62, 73, 74].

In the past two decades, the questions of understanding aging in activated dynamics have attracted a great interest in the mathematics community. From the bulk of works carried out on mean-field and other models, a *universal aging mechanism* could be identified that links aging of the classical two-time correlation functions to the arcsine law for α-stable subordinators in the theory of Lévy processes. The purpose of this section is to spell out this aging scheme while providing key tools and ideas that enable its effective implementation in the context of mean-field spin glass dynamics.

Let us now introduce the main objects that come into play.

The models. The Hamiltonians we consider are centered Gaussian processes $(H_N(\sigma), \sigma \in \mathcal{V}_N)$ indexed by the vertices σ (or configurations) of the discrete hypercube $\mathcal{V}_N = \{-1, 1\}^N$. The choice of the covariance completely determines the model. Given an integer $p \geq 2$, the p-spin SK models have covariance

$$\mathbb{E} H_N(\sigma) H_N(\eta) = N \left[R_N(\sigma, \eta) \right]^p, \tag{31.35}$$

where $R_N(\sigma, \eta) \equiv \frac{1}{N} \sum_{i=1}^{N} \sigma_i \eta_i$ denotes the usual normalised overlap. We can see from (31.35) that as p increases the correlations weaken. Formally taking the limit $p \to \infty$ yields a collection of independent Gaussians that defines the random energy model (REM),

$$\mathbb{E} H_N(\sigma) H_N(\eta) = N \delta(\sigma, \eta). \tag{31.36}$$

These sequences of random Hamiltonians are defined on some abstract probability space, $(\Omega, \mathcal{F}, \mathbb{P})$. $\mathbb{E}$ denotes the expectation with respect to $\mathbb{P}$. We refer to this space as the *disorder* (also called the *random environment*).

What dynamics to choose? Relevant models of spin glass dynamics are Glauber dynamics on state space $\mathcal{V}_N$, reversible with respect to the Gibbs measure at inverse temperature $\beta > 0$ associated to the random Hamiltonian of the model considered.

Typical examples of such dynamics are single spin-flip continuous-time Markov jump processes $(X_N(t), t > 0)$ on $\mathcal{V}_N$ whose jump rates $\lambda_N(\eta, \sigma)$ obey the detailed balance equation

$$\mathrm{e}^{-\beta H_N(\sigma)} \lambda_N(\sigma, \eta) = \mathrm{e}^{-\beta H_N(\eta)} \lambda_N(\eta, \sigma) \quad \text{if } \sigma \sim \eta \tag{31.37}$$

and $\lambda_N(\sigma, \eta) = 0$ else, where $\sigma \sim \eta$ if the configurations σ and η differ in exactly one coordinate. This still leaves considerable freedom of choice. The one that has drawn the most attention and publications to date is the *random hopping dynamics* whose jump rates,

$$\lambda_N(\sigma, \eta) = \frac{1}{N} \mathrm{e}^{+\beta H_N(\sigma)} \quad \text{if } \sigma \sim \eta \tag{31.38}$$

only depend on the initial configuration, σ. Although physically unrealistic (the trajectories of this process are independent of the random Hamiltonian), this choice has played an important role in understanding activated aging. A choice that is advocated in physics as being more satisfactory is that of *Metropolis dynamics*, whose rates are given by

$$\lambda_N(\sigma, \eta) = \frac{1}{N} \mathrm{e}^{-\beta [H_N(\eta) - H_N(\sigma)]^+} \quad \text{if } \sigma \sim \eta \tag{31.39}$$

and $\lambda_N(\sigma, \eta) = 0$ else, were $a^+ = \max\{a, 0\}$. The trajectories of the process now do depend on the random Hamiltonian and are biased against increasing the energy.

Note that the law of the dynamics depends on the disorder. In the sequel we call $\mathcal{P}_{\pi_N}$ the law of X_N conditional on the σ-algebra $\mathcal{F}$, i.e., for fixed realisation of the disorder, started in the initial condition π_N.

Two-time correlation functions. A natural observable to quantify aging is the overlap between the states of the process at two far distant points in time, $c_N t$ and $c_N(t + s)$, where c_N is the timescale on which we observe the process. Such an overlap is a random variable that depends both on the disorder and on the process X_N. Instead of averaging, we fix a realisation of the disorder and choose for two-time correlation function the probability

$$\mathcal{C}_{N,\varepsilon}(t, s) \equiv \mathcal{P}_{\pi_N}\left(R_N\big(X_N\left(c_N t\right), X_N\left(c_N(t + s)\right)\big) \geq 1 - \varepsilon \right) \tag{31.40}$$

where $0 \leq \varepsilon < 1$. Our aim is then to study the asymptotic behaviour of $\mathcal{C}_{N,\varepsilon}(t, s)$ when $N \to \infty$, trying to obtain results that are valid for typical realisations of the disorder, namely, $\mathbb{P}$-*almost surely* (i.e., *quenched results* in the terminology of physics). Depending on the model, substitutes for (31.40) can be used, such as the *no-jump* correlation function from trap models

$$\Pi_N(t, s) = \mathcal{P}_{\pi_N}\left(X_N\left(c_N t\right) = X_N\left(c_N(t + u)\right) \, \forall t \leq u < t + s \right). \tag{31.41}$$

We will now endow our models with different dynamics and study their correlation functions when the initial distribution π_N is the uniform measure on $\mathcal{V}_N$ (to mimic a deep quench) and for time-scales c_N that diverge exponentially fast with N (this puts us in the setting of *activated* dynamics).

31.2.2. *The random hopping dynamics of the REM*

Consider the Hamiltonian (31.36) equipped with the dynamics (31.38) and define the one-parameter sequence

$$c_N(\gamma) = \exp\left\{\beta\gamma N - \frac{\beta}{2\gamma}\left(\ln(\gamma^2 N/2) + \ln 4\pi\right)\right\}, \quad \gamma > 0. \tag{31.42}$$

The dynamical phase diagram of the REM on timescale $c_N = c_N(\gamma)$ is fully understood for all $\gamma, \beta > 0$. Denote by Asl_α the probability distribution function of the generalised arcsine law of parameter α, $0 < \alpha < 1$,

$$\mathrm{Asl}_\alpha(u) \equiv \frac{\sin\alpha\pi}{\pi}\int_0^u (1-x)^{-\alpha}x^{\alpha-1}\,\mathrm{d}x, \quad 0 \le u \le 1. \tag{31.43}$$

Theorem 1. *Given $\gamma > 0$ let $c_N = c_N(\gamma)$. For all β and γ satisfying*

$$0 < \gamma < \min\left(\beta, \sqrt{2\ln 2}\right) \tag{31.44}$$

we have that for all $\varepsilon \in [0,1)$, $t > 0$ and $s > 0$, $\mathbb{P}$-almost surely

$$\lim_{N\to\infty} \mathcal{C}_{N,\varepsilon}(t,s) = \mathrm{Asl}_{\gamma/\beta}\left(t/(t+s)\right). \tag{31.45}$$

The same result holds true for the function $\Pi_N(t,s)$ defined in (31.41).

Theorem 1 was proved in Ref. [75]. It improves on previous results of Ref. [76] obtained in a sub-region of (31.44). Furthermore, it was proved in the seminal papers [77, 78] that in the case $\gamma = \sqrt{2\ln 2}$ and $\beta > \sqrt{2\ln 2}$, (31.45) remains true albeit in $\mathbb{P}$-probability only, on time-scales of the form $c_N = \rho c_N(\sqrt{2\ln 2})$, and taking the double limit $N \uparrow \infty$ first and $\rho \downarrow 0$ next. These are the longest time-scales before stationarity. When $\gamma > \min(\beta, \sqrt{2\ln 2})$ the process X_N is stationary. We refer the reader to Ref. [75] for exhaustive references and a complete description of the dynamical phase diagram, including its transition lines.

Let us now outline the strategy of the proof of Theorem 1.

Clock process and jump chain. All Markov jump processes X_N can be constructed as the time change of a *jump chain* by the inverse of a *clock process*: the former describes the trajectories of X_N and the latter the time elapsed along them. In the random hopping dynamics, the jump chain $(J_N(k), k \in \mathbb{N})$ is the simple random walk (SRW) on $\mathcal{V}_N$ and, setting

$$\tau_N(\sigma) = \exp(-\beta H_N(\sigma)), \tag{31.46}$$

the *clock process* is the partial sum process

$$\widetilde{S}_N(k) = \sum_{i=1}^{k} \tau_N(J_N(i))e_{N,i}, \quad k \in \mathbb{N}, \tag{31.47}$$

where $(e_{N,i}, n \in \mathbb{N}, i \in \mathbb{N})$ is a family of independent mean one exponential random variables, independent of J_N. Then

$$X_N(t) = J_N(\widetilde{S}_N^{-1}(t)), \quad t > 0. \tag{31.48}$$

The arcsine law as a universal aging mechanism. One readily sees that the two-time correlation function (31.41) can be rewritten as

$$\Pi_N(t, s) = \mathcal{P}_{\pi_N}\big(\mathcal{R}_N \cap (t, (t+s)) = \emptyset\big), \quad t, s > 0, \tag{31.49}$$

where $\mathcal{R}_N \equiv \{c_N^{-1}\widetilde{S}_N(k), k \in \mathbb{N}\}$ is the range of the time re-scaled clock process (31.47). This observation places the clock process in the limelight as it is clear that the predicted slowdown of the time de-correlations can only be attributed to some asymptotic ($N \to \infty$) properties of the clock.

Among the known possible limits, stable subordinators of exponent $0 < \alpha < 1$ play a special role. These are non-negative processes S with independent and stationary increments that increase only by jumps, the pairs of their *jump times* and *jump sizes* being given by the points $\{(t_k, \xi_k)\}$ of a Poisson point process of intensity measure $\mathrm{d}t \times \mathrm{d}\nu$,

$$S(t) = \sum_{t_k \leq t} \xi_k, \quad t > 0, \tag{31.50}$$

and ν, the so-called Lévy measure, takes the specific form

$$\nu(u, \infty) = cu^{-\alpha}, \quad u > 0, \tag{31.51}$$

where $c > 0$ is a constant and $0 < \alpha < 1$. A simple aging mechanism is then provided by the arcsine law, which states that if S is a stable subordinator of exponent $\alpha \in (0, 1)$ then, denoting by $\mathcal{R}$ its range and recalling (31.43)

$$\mathcal{P}\big(\mathcal{R} \cap (t, (t+s)) = \emptyset\big) = \mathrm{Asl}_\alpha\left(\frac{t}{t+s}\right), \quad t, s > 0. \tag{31.52}$$

Convergence of clock processes. Our immediate goal is thus to find criteria for the convergence of the clock process (31.47) under proper scaling, i.e., we ask whether there are sequences, a_N, c_N, such that the process

$$S_N(t) \equiv c_N^{-1}\widetilde{S}_N(\lfloor a_N t \rfloor) = c_N^{-1} \sum_{i=1}^{\lfloor a_N t \rfloor} \tau_N(J_N(i))e_{N,i}, \quad t > 0, \tag{31.53}$$

converges to a subordinator. Note that c_N is the timescale on which we observe the process X_N while a_N is an auxiliary timescale associated to the number of steps the jump chain, J_N, takes. This links aging to a classical and well studied problem of probability theory: given an arbitrary array of positive random variables $\{Z_{N,i}, i \geq 1, N \geq 1\}$, find sequences, a_N, c_N, such that the sequence of partial sum processes

$$S_N(t) = c_N^{-1} \sum_{i=1}^{\lfloor a_N t \rfloor} Z_{N,i}, \quad t > 0 \tag{31.54}$$

converges to a Lévy processes. Among all known convergence criteria, those obtained in Ref. [79] are specially well suited to situations where there is a temporal structure as is the case in clock processes. There are three conditions.[a] The first two of them are

---

[a]The results of [79] are more general than those we present, which we limit to the convergence to stable subordinators that interest us most.

sufficient conditions for the point process $\{(i/a_N, Z_{N,i}/c_N)\}$ to converge in a suitable sense to a Poisson point process $\{(t_k, \xi_k)\}$ with intensity measure $\mathrm{d}t \times \mathrm{d}\nu$. The third one is needed to guarantee that the sum (31.54) converges to the corresponding sum of these Poisson points, and so, to a process of the form (31.50) if the limiting measure ν in (31.55) is of the form (31.51).

To illustrate our strategy, let us consider the first of these conditions which contains the most interesting information from the point of view of theoretical physics (see, e.g., Ref. [80] for a complete statement or the three conditions). It asks that for all $t > 0$ and all $u > 0$, as $N \to \infty$, in $\mathcal{P}_{\pi_N}$-probability,

$$\lim_{N \uparrow \infty} \sum_{i=1}^{\lfloor a_N t \rfloor} \mathcal{P}_{\pi_N}\left(c_N^{-1} Z_{N,i} > u | \mathcal{F}_{N,i-1}\right) = t\nu(u, \infty), \tag{31.55}$$

where $\mathcal{F}_{N,i}$ denotes the σ-algebra generated by the $Z_{N,j}$'s with $j \leq i$. Going back to the REM, here is how we can implement it. In view of (31.53) we naturally take

$$Z_{N,i} = \tau_N(J_N(i))e_{N,i}. \tag{31.56}$$

These $Z_{N,i}$'s are random variables that depend both on the simple random walk J_N and on the disorder. We deal with these two randomness as follows. We observe first that J_N is "fast-mixing". Indeed, setting $\ell_N = 2N^2$ and denoting by P_{π_N} the law of J_N started in the uniform distribution, we have that for any $\sigma, \eta \in \mathcal{V}_N$ and any $i \geq 0$ (note that J_N is 2-periodic),

$$\left| \sum_{q=0}^{1} P_{\pi_N}\left(J_N(\ell_N + i + q) = \eta, J_N(0) = \sigma\right) - 2\pi_N(\sigma)\pi_N(\eta) \right| \leq 2^{-3n+1}.$$

Assuming that $a_N \gg \ell_N$, this enables us to replace our chain-dependent condition (31.55), through an ergodic theorem, by a condition that now only depends on the disorder. Doing this, (31.55) becomes

$$\lfloor a_N t \rfloor \sum_{\sigma \in \mathcal{V}_N} \pi_N(\sigma)Q_N^u(\sigma) \to t\nu(u, \infty), \quad u > 0, \tag{31.57}$$

where $Q_N^u(\sigma) \equiv \mathcal{P}_\sigma\left(Z_{N,i} > c_N u\right)$ is the tail distribution of $Z_{N,i}$ when the process X_N starts in σ. The highlight of this approach is that since $Q_N^u(\sigma)$ now only depends on the disorder, (31.57) takes the form of a law of large numbers under the law $\mathbb{P}$, and this makes it possible to try to obtain almost sure (quenched) results. This in turn will condition the choice of the a_N and c_N. Observing that for $a_N = e^{N\gamma^2/2}$ and $c_N = c_N(\gamma)$ the re-scaled increments (31.56) are heavy tailed,[b]

$$a_N \mathbb{P}(\tau_N(\sigma)e_{N,i} > c_N u) \sim u^{\gamma/\beta}, \tag{31.58}$$

we readily obtain that, under the assumptions of Theorem 1, convergence in (31.57) holds $\mathbb{P}$-almost surely to the limiting measure

$$\nu(u, \infty) = u^{\gamma/\beta}(\gamma/\beta)\Gamma(\gamma/\beta), \quad u > 0. \tag{31.59}$$

The remaining two convergence conditions are dealt with in a similar way.

---

[b]Note that for this choice, c_N is the size of the maximum of τ_N along trajectories of J_N of length a_N. This explains the specific form of (31.42).

Back to two-time correlation functions. The above strategy enables us to prove that under the assumptions of Theorem 1, $\mathbb{P}$-almost surely

$$S_N \Rightarrow_{J_1} V_{\gamma/\beta} \tag{31.60}$$

where S_N is defined in (31.53) and $V_{\gamma/\beta}$ is the stable subordinator of parameter γ/β. The symbol $\Rightarrow_{J_1}$ denotes weak convergence in Skorokhod space equipped with the J_1-topology. This space is designed to describe the trajectories of stochastic processes admitting jumps, such as those of Poisson processes and Lévy processes. Among the topologies on this space, J_1 is the finest. It guarantees that each jump in the limiting process corresponds to exactly one jump before the limit. No other topology fulfils this condition, which is essential if one wants to be able to relate the convergence (31.59) to that of the two-time correlation function (31.49) and, *a fortiori*, to (31.40).

In the REM, convergence in the J_1-topology easily follows from the facts that (i) the leading contributions to the clock (31.53) come from the visits of J_N to configurations such that $\tau_N(\sigma) \sim c_N$, which can be seen as *deep traps*, (ii) these deep traps are typically far apart from each other and (iii) after visiting one of them, the simple random walk typically does not revisit it: each jump of the limiting subordinator then corresponds to exactly one such visit.

These and other fine properties of the simple random walk will finally imply that (31.40) and (31.41) are equal in the limit $N \to \infty$.

31.2.3. *The random hopping dynamics of the p-spin SK model*

We will now see that the same aging behaviour as that found in the REM is also present in the p-spin SK model (31.35) equipped with the dynamics (31.38) when $p \geq 3$. Let $c_N(\gamma)$ be as in (31.42).

Theorem 2. *Given $\gamma > 0$ let $c_N = c_N(\gamma)$. For any $p \geq 3$, there exists a function $\zeta(p)$ such that for all β and γ satisfying*

$$0 < \gamma < \min\left(\beta, \zeta(p)\right) \tag{31.61}$$

we have that for all $\varepsilon \in (0, 1)$, $t > 0$ and $s > 0$,

$$\lim_{N \to \infty} \mathcal{C}_{N,\varepsilon}(t, s) = \mathrm{Asl}_{\gamma/\beta}\left(t/(t + s)\right). \tag{31.62}$$

Convergence holds $\mathbb{P}$-almost surely if $p > 4$, and in $\mathbb{P}$-probability if $p = 3, 4$.

The function $\zeta(p)$ is increasing and it satisfies

$$\zeta(3) \simeq 1.0291 \qquad and \qquad \lim_{p \to \infty} \zeta(p) = \sqrt{2 \log 2}. \tag{31.63}$$

This quenched result was proved in Ref. [80]. In Ref. [81] an analogous result was obtained, with the same constants $\zeta(p)$ and K_p, but convergence there is in law with respect to the disorder. These results do not cover the case of the SK model ($p = 2$) which seems to belong to a different universality class.

The method of proof is that of Sec. 31.2.2. The jump chain and clock process representation (31.47)–(31.48) of X_N is unchanged. However, because H_N in (31.46) now is defined through (31.35), the $\tau_N(\sigma)$'s are correlated random variables with respect to the disorder, and we no longer can expect the leading contributions to the re-scaled clock process (31.53) to come from widely separated single configurations (deep traps) as in the REM. Instead, such contributing terms form clusters (deep valleys). The idea to deal with this situation is to coarse-grain S_N over suitable blocks. Namely, we introduce a new scale, $\theta_N \ll a_N$, and instead of (31.53) consider the process

$$S_N^b(t) = c_N^{-1} \sum_{i=1}^{\lfloor \lfloor a_N t \rfloor / \theta_N \rfloor} Z_{N,i}, \quad t > 0, \tag{31.64}$$

where the increments are the block variables

$$Z_{N,i} \equiv \sum_{j=\theta_N(i-1)+1}^{\theta_N i} \tau_N(J_N(i)) e_{N,i}, \quad i \geq 1. \tag{31.65}$$

The point of this procedure is that, using the fast-mixing property of J_N and choosing $2N^2 \ll \theta_N \ll a_N$, the random variables $Z_{N,i}$ can be made close to independent and identically distributed. The strategy presented in Sec. 31.2.2 for proving convergence of clock processes then carries forward unchanged, the main difference being that the distribution $Q_N^u(\sigma)$ of the increments (31.65) that enters condition (31.57) is now much more complex, and is a random variable depending on the disorder. Nevertheless, along the trajectories of J_N the shape and width of the deep valleys that give the leading contributions to S_N^b can be described quite precisely, and the distribution of the $\tau_N(\sigma)$'s across these valleys can be well approximated using Gaussian interpolation techniques. This enables us to prove that under the assumptions of Theorem 2, choosing a_N and c_N as in (31.58) the increments (31.65) are heavy tailed, and S_N^b converges to a stable subordinator of exponent γ/β in Skorokhod space equipped with the J_1-topology, $\mathbb{P}$-almost surely if $p > 4$, and in $\mathbb{P}$-probability if $p = 3, 4$.

Finally, we must prove that the convergence of the coarse-grained process S_N^b allows to control the two-time correlation function (31.40). This will follow from the fact that in a block of lenght θ_N, essentially all the time is spent in a single visit to quite small "valley", within which the process does not make more than $o(N)$ steps.

31.2.4. *Metropolis dynamics of the REM*

The following result, proved in Ref. [65], establishes that despite their widely different microscopic structure, Metropolis dynamics of the REM with jump rates (31.39) and the random hopping dynamics exhibits the same aging behaviour in the same domain of temperature and timescale.

Theorem 3. *Let $c_N = c_N(\gamma)$. For all β and γ satisfying*

$$0 < \gamma < \min\left(\beta, \sqrt{2\ln 2}\right) \tag{31.66}$$

we have that for $\varepsilon = 0$ and all $t > 0$ and $s > 0$, $\mathbb{P}$-almost surely

$$\lim_{N \to \infty} \mathcal{C}_{N,\varepsilon}(t,s) = \mathrm{Asl}_{\gamma/\beta}\big(t/(t+s)\big). \tag{31.67}$$

Although still valid, the jump chain and clock process representation (31.47)–(31.48) of X_N is no longer efficient in the framework of Metropolis dynamics. Indeed, it was shown in Ref. [82] for a truncated REM that, due to metastable trapping in local valleys of the energy landscape, the jump chain of Metropolis dynamics is itself an aging process that presents the same complexity as X_N. In particular, its mixing time is exponential in N. This calls for a complete rethink of the process representation scheme.

A continuous-time representation scheme. We call *exploration process* any continuous-time Markov jump process Y_N on $\mathcal{V}_N$ that has the same trajectories as X_N. Denoting by $\widetilde{\lambda}_N(\sigma, \eta)$ and $\lambda_N(\sigma, \eta)$ the jump rates of Y_N and X_N respectively, and by $\widetilde{\lambda}_N(\sigma) \equiv \sum_{\eta \sim \sigma} \widetilde{\lambda}_N(\sigma, \eta)$ and $\lambda_N(\sigma) \equiv \sum_{\eta \sim \sigma} \lambda_N(\sigma, \eta)$ their mean holding times at σ, we have

$$X_N(t) = Y_N(\widetilde{S}_N^{-1}(t)), \quad t > 0, \tag{31.68}$$

where the now *continuous-time clock process* $\widetilde{S}_N$ is given by

$$\widetilde{S}_N(t) = \int_0^t \lambda_N^{-1}(Y_N(s))\widetilde{\lambda}_N(Y_N(s))\,\mathrm{d}s, \quad t > 0. \tag{31.69}$$

To bring us back to the setting of partial sum processes for which the convergence conditions of Ref. [79] apply, we proceed as in the p-spin SK model, i.e., introduce a new scale, θ_N, and coarse-grain the time re-scaled clock process $S_N(t) \equiv c_N^{-1}\widetilde{S}_N(\lfloor a_N t \rfloor)$ over blocks of length θ_N. The resulting clock, $S_N^b(t)$, takes the form (31.64) with increments

$$Z_{N,i} \equiv \int_{\theta_N(i-1)}^{\theta_N i} \lambda_N^{-1}(Y_N(s))\widetilde{\lambda}_N(Y_N(s))\,\mathrm{d}s. \tag{31.70}$$

The gist of this construction is that we are now free to choose the exploration process Y_N, the idea being to choose it in such a way that it mimics the jump chain J_N of the random hopping dynamics, i.e., we ask that (i) it be fast-mixing and that (ii) its invariant measure μ_N resembles the uniform distribution π_N on $\mathcal{V}_N$. As before, the mixing condition serves to reduce the clock process convergence conditions to laws of large numbers under the law $\mathbb{P}$ on the disorder. In particular, (31.55) with increments (31.70) takes the form (31.57) with π_N replaced by μ_N. From there, the strategy is unchanged: prove the convergence of the clock $S_N^b(t)$ in the fine J_1-topology and then prove that this enables us to control some useful two-time correlation function.

The proof of Theorem 3 then relies on detailed information on the properties of the exploration process combined with the knowledge of the valley structure of the energy landscape. This is in sharp contrast with the random hopping dynamics where it suffices to describe the valley structure along the trajectories of the simple random walk J_N. Nevertheless, in the REM, questions about the valley structure of the energy landscape can be rephrased in terms of the well-studied graph structure of the percolation cloud in site percolation on $\mathcal{V}_N$, and thus, they can be answered fully.

31.2.5. *Conclusions and perpectives*

We have seen that subordinators arise as universal aging mechanisms within the emblematic class of the p-spin SK models, including the REM. Beyond models on the hypercube $\mathcal{V}_N$, it has also explained aging in a wide class of models and graphs that cover trap models on the complete graph, on hierarchical graphs and on $\mathbb{Z}^d$ (see [83–85] and the references therein). Understanding the activated aging behavior of the p-spin SK model endowed with Metropolis dynamics remains an open problem. Here we are up against the difficulty that we do not as yet have a good enough understanding of the properties of the energy landscape, either rigorously or theoretically, although several recent papers tackle this problem through, in particular, numerical simulations [86–89]. The subordinator-based mechanism is also present in another important family of spin glasses, the GREM, whose analysis has been initiated in Ref. [90], paving the way for further progress in the area of models with hierarchically structured energy landscape.

References

[1] D. Sherrington and S. Kirkpatrick, *Phys. Rev. Lett.* **35**, 1792–1796, (1975).
[2] M. Mézard, G. Parisi, and M. A. Virasoro, *Spin glass theory and beyond.* vol. 9, (World Scientific, 1987).
[3] B. Derrida, *Phys. Rev. Lett.* **45**(2), 79–82, (1980).
[4] T. Eisele, *Commun. Math. Phys.* **90**(1), 125–159, (1983).
[5] E. Olivieri and P. Picco, *Commun. Math. Phys.* **96**(1), 125–144, (1984).
[6] L. A. Pastur, *Math. notes.* **46**(3), 712–716, (1989).
[7] B. Derrida, *Phys. Rev. B.* **24**(5), 2613, (1981).
[8] C. Moukarzel and N. Parga, *Physica A.* **177**(1-3), 24–30, (1991).
[9] B. Derrida, *Physica A.* **177**(1-3), 31–37, (1991).
[10] D. Saakian, *Phys. Rev. E.* **61**(6), 6132, (2000).
[11] A. Gutin and E. Shakhnovich, *J. Chem. Phys.* **98**(10), 8174–8177, (1993).
[12] K. Ogure and Y. Kabashima, *Prog. Theor. Phys.* **111**(5), 661–688, (2004).
[13] K. Ogure and Y. Kabashima, *J. Stat. Mech.: Theory Exp.* **2009**(03), P03010, (2009).
[14] B. Derrida and P. Mottishaw, *arXiv:2202.12584.* (2022).
[15] B. Derrida and H. Flyvbjerg, *J. Phys. A.* **20**(15), 5273, (1987).
[16] B. Derrida, *Physica D.* **107**(2-4), 186–198, (1997).
[17] A. Galves, S. Martinez, and P. Picco, *J. Stat. Phys.* **54**(1), 515–529, (1989).
[18] J.-P. Bouchaud and M. Mézard, *J. Phys. A.* **30**(23), 7997, (1997).
[19] B. Derrida and G. Toulouse, *J. Physique Lett.* **46**(6), 223–228, (1985).
[20] B. Derrida and P. Mottishaw, *J. Stat. Mech.: Theory Exp.* **2015**(1), P01021, (2015).
[21] D. Ruelle, *Commun. Math. Phys.* **108**(2), 225–239, (1987).
[22] E. Bolthausen and A.-S. Sznitman, *Commun. Math. Phys.* **197**(2), 247–276, (1998).
[23] M. Pain and O. Zindy, *Ann. Henri Poincaré.* **57**(2), 685–699, (2021).
[24] B. Derrida and P. Mottishaw, *J. Phys. A.* **54**(4), 045002, (2021).
[25] G. Parisi, *J. Phys. A.* **13**(4), L115, (1980).
[26] E. Gardner and B. Derrida, *J. Phys. A.* **22**(12), 1975, (1989).
[27] V. Dotsenko, *EPL.* **95**(5), 50006, (2011).
[28] D. J. Gross and M. Mézard, *Nucl. Phys. B.* **240**(4), 431–452, (1984).
[29] E. Gardner, *Nucl. Phys. B.* **257**, 747–765, (1985).
[30] M. Talagrand, *Probab. Theory Relat. Fields.* **117**(3), 303–360, (2000).
[31] M. Talagrand, *Comptes Rendus Mathematique.* **337**(2), 111–114, (2003).
[32] A. Crisanti and H.-J. Sommers, *Z. Phys. B.* **87**(3), 341–354, (1992).
[33] M. Talagrand, *Probab. Theory Relat. Fields.* **134**(3), 339, (2006).
[34] M. Campellone, G. Parisi, and M. A. Virasoro, *J. Stat. Phys.* **138**(1), 29–39, (2010).
[35] B. Derrida, *J. Physique Lett.* **46**, 401–407, (1985).
[36] A. Bovier and I. Kurkova, *Ann. Henri Poincaré.* **40**(4), 439–480, (2004).

[37] A. Bovier and I. Kurkova, *Ann. Henri Poincaré.* **40**(4), 481–495, (2004).

[38] A. Bovier and I. Kurkova. In *Spin glasses*, pp. 81–115. Springer, (2007).

[39] T. Dorlas and W. Dukes, *J. Phys. A.* **35**(20), 4385, (2002).

[40] B. Derrida and E. Gardner, *J. Phys. C.* **19**(29), 5783, (1986).

[41] T. Obuchi, K. Takahashi, and K. Takeda, *J. Phys. A.* **43**(48), 485004, (2010).

[42] B. Derrida and E. Gardner, *J. Phys. C.* **19**(13), 2253, (1986).

[43] D. Capocaccia, M. Cassandro, and P. Picco, *J. Stat. Phys.* **46**(3), 493–505, (1987).

[44] B. Derrida and P. Mottishaw, *J. Stat. Phys.* **172**(2), 592–610, (2018).

[45] J. Cook and B. Derrida, *J. Stat. Phys.* **63**(3), 505–539, (1991).

[46] C. Monthus and T. Garel, *Phys. Rev. E.* **75**(5), 051119, (2007).

[47] B. Derrida and H. Spohn, *J. Stat. Phys.* **51**(5), 817–840, (1988).

[48] M. D. Bramson, *Commun. Pure Appl. Math.* **31**(5), 531–581, (1978).

[49] M. Bramson, *Convergence of solutions of the Kolmogorov equation to travelling waves.* vol. 285, (American Mathematical Soc., 1983).

[50] X. Cao, Y. Fyodorov, and P. Le Doussal, *SciPost Physics.* **1**(2), 011, (2016).

[51] B. Derrida and P. Mottishaw, *EPL.* **115**(4), 40005, (2016).

[52] É. Brunet and B. Derrida, *EPL.* **87**(6), 60010, (2009).

[53] É. Brunet and B. Derrida, *J. Stat. Phys.* **143**(3), 420–446, (2011).

[54] E. Aïdékon, J. Berestycki, É. Brunet, and Z. Shi, *Probab. Theory Relat. Fields.* **157**(1), 405–451, (2013).

[55] L.-P. Arguin, A. Bovier, and N. Kistler, *Ann. Appl. Probab.* **22**(4), 1693–1711, (2012).

[56] L.-P. Arguin, A. Bovier, and N. Kistler, *Probab. Theory Relat. Fields.* **157**(3), 535–574, (2013).

[57] M. Schmidt and N. Kistler, *Electron. Commun. Probab.* **20**, 1–12, (2015).

[58] C. De Dominicis, H. Orland, and F. Lainée, *J. Physique Lett.* **46**(11), 463–466, (1985).

[59] G. Koper and H. Hilhorst, *Europhys. Lett.* **3**(11), 1213, (1987).

[60] E. Shakhnovich and A. Gutin, *Europhys. Lett.* **9**(6), 569, (1989).

[61] D. Saakyan, *Theor. Math. Phys.* **94**(1), 123–125, (1993).

[62] J.-P. Bouchaud and D. S. Dean, *J. Physique I.* **5**(3), 265–286, (1995).

[63] C. Monthus and J.-P. Bouchaud, *J. Phys. A.* **29**(14), 3847, (1996).

[64] L. Faoro, M. V. Feigel'man, and L. Ioffe, *Ann. Phys. (N. Y.).* **409**, 167916, (2019).

[65] V. Gayrard, *Probab. Theory Related Fields.* **174**(1-2), 501–551, (2019).

[66] C. Manai and S. Warzel, *J. Stat. Phys.* **180**(1), 654–664, (2020).

[67] C. Manai and S. Warzel, *arXiv:2007.03290.* (2020).

[68] J. D. Bryngelson and P. G. Wolynes, *J. Phys. Chem.* **93**(19), 6902–6915, (1989).

[69] S. Franz, L. Peliti, and M. Sellitto, *J. Phys. A.* **26**(23), L1195, (1993).

[70] N. Sourlas, *Nature.* **339**(6227), 693–695, (1989).

[71] T. Dorlas and J. Wedagedera, *Phys. Rev. Lett.* **83**(21), 4441, (1999).

[72] T. C. Dorlas and J. R. Wedagedera, *Int. J. Mod. Phys. B.* **15**(01), 1–15, (2001).

[73] J.-P. Bouchaud, L. Cugliandolo, J. Kurchan, and M. Mézard. In ed. A. P. Young, *Spin glasses and random fields*, pp. 161–223. World Scientific, (1998).

[74] J.-P. Bouchaud, *J. Phys. I (France).* **2**, 1705–1713, (1992).

[75] V. Gayrard and L. Hartung. In *Statistical mechanics of classical and disordered systems*, vol. 293, *Springer Proc. Math. Stat.*, pp. 111–170. Springer, Cham, (2019).

[76] G. Ben Arous and J. Černý, *Comm. Pure Appl. Math.* **61**(3), 289–329, (2008).

[77] G. Ben Arous, A. Bovier, and V. Gayrard, *Commun. Math. Phys.* **235**(3), 379–425, (2003).

[78] G. Ben Arous, A. Bovier, and V. Gayrard, *Commun. Math. Phys.* **236**(1), 1–54, (2003).

[79] R. Durrett and S. I. Resnick, *Ann. Probab.* **6**(5), 829–846, (1978).

[80] A. Bovier and V. Gayrard, *Ann. Probab.* **41**(2), 817–847, (2013).

[81] G. Ben Arous, A. Bovier, and J. Černý, *Commun. Math. Phys.* **282**(3), 663–695, (2008).

[82] V. Gayrard, *Ann. Henri Poincaré.* **17**(3), 537–614, (2016).

[83] V. Gayrard, *Electron. J. Probab.* **17**(58), 1–33, (2012).

[84] V. Gayrard and O. Gün, *Markov Process. Related Fields.* **22**(1), 165–202, (2016).

[85] V. Gayrard and A. Švejda, *ALEA, Lat. Am. J. Probab. Math. Stat.* **11**, no. 2, 781–822, (2015).

[86] D. A. Stariolo and L. F. Cugliandolo, *EPL.* **127**(1), 16002, (2019).

[87] D. A. Stariolo and L. F. Cugliandolo, *Phys. Rev. E.* **102**, 022126, (2020).

[88] M. Baity-Jesi, A. Achard-de Lustrac, and G. Biroli, *Phys. Rev. E.* **98**, 012133, (2018).

[89] I. Hartarsky, M. Baity-Jesi, R. Ravasio, A. Billoire, and G. Biroli, *J. Stat. Mech.: Theory Exp.* **2019**(9), 093302, (2019).

[90] L. R. Fontes and V. Gayrard, *Electron. J. Probab.* **24**, 142, (2019).

Chapter 32

Rigorous Results: Random Constraint Satisfaction Problems

Amin Coja-Oghlan[*], Allan Sly[†] and Nike Sun[‡]

TU Dortmund, Department of Computer Science, Dortmund, Germany
amin.coja-oghlan@tu-dortmund.de
†*Department of Mathematics, Princeton University, USA*
asly@princeton.edu
‡*Department of Mathematics, MIT, USA*
nsun@mit.edu

This chapter surveys some of the rigorous mathematical results in the theory of random constraint satisfaction problems (random CSPs). The first part covers the replica symmetric regime, where the so-called "planting trick" has been leveraged to gain understanding of the behavior of typical solutions. Moreover, the onset of replica symmetry breaking has been shown to coincide with information-theoretic thresholds in many interesting models. The second part of the survey covers the regime of (one-step) replica symmetry breaking, where combinatorial models of solution clusters have been analyzed to produce sharp asymptotic results such as satisfiability thresholds.

32.1. Introduction

In a *random constraint satisfaction problem* (CSP), we have n variables taking values in a (finite) alphabet $\mathcal{X}$, subject to a random set of constraints. Examples include (proper) colorings and independent sets of random graphs, and random boolean formulas such as the random k-SAT model. Questions of when these CSPs have solutions, and whether they can be found algorithmically, were of natural interest to the combinatorics and theoretical computer science communities. However, it was only through ideas from statistical physics, starting with Parisi's work on spin glasses, that a more full understanding of the complex nature of the random CSP solution space has emerged. For a time, the physics predictions were largely inaccessible to mathematicians. However, in recent years, rigorous mathematical techniques have been developed to gradually prove more aspects of the rich picture developed by physics methods.

As early as the 1980s it was observed in work of Mézard and Parisi [33] that the theory of spin glasses had implications for random CSPs. Over time this matured into a detailed description of a series of phase transitions that the space of solutions undergoes as the density of constraints increases [1]. Figure 32.1 abstractly depicts how, at various

679

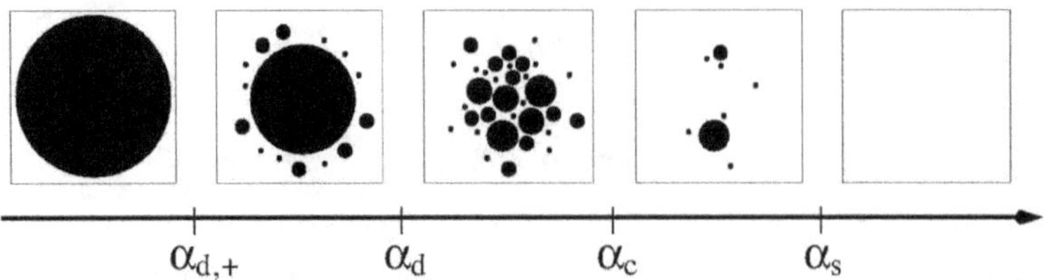

Fig. 32.1. (Figure from [1].) Each panel depicts the solution space of a typical instance of random regular k-NAE-SAT in a certain regime of the clause density $\alpha = m/n$.

constraint densities α, the solution space decomposes into a collection of clusters:

- At low constraint densities, all (or almost all) of the solutions lie in a single well-connected cluster.
- At the first transition α_d, called the *clustering* threshold (also the *dynamical replica symmetry breaking threshold*), the space of solutions splits into exponentially many clusters, each with an exponentially small fraction of the solutions.
- At the *condensation threshold* (or *Kauzmann transition*) α_{cond}, the *free energy* ($f = \lim_n (Z_n)^{1/n}$ where $Z \equiv Z_n$ is the number of solutions in an instance with n variables) is non-analytic in α. Beyond α_{cond}, solutions still occur in clusters, but most of the solutions are contained in a large constant number of clusters.
- The final transition depicted is the *satisfiability threshold* α_{sat}, the point beyond which there are no more solutions. Beyond the satisfiability threshold, there is a *Gardner transition* (not depicted) where the set of ground state configurations changes from 1RSB to full RSB, and the ground state energy is non-analytic in α.

While the above description is rather informal, the physics predictions include quantitative predictions for the locations of the phase transitions, the number of solutions and cluster sizes at each constraint density α, and the behavior of typical solutions.

In the remainder of the chapter, we will describe the progress that has been made in making these prediction rigorous. The chapter is divided into two parts: Section 32.2 covers the replica symmetric regime $\alpha \leq \alpha_{\text{cond}}$ and the idea of "quiet planting." Section 32.3 covers the regime $\alpha > \alpha_{\text{cond}}$, where we see (one-step) replica symmetry breaking, condensation, and the satisfiability transition. To better illustrate the ideas we focus on the random k-NAE-SAT problem, a random boolean formula that, because of its symmetries, is the mathematically best understood random CSP (apart from conceptually simpler cases such as random k-XORSAT). Let us emphasize, however, that we expect this behavior to be universal among a wide class of interesting models. In particular, we expect to see qualitatively similar phase transitions for the random k-SAT problem, as well as for colorings or independent sets of random graphs.[a]

---

[a]At least in the setting of random graphs where the average degree is a large enough constant.

32.2. The Replica Symmetric Phase

Given a CNF boolean formula, a *not-all-equal-SAT* (*NAE-SAT*) solution is an assignment $\underline{x}$ of truth values to variables such that under both $\underline{x}$ and $\neg\underline{x}$ all clauses evaluate to TRUE — equivalently, such that no clause gives the same evaluation to all its variables. A k-NAE-SAT problem is one in which each clause has exactly k literals. Sampling such a formula in a uniformly random manner gives rise to the *random k-NAE-SAT model*. The appeal of this model is that it has certain symmetries making the analysis particularly tractable, yet it is expected to share most of the interesting qualitative phenomena exhibited by other commonly studied problems, including random k-SAT and random graph colorings. Following convention, we fix k and then parameterize the model by its clause-to-variable ratio, $\alpha \equiv m/n$. The *partition function*, denoted $Z \equiv Z_n$, is the number of valid NAE-SAT assignments for an instance on n variables.

Random constraint satisfaction problems usually start their life in the replica symmetric phase, and many remain replica symmetric throughout almost the entire satisfiable phase. Furthermore, within the replica symmetric phase, phenomena such as *dynamical replica symmetry breaking* can occur, which appear to have an impact on the performance of certain types of algorithms.

To illustrate the evolution of random CSPs within the replica symmetric phase, we consider the example of the *random k-NAE-SAT* problem. Hence, let $\underline{\Phi} = \underline{\Phi}_k(n,m)$ be a random propositional formula over the boolean variables $V_n = \{x_1, \ldots, x_n\}$ with $m \sim \alpha n$ uniform and independent random clauses. We may assume that no clause contains the same variable twice. Representing the boolean values 'true' and 'false' by ± 1, we let Z be the number of NAE-SAT assignments $\sigma \in \{\pm 1\}^n$ of $\underline{\Phi}$, i.e., assignments such that both σ and its negation $-\sigma$ are satisfying.

The random formula Φ can be represented by a factor graph with variable nodes V_n and factor nodes $F_m = \{a_1, \ldots, a_m\}$ representing the clauses. Hence, x_j is adjacent to a_i iff x_j appears in the i-th clause of $\underline{\Phi}$. Furthermore, we decorate the edges of the factor graph with the signs of the literals.

On this factor graph representation of Φ we can run the *belief propagation* message passing algorithm. Depending on the initialization and on the values of k and α, the algorithm may or may not converge to a unique fixed point. But due to the inherent symmetry of the problem (i.e., the requirement that both σ and $-\sigma$ be satisfying), there always exists a trivial belief propagation fixed point whose messages are all uniform on $\{\pm 1\}$.

For very small values of α this is indeed the unique fixed point. Specifically, if $\alpha < 1/(k-1)$, then the random factor graph representation of Φ is subcritical. Thus, the factor graph decomposes into many disjoint components that are mostly acyclic. Because belief propagation on finite acyclic graphs has a unique fixed point, the all-uniform messages constitute the unique fixed point. Furthermore, for each of the tree components of the factor graph the number of NAE-SAT assignments can be calculated from the messages via the Bethe free entropy formula [2]. As a consequence, for $\alpha < 1/(k-1)$ we obtain the asymptotic formula

$$\lim_{n \to \infty} Z^{1/n} = 2(1 - 2^{1-k})^\alpha \equiv \mathsf{f}^{\mathrm{RS}}(\alpha) \qquad \text{in probability.} \tag{32.1}$$

The quantity $\mathsf{f}^{\mathrm{RS}}(\alpha)$ is the *replica symmetric free energy*.

In fact, with a bit more care, (32.1) can be sharpened to obtain the precise limiting distribution of Z itself, without taking the n-th root on the left-hand side. To this end we would need to investigate the impact of the (few) components of the factor graph that contain a single cycle of a given length. Each such component incurs a constant correction factor. Moreover, routine arguments show that the joint distribution of the bounded-length cycles converges to that of a family of independent Poisson variables [3].

The first-order approximation (32.1) extends to far larger values of α. In fact, the influential contribution of Achlioptas and Moore [4] on the use of the second moment method implies (together with sharp threshold arguments) that (32.1) holds for $\alpha < 2^{k-1} \ln 2 - 2$ for all $k \geq 3$. This result already comes quite close to the density

$$\alpha_{\mathrm{sat}} = 2^{k-1} \ln 2 - \left(\frac{\ln 2}{2} + \frac{1}{4} \right) + o_k(1). \tag{32.2}$$

beyond which NAE-SAT assignments cease to exist.

The proof of Achlioptas and Moore is based on calculating the expected number of pairs of NAE-SAT assignments σ, τ with a given overlap $x = \sigma \cdot \tau / n$: the expectation is roughly $\exp(n\varphi_{k,\alpha}(x))$, where

$$\begin{aligned}
\varphi_{k,\alpha}(x) = {} & 2 \ln 2 - \frac{1+x}{2} \ln(1+x) - \frac{1-x}{2} \ln(1-x) \\
& + \alpha \ln \left[1 - 2^{2-k} + 2^{1-2k} \left((1+x)^k + (1-x)^k \right) \right].
\end{aligned}$$

A bit of calculus reveals that for $\alpha < 2^{k-1} \ln 2 - 2$ this expression attains its unique maximum at $x = 0$; see Fig. 32.2. An immediate consequence of this calculation and of the asymptotic formula (32.1) is that the overlap of two independent random satisfying assignments $\underline{\sigma}, \underline{\tau}$ of Φ satisfy

$$\lim_{n \to \infty} \frac{1}{n} |\underline{\sigma} \cdot \underline{\tau}| = 0 \quad \text{in probability.} \tag{32.3}$$

Hence, the overlap of a pair of random assignments concentrates on a single point. In physics terminology, this means that the random NAE-SAT problem is *replica symmetric* for $\alpha < 2^{k-1} \ln 2 - 2$.

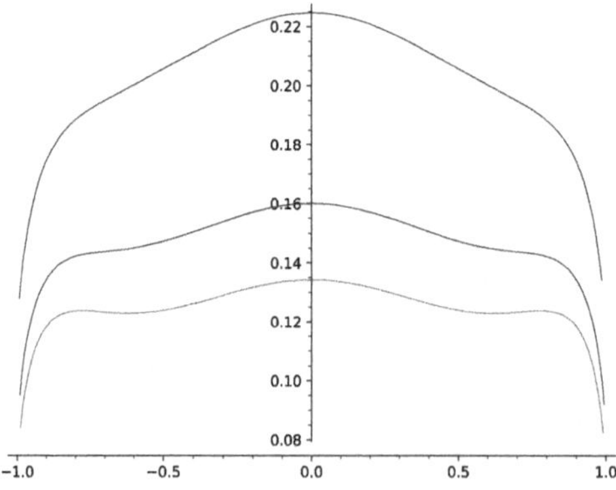

Fig. 32.2.   The function $\varphi_{k,\alpha}(x)$ for $k = 5$ and $\alpha = 9, 9.5, 9.7$ (top to bottom).

According to physics predictions [1], there exists a sharp threshold $\alpha_{\mathrm{cond}} < \alpha_{\mathrm{sat}}$ up to which the replica symmetry condition (32.3) is satisfied, and beyond which it is violated. In the limit of large k, this predicted threshold is asymptotically given by the expression

$$\alpha_{\mathrm{cond}} = 2^{k-1}\ln 2 - \ln 2 + o_k(1).$$

Thus, α_{cond} exceeds the bound of Achlioptas and Moore by an additive constant, and is itself within an additive constant of the satisfiability threshold α_{sat} (see (32.2)).

Physics methods yield a prediction as to the precise value of α_{cond} for any given value of k. However, this prediction does not come as a simple explicit expression, but rather takes a variational form. Specifically, the formula asks to optimize a functional $\mathcal{B}$ that we call the *Bethe free entropy*. This functional does not coincide with the Bethe free entropy formula from (32.1). Rather $\mathcal{B}$ is a 'planted' version of that formula, a point that we will revisit in due course.

The functional $\mathcal{B}$ ranges over the set $\mathcal{P}_*[0,1]$ of all probability distributions π on the unit interval with mean $1/2$. For a specific distribution $\pi \in \mathcal{P}_*[0,1]$ let $(\varrho_i^{(\pi)})_{i\geq 1}$ be a family of independent random variables with distribution π. Moreover, let $\underline{\gamma}$ be a Poisson variable with mean $k\alpha$ that is independent of the $\varrho_i^{(\pi)}$. Finally, let $\Lambda(x) = x\ln x$, with the convention $\Lambda(0) = 0$. Then the Bethe functional reads

$$\mathcal{B}_k(\alpha, \pi) = \mathbb{E}\left[\frac{\Lambda\left(\prod_{i=1}^{\gamma}\left(1 - \prod_{j=1}^{k-1}\varrho_{ki+j}^{(\pi)}\right)\right) + \prod_{i=1}^{\gamma}\left(1 - \prod_{j=1}^{k-1}(1 - \varrho_{ki+j}^{(\pi)})\right)}{2(1 - 2^{1-k})\gamma} \right.$$
$$\left. - \frac{\alpha(k-1)}{1 - 2^{1-k}}\Lambda\left(1 - \prod_{j=1}^{k}\varrho_j^{(\pi)} - \prod_{j=1}^{k}(1 - \varrho_j^{(\pi)})\right) \right],$$

$$\mathcal{B}_k(\alpha) = \sup_{\pi \in \mathcal{P}_*[0,1]} \mathcal{B}(\alpha, \pi).$$

The predicted threshold can now be expressed in terms of $\mathcal{B}_k(\alpha)$:

$$\alpha_{\mathrm{cond}} = \inf\left\{\alpha > 0 : \mathcal{B}_k(\alpha) > \ln 2 + \alpha\ln(1 - 2^{1-k})\right\}.$$

Theorem 32.2.1 ([5]). *For all $\alpha < \alpha_{\mathrm{cond}}$,*

$$\sqrt[n]{Z(\mathbb{F}_k(n, \underline{m}))} \xrightarrow{n \to \infty} 2(1 - 2^{1-k})^{d/k} \qquad \textit{in probability.}$$

Furthermore, the condition (32.3) is satisfied for all $\alpha < \alpha_{\mathrm{cond}}$.

The proof of Theorem 32.2.1 combines relatively abstract ideas from the mathematical physics of spin glasses such as the interpolation method and the Aizenman–Sims–Starr scheme with a powerful technique called 'pinning'. This method was originally invented in the context of coding theory, but also rediscovered in the study of approximation algorithms [6, 7]. The pinning method is applied somewhat indirectly — not to the random formula $\underline{\Phi}$ itself, but to a reweighted distribution $\underline{\Phi}^*$ that we will learn about shortly.

It is possible to show that Theorem 32.2.1 is tight in the sense that for any $\alpha > \alpha_{\mathrm{cond}}$ there exists $\eta > 0$ such that

$$\limsup_{n \to \infty} \mathbb{P}\left[\sqrt[n]{Z(\mathbb{F}_k(n, \underline{m}))} > 2(1 - 2^{1-k})^{d/k} - \eta \right]^{\frac{1}{n}} < 1. \tag{32.4}$$

Thus, Theorem 32.2.1 determines the precise extent of the replica symmetric phase.

The proof of Theorem 32.2.1 proceeds by way of a reweighted distribution on random formulas called the *planted model*. While the statement (32.3) deals with the experiment of first drawing a random formula $\underline{\Phi}$ and then sampling a (pair of) satisfying assignment(s), in the planted model we put the cart before the horse, as it were, by first choosing a solution and then generating a formula to go with it. More precisely, in the first step we draw an assignment $\underline{\sigma}^* \in \{\pm 1\}^n$ uniformly at random. Second, we choose a formula $\underline{\Phi}^* = \underline{\Phi}^*(\underline{\sigma}^*)$ with m clauses uniformly among all formulas that $\underline{\sigma}^*$ satisfies. In effect, $\underline{\Phi}^*$ consists of m independent random clauses that are chosen uniformly among the $2^{k-1}\binom{n}{k}$ clauses that $\underline{\sigma}^*$ satisfies. In effect, $\underline{\Phi}^*$ has a size-biased distribution in that the probability that a specific formla Φ comes up is proportional to its number of satisfying assignments:

$$\mathbb{P}[\underline{\Phi}^* = \Phi] = \frac{Z(\Phi)\mathbb{P}[\underline{\Phi} = \Phi]}{\mathbb{E}[Z]}. \tag{32.5}$$

Clearly, unless Z is *extremely* concentrated about its mean, one should expect that the distributions of $\underline{\Phi}^*$ and of $\underline{\Phi}$ differ significantly. But remarkably, an unintended consequence of the inherent symmetry of the NAE-SAT problem is that throughout the replica symmetric phase, the distributions of $\underline{\Phi}$ and $\underline{\Phi}^*$ are actually quite 'close'. Formally, they are mutually contiguous. The proof of this contiguity result actually reveals the precise limiting distribution of $Z(\underline{\Phi})$, which turns out to be the natural continuation of the formula that we obtained in the sub-critical case by counting short cycles.

Theorem 32.2.2 ([5]). *Let $k \geq 3$ and $\alpha < \alpha_{\mathrm{cond}}$. Then $\underline{\Phi}$ and $\underline{\Phi}^*$ are mutually contiguous.*

The proof of Theorem 32.2.2 combines Theorem 32.2.1 with a truncated moment calculation and small subgraph conditioning, an argument that was originally developed to prove that random regular graphs are Hamiltonian [8]. Small subgraph conditioning also plays a key role in the study of the stochastic block model (and other inference problems) [9].

Theorem 32.2.2 opens the door to the analysis of the random formula $\underline{\Phi}$ for all $\alpha < \alpha^*$. Indeed, thanks to contiguity any property that we can establish for $(\underline{\Phi}^*, \underline{\sigma}^*)$ with high probability carries over to the pair $(\underline{\Phi}, \underline{\sigma})$ immediately. This approach, which is a refinement of arguments from [10, 11], has come to be called *quiet planting*.

The merit of quiet planting is that we obtain direct access to a random satisfying assignment. To elaborate, once we 'quench' (condition on) the random formula $\underline{\Phi}$, there does generally not seem to be an easy way to sample a random satisfying assignment. For instance, one would have to take into account all sorts of local dependencies amongst the variables. In fact, throughout much of the replica symmetric phase we do not know an efficient method for constructing even a single satisfying assignment. In other words, analysing combinatorial properties of random satisfying assignments directly, by first sampling $\underline{\Phi}$ and then taking a good long look, seems like a daunting task.

In the planted model it is quite the opposite. Here we expressly know the satisfying assignment $\underline{\sigma}^*$, and routine methods from probabilistic combinatorics make it easy to study all manner of properties of the formula $\underline{\Phi}^*$. But Theorem 32.2.2 shows that both problems are equivalent.

This connection makes it easy, for example, to study effects such as freezing or dynamic replica symmetry breaking (a.k.a. the reconstruction property) on the random formula $\underline{\Phi}$. For example, a straightforward coupling argument shows that the reconstruction threshold on a Galton–Watson tree that mimics the local topology of $\underline{\Phi}$ coincides with the reconstruction threshold on the random formula $\underline{\Phi}$ itself.

Actually the planted model $\underline{\Phi}^*$ also plays a key role in the proof of Theorem 32.2.1, which builds upon proofs for models with soft constraints from Ref. [5]. The proof proceeds not directly by investigating the number of solutions of the random formula $\underline{\Phi}$, but indirectly via counting satisfying assignments of $\underline{\Phi}^*$. This approach enables the use of the pinning technique, a vital ingredient of the proof of Theorem 32.2.1. The basic insight behind pinning is that conditioning on the truth values of even a small number of variables (any number that diverges as $n \to \infty$ will do) will ensure that the planted model $\underline{\Phi}^*$ becomes replica symmetric. Hence, if we let $\ell = \ell(n) \to \infty$ be any sequence that grows to infinity, and if $\underline{\tau}^*, \underline{\tau}^{**}$ are two random solutions of $\underline{\Phi}^*$ given that $\tau_i^* = \tau_i^{**} = \sigma_i^*$ for $i = 1, \ldots, \ell$, then the overlap $\frac{1}{n}|\underline{\tau}^* \cdot \underline{\tau}^{**}|$ will concentrate on a single value (that may depend on $\underline{\Phi}$). This innocuous fact adds substantial power to techniques such as the interpolation method and the Aizenman–Sims–Starr coupling argument. In particular, we can derive the asymptotic formula

$$\lim_{n \to \infty} \sqrt[n]{Z(\underline{\Phi}^*)} = \mathcal{B}_k(\alpha) \text{ in probability.} \tag{32.6}$$

Comparing (32.6) with (32.1), we see that the threshold α_{cond} from Theorem (32.2.1) is nothing but the point up to which $\sqrt[n]{Z(\underline{\Phi}^*)}$ coincides with the 'obvious' bound (32.1) on the number of satisfying assignments of $\underline{\Phi}$. Thus, Theorem 32.2.1 provides that α_{cond} equals the largest density up to which the exponential order of the numbers of satisfying assignments of $\underline{\Phi}$ and $\underline{\Phi}^*$ coincide.

The planted model is a powerful tool for understanding the behaviour of a typical solution. This has been exploited in order to understand the clustering of solutions. The simplest definition of a cluster is the connected component of solutions in the solution space such that two are adjacent if they differ at only $O(1)$ number of variables. Above the clustering transition α_{d}, the solution space becomes broken up into exponentially many well-separated pieces, or *clusters* (see [10, 12–14]). Conjecturally, α_{d} also coincides with the *reconstruction threshold* [1, 15, 16], and is small relative to α_{sat} when k is large, with $\alpha_{\text{d}}/\alpha_{\text{sat}} \asymp (\ln k)/k$. The planted model gives a simple way to establish clustering because one can calculate the expected number of solutions at a given distance from a random solution in terms of $\varphi_{k,\alpha}(x)$. If this is $o(1)$ at distance xn then with high probability most solutions lie within clusters of radius at most xn. By contrast, we also know that since the overlap is concentrated around 0, most pairs of solutions are at distance $n/2$ and each individual cluster is small.

32.3. Replica Symmetry Breaking

As the density of constraints increases beyond the condensation threshold α_{cond}, we enter the *replica symmetry breaking (RSB)* regime. In this section we will discuss RSB in the setting of the *random d-regular NAE-SAT model*. As in the previous section, there are n variables subject to m random clauses each of degree k; the main difference now is that each variable must have the same degree d. As a result $\alpha = m/n = d/k$. The corresponding factor graph is bi-regular, and its local homogeneity greatly simplifies the analysis, as we will describe below.

It is conjectured that for each $k \geq 3$, the model has an exact satisfiability threshold $\alpha_{\text{sat}}(k)$: for $\alpha < \alpha_{\text{sat}}$ it is satisfiable ($Z > 0$) with high probability, but for $\alpha > \alpha_{\text{sat}}$ it is unsatisfiable ($Z = 0$) with high probability. This has been proved [17, Thm. 1] for all k exceeding an absolute constant k_0, together with an exact formula for α_{sat} which matches the physics prediction. It can be approximated for large k by (32.2).

Recall from (32.1) the calculation of the replica symmetric free energy $\mathsf{f}^{\text{RS}}(\alpha)$. For this model, the replica symmetric free energy also coincides with the first moment estimate of Z_n:

$$\mathbb{E}Z = 2^n \left(1 - \frac{2}{2^k}\right)^{n\alpha} = \mathsf{f}^{\text{RS}}(\alpha)^n.$$

It then follows by Markov's inequality and Jensen's inequality that $\mathsf{f}^{\text{RS}}(\alpha)$ is with high probability an upper bound on the true limiting free energy $\mathsf{f}(\alpha) = \lim_n (Z_n)^{1/n}$.

As mentioned previously, one of the intriguing predictions from the physics analysis [18, 19] is that there is a critical value α_{cond} strictly below α_{sat}, such that $\mathsf{f}(\alpha)$ and $\mathsf{f}^{\text{RS}}(\alpha)$ agree up to $\alpha = \alpha_{\text{cond}}$ and diverge thereafter. In particular, this implies that the function $\mathsf{f}(\alpha)$ must be non-analytic at $\alpha = \alpha_{\text{cond}}$. This is the *condensation transition*, and will be further described below in Sec. 32.3.1. For all $0 \leq \alpha < \alpha_{\text{sat}}$, the free energy is predicted to be given by a formula

$$\mathsf{f}(\alpha) = \mathsf{f}^{\text{1RSB}}(\alpha) \begin{cases} = \mathsf{f}^{\text{RS}}(\alpha) & \text{for } 0 \leq \alpha \leq \alpha_{\text{cond}}, \\ < \mathsf{f}^{\text{RS}}(\alpha) & \text{for } \alpha > \alpha_{\text{cond}}. \end{cases}$$

The function $\mathsf{f}^{\text{1RSB}}(\alpha)$ is quite explicit, although not extremely simple to state; it is formally presented below in Definition 32.3.2. The formula for $\mathsf{f}^{\text{1RSB}}(\alpha)$ is derived via the *one-step replica symmetry breaking* (1RSB) heuristic, discussed further below. The following result gives some characterization of the condensation regime in the regular NAE-SAT model:

Theorem 32.3.1. *In random regular k-NAE-SAT with $k \geq k_0$:*

(1) *For all $\alpha < \alpha_{\text{sat}}(k)$, the free energy $\mathsf{f}(\alpha)$ exists and equals the predicted value $\mathsf{f}^{\text{1RSB}}(\alpha)$.*

(2) *For all $\alpha_{\text{cond}} < \alpha < \alpha_{\text{sat}}$ and $\epsilon > 0$, there exists a large enough constant $m_0 = m_0(k, \alpha, \epsilon)$ such that, with probability $\geq 1 - \epsilon$, the m_0 largest clusters contain at least $1 - \epsilon$ fraction of the solutions. Further, there exists $\rho(\alpha, k) \in (0, 1)$ such that the overlap distribution (the law of $(\sigma, \tau)/n$ for two uniformly random solutions*

σ, τ *of the same instance) is concentrated around the two values* $\{0, \rho\}$ *in the limit* $n \to \infty$.

The first item is proved in Ref. [20]; the second item is proved in Ref. [21].

In the physics literature, having the overlap distributed concentrated on $r+1$ values is often taken as the definition of r-step replica symmetry breaking, so the result of Ref. [21] verifies that the regular NAE-SAT model is 1RSB in the condensation regime. The discussion in the current section (Sec. 32.3) has been adapted in part from Refs. [20, 21].

32.3.1. *Statistical physics predictions*

According to the heuristic analysis by statistical physics methods, the random regular NAE-SAT model has a single level of replica symmetry breaking (1RSB). We summarize here some of the key phenomena that are predicted from the 1RSB framework [1, 18, 19], referring the reader to [2, Chapter 19] for a full expository account. While much of the following description remains conjectural, some of the key implications (in terms of free energy and overlap distribution) are established in Refs. [20, 21]. Throughout the following we write $\doteq$ to indicate equality up to subexponential factors ($\exp\{o(n)\}$).

For α above α_{d} it is expected that the number of clusters of size $\exp\{ns\}$ has mean value $\exp\{n\Sigma(s; \alpha)\}$, and is *concentrated* about this mean. The function $\Sigma(s) \equiv \Sigma(s; \alpha)$ is referred to as the "cluster complexity." The 1RSB framework of statistical physics gives an *explicit* conjecture for Σ, discussed below in Sec. 32.3.2. Then, summing over cluster sizes $0 \le s \le \ln 2$ gives that the total number Z of NAE-SAT solutions has mean

$$\mathbb{E}Z \doteq \sum_s \exp\{n[s + \Sigma(s)]\} \doteq \exp\{n[s_1 + \Sigma(s_1)]\}, \tag{32.7}$$

where $s_1 = \arg\max[s + \Sigma(s)]$. It is expected that Σ is continuous and strictly concave in s, and also that $s + \Sigma(s)$ has a unique maximizer s_1 with $\Sigma'(s_1) = -1$. For NAE-SAT and related models, this explicit calculation reveals a critical value $\alpha_{\mathrm{cond}} \in (\alpha_{\mathrm{d}}, \alpha_{\mathrm{sat}})$, characterized as

$$\alpha_{\mathrm{cond}} = \sup\{\alpha \ge \alpha_{\mathrm{d}} : \Sigma(s_1(\alpha); \alpha) \ge 0\}.$$

By contrast, the satisfiability threshold can be characterized as

$$\alpha_{\mathrm{sat}} = \sup\{\alpha \ge \alpha_{\mathrm{d}} : \max_s \Sigma(s; \alpha) \ge 0\}. \tag{32.8}$$

For all $\alpha \ge \alpha_{\mathrm{d}}$, the expected partition function $\mathbb{E}Z$ is dominated by clusters of size $\exp\{ns_1\}$. However, for $\alpha > \alpha_{\mathrm{cond}}$, we have $\Sigma(s_1) < 0$, so the expected number of clusters of this size is very small: $\exp\{n\Sigma(s_1)\}$ tends to zero exponentially fast as $n \to \infty$. This means that clusters of size $\exp\{ns_1\}$ are highly unlikely to appear in a typical realization of the model. Instead, in a typical realization we only expect to see clusters of size $\exp\{ns\}$ with $\Sigma(s) \ge 0$. As a result the solution space should be dominated (with high probability) by clusters of size $s_{\max}$ where

$$s_{\max} \equiv s_{\max}(\alpha) \equiv \arg\max\{s + \Sigma(s) : \Sigma(s) \ge 0\}.$$

Since Σ is continuous, $s_{\max}$ is the largest root of Σ, and for $\alpha \in (\alpha_{\text{cond}}, \alpha_{\text{sat}})$ we should have

$$Z \doteq \exp\{ns_{\max}\} \ll \mathbb{E}Z = \exp\{n[s_1 + \Sigma(s_1)]\}$$

(where the approximation for Z holds with high probability). The *1RSB free energy*, formally given by Definition 32.3.2 below, should be interpreted as an expression for the function $\mathsf{f}^{1\text{RSB}}(\alpha) = s_{\max}(\alpha)$.

32.3.2. *The tilted cluster partition function*

From the discussion of Sec. 32.3.1 we see that once the function $\Sigma(s; \alpha)$ is determined, it is possible to derive α_{cond}, α_{sat}, and $\mathsf{f}(\alpha)$. In order to compute the free energy, the function Σ can be computed using a physics-inspired approach. First consider the λ-tilted partition function

$$\bar{Z}_\lambda \equiv \sum_{\gamma \in \mathsf{CL}(\mathscr{G})} |\gamma|^\lambda, \tag{32.9}$$

where $\mathsf{CL}(\mathscr{G})$ denotes the set of solution clusters of $\mathscr{G}$, and $|\gamma|$ denotes the number of satisfying assignments inside the cluster γ. According to the conjectural picture described above, we should have

$$\mathbb{E}\bar{Z}_\lambda \doteq \sum_s (\exp\{ns\})^\lambda \exp\{n\Sigma(s)\} \doteq \exp\{n\mathfrak{F}(\lambda)\}$$

where $\mathfrak{F}$ is the Legendre dual of $-\Sigma$:

$$\mathfrak{F}(\lambda) \equiv (-\Sigma)^\star(\lambda) \equiv \max_s\{\lambda s + \Sigma(s)\} = \lambda s_\lambda + \Sigma(s_\lambda), \tag{32.10}$$

where $s_\lambda \equiv \arg\max_s[\lambda s + \Sigma(s)]$. Moreover, if $\Sigma(s_\lambda) \geq 0$, then Z_λ should concentrate near $\mathbb{E}Z_\lambda$, and in this regime physicists have an exact prediction for $\mathfrak{F}(\lambda)$, which will be further discussed below in Sec. 32.3.4. In short, the physics approach to computing Σ is to first compute $\mathfrak{F}(\lambda)$ (in the regime where $\Sigma(s_\lambda) \geq 0$), and then set $\Sigma = -\mathfrak{F}^\star$. Note that by differentiating $\mathfrak{F}(\lambda) = n^{-1} \ln \mathbb{E}\bar{Z}_\lambda$ we find that $\mathfrak{F}$ is convex in λ, so the resulting Σ will indeed be concave.

At first glance the reduction to computing $\mathfrak{F}(\lambda)$ may not seem to improve matters. It is not immediately clear how "clusters" should be defined. It turns out that in the regime we are studying, a reasonable definition is that two NAE-SAT solutions are connected if they differ by a single bit, and the *clusters* are the connected components of the solution space. A typical NAE-SAT solution will have a positive density of variables which are *free*, meaning their value can be changed without violating any clause; any such solution must belong in a cluster of exponential size. Each cluster may be a complicated subset of $\{0,1\}^n$ — changing the value at one free variable may affect whether its neighbors are free, so a cluster need not be a simple subcube of $\{0,1\}^n$. Nevertheless, we wish to sum over the cluster sizes raised to non-integer powers. This computation is made tractable by constructing more explicit combinatorial models for the NAE-SAT solution clusters, as we next describe.

32.3.3. *Modeling solution clusters*

Near the condensation threshold (at least when k is large), the analysis of NAE-SAT solution clusters is greatly simplified by the fact that in every satisfying assignment the vast majority of variables are *frozen* rather than free. The result of this, roughly speaking, is that a cluster $\gamma \in \mathsf{CL}(\mathscr{G})$ can be encoded by a configuration $\underline{x} \in \{0, 1, \mathtt{f}\}^n$ (representing its circumscribed subcube, so $x_v = \mathtt{f}$ indicates a free variable) with no essential loss of information. We say that a variable within a clause is forced if, given the other variables in the clause, it has only one option to satisfy the clause. This is formalized by a combinatorial model of "frozen configurations" representing the clusters which can be viewed as the solutions of a certain CSP that requires:

- All frozen variables are forced by at least one clusters.
- Free variables are not forced by any cluster.
- All clauses with only frozen variables are satisfied.

The physics heuristics can be applied again to this CSP on clusters.

Variations on this idea appear in several places in the physics literature; in the specific context of random CSPs we refer to Refs. [22–24]. Analyzing the number of frozen configurations, corresponding to (32.9) with $\lambda = 0$, yields the satisfiability threshold for this model [17].

Analyzing (32.9) for general λ requires deeper investigation of the arrangement of free variables in a typical frozen configuration $\underline{x}$. A key piece of intuition is that if we consider the subgraph of $\mathscr{G}$ induced by the free variables, together with the clauses through which they interact, then this subgraph is predominantly comprised of disjoint components T of bounded size. (In fact, the majority of free variables are simply isolated vertices; a smaller fraction occurs in linked pairs; a yet smaller fraction occurs in components of size three or more.) Each free component T is surrounded by frozen variables, and we let $z(T)$ be the number of NAE-SAT assignments on T which are consistent with the frozen boundary. Since disjoint components T, T' do not interact, the size of the cluster represented by $\underline{x}$ is simply the product of $z(T)$ over all T.

Another key observation is that the random NAE-SAT graph has few short cycles, so almost all of the free components will be *trees*. As a result, their weights $z(T)$ can be evaluated recursively by belief propagation (analogous to the BP calculation leading to (32.1)). In the RSB heuristic framework, a cluster is represented by a vector $\underline{m}$ of "messages," indexed by the directed edges of the NAE-SAT graph $\mathscr{G}$. Informally, for a given cluster, and for any variable v adjacent to any clause a,

$$\mathtt{m}_{v \to a} = \text{"within-cluster law of } \boldsymbol{x}_v \text{ in absence of } a\text{"};$$
$$\mathtt{m}_{a \to v} = \text{"within-cluster law of } \boldsymbol{x}_v \text{ in absence of } \partial v \setminus a\text{"}, \tag{32.11}$$

where ∂v denotes the neighboring clauses of v. Each message is a probability measure on $\{0, 1\}$, and the messages are related to one another via local consistency equations, which are known as the BP equations. A configuration $\underline{m}$ which satisfies all the local consistency equations is a *BP solution*. Thus a cluster γ can be encoded either by a frozen configuration $\underline{x}$ or by a BP solution $\underline{m}$; the latter has the key advantage that *the size of γ can be easily read off from $\underline{m}$, as a certain product of local functions.* For the cluster size raised to power λ, simply raise each local function to power λ. Thus the configurations $\underline{m}$ with λ-tilted weights form a *spin system* (Markov random field), whose partition function is the quantity of interest (32.9). This new spin system is sometimes termed the "auxiliary model" (e.g. [2, Chapter 19]).

32.3.4. *One-step replica symmetry breaking*

In Sec. 32.3.3 we described informally how a solution cluster γ can be encoded by a frozen configuration $\underline{x}$, or a BP solution $\underline{m}$. An important caveat is that the converse need not hold. In the NAE-SAT model, for any value of α, a trivial BP solution is always given by the "replica symmetric fixed point" (also called the factorized fixed point), where every $m_{v \to a}$ is the uniform measure on $\{0,1\}$. However, above α_{cond}, this is a spurious solution. One way to see this is via the heuristic cavity calculation of $f^{\mathrm{RS}}(\alpha)$, which we now describe to motivate the more complicated expression for $f^{\mathrm{1RSB}}(\alpha)$.

Given a random regular NAE-SAT instance $\mathscr{G}$ on n variables, choose k uniformly random variables $v_1, \ldots, v_k$, and assume for simplicity that no two of these share a clause. Remove the k variables along with their kd incident clauses, producing the "cavity graph" $\mathscr{G}''$. Then add $d(k-1)$ new clauses to $\mathscr{G}''$, producing the graph $\mathscr{G}'$. Under this operation [25], $\mathscr{G}'$ is distributed as a random regular NAE-SAT instance on $n - k$ variables. If the free energy $f(\alpha) = \lim_{n \to \infty} Z^{1/n}$ exists, then we would expect it to agree asymptotically with

$$\left(\frac{Z(\mathscr{G})}{Z(\mathscr{G}')} \right)^{1/k} = \left(\frac{Z(\mathscr{G})}{Z(\mathscr{G}'')} \right)^{1/k} \Big/ \left(\frac{Z(\mathscr{G}')}{Z(\mathscr{G}'')} \right)^{1/k}. \tag{32.12}$$

Let U denote the set of "cavity neighbors", i.e., the variables in $\mathscr{G}''$ of degree $d-1$, which neighbored the clauses that were deleted from $\mathscr{G}$. Then $\mathscr{G}$ and $\mathscr{G}'$ differ from $\mathscr{G}''$ only in the addition of a few small subgraphs which are attached to U. Computing $Z(\mathscr{G})/Z(\mathscr{G}'')$ or $Z(\mathscr{G}')/Z(\mathscr{G}'')$ reduces to understanding the joint law of the spins $(x_u)_{u \in U}$ under the NAE-SAT model defined by $\mathscr{G}''$. Since $\mathscr{G}$ is unlikely to have many cycles, the vertices of U are typically far apart from one another in $\mathscr{G}''$. Therefore, one plausible scenario is that their spins are approximately independent under the NAE-SAT model on $\mathscr{G}''$, with x_u marginally distributed according to $m_{u \to a}$ where a is the deleted clause that neighbored u in $\mathscr{G}$. If this is the case, then each $m_{u \to a}$ must be uniform over $\{0,1\}$, by the negation symmetry of NAE-SAT. Under this assumption, we can calculate

$$\left(\frac{Z(\mathscr{G})}{Z(\mathscr{G}'')} \right)^{1/k} = 2(1 - 2/2^k)^d,$$

$$\left(\frac{Z(\mathscr{G}')}{Z(\mathscr{G}'')} \right)^{1/k} = (1 - 2/2^k)^{\alpha(k-1)}. \tag{32.13}$$

Substituting into (32.12) gives the replica symmetric free energy prediction $f(\alpha) \doteq f^{\mathrm{RS}}(\alpha)$, which we know to be false for large α (in particular, it is inconsistent with the known satisfiability threshold). Thus the replica symmetric fixed point, $m_{u \to a} = \mathrm{unif}(\{0,1\})$ for all $u \to a$, is a spurious BP solution. In reality the x_u are *not* approximately independent in $\mathscr{G}''$, even though the u's are far apart. This phenomenon of *non-negligible long-range dependence* may be taken as a definition of replica symmetry breaking (RSB) in this setting, and occurs precisely for α larger than α_{cond}.

Since above α_{cond} the partition function cannot be estimated by (32.13) due to replica symmetry breaking, a different approach is needed. To this end, the *one-step RSB* (1RSB) heuristic posits that even when the original NAE-SAT model exhibits RSB, the (seemingly more complicated) auxiliary model of λ-weighted BP solutions $\underline{m}$ *is replica symmetric, for λ small enough:* conjecturally, as long as $\Sigma(s_\lambda) \geq 0$ for $s_\lambda \equiv \arg\max_s\{\lambda s + \Sigma(s)\}$ (cf. the discussion below (32.10)). That is, for such λ, the auxiliary model is predicted to have correlation decay, in contrast with the long-range correlations of the original model. This would mean that in the auxiliary model of the cavity graph $\mathscr{G}''$, the spins $(\underline{m}_{u\to a})_{u\in U}$ are approximately independent, with each $\underline{m}_{u\to a}$ marginally distributed according to some law $\dot{q}_{u\to a}$. The model has a replica symmetric fixed point, $\dot{q}_{u\to a} = \dot{q}_\lambda$ for all $u \to a$ (the analogue of $\underline{m}_{u\to a} = \text{unif}(\{0,1\})$ for all $u \to a$). If we substitute this assumption into the cavity calculation (the analogues of (32.12) and (32.13)), we obtain the replica symmetric prediction for the auxiliary model free energy $\mathfrak{F}(\lambda)$, expressed as a function of $\dot{q}_\lambda$. As explained above, from $\mathfrak{F}(\lambda)$ we can derive the complexity function $\Sigma(s)$ and the 1RSB NAE-SAT free energy $\mathsf{f}^{1\text{RSB}}(\alpha)$.

32.3.5. *The 1RSB free energy prediction*

Having described the heuristic reasoning, we now proceed to formally state the 1RSB free energy prediction. We first describe $\dot{q}_\lambda$ as a certain discrete probability measure over $\underline{m}$. Since $\underline{m}$ is a probability measure over $\{0,1\}$, we encode it by $x \equiv \underline{m}(1) \in [0,1]$. A measure q on $\underline{m}$ can thus be encoded by an element $\mu \in \mathscr{P}$ where $\mathscr{P}$ denotes the set of discrete probability measures on $[0,1]$. For measurable $B \subseteq [0,1]$, define

$$\hat{\mathscr{R}}_\lambda\mu(B) \equiv \frac{1}{\hat{\mathscr{Z}}(\mu)} \int \left(2 - \prod_{i=1}^{k-1} x_i - \prod_{i=1}^{k-1}(1-x_i)\right)^\lambda$$

$$\times 1\left\{\frac{1 - \prod_{i=1}^{k-1} x_i}{2 - \prod_{i=1}^{k-1} x_i - \prod_{i=1}^{k-1}(1-x_i)} \in B\right\} \prod_{i=1}^{k-1} \mu(dx_i)$$

as well as

$$\dot{\mathscr{R}}_\lambda\mu(B) \equiv \frac{1}{\dot{\mathscr{Z}}(\mu)} \int \left(\prod_{i=1}^{d-1} y_i + \prod_{i=1}^{d-1}(1-y_i)\right)^\lambda 1\left\{\frac{\prod_{i=1}^{d-1} y_i}{\prod_{i=1}^{d-1} y_i + \prod_{i=1}^{d-1}(1-y_i)} \in B\right\} \prod_{i=1}^{d-1} \mu(dy_i),$$

$$(32.14)$$

where $\hat{\mathscr{Z}}(\mu)$ and $\dot{\mathscr{Z}}(\mu)$ are the normalizing constants such that $\hat{\mathscr{R}}_\lambda\mu$ and $\dot{\mathscr{R}}_\lambda\mu$ are also probability measures on $[0,1]$. (In the context of $\lambda = 0$ we take the convention that $0^0 = 0$.) Denote $\mathscr{R}_\lambda \equiv \dot{\mathscr{R}}_\lambda \circ \hat{\mathscr{R}}_\lambda$. The map $\mathscr{R}_\lambda : \mathscr{P} \to \mathscr{P}$ represents the BP recursion for the auxiliary model. We let $\dot{\mu}_{\lambda,0} \equiv \frac{1}{2}\delta_0 + \frac{1}{2}\delta_1 \in \mathscr{P}$, and define recursively $\dot{\mu}_{\lambda,l+1} = \mathscr{R}_\lambda\dot{\mu}_{\lambda,l} \in \mathscr{P}$ for all $l \geq 0$. For k in the condensation regime, $\dot{\mu}_{\lambda,l}$ converges to a limit $\dot{\mu}_\lambda \in \mathscr{P}$ as $l \to \infty$ satisfying the fixed point equation $\dot{\mu}_\lambda = \mathscr{R}_\lambda\dot{\mu}_\lambda$.

The limit $\dot{\mu}_\lambda$ encodes the desired replica symmetric solution $\dot{q}_\lambda$ for the auxiliary model. We can then express $\mathfrak{F}(\lambda)$ in terms of $\dot{\mu}_\lambda$ as follows. Writing $\hat{\mu}_\lambda \equiv \hat{\mathscr{R}}_\lambda\dot{\mu}_\lambda$, let

$\dot{w}_\lambda, \hat{w}_\lambda, \bar{w}_\lambda \in \mathscr{P}$ be defined by

$$\dot{w}_\lambda(B) = \frac{1}{\dot{3}_\lambda} \int \left(\prod_{i=1}^{d} y_i + \prod_{i=1}^{d}(1-y_i)\right)^\lambda \mathbf{1}\left\{\prod_{i=1}^{d} y_i + \prod_{i=1}^{d}(1-y_i) \in B\right\} \prod_{i=1}^{d} \hat{\mu}_\lambda(dy_i),$$

$$\hat{w}_\lambda(B) = (\hat{3}_\lambda)^{-1} \int \left(1 - \prod_{i=1}^{k} x_i - \prod_{i=1}^{k}(1-x_i)\right)^\lambda \mathbf{1}\left\{1 - \prod_{i=1}^{k} x_i - \prod_{i=1}^{k}(1-x_i) \in B\right\} \prod_{i=1}^{k} \dot{\mu}_\lambda(dx_i),$$

$$\bar{w}_\lambda(B) = (\bar{3}_\lambda)^{-1} \iint (xy + (1-x)(1-y))^\lambda \mathbf{1}\{xy + (1-x)(1-y) \in B\} \dot{\mu}_\lambda(dx)\hat{\mu}_\lambda(dy),$$

with $\dot{3}_\lambda, \hat{3}_\lambda, \bar{3}_\lambda$ the normalizing constants. The analogue of (32.13) for this model is

$$\left(\frac{\bar{Z}_\lambda(\mathscr{G})}{\bar{Z}_\lambda(\mathscr{G}'')}\right)^{1/k} = \dot{3}_\lambda(\hat{3}_\lambda/\bar{3}_\lambda)^d,$$

$$\left(\frac{\bar{Z}_\lambda(\mathscr{G}')}{\bar{Z}_\lambda(\mathscr{G}'')}\right)^{1/k} = (\hat{3}_\lambda)^{\alpha(k-1)},$$

and substituting into (32.12) gives the 1RSB prediction $\bar{Z}_\lambda \doteq \exp\{\mathfrak{F}(\lambda)\}$ where

$$\mathfrak{F}(\lambda) \equiv \mathfrak{F}(\lambda; \alpha) \equiv \ln \dot{3}_\lambda + \alpha \ln \hat{3}_\lambda - k\alpha \ln \bar{3}_\lambda. \tag{32.15}$$

Further, the maximizer of $s \mapsto (\lambda s + \Sigma(s))$ is predicted to be given by

$$s_\lambda \equiv s_\lambda(\alpha) \equiv \int \ln(x)\dot{w}_\lambda(dx) + \alpha \int \ln(x)\hat{w}_\lambda(dx) - k\alpha \int \ln(x)\bar{w}_\lambda(dx). \tag{32.16}$$

If $s = s_\lambda$ for $\lambda \in [0,1]$ then we define

$$\Sigma(s) \equiv \Sigma(s; \alpha) \equiv \mathfrak{F}(\lambda; \alpha) - \lambda s_\lambda(\alpha). \tag{32.17}$$

We then use (32.17) to define the thresholds

$$\alpha_{\text{cond}} \equiv \sup\{\alpha : \Sigma(s_1; \alpha) > 0\},$$
$$\alpha_{\text{sat}} \equiv \sup\{\alpha : \Sigma(s_0; \alpha) > 0\}.$$

We can now formally state the predicted free energy of the original NAE-SAT model:

Definition 32.3.2. For $\alpha \in k^{-1}\mathbb{Z}$, 1RSB free energy prediction $\mathsf{f}^{1\text{RSB}}(\alpha)$ is defined as

$$\mathsf{f}^{1\text{RSB}}(\alpha) = \begin{cases} \mathsf{f}^{\text{RS}}(\alpha) = 2(1 - 2/2^k)^\alpha & \text{for } \alpha \le \alpha_{\text{cond}}, \\ \exp[\sup\{s : \Sigma(s) \ge 0\}] & \text{for } \alpha_{\text{cond}} \le \alpha < \alpha_{\text{sat}} \\ 0 & \text{for } \alpha > \alpha_{\text{sat}}. \end{cases} \tag{32.18}$$

(In regular k-NAE-SAT we must have integer $d = k\alpha$, so we need not consider $\alpha \notin k^{-1}\mathbb{Z}$.)

32.3.6. *Rigorous analysis of the free energy*

We now give some ideas of the proof of Theorem 32.3.1. Since $\mathsf{f} = \mathsf{f}(\alpha)$ is *a priori* not well-defined, let us write $\mathsf{f} \le \mathsf{g}$ to mean that for all $\epsilon > 0$, $\mathbb{P}(Z^{1/n} \ge \mathsf{g} + \epsilon)$ tends to zero as $n \to \infty$. With this notation, the first assertion of Theorem 32.3.1 is obtained by proving separately the upper bound $f(\alpha) \leq f^{1RSB}(\alpha)$, and the matching lower bound $f(\alpha) \geq f^{1RSB}(\alpha)$.

The upper bound is proved by an interpolation argument, which is a kind of subadditive argument. It builds on similar bounds for spin glasses on Erdős–Rényi graphs [26, 27], together with ideas from Refs. [28, 29] for interpolation in random regular models. Let $Z_n(\beta)$ denote the partition function of NAE-SAT at inverse temperature $\beta > 0$. A consequence of the interpolation method is that $\mathbb{E} \ln Z_n(\beta)$ can be expressed as the infimum of a certain functional $\mathcal{P}(\mu; \beta)$, with μ ranging over probability measures on $[0, 1]$. Optimising over the choice of μ here is quite non-trivial. However, each μ gives an upper bound and choosing μ according to the fixed point solution gives the conjectured upper bound for each $\beta > 0$. The free energy is a decreasing function in β and taking the limit $\beta \to \infty$ gives the desired bound $f(\alpha) \leq f^{1RSB}(\alpha)$.

Deriving a matching lower bound is then the main challenge. The proof strategy of Ref. [20] is inspired by the physics heuristics described above, and at a high level proceeds as follows. Take any λ such that $\Sigma(s_\lambda)$ (as defined by (32.16) and (32.17)) is nonnegative, and let Y_λ be the contribution to the partition function of clusters of size roughly $\exp\{ns_\lambda\}$. (As discussed in Sec. 32.3.2, we shall think of a cluster as a connected component of the solution space.) The informal statement of the main technical result of Ref. [20] is that

$$Y_\lambda \doteq \exp\{n[\lambda s_\lambda + \Sigma(s_\lambda)]\}. \tag{32.19}$$

Adjusting λ as indicated by (32.18) then Eq. (32.19) implies the desired bound $f(\alpha) \geq f^{1RSB}(\alpha)$.

Recall from Sec. 32.3.3 that a solution cluster γ can be encoded by a BP solution $\underline{m}$. For technical reasons, it is useful to introduce slightly modified versions of the messages m, which record information on the topology of *free trees* incident to each edge. Ref. [20] considered a restricted model in which every free tree has at most L variables; this describes a subset of valid encodings. The approach then was to establish a version of (32.19), and thus a lower bound on the free energy, for every fixed L. In the limit $L \to \infty$ this yields the sharp lower bound, matching the upper bound obtained from the interpolation method.

The proof of (32.19) for fixed L is via the (first and second) moment method for the restricted model described above. Moreover, by a straightforward combinatorial calculation together with Stirling's formula, the moment calculation reduces to an optimization problem over the space of empirical distributions (proportions of message configurations incident to variables and clauses in the graph). The dimension of the space of empirical distributions is fixed in n, but grows with k and d. Most of the technical difficulty of Ref. [20] (and related works) lies in the problem of solving this optimization.

The first observation towards solving the optimization problem is as follows. It is known (see e.g. [17, Lem. 3.6]) that maximizers of the optimization problem correspond to BP fixed points of measures $Q_{v \to a}(m_{v \to a}, m_{a \to v})$ on the pairs of messages. Unfortunately, this is a more complicated fixed point equation than the one given in Eq. (32.14), which is a "one-sided" measure of the form $q_{v \to a}(m_{v \to a})$. In general, it is not clear how to characterize all the two-sided BP fixed points.

To address this issue, Ref. [20] develops a *resampling argument* to reduce the problem to *one-sided* BP fixed points. The basic procedure is as follows. Start with a pair $(G, \underline{m})$ sampled from the planted model. Select at random a small fraction of variables S. Then resample the clauses joining S to the rest of the graph $G \setminus S$, and resample the configuration on S according to the law of the planted model. This gives rise to a new pair $(G', \underline{m}')$. These dynamics are reversible, and so both $\underline{m}$ and $\underline{m}'$ have nearly the optimal empirical distribution with high probability. This idea leads to a fixed-point equation which turns out to be essentially the same as the one-sided BP fixed-point equation. This is the main idea in the implementation of the second moment method in Ref. [20].

For the second part of Theorem 32.3.1, Ref. [21] gave a refined analysis estimating the partition function up to a constant multiplicative factor. To achieve this level of precision, it is no longer possible to truncate on the size of free trees, so the message configurations $\underline{m}$ have an alphabet of diverging size. This is handled in Ref. [21] by splitting the calculation into the number of arrangements of a core of frozen variables, together with the number of ways (with weights) to embed free trees into the frozen core. Via the second moment method again, this approach leads to the conclusion of Theorem 32.3.1.

32.3.7. *Proofs of satisfiability thresholds*

Recall from (32.8) the connection between the satisfiability threshold α_{sat} and the cluster complexity function Σ. Determining α_{sat} is simpler than calculating the free energy, since it can be done by applying the moment method to the untilted cluster partition function — (32.9) with $\lambda = 0$. In this case, since each cluster has unit weight regardless of how many solutions it contains, it is no longer necessary to keep track of topologies of free trees, and it suffices simply to count the "frozen configurations" described in Sec. 32.3.3. Applying the moment method to this count again results in an optimization problem, but over a much simpler space than in the tilted case. With this approach the satisfiability threshold was determined for random regular k-NAESAT [17], as well as the closely related random regular k-SAT [30] model, in both cases for $k \geq k_0$ (a large absolute constant). A similar approach was applied in [31], with a finer analysis, to pin down the asymptotics of the maximum size of independent sets in random d-regular graphs, with $d \geq d_0$.

Establishing satisfiability thresholds when the system is not regular is substantially more challenging. From the physics perspective, it is still possible to write the 1RSB prediction: it looks similar to the one described in Sec. 32.3.5, but involves a more complicated measure-valued recursion. From the mathematical perspective, however, there is a new problem with the second moment approach. In a random regular graph, almost all local neighborhoods look like the same regular tree. In general random graphs, however, the local neighborhoods are random, and their empirical counts (the "neighborhood profile") have central-limit-theorem-type fluctuations. As a result, we expect the logarithm of the partition function and the number of clusters to be asymptotically normal with order-$\sqrt{n}$ fluctuations, which are too large for the second moment method.

The work Ref. [32] gives (to date) the only rigorous determination of a satisfiability threshold in a non-regular 1RSB model, the random k-SAT model with $k \geq k_0$. In an important prior work [30] the satisfiability threshold was computed up to $o_k(1)$ error. The work [30] applies the moment method conditional on the degree distribution (depth-one neighborhood profile), after pruning high-degree variables, and counting a carefully chosen subset of solutions. The work [32] determines α_{sat} by conditioning on the depth-r neighborhood profile, and pruning an $o_R(1)$ fraction of bad r-neighborhoods. The resulting conditional second moment calculation is carried out by a (more difficult) version of the resampling argument described in Sec. 32.3.6.

References

[1] F. Krząkała, A. Montanari, F. Ricci-Tersenghi, G. Semerjian, and L. Zdeborová, *Proc. Natl. Acad. Sci. USA.* **104**(25), 10318–10323, (2007).

[2] M. Mézard and A. Montanari, *Information, physics, and computation.* (Oxford University Press, 2009).

[3] S. Janson, *Comb. Probab. Comput.* **4**, 369–405, (1995).

[4] D. Achlioptas and C. Moore, *SIAM J. Comput.* **36**(3), 740–762, (2006).

[5] A. Coja-Oghlan, C. Efthymiou, N. Jaafari, M. Kang, and T. Kapetanopoulos, *Comm. Math. Phys.* **359**(2), 603–698, (2018).

[6] A. Montanari, *Eur. Trans. Telecommun.* **19**(4), 385–403, (2008).

[7] P. Raghavendra and N. Tan. In *Proc. 23rd SODA*, pp. 373–387. SIAM, (2012).

[8] R. W. Robinson and N. C. Wormald, *Random Struct. Algorithms.* **3**(2), 117–126, (1992).

[9] E. Mossel, J. Neeman, and A. Sly, *Probab. Theory Related Fields.* **162**(3-4), 431–461, (2015).

[10] D. Achlioptas and A. Coja-Oghlan. In *Proc. 49th FOCS*, pp. 793–802. IEEE, (2008).

[11] F. Krzakala and L. Zdeborová, *Phys. Rev. Lett.* **102**, 238701 (2009).

[12] M. Mézard, T. Mora, and R. Zecchina, *Phys. Rev. Lett.* **94**(19), 197205, (2005).

[13] D. Achlioptas and F. Ricci-Tersenghi. In *Proc. 38th STOC*, pp. 130–139. ACM, New York, (2006).

[14] D. Achlioptas, A. Coja-Oghlan, and F. Ricci-Tersenghi, *Random Struct. Algor.* **38**(3), 251–268, (2011).

[15] A. Gerschenfeld and A. Montanari. In *Proc. 48th FOCS*, pp. 194–204. IEEE, (2007).

[16] A. Montanari, R. Restrepo, and P. Tetali, *SIAM J. Discrete Math.* **25**(2), 771–808, (2011).

[17] J. Ding, A. Sly, and N. Sun, *Comm. Math. Phys.* **341**(2), 435–489, (2016).

[18] L. Zdeborova and F. Krząkała, *Phys. Rev. E.* **76**(3), 031131, (2007).

[19] A. Montanari, F. Ricci-Tersenghi, and G. Semerjian, *J. Stat. Mech.* **2008**(04), P04004, (2008).

[20] A. Sly, N. Sun, and Y. Zhang, *Probab. Theory and Relat. Fields.* **182**, 1–109, (2022).

[21] D. Nam, A. Sly, and Y. Sohn. *arXiv:2011.14270.* (2020).

[22] G. Parisi, *arXiv:0212047.* (2002).

[23] A. Braunstein, M. Mézard, and R. Zecchina, *Random Struct. Algor.* **27**(2), 201–226, (2005).

[24] E. Maneva, E. Mossel, and M. J. Wainwright, *J. ACM.* **54**(4), Art. 17, 41, (2007).

[25] M. Aizenman, R. Sims, and S. L. Starr, *Phys. Rev. B.* **68**(21), 214403, (2003).

[26] S. Franz and M. Leone, *J. Statist. Phys.* **111**(3-4), 535–564, (2003).

[27] D. Panchenko and M. Talagrand, *Probab. Theory Related Fields.* **130**(3), 319–336, (2004).

[28] M. Bayati, D. Gamarnik, and P. Tetali, *Ann. Probab.* **41**(6), 4080–4115, (2013).

[29] D. Gamarnik, *Probab. Theory Related Fields.* **160**(1-2), 253–278, (2014).

[30] A. Coja-Oghlan and K. Panagiotou, *Adv. Math.* **288**, 985–1068, (2016).

[31] J. Ding, A. Sly, and N. Sun, *Acta Math.* **217**(2), 263–340, (2016).

[32] J. Ding, A. Sly, and N. Sun, *Ann. of Math. (2)* **196**(1), 1–388, (2022).

[33] M. Mézard and G. Parisi, *J. Physique Lett.* **46**(17), 771–778 (1985).

Chapter 33

Metastates and Replica Symmetry Breaking

Charles M. Newman[*], Nicholas Read[†] and Daniel L. Stein[‡]

Courant Institute of Mathematical Sciences, New York University, USA
newman@cims.nyu.edu
†*NYU-ECNU Institute of Mathematical Sciences at NYU Shanghai, China*
nicholas.read@yale.edu
‡*Department of Physics, Yale University, USA,*
NYU-ECNU Institutes of Physics and Mathematical Sciences at NYU Shanghai, China
and Santa Fe Institute, USA
daniel.stein@nyu.edu

In this chapter we define and discuss metastates, mathematical tools with general applicability to thermodynamic systems which are particularly useful when working with disordered or inhomogeneous short-range systems. In an infinite such system there may be many competing thermodynamic states, which can lead to the absence of a straightforward thermodynamic limit of local correlation functions. A metastate is a probability measure on the infinite-volume thermodynamic states that restores the connection between those states and the Gibbs states observed in finite volumes. After introducing the basic metastates and discussing their properties, we present possible scenarios for the spin-glass phase and discuss what the metastate approach reveals about how replica symmetry breaking would manifest itself in finite-dimensional short-range spin glasses.

33.1. Introduction

The presence of quenched disorder in condensed matter systems creates special challenges for statistical mechanics, designed primarily to deal with thermal disorder. A proper statistical mechanical treatment of a system whose Hamiltonian contains quenched random variables requires averaging the free energy, rather than the partition function, over these variables. This led to the so-called "replica trick", first used in the context of spin glasses by Edwards and Anderson [1] (EA). Sherrington and Kirkpatrick (SK) [2] applied the replica trick to an infinite-range spin glass model, using the "spin freezing" order parameter proposed in [1], but found the solution to be thermodynamically unstable at low temperature. The solution, found by Giorgio Parisi in 1979 [3], required an exotic and non-intuitive notion of "replica symmetry breaking" (RSB); it was a stunning result that led (in Phil Anderson's words [4]) to a "cornucopia" of applications, to which this volume is dedicated.

A related problem, on which the effectiveness of theoretical statistical mechanics depends, is the existence of a thermodynamic limit for the state in which a system resides. When encountering the subject for the first time a student typically learns that for a macroscopic system comprising $N \sim 10^{24} - 10^{25}$ degrees of freedom with short-range interactions, the effects of surfaces on bulk thermodynamic properties vanishes for large system size, so that a straightforward $N \to \infty$ limit describes the thermodynamics of a large but finite sample. This approach works well in describing the condensed phase for systems without quenched disorder (so long as an appropriate order parameter is identified), as well as for some systems *with* quenched disorder. But when quenched disorder is present, its success cannot be guaranteed, particularly if the low-temperature phase consists of many pure states unrelated by any simple symmetry transformation.

This is not merely a theoretical issue. Consider for example a dilute magnetic alloy such as CuMn, which for a range of Mn concentrations displays spin glass behavior, and two labs which prepare their samples under similar conditions. The locations of the magnetic impurity Mn atoms within the Cu lattice will differ in the two samples, leading to a different distribution of ferromagnetic and antiferromagnetic couplings; in more formal language, the two samples have different realizations of the spin-spin couplings. It now becomes crucial to understand what effect the difference in coupling realizations will have on the system thermodynamics: if there is too much dependence then universal behavior would be absent, i.e., different samples would behave differently.

Fortunately, it can be shown that measurable *global* properties (i.e., quantities which do not depend on the configuration of any finite subset of an infinite system) do *not* in general depend on coupling realization:[a] these global quantities include energy/free energy per spin, magnetization per spin, transition temperature, and so on. Thermodynamic *states*, however, are local: they can be considered as enumerations of all k-spin correlation functions, where $k = 1, 2, 3, \ldots$. As such they are exquisitely sensitive to coupling realization, and the usual straightforward approach of taking a simple thermodynamic limit can break down. As we will see, this is especially important when dealing with systems in which the ordering at low temperature is described by RSB.

In what follows we will discuss in further detail the breakdown in certain cases of the straightforward thermodynamic limit (i.e., one not conditioned on the quenched disorder), and present the concept of a metastate as a statistical-mechanical tool designed to handle this. We will show how metastates are useful for describing the properties of large finite volumes in the absence of a straightforward thermodynamic limit, and investigate some of their uses and applications. Given that the volume in which this contribution appears is dedicated to the many applications of RSB, we will focus our attention on how the metastate is especially useful when working with systems in which the low-temperature ordering is or may be described by RSB, such as EA spin glasses.

---

[a]An important exception is the spin or edge overlap between two states in a system with RSB; the fact that this global quantity is "non-self-averaging" was one of the surprises of RSB. Non-self-averaging in the context of short-range models is discussed in Sec. 33.4.4.1.

33.2. Chaotic Size Dependence and the Thermodynamic Limit

We will be primarily interested in the EA Ising spin glass [1] in zero field. Its (infinite-volume) Hamiltonian is given by

$$H_J(\sigma) = - \sum_{\{\mathbf{x},\mathbf{y}\}} J_{\mathbf{xy}} \sigma_{\mathbf{x}} \sigma_{\mathbf{y}} \tag{33.1}$$

where $\mathbf{x}, \mathbf{y} \ldots \in \mathbb{Z}^d$ are sites in the d-dimensional hypercubic lattice $\mathbb{Z}^d$, $\sigma_{\mathbf{x}} = \pm 1$ is an Ising spin at site $\mathbf{x}$ and $\{\mathbf{x},\mathbf{y}\}$ denotes an "edge" in the set E of nearest-neighbor pairs. The couplings (or bonds) $J_{\mathbf{xy}} = J_{\mathbf{yx}}$ are independent, identically-distributed continuous random variables chosen from a distribution $\nu(\mathrm{d}J_{\mathbf{xy}})$, with random variable $J_{\mathbf{xy}}$ assigned to the edge $\{\mathbf{x},\mathbf{y}\}$. For simplicity we will assume that ν is supported on the entire real line, is distributed symmetrically about zero, and has finite variance; e.g., a Gaussian with mean zero and variance one. We denote by J a particular realization of the couplings.

Theoretically and numerically (not to mention experimentally!) one necessarily works with finite volumes. Let $\Lambda_L \subset \mathbb{Z}^d$ denote a cube of side L centered at the origin, $|\Lambda_L|$ denote its volume, i.e., the number of spins contained within Λ_L, and $\partial\Lambda_L$ its boundary. One then considers $H_{J,L}(\sigma)$, the Hamiltonian (33.1) restricted to Λ_L with a specified boundary condition on $\partial\Lambda_L$, usually taken to be periodic, which among other advantages preserves the spin-flip symmetry of the Hamiltonian. The thermodynamics within Λ_L is described by the finite-volume Gibbs distribution $\rho^{(L)}$: for any (well-behaved) function $f(\sigma)$ of some subset of the spins within Λ_L, its expectation at inverse temperature $\beta = 1/T$ is given by

$$\langle f(\sigma) \rangle_{\rho^{(L)}} = \sum_{\{\sigma_L\}} f(\sigma) e^{-\beta H_{J,L}(\sigma)} \Big/ \sum_{\{\sigma_L\}} e^{-\beta H_{J,L}(\sigma)} \tag{33.2}$$

where $\sum_{\{\sigma_L\}}$ denotes a sum over all $2^{|\Lambda_L|}$ spin configurations within Λ_L. The usual procedure is to solve for $\rho^{(L)}$ in some Λ_L with L large, followed by taking some infinite sequence of volumes Λ_L with $L \to \infty$. The question then arises, under what conditions do the thermodynamic quantities under investigation converge in the thermodynamic limit?

The question of convergence (not depending on the choice of sequence of volumes) typically does not arise in theoretical physics (outside of mathematical physics), because it usually does not present a problem. In both the EA and SK spin glasses, most global quantities, such as those mentioned in the Introduction, can be shown to converge [5–7] (with probability one in the coupling realizations[b]). But if we're interested in studying the thermodynamic states themselves (i.e., as mentioned above, the set of all finite-spin correlation functions), then a problem may arise at low temperatures, particularly if many pure states are present.

This was addressed in Ref. [8], which considered the EA Hamiltonian (33.1) in an infinite sequence of volumes Λ_L. The focus there was on "gauge-related" boundary

---

[b]Throughout this chapter, all conclusions drawn about spin glasses should be understood as occurring with probability one in the coupling realizations unless otherwise noted.

conditions, i.e., boundary conditions related by a gauge transformation, such as periodic and antiperiodic or any two fixed boundary conditions (for a definition and detailed discussion of gauge-related boundary conditions, see Sec. IX of Ref. [9]). Several theorems were proved in Ref. [8], but both their statements and proofs will be omitted here. For our purposes, the consequences of the theorems can be summarized as follows.

Consider an infinite sequence of volumes with periodic boundary conditions as described above, and suppose that there exists only a single pair of globally spin-flip related pure states (at positive temperature) or ground states (at zero temperature), such as would occur in either the scaling-droplet (SD) [10–13] or trivial–non-trivial (TNT) [14, 15] pictures. Then any infinite sequence, chosen independently of the couplings, will converge to a limiting thermodynamic state: namely, a mixed state comprising the two globally reversed pure/ground states, each with probability $1/2$.

Suppose, on the other hand, that the Hamiltonian (33.1) supports infinitely many incongruent [16] (i.e., differing by relative interfaces with dimensionality equal to the space dimension) pure/ground states, as predicted by the RSB [3, 17–22] or chaotic pairs (CP) [23–25] pictures. Then an infinite sequence of volumes chosen independently of the couplings will generally *not* converge to an infinite-volume (pure or mixed) thermodynamic state, a phenomenon referred to as *chaotic size dependence* (CSD) [8, 26]. Instead, there are infinitely many convergent *sub*sequences of volumes, each of which converges to a thermodynamic state different from the others. Although compactness of the space of spin configurations ensures [27] that the thermodynamic states of appropriately chosen subsequences of volumes will converge, in general these subsequences must be chosen dependent on the coupling realization.

Before proceeding, it may be worthwhile to step back and note that nonconvergence of the above type can occur in any system, if the boundary conditions are not chosen appropriately. Consider for example a simple uniform Ising ferromagnet in zero field in two or higher dimensions. An infinite sequence of volumes with periodic or free boundary conditions will of course converge to a mixture of the positive and negatively magnetized states, each with probability $1/2$. But suppose one chose instead fixed random boundary conditions, where for every volume the spins at the boundary are chosen to be $+1$ or -1 independently in accordance with a fair coin toss. In that case the sequence will not converge, in the following sense: consider any fixed volume Λ_W, and consider the spin configuration (at zero temperature) or correlation functions (at positive temperature), within this fixed volume, which we hereafter refer to as a "window". Then at low temperature, for a sequence of Λ_L's with fixed random boundary conditions, the thermodynamic state within the window Λ_W will continually flip between the positively and negatively magnetized states (depending on whether the boundary condition on $\partial \Lambda_L$ has an excess of plus or minus spins) as $L \to \infty$, never tending toward a limit. In this case there are two subsequences of boundary conditions leading to separate limits, one being the positively magnetized and the other the negatively magnetized state.

Of course for the uniform ferromagnet we understand the nature of the broken symmetry and the order parameter, and how to choose appropriate boundary conditions to arrive at the desired thermodynamic limit. For the spin glass and similar systems with quenched disorder, however, the situation is far more complicated: even knowing the order parameter, whether the EA order parameter [1] or the Parisi order parameter [3, 17–20], or something else, will not solve the problem. We simply don't know how to choose coupling-dependent boundary conditions that lead to thermodynamic convergence, and even if we did, these coupling-dependent boundary conditions would lead to non-measurability and consequently no clear way of averaging over coupling realizations. Put another way, there is likely no finite procedure for selecting convergent subsequences, thereby generating thermodynamic states. CSD arising in this way appears to be a fundamental property of Hamiltonians with quenched randomness, and cannot be transformed away by any known methods.[c]

The metastate concept was introduced as a tool for handling these sorts of situations; we turn to its definition, construction, and properties in the next section.

33.3. Metastates

33.3.1. *Analogy to chaotic dynamical systems*

The term "chaotic size dependence" provides more than a picturesque description of the nonconvergence of correlation functions in a coupling-independent sequence of volumes: there is a deep analogy to dynamical chaos which provides a clue to resolving the difficulties posed by CSD. Consider the chaotic orbit of a particle in a dynamical system: its behavior in time t is deterministic but effectively unpredictable, and can be treated as if it were a random sampling from some distribution κ on the particle's space of states. One way to construct κ is through a histogram that records the proportion of time the particle spends in each (coarse-grained) region of states.

Similarly, for systems with quenched disorder such as spin glasses, the behavior of correlation functions as L changes is analogous to the particle's chaotic behavior in time t. Roughly speaking, the fraction of Λ_L's in which a given thermodynamic state appears can be shown to converge as $L \to \infty$ [28–30], just as the κ describing the chaotic behavior of a dynamical system converges as $t \to \infty$. The resulting distribution over thermodynamic states carries information on how often a given state appears within Λ_L's in the infinite sequence.

Strictly speaking, a thermodynamic state Γ is an infinite-volume quantity; by saying that it "appears" within a finite volume Λ_L, we mean the following. Fix a window Λ_W deep inside Λ_L, i.e., with $W \ll L$; within this window all correlation functions computed using the *finite-volume* Gibbs state $\rho^{(L)}$ are the same as those computed using Γ (with negligibly small deviations going to zero as $L \to \infty$ with W fixed).

33.3.2. *Constructions of metastates*

There are several kinds of metastate which carry different kinds of information; here we focus on the simplest variety. A metastate depends on the Hamiltonian (which we will hereafter assume to be (33.1)), the dimension d, temperature T (which can be zero [31] or nonzero [32]), disorder realization (corresponding here to J), and an infinite sequence of volumes Λ_L each with a specified boundary condition. We will hereafter assume that every Λ_L has periodic boundary conditions unless otherwise specified. We will denote

---

[c]CSD occurs also in the SK model, though in the sense of overlap distributions; see Sec. 5.1 of Ref. [26].

a resulting "periodic boundary condition metastate" by κ_J, where dependence on all other quantities is suppressed but understood.

There are two independent constructions of metastates, one initially constructed for random-field magnets [33] and one initially constructed for spin glasses [28]. It was proved in Ref. [29] (see also [30]) that there exists an infinite sequence of volumes, chosen independently of J, for which the two constructions give the same metastate, and so either method can be used, depending on which is more convenient to address the problem at hand. Both constructions are sufficiently general that they can be used for a wide variety of applications, including mean-field (MF) Curie–Weiss ferromagnets with random couplings [34, 35], neural networks [34, 36], and other disordered systems.

The first construction, due to Aizenman and Wehr (AW) [33], uses a canonical ensemble approach based on varying the couplings *outside* Λ_L. Let $\rho^{(L)}$ denote the finite-volume Gibbs state (or ground state pair at zero temperature) in Λ_L with periodic boundary conditions, and consider for each Λ_L the random pair $(J_L, \rho^{(L)})$, where J_L is the restriction of J to E_L, and take the limit (using compactness [27]) of these finite-dimensional distributions along a J-independent subsequence of L's. This yields a probability distribution κ on infinite-volume pairs (J, Γ), where Γ denotes a thermodynamic state, which is translation-invariant (because of the use of periodic boundary conditions) under simultaneous lattice translations of J and $\rho^{(L)}$. The metastate is then the conditional distribution κ_J of κ given a fixed J; it is supported on the infinite-volume thermodynamic states arising from (sub)sequence limits of finite-volume Gibbs states.

The second construction, due to Newman and Stein (NS) [28], is motivated by the chaotic orbits analogy. Given an infinite sequence of volumes $\Lambda_{L_1}, \Lambda_{L_2}, \ldots$ with $L_1 \ll L_2 \ll \ldots$ such that $L_k \to \infty$ as $k \to \infty$, construct a microcanonical ensemble κ_N in which each of the finite-volume Gibbs states (or ground states at zero temperature) $\rho^{(L_1)}, \rho^{(L_2)}, \ldots, \rho^{(L_N)}$ has weight N^{-1}. The ensemble κ_N converges to the metastate κ_J as $N \to \infty$ (again, possibly with use of a subsequence) in the sense that, for every well-behaved function $g(\cdot)$ on thermodynamic states Γ (e.g., a function on finitely many spins),

$$\lim_{N \to \infty} N^{-1} \sum_{k=1}^{N} g(\rho^{(L_k)}) = \int g(\Gamma)\, \mathrm{d}\kappa_J(\Gamma). \tag{33.3}$$

From (33.3) we see that $\int \mathrm{d}\kappa_J(\Gamma) = 1$ and κ_J can therefore be interpreted as a probability measure on thermodynamic states: the finite-volume probability of any event depending on a finite set of spins and/or couplings converges in the infinite-volume limit to the κ_J-probability of that event.

33.3.3. *Large finite volumes and the thermodynamic limit*

A metastate reconciles how nonconvergence in the thermodynamic limit can be used to provide information on the state of a typical macroscopically large volume. The information contained in κ_J includes the fraction of cube sizes L_k which the system spends in different *infinite-volume thermodynamic states* as $k \to \infty$. If there is only a single pair of pure/ground states, as in SD [10–13], then along any deterministic (i.e., not conditioned on J) sequence of volumes the distribution of spin configurations in any fixed window Λ_W generated by the finite-volume Gibbs states will eventually settle down to a fixed state, which as discussed above is the restriction of the infinite-volume thermodynamic state to Λ_W.

On the other hand, if there are many infinite-volume thermodynamic states, as in RSB [3, 17–22] (see below), then CSD occurs and the set of correlation functions in Λ_W never converges to a limit. Instead, for any Λ_{L_k} with L_k sufficiently large, the set of all correlation functions in Λ_W will be identical to that of one of the many (pure or mixed) infinite-volume thermodynamic states available for the system to choose from, and the "chosen" state varies with L_k. Although the correlation function values in Λ_W never settle down, the *fraction of volumes* Λ_{L_k} in which a particular thermodynamic states appears in Λ_W *does* converge (along the subsequence) to a limit, and this information is contained within κ_J [29, 30].

33.3.4. *Formal definition and covariance properties of a metastate*

As mentioned earlier, there are more complex metastate constructions that contain more information than the "simplest" metastate discussed above. A particularly useful construct at zero temperature is a so-called excitation metastate [37–40], which contains information not only on the probability of appearance of different ground states but also all possible local excitations above each ground state. We do not discuss these other metastates here but refer the reader to the references for more details.

For the simple periodic boundary condition metastate, we saw in the previous section two different but equivalent constructions. By themselves they do not define a metastate, considering that there may be other constructions that also lead to the same result. To arrive at a formal definition, we would like a metastate to satisfy certain properties: it must be supported on (infinite-volume) thermodynamic states of the Hamiltonian at positive temperature or ground states at zero temperature, and it must be a probability distribution on these thermodynamic states in the sense of (33.3). We would also like a metastate to satisfy certain useful covariance properties, to be discussed below.

We begin by formally defining thermodynamic states (i.e., infinite-volume Gibbs states) as probability measures on spin configurations. Let $\Sigma = \{-1, +1\}^{\mathbb{Z}^d}$ be the set of all infinite-volume spin configurations and let $\mathcal{M}_1(\Sigma)$ be the set of (regular Borel) probability measures on Σ. An infinite-volume Gibbs state Γ for the Hamiltonian H_J (33.1) is an element of $\mathcal{M}_1(\Sigma)$ that (at a given temperature T) satisfies the Dobrushin–Lanford–Ruelle (DLR) equations [41] for that Hamiltonian. Essentially, the DLR equations require that the conditional probability in Γ of the occurrence of an event in any finite subregion Λ_L (in particular, of a given configuration of a finite set of spins $\mathcal{S} \subseteq \Lambda_L$), conditioned on the spins outside Λ_L, be equal to that obtained from the *finite*-volume Gibbs distribution $\rho^{(L)}$, using the boundary condition on $\partial \Lambda_L$ determined by the spin configuration outside Λ_L. An infinite-volume Gibbs state may be pure or mixed, i.e., a convex combination of two or more pure states. (A pure state is a Gibbs state that cannot be expressed as a convex combination of other Gibbs states; see also

Sec. 33.4.2.) We denote the set of infinite-volume Gibbs states corresponding to the coupling realization J by $\mathcal{G}_J$.

We can now formally define metastates κ_J for the EA Hamiltonian (33.1) on $\mathbb{Z}^d$ as follows:

Definition 3.1. A metastate κ_J is a measurable mapping

$$\mathbb{R}^E \to \mathcal{M}_1(\Sigma)$$
$$J \mapsto \kappa_J \tag{33.4}$$

with the following properties:

(1) **Support on Gibbs states.** Every state sampled from κ_J is a thermodynamic state for the realization J:

$$\kappa_J(\mathcal{G}_J) = 1.$$

(2) **Coupling Covariance.** For $B \subset \mathbb{Z}^d$ finite, $J_B \in \mathbb{R}^{E(B)}$ (the set of edges in B), and any measurable subset A of $\mathcal{M}_1(\Sigma)$, we define the operation $\mathcal{L}_{J_B} : \Gamma \mapsto \mathcal{L}_{J_B}\Gamma$ by its effect on expectation $\langle \cdots \rangle_\Gamma$ in Γ,

$$\langle f(\sigma)\rangle_{\mathcal{L}_{J_B}\Gamma} = \frac{\langle f(\sigma)\exp(-\beta H_{J_B}(\sigma))\rangle_\Gamma}{\langle \exp(-\beta H_{J_B}(\sigma))\rangle_\Gamma}, \tag{33.5}$$

which describes the effect of modifying the couplings within a finite subset B of $\mathbb{Z}^d$. We then require that the metastate be covariant under local modifications of the couplings, i.e.,

$$\kappa_{J+J_B}(A) = \kappa_J(\mathcal{L}_{J_B}^{-1}A)$$

where $\mathcal{L}_{J_B}^{-1}A = \{\Gamma \in \mathcal{M}_1(\Sigma) : \mathcal{L}_{J_B}\Gamma \in A\}$.

We further define a translation-covariant metastate:

Definition 3.2. A translation-covariant metastate is a metastate κ_J with the additional property of

(1) **Translation Covariance.** For any translation τ of $\mathbb{Z}^d$ and any measurable subset A of $\mathcal{M}_1(\Sigma)$,

$$\kappa_{\tau J}(A) = \kappa_J(\tau^{-1}A).$$

These requirements, including translation covariance, are satisfied by both the AW and NS periodic boundary condition metastate constructions. Translation covariance follows easily in the thermodynamic limit from the torus-translation-covariance of periodic boundary conditions. For other coupling-independent boundary conditions, metastates can be obtained in a similar way as for periodic boundary conditions, but are not necessarily translation covariant; however, translation covariance can be recovered by taking an average of the translates of the finite-volume Gibbs measures [38, 39]. In practice, translation covariance is a crucial property without which few conclusions can be drawn.

The importance of coupling covariance, i.e., covariance of a (possibly not translation-covariant) metastate under a local modification of the couplings, is less obvious. We note first that under any finite change in coupling values, pure states transform to pure states (with some local changes in correlation functions). An important consequence of coupling covariance is that if a metastate is supported on some set of pure states, then under any finite coupling transformation $J \to J'$ the transformed metastate $\kappa_{J'}$ will be supported on the *same* set of pure states as κ_J (modulo finite changes in certain correlation functions due to the coupling transformation). Coupling covariance is useful because it helps make explicit the dependence of the metastate on any finite set of couplings. This is crucial because numerous applications, particularly taking derivatives with respect to couplings, require taking into account the dependence of free energies or other thermodynamic quantities on all of the couplings. Moreover, covariance with respect to changes of couplings ensures that taking derivatives with respect to couplings will not generate difficult-to-handle boundary terms induced by pure states flowing into or out of a region of integration.

33.3.4.1. *Gauge invariance of metastates*

Definition 3.1, along with the equivalence of AW and NS metastates obtained along certain deterministic sequences of volumes, leads to another covariance property of such metastates, proved in Ref. [25], namely that they display gauge invariance with respect to boundary conditions. Recall that constructing a metastate requires specification in advance of the boundary conditions on an infinite sequence of volumes. The theorem of Ref. [25] shows that a metastate is unchanged by *any* gauge transformation along all or any subset of boundaries $\partial \Lambda_L$ in the sequence. In other words periodic and antiperiodic boundary condition metastates are identical, as are any metastates constructed with any combination of periodic and antiperiodic boundary conditions within or between volumes. Similarly, all fixed boundary condition metastates are equivalent, for any way of determining the fixed boundary conditions, so long as it is independent of J.

This leads to several powerful conclusions; among them is that our restriction in this contribution to periodic boundary condition metastates incurs little loss of generality. What *is* important is that Definition 3.1 almost certainly requires the use of *coupling-independent* boundary conditions to generate metastates. The use of coupling-*dependent* boundary conditions, though potentially useful for some purposes, would almost certainly result in losing the essential properties of measurability, translation-covariance, and coupling-covariance.

Now that metastates have been defined and their basic properties enumerated, we can turn to some applications. Our main interest in this contribution is how the metastate construct can be used to specify what RSB can (and cannot) mean in the EA model in finite dimensions. We turn to this question in the next section.

33.4. Metastates and Pure States

Next we will make some further definitions, and then describe distinct classes of scenarios that are possible within the metastate framework. The entire discussion in this section is for infinite-volume systems.

33.4.1. *Trivial versus non-trivial metastates and the metastate-average state (barycenter)*

We begin by defining what we will mean by a "trivial metastate". We say a metastate is trivial if κ_J consists of a single atom, in other words a point mass or δ-function on a single Gibbs (i.e. DLR) state; otherwise, it is nontrivial or "dispersed".

An additional construction based on the metastate will be used. Given a metastate, the Gibbs states can be averaged using the metastate, to produce the metastate-average state (MAS) or barycenter $\rho_J(\sigma)$ [24, 26, 28, 33], which is itself a Gibbs state (though a rather special one), and which still depends on the sample of J. That is, $\rho_J(\sigma) = [\Gamma(\sigma)]_{\kappa_J}$, where the square bracket $[\cdots]_{\kappa_J}$ denotes metastate average, in other words

$$\rho_J(\sigma) = \int \Gamma(\sigma) \mathrm{d}\kappa_J(\Gamma). \tag{33.6}$$

If the metastate is trivial, then the MAS $\rho_J = \Gamma$, the Gibbs state on which κ_J is concentrated.

33.4.2. *Pure-state decomposition of a Gibbs state*

A convex combination (or mixture) of distinct Gibbs states for the same H_J is again a Gibbs state; in general, a convex combination could involve an average taken using a probability measure on Gibbs states. A Gibbs state that cannot be expressed as such a combination of other Gibbs states is called an extremal or pure (Gibbs) state. Any Gibbs state can be decomposed uniquely into a mixture of pure states for the same H [41, 42], in the form

$$\Gamma(\sigma) = \sum_{\alpha} w_\Gamma(\alpha) \Gamma_\alpha(\sigma), \tag{33.7}$$

where Γ_α are pure states, and for any given Γ the weights $w_\Gamma(\alpha) \geq 0$ sum to 1. [In practice the decomposition might be continuous and the sum over α would be replaced with an integral using the measure $w_\Gamma(\alpha)$, but we will usually not show this explicitly.] Pure states can also be characterized in other, more intrinsic, ways; one of these is that they exhibit clustering of correlations [41, 42]. For example, a simple consequence of clustering is that if the Gibbs state Γ is pure then

$$\langle \sigma_\mathbf{x} (\tau^{-1}\sigma)_\mathbf{x} \rangle_\Gamma \to \langle \sigma_\mathbf{x} \rangle_\Gamma \langle (\tau^{-1}\sigma)_\mathbf{x} \rangle_\Gamma \tag{33.8}$$

as $|\mathbf{x} - \tau(\mathbf{x})| \to \infty$ [again, $(\tau^{-1}\sigma)_\mathbf{x} = \sigma_{\tau(\mathbf{x})}$ is a translation of $\sigma_\mathbf{x}$], and a similar statement holds for any two local functions $A(\sigma)$ and $B(\sigma)$ built from spins near $\mathbf{x}$ taking the place of the two $\sigma_\mathbf{x}$'s. The pure states correspond to the "ordered" states, which should be familiar in cases such as the uniform Ising ferromagnet in zero magnetic field, which at low temperature (for dimension ≥ 2) has (at least) two ordered states; in one of these, the majority of spins in any finite region in a typical configuration are $+1$, while in the other, they are -1.

The Hamiltonian H_J for a classical spin system with quenched disorder may possess a nontrivial group of global "internal" symmetry operations that act locally on all spins simultaneously, and leave H_J invariant. For example, the EA Hamiltonian in Eq. (33.1) is invariant under a global spin flip which maps $\sigma_\mathbf{x} \to -\sigma_\mathbf{x}$ for all $\mathbf{x}$. If a magnetic field were included, by adding $-h \sum_{\mathbf{x}} \sigma_{\mathbf{x}}$ to H_J, this symmetry would be lost. From here on we will assume that a metastate is obtained using a boundary condition that respects the internal symmetry of the Hamiltonian, in which case the metastate constructions preserve any such symmetries: a Gibbs state drawn from a metastate κ_J will be invariant under the full symmetry group of the Hamiltonian, which in turn implies symmetries (Ward identities) of correlation functions in that Gibbs state.

In the high-temperature region, there is a unique Gibbs state, which is pure, and the metastate is unique and trivial. In this case, the pure state is invariant under the symmetry operations. In a low-temperature phase, it may be that a given pure state is not invariant under the full symmetry group (when the group is nontrivial), in which case it is said to exhibit spontaneous symmetry breaking [41, 42]. In general, the pure states can be partitioned into *orbits*, defined such that the symmetry group acts transitively on each orbit. Each orbit consists either of a single invariant pure state, or of more than one pure state. As a Gibbs state drawn from the metastate κ_J must be invariant under the symmetry, the pure-state decomposition of a Gibbs state drawn from κ_J must consist of symmetry orbits. We will call a Gibbs state *trivial* if its pure-state decomposition consists of a single symmetry orbit, and *nontrivial* if it consists of more than one. (While spontaneous symmetry breaking is certainly a nontrivial phenomenon, and is expected to occur at low temperature in many spin-glass systems with nontrivial symmetry groups, this terminology will be useful for our analysis of spin-glass phases.) Thus this definition using symmetry orbits can handle all cases, including high and low temperature, both discrete and continuous symmetries, and zero and nonzero magnetic field.

For the MAS, we also define its pure-state decomposition

$$\rho_J(\sigma) = \sum_{\Gamma} \kappa_J(\Gamma) \sum_{\alpha \in \Gamma} w_\alpha(\Gamma) \Gamma_\alpha(\sigma) \tag{33.9}$$

$$= \sum_{\alpha} \mu(\alpha) \Gamma_\alpha(\sigma), \tag{33.10}$$

where the weights are $\mu(\alpha) = \sum_{\Gamma} \kappa_J(\Gamma) w_\Gamma(\alpha) = [w_\Gamma(\alpha)]_{\kappa_J}$, and implicitly depend on J. Here again we have written sums, though some of these may in fact be integrals over a probability measure. The same distinction between trivial and nontrivial decompositions of a Gibbs state can be applied to this one.

33.4.3. *Classes of scenarios for spin glasses*

The preceding definitions of trivial and nontrivial, both for metastates and for Gibbs states, now lead to four combinations [22, 24, 28] that provide a broad-brush classification of scenarios for short-range spin glasses, such as the EA model. To simplify the description, we assume the Gibbs states have the same character (i.e., either trivial or non-trivial) for almost every Gibbs state drawn from the metastate (it is unknown whether this must be true, however, the same conclusions would hold if we replaced "almost surely non-trivial Gibbs states" with "nonzero probability of non-trivial Gibbs states"). As far as is known to the authors at the time of writing, all four classes remain open as possibilities that may occur in some model systems, possibly in different dimensions of space, or at different parameter values, for example different temperatures or magnetic fields. They are:

1) Both the metastate and the Gibbs states are trivial. This is the case in the important SD scenario [10–13], as assumed either implicitly [10, 11], or (for the Gibbs states) explicitly, following some discussion [13]. Scenarios in this class still allow for rich physical phenomena at low temperature [13]. It is also the case that occurs at high temperature.

2) Nontrivial metastate and trivial Gibbs states. NS [23, 24, 28] termed this class chaotic pairs (CPs), referring to the Ising EA model at zero magnetic field (the pairs being the symmetry orbits), while the term "chaotic singles" has been used for the same but with a magnetic field [22].

3) Trivial metastate and nontrivial Gibbs states. There is no widely accepted name for this class of scenarios, but below we will mention its connection with the literature. (NS [23, 24, 28] originally termed one scenario in this class the *standard SK picture*, but we discuss this point in the following subsection.)

4) Both the metastate and the Gibbs states are nontrivial. This class is the broadest, and its instances have the richest structure. Below we review arguments that the scenario predicted by RSB [3, 17–22] is in this class in general. (NS [23, 24, 28] originally referred to a scenario in this class as *non-standard SK*.)

It follows from this classification that in all classes, except class 1), the MAS is a nontrivial Gibbs state.

Although we mainly discuss positive temperature, it may be useful to say something about $T = 0$ also. If the probability distribution of the bonds J is continuous without atoms (so *not*, for example, the bimodal model, in which $J_{\mathbf{xy}} = \pm J_0$ for $J_0 > 0$ constant), as assumed so far and as we will continue to assume in this paragraph, then at zero temperature a pure state is a ground state (with probability one), that is a single spin configuration. For classical spins, ground states always form non-trivial symmetry orbits. Some reflection on the metastate constructions shows that at $T = 0$ the Gibbs states drawn from the metastate are trivial with probability one. Hence, at $T = 0$, only classes 1) and 2) can occur. We may expect that if 3) or 4) occur at $T > 0$, then as $T \to 0$, assuming that no other phase transition intervenes, a scenario in class 3) will reduce to one in 1), and one in 4) to one in 2).

33.4.4. *Constraints on the scenarios*

Next we discuss some rigorous constraints on the behavior of the scenarios within the preceding classification.

33.4.4.1. *Non-self-averaging of overlap distributions*

Here we will need to refer to the overlaps of pure states, and to a version [24] of Parisi's overlap distribution function $P(q)$ [17] for the EA model. Given two pure states $\Gamma_\alpha, \Gamma_{\alpha'}$, we can define the average overlap $q_{\alpha\alpha'}$ in the window Λ_W, and take $W \to \infty$:

$$q_{\alpha\alpha'} = \lim_{W\to\infty} \frac{1}{W^d} \sum_{\mathbf{x}\in\Lambda_W} \langle\sigma_{\mathbf{x}}\rangle_\alpha \langle\sigma_{\mathbf{x}}\rangle_{\alpha'}. \qquad (33.11)$$

When (J,Γ) are drawn from the distribution κ, which is translation invariant, and Γ_α, $\Gamma_{\alpha'}$ are drawn from the distribution $w_\Gamma(\alpha)w_\Gamma(\alpha')$ on pairs of pure states in Γ [and note that $\kappa(J,\Gamma)w_\Gamma(\alpha)w_\Gamma(\alpha')$ is translation invariant], then the ergodic theorem (for translations) implies that the $W \to \infty$ limit of the random variable $q_{\alpha\alpha'}$ exists almost surely; the limit is translation invariant. Similarly to Parisi [17], we then define the probability distribution of overlaps for (J,Γ) by

$$P_{J,\Gamma}(q) = \sum_{\alpha,\alpha'} w_\Gamma(\alpha)w_\Gamma(\alpha')\delta(q - q_{\alpha\alpha'}). \qquad (33.12)$$

We define $P_J(q) = [P_{J,\Gamma}(q)]_{\kappa_J}$ to be the metastate average of $P_{J,\Gamma}(q)$ over Γ; thus if the metastate is trivial, $P_J(q) = P_{J,\Gamma}(q)$. Finally, writing $[\cdots]_\nu$ for expectation using the distribution $\nu(J)$ on J, we define $P(q) = [P_J(q)]_\nu$. For the MAS ρ_J, we define $P_{J,\rho}(q)$ similarly to $P_{J,\Gamma}$, using the pure-state decomposition of ρ_J introduced earlier. Each of these distributions is invariant under translations of (J,Γ). We note that for the EA model at zero magnetic field, the overlaps for the two members of a non-trivial symmetry orbit with another fixed pure state have opposite signs, and then $P_{J,\Gamma}(q)$ is an even function of q.

A feature of the RSB MF theory obtained for the infinite-range SK model is that, while the thermodynamic functions such as the free energy per spin self-average (that is, its thermodynamic limit exists for given disorder, and is almost surely a constant without fluctuations due to the disorder) [5–7], the same is not true for the distribution of overlaps in a given sample of the SK model [19, 43]. In contrast, for short-range models such as the EA model, both $P_J(q)$ and $P_{J,\rho}(q)$ must self average, as a consequence of translation invariance and the ergodicity of the distribution $\nu(J)$ [23]. Consequently, the picture of RSB in short-range models as belonging to class 3), as seemed to be assumed within the standard interpretations of that time, was shown to be inconsistent with the behavior that would be expected on the basis of the RSB MF theory. Given the ergodicity of ν, what was called non-self-averaging (NSA) behavior is permitted in a short-range model only for $P_{J,\Gamma}(q)$ and only if κ is not ergodic, and hence only if κ_J is non-trivial [24, 28]. Further, within the RSB scheme (discussed further below), NSA behavior can arise only within class 4), with both a non-trivial metastate and non-trivial Gibbs states [22].

33.4.4.2. *Cardinality and structure of pure-state decompositions*

The results of the preceding subsection can be refined further. Using both coupling covariance and translation covariance, it was shown in Ref. [44] that if the Gibbs states drawn from the metastate are nontrivial, then the pure-state decomposition of the MAS must be uncountable, forming a continuum without any atoms. Hence for scenarios in class 4), such as RSB, if the Gibbs states have a decomposition into a countable number of symmetry orbits, as suggested by RSB, then the metastate not only must be non-trivial but also must be a continuous atomless distribution on Gibbs states. Also, in class 3) the nontrivial Gibbs state must have a decomposition into a continuous atomless distribution on pure states. On the other hand, for scenarios in class 2), such as CPs, the metastate is permitted to have support on a countable or even a finite number (> 1) of trivial Gibbs states. We suspect that here too for spin glasses the metastate must be supported on infinitely many such Gibbs states, but as of now the question remains open.

33.4.4.3. *Complexity of Gibbs states and metastates*

A further refinement invokes the idea of *complexity* of a pure-state decomposition. In the form suggested by Palmer [45], complexity is the entropy of the set of weights $w_\Gamma(\alpha)$ occurring in the decomposition of a given Γ; crudely, this corresponds to the logarithm of the number of pure states, at least if they all have approximately the same weight. This notion of entropy is well defined, but less useful if it turns out to be infinite. In the latter case, Palmer suggested calculating it in finite size, and that it might even be extensive, increasing proportionally to the volume as the system size increases. But this runs into the problem that, in finite size, pure states and hence the decomposition are not well defined. Ignoring that difficulty for a moment, it was recognized that the complexity cannot be extensive [46]. Working with well-defined pure states in infinite size, the idea for a given Gibbs state of counting the number of pure states that can be distinguished when examining the spin configuration in a finite window was proposed [24, 26, 28]. For a (hyper-)cubic window $\Lambda = \Lambda_W$ of side W, centered say at the origin, it was expected in a short-range model that the logarithm of the number of distinguishable pure states could not grow with W faster than W^{d-1} [24, 26, 28]. For Ising spins with nearest-neighbor interactions, this arises from counting the number of boundary conditions on the hypercube that could produce different ground states, and the expectation that the same bound would apply for $T > 0$.

All these issues can be dealt with in a well-defined way by using some information theory [47]. A pure state corresponds to a boundary condition, effectively at infinity. The weights and the pure states allow us to consider the joint distribution $w_\Gamma(\alpha)\Gamma_\alpha(\sigma)$ of pure states α and spin configurations σ (for given Γ). If we restrict σ to the spin configuration σ_Λ in the hypercube $\Lambda = \Lambda_W$ as before, then the mutual information $I(\sigma_\Lambda; \alpha) \geq 0$ between σ_Λ and α can be defined in terms of the joint distribution of those random variables, and we now call this Λ_W-dependent quantity the *complexity* $K_\Gamma(\Lambda_W)$ of the Gibbs state Γ [48, 49]:

$$K_\Gamma(\Lambda_W) \equiv I_\Gamma(\sigma_\Lambda; \alpha) = \sum_{\sigma_\Lambda, \alpha} w_\Gamma(\alpha)\Gamma_\alpha(\sigma_\Lambda) \ln \frac{w_\Gamma(\alpha)\Gamma_\alpha(\sigma_\Lambda)}{w_\Gamma(\alpha)\Gamma(\sigma_\Lambda)} \tag{33.13}$$

[recall that $\Gamma(\sigma_\Lambda) = \sum_\alpha w_\Gamma(\alpha)\Gamma_\alpha(\sigma_\Lambda)$]. This definition does not use any notion of distinguishability of pure states within a window. As $W \to \infty$, $K_\Gamma(\Lambda_W)$ increases monotonically, and tends to the same value as for Palmer's definition of complexity. We can similarly define the complexity $K_{\rho_J}(\Lambda_W)$ of the MAS ρ_J in place of Γ, and also the complexity $K_{\kappa_J}(\Lambda_W)$ of the metastate κ_J itself: $K_{\kappa_J}(\Lambda_W)$ is defined as the mutual information between the Gibbs (not pure) state Γ and σ_Λ, using the joint distribution $\kappa_J(\Gamma)\Gamma(\sigma_\Lambda)$ [49]. These three quantities are related (for given J and Λ_W) by

$$K_{\rho_J}(\Lambda_W) = [K_\Gamma(\Lambda_W)]_{\kappa_J} + K_{\kappa_J}(\Lambda_W). \tag{33.14}$$

For any of these complexities, if it (or its expectation using κ_J or κ) diverges as $W \to \infty$, then we can look for the manner in which it diverges. If the leading behavior is $\sim W^{d-\zeta'}$, then $d - \zeta' > 0$ indicates an uncountable number of pure states (or Gibbs states in the case of K_{κ_J}). These definitions help to quantify the structures in the above classification, and the exponents $d - \zeta'$ are expected to be universal within a phase, for example, independent of temperature.

In the nearest-neighbor EA model of Ising spins in Eq. (33.1), a simple argument, similar to counting boundary conditions, then produces a bound on the κ-expectation of the complexity $K_\Gamma(\Lambda_W)$ of the Gibbs states by a constant times the surface area W^{d-1} [48]. More generally, a bound of the same form can be obtained for short-range models of classical spins [49], though the argument was valid only for $T > 0$. (A corresponding result for long-range models was also obtained.) The same bounds also apply to the expectations of the other two complexities; thus $\zeta' \geq 1$. Within the usual interpretation of RSB theory, the expected complexity of a Gibbs state as $W \to \infty$ is $\lim_{W\to\infty} \left[[K_\Gamma(\Lambda_W)]_{\kappa_J}\right]_\nu = \psi(1) - \psi(1 - x_1)$ [50], where ψ is the digamma function and $1 - x_1$ is the weight in the δ-function in $P(q)$ at $q(1)$, interpreted as $1 - x_1 = \left[\left[\sum_\alpha w_\Gamma(\alpha)^2\right]_{\kappa_J}\right]_\nu \leq 1$.

33.4.5. *Correlations in the MAS*

Like other states, the MAS can be characterized by its spin correlations, and it will be useful for what follows to introduce one. Due to the quenched disorder, correlation functions in a spin glass will be random with zero mean, and the basic quantities are expectations of squared correlations. Thus we define for Ising spins [22, 48]

$$C_{\mathrm{MAS}}(\mathbf{x},\mathbf{y}) = \left[\left(\langle\sigma_\mathbf{x}\sigma_\mathbf{y}\rangle_{\rho_J} - \langle\sigma_\mathbf{x}\rangle_{\rho_J}\langle\sigma_\mathbf{y}\rangle_{\rho_J}\right)^2\right]_\nu \tag{33.15}$$

$$= \left[\left([\langle\sigma_\mathbf{x}\sigma_\mathbf{y}\rangle_\Gamma]_{\kappa_J} - [\langle\sigma_\mathbf{x}\rangle_\Gamma]_{\kappa_J}[\langle\sigma_\mathbf{y}\rangle_\Gamma]_{\kappa_J}\right)^2\right]_\nu \tag{33.16}$$

using the definition of ρ_J. When spin-flip symmetry is present this simplifies, because then $\langle\sigma_\mathbf{x}\rangle_\Gamma = 0$ for all $\mathbf{x}$. This expression resembles the basic correlation function χ for a spin glass, that is, taking account of the metastate,

$$\chi(\mathbf{x},\mathbf{y}) = \left[\left[\left(\langle\sigma_\mathbf{x}\sigma_\mathbf{y}\rangle_\Gamma - \langle\sigma_\mathbf{x}\rangle_\Gamma\langle\sigma_\mathbf{y}\rangle_\Gamma\right)^2\right]_{\kappa_J}\right]_\nu, \tag{33.17}$$

but C_{MAS} differs in that the square is taken *after* the metastate averages. If the metastate is trivial, this of course makes no difference, so $C_{\mathrm{MAS}} = \chi$. In the case with spin-flip symmetry, $\chi(\mathbf{x},\mathbf{y}) \geq C_{\mathrm{MAS}}(\mathbf{x},\mathbf{y})$. The translation invariance of κ implies that these correlation functions depend on $\mathbf{x} - \mathbf{y}$, not $\mathbf{x}, \mathbf{y}$ separately.

In a spin glass phase, if the decomposition of Γ contains more than one pure state (due to either spontaneous symmetry breaking or Γ being nontrivial), then in most scenarios (at $T > 0$) χ tends to a non-zero constant as $|\mathbf{x} - \mathbf{y}| \to \infty$. For a non-trivial metastate, $C_{\mathrm{MAS}}(\mathbf{x},\mathbf{y})$ may decay to values $\leq \chi(\mathbf{x},\mathbf{y})$, especially in those cases in which the MAS has an uncountable pure-state decomposition. There are models [51–53] in which C_{MAS} tends to zero and the leading asymptotic behavior is a power law:

$$C_{\mathrm{MAS}}(\mathbf{x} - \mathbf{y}) \sim |\mathbf{x} - \mathbf{y}|^{-(d-\zeta)} \tag{33.18}$$

(times a non-universal constant in general) as $|\mathbf{x} - \mathbf{y}| \to \infty$, and ζ is known. In the scenarios of class 3), $\rho_J = \Gamma$, and $\chi = C_{\mathrm{MAS}}$ itself may behave in the fashion described here. In general, when the power law form holds, we expect $d - \zeta$ to be a universal constant within a phase. Heuristic arguments in the EA model, to be discussed in the following section, further support parts of this picture. The relation $\zeta = \zeta'$ was proposed, based on those models and a fractal picture of ground states [22], but it is not known if it must always hold.

33.5. Metastate Interpretation of Replica Symmetry Breaking

In this section we explicitly connect RSB and metastate concepts and results. The final arguments are at a theoretical physics level of rigor that involve the use of RSB MF theory and fluctuations within replica field theory in short-range models.

We begin with a technical point: even when the magnetic field is nominally zero, the development of RSB appears to assume that an "ordering field" is present, that is a small magnetic field that is taken to zero as the system size tends to infinity, but sufficiently slowly that spin-flip symmetry of the EA model is absent in the states in the limit. It then turns out that the overlaps $q_{\alpha\alpha'}$ inferred from the RSB MF theory are almost surely nonnegative. In the following, we will assume this holds.

33.5.1. $q(x)$ *function*

We can define a function $q(x)$ from first principles, motivated by the interpretation of RSB results [17, 19, 20, 22]. From $P(q) = P_J(q)$ we first define the cumulative distribution $x(q) = \int_{0-}^{q} P(q')\,\mathrm{d}q'$ of q as a function on the support of $P(q)$. On the graph of $x(q)$ versus q we now interchange the axes to produce the graph of a function $q(x)$ for $x \in (0, 1)$, with the convention that a jump in $x(q)$ becomes a constant region of $q(x)$, while a constant region of $x(q)$ becomes a jump discontinuity of $q(x)$; $q(x)$ is a monotonically-increasing function for $x \in (0, 1)$. [The value assigned to $q(x)$ at a discontinuity in the open interval $(0, 1)$ has no known significance.] We further define $q(1) = \left[\left[\sum_\alpha w_\Gamma(\alpha) q_{\alpha\alpha} \right]_{\kappa_J} \right]_\nu = \left[\sum_\alpha \mu(\alpha) \langle \sigma_{\mathbf{x}} \rangle_\alpha^2 \right]_\nu$ (for any $\mathbf{x}$), where the self-overlap $q_{\alpha\alpha}$, or equivalently the average over positions of the time autocorrelation of single spins [1], is the EA order parameter q_{EA} in the pure state Γ_α. (We have recently shown that q_{EA} must be the same for all pure states in the decomposition of a given Γ drawn from the metastate [54], but whether it is the same for all Γ is not known for short-range systems.) Similarly, motivated by RSB arguments [22] given below, we define $q(0) = \left[\sum_{\alpha,\alpha'} \mu(\alpha)\mu(\alpha') q_{\alpha\alpha'} \right]_\nu = \left[\langle \sigma_{\mathbf{x}} \rangle_{\rho_J}^2 \right]_\nu$. Then $q(x)$ is now defined on $[0, 1]$, and may be discontinuous at $x = 0$ or 1. For $q(1)$, this can occur if the measure $w_\Gamma(\alpha)$ is atomless (i.e. continuous) for a set of (J, Γ) of nonzero κ probability; for those Γ, the probability $w_\Gamma(\alpha)^2$ of drawing a pure state Γ_α twice from Γ is zero, and so the $\nu(J)\mu(\alpha)$-expected self-overlap $q(1)$ could differ from (in particular, exceed) the supremum of the support of $P(q)$. For $q(0)$, the pairwise overlaps in pure states in the MAS could differ from those in the pure states in a single Γ, with nonzero κ probability, and so $q(0)$ could differ from (even lie below) the infimum of the support of $P(q)$. It is not clear whether $q(x)$ as we have defined it must necessarily be monotonic for all $x \in [0,1]$; in any case, it contains more information than $P(q)$ does.

We remark that, defining $\bar{q} = \int_0^1 dx\, q(x) = \int_{0^-}^{1^+} dq'\, P(q')q'$, $q(x)$ obeys $q(1) - \bar{q} \geq 0$ and $\bar{q} - q(0) \geq 0$, which follow from the definitions (both quantities are sums of variances). If $q(1) - \bar{q} > 0$ then the Gibbs states drawn from the metastate are nontrivial, while if $\bar{q} - q(0) > 0$ then the metastate is nontrivial. If $q(x)$ were monotonic on $[0,1]$, as it is in RSB theory, then both of these would hold whenever $q(x)$ is not constant on $(0,1)$ [22]. The Cauchy–Schwarz inequality yields $q_{\alpha\alpha'} \leq q_{\alpha\alpha}^{1/2} q_{\alpha'\alpha'}^{1/2}$, which would give monotonicity at $x = 1$ if $q_{\alpha\alpha}$ were independent of α, so that $q_{\alpha\alpha} = q_{\alpha'\alpha'}$ for all α, α'.

Next we briefly review the basics of RSB (for more detail, see Refs. [3, 17, 19, 20]). At MF level, the free energy per spin has to be obtained by maximizing a functional of the symmetric matrix Q_{ab}, where a, b index the "replicas" and run from 1 to n, $Q_{aa} = 0$ for all a, and the functional must be evaluated in the limit $n \to 0$ before maximizing. (The maximization rather than the usual minimization is a feature of replicas, and is due to the $n \to 0$ limit.) Parisi's hierarchical scheme [3] for breaking the symmetry S_n of the functional under permutations of the replicas is to first divide n into n/m_1 blocks of size m_1, and assign the value q_0 to elements in the off-diagonal blocks of Q_{ab}. Each diagonal block is then divided into sub-blocks of size m_2 in the same fashion (the same for each one), with the value q_1 assigned to its off-diagonal sub-blocks. This procedure is iterated at most a countably-infinite number of times. Finally, when $n \to 0$, the block sizes are assumed to obey $0 = n \leq m_1 \leq m_2 \leq \cdots \leq 1$, giving a countable partition of $[0,1]$, and maximization of the functional is performed with respect to all possible such partitions. At $n = 0$, for a partition, $(q_r)_r$ can be viewed as a function $q(x)$, where $q(x) = q_r$ when $m_r < x < m_{r+1}$ (where $m_0 = n = 0$), $q(0) = q_0$, and $q(1)$ is defined as $q_{r_{\max}}$ (where $r_{\max}$ is the largest r) for a finite partition, and as $q(1) = \limsup_{r \to \infty} q_r$ for an infinite one. $q(x)$ is found to be a non-negative monotonically increasing function of $x \in [0,1]$; in many situations, $q(x)$ is continuous on the open interval $(0,1)$. Its interpretation for $x > 0$, similar to that above, has long been standard [17].

$q(x)$ as obtained from RSB is not always continuous at $x = 0$ or 1, which brings up an important point. The Parisi functional essentially consists of multiple integrals over x's of (products of) $q(x)$, so the maximization over functions $q(x)$ is unaffected by changes in the value of $q(x)$ on sets of x of measure zero; hence the values $q(0)$, $q(1)$ do not affect the free energy per spin. Sometimes in a given problem, distinct stationary points $q(x)$ are found which differ only in the value of $q(1)$ or $q(0)$, and still have the same MF free energy per spin; we have seen that the values of these are important for the interpretation.

As particular examples, in class 1), SD, $q(x)$ would be constant. In the scenarios of class 2), such as CPs, which with an ordering field reduce to chaotic singles, pairwise- and self-overlaps of pure states in the MAS should be different, while $P(q)$ consists of a single δ-function at q_{EA}, and then $q(0) \neq q(x) = q(1)$ for $x > 0$. Similarly, scenarios in class 3) can have $q(1) \neq q(x) = q(0)$ for $x < 1$ (see the next paragraph). In class 4), there are many possible forms, including $q(x)$ continuous but not constant on $[0,1]$. Thus examples in all four classes of scenarios can be characterized by a $q(x)$ function, and examples even of classes 2) [55] and 3) (see below) can be found at MF level in RSB. However, in the absence of rigorous results stating that $q(x)$ is monotonic on $[0,1]$, it is not possible to say that if $q(x)$ is non-constant on $(0,1)$ then both the Gibbs states and the metastate are non-trivial (as is the case in RSB); apparently $P(q) = P_J(q)$ could be non-trivial (not a single δ-function) due to fluctuations in only one of them.

In MF spin glass models lacking inversion symmetry (i.e. spin-flip symmetry, in the Ising case), the form of $q(x)$ in class 3) just described was found to occur in RSB MF theory for a range of temperatures, and to correspond to a "dynamically-frozen" phase in a dynamical approach [56–59]. It was later argued that in a short-range spin glass, this phase, which appeared to possess extensive complexity, would be destroyed by entropic effects [60, 61], so that there would be no transition into it on lowering the temperature (there was still supposed to be another transition at lower temperature, which was termed a "random first-order transition" [60, 61]). However, it does not seem clear that such effects must completely destroy such a frozen phase; instead they could leave a similar phase, still in class 3), now having a subextensive complexity that obeys the bounds discussed above [48, 49].

33.5.2. *Application of RSB to the AW metastate*

Now we turn to the use of RSB to study the AW metastate for the EA model [22]. We consider a finite system in the hypercube Λ_L, with free or periodic boundary conditions. A sub-hypercube Λ_R will be viewed as the "inner" region, while the sites and edges in $\Lambda_L - \Lambda_R$ constitute the "outer" region. We will consider copies of the system that all experience the same disorder (bonds) in the inner region, but some of which experience different (independently sampled) disorder in the outer region. An expectation over the disorder in the outer region corresponds to an AW metastate expectation using κ_J, while an expectation over disorder in the inner region corresponds to the disorder expectation using ν (when the limits $L \to \infty$ with R fixed, followed by $R \to \infty$ are taken after all the expectations). With this we can study different types of moments of spin correlation functions, with metastate and disorder averages taken at separate stages; disorder expectations are taken last, after all metastate expectations have been done.

To carry out the expectations using the replica formalism, we introduce l "groups" of n_k copies or replicas of the system for the kth independent sample of disorder in the outer region ($k = 1, \ldots, l$); replica indices run from 1 to $\sum_k n_k = n$, the total number of replicas in all groups; the replica limit $n_k \to 0$ for all k must be taken. The replicated theory has permutation symmetry $S_{n_1} \times S_{n_2} \times \cdots S_{n_l}$, broken from S_n because of the different disorder experienced by replicas in different groups in the outer region. However, locally in the inner region the theory has full S_n symmetry, so the effect is that of a symmetry-breaking perturbation that is at infinity once the $L, R \to \infty$ limits have been taken.

At MF level, applying the hierarchical ansatz, in the outer region the replicas that experience distinct disorder should have small mutual overlaps, but otherwise the structure of the order-parameter matrix Q_{ab} (locally in the outer region) within each group will be the same as usual (with n_k in place of n). In the inner region, the local Q_{ab} matrix will have the same form as when only one group of replicas is used. The presence of the additional partition into blocks of sizes n_k (which can be taken all equal) which $\to 0$ does not affect the free-energy functional, and the overlaps between replicas in distinct groups will here be q_0, reflecting the explicit breaking of the S_n symmetry by the outer region, with subsequent further breaking as in the usual scheme.

As a simple example, we first consider the disorder and metastate expectation $[[\langle \sigma_{\mathbf{x}} \rangle_\Gamma^2]_{\kappa_J}]_\nu$ for $\mathbf{x}$ at say the origin. For this, we choose distinct replicas a, b in say the first group, and because of the distinct stationary points of the MF theory that differ by permutations in S_{n_1}, we should average over those choices; we obtain

$$\big[\, [\langle \sigma_{\mathbf{x}} \rangle_\Gamma^2]_{\kappa_J} \,\big]_\nu = \lim_{n_1 \to 0} \frac{1}{n_1(n_1 - 1)} \sum_{a,b=1}^{n_1} Q_{ab} \tag{33.19}$$

$$= \int_0^1 \mathrm{d}x\, q(x) = \overline{q}. \tag{33.20}$$

On the other hand, if we take the metastate expectation before squaring, we must take two replicas from distinct groups, and then averaging within each group has no effect; we obtain

$$\big[\, [\langle \sigma_{\mathbf{x}} \rangle_\Gamma]_{\kappa_J}^2 \,\big]_\nu = q_0 = q(0), \tag{33.21}$$

the result claimed earlier [22].

Similar results are found for more complicated moments. If the metastate and disorder expectations are taken together, the results are the same as in the old RSB forms. But when some algebraic operation such as a square occurs between the expectations, the results differ. In particular, the so-called non-self-averaging (NSA) of $P_{J,\Gamma}(q)$ was found in RSB by using the former type of expectations; it occurs whenever $q(x)$ is not constant on $(0,1)$, so NSA occurs in RSB only if both the metastate and the typical Gibbs states are non-trivial. When the present formalism is applied to moments of metastate averages, no NSA is found for $P_J(q)$, in complete agreement with the considerations of NS [23, 24, 28]. Thus within RSB, fluctuations of $P_{J,\Gamma}(q)$ are associated with fluctuations of (nontrivial) Γs due to a nontrivial metastate, not the disorder distribution ν on J [22, 24].

Next we turn to correlation functions. For the correlations in which the metastate and disorder expectations are performed together, for example for $\chi(\mathbf{x}, \mathbf{y})$, the results take the traditional form; the replicas used are in the same group. On the other hand, for the MAS correlation $C_{\mathrm{MAS}}(\mathbf{x}, \mathbf{y})$ one must choose two replicas from distinct groups. In this case it is known in RSB field theory [62, 63] (though not applied there to the MAS) that the correlation function in the spin glass phase of the EA model at zero magnetic field has the asymptotic form

$$C_{\mathrm{MAS}}(\mathbf{x}, \mathbf{y}) \sim |\mathbf{x} - \mathbf{y}|^{-(d-4)} \tag{33.22}$$

(within a constant factor), so that $\zeta = 4$ [22]. The calculation here, within a statistical field theory at lowest order without any loop corrections, should be valid for dimensions

$d > 6$. It can be extended to obtain the distribution $P_{J,\rho,W}(q)$ of window overlaps, with the overlaps defined as in (33.11) but with W kept fixed, for the MAS ρ_J. In leading order as $W \to \infty$, again for the EA model in zero magnetic field, the disorder expectation $[P_{J,\rho,W}(q)]_\nu$ of this distribution is found to be a Gaussian of variance $\sim W^{-(d-4)}$ for $d > 6$, and further the distribution $P_{J,\rho,W}(q)$ is found to equal its disorder expectation at leading order as $W \to \infty$ [22]. Thus in the limit $W \to \infty$, $P_{J,\rho}(q)$ is found to be a δ-function at $q = q(0)$, and it self-averages, as expected from Refs. [23, 24, 28].

Some authors carried out a direct numerical study of the AW MAS along these lines, in the three-dimensional nearest-neighbor EA model at moderate sizes, and found evidence of a non-trivial metastate [64]. Another study looked at a dynamical analog [52] in a one-dimensional power-law model, and found quantitative agreement with the exponent that corresponds to $\zeta = 4$ in the short-range case for $d > 6$ [65]; that work has been extended further [66].

33.6. Conclusion

In spin glass theory there are outstanding controversies surrounding the nature of the spin glass phase: is it a single (pair of) ordered state(s), as suggested by the scaling-droplet theory, or are there many ordered states, as suggested by replica-symmetry breaking (RSB) mean-field theory? The notion of distinct ordered (or "pure") states, and hence the question itself, is not even well-defined except in an infinite system; hence some sort of infinite-size limit must be taken. Due to the possible presence of chaotic size dependence, the limit is not straightforward. The metastate constructions provide a way out of this problem. A metastate is an additional layer of structure in the theoretical framework: it is a probability distribution on Gibbs states for given disorder, and each Gibbs state could be a mixture of many pure states. A metastate contains information about how the states in finite size vary with size or depend on the disorder far from the origin, asymptotically at large sizes. Within this framework, a number of significant results that constrain the allowed scenarios for a spin glass have been obtained, and some of these results were reviewed in this contribution.

RSB theory initially takes the form of a mean-field theory for thermodynamic properties. When applied to short-range spin glasses, it makes a number of remarkable predictions about the pure states and their dependence on the sample of disorder. It turns out, at least from a heuristic or physical point of view, that RSB, when properly interpreted, has so far passed all the consistency tests available from metastate theory, and at least for some cases makes predictions about the metastate itself.

The ultimate answers to the controversies of short-range spin glasses are still unknown. The nature of the problem raises severe difficulties for traditional analytical methods of theoretical physics, while numerical methods are subject to the limitations of finite size. It may be that rigorously-proved theorems will play a definitive role in resolving the remaining controversies and uncovering the true behavior of these fascinating systems.

Acknowledgments

NR is grateful for the support of NSF grant no. DMR-1724923.

References

[1] S. Edwards and P. W. Anderson, *J. Phys. F.* **5**, 965–974, (1975).
[2] D. Sherrington and S. Kirkpatrick, *Phys. Rev. Lett.* **35**, 1792–1796, (1975).
[3] G. Parisi, *Phys. Rev. Lett.* **43**, 1754–1756, (1979).
[4] P. W. Anderson, *Physics Today.* **42(9)**, 9–11, (1989).
[5] F. Guerra and F. L. Toninelli, *Commun. Math. Phys.* **230**, 71–79, (2002).
[6] F. Guerra, *Commun. Math. Phys.* **233**, 1–12, (2003).
[7] M. Talagrand, *Spin Glasses: A Challenge for Mathematicians.* (Springer-Verlag, 2003).
[8] C. M. Newman and D. L. Stein, *Phys. Rev. B.* **46**, 973–982, (1992).
[9] C. M. Newman and D. L. Stein, *Phys. Rev. E.* **105**, 044132, (2022).
[10] W. L. McMillan, *J. Phys. C.* **17**, 3179–3187, (1984).
[11] A. J. Bray and M. A. Moore, *Phys. Rev. B.* **31**, 631–633, (1985).
[12] D. S. Fisher and D. A. Huse, *Phys. Rev. Lett.* **56**, 1601–1604, (1986).
[13] D. S. Fisher and D. A. Huse, *Phys. Rev. B.* **38**, 386–411, (1988).
[14] F. Krzakala and O. C. Martin, *Phys. Rev. Lett.* **85**, 3013–3016, (2000).
[15] M. Palassini and A. P. Young, *Phys. Rev. Lett.* **85**, 3017–3020, (2000).
[16] D. A. Huse and D. S. Fisher, *J. Phys. A.* **20**, L997–L1003, (1987).
[17] G. Parisi, *Phys. Rev. Lett.* **50**, 1946–1948, (1983).
[18] M. Mézard, G. Parisi, N. Sourlas, G. Toulouse, and M. Virasoro, *Phys. Rev. Lett.* **52**, 1156–1159, (1984).
[19] M. Mézard, G. Parisi, N. Sourlas, G. Toulouse, and M. Virasoro, *J. Phys. (France).* **45**, 843–854, (1984).
[20] M. Mézard, G. Parisi, and M. A. Virasoro, Eds., *Spin Glass Theory and Beyond.* (World Scientific, 1987).
[21] E. Marinari, G. Parisi, F. Ricci-Tersenghi, J. J. Ruiz-Lorenzo, and F. Zuliani, *J. Stat. Phys.* **98**, 973–1047, (2000).
[22] N. Read, *Phys. Rev. E.* **90**, 032142, (2014).
[23] C. M. Newman and D. L. Stein, *Phys. Rev. Lett.* **76**, 515–518, (1996).
[24] C. M. Newman and D. L. Stein, *Phys. Rev. E.* **55**, 5194–5211, (1997).
[25] C. M. Newman and D. L. Stein, *Phys. Rev. E.* **57**, 1356–1366, (1998).
[26] C. M. Newman and D. L. Stein, *J. Phys.: Cond. Mat.* **15**, R1319–R1364, (2003).
[27] K. L. Chung, *A First Course in Probability Theory, 3rd Ed.* (Academic, 2001).
[28] C. M. Newman and D. L. Stein, *Phys. Rev. Lett.* **76**, 4821–4824, (1996).
[29] C. M. Newman and D. L. Stein. In eds. A. Bovier and P. Picco, *Mathematics of Spin Glasses and Neural Networks*, pp. 243–287. Birkhauser, (1998).
[30] C. M. Newman, *Topics in Disordered Systems.* (Birkhauser, 1997).
[31] L.-P. Arguin, C. M. Newman, D. L. Stein, and J. Wehr, *J. Stat. Phys.* **165**, 1069–1078, (2016).
[32] L.-P. Arguin, C. M. Newman, D. L. Stein, and J. Wehr, *J. Stat. Phys.* **156**, 221–238, (2014).
[33] M. Aizenman and J. Wehr, *Commun. Math. Phys.* **130**, 489–528, (1990).
[34] C. Külske. In eds. A. Bovier and P. Picco, *Mathematics of Spin Glasses and Neural Networks*, pp. 151–160. Birkhauser, (1998).
[35] C. Külske, *J. Stat. Phys.* **91**, 155–176, (1998).
[36] A. C. D. van Enter and H. G. Schaap, *J. Phys. A.* **35**, 2581–2592, (2001).

[37] C. M. Newman and D. L. Stein, *Phys. Rev. Lett.* **84**, 3966–3969, (2000).

[38] C. M. Newman and D. L. Stein, *Commun. Math. Phys.* **224**, 205–218, (2001).

[39] L.-P. Arguin, M. Damron, C. M. Newman, and D. L. Stein, *Commun. Math. Phys.* **300**, 641–657, (2010).

[40] L.-P. Arguin, C. M. Newman, and D. L. Stein, *Commun. Math. Phys.* **367**, 1019–1043, (2019).

[41] H. O. Georgii, *Gibbs Measures and Phase Transitions.* (de Gruyter, 1988).

[42] B. Simon, *The Statistical Mechanics of Lattice Gases.* (Princeton University Press, 1993).

[43] A. P. Young, A. J. Bray, and M. A. Moore, *J. Phys. C.* **17**, L149, (1984).

[44] C. M. Newman and D. L. Stein. In eds. E. Bolthausen and A. Bovier, *Spin Glass Theory*, pp. 159–175. Springer, (2006).

[45] R. G. Palmer, *Adv. Phys.* **31**, 669–735, (1982).

[46] A. C. D. van Enter and J. L. van Hemmen, *Phys. Rev. A.* **29**, 355–365, (1984).

[47] T. M. Cover and J. A. Thomas, *Elements of Information Theory.* (John Wiley & Sons, 2006). Chs. 2 and 8.

[48] J. Höller and N. Read, *Phys. Rev. E.* **101**, 042114, (2020).

[49] N. Read, *Phys. Rev. E.* **105**, 054134, (2022).

[50] D. Gross and M. Mézard, *Nucl. Phys. B.* **240**, 431–452, (1984).

[51] C. M. Newman and D. L. Stein, *Phys. Rev. Lett.* **72**, 2286–2289, (1994).

[52] O. L. White and D. S. Fisher, *Phys. Rev. Lett.* **96**, 137204, (2006).

[53] T. S. Jackson and N. Read, *Phys. Rev. E.* **81**, 021130, (2010).

[54] C. M. Newman, N. Read, and D. L. Stein.

[55] J. Höller and N. Read in preparation.

[56] T. R. Kirkpatrick and D. Thirumalai, *Phys. Rev. Lett.* **58**, 2091, (1987).

[57] T. R. Kirkpatrick and D. Thirumalai, *Phys. Rev. B.* **36**, 5388, (1987).

[58] T. R. Kirkpatrick and D. Thirumalai, *Phys. Rev. B.* **37**, 5342, (1988).

[59] T. R. Kirkpatrick and D. Thirumalai, *Phys. Rev. B.* **38**, 4881, (1988).

[60] T. R. Kirkpatrick, D. Thirumalai, and P. G. Wolynes, *Phys. Rev. A.* **40**, 1045, (1989).

[61] J.-P. Bouchaud and G. Biroli, *J. Chem. Phys.* **121**, 7347, (2004).

[62] C. D. Dominicis, I. Kondor, and T. Temesvari. In ed. A. P. Young, *Spin Glasses and Random Fields.* World Scientific, (1998).

[63] C. D. Dominicis and I. Giardina. In ed. A. P. Young, *Random Fields and Spin Glasses.* Cambridge University Press, (2006).

[64] A. Billoire, L. A. Fernandez, A. Maiorano, E. Marinari, V. Martin-Mayor, J. Moreno-Gordo, G. Parisi, F. Ricci-Tersenghi, and J. Ruiz-Lorenzo, *Phys. Rev. Lett.* **119**, 037203, (2017).

[65] M. Wittmann and A. P. Young, *J. Stat. Mech.* p. 013301, (2016).

[66] S. Jensen, N. Read, and A. P. Young, *Phys. Rev. E.* **104**, 034105, (2021).

Chapter 34

Future Perspectives

Giorgio Parisi

Department of Physics, Sapienza Università di Roma, Rome, Italy
Istituto Nazionale di Fisica Nucleare, Sezione di Roma I, Rome, Italy
Institute of Nanotechnology (NANOTEC) - CNR, Rome unit, Rome, Italy

This chapter presents a brief introduction to the theory of multiple equilibria based on the formalism of spontaneous replica symmetry breaking, in both the algebraic and the probabilistic formulations. I also present some of the most important open problems in both infinite-range and finite-dimensional models.

34.1. Multiple Equilibria

The possibility for a system to form multiple equilibria is the key feature that underlies spontaneous replica symmetry breaking (SRSB) in physics and beyond. Interestingly, the idea did not originate in physics but previously appeared in various other contexts.

In 1972 Niles Eldredge and Stephen Jay Gould [1] proposed the evolutionary theory of punctuated equilibria. From this point of view the evolution of the species is not a continuous gradual process. Long periods of stasis, during which there is practically no change in the morphology, are punctuated by rare bursts of evolutionary change.

In the modern theory of memory (Hebb [2], Little [3], Hopfield [4], Amit [5]), the part of the brain that is responsible for memory may stay in an extremely large number of different equilibrium states, each corresponding to the recollection of a different item: this region may remain in that situation for a long period. The extremely large number of items that we can memorize and recall then depends on the extremely large number of possible equilibrium states.

Many other complex systems exhibit long periods of equilibrium separated by fast transitions to a new equilibrium point, such as ecosystems, climate (glaciations), geology (eras), animal behavior, etc. "Multiple equilibria" is also a well-known concept to economists. For example, in 1970 the Nobel Laureate Gérard Debreu wrote about *Economies with a Finite Set of Equilibria* [6].

Closer to physics, similar ideas were put forward by Goldstein [7] in 1969 to describe glasses; *Goldstein's idea is that at low enough temperatures a supercooled liquid explores the phase space mainly through activated jumps between different amorphous minima, separated by potential energy barriers.*

These ideas, however, only started to have a precise formulation in the contest of spin glasses [8], which are now considered to be the basis of the theoretical approach to complexity.

34.2. The Replica Approach to Spin Glasses

The simplest model for spin glasses is given by the Sherrington–Kirkpatrick [9] Hamiltonian (1975) for N spins

$$H_J[\{\sigma\}] = -\frac{1}{2} \sum_{i,k=1,N} J_{i,k}\sigma_i\sigma_k \; - h \sum_{i=1,N} \sigma_i, \qquad \overline{J_{i,k}^2} = \frac{1}{N},$$

where the couplings $J_{i,k}$ are different from zero for all i and k (they are independent random variables), h is the magnetic field and the spins are Ising variables ($\sigma_i = \pm 1$).

The strategy to solve the model [10] is to write exact formulas for $\overline{Z_J^n}$,[a] and to compute the average free energy F defined as

$$- \beta F = \overline{\log(Z_J)} \qquad Z_J = \sum_{\{\sigma\}} \exp\left(-H_J[\{\sigma\}]\right),$$

using the formula

$$\overline{\log(Z_J)} = \lim_{n\to 0} \frac{\mathrm{d}\,\overline{Z_J^n}}{\mathrm{d}\,n}.$$

Sherrington and Kirkpatrick (SK) proved that for a system of N spins it is possible to write the exact replica formula:

$$\overline{Z_J^n} \propto \int \mathrm{d}\,Q \exp(-N\beta F(Q)),$$

where the integral runs over symmetric $n \times n$ matrices with zero diagonal elements, i.e. $n(n-1)/2$ variables. Because the number of integration variables must be an integer, we should not use the previous formula for non-integer n. SK nevertheless proposed to approximate the integral as

$$\overline{Z_J^n} \approx \exp\left(-N\beta F(Q^*)\right),$$

where $F(Q)$ must have a minimum at Q^*. Eventually one could compute the corrections to the saddle point value by Gaussian integrals.

SK further made an innocent-looking assumption:

$$Q_{a,b}^* = q, \text{ for } a \neq b.$$

Unfortunately, the results they obtained were not physically consistent, in that the entropy was negative at low temperatures. The underlying reason remained mysterious until de Almeida and Thouless [11] proved that $Q_{a,b}^* = q$ is not a minimum.

But which is the value of the minimum Q^*? We have to take Q^* as a matrix where the matrix elements are not all equal to q. In a first SRSB computations by Blandin [12, 13], based on a physical interpretation of the Edwards–Anderson order parameter as the zero-coupling limit of the correlation of two coupled replicas, the n

---

[a]The overline denotes averaging over J.

replicas are divided into two groups of $n/2$ replicas, and the value of the matrix element depends on which group the indices belong to. The calculation can then be generalized to m groups of n/m replicas, with m integer. After some attempts, it turned out [8] that also m must be non-integer. Such a procedure does not make sense in the same way that a regular polygon with 3.5 or π sides doesn't, yet it is still amenable to computations.[b]

The stability problem identified by de Almeida, Kosterlitz and Thouless was less acute [14]. Generalizing this ansatz one finds [8] a solution which is not unstable [15]:

$$F = \max_{q(x)} F[q(x)],$$

where $F[q(x)]$ is a functional of the function $q(x)$ that plays the role of order parameter. At zero magnetic field, we have

$$F[q(x)] = -\frac{\beta}{4}\left[1 + \int_0^1 d\,x\, q^2(x) - 2q(1)\right] - \frac{1}{\beta}f(0,0),$$

where $f(x,h)$ is an auxiliary function defined over the interval $0 \leq x \leq 1$. It is the solution to the non-linear anti-parabolic equation

$$\frac{\partial f(x,h)}{\partial x} = -\frac{1}{2}\frac{dq}{dx}\left[\frac{\partial^2 f}{\partial h^2} + x\left(\frac{\partial f}{\partial h}\right)^2\right],$$

with the initial condition $f(1,h) = \ln(2\cosh(\beta h))$.

After a lot of crazy mathematics, one therefore comes back to respectable mathematics, albeit with one big surprise: the order parameter is a function.

34.3. The Physical Meaning of the Order Parameter

From the above treatment, the physical meaning of $q(x)$ is not transparent. However it possible to show [8] that a spin glass sample has many equilibrium states, labeled by an index α, and that each of these states appears at equilibrium with a probability w_α.

$$\langle \mathcal{O} \rangle = \sum_{w_\alpha} w_\alpha \mathcal{O}_\alpha.$$

Each of these states is further characterized by its own magnetization m_i^α. One could define a matrix of overlaps

$$q_{\alpha,\gamma} = \mathrm{Av}\,(m_i^\alpha m_i^\gamma),$$

noting that $q_{\mathrm{EA}} = q_{\alpha,\alpha}$. For each sample, we could further define a descriptor $\mathcal{D}_J$ that is formed by the matrix q and the weights w's. After a long computation, one can compute the probability distribution of the descriptors, i.e., $\mathcal{P}(\mathcal{D})$.

In the standard replica approach states satisfy the ultrametricity property. In other words, states lie on the leaves of a tree and the distance between them is proportional to the distance on the tree to reach one from the other. Surprisingly, the tree of states branches at all levels and there is an infinite number of branches. Even more so, this intricate construction was initially completely unexpected.

---

[b]For instance, the perimeter of a regular polygon of radius 1 with n sides is given by: $C(n) = n(2\sin(\pi/n))$, and turns negative for $n < 1$.

A standard taxonomy, i.e. a hierarchical classification, is possible only if the relevant properties have an ultrametric structure. While the standard taxonomic classification of living beings is related to the history of evolution, in the case of spin glasses it turns out to be intrinsic to the equilibrium properties of the system.

34.4. Mathematicians Come to Rescue

The crazy form of the Q matrix used in the replica is equivalent to this extremely complex probability distribution. Why we have this probability distribution and why ultrametricity? Ultrametricity is not a self-evident requirement! For a long time, I was not fully convinced that this solution was the correct one: maybe the correct one was still more complex.

This probabilistic approach was a starting point for mathematicians. From the end of the nineties, Francesco Guerra introduced new ideas in the field [16, 17]. The correctness of the previous formulas was proved by Talagrand [18] in 2003 tweaking Guerra's lower bound in an upper bound.

So, it has been proved that the free energy is correct; but what about the $\mathcal{P}(\mathcal{D})$? Aizenman, Sims, and Starr [19] proved that a variational equation [20] holds:

$$F = \max_{\mathcal{P}} F[\mathcal{P}(\mathcal{C})]. \tag{34.1}$$

It can be proven that the same formula holds if you consider only stochastic stable $\mathcal{P}(\mathcal{D})$ (stochastic stability is a nickname [21] for a system that satisfies Ghirlanda–Guerra and Aizenman–Contucci [22] identities). It is simple to prove that, if $\mathcal{P}(\mathcal{D})$ is stochastic stable and ultrametric, $\mathcal{P}(\mathcal{D})$ coincides with the probability given by the replica method. So the big question was: *does stochastic stability imply ultrametricity?*

After a series of partial results, with a beautiful proof Panchenko [23] proved in general that stochastic stability implies ultrametricity, vindicating the replica formula for $\mathcal{P}(\mathcal{D})$.

34.5. Open Problems in Infinite Range Models

Let me present some open problems in order of estimated increasing difficulty.

34.5.1. *Diluted models*

In the case of diluted models (i.e., models on Bethe lattices), the spins interact with only a finite number (z) of other spins [24].

At the end of very long computations, one finds that Eq. (34.1) is correct [25, 26]: unfortunately, we need to consider also multiple overlaps in the descriptor $\mathcal{D}_J$

$$q_{\alpha,\beta,\gamma} = \mathrm{Av}\left(m_i^\alpha m_i^\beta m_i^\gamma\right).$$

In the explicit formulas written with Marc Mézard, we assumed [27] that there is a function Q_3 such that

$$q_{\alpha,\beta,\gamma} = Q_3(q_{\alpha,\beta}, q_{\alpha,\gamma}, q_{\beta,\gamma}). \tag{34.2}$$

This property was called by Mézard and Virasoro reproducibility [28]. If reproducibility is correct the correct solution is given by the generalization of the Mézard–Parisi formulas [29].

Unfortunately, Panchenko was able to prove that Eq. (34.2) holds only in particular cases, not in general. More precisely the previous formula is true if the overlaps assume a finite number of possible different values, as in the case of the K steps replica symmetry breaking. My personal opinion is that formula (34.2) is correct and its violations should bring some contradiction, however it is not easy to pinpoint which one. If formula (34.2) would not be valid everything would be very strange and the solution of the model could not be approximated as the limit of K steps replica symmetry breaking for $K \to \infty$. It is very important to know if something strange happens in the dilute model because the finite dimensional model can be considered as Bethe lattices with correlations.

One possible way to arrive at some results could be the following. We know that in the limit $z \to \infty$ the free energy of the diluted model converges to that of the SK model. Using the replica method the free energy can be expanded in powers of $1/z$ with well-defined coefficients [30, 31]. I can hope that one could prove that this expansion is an asymptotic expansion of the correct results and that formula (34.2) is correct at least for large z.

34.5.2. *Finite volume corrections*

Most of the efforts have been devoted to the computation of infinite volume limit. However finite volume corrections are very important and often related to finite-dimensional corrections.

Let us consider the average free energy. We could conjecture some asymptotic expansion of the kind:

$$\overline{\log(Z_J(N))} = -N\beta F + AN^\omega + B\ln(N) + C.$$

What about ω, A, B and C? We have strong numerical indications [32] that in the SK model $\omega \approx \frac{1}{3}$, but why? In a recent paper [33], it was shown that doing an over-simplified computation one gets $\omega \approx \frac{1}{5}$

We need to understand better the structure of zero-modes in the model. In simpler models we have to do the integral on the manifold spanned by zero modes: e.g. for the infinite range ferromagnetic $O(n)$ model

$$\log(Z(N)) = -N\beta F - \frac{n-1}{2}\ln(N) + C.$$

Similar problems arise in the case of the p-spin model where a possible solution was proposed in [34] (see also next subsection).

34.5.3. *Replicae ab omni naevo vindicatae?*

Can we twist the replica original formulation to get rigorous results? Unfortunately at the present moment, nobody can transform the original approach with replicas into rigorous proof. Following [34] let me propose a possible approach that is based on some general mathematics conjectures: I am unable to even think how they could be proved.

Let us start with precise definitions.

$$Z_n(N) = \overline{Z_J(N)^n} = \int \mathrm{d}\,Q \exp(-N\beta F_n(Q))\,, n \in \mathcal{N},$$

$$Z(z,N) = \overline{Z_J(N)^z}\,, \qquad\qquad z \in \mathcal{C}.$$

The first conjecture (quite likely easy to be proved): $Z(z,N)$ is the unique (or essentially unique) analytic extension of $Z_n(N)$ from integers to complex numbers satisfying some restrictions (e.g. on the behavior for large Im z). Carleman's condition does not work because $Z_n(N) \propto \exp(An^2)$

We define the sum over all the critical points of $F_n(Q)$ (an improved saddle point method):

$$\mathcal{Z}_n(N) = \sum_{\alpha} \exp(-N\beta F_n(Q_\alpha)), \qquad\qquad \left.\frac{\partial F_n(Q)}{\partial Q}\right|_{Q=Q_\alpha} = 0.$$

We conjecture that

- There exists a unique (or essentially unique) analytic extension of $\mathcal{Z}_n(N)$ from integers to complex numbers satisfying some restrictions. Let us call it $\mathcal{Z}(z,N)$.
- For real $n > 0$:

$$\mathcal{F}(n) \equiv \lim_{N\to\infty} \frac{\log(\mathcal{Z}(n,N))}{N} = \lim_{N\to\infty} \frac{\log(Z_n(N))}{N} \equiv F(n).$$

- There are direct algebraic ways to evaluate directly $\mathcal{F}(n)$ as discussed in Ref. [34].

34.6. Finite Dimensions: The Renormalization Group

I have no space to discuss here the many gigantic efforts to understand numerically the finite-dimensional behavior of spin glasses and compare it with the predictions of the replica theory (e.g. the work of the Janus collaboration [35] in part summarized in Chapter 5). Here I will concentrate on analytic approaches.

34.6.1. *The hierarchical model*

The Dyson–Wilson–Bleher–Sinai hierarchical model [36] is the simplest model sharing with more standard finite-dimensional models many properties at the level of the renormalization group: there is a parameter ρ that is a proxy of the dimension for finite-dimensional models. The model is a proxy of the one-dimensional long-range model where the interaction decay as $d^{-\rho}$.

In the ferromagnetic Ising model, one can write in an explicit way the renormalization group transformation

$$P_{2N}(m) = \mathcal{R}[P_N(m)],$$

where $P_N(m)$ is the probability distribution of the magnetization for a system of N spins. The equation can be studied both numerically and analytically. Many theorems can be proved, among them some regarding an appropriate ϵ expansion for the critical exponents.

A similar equation could be written for spin glasses, where now P is a function of all overlaps of an arbitrary number of replicas. However, (as far as I understand) there are no Ghirlanda–Guerra-like relations, no ultrametricity. It is quite possible that some numerical approximations can be done and that rigorous theorems could be established. This would be extremely important because the understanding of the model would provide a clue on the existence of replica symmetry breaking in finite-dimensional cases.

Moreover, approximate analytic computation of the critical exponents would be extremely interesting, especially in a non-zero magnetic field, where the dimension temperature diagram is not clear.

34.6.2. *The renormalization group: One loop computation*

De Dominicis and Kondor computed the correlation functions of the theory at zero loops [37]. They are a very complex function of the replica indices and the momenta p. Depending on the replica indices we could have the following behaviors at small p:

$$1/p^2, \qquad 1/p^3, \qquad 1/p^4.$$

De Dominicis, Kondor and Temesvari analyzed the field theory. They found a very complex structure of Ward's identities [38]. If one starts to do the one loop computation one finds very many cancellations (e.g. in Ref. [39]) as it happens in the non-linear sigma model in the low-temperature case.

The full one-loop computation was never done: a naive estimate gives $O(10^5)$–$O(10^6)$ terms. The computation should be within the reach of modern computer algebra.

However, we need smart ideas for doing the computation exposing the cancellations. The lack of explicit cancellations is a well-known problem in many models: cancellations stem from Ward identities and single Feynman diagrams do not satisfy the Ward identities. Partial resummations are needed to expose them.

Suggestions and explicit computations are very welcome.

34.6.3. *The renormalization group: Random lasers*

Random lasers [40] are a very important example of an experimental system with continuous replica symmetry breaking that has also been extensively quoted in the motivation for my Nobel prize.

They are quite different from spin glasses. There are still some open issues already in the mean-field approximation, however, some progress has recently done in Ref. [41].

It is possible that we should redo the De Dominicis, Kondor, and Temesvari analysis for this model. It is quite possible that the effects are smaller here than in other models.

34.6.4. *Hard spheres*

In 1999 we studied the replica theory for structural glasses with Marc Mézard [42], but we found that the case of hard spheres was too difficult for us. Around 2004 Francesco

Zamponi started to work with me. In 2005 we extended the theory to hard spheres. We continued to work in the field and in 2010 we collected all our results in a 60 pages paper [43].

There were some discrepancies with the theory, also near jamming. I believed that they were nothing important and that they would be cured by computing corrections to mean field theory, a very boring job, nothing very deep. Francesco was convinced that there was a conceptual problem. He decided that we should attack the problem both numerically and analytically.

To make a long story short, with Charbonneau and Corwin [44] we showed that the discrepancies were mostly independent of the space dimensions in the range $D = [3 : 10]$. Kurchan and Zamponi (with some aid from me) arrived at a convincing proof that in infinite dimensions the corrections to the mean field were negligible [45].

I understood that there was something strange. Kurchan, Urbani and Zamponi started to investigate the possibility of a second replica symmetry breaking. I was skeptical. When they showed me a computation that a second replica symmetry breaking was going in the right direction, I was quite excited and I started to be very active in the program [46].

Finally, also in collaboration with Patrick Charbonneau, we showed that, by introducing continuous replica symmetry breaking, everything was perfect [47, 48]. We could compute the exponents at the jamming transition, finding them in wonderful agreement with the three-dimensional results.

We know that the critical exponents for the decay of correlations in spin glasses have a very strong dependence on the dimension (quite likely for dimensions less than 6): e.g. the mean squared displacement as a function of the pressure P behaves as $\langle \Delta^2 \rangle \propto P^{-\kappa}, (\kappa = 1.41574\ldots)$

Why we do not see corrections to the jamming exponents as functions of the dimensions? There should be a clear answer to this question.

Here we miss the De Dominicis-Kondor analysis of the correlations, and we do not know which are the predictions for the correlations. Maybe the local exponents like κ do not renormalize and the correlations exponents do renormalize. Who knows?

Acknowledgments

A big thank to all the more than one hundred people I was lucky to work with in this subject!

References

[1] N. Eldredge and S. J. Gould, *Punctuated Equilibria: An Alternative to Phyletic Gradualism*, in Thomas J. M. Schopf (ed.), *Models in Paleobiology* (Freeman Cooper, 1972) pp. 82-115.

[2] D. O. Hebb, *The Organization of Behavior* (Wiley, 1949).

[3] W. A. Little, *Math. Biosci.* **19**, 101 (1974).

[4] J. J. Hopfield, *Proc. Natl. Acad. Sci.* USA, **79**, 2554 (1982).

[5] D. Amit, *Modeling Brain Function* (Cambridge University Press, 1989).

[6] G. Debreu, *Econometrica* **38**, 387 (1970).

[7] M. Goldstein, *J. Chem. Phys.* **51**, 3728 (1969).

[8] M. Mézard, G. Parisi and M. A. Virasoro, *Spin glass theory and beyond* (World Scientific, 1987).

[9] D. Sherrington and S. Kirkpatrick, *Phys. Rev. Lett.* **35**, 1792 (1975).

[10] S. F. Edwards and P. W. Anderson (1975), *J. Phys. F: Metal Physics* **5**, 965 (1975).

[11] J. R. L. de Almeida and D. J. Thouless, *J. Phys. A: Math. Gen.* 11, 983 (1978).

[12] A. Blandin, *J. Physique Coll.*, **39**, C6-1499 (1978).

[13] A. Blandin, M. Gabay, T. Garel, *J. Phys. C: Solid State Phys.*, **13**, 403 (1980).

[14] D.J., Thouless, J. R. L. De Almeida and J. M. Kosterlitz, *J. Phys. C: Solid State Phys.* **13**, 327 (1980).

[15] C. De Dominicis and I. Kondor, *Phys. Rev. B* **27**, 606 (1983).

[16] F. Guerra, *Int. J. Mod. Phys. B* **10**, 1675 (1996); *Comm. Math. Phys.* **233**, 1 (2003).

[17] S. Ghirlanda and F. Guerra, *J. Phys. A* **31**, 9149 (1998).

[18] M. Talagrand, *C.R.A.S.* **337**, 111 (2003); *Ann. Math.* **163**, 221 (2006).

[19] M. Aizenman, R. Sims, and S. L. Starr, *Phys. Rev. B* **68**, 214403 (2003).

[20] G. Parisi, *Physica Scripta* **T19A**, 27 (1987).

[21] G. Parisi, *Int. J. Mod. Phys. B* **18**, 733 (2004).

[22] M. Aizenman and P. Contucci, *J. Stat. Phys.* **92**, 765 (1998).

[23] D. Panchenko, *Ann. Math.* **177**, 383 (2013).

[24] L. Viana and A. J. Bray, *J. Phys. C* **18**, 3037 (1985).

[25] D. Panchenko, *Ann. Prob.* **41**, 1315 (2013).

[26] D. Panchenko, *J. Stat. Phys.* **162**, 1 (2016).

[27] M. Mézard and G. Parisi *Eur. Phys. J. B* **20**, 217 (2001).

[28] M. Mézard and M. A. Virasoro, *J. Physique* **46**, 1293 (1985).

[29] G. Parisi, *J. Stat. Phys.* **167**, 515 (2017).

[30] G. Parisi and F. Tria, *Eur. Phys. J. B* **30**, 533 (2002).

[31] G. Boschi and G. Parisi, *arXiv:2001.01966* (2020).

[32] M. Palassini, *J. Stat. Mech.* 2008.10, P10005 (2008).

[33] G. Parisi, L. Sarra and L. Talamanca, *J. Stat. Mech.* 033302 (2019).

[34] Campellone, Parisi, Virasoro *J. Stat. Phys* **138**, 29 (2010)

[35] R. Alvarez Banos, A. Cruz, L. A. Fernandez, J. M. Gil-Narvion, A. Gordillo-Guerrero, M. Guidetti, A. Maiorano, F. Mantovani, E. Marinari, V. Martin-Mayor, J. Monforte-Garcia, A. Munoz Sudupe, D. Navarro, G. Parisi, S. Perez-Gaviro, J. J. Ruiz-Lorenzo, S.F. Schifano, B. Seoane, A. Tarancon, R. Tripiccione, and D. Yllanes, *Phys. Rev. Lett.* **105**, 177202 (2010); *J. Stat. Mech.* P06026 (2010).

[36] F. J. Dyson, *Comm. Math. Phys.* **12**, 91 (1969); K. G. Wilson, *Phys. Rev. B* **4**, 3174 (1971); P. M. Bleher and Ja. G. Sinai, *Commun. Math. Phys.* **33**, 23 (1973).

[37] C. De Dominicis and I. Kondor, *J. Physique Lett.* **45**, 205 (1984).

[38] C. De Dominicis, I. Kondor and T. Temesvari *J. Phys. I* (France), **4**, 1287 (1994).

[39] M. E. Ferrero and G. Parisi, *J. Phys. A.* **29**, 3795 (1996)

[40] N. Ghofraniha, I. Viola, F. Di Maria, G. Barbarella, G. Gigli, L. Leuzzi, C. Conti, *Nat. Commun.* **6**, 6058 (2015).

[41] J. Niedda, G. Gradenigo, L Leuzzi, and G. Parisi *arXiv:2210.04362* (2022).

[42] M. Mézard, and G. Parisi. *J. Phys.: Cond. Matt.* **11**, A157 (1999).

[43] G. Parisi and F. Zamponi. *Rev. Mod. Phys.* **82**, 789 (2010).

[44] P. Charbonneau, E.I. Corwin, G. Parisi, F. Zamponi, *Phys. Rev. Lett.*, **109**, 205501 (2012).

[45] J. Kurchan, G. Parisi, F. Zamponi, *J. Stat. Mech.* P10012 (2012);

[46] J. Kurchan, G. Parisi, P. Urbani, F. Zamponi *J. Phys. Chem. B*, **117**, 12979 (2013);

[47] P. Charbonneau, J. Kurchan, G. Parisi, P. Urbani and F. Zamponi, *Nature Comm.* **5**, 3725 (2014), *J. Stat. Mech.* P10009 (2014).

[48] G. Parisi, P. Urbani, and F. Zamponi. *Theory of simple glasses: exact solutions in infinite dimensions.* (Cambridge University Press, 2020).